◀ Table of Atomic Masses* ▶

Element	Symbol	Atomic Number	Atomic Mass
Actinium	Ac	89	(227)†
Aluminum	Al	13	26.98
Americium	Am	95	(243)
Antimony	Sb	51	121.8
Argon	Ar	18	39.95
Arsenic	As	33	74.92
Astatine	At	85	(210)
Barium	Ba	56	137.3
Berkelium	Bk	97	(247)
Beryllium	Be	4	9.012
Bismuth	Bi	83	209.0
Boron	B	5	10.81
Bromine	Br	35	79.90
Cadmium	Cd	48	112.4
Calcium	Ca	20	40.08
Californium	Cf	98	(251)
Carbon	C	6	12.01
Cerium	Ce	58	140.1
Cesium	Cs	55	132.9
Chlorine	Cl	17	35.45
Chromium	Cr	24	52.00
Cobalt	Co	27	58.93
Copper	Cu	29	63.55
Curium	Cm	96	(247)
Dysprosium	Dy	66	162.5
Einsteinium	Es	99	(252)
Erbium	Er	68	167.3
Europium	Eu	63	152.0
Fermium	Fm	100	(257)
Fluorine	F	9	19.00
Francium	Fr	87	(223)
Gadolinium	Gd	64	157.3
Gallium	Ga	31	69.72
Germanium	Ge	32	72.59
Gold	Au	79	197.0
Hafnium	Hf	72	178.5
Helium	He	2	4.003
Holmium	Ho	67	164.9
Hydrogen	H	1	1.008
Indium	In	49	114.8
Iodine	I	53	126.9
Iridium	Ir	77	192.2
Iron	Fe	26	55.85
Krypton	Kr	36	83.80
Lanthanum	La	57	138.9
Lawrencium	Lr	103	(260)
Lead	Pb	82	207.2
Lithium	Li	3	6.941
Lutetium	Lu	71	175.0
Magnesium	Mg	12	24.31
Manganese	Mn	25	54.94
Mendelevium	Md	101	(258)
Mercury	Hg	80	200.6
Molybdenum	Mo	42	95.94
Neodymium	Nd	60	144.2
Neon	Ne	10	20.18
Neptunium	Np	93	(237)
Nickel	Ni	28	58.69
Niobium	Nb	41	92.91
Nitrogen	N	7	14.01
Nobelium	No	102	(259)
Osmium	Os	76	190.2
Oxygen	O	8	16.00
Palladium	Pd	46	106.4
Phosphorus	P	15	30.97
Platinum	Pt	78	195.1
Plutonium	Pu	94	(244)
Polonium	Po	84	(209)
Potassium	K	19	39.10
Praseodymium	Pr	59	140.9
Promethium	Pm	61	(145)
Protactinium	Pa	91	(231)
Radium	Ra	88	226
Radon	Rn	86	(222)
Rhenium	Re	75	186.2
Rhodium	Rh	45	102.9
Rubidium	Rb	37	85.47
Ruthenium	Ru	44	101.1
Samarium	Sm	62	150.4
Scandium	Sc	21	44.96
Selenium	Se	34	78.96
Silicon	Si	14	28.09
Silver	Ag	47	107.9
Sodium	Na	11	22.99
Strontium	Sr	38	87.62
Sulfur	S	16	32.07
Tantalum	Ta	73	180.9
Technetium	Tc	43	(98)
Tellurium	Te	52	127.6
Terbium	Tb	65	158.9
Thallium	Tl	81	204.4
Thorium	Th	90	232.0
Thulium	Tm	69	168.9
Tin	Sn	50	118.7
Titanium	Ti	22	47.88
Tungsten	W	74	183.9
Uranium	U	92	238.0
Vanadium	V	23	50.94
Xenon	Xe	54	131.3
Ytterbium	Yb	70	173.0
Yttrium	Y	39	88.91
Zinc	Zn	30	65.38
Zirconium	Zr	40	91.22

*The values given here are to four significant figures where possible.
†A value given in parentheses denotes the mass of the longest-lived isotope.

CHEMISTRY

Steven S. Zumdahl
University of Illinois

CHEMISTRY

Third Edition

D. C. HEATH AND COMPANY
Lexington, Massachusetts Toronto

Address editorial correspondence to

D. C. Heath and Company
125 Spring Street
Lexington, MA 02173

Acquisitions Editor: Kent Porter Hamann
Project Consultant: Richard E. Morel
Production Editor: Karen Wise
Designer: Kenneth Hollman
Production Coordinator: Lisa Merrill
Art Editor: Gary Crespo
Photo Researcher: Mark Corsey
Text Permissions Editor: Margaret Roll

Published simultaneously in Canada.

Printed in the United States of America.

International Standard Book Number: 0-669-32462-0

Library of Congress Catalog Number: 92-70801

10 9 8 7 6 5 4

◄ To the Professor ►

Because of the enthusiastic response to the second edition of this text, the third edition of *Chemistry* continues in the same spirit: a presentation of the concepts of chemistry in a clear, interesting, and student-friendly manner. However, I have gone over every page in the second edition thoroughly, fine-tuning in some cases and substantially rewriting in others. In doing so, I have incorporated numerous constructive suggestions from instructors who used the previous edition.

Since visual material is especially important for learning general chemistry, which typically presents a pictorial view of chemical concepts, the use of color has been markedly increased in this edition. Special illustrations and color photographs integrate descriptive chemistry with chemical principles, and many new *Chemical Impact* features emphasize practical applications of newly learned concepts.

Important Features of the Third Edition

- With a strong **problem-solving orientation,** this text talks to the student about how to approach and solve chemical problems. I have made a strong pitch to the student for using a thoughtful and logical approach rather than simply memorizing procedures. In particular, an innovative method is given for dealing with acid–base equilibria, the material the typical student finds most difficult and frustrating. The key to this approach involves first deciding what species are present in solution, then thinking about the chemical properties of these species. This method provides a general framework for approaching all types of solution equilibria.

  The text contains almost 300 sample exercises, with many more examples given in the discussions leading to sample exercises or used to illustrate general strategies. When a specific strategy is presented, it is summarized, and the sample exercise that follows it reinforces the step-by-step attack on the problem (see p. xix).

- I have presented a thorough **treatment of reactions** that occur in solution, including acid–base reactions. This material appears in Chapter 4, directly after the chapter on chemical stoichiometry, to emphasize the connection between solution reactions and chemical reactions in general. The early presentation of this material provides an opportunity to cover some interesting descriptive chemistry and also supports the lab, which typically involves a great deal of aqueous chemistry. Chapter 4 also includes oxidation–reduction reactions, because a large number of interesting and important chemical reactions involve redox processes. However, coverage of oxidation–reduction is optional at this point and depends on the needs of a specific course.

- **Descriptive chemistry** and chemical principles are thoroughly integrated in this text. Chemical models may appear sterile and confusing without the observations that stimulated their invention. On the other hand, facts without organizing principles may seem overwhelming. A combination of observations and models can make chemistry both interesting and understandable. In addition, in those chapters that deal with the chemistry of the elements systematically, I have made a continuous effort to show how properties and models correlate. Descriptive chemistry is presented in a variety of ways—as applications of the principles in separate sections, in sample exercises and exercise sets, in photographs, and in *Chemical Impact* features.

- Throughout the book a strong **emphasis on models** prevails (see p. xviii). Coverage includes how they are constructed, how they are tested, and what we learn when they inevitably fail. Models are developed naturally, with pertinent observations always presented first to show why a particular model was invented.

- Everyday-life **applications** of chemistry that should be of interest to the students taking general chemistry appear throughout the text. For example, the *Chemical Impact* "Refurbishing the Lady" illustrates the chemistry behind the restoration of the Statue of Liberty, while "Nature Has Hot Plants" discusses several fascinating species of heat-producing plants, including the voodoo lily. Many industrial applications have also been incorporated into the text. Interesting careers in chemistry are highlighted through profiles of real people who work in the chemical sciences (see p. xv).

- Judging from the favorable comments of instructors and students who have used the second edition, the text seemed to work very well in a variety of courses. I was especially pleased that **readability** was cited as a key strength when students were asked to assess the text. Thus, although the text has been fine-tuned in many areas, I have endeavored to build on the basic descriptions, strategies, analogies, and explanations that were successful in the second edition.

Changes in the Third Edition

- To assist instructors in providing interesting and relevant classroom demonstrations of chemical phenomena for their students, the *Instructor's Edition* indicates via the marginal icon (flask with stirring rod) direct references to more than 750 demonstrations from several authoritative sources. The sources are provided in a separate booklet, the *Lecture Demonstration Guide,* that is available to adopters of the Third Edition.

- In this edition, the effective problem-solving emphasis is further reinforced by the division of the exercise sets into five discrete, increasingly challenging groups (see p. xx). Each set begins with Questions that test students' conceptual grasp of the material. Following these, Exercises, now paired and organized by topic, reinforce students' understanding of each section. Additional Exercises are not keyed by topic, so that students must identify and apply the appropriate concepts themselves. The fourth type of exercises, Challenge Problems, require students to go still further and combine skills and concepts. Finally, Marathon Problems are even more comprehensive (see below).

- New to this edition is the inclusion of "marathon" problems at the end of many of the chapters. The use of these problems in the general chemistry course was described in a recent issue of the *Journal of Chemical Education.*[*] Marathon problems can serve several purposes: to introduce chapter material, since they provide a way for the students to see a large number of the concepts in a given chapter in a single problem; to enable students to discern relationships among the main points of a chapter (and sometimes among different chapters) in a way not possible with shorter, narrowly defined problems; and to provide a mechanism for increasing the interaction between the instructor and the students, resulting in a more active learning environment.

- Chapter 4, "Types of Chemical Reactions and Solution Stoichiometry," has been tightened and condensed to

[*]Burness, James H. *J. Chem. Educ*. 1991, *68*, 919.

simplify and clarify this important material as much as possible. In particular, great pains have been taken to explain how to predict the products of reactions. Problem-solving strategies and sample exercises have been increased, while a more detailed discussion of qualitative analysis moves to later chapters. A careful reading of this chapter will show that its length is due mainly to careful explanations of the concepts related to reactions in solution.

- Many of the illustrations have been reconceived for additional visual clarification of chemical concepts and all have been rerendered to achieve a new standard of accuracy and clarity. Pedagogical consistency in the use of color has been a focus in the generation of this new artwork.

Flexibility of Topic Order

The order of topics in the text was chosen because it is preferred by the majority of instructors. However, I consciously constructed the book so that many other orders are possible. For example, at the University of Illinois, for a two-semester sequence we use the chapters in the order 1–6, 13–15, 7–9, 21, 20, 12, 10, 11, 16, 17, and 22. Sections of Chapters 18, 19, and 23 are used throughout the two semesters as appropriate. This order, chosen because of the way the laboratory is organized, is not necessarily recommended, but it illustrates the flexibility of order built into the text.

Some specific points about topic order:

- About half of chemistry courses present kinetics before equilibria, while the other half present equilibria first. This text is written to accommodate either order.

- The introductory aspects of thermodynamics are presented relatively early (in Chapter 6) because of the importance of energy in various chemical processes and models, but the more subtle thermodynamic concepts are left until later (Chapter 16). These two chapters may be used together if desired.

- To make the book more flexible, the derivation of the ideal gas law from the kinetic-molecular theory and quantitative analysis using spectroscopy are presented in the appendixes. While mainstream general chemistry courses typically do not cover this material, some courses may find it appropriate. By using the optional material in the appendixes and by assigning the more difficult end-of-chapter exercises (from the additional exercises section), an instructor will find the level of the text appropriate for many majors courses or for other courses requiring a more extensive coverage of these topics.

- Because some courses cover bonding using only a Lewis-structure approach, orbitals are not presented in the introductory chapter on bonding (Chapter 8). In Chapter 9 both hybridization and the molecular orbital model are covered, but either or both of these topics may be omitted if desired.

- Chapter 4 can be tailored to fit the specific course involved. Used in its entirety where it stands in the book, it provides interesting examples of descriptive chemistry and supports the laboratory program. Material in this chapter can also be skipped entirely or covered at some later point whenever appropriate. For example, the sections on oxidation and reduction can be taught with electrochemistry. Although many instructors prefer early introduction of this concept, these sections can be omitted without complication since the next few chapters do not depend on this material.

Supplements

An extensive supplements package has been designed to make this book more useful to both student and instructor. These supplements include:

- *Study Guide,* by Paul B. Kelter of the University of Wisconsin, Oshkosh. Written to be a self-study aid for students, this guide includes alternate strategies for solving various types of problems, supplemental explanations for the most difficult material, and self-tests. There are approximately 400 worked examples and 700 practice problems (with answers) designed to give students mastery and confidence.

- *Solutions Guide,* by Kenneth C. Brooks, Thomas J. Hummel, and Steven S. Zumdahl, all of the University of Illinois, Urbana, provides detailed solutions for half of the end-of-chapter exercises (designated by blue question numbers or letters) using the strategies emphasized in the text. To ensure the accuracy of the solutions, this supplement and the *Complete Solutions Guide* were checked independently by several instructors.

- *Complete Solutions Guide,* by Kenneth C. Brooks, Thomas J. Hummel, and Steven S. Zumdahl, presents detailed solutions for **all** of the end-of-chapter exercises in the text for the convenience of faculty and staff in-

volved in instruction and for instructors who wish their students to have solutions for all exercises. Departmental approval is required for the sale of the *Complete Solutions Guide* to students.

- *Instructor's Guide,* by Kenneth C. Brooks, includes suggestions for alternative orders of topics, amplification of strategies used in various chapters, suggested sources of additional information, and a section on notes for teaching assistants.

- *Solving Equilibrium Problems with Applications to Qualitative Analysis,* by Steven S. Zumdahl. Revised from a text successfully used by thousands of students over the last ten years, this book offers thorough, step-by-step procedures for solving problems related to equilibria taking place both in the gas phase and in solution. Containing hundreds of sample exercises, test exercises with complete solutions, and end-of-chapter exercises with answers, the text utilizes the same problem-solving methods found in *Chemistry* and is an excellent source of additional drill-type problems. The last chapter presents an exploratory qualitative analysis experiment with explanations based on the principles of aqueous equilibria.

- *Experimental Chemistry,* Third Edition, by James F. Hall of the University of Lowell, provides an extensively revised laboratory program compatible with the text. The 43 experiments present a wide variety of chemistry, and many experiments offer choices of procedures. Safety is strongly emphasized throughout the program.

- *Instructor's Resource Guide* for *Experimental Chemistry,* Third Edition, by James F. Hall, contains tips including hints on running experiments, approximate times for each experiment, and answers to all prelab and postlab questions posed in the laboratory guide.

- *Test Item File,* by Susan Arena (available to adopters), offers a printed version of more than 2000 exam questions referenced to the appropriate text section. Questions are available in multiple-choice, open-ended, and true-false formats.

- *Computerized Testing* presents the *Test Item File* questions in a computerized testing program by ESATest. Instructors can produce chapter tests, midterms, and final exams easily and with excellent graphics capability. The instructor can also edit existing questions or add new ones as desired, or preview questions on screen and add them to the test with a single keystroke. The testing program is available for Apple II, Macintosh, and IBM computers.

- *University of Illinois Film Center General Chemistry Videotapes,* which may also be purchased by adopters, reinforce the major concepts found in the text.

- *Transparencies,* a set of 245 transparencies (many in color), are available to adopters of the third edition of the text.

New Supplements

- *Chemistry in Motion Videotape and Videodisc Supplments.* D. C. Heath has two exciting and pedagogically valuable sets of video demonstrations of chemical experiments:

  Available on videotape only is the Project SERAPHIM and JCE:Software 60-minute collection of 37 demonstrations done by John W. Moore of the University of Wisconsin, Madison, with the assistance of Lynn Hunsberger.

  Available on videotape *and* videodisc is a series of 34 demonstrations done by Patricia L. Samuel of Boston University, with the assistance of Lorraine Kelly. The *Chemistry in Motion Videodisc* also includes a complete set of the approximately 550 illustrations in the third edition of *Chemistry.*

- *Chemistry in Motion Software.* This Macintosh software by Leonard J. Soltzberg of Simmons College provides animations of concepts and processes that are best understood when actually viewed in motion and with dimensionality, e.g., Le Châtelier's principle, crystal structure, states of matter, molecular motion, entropy, and so on.

- *Lecture Demonstration Guide.* (See p. vi for a description of this helpful resource reference by Fred Juergens of the University of Wisconsin, Madison.)

Acknowledgments

The success of this text is due to the efforts of many talented people. It is a great privilege and pleasure to work with Kent Porter Hamann, Editorial Director for Science. Kent is simply the best in the business. She combines remarkable market expertise and editorial skills with incredible energy and continuous good humor. Karen Wise, Senior Production Editor, did a truly amazing job of holding everything together. Karen's outstanding organizational and editorial skills, combined with her endless supply of good cheer, made this project a real pleasure.

I am especially grateful to my multitalented wife Eunice who is truly a partner in this project, providing constant moral support and spending long hours discussing, typing, checking, and proofreading. I also greatly appreciate the continuing understanding and support of Whitney and Leslie.

I owe much to Ken Brooks, who collaborated in writing the end-of-chapter exercises and who has contributed greatly to the project through his enthusiastic attitude and unerring suggestions concerning content and approach. In addition, Tom Hummel contributed tremendously to this project through his efforts to make the end-of-chapter problems clear and the answers accurate. My thanks also to my colleagues in the general chemistry program at the University of Illinois, particularly Roxy Wilson, Barbara Whitmarsh, and Loretta Jones,[*] who have made many constructive suggestions.

Many other people at D. C. Heath supplied invaluable assistance during this project: Jim Porter Hamann, Senior Product Manager, whose energy and thorough understanding of the marketplace have contributed greatly to the success of this book; Mark Corsey, Photo Researcher, who showed real creativity in securing new photos for this edition; Gary Crespo, Art Editor, who coordinated the revision of the entire illustration program; Kenneth Hollman, Senior Designer, who developed a beautiful and functional design; and Joanne Williams, Editorial Associate, whose efficient and cheerful assistance was always greatly appreciated. Last, but surely not least, I want to express my gratitude to the D. C. Heath book reps, a very impressive group of hard-working people, many of whom I am proud to call friends.

Finally, I want to extend special thanks to the following people, who reviewed all or part of the manuscript at various stages:

Robert D. Allendoerfer, State University of New York, Buffalo
Patricia G. Amateis, Virginia Polytechnic Institute and State University
J. Aaron Bertrand, Georgia Institute of Technology
James R. Bowser, SUNY College, Fredonia
Albert W. Burgstahler, University of Kansas
Mike L. Buttram, Texarkana College
William C. Deese, Louisiana Tech University
Michael L. Denniston, Dekalb College
George W. Eastland, Jr., Saginaw Valley State University
Abraham S. Endler
C. W. Finley, Penn State University, New Kensington Campus

[*]Now at the University of Northern Colorado.

Ronald P. Furstenau, United States Air Force Academy
Marcia L. Gillette, Indiana University at Kokomo
Marian Chu Hallada, University of Michigan
Forrest C. Hentz, Jr., North Carolina State University
Peter E. Hurlimann, Citrus College
John Judkins
A. H. Kalantar, University of Alberta, Edmonton
Catherine A. Keenan, Chaffey College
Mariusz A. Klobukowski, University of Alberta, Edmonton
Frank William Kutzler, Tennessee Technological University
John Langston, Yuba College
Alfred Lee, City College of San Francisco
Curtis L. McLendon, Saddleback College

David Munch, Seattle Central Community College
Theodore P. Perros, George Washington University
James A. Plambeck, University of Alberta, Edmonton
B. Ken Robertson, University of Missouri, Rolla
Theodore Sakano, Rockland Community College
William E. Stanclift, Northern Virginia Community College, Annandale Campus
Roger W. Strassburg, University of Akron
Josef Takats, University of Alberta, Edmonton
William P. Tucker, North Carolina State University
Jay H. Worrell, University of South Florida

S. S. Z.

◀ To the Student ▶

The major purpose of this book, of course, is to help you learn chemistry. However, this main thrust is closely linked to two other goals: to show how important and how interesting the subject is, and to show how to think like a chemist. To solve complicated problems the chemist uses logic, trial and error, intuition, and, above all, patience. A chemist is used to being wrong. The important thing is to learn from a mistake, recheck assumptions, and try again. A chemist thrives on puzzles that seem to defy solutions.

Many of you using this text do not plan to be practicing chemists. However, the nonchemist can benefit from the chemist's attitude. Problem solving is important in all professions and in all walks of life. The techniques you will learn from this book will serve you well in any career you choose. Thus, I believe that the study of chemistry has much to offer the nonmajor, including an understanding of many fascinating and important phenomena and a chance to hone problem-solving skills.

This book attempts to present chemistry in a manner that is sensible to the novice. Chemistry is not the result of an inspired vision. It is the product of countless observations and many attempts, using logic and trial and error, to account for these observations. In this book the concepts are developed in a natural way: the observations come first and then models are constructed to explain the observed behavior.

Models are a major focus in this book. The uses and limitations of models are emphasized, and science is treated as a human activity, subject to all the normal human foibles. Mistakes are discussed as well as successes.

A central theme of this book is a thoughtful, systematic approach to problem solving. Learning encompasses much more than simply memorizing facts. Truly educated people use their factual knowledge as a starting point—a base for creative approaches to solving problems.

As you have probably heard, learning chemistry can be frustrating. It is easy to lose sight of how really important and interesting chemistry is. You *can* learn chemistry and even enjoy the process, but you must understand that finesse works much better than brute force. Chemistry can be difficult not so much because the concepts are hard, but

because it deals with complicated systems. Before a problem can be solved, a lot of facts must be sifted to find the pertinent ones. There is no alternative to thinking things through.

Read through the material in the text carefully. For most concepts, illustrations or photos will help you visualize what is going on. Often a given type of problem is "walked through" in the text before the corresponding sample exercises appear. Strategies for solving problems are given throughout the text.

Thoroughly examine the sample exercises and the problem-solving strategies. The strategies summarize the approach taken in the text; the sample exercises follow the strategies step-by-step. Schematics in Chapter 15 also illustrate the logical pathways to solving aqueous equilibrium problems.

Throughout the text, I have used margin notes to highlight key points, to comment on an application of the text material, or to reference material in other parts of the book. The boxed features called *Chemical Impacts* discuss especially interesting applications of chemistry to the everyday world.

Each chapter has a summary and key terms list for review, and the glossary gives a quick reference for definitions.

Learning chemistry requires working the end-of-chapter exercises assigned by your professor. Answers to exercises denoted by blue question numbers are in the back of the book, while complete solutions to those exercises are in the *Solutions Guide*.

The *Study Guide* contains extra practice problems and many examples. The supplement *Solving Equilibrium Problems with Applications to Qualitative Analysis* reinforces in great detail the text's step-by-step approach to solving equilibrium problems and contains many worked examples and self-quiz questions to help you assess your level of proficiency.

It is very important to use the exercises to your best advantage. Your main goal should not be to simply get the correct answer but to *understand the process* for getting the answer. Memorizing the solutions for specific problems is not a very good way to prepare for an exam. There are too many pigeonholes required to cover every possible problem type. Look within the problem for the solution. Use the concepts you have learned along with a systematic, logical approach to find the solution. Learn to trust yourself to think it out. You will make mistakes, but the important thing is to learn from these errors. The only way to gain confidence is to do lots of practice problems and use these to diagnose your weaknesses.

Be patient and thoughtful and work hard to understand rather than simply memorize. I wish you an interesting and satisfying year.

◀ About the Author ▶

STEVEN S. ZUMDAHL received his B.S. degree in Chemistry from Wheaton College (Illinois) in 1964 and his Ph.D. in Chemistry from the University of Illinois, Urbana, in 1968.

In 25 years of teaching he has been a faculty member at the University of Colorado, Boulder; Parkland College (Illinois); and the University of Illinois, Urbana. Currently he is Professor and Associate Head of Chemistry and Director of Undergraduate Programs in Chemistry at the University of Illinois.

Professor Zumdahl is known at the University of Illinois for his rapport with students and for his outstanding teaching ability. During his tenure at the University, he has received the University of Illinois Award for Excellence in Teaching, the Liberal Arts and Sciences College Award for Distinguished Teaching, and the School of Chemical Sciences Teaching Award (four times).

Dr. Z., as he is known to his students, greatly enjoys ''mechanical things,'' including bicycles and cars. He collects and restores classic automobiles, having a special enthusiasm for vintage Corvettes.

◀ A Note from the Author ▶

◀ CHEMICAL IMPACT ▶

Titanium Makes Great Bicycles

One of the most interesting characteristics of the world of bicycling is the competition among various frame materials. Bicycle frames are now built from steel, aluminum, carbon fiber composites, and titanium, with each material having advantages and disadvantages. Steel is strong, economical, adaptable, and (unfortunately) "rustable." Aluminum is light and stiff but has relatively low fatigue limits (resistance to repeated stresses). Carbon fiber composites have amazing strength-to-mass ratios and have shock- and vibration-dampening properties superior to any metal; however, they are very expensive. Titanium has a density approximately 43% less than that of steel, a yield strength (when alloyed with metals such as aluminum and tin) that is 30% greater than that of steel, an extraordinary resistance to fatigue, and a high resistance to corrosion, but it is expensive and difficult to work.

Of all these materials, titanium gives the bicycle that fanatics seem to love the most. After their first ride on a bicycle with a titanium frame, most experienced cyclists find themselves shaking their heads and searching hard for the right words to describe the experience. Typically, the word *magic* is used a great deal in the ensuing description.

The magic of titanium results from its combination of toughness, stretchability, and resilience. A bicycle that is built stiff to resist pedaling loads usually responds by giving a harsh, uncomfortable ride. A titanium bike is very stiff against high pedaling torques, but it seems to transmit much less road shock than bikes made of competitive materials. Why titanium excels in dampening vibrations is not entirely clear. Despite titanium's significantly lower density than steel's, shock waves travel more slowly in titanium than in steel. Whatever the explanation for its shock-absorbing abilities, titanium pro-

A titanium bicycle.

vides three things that cyclists find crucial: light weight, stiffness, and a smooth ride—magic.

Titanium is quite abundant in the earth's crust, ranking ninth of all the elements and second among the transition elements. The metallurgy of titanium presents special challenges. Carbon, the reducing agent most commonly used to obtain metals from their oxides ores, cannot be used because it forms intractable interstitial carbides with titanium. These carbides are extraordinarily hard and have melting points close to 3000°C. However, if chlorine gas is used in conjunction with carbon to treat the ore, volatile $TiCl_4$ is formed, which can be distilled off and then reduced with magnesium or sodium at approximately 1000°C to form a titanium "sponge." This sponge is then ground up, cleaned with aqua regia (a 1:3 mixture of concentrated HNO_3 and con-

centrated HCl), melted under a blanket of inert gas (to prevent reaction with oxygen), and cast into ingots. Titanium, a lustrous, silvery metal with a high melting point (1667°C), crystallizes in a hexagonal closest packed structure. Because titanium tends to become quite brittle when trace impurities such as C, N, and O are present, it must be fabricated with great care.

Titanium's unusual ability to stretch makes it hard to machine. It tends to push away even from a very sharp cutting blade, giving a rather unpredictable final dimension. Also, because titanium is embrittled by reaction with oxygen, all welding operations must be carried out under a shielding gas such as argon.

However, the bicycle that results is worth all these difficulties. One woman described a titanium bicycle as "the one God rides on Sunday."

- In 25 years of teaching chemistry, I have noticed that students often approach the course with apprehension because they have heard how difficult chemistry can be. One of my main goals is to motivate students by showing them just how important and interesting chemistry really is.

a nationally recognized expert in the areas of monitoring and
...missions from hazardous substances and is a frequent lecturer at
...ps. He has over 10 publications and 20 conference presentations

...interest in a career in environmental science was fostered by two
...mistry courses and two ecology courses he took as an undergrad-
...plan to gain several years of industrial experience and then to
...r a graduate degree was changed when he found that professional
... a B.S. degree was possible in the environmental research field.
...ary nature of most environmental problems has allowed him to
...sts in several fields. His specialty is really in being a generalist.
...ntal consulting field provides Bart with a number of attractions:
...ne and solve a number of research problems; the simultaneous
...of diverse projects (he has had a major role in over 40 projects
...k of desk, field, and laboratory work; the travel; and the opportu-
...warding work that has a positive effect on people's lives. In his
... manages a research group consisting of two Ph.D., two M.S.,
...entists with chemistry, physics, and atmospheric science back-

...eer highlights are
...er month doing air sampling in the Grand Tetons, where he also
...d learned to ski
...g pipes by hand into the rocky ground of Death Valley Monument
...ly with experts in their fields and with people who enjoy what

- Doing vigorous work in 100°F weather while wearing a rubberized suit, double gloves, and a respirator
- Getting to work in and see Alaska, Yosemite Park, Niagara Falls, Hong Kong, the People's Republic of China, Mesa Verde, New York City, and dozens of other interesting places

Heidi Piper Flatley went to work for Procter and Gamble after her graduation from the University of Illinois at Champaign-Urbana in 1987 with a B.S. degree in chemical engineering. Combining her technical expertise with her interests in psychology and marketing, Ms. Flatley took a position in the area of Products Research, where she tries to discover "unmet consumer needs" and then to design products to meet these needs. Heidi describes herself as a "technology broker"—someone who looks for ways to use her company's technical expertise to improve people's lives. After a possible application is identified, she then works closely with the personnel in Research and Development as the concept is brought from the idea stage to a finished product that can be market tested.

Heidi says, "I have become an expert in market research and am continuing to learn about marketing and about management skills (personal and interpersonal) and am gaining excellent experience in product development."

By 1990, Heidi was living in a French-speaking neighborhood in Brussels, Belgium, where she does market research throughout Europe for Procter and Gamble. Heidi says, "As a sample slice of my job, I'll tell you what I did last week. I spent Monday, Tuesday, and Wednesday in London with a Belgian woman I hired to help

Heidi Piper Flatley

- Chemistry is a *human activity,* and throughout the text I try to show not just the history of chemistry but also that chemists are indeed real people.

Notice from Sample Exercise 4.12 that the procedures for doing stoichiometric calculations for solution reactions are very similar to those for other types of reactions. It is useful to think in terms of the following steps for reactions in solution.

STOICHIOMETRY FOR REACTIONS IN SOLUTION

STEP 1
Identify the species present in the combined solution, and determine what reaction occurs.

STEP 2
Write the balanced net ionic equation for the reaction.

STEP 3
Calculate the moles of reactants.

STEP 4
Determine which reactant is limiting.

STEP 5
Calculate the moles of product or products, as required.

STEP 6
Convert to grams or other units, as required.

Sample Exercise 4.13

When aqueous solutions of Na_2SO_4 and $Pb(NO_3)_2$ are mixed, $PbSO_4$ precipitates. Calculate the mass of $PbSO_4$ formed when 1.25 L of 0.0500 M $Pb(NO_3)_2$ and 2.00 L of 0.0250 M Na_2SO_4 are mixed.

Solution

STEP 1

Identify the species present in the combined solution, and determine what reaction occurs. When the aqueous solutions of Na_2SO_4 (containing Na^+ and SO_4^{2-} ions) and $Pb(NO_3)_2$ (containing Pb^{2+} and NO_3^- ions) are mixed, the resulting solution contains the ions Na^+, SO_4^{2-}, Pb^{2+}, and NO_3^-. Since $NaNO_3$ is soluble and $PbSO_4$ is insoluble (see Rule 4 in Table 4.1), solid $PbSO_4$ will form.

STEP 2

Write the balanced net ionic equation for the reaction. The net ionic equation is

$$Pb^{2+}(aq) + SO_4^{2-}(aq) \rightarrow PbSO_4(s)$$

STEP 3

Calculate the moles of reactants. Since 0.0500 M $Pb(NO_3)_2$ c[...] Pb^{2+} ions, we can calculate the moles of Pb^{2+} ions in 1.25 L [...] follows:

$$1.25\ \cancel{L} \times \frac{0.0500\ \text{mol}\ Pb^{2+}}{\cancel{L}} = 0.0625\ \text{mol}\ Pb^{2[...]}$$

The 0.0250 M Na_2SO_4 solution contains 0.0250 M SO_4^{2-} ions, [...] moles of SO_4^{2-} ions in 2.00 L of this solution is

$$2.00\ \cancel{L} \times \frac{0.0250\ \text{mol}\ SO_4^{2-}}{\cancel{L}} = 0.0500\ \text{mol}\ SO_4[...]$$

- Chemistry is not the result of an inspired vision. It is the product of countless observations and many attempts, using logic and trial and error, to account for these observations. In this book I try to develop key chemical concepts in the same way—to show the observations first and then discuss the models that have been constructed to explain the observed behavior. I hope students will practice ''thinking like a chemist'' by carefully studying the observations to see if they can follow the thought process, rather than just jumping ahead to the equation or model that will follow.

- Another goal I have is to show students how to think like a chemist. Most students using this text do not plan to be practicing chemists. However, problem solving is important in all professions and all walks of life. The same skills and attitudes a chemist uses—logic, trial and error, intuition, and above all, patience—students will find useful whatever their career goals.

---

relationships among the properties can be discovered. These relationships are often represented pictorially by means of graphs (plots).

We will take an historical approach to these laws to give you some perspective on the scientific method in action.

Boyle's Law

The first quantitative experiments on gases were performed by an Irish chemist, Robert Boyle (1627–1691). Using a J-shaped tube closed at one end (Fig. 5.4), which he reportedly set up in the multistory entryway of his house, Boyle studied the relationship between the pressure of the trapped gas and its volume. Representative values from Boyle's experiments are given in Table 5.1. These data show that the product of the pressure and volume for the trapped air sample is constant within the accuracies of Boyle's measurements (note the third column in Table 5.1). This behavior can be represented by the equation

$$PV = k$$

which is called **Boyle's law** and where k is a constant for a given sample of air at a specific temperature.

It is convenient to represent the data in Table 5.1 by using two different plots. The first type of plot, P versus V, forms a curve called a **hyperbola** shown in Fig. 5.5(a) on p. 188. Looking at this plot, note that as the pressure drops by about half (from 58.8 to 29.1), the volume doubles (from 24.0 to 48.0). In other words, there is an *inverse relationship* between pressure and volume. The second type of plot can be obtained by rearranging Boyle's law to give

$$V = \frac{k}{P} = k\frac{1}{P}$$

which is the equation for a straight line of the type

$$y = mx + b$$

where m represents the slope and b the intercept of the straight line. In this case, $y = V$, $x = 1/P$, $m = k$, and $b = 0$. Thus a plot of V versus $1/P$ using Boyle's data gives a straight line with an intercept of zero, as shown in Fig. 5.5(b).

Figure 5.4
A J-tube similar to the one used by Boyle.

Boyle's law: $V \propto 1/P$ at constant temperature.

Graphing is reviewed in Appendix 1.3.

Table 5.1		
Actual Data from Boyle's Experiment		
Volume (in³)	Pressure (in Hg)	Pressure × Volume (in Hg × in³)
117.5	12.0	14.1×10^2
87.2	16.0	14.0×10^2
70.7	20.0	14.1×10^2
58.8	24.0	14.1×10^2
44.2	32.0	14.1×10^2
35.3	40.0	14.1×10^2
29.1	48.0	14.0×10^2

4.1 Water, the Common Solvent

Purpose

• To show why the polar nature of water makes it an effective solvent.

Water is one of the most important substances on earth. It is essential for sustaining the reactions that keep us alive, but it also affects our lives in many indirect ways. Water helps moderate the earth's temperature; it cools automobile engines, nuclear power plants, and many industrial processes; it provides a means of transportation on the earth's surface and a medium for the growth of a myriad of creatures we use as food; and much more.

One of the most valuable properties of water is its ability to dissolve many different substances. For example, salt disappears when you sprinkle it into the water used to cook vegetables, as does sugar when you add it to your iced tea. In each case the "disappearing" substance is obviously still present—you can taste it. What happens when a solid dissolves? To understand this process, we need to consider the nature of water. Liquid water consists of a collection of H_2O molecules. An individual H_2O molecule is "bent" or V-shaped, with an H—O—H angle of approximately 105 degrees:

$$H \overset{105°}{\underset{O}{\wedge}} H$$

The O—H bonds in the water molecule are covalent bonds formed by electron sharing between the oxygen and hydrogen atoms. However, the electrons of the bond are not shared equally between these atoms. For reasons we will discuss in later chapters, oxygen has a greater attraction for electrons than does hydrogen. If the electrons were shared equally between the two atoms, both would be electrically neutral because, on average, the number of electrons around each would equal the number of protons in that nucleus. However, because the oxygen atom has a greater attraction for electrons, the shared electrons tend to spend more time close to the oxygen than to either of the hydrogens. Thus the oxygen atom gains a slight excess of negative charge, and the hydrogen atoms become slightly positive. This is shown in Fig. 4.1, where δ (delta) indicates a *partial* charge *(less than one unit of charge)*. Because of this unequal charge distribution, water is said to be a **polar molecule.** It is this polarity that gives water its great ability to dissolve compounds.

A schematic of an ionic solid dissolving in water is shown in Fig. 4.2. Note that the "positive ends" of the water molecules are attracted to the negatively charged anions and that the "negative ends" are attracted to the positively charged cations. This process is called **hydration.** The hydration of its ions tends to cause a salt to "fall apart" in the water, or to dissolve. The strong forces present among the positive and negative ions of the solid are replaced by strong water–ion interactions.

It is very important to recognize that when ionic substances (salts) dissolve in water, they break up into the *individual* cations and anions. For instance, when ammonium nitrate (NH_4NO_3) dissolves in water, the resulting solution contains NH_4^+ and NO_3^- ions moving around independently. This proc[ess is repre]sented as

$$NH_4NO_3(s) \xrightarrow{H_2O(l)} NH_4^+(aq) + NO_3^-(aq)$$

where (aq) designates that the ions are hydrated by unspecified [numbers of water] molecules.

Figure 4.1
(a) The water molecule is polar.
(b) A space-filling model of the water molecule.

Figure 4.2
Polar water molecules interact with the positive and negative ions of a salt, assisting in the dissolving process.

The solubility of ionic substances in water varies greatly. For example, sodium chloride is quite soluble in water, whereas silver chloride (contains Ag^+ and Cl^- ions) is only very slightly soluble. The differences in the solubilities of ionic compounds in water typically depend on the relative attractions of the ions for each other (these forces hold the solid together) and the attractions of the ions for water molecules (which cause the solid to disperse [dissolve] in water). Solubility is a complex

• Visual material is especially important for learning general chemistry, which typically presents a pictorial view of chemical concepts. All of the illustrations in this edition have been reworked to increase student understanding.

---

768 Chapter Sixteen Spontaneity, Entropy, and Free Energy

The first law of thermodynamics is used mainly for energy bookkeeping, that is, to answer such questions as

How much energy is involved in the change?

Does energy flow into or out of the system?

What form does the energy finally assume?

The first law of thermodynamics: the energy of the universe is constant.

Although the first law of thermodynamics provides the means for accounting for energy, it gives no hint as to *why* a particular process occurs in a given direction. This is the main question to be considered in this chapter.

16.1 Spontaneous Processes and Entropy

Purpose

• To define a spontaneous process.

• To define entropy in terms of positional probability.

Spontaneous does not mean fast.

A process is said to be **spontaneous** if it *occurs without outside intervention.* **Spontaneous processes** may be fast or slow. As we will see in this chapter, thermodynamics can tell us the *direction* in which a process will occur but can say nothing about the *speed* of the process. As we saw in Chapter 12, the rate of a reaction depends on many factors, such as activation energy, temperature, concentration, and catalysts, and we were able to explain these effects using a simple collision model. In describing a chemical reaction, the discipline of chemical kinetics focuses on the pathway between reactants and products; thermodynamics only considers the initial and final states and does not require knowledge of the pathway between reactants and products (see Fig. 16.2).

In summary, thermodynamics lets us predict whether a process will occur but gives no information about the amount of time required for the process. For example, according to the principles of thermodynamics, a diamond should change spontaneously to graphite. The fact that we do not observe this process does not mean the prediction is wrong; it simply means the process is very slow. Thus we need both thermodynamics and kinetics to describe reactions fully.

To explore the idea of spontaneity, consider the following physical and chemical processes:

A ball rolls down a hill but never spontaneously rolls back up the hill.

If exposed to air and moisture, steel rusts spontaneously. However, the iron oxide in rust does not spontaneously change back to iron gas.

A gas fills its container uniformly. It never spontaneously col the container.

Heat flow always occurs from a hot object to a cooler one. T never occurs spontaneously.

Wood burns spontaneously in an exothermic reaction to form d water, but wood is not formed when carbon dioxide and together.

• Throughout the text I have used margin notes to highlight key points, to comment on an application of the text material, or to reference material in other parts of the text. I have also included ''Purpose'' statements at the beginning of each section of a chapter to identify the key concepts that will be covered. This book attempts to present chemistry in a manner that makes sense to the student.

8.7 The Covalent Chemical Bond: A Model   **363**

◀ **CHEMICAL IMPACT** ▶

Testing for Toxicity by Computer

When a new compound that will come in contact with humans is synthesized, the compound's safety must be tested. Currently this is done with expensive bacterial or animal tests. However, computers are now being introduced to screen new compounds to detect those which are likely to be toxic in some way.

The fundamental idea is that the toxicity of a compound is due to some part or parts of the molecular structure. That is, certain types of molecular fragments seem to always lead to a particular kind of toxicity, such as carcinogenicity (ability to cause cancer). The new procedure involves entering known structure–toxicity relationships into the computer database. When a new compound is prepared, its structure is compared by the computer with this database. If the computer finds a fragment in the new molecule that is known to cause a toxic response, this information will alert the researcher to the possible problems. The hope is that this approach will prevent many compounds from being tested only to be rejected after much time and money have already been spent. This should make products both safer and less expensive.

as constructed of individual bonds, C—C, C—H, C—N, C—O, N—H, and so on, it helps tremendously in predicting and understanding the protein's behavior. The essential idea is that we expect a given bond to behave about the same in any molecular environment. Used in this way, the model of the chemical bond has helped chemists to systematize the reactions of the millions of existing compounds.

In addition to being very useful, the bonding model is also physically sensible. It makes sense that atoms can form stable groups by sharing electrons; shared electrons give a lower energy state because they are simultaneously attracted by two nuclei.

Also, as we will see in the next section, bond energy data support the existence of discrete bonds that are relatively independent of the molecular environment. It is very important to remember, however, that the chemical bond is only a model. Although our concept of discrete bonds in molecules agrees with many of our observations, some molecular properties require that we think of a molecule as a whole, with the electrons free to move through the entire molecule. This is called **delocalization** of the electrons, a concept that will be discussed more completely in the next chapter.

Fundamental Properties of Models

• Models are human inventions, always based on an incomplete understanding of how nature works. *A model does not equal reality.*

• Models are often wrong. This property derives from the first property. Models are based on speculation and are always oversimplifications.

• Models tend to become more complicated as they age. As flaws are discovered in our models, we ''patch'' them and thus add more detail.

• It is very important to understand the assumptions inherent in a particular model before you use it to interpret observations or to make predictions. Simple models usually involve very restrictive assumptions and can only be expected to yield qualitative information. Asking for a sophisticated explanation from a simple model is like expecting to get an accurate mass for a diamond using a bathroom scale.

For a model to be used effectively, we must understand its strengths and weaknesses and ask only appropriate questions. An illustration of this point is the

---

• Models are a central theme in this book. The uses and limitations of models are emphasized to show chemistry as a dynamic process. Mistakes are discussed as well as the successes to further illustrate this process. Throughout the text I emphasize that *a model does not equal reality.*

102 Chapter Three Stoichiometry

Since C_2H_5OH contains six hydrogen atoms, the hydrogen atoms can be balanced by placing a 3 before the H_2O:

$$C_2H_5OH(l) + O_2(g) \rightarrow 2CO_2(g) + 3H_2O(g)$$
$$(5 + 1)\ H \qquad\qquad\qquad (3 \times 2)\ H$$

Last, we balance the oxygen atoms. Note that the right side of the preceding equation contains seven oxygen atoms, whereas the left side has only three. We can correct this by putting a 3 before the O_2 to produce the balanced equation:

$$C_2H_5OH(l) + 3O_2(g) \rightarrow 2CO_2(g) + 3H_2O(g)$$
$$\underline{1\ O \qquad\qquad 6\ O} \qquad \underline{(2 \times 2)\ O \quad 3\ O}$$
$$7\ O \qquad\qquad\qquad 7\ O$$

Now we check:

$$C_2H_5OH(l) + 3O_2(g) \rightarrow 2CO_2(g) + 3H_2O(g)$$

2 C atoms	2 C atoms
6 H atoms	6 H atoms
7 O atoms	7 O atoms

The equation is balanced.

WRITING AND BALANCING THE EQUATION FOR A CHEMICAL REACTION

STEP 1
Determine what reaction is occurring. What are the reactants, the products, and the physical states involved?

STEP 2
Write the *unbalanced* equation that summarizes the reaction described in Step 1.

STEP 3
Balance the equation by inspection, starting with the most complicated molecule(s). Determine what coefficients are necessary so that the same number of each type of atom appears on both reactant and product sides. Do not change the identities (formulas) of any of the reactants or products.

Sample Exercise 3.14

Chromate and dichromate compounds are carcinogens (cancer-inducing agents) and should be handled very carefully.

Chromium compounds exhibit a variety of bright colors. When solid ammonium dichromate, $(NH_4)_2Cr_2O_7$, a vivid orange compound, is ignited, a spectacular reaction occurs, as shown in the two photographs. Although the reaction is actually somewhat more complex, let's assume here that the pro chromium(III) oxide, nitrogen gas (consisting of N_2 molecules), Balance the equation for this reaction.

Solution

3.3

STEP 1
From the description given, the reactant is solid ammoni $(NH_4)_2Cr_2O_7(s)$, and the products are nitrogen gas, $N_2(g)$, wate and solid chromium(III) oxide, $Cr_2O_3(s)$. The formula for chromiu

---

3.7 Balancing Chemical Equations **103**

be determined by recognizing that the Roman numeral III means that Cr^{3+} ions are present. For a neutral compound, the formula must then be Cr_2O_3, since each oxide ion is O^{2-}.

STEP 2
The unbalanced equation is

$$(NH_4)_2Cr_2O_7(s) \rightarrow Cr_2O_3(s) + N_2(g) + H_2O(g)$$

STEP 3
Note that nitrogen and chromium are balanced (two nitrogen atoms and two chromium atoms on each side), but hydrogen and oxygen are not. A coefficient of 4 for H_2O balances the hydrogen atoms:

$$(NH_4)_2Cr_2O_7(s) \rightarrow Cr_2O_3(s) + N_2(g) + 4H_2O(g)$$
$$(4 \times 2)\ H \qquad\qquad\qquad\qquad (4 \times 2)\ H$$

Note that in balancing the hydrogen we also have balanced the oxygen, since there are seven oxygen atoms in the reactants and in the products.

CHECK:

$$2\ N,\ 8\ H,\ 2\ Cr,\ 7\ O \rightarrow 2\ N,\ 8\ H,\ 2\ Cr,\ 7\ O$$
$$\text{Reactant} \qquad\qquad \text{Product}$$
$$\text{atoms} \qquad\qquad\quad \text{atoms}$$

The equation is balanced.

Decomposition of ammonium dichromate.

Sample Exercise 3.15

Propane (C_3H_8), a liquid at 25°C under high pressure, is often used as a fuel in rural areas where there is no natural gas pipeline. When liquid propane is released from its storage tank, the pressure on it is lowered and it changes to a gas. Propane gas reacts with oxygen gas (a combustion reaction) in a furnace to produce gaseous carbon dioxide and water vapor. Balance the equation for this reaction.

Solution

The reactants are propane and oxygen; the products are carbon dioxide and water. All are in the gaseous state. Thus the unbalanced equation for the reaction is

$$C_3H_8(g) + O_2(g) \rightarrow CO_2(g) + H_2O(g)$$

We start with C_3H_8 because it is the most complicated molecule. Since C_3H_8 contains three carbon atoms per molecule, a coefficient of 3 is needed for CO_2:

$$C_3H_8(g) + O_2(g) \rightarrow 3CO_2(g) + H_2O(g)$$

Also, each C_3H_8 molecule contains eight hydrogen atoms, so a coefficient of 4 is required for H_2O:

$$C_3H_8(g) + O_2(g) \rightarrow 3CO_2(g) + 4H_2O(g)$$

The final element to be balanced is oxygen. Note that the left side of the equation

Propane burns readily in the presence of oxygen, giving this characteristic blue flame.

• A central theme of this book is to present a thoughtful, systematic approach to problem solving. Often I will ''walk through'' a problem in the text and provide guidelines for developing effective problem-solving techniques. Whenever you see problem-solving strategies set apart in the text followed by a Sample Exercise, you will find that the exercise follows the strategies step-by-step. My goal is to help the student *understand the process*, not *memorize the example*.

A blue question or exercise number indicates that the answer to that question or exercise appears at the back of the book and a solution appears in the Solutions Guide.

Questions

1. The atomic mass of boron (B) is given in the periodic table as 10.81, yet no single atom of boron has a mass of 10.81 amu. Explain.

2. The listed atomic mass of chromium is 52.00 amu. Does this mean that chromium can have only a single isotope with mass 52.00 amu? Explain.

3. What is the difference between the empirical and molecular formulas of a compound? Can they ever be the same? Explain.

4. Why is the actual yield of a reaction often less than the theoretical yield?

Exercises

In this section similar exercises are paired.

Atomic Masses and the Mass Spectrometer

5. The element magnesium (Mg) has three stable isotopes with the following masses and abundances:

Isotope	Mass (amu)	Abundance
^{24}Mg	23.9850	78.99%
^{25}Mg	24.9858	10.00%
^{26}Mg	25.9826	11.01%

Calculate the average atomic mass (the atomic weight) of magnesium from these data.

6. Assume that element Uus is synthesized and that it has the following stable isotopes:

^{284}Uus (283.4 amu)	34.60%
^{285}Uus (284.7 amu)	21.20%
^{288}Uus (287.8 amu)	44.20%

What is the value of the average atomic mass for Uus that would be listed on the periodic table?

7. The element europium exists in nature as two isotopes: ^{151}Eu has a mass of 150.9196 amu, and ^{153}Eu has a mass of 152.9209 amu. The average atomic mass of europium is 151.96 amu. Calculate the relative abundance of the two europium isotopes.

8. The element silver (Ag) has two naturally occurring isotopes: ^{109}Ag and ^{107}Ag with a mass of 106.905 amu. Silver consists of 51.82% ^{107}Ag and has an average atomic mass of 107.868 amu. Calculate the mass of ^{109}Ag.

9. The mass spectrum of bromine (Br_2) consists of three peaks with the following characteristics:

Mass (amu)	Relative size
157.84	0.2534
159.84	0.5000
161.84	0.2466

How do you interpret these data?

10. Naturally occurring tellurium (Te) has the following isotopic abundances:

Isotope	Abundance	Mass (amu)
^{120}Te	0.09%	119.90
^{122}Te	2.46%	121.90
^{123}Te	0.87%	122.90
^{124}Te	4.61%	123.90
^{125}Te	6.99%	124.90
^{126}Te	18.71%	125.90
^{128}Te	31.79%	127.90
^{130}Te	34.48%	129.91

Draw the mass spectrum of H_2Te, assuming that the only hydrogen isotope present is ^{1}H (mass 1.008).

b. What masses of anthraquinone and of water are produced assuming 100% yield?

c. If 1.96×10^3 g anthraquinone is actually obtained, what is the percent yield of the reaction?

Additional Exercises

85. Calculate the molar mass for each of the following substances:
   a. $Cu(H_2O)_6Cl_2$
   b. $NaBrO_3$
   c. $(C_2F_4)_{500}$ (the polymer Teflon), which is made of the unit

   F F
   | |
   —C—C—
   | |
   F F

   d. H_3PO_4
   e. $CaCO_3$

86. Chloral hydrate ($C_2H_3Cl_3O_2$) is a drug formerly used as a sedative and hypnotic. It is the compound used to make "Mickey Finns" in detective stories.
   a. Calculate the molar mass of chloral hydrate.
   b. How many moles of $C_2H_3Cl_3O_2$ molecules are in 500.0 g chloral hydrate?
   c. What is the mass in grams of 2.0×10^{-2} mol chloral hydrate?
   d. How many chlorine atoms are in 5.0 g chloral hydrate?

87.

is made from 1.00×10^3 g adipic acid?

Challenge Problems

104. In the spring of 1984 concern arose over the presence of ethylene dibromide, or EDB, in grains and cereals. EDB has the molecular formula $C_2H_4Br_2$ and until 1984 was commonly used a plant fumigant. The federal limit for EDB in finished cereal products is 30.0 parts per billion (ppb), where 1.0 ppb = 10^{-9} g EDB for every 1.0 g sample. How many molecules of EDB in 1.0 lb flour if 30.0 ppb EDB is present?

105. When aluminum metal is heated with an element from Group 6A of the periodic table, an ionic compound forms. When the experiment is performed with an unknown Group 6A element, the product is 18.56% Al by mass. What is the formula of the compound?

106. A salt contains only barium and one of the halide ions. A 0.158-g sample of the salt was dissolved in water, and an excess of sulfuric acid was added to form barium sulfate ($BaSO_4$), which was filtered, dried, and weighed. Its mass was found to be 0.124 g. What is the formula of the barium halide?

107. Hydrogen cyanide is produced industrially from the reaction of gaseous ammonia, oxygen, and methane:

$$2NH_3(g) + 3O_2(g) + 2CH_4(g) \rightarrow 2HCN(g) + 6H_2O(g)$$

If 5.00×10^3 kg each of NH_3, O_2, and CH_4 are reacted, what mass of HCN and of H_2O would be produced, assuming 100% yield?

111. A 1.500-g sample of a mixture containing only Cu_2O and CuO was treated with hydrogen to produce 1.252 g pure copper metal. Calculate the percentage composition (by mass) of the mixture.

Marathon Problem*

112. From the information below, determine the mass of substance C that will be formed if 45.0 grams of substance A reacts with 23.0 grams of substance B. (Assume that the reaction between A and B goes to completion.)
   a. Substance A is a gray solid that consists of an alkaline earth metal and carbon (37.5% by mass). It reacts with substance B to produce substances C and D. Forty million trillion formula units of A have a mass of 4.26 milligrams.
   b. 47.9 grams of substance B contains 5.36 grams of hydrogen and 42.5 grams of oxygen.
   c. When 10.0 grams of C is burned in excess oxygen, 33.8 grams of carbon dioxide and 6.92 grams of water are produced. A mass spectrum of substance C shows a parent molecular ion with a charge-to-mass ratio of 26.
   d. Substance D is the hydroxide of the metal in substance A.

*This Marathon Problem was developed by James H. Burness of Penn State University, York Campus.

(Excerpts from pp. 123 and 125.)

• It is very important that students use the exercise sets to their best advantage. And in this edition the exercise sets have undergone a major change. First there are the "Questions," which require a short written answer. These test conceptual understanding rather than number crunching. Next are the "Exercises," generally drill-type in nature, keyed by topic in the chapter and now in matched pairs. Students will have access to the answer to each odd-numbered problem in the back of the book, and the solution for each is included in the *Solutions Guide*. For the matching even-numbered problems, there is no student help. This both gives versatility to homework assignments and builds student self-confidence in mastering problem-solving skills. The third group, "Additional Exercises," requires more student thought—these exercises require more synthesis of various concepts and are not listed by chapter topic. "Challenge Exercises" are exactly that, and have been included to offer a wider range of difficulty in the problem sets. The final "Marathon Problem" is more comprehensive, helping students to see relationships. It may be done in class as a group problem, helping students to develop yet another problem-solving technique—working as a member of a team.

◀ Contents ▶

Chapter 8 Bonding: General Concepts   341

Chapter 12 Chemical Kinetics 543

Chapter 13 Chemical Equilibrium 595

CHAPTER 1

Chemical Foundations

CONTENTS

C*hemistry.* It is a word that is impossible to define concisely because the field is so diverse and because its practitioners perform such an incredible variety of jobs. Chemistry deals mainly with situations in which the nature of a substance is changed by altering its composition so that entirely new substances are synthesized or particular properties of existing substances are enhanced.

There are many misconceptions about the practitioners of chemistry. Many people picture a chemist as a solitary figure who works in a laboratory and does not talk to anyone else for days at a time. Nothing could be further from the truth. Many chemists do indeed work in laboratories, but rarely by themselves. A typical day for a modern chemist would be spent as a member of a team solving a problem important to his or her company. This team might consist of chemists from various specialities: chemical engineers, marketing and development specialists, and possibly even lawyers. Figure 1.1 represents the people and organizations with which typical laboratory chemists might expect to interact in the course of their jobs.

On the other hand, many persons trained in the chemical sciences do not perform actual laboratory work but may work as patent attorneys, financial analysts, plant managers, salespeople, personnel managers, and so on. Also, it is quite common for a person trained in the chemical sciences to have many different jobs during a career. To give specific examples, profiles of two "real people" appear at the end of this chapter.

In their work, chemical scientists deal with many different phenomena and do research to solve a wide variety of problems. These are a few of the questions that chemists are currently considering:

What causes acid rain, and how can it be prevented?

< The processes of learning and memory are being investigated through positron emission tomography (PET) scans of the human brain.

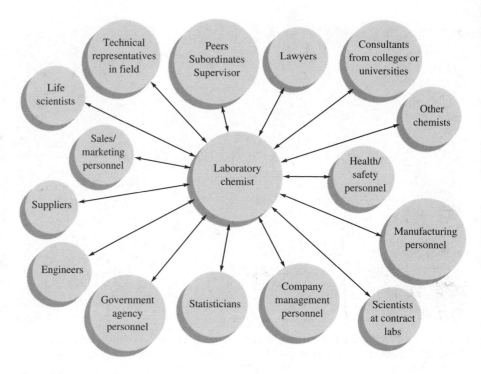

Figure 1.1

The typical chemist interacts with a great variety of other people in doing his or her job.

How can we save the millions of books containing acidic paper that are now crumbling on library shelves everywhere?

Can our large supplies of coal be economically turned into natural gas?

Why do certain substances cause cancer and others seem to protect us from cancer?

How does lithium affect mental health?

Can batteries be designed that would make electric cars feasible?

How can bacteria be modified so that they produce useful chemicals?

Chemical knowledge is expanding at a phenomenal rate. At present, about 400,000 research reports in the various areas of chemistry are published each year. This amounts to more than a thousand articles per day. Clearly it is not humanly possible to master the entirety of chemical knowledge. However, it is important for everyone to understand at least the basics of chemistry. Chemistry is at the heart of the processes that sustain our life and allow us to learn, work, keep warm, and travel. In fact, chemistry is vital to most of the activities of our lives. Understanding the chemical processes that maintain life and control the events in the world around us is essential to our continued well-being.

This textbook introduces you to the types of problems chemical scientists deal with and the methods and models used to solve them. A major goal of this book is to acquaint you with the fundamental principles that chemical scientists use to describe the behavior of matter and to solve real-life problems. Another goal is to help you become a better problem solver. As you

Acidic paper literally crumbles with age.

A scene from the lab of Justus von Liebig (1803–1873), one of the greatest chemistry teachers of all time. Liebig was instrumental in making Germany preeminent in chemistry during the eighteenth century.

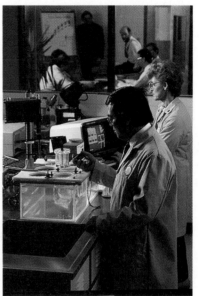

The modern chemical laboratory provides a safe, pleasant environment that allows easy interaction among the scientists.

will see, chemical systems tend to be complex, but critical thought, intelligent approximations, and creative use of fundamental knowledge can make them comprehensible. You cannot simply rely on memorization. You have to *think* to solve chemistry problems. This makes chemistry challenging and sometimes frustrating, but it also gives you a chance to improve your problem-solving skills, which will come in handy in other parts of your life.

This text stresses thoughtful problem solving rather than rote memorization.

Thus this textbook will

1. help you understand the fundamental models of chemistry,
2. show you how chemistry is involved in the real world, and
3. help you develop your skills as a problem solver.

In this chapter we will develop a general idea of science as a discipline and will demonstrate how to handle one of the most important tools of science, the measurement.

1.1 Thinking Like a Chemist

Purpose

• To appreciate the importance of creative problem solving.

Much of your life, both personal and professional, will involve problem solving. Most likely, the more creative you are at solving problems, the more effective and successful you will be. Chemists are usually excellent problem solvers because they get a lot of practice. Chemical problems are frequently very complicated—there is usually no neat and tidy solution. Often it is difficult to know where to begin. In response to this dilemma, a chemist makes an educated guess (formulates a hypothesis) and then tests it to see if the proposed solution correctly predicts the observed behavior of the system. This process of trial and error is virtually a way of life for a chemist. Chemists rarely solve a complex problem in a straightforward, elegant manner. More commonly, they poke and prod the problem and make progress only in fits and starts.

It's very important to keep this in mind as you study chemistry. Although ''plug and chug'' exercises are necessary to familiarize you with the relationships that govern chemical behavior, your ultimate goal should be to advance beyond this stage to true problem solving. Unfortunately, it is very difficult to give a formula for developing into a successful problem solver. Creative problem solving is a rather mysterious activity that defies simple analysis. However, it is clear that practice helps in developing this talent. That's why we will make every attempt in this text to challenge you to be creative with the knowledge of chemistry you will be acquiring. Although this process can be frustrating at times, it is definitely worth the struggle—both because it is one of the most valuable skills you can develop and because it helps you test your understanding of chemical concepts. If your understanding of these concepts is not sufficient to allow you to solve problems involving ''twists'' that you have never encountered before, your knowledge is not very useful to you. The only way to develop your creativity is to expose yourself to new situations where you need to make new connections. A substantial part of creative problem solving involves developing the confidence necessary to think your way through unfamiliar situations. You must recognize that for a complex problem the entire solution is almost never visible in the beginning. Typically, one tries first to understand pieces of the problem and then puts these pieces together to form the solution.

1.2 The Scientific Method

Purpose

• To identify the principal operations and limitations of the scientific method.

Science is a framework for gaining and organizing knowledge. Science is not simply a set of facts but is also a plan of action—a *procedure* for processing and understanding certain types of information. Scientific thinking is useful in all aspects of life, but in this text we will use it to understand how the chemical world operates. The process that lies at the center of scientific inquiry is called the **scientific method.** There are actually many scientific methods, depending on the nature of the specific problem under study and on the particular investigator involved. However, it is useful to consider the following general framework for a generic scientific method:

Steps in the Scientific Method

1. *Making observations*. Observations may be *qualitative* (the sky is blue; water is a liquid) or *quantitative* (water boils at 100°C; a certain chemistry book weighs 2 kilograms). A qualitative observation does not involve a number. A quantitative observation (called a **measurement**) involves both a number and a unit.

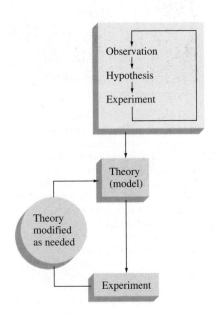

The fundamental steps of the scientific method.

2. *Formulating hypotheses*. A hypothesis is a *possible* explanation for an observation.

3. *Performing experiments*. An experiment is carried out to test a hypothesis. This involves gathering new information that enables a scientist to decide whether or not the hypothesis is valid—that is, whether it is supported by the new information learned from the experiment. Experiments always produce new observations, and this brings the process back to the beginning again.

To understand a given phenomenon, these steps are repeated many times, gradually accumulating the knowledge necessary to provide a possible explanation of the phenomenon.

Once a set of hypotheses that agrees with the various observations is obtained, the hypotheses are assembled into a theory. A **theory,** which is often called a **model,** is a set of tested hypotheses that gives an overall explanation of some natural phenomenon.

It is very important to distinguish between observations and theories. An observation is something that is witnessed and can be recorded. A theory is an *interpretation*—a possible explanation of *why* nature behaves in a particular way. Theories inevitably change as more information becomes available. For example, the motions of the sun and stars have remained virtually the same over the thousands of years during which humans have been observing them, but our explanations—our theories—for these motions have changed greatly since ancient times. (See the Chemical Impact on Observations, Theories, and the Planets, on p. 6.)

The point is that scientists do not stop asking questions just because a given theory seems to account satisfactorily for some aspect of natural behavior. They continue doing experiments to refine or replace the existing theories. This is generally done by using the currently accepted theory to make a prediction and then performing an experiment (making a new observation) to see whether the results bear out this prediction.

Always remember that theories (models) are human inventions. They represent attempts to explain observed natural behavior in terms of human experiences. A theory is actually an educated guess. We must continue to do experiments and to refine our theories (making them consistent with new knowledge) if we hope to approach a more nearly complete understanding of nature.

As scientists observe nature, they often see that the same observation applies to many different systems. For example, studies of innumerable chemical changes have shown that the total observed mass of the materials involved is the same before and after the change. Such generally observed behavior is formulated into a statement called a **natural law.** For example, the observation that the total mass of materials is not affected by a chemical change in those materials is called the **law of conservation of mass.**

Note the difference between a natural law and a theory. A natural law is a summary of observed (measurable) behavior, whereas a theory is an explanation of behavior. *A law summarizes what happens; a theory (model) is an attempt to explain why it happens.*

In this section we have described the scientific method as it might ideally be applied (see Fig. 1.2). However, it is important to remember that science does not always progress smoothly and efficiently. For one thing, hypotheses and observations are not totally independent of each other, as we have assumed in the description of the idealized scientific method. The coupling of observations and hypotheses

Robert Boyle (1627–1691) was born in Ireland. He became especially interested in experiments involving air and developed an air pump with which he produced evacuated cylinders. He used these cylinders to show that a feather and a lump of lead fall at the same rate in the absence of air resistance and that sound cannot be produced in a vacuum. His most famous experiments involved careful measurements of the volume of a gas as a function of pressure. In his book *The Skeptical Chymist,* Boyle urged that the ancient view of elements as mystical substances should be abandoned and that an element should instead be defined as anything that cannot be broken down into simpler substances. This conception was an important step in the development of modern chemistry.

◀ **CHEMICAL IMPACT** ▶

Observations, Theories, and the Planets

Humans have always been fascinated by the heavens, by the behavior of the sun by day and the stars by night. Although more accurately measured now because of precise instruments, the basic *observations* of these events have remained the same over the past 4000 years. However, our *interpretations* of the events have changed dramatically. For example, about 2000 B.C. the Egyptians postulated that the sun was a boat inhabited by the god Ra, who daily sailed across the sky.

Over the years, patterns in the changes in the heavens were recognized and, through marvelous devices such as Stonehenge in England, were connected to the seasons of the year. People also noted that seven objects seemed to move against the background of "fixed stars." These objects, actually the sun, the moon, and the planets Mercury, Venus, Mars, Jupiter, and Saturn, were called the "wanderers." The planets appeared to move from west to east, except Mars, which seemed to slow down and even move backwards for a few weeks.

One of the first explanations for these observations came from Eudoxus, born in 400 B.C. He imagined the earth as fixed, with the planets attached to a nested set of transparent spheres that moved at different rates around the earth. The stars were attached to the outermost sphere. This model, although clever, still did not account for the strange behavior of Mars. Five hundred years later, Ptolemy, a Greek scholar, worked out a plan more complex than that of Eudoxus, in which the planets were attached to the edges of spheres that "rolled around" the spheres of Eudoxus (see time line). This model accounted for the behavior of all the planets, including the apparent reversals in the motion of Mars.

Because of human prejudice that the earth should be the center of the universe, Ptolemy's model was assumed to be cor-

rect for more than a thousand years, and its wide acceptance actually inhibited the advancement of astronomy. Finally, in 1543, a Polish cleric, Nicholas Copernicus, postulated that the earth was only one of the planets, all of which revolved around the sun. This "demotion" of the earth's status produced violent opposition to the new model, and in fact, Copernicus's writings were "corrected" by religious officials before scholars were allowed to use them.

The Copernican theory persisted and was finally given a solid mathematical base by Johannes Kepler. Kepler postulated elliptical rather than circular orbits for the planets in order to account more completely for their observed motions. Kepler's hypotheses were in turn further refined 36 years after his death by Isaac Newton, who recognized that the concept of gravitation could account for the positions and motions of the planets. However, even the brilliant models of Newton were found incomplete by Albert Einstein, who showed that Newton's mechanics was a special case of a much more general model.

Thus the same basic observations were made for several thousand years, but the explanations—the models—have changed remarkably from the Egyptians' boat of Ra to Einstein's relativity.

The lesson here is that our models will inevitably change, and we should expect them to do so. They can help us make scientific progress, or they can inhibit progress if we become too attached to them. Although the fundamental facts of chemistry will remain the same, the models in a chemistry text written a century from now will certainly be quite different from the ones presented here.

A time line showing how models of the solar system changed over 4000 years.

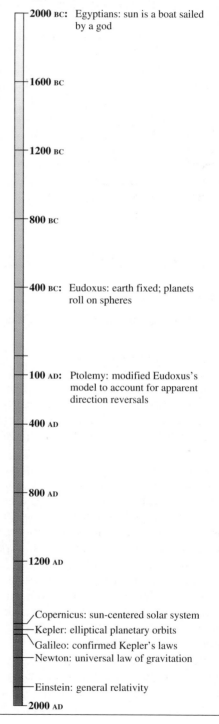

2000 BC: Egyptians: sun is a boat sailed by a god

1600 BC

1200 BC

800 BC

400 BC: Eudoxus: earth fixed; planets roll on spheres

100 AD: Ptolemy: modified Eudoxus's model to account for apparent direction reversals

400 AD

800 AD

1200 AD

Copernicus: sun-centered solar system

Kepler: elliptical planetary orbits

Galileo: confirmed Kepler's laws

Newton: universal law of gravitation

Einstein: general relativity

2000 AD

occurs because once we begin to proceed down a given theoretical path, our hypotheses are unavoidably couched in the language of that theory. In other words, we tend to see what we expect to see and often fail to notice things that we do not expect. Thus the theory we are testing helps us because it focuses our questions. However, at the very same time, this focusing process may limit our ability to see other possible explanations.

It is also important to keep in mind that scientists are human. They have prejudices; they misinterpret data; they become emotionally attached to their theories and thus lose objectivity; and they play politics. Science is affected by profit motives, budgets, fads, wars, and religious beliefs. Galileo, for example, was forced to recant his astronomical observations in the face of strong religious resistance. Lavoisier, the father of modern chemistry, was beheaded because of his political affiliations. And great progress in the chemistry of nitrogen fertilizers resulted from the desire to produce explosives to fight wars. The progress of science is often affected more by the frailties of humans and their institutions than by the limitations of scientific measuring devices. The scientific methods are only as effective as the humans using them. They do not automatically lead to progress.

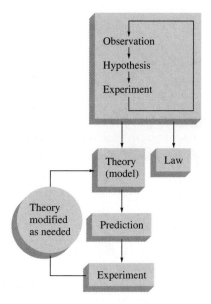

Figure 1.2

The various parts of the scientific method.

1.3 Units of Measurement

Purpose

- To describe the SI system of units and prefixes.

Making observations is fundamental to all science. A quantitative observation, or **measurement**, always consists of two parts: a **number** and a scale (called a **unit**). Both parts must be present for the measurement to be meaningful.

In this textbook we will use measurements of mass, length, time, temperature, electric current, and the amount of a substance, among others. Scientists recognized long ago that standard systems of units had to be adopted if measurements were to be useful. If every scientist had a different set of units, complete chaos would result. Unfortunately, different standards were adopted in different parts of the world. The two major systems are the *English system* used in the United States (and a few African countries) and the *metric system* used by most of the rest of the industrialized world. This duality causes a good deal of trouble; for example, parts as simple as bolts are not interchangeable between machines built using the two systems. As a result, the United States has begun to adopt the metric system.

Most scientists in all countries have for many years used the metric system. In 1960, an international agreement set up a system of units called the **International System (le Système International** in French), or the **SI system.** This system is based on the metric system and units derived from the metric system. The fundamental SI units are listed in Table 1.1. We will discuss how to manipulate these units later in this chapter.

Because the fundamental units are not always convenient (expressing the mass of a pin in kilograms is awkward), the SI system employs prefixes to change the size of the unit. These are listed in Table 1.2. Some common objects and their measurements in SI units are listed in Table 1.3.

Figure 1.3

The largest cube has sides 1 m in length and a volume of 1 m³. The middle-sized cube has sides 1 dm in length and a volume of 1 dm³, or 1 L. The smallest cube has sides 1 cm in length and a volume of 1 cm³, or 1 mL.

Table 1.1		
The Fundamental SI Units		
Physical Quantity	Name of Unit	Abbreviation
Mass	kilogram	kg
Length	meter	m
Time	second	s
Temperature	Kelvin	K
Electric current	ampere	A
Amount of substance	mole	mol
Luminous intensity	candela	cd

Table 1.2			
The Prefixes Used in the SI System. **Those most commonly encountered are shown in color.**			
Prefix	Symbol	Meaning	Exponential Notation*
exa	E	1,000,000,000,000,000,000	10^{18}
peta	P	1,000,000,000,000,000	10^{15}
tera	T	1,000,000,000,000	10^{12}
giga	G	1,000,000,000	10^{9}
mega	M	1,000,000	10^{6}
kilo	k	1,000	10^{3}
hecto	h	100	10^{2}
deka	da	10	10^{1}
—	—	1	10^{0}
deci	d	0.1	10^{-1}
centi	c	0.01	10^{-2}
milli	m	0.001	10^{-3}
micro	μ	0.000001	10^{-6}
nano	n	0.000000001	10^{-9}
pico	p	0.000000000001	10^{-12}
femto	f	0.000000000000001	10^{-15}
atto	a	0.000000000000000001	10^{-18}

*See Appendix 1.1 if you need a review of exponential notation.

Table 1.3	
Some Examples of Commonly Used Units	
Length	A dime is 1 mm thick. A quarter is 2.5 cm in diameter. The average height of an adult man is 1.8 m.
Mass	A nickel has a mass of about 5 g. A 120-lb person has a mass of about 55 kg.
Volume	A 12-oz can of soda has a volume of about 360 mL.

One physical quantity that is very important in chemistry is *volume*, which is not a fundamental SI unit but is derived from length. A cube that measures 1 meter (m) on each edge is represented in Fig. 1.3. This cube has a volume of $(1 \text{ m})^3 = 1 \text{ m}^3$. Recognizing that there are 10 decimeters (dm) in a meter, the volume of this cube is $(1 \text{ m})^3 = (10 \text{ dm})^3 = 1000 \text{ dm}^3$. A cubic decimeter, that is $(1 \text{ dm})^3$, is commonly called a **liter (L),** which is a unit of volume slightly larger than a quart. As shown in Fig. 1.3, 1000 liters are contained in a cube with a volume of 1 cubic meter. Similarly, since 1 decimeter equals 10 centimeters (cm), the liter can be divided into 1000 cubes each with a volume of 1 cubic centimeter:

$$1 \text{ liter} = (1 \text{ dm})^3 = (10 \text{ cm})^3 = 1000 \text{ cm}^3$$

Calibration mark indicates 25-mL volume

Valve (stopcock) controls the liquid flow

100-mL graduated cylinder   25-mL pipet   50-mL buret

Calibration mark indicates 250-mL volume

250-mL volumetric flask

Figure 1.4

Common types of laboratory equipment used to measure liquid volume.

Also, since 1 cm^3 = 1 milliliter (mL),

$$1 \text{ liter} = 1000 \text{ cm}^3 = 1000 \text{ mL}$$

Thus 1 liter contains 1000 cubic centimeters, or 1000 milliliters.

Chemical laboratory work frequently requires measurement of the volumes of liquids. Several devices for the accurate determination of liquid volume are shown in Fig. 1.4.

An important point concerning measurements is the relationship between mass and weight. Although these terms are sometimes used interchangeably, they are *not* the same. *Mass is a measure of the resistance of an object to a change in its state of motion.* Mass is measured by the force necessary to give an object a certain acceleration. On earth we use the force that gravity exerts on an object to measure its mass. We call this force the object's **weight.** Since weight is the response of mass to gravity, it varies with the strength of the gravitational field. Therefore, your body mass is the same on the earth or on the moon, but your weight would be much less on the moon than on earth because of the moon's smaller gravitational field.

Because weighing something on a chemical balance (see Fig. 1.5) involves comparing the mass of that object to a standard mass, the terms **weight** and **mass** are sometimes used interchangeably.

1.4 Uncertainty in Measurement

Purpose

- To identify causes of uncertainty in measurement.
- To show how significant figures are used.
- To compare precision and accuracy in measurement.

Figure 1.5

An electronic analytical balance.

Buret

Figure 1.6

Measurement of volume using a buret. The volume is read at the bottom of the liquid curve (called the *meniscus*).

A measurement always has some degree of uncertainty.

Uncertainty in measurement is discussed in more detail in Appendix 1.5.

The number associated with a measurement is obtained using some measuring device. For example, consider the measurement of the volume of a liquid using a buret (shown in Fig. 1.6 with the scale greatly magnified). Notice that the meniscus of the liquid occurs at about 22.15 milliliters. This means that about 22.15 mL of liquid has been delivered from the buret (if the initial position of the liquid meniscus was 0.00 mL). Note that we must estimate the last number of the volume reading by interpolating between the 0.1-mL marks. Since the last number is estimated, its value may be different if another person makes the same measurement. If five different people read the same volume, the results might be as follows:

Person	Results of Measurement
1	22.15 mL
2	22.14 mL
3	22.16 mL
4	22.17 mL
5	22.16 mL

These results show that the first three numbers (22.1) remain the same regardless of who makes the measurement; these are called **certain** digits. However, the digit to the right of the 1 must be estimated and therefore varies; it is called an **uncertain** digit. We customarily report a measurement by recording all the certain digits plus the *first* uncertain digit. In our example it would not make any sense to try to record the volume to thousandths of a milliliter because the value for hundredths of a milliliter must be estimated when using the buret.

It is very important to realize that a *measurement always has some degree of uncertainty.* The uncertainty of a measurement depends on the precision of the measuring device. For example, using a bathroom scale, you might estimate the mass of a grapefruit to be approximately 1.5 pounds. Weighing the same grapefruit on a highly precise balance might produce a result of 1.476 pounds. In the first case, the uncertainty occurs in the tenths of a pound place; in the second case, the uncertainty occurs in the thousandths of a pound place. Suppose we weigh two similar grapefruits on the two devices and obtain the following results:

	Bathroom Scale	Balance
Grapefruit 1	1.5 lb	1.476 lb
Grapefruit 2	1.5 lb	1.518 lb

Do the two grapefruits have the same mass? The answer depends on which set of results you consider. Thus a conclusion based on a series of measurements depends on the certainty of those measurements. For this reason, it is important to indicate the uncertainty in any measurement. This is done by always recording the certain digits and the first uncertain digit (the estimated number). These numbers are called the **significant figures** of a measurement.

The convention of significant figures automatically indicates something about the uncertainty in a measurement. The uncertainty in the last number (the estimated number) is usually assumed to be ±1 unless otherwise indicated. For example, the measurement 1.86 kilograms can be taken to mean 1.86 ± 0.01 kilograms.

Sample Exercise 1.1

In analyzing a sample of polluted water, a chemist measured out a 25.00-mL water sample with a pipet (see Fig. 1.4). At another point in the analysis, the chemist used a graduated cylinder (see Fig. 1.4) to measure 25 mL of a solution. What is the difference between the measurements 25.00 mL and 25 mL?

Solution

Even though the two volume measurements appear to be equal, they really convey different information. The quantity 25 mL means that the volume is between 24 mL and 26 mL, whereas the quantity 25.00 mL means that the volume is between 24.99 mL and 25.01 mL. The pipet measures volume with much greater precision than does the graduated cylinder.

When making a measurement, it is important to record the results to the appropriate number of significant figures. For example, if a certain buret can be read to ±0.01 mL, you should record a reading of twenty-five milliliters as 25.00 mL, not 25 mL. This way at some later time when you are using your results to do calculations, the uncertainty in the measurement will be known to you.

Precision and Accuracy

Two terms often used to describe the reliability of measurements are precision and accuracy. Although these words are frequently used interchangeably in everyday life, they have different meanings in the scientific context. **Accuracy** refers to the agreement of a particular value with the true value. **Precision** refers to the degree of agreement among several measurements of the same quantity. Precision reflects the *reproducibility* of a given type of measurement. The difference between these terms is illustrated by the results of three different dart throws shown in Fig. 1.7.

Two different types of errors are illustrated in Fig. 1.7. A **random error** (also called an **indeterminate error**) means that a measurement has an equal probability of being high or low. This type of error occurs in estimating the value of the last digit of a measurement. The second type of error is called **systematic error** (or **determinate error**). This type of error occurs in the same direction each time; it is either always high or always low. Figure 1.7(a) indicates large random errors (poor technique). Figure 1.7(b) indicates small random errors but a large systematic error, and Figure 1.7(c) indicates small random errors and no systematic error.

In quantitative work, precision is often used as an indication of accuracy; we assume that the *average* of a series of precise measurements (which should ''average out'' the random errors because of their equal probability of being high or low) is accurate, or close to the ''true'' value. However, this assumption is only valid if

(a)

(b)

(c)

Figure 1.7

The results of several dart throws show the difference between *precise* and *accurate*. (a) Neither accurate nor precise (large random errors). (b) Precise but not accurate (small random errors, large systematic error). (c) Bull's-eye! Both precise and accurate (small random errors, no systematic error).

systematic errors are absent. Suppose we weigh a piece of brass five times on a very precise balance and obtain the following results:

Weighing	Result
1	2.486 g
2	2.487 g
3	2.485 g
4	2.484 g
5	2.488 g

Normally we would assume that the true mass of the piece of brass is very close to 2.486 grams, which is the average of the five results:

$$\frac{2.486 \text{ g} + 2.487 \text{ g} + 2.485 \text{ g} + 2.484 \text{ g} + 2.488 \text{ g}}{5} = 2.486 \text{ g}$$

However, if the balance has a defect causing it to give a result that is consistently 1.000 gram too high (a systematic error of $+1.000$ gram), then the measured value of 2.486 grams would be seriously in error. The point here is that high precision among several measurements is an indication of accuracy *only* if systematic errors are absent.

Precision is an indication of accuracy only if there are no systematic errors.

Sample Exercise 1.2

To check the accuracy of a graduated cylinder, a student filled the cylinder to the 25-mL mark using water delivered from a buret (see Fig. 1.4) and then read the volume delivered. Following are the results of five trials:

Trial	Volume Shown by Graduated Cylinder	Volume Shown by the Buret
1	25 mL	26.54 mL
2	25 mL	26.51 mL
3	25 mL	26.60 mL
4	25 mL	26.49 mL
5	25 mL	26.57 mL
Average	25 mL	26.54 mL

Is the graduated cylinder accurate?

Solution

The results of the trials show very good precision (for a graduated cylinder). The student has good technique. However, note that the average value measured using the buret is significantly different from 25 mL. Thus this graduated cylinder is not very accurate. It produces a systematic error (in this case, the indicated result is low for each measurement).

1.5 Significant Figures and Calculations

Purpose

- To show how to determine the number of significant figures in a calculated result.

Calculating the final result for an experiment usually involves adding, subtracting, multiplying, or dividing the results of various types of measurements. Since it is very important that the uncertainty in the final result is known correctly, we have developed rules for counting the significant figures in each number and for determining the correct number of significant figures in the final result.

Rules for Counting Significant Figures

1. *Nonzero integers.* Nonzero integers always count as significant figures.

2. *Zeros.* There are three classes of zeros:

   a. **Leading zeros** are zeros that *precede* all the nonzero digits. These do not count as significant figures. In the number 0.0025, the three zeros simply indicate the position of the decimal point. This number has only two significant figures.

   b. **Captive zeros** are zeros *between* nonzero digits. These always count as significant figures. The number 1.008 has four significant figures.

   c. **Trailing zeros** are zeros at the *right end* of the number. They are significant only if the number contains a decimal point. The number 100 has only one significant figure, whereas the number 1.00×10^2 has three significant figures. The number one hundred written as 100. also has three significant figures.

3. *Exact numbers.* Many times calculations involve numbers that were not obtained using measuring devices but were determined by counting: 10 experiments, 3 apples, 8 molecules. Such numbers are called **exact numbers.** They can be assumed to have an infinite number of significant figures. Other examples of exact numbers are the 2 in $2\pi r$ (the circumference of a circle) and the 4 and the 3 in $\frac{4}{3}\pi r^3$ (the volume of a sphere). Exact numbers also can arise from definitions. For example, one inch is defined as *exactly* 2.54 centimeters. Thus in the statement 1 in = 2.54 cm, neither the 2.54 nor the 1 limits the number of significant figures when used in a calculation.

Note that the number 1.00×10^2 above is written in **exponential notation.** This type of notation has at least two advantages: the number of significant figures can be easily indicated, and fewer zeros are needed to write a very large or very small number. For example, the number 0.000060 is much more conveniently represented as 6.0×10^{-5}. (The number has two significant figures.)

> Leading zeros are never significant figures.

> Captive zeros are always significant figures.

> Trailing zeros are sometimes significant figures.

> Exact numbers never limit the number of significant figures in a calculation.

> Exponential notation is reviewed in Appendix 1.1.

Sample Exercise 1.3

Give the number of significant figures for each of the following results.
a. A student's extraction procedure on tea yields 0.0105 g of caffeine.
b. A chemist records a weight of 0.050080 g in an analysis.
c. In an experiment a span of time is determined to be 8.050×10^{-3} s.

Caffeine, which occurs in such items as tea, coffee, and cola nuts, is a respiratory and cardiac stimulant.

Solution

a. The number contains three significant figures. The zeros to the left of the 1 are leading zeros and are not significant, but the remaining zero (a captive zero) is significant.

b. The number contains five significant figures. The leading zeros (to the left of the 5) are not significant. The captive zeros between the 5 and the 8 are significant, and the trailing zero to the right of the 8 is significant because the number contains a decimal point.

c. This number has four significant figures. Both zeros are significant.

To this point we have learned to count the significant figures in a given number. Next we must consider how uncertainty accumulates as calculations are carried out. The detailed analysis of the accumulation of uncertainties depends on the type of calculation involved and can be complex. However, in this textbook we will employ the following simple rules that have been developed for determining the appropriate number of significant figures in the result of a calculation.

Rules for Significant Figures in Mathematical Operations*

1. *For multiplication or division* the number of significant figures in the result is the same as the number in the least precise measurement used in the calculation. For example, consider the calculation

$$4.56 \times 1.4 = 6.38 \xrightarrow{\text{Corrected}} 6.4$$

Limiting term has two significant figures   Two significant figures

The product should have only two significant figures, since 1.4 has two significant figures.

2. *For addition or subtraction* the result has the same number of decimal places as the least precise measurement used in the calculation. For example, consider the sum

$$
\begin{array}{r}
12.11 \\
18.0 \quad \leftarrow\text{limiting term has one decimal place} \\
\underline{1.013} \\
31.123 \xrightarrow{\text{Corrected}} 31.1
\end{array}
$$

One decimal place

The correct result is 31.1, since 18.0 has only one decimal place.

Note that for multiplication and division, significant figures are counted. For addition and subtraction, the decimal places are counted.

*Although these simple rules work well for most cases, they can give misleading results in certain cases. For more information, see L. M. Schwartz, Propagation of significant figures, *J. Chem. Ed.* **62** (1985): 693; and H. Bradford Thompson, Is 8°C equal to 50°F? *J. Chem. Ed.* **68** (1991): 400.

In most calculations you will need to round numbers to obtain the correct number of significant figures. The following rules should be applied when rounding.

Rules for Rounding

1. In a series of calculations, carry the extra digits through to the final result, *then* round.

2. If the digit to be removed
   a. is less than 5, the preceding digit stays the same. For example, 1.33 rounds to 1.3.
   b. is equal to or greater than 5, the preceding digit is increased by 1. For example, 1.36 rounds to 1.4.

Rule 2 is consistent with the operation of electronic calculators.

Although rounding is generally straightforward, one point requires special emphasis. As an illustration, suppose that the number 4.348 needs to be rounded to two significant figures. In doing this, we look *only* at the *first number* to the right of the 3:

$$4.3\overset{\uparrow}{4}8$$

Look at this
number to round
to two significant figures.

The number is rounded to 4.3 because 4 is less than 5. It is incorrect to round sequentially. For example, do *not* round the 4 to 5 to give 4.35 and then round the 3 to 4 to give 4.4.

Do not round sequentially. The number 6.8347 rounded to three significant figures is 6.83, not 6.84.

When rounding, *use only the first number to the right of the last significant figure*.

It is important to note that Rule 1 above will not usually be followed in the Sample Exercises in this text because we want to show the correct number of significant figures in *each step* of a problem. This same practice is followed for the detailed solutions given in the Solutions Guide. However, as stated in Rule 1, the best procedure is to carry extra digits throughout a series of calculations and round to the correct number of significant figures only at the end. This is the practice you should follow. The fact that your rounding procedures are different from those used in this text must be taken into account when you check your answer with the one given at the end of the book or in the Solutions Guide. Your answer (based on rounding only at the end of a calculation) may differ in the last place from that given here as the ''correct'' answer because we have rounded after each step. To help you understand the difference between these rounding procedures, we will consider them further in Sample Exercise 1.4.

Sample Exercise 1.4

Carry out the following mathematical operations and give each result with the correct number of significant figures.

a. $1.05 \times 10^{-3} \div 6.135$

b. $21 - 13.8$

c. As part of a lab assignment to determine the value of the gas constant (R), a student measured the pressure (P), volume (V), and temperature (T) for a sample of gas, where

$$R = \frac{PV}{T}$$

The following values were obtained: $P = 2.560$, $T = 275.15$, and $V = 8.8$. (Gases will be discussed in detail in Chapter 5; we will not be concerned at this time about the units for these quantities.) Calculate R to the correct number of significant figures.

Solution

a. The result is 1.71×10^{-4}, which has three significant figures because the term with the least precision (1.05×10^{-3}) has three significant figures.

b. The result is 7 with no decimal place because the number with the least number of decimal places (21) has none.

c.
$$R = \frac{PV}{T} = \frac{(2.560)(8.8)}{275.15}$$

The correct procedure for obtaining the final result can be represented as follows:

$$\frac{(2.560)(8.8)}{275.15} = \frac{22.528}{275.15} = 0.0818753$$
$$= 0.082 = 8.2 \times 10^{-2} = R$$

The final result must be rounded to two significant figures because 8.8 (the least precise measurement) has two significant figures. To show the effects of rounding at intermediate steps, we will carry out the calculation as follows:

Rounded to
two significant figures
↓

$$\frac{(2.560)(8.8)}{275.15} = \frac{22.528}{275.15} = \frac{23}{275.15}$$

Now we proceed with the next calculation:

$$\frac{23}{275.15} = 0.0835908$$

Rounded to two significant figures, this result is

$$0.084 = 8.4 \times 10^{-2}$$

Note that intermediate rounding gives a significantly different result than was obtained by rounding only at the end. Again, we must reemphasize that in *your* calculations you should round *only at the end*. However, because rounding is carried out at intermediate steps in this text (to always show the correct number of significant figures), the final answer given in the text may differ slightly from the one you obtain (rounding only at the end).

There is a useful lesson to be learned from part (c) of Sample Exercise 1.4. The student measured the pressure and temperature to greater precision than the volume. A more precise value of R (one with more significant figures) could have been obtained if a more precise measurement of V had been made. As it is, the efforts expended to measure P and T very precisely were wasted. Remember that a series of measurements to obtain some final result should all be done to about the same precision.

1.6 Dimensional Analysis

Purpose

• To show how to convert units between the English and metric systems.

It is often necessary to convert a given result from one system of units to another. The best way to do this is by a method called the **unit factor method,** or more commonly **dimensional analysis.** To illustrate the use of this method, we will consider several unit conversions. Some equivalents in the English and metric systems are listed in Table 1.4. A more complete list of conversion factors given to more significant figures appears inside the back cover of the text.

Consider a pin measuring 2.85 centimeters in length. What is its length in inches? To accomplish this conversion we must use the equivalence statement

$$2.54 \text{ cm} = 1 \text{ in}$$

If we divide both sides of this equation by 2.54 cm, we get

$$\frac{2.54 \text{ cm}}{2.54 \text{ cm}} = 1 = \frac{1 \text{ in}}{2.54 \text{ cm}}$$

Note that the expression 1 in/2.54 cm equals 1. This expression is called a **unit factor.** Since 1 inch and 2.54 centimeters are exactly equivalent, multiplying any expression by this unit factor will not change its *value*.

The pin has a length of 2.85 centimeters. Multiplying this length by the appropriate unit factor gives

$$2.85 \text{ cm} \times \frac{1 \text{ in}}{2.54 \text{ cm}} = \frac{2.85}{2.54} \text{ in} = 1.12 \text{ in}$$

Note that the centimeter units cancel to give inches for the result. This is exactly what we wanted to accomplish. Note also that the result has three significant figures, as required by the number 2.85. Recall that the 1 and 2.54 in the conversion factor are exact numbers by definition.

Table 1.4
English-Metric Equivalents
Length
1 m = 1.094 yd
2.54 cm = 1 in
Mass
1 kg = 2.205 lb
453.6 g = 1 lb
Volume
1 L = 1.06 qt
1 ft³ = 28.32 L

Sample Exercise 1.5

A pencil is 7.00 in long. What is its length in centimeters?

Solution

In this case we want to convert from inches to centimeters. Therefore, we must use the reciprocal of the unit factor used above to do the opposite conversion:

$$7.00 \text{ in} \times \frac{2.54 \text{ cm}}{1 \text{ in}} = (7.00)(2.54) \text{ cm} = 17.8 \text{ cm}$$

Here the inch units cancel, leaving centimeters, as requested.

Note that two unit factors can be derived from each equivalence statement. For example, from the equivalence statement 2.54 cm = 1 in, the two unit factors are

$$\frac{2.54 \text{ cm}}{1 \text{ in}} \quad \text{and} \quad \frac{1 \text{ in}}{2.54 \text{ cm}}$$

How do you choose which one to use in a given situation? Simply look at the *direction* of the required change. To change from inches to centimeters, the inches must cancel. Thus the factor 2.54 cm/1 in is used. To change from centimeters to inches, centimeters must cancel, and the factor 1 in/2.54 cm is appropriate.

Consider the direction of the required change to select the correct unit factor.

Converting from One Unit to Another

- To convert from one unit to another, use the equivalence statement that relates the two units.
- Derive the appropriate unit factor by looking at the direction of the required change (to cancel the unwanted units).
- Multiply the quantity to be converted by the unit factor to give the quantity with the desired units.

Sample Exercise 1.6

You want to order a bicycle with a 25.5-in frame, but the sizes in the catalog are given only in centimeters. What size should you order?

Solution

You need to go from inches to centimeters, so 2.54 cm/1 in is appropriate:

$$25.5 \text{ in} \times \frac{2.54 \text{ cm}}{1 \text{ in}} = 64.8 \text{ cm}$$

To ensure that the conversion procedure is clear, a multistep problem is considered in Sample Exercise 1.7.

Sample Exercise 1.7

A student has entered a 10.0-km run. How long is the run in miles?

Solution

This conversion can be accomplished in several different ways. Since we have the equivalence statement 1 m = 1.094 yd, we will proceed by a path that uses this fact. Before we start any calculations, let us consider our strategy. We have kilometers, which we want to change to miles. We can do this by the following route:

$$\text{kilometers} \rightarrow \text{meters} \rightarrow \text{yards} \rightarrow \text{miles}$$

To proceed in this way, we need the following equivalence statements:

$$1 \text{ km} = 1000 \text{ m}$$
$$1 \text{ m} = 1.094 \text{ yd}$$
$$1760 \text{ yd} = 1 \text{ mi}$$

To make sure the process is clear, we will proceed step by step:

KILOMETERS TO METERS:

$$10.0 \text{ km} \times \frac{1000 \text{ m}}{1 \text{ km}} = 1.00 \times 10^4 \text{ m}$$

METERS TO YARDS:

$$1.00 \times 10^4 \text{ m} \times \frac{1.094 \text{ yd}}{1 \text{ m}} = 1.094 \times 10^4 \text{ yd}$$

Note that we should have only three significant figures in the result. Since this is an intermediate result, however, we will carry the extra digit. Remember, round off only the final result.

YARDS TO MILES:

$$1.094 \times 10^4 \text{ yd} \times \frac{1 \text{ mi}}{1760 \text{ yd}} = 6.216 \text{ mi}$$

Note in this case that 1 mi equals exactly 1760 yd *by designation*. Thus 1760 is an exact number.

Since the distance was originally given as 10.0 km, the result can have only three significant figures and should be rounded to 6.22 mi. Thus

$$10.0 \text{ km} = 6.22 \text{ mi}$$

Alternatively, we can combine the steps:

$$10.0 \text{ km} \times \frac{1000 \text{ m}}{1 \text{ km}} \times \frac{1.094 \text{ yd}}{1 \text{ m}} \times \frac{1 \text{ mi}}{1760 \text{ yd}} = 6.22 \text{ mi}$$

In using dimensional analysis, your verification that everything has been done correctly is that you end up with the correct units. *In doing chemistry problems, you should always include the units for the quantities used.* Always check to see that the units cancel to give the correct units for the final result. This provides a very valuable check, especially for complicated problems.

Study the procedures for unit conversions in the following Sample Exercises.

Sample Exercise 1.8

The speed limit on highways in the United States is 55 mi/h. What number would be posted in kilometers per hour?

Solution

Result obtained by rounding only at the end of the calculation

$$\frac{55 \text{ mi}}{\text{h}} \times \frac{1760 \text{ yd}}{1 \text{ mi}} \times \frac{1 \text{ m}}{1.094 \text{ yd}} \times \frac{1 \text{ km}}{1000 \text{ m}} = 88 \text{ km/h}$$

Note that all units cancel except the desired kilometers per hour.

Sample Exercise 1.9

A Japanese car is advertised as having a gas mileage of 15 km/L. Convert this rating to miles per gallon.

Solution

Result obtained by rounding only at the end of the calculation

$$\frac{15 \text{ km}}{\text{L}} \times \frac{1000 \text{ m}}{1 \text{ km}} \times \frac{1.094 \text{ yd}}{1 \text{ m}} \times \frac{1 \text{ mi}}{1760 \text{ yd}} \times \frac{1 \text{ L}}{1.06 \text{ qt}} \times \frac{4 \text{ qt}}{1 \text{ gal}} = 35 \text{ mi/gal}$$

1.7 Temperature

Purpose

• To demonstrate conversions among the Fahrenheit, Celsius, and Kelvin temperature scales.

Three systems for measuring temperature are widely used: the Celsius scale, the Kelvin scale, and the Fahrenheit scale. The first two temperature systems are used in the physical sciences, and the third is used in many of the engineering sciences. Our purpose here is to define the three temperature scales and show how conversions from one scale to another can be performed. Although these conversions can be carried out routinely on most calculators, we will consider the process in some detail here to illustrate methods of problem solving.

The three temperature scales are defined and compared in Fig. 1.8. Note that the size of the temperature unit (the **degree**) is the same for the Kelvin and Celsius scales. The fundamental difference between these two temperature scales is in their zero points. Conversion between these two scales simply requires an adjustment for the different zero points.

Figure 1.8
The three major temperature scales.

Temperature (Kelvin) = temperature (Celsius) + 273.15

or   Temperature (Celsius) = temperature (Kelvin) − 273.15

$T_K = T_C + 273.15$

$T_C = T_K - 273.15$

For example, to convert 300.00 K to the Celsius scale, we do the following calculation:

$$300.00 - 273.15 = 26.85°C$$

Note that, in expressing temperature in Celsius units, the designation °C is used. The degree symbol is not used when writing temperature in terms of the Kelvin scale. The unit of temperature on this scale is called a **Kelvin** and is symbolized by the letter K.

Converting between the Fahrenheit and Celsius scales is somewhat more complicated because both the degree sizes and the zero points are different. Thus we need to consider two adjustments: one for degree size and one for the zero point. First, we must account for the difference in degree size. This can be done by reconsidering Fig. 1.8. Notice that since 212°F = 100°C and 32°F = 0°C,

212 − 32 = 180 Fahrenheit degrees = 100 − 0 = 100 Celsius degrees

Thus 180° on the Fahrenheit scale is equivalent to 100° on the Celsius scale, and the unit factor is

$$\frac{180°F}{100°C} \quad \text{or} \quad \frac{9°F}{5°C}$$

or the reciprocal, depending on the direction in which we need to go.

Next, we must consider the different zero points. Since 32°F = 0°C, we obtain the corresponding Celsius temperature by first subtracting 32 from the Fahrenheit temperature to account for the different zero points. Then the unit factor is applied to adjust for the difference in the degree size. This process is summarized by the equation

$$(T_F - 32°F)\frac{5°C}{9°F} = T_C \tag{1.1}$$

where T_F and T_C represent a given temperature on the Fahrenheit and Celsius scales, respectively. In the opposite conversion, we first correct for degree size and then correct for the different zero point. This process can be summarized in the following general equation:

$$T_F = T_C \times \frac{9°F}{5°C} + 32°F \tag{1.2}$$

Equations (1.1) and (1.2) are really the same equation in different forms. See if you can obtain Equation (1.2) by starting with Equation (1.1) and rearranging.

At this point it is worthwhile to weigh the two alternatives for learning to do temperature conversions: you can simply memorize the equations, or you can take the time to learn the differences between the temperature scales and to understand the processes involved in converting from one scale to another. The latter approach may take a little more effort, but the understanding you gain will stick with you much longer than the memorized formulas. This choice also will apply to many of the other chemical concepts. Try to think things through!

Understand the process of converting from one temperature scale to another; do not simply memorize the equations.

Sample Exercise 1.10

Normal body temperature is 98.6°F. Convert this temperature to the Celsius and Kelvin scales.

Solution

Rather than simply using the formulas to solve this problem, we will proceed by thinking it through. The situation is diagramed in Fig. 1.9. First, we want to convert 98.6°F to the Celsius scale. The number of Fahrenheit degrees between 32.0°F and 98.6°F is 66.6°F. We must convert this difference to Celsius degrees:

$$66.6°F \times \frac{5°C}{9°F} = 37.0°C$$

Thus 98.6°F corresponds to 37.0°C.

Now we can convert to the Kelvin scale:

$$T_K = T_C + 273.15 = 37.0 + 273.15 = 310.2 \text{ K}$$

Note that the final answer has only one decimal place (37.0 is limiting).

Fahrenheit   Celsius   Kelvin

98.6° F ——————— ?° C ——————— ? K

66.6° F ——| 66.6° F × $\dfrac{5°\text{C}}{9°\text{F}}$ = 37.0° C   37.0 + 273.15 K = 310.2 K

32° F ——————— 0° C ——————— 273.15 K

Figure 1.9
Normal body temperature on the Fahrenheit, Celsius, and Kelvin scales.

Sample Exercise 1.11

One interesting feature of the Celsius and Fahrenheit scales is that $-40°$C and $-40°$F represent the same temperature, as shown in Fig. 1.8. Verify that this is true.

Solution

The difference between 32°F and $-40°$F is 72°F. The difference between 0°C and $-40°$C is 40°C. The ratio of these is

$$\frac{72°\text{F}}{40°\text{C}} = \frac{8 \times 9°\text{F}}{8 \times 5°\text{C}} = \frac{9°\text{F}}{5°\text{C}}$$

as required. Thus $-40°$C is equivalent to $-40°$F.

Since, as shown in Sample Exercise 1.11, $-40°$ on both the Fahrenheit and Celsius scales represents the same temperature, this point can be used as a reference point (like 0°C and 32°F) for a relationship between the two scales:

$$\frac{\text{Number of Fahrenheit degrees}}{\text{Number of Celsius degrees}} = \frac{T_F - (-40)}{T_C - (-40)} = \frac{9°\text{F}}{5°\text{C}}$$

or

$$\frac{T_F + 40}{T_C + 40} = \frac{9°\text{F}}{5°\text{C}} \tag{1.3}$$

where T_F and T_C represent the same temperature (but not the same number). This equation can be used to convert Fahrenheit temperatures to Celsius and vice versa and may be easier to remember than Equations (1.1) and (1.2).

Liquid nitrogen is so cold that water condenses out of the surrounding air, forming a cloud as the nitrogen is poured.

Sample Exercise 1.12

Liquid nitrogen, which is often used as a coolant for low-temperature experiments, has a boiling point of 77 K. What is this temperature on the Fahrenheit scale?

Solution

We will first convert 77 K to the Celsius scale:

$$T_C = T_K - 273.15 = 77 - 273.15 = -196°C$$

To convert to the Fahrenheit scale, we will use Equation (1.3):

$$\frac{T_F + 40}{T_C + 40} = \frac{9°F}{5°C}$$

$$\frac{T_F + 40}{-196°C + 40} = \frac{T_F + 40}{-156°C} = \frac{9°F}{5°C}$$

$$T_F + 40 = \frac{9°F}{5°C}(-156°C) = -281°F$$

$$T_F = -281°F - 40 = -321°F$$

1.8 Density

Purpose

• To illustrate calculations involving density.

A property of matter that is often used by chemists as an "identification tag" for a substance is **density,** the mass of substance per unit volume of the substance:

$$\text{Density} = \frac{\text{mass}}{\text{volume}}$$

The density of a liquid can be easily determined by weighing an accurately known volume of the liquid. This procedure is illustrated in Sample Exercise 1.13.

Sample Exercise 1.13

A chemist, trying to identify the main component in a compact disc cleaner, finds that 25.00 cm³ of the substance has a mass of 19.625 g at 20°C. The following are the names and densities of the compounds that might be the main component:

Compound	Density in g/cm³ at 20°C
Chloroform	1.492
Diethyl ether	0.714
Ethanol	0.789
Isopropyl alcohol	0.785
Toluene	0.867

Which of these compounds is the most likely to be the main component of the compact disc cleaner?

Solution

To identify the unknown substance, we must determine its density. This can be done by using the definition of density:

$$\text{Density} = \frac{\text{mass}}{\text{volume}} = \frac{19.625 \text{ g}}{25.00 \text{ cm}^3} = 0.7850 \text{ g/cm}^3$$

This density corresponds exactly to that of isopropyl alcohol, which is therefore the most likely main component of the cleaner. However, note that the density of ethanol is also very close. In order to be sure that the compound is isopropyl alcohol, we should run several more density experiments. (In the modern laboratory, many other types of tests could be done to distinguish between these two liquids.)

Besides being a tool for the identification of substances, density has many other uses. For example, the liquid in your car's lead storage battery (a solution of sulfuric acid) changes density because the sulfuric acid is consumed as the battery discharges. In a fully charged battery, the density of the solution is about 1.30 g/cm³. If the density falls below 1.20 g/cm³, the battery will have to be recharged. Density measurement is also used to determine the amount of antifreeze, and thus the level of protection against freezing, in the cooling system of a car.

The densities of various common substances are given in Table 1.5.

Table 1.5		
Densities of Various Common Substances* at 20°C		
Substance	Physical State	Density (g/cm³)
Oxygen	Gas	0.00133
Hydrogen	Gas	0.000084
Ethanol	Liquid	0.789
Benzene	Liquid	0.880
Water	Liquid	0.9982
Magnesium	Solid	1.74
Salt (sodium chloride)	Solid	2.16
Aluminum	Solid	2.70
Iron	Solid	7.87
Copper	Solid	8.96
Silver	Solid	10.5
Lead	Solid	11.34
Mercury	Liquid	13.6
Gold	Solid	19.32
*At 1 atmosphere pressure		

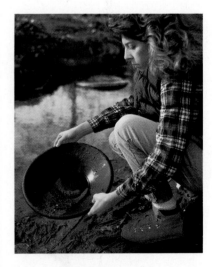

Because gold has a higher density than sand, it settles to the bottom of a prospector's pan.

1.9 Classification of Matter

Purpose

• To show how matter can be classified into subgroups.

Before we can hope to understand the changes we see going on around us—the growth of plants, the rusting of steel, the aging of people, rain becoming more acidic—we must find out how matter is organized. **Matter,** best defined as anything occupying space and having mass, is the material of the universe. Matter is complex and has many levels of organization. In this section we introduce basic ideas about the structure of matter and its behavior.

We will start by considering the definitions of the fundamental properties of matter. Matter exists in three **states:** solid, liquid, and gas. A **solid** is rigid; it has a fixed volume and shape. A **liquid** has a definite volume but no specific shape; it assumes the shape of its container. A **gas** has no fixed volume or shape; it takes on the shape and volume of its container. In contrast to liquids and solids, which are only slightly compressible, gases are highly compressible; it is relatively easy to decrease the volume of a gas. Table 1.5 gives the states of some common substances at 20°C and 1 atmosphere of pressure.

Most of the matter around us consists of **mixtures** of pure substances. Wood, gasoline, wine, soil, and air are all mixtures. The main characteristic of a mixture is that it has *variable composition.* For example, wood is a mixture of many substances, the proportions of which vary depending on the type of wood and where it grows. Mixtures can be classified as **homogeneous** [having visibly (to the naked eye) indistinguishable parts] or **heterogeneous** [having visibly distinguishable parts].

A homogeneous mixture is called a **solution.** Air is a solution consisting of a mixture of gases. Wine is a complex liquid solution. Brass is a solid solution of copper and zinc. Sand in water and iced tea with ice cubes are examples of heterogeneous mixtures. Heterogeneous mixtures can usually be separated into two or more homogeneous mixtures or pure substances (for example, the ice cubes can be separated from the tea).

Mixtures can be separated into pure substances by physical methods. A **pure substance** is one with constant composition. Water is a good illustration of these ideas. As we will discuss in detail later, pure water is composed solely of H_2O molecules, but the water found in nature (groundwater or the water in a lake or ocean) is really a mixture. Seawater, for example, contains large amounts of dissolved minerals. Boiling seawater produces steam, which can be condensed to pure water, leaving the minerals behind as solids. The dissolved minerals in seawater also can be separated out by freezing the mixture, since pure water freezes out. The processes of boiling and freezing cause **physical changes:** when water freezes or boils, it changes its state but remains water; it is still composed of H_2O molecules. A physical change is a change in the form of a substance, not in its chemical composition. A physical change can be used to separate a mixture into pure compounds, but it will not break compounds into elements.

One of the most important methods for separating the components of a mixture is **distillation,** a process that depends on differences in the volatility (how readily substances become gases) of the components. In simple distillation, a mixture is heated in a device such as that shown in Fig. 1.10. The most volatile component vaporizes at the lowest temperature, and the vapor passes through a cooled tube (a condenser), where it condenses back into its liquid state.

The simple, one-stage distillation apparatus shown in Fig. 1.10 works very well when only one component of the mixture is volatile. For example, a mixture of water and sand is easily separated by boiling off the water. Water containing dissolved minerals behaves in much the same way. As the water is boiled off, the minerals remain behind as nonvolatile solids. Simple distillation of seawater using the sun as the heat source is an excellent way to desalinate (remove the minerals from) seawater.

The term **volatile** refers to the ease with which a substance can be changed to its vapor.

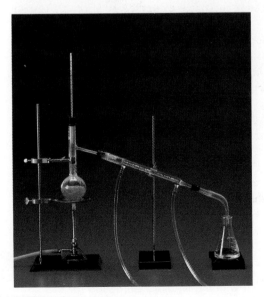

Figure 1.10

Simple laboratory distillation apparatus. Cool water circulates through the outer portion of the condenser, causing vapors from the distilling flask to condense into a liquid. The nonvolatile component of the mixture remains in the distilling flask.

However, when a mixture contains several volatile components, the one-step distillation does not give a pure substance in the receiving flask, and more elaborate methods are required.

Another method of separation is simple **filtration,** which is used when a mixture consists of a solid and a liquid. The mixture is poured onto a mesh, such as filter paper, which passes the liquid and leaves the solid behind.

A third method of separation is called **chromatography.** Chromatography is the general name applied to a series of methods that employ a system with two **phases** (states) of matter: a mobile phase and a stationary phase. The **stationary phase** is a solid, and the **mobile phase** is either a liquid or a gas. The separation process occurs because the components of the mixture have different affinities for the two phases and thus move through the system at different rates. A component with a high affinity for the mobile phase moves relatively quickly through the chromatographic system, whereas one with a high affinity for the solid phase moves more slowly.

One simple type of chromatography, **paper chromatography,** employs a strip of porous paper, such as filter paper, for the stationary phase. A drop of the mixture to be separated is placed on the paper, which is then dipped into a liquid (the mobile phase) that travels up the paper as though it were a wick (see Fig. 1.11). This method of separating a mixture is often used by biochemists, who study the chemistry of living systems.

(a)   (b)   (c)

Figure 1.11

Paper chromatography of ink. (a) A line of the mixture to be separated is placed at one end of a sheet of porous paper. (b) The paper acts as a wick to draw up the liquid. (c) The component with the weakest attraction for the paper travels faster than those that cling to the paper.

It should be noted that when a mixture is separated, the absolute purity of the separated components is an ideal. Because water, for example, inevitably comes into contact with other materials when it is synthesized or separated from a mixture, it is never absolutely pure. With great care, however, substances can be obtained in very nearly pure form.

Pure substances contain compounds (combinations of elements) or free elements. A **compound** is a substance with *constant composition* that can be broken down into elements by chemical processes. An example of a chemical process is the electrolysis of water (see Fig. 1.12), in which an electric current is passed through water to break it down into the free elements hydrogen and oxygen. This process produces a chemical change because the water molecules have been broken down. The water is gone, and in its place we have the free elements hydrogen and oxygen. A **chemical change** is one in which a given substance becomes a new substance or substances with different properties and different composition. **Elements** are substances that cannot be decomposed into simpler substances by chemical or physical means.

We have seen that the matter around us has various levels of organization. The most fundamental substances we have discussed so far are elements. As we will see in later chapters, elements also have structure: they are composed of atoms, which in turn are composed of nuclei and electrons. Even the nucleus has structure: it is composed of protons and neutrons. And even these can be broken down further, into elementary particles called **quarks.** However, we need not concern ourselves with such details at this point. Figure 1.13 summarizes our discussion of the organization of matter.

Figure 1.12

Electrolysis is an example of a chemical change. In this apparatus, water is decomposed to hydrogen gas (filling the red balloon) and oxygen gas (filling the blue balloon). This process will be discussed in detail in Chapter 17.

Figure 1.13
The organization of matter.

The element mercury (top left) combines with the element iodine (top right) to form the compound mercuric iodide (bottom). This is an example of a chemical change.

1.10 *Profiles of People Working in the Chemical Sciences*

Purpose

• To illustrate "real-life" chemical scientists.

As mentioned earlier in this chapter, people trained in the chemical sciences hold an amazing variety of jobs. Because most positions in chemically based industries require a sound technical background, it is common for these industries to hire people with degrees in the chemical sciences and then to encourage these people to learn new skills that will allow them to assume the other responsibilities connected with the manufacture, sale, and use of chemicals. It is quite common for newly graduated chemistry majors to take entry-level positions as laboratory chemists who carry out experiments to help their companies develop new products (research and development). Other entry-level positions might involve ensuring that products meet company standards (quality control or quality assurance) or assisting customers in the use of the company's products (technical sales and service). A person may make a career of laboratory work or, in a few years, may move out of the laboratory into areas such as marketing and sales, eventually becoming a manager and perhaps reaching the highest levels of management. The chief executive officer of a chemically based industry is usually a person with a technical degree.

People who want to make a career of laboratory research in industry often attend graduate school and earn a Ph.D. Graduate study provides a deeper understanding of a particular field and provides the training needed to carry out independent research. A person with a Ph.D. usually manages pure research activities that seek to establish new knowledge that will eventually lead to new products. A career in research often proceeds through a series of management positions, with increasing responsibility and scope, and can lead to the highest levels of management in the company.

Of course, someone interested in research also may pursue an academic career following completion of a Ph.D. and (often) postdoctoral studies. Academic research is pure research most often supported by government agencies such as the National Science Foundation (NSF) or the National Institutes of Health (NIH). Although an academic career might not be as financially lucrative as a career in private industry, an academic career can be extraordinarily satisfying and typically provides a great deal of personal freedom.

The following two profiles are meant to provide just a sampling of careers open to persons trained in the chemical sciences.

Bart M. Eklund is a senior scientist with Radian Corporation in Austin, Texas, where he manages the Atmospheric Chemistry Group. He earned a B.S. in Chemistry from the University of Illinois at Champaign-Urbana in 1979 and has spent his entire career with Radian in the environmental consulting business. Mr. Eklund's primary duties involve directing custom research programs to solve specific problems for client firms. He is responsible for the design and execution of the projects, the quality of the work performed, fiscal management, and client contacts. His other responsibilities at Radian include business development, recruiting, and staff development.

Bart Eklund

Mr. Eklund is a nationally recognized expert in the areas of monitoring and modeling of air emissions from hazardous substances and is a frequent lecturer at specialty workshops. He has over 10 publications and 20 conference presentations to his credit.

Bart's specific interest in a career in environmental science was fostered by two environmental chemistry courses and two ecology courses he took as an undergraduate. His original plan to gain several years of industrial experience and then to return to school for a graduate degree was changed when he found that professional advancement with a B.S. degree was possible in the environmental research field. The multidisciplinary nature of most environmental problems has allowed him to develop his interests in several fields. His specialty is really in being a generalist.

The environmental consulting field provides Bart with a number of attractions: the chance to define and solve a number of research problems; the simultaneous work on a number of diverse projects (he has had a major role in over 40 projects in his career); the mix of desk, field, and laboratory work; the travel; and the opportunity to perform rewarding work that has a positive effect on people's lives. In his current position he manages a research group consisting of two Ph.D., two M.S., and four B.S. scientists with chemistry, physics, and atmospheric science backgrounds.

Among his career highlights are

- Spending a winter month doing air sampling in the Grand Tetons, where he also met his wife and learned to ski

- Driving sampling pipes by hand into the rocky ground of Death Valley Monument in California

- Working regularly with experts in their fields and with people who enjoy what they do

- Doing vigorous work in 100°F weather while wearing a rubberized suit, double gloves, and a respirator

- Getting to work in and see Alaska, Yosemite Park, Niagara Falls, Hong Kong, the People's Republic of China, Mesa Verde, New York City, and dozens of other interesting places

Heidi Piper Flatley went to work for Procter and Gamble after her graduation from the University of Illinois at Champaign-Urbana in 1987 with a B.S. degree in chemical engineering. Combining her technical expertise with her interests in psychology and marketing, Ms. Flatley took a position in the area of Products Research, where she tries to discover ''unmet consumer needs'' and then to design products to meet these needs. Heidi describes herself as a ''technology broker''— someone who looks for ways to use her company's technical expertise to improve people's lives. After a possible application is identified, she then works closely with the personnel in Research and Development as the concept is brought from the idea stage to a finished product that can be market tested.

Heidi says, ''I have become an expert in market research and am continuing to learn about marketing and about management skills (personal and interpersonal) and am gaining excellent experience in product development.''

By 1990, Heidi was living in a French-speaking neighborhood in Brussels, Belgium, where she does market research throughout Europe for Procter and Gamble. Heidi says, ''As a sample slice of my job, I'll tell you what I did last week. I spent Monday, Tuesday, and Wednesday in London with a Belgian woman I hired to help

Heidi Piper Flatley

me interview people in their homes. We did 20 interviews in 3 days, each involving a 45-minute session in which we observe a person using our products and then complete a questionnaire which I designed. Thursday and Friday I managed concept workshops (that I designed the previous weekend) to gain information about attitudes and habits. The results of these workshops then were analyzed in a session (that I chaired) with two Germans from a European advertising agency, a German from the Procter and Gamble Advertising Department, a French perfumer from Procter and Gamble, a Belgian formulation chemist, a German market research expert, and a Belgian market researcher. The six new concepts which came out of these sessions will be further market tested before we make a recommendation to the management at Procter and Gamble as to how to proceed.''

Heidi is not sure how her career will develop in the next 10 to 15 years, but she greatly enjoys chemistry and its applications to consumer products. She is considering such possibilities as starting her own market research company or aspiring to the upper levels of management in a technically based company where she feels she can provide an excellent role model for young women just starting out. ''Maybe to be a successful career woman and yet remain balanced and 'human' is the best example I could set.''

FOR REVIEW

Summary

Ideally, the progress of any science occurs by use of the scientific method, which first makes observations of nature and then looks for patterns in the observations that often lead to the formulation of natural laws. A theory or model is then constructed to provide an interpretation of the behavior of nature. The theory is tested by further experiments and is modified as necessary.

Quantitative observations are called measurements and always consist of a number and a scale or unit. Measurement always involves some uncertainty. Drawing conclusions from the results of measurements requires that the extent of the uncertainty be known. This information is conveyed by using the correct number of significant figures. The preferred system of units among scientists is the SI system. Converting results from one set of units to another is accomplished with unit factors (dimensional analysis).

Matter can exist in three states—solid, liquid, and gas—and has many levels of organization. Mixtures of compounds can be separated by methods involving only physical changes, such as distillation, filtration, and various forms of chromatography. On the other hand, compounds can be broken down to elements only through chemical changes.

Key Terms

Section 1.2	hypothesis	*Section 1.4*	*Section 1.5*
scientific method	*Section 1.3*	uncertainty	significant figures
measurement	SI system	accuracy	exponential notation
natural law	mass	precision	
theory	weight	random error	
model		systematic error	

Section 1.6	Section 1.9	solution	chromatography
dimensional analysis	matter	pure substance	paper chromatography
unit factor	states (of matter)	physical change	compound
Section 1.8	homogeneous mixture	distillation	chemical change
density	heterogeneous mixture	filtration	element

A blue question or exercise number indicates that the answer to that question or exercise appears at the back of this book and a solution appears in the Solutions Guide.

Questions

1. Define and explain the differences between the following terms:
   a. law and theory
   b. theory and experiment
   c. qualitative and quantitative
   d. hypothesis and theory

2. Is the scientific method suitable for solving problems only in the sciences? Explain.

3. Which of the following statements (hypotheses) could be tested by quantitative measurement?
   a. Ty Cobb was a better hitter than Pete Rose.
   b. Ivory soap is $99\frac{44}{100}\%$ pure.
   c. Rolaids consumes 47 times its weight in excess stomach acid.

4. Paracelsus, a sixteenth-century alchemist and healer, adopted as his slogan: ''The patients are your textbook, the sickbed is your study.'' Is this view consistent with using the scientific method?

5. What is the difference between precision and accuracy?

6. A student performed an analysis of a sample for its calcium content and got the following results:

   14.92%, 14.91%, 14.88%, 14.91%

   The actual amount of calcium in the sample is 15.70%. What conclusion can you draw about the accuracy and precision of these results?

7. What is wrong with the following statement?

   ''The results of the experiment do not agree with the theory. Something must be wrong with the experiment.''

8. Why is it incorrect to say that the results of a measurement were accurate but not precise?

9. Distinguish between physical changes and chemical changes.

10. Why is the separation of mixtures into pure or relatively pure substances so important when performing a chemical analysis?

Exercises

In this section similar exercises are paired.

Uncertainty, Precision, Accuracy, and Significant Figures

11. Which of the following are exact numbers?
    a. The elevation of Breckenridge, Colorado, is *9600* ft.
    b. There are *12* eggs in a dozen.
    c. One yard is equal to *0.9144* m.
    d. The announced attendance at a football game was *52,806*.
    e. In 1983, *1759* Ph.D.s in chemistry were awarded in the United States.
    f. The budget deficit of the U.S. government in fiscal year 1990 was *$269 billion*.

12. Which of the following are exact numbers?
    a. There are *100* cm in *1* m.
    b. One meter equals *1.094* yard.
    c. We can use the equation

    $$°F = \tfrac{9}{5}°C + 32$$

    to convert from Celsius to Fahrenheit temperature. Are the numbers $\tfrac{9}{5}$ and *32* exact or inexact?
    d. $\pi = 3.1415926$.

13. How many significant figures are in each of the following?
    a. 0.0012
    b. 437,000
    c. 900.0
    d. 106
    e. 125,904,000
    f. 1.0012
    g. 2006
    h. 3050
    i. 0.001060
    Express each number in exponential form.

14. How many significant figures are in each of the following?
    a. 100
    b. 1.0×10^2
    c. 1.00×10^3
    d. 100.
    e. 0.0048
    f. 0.00480
    g. 4.80×10^{-3}
    h. 4.800×10^{-3}

15. Use exponential notation to express the number 582,000,000 to
    a. one significant figure
    b. two significant figures
    c. three significant figures
    d. five significant figures
    e. seven significant figures

16. Use exponential notation to express the number 480 to
    a. one significant figure
    b. two significant figures
    c. three significant figures
    d. four significant figures

17. Perform the following mathematical operations and express each result to the correct number of significant figures.
    a. $4.184 \times 100.62 \times (25.27 - 24.16)$
    b. $\dfrac{8.925 - 8.904}{8.925} \times 100$

    (This type of calculation is done many times in calculating a percentage error. Assume that this example is such a calculation; thus 100 can be considered to be an exact number.)
    c. $(9.04 - 8.23 + 21.954 + 81.0) \div 3.1416$
    d. $\dfrac{9.2 \times 100.65}{8.321 + 4.026}$
    e. $0.1654 + 2.07 - 2.114$
    f. $8.27(4.987 - 4.962)$
    g. $\dfrac{9.5 + 4.1 + 2.8 + 3.175}{4}$

    (Assume that this operation is taking the average of four numbers. Thus 4 in the denominator is exact.)
    h. $\dfrac{9.025 - 9.024}{9.025} \times 100$ (100 is exact)

18. Perform the following mathematical operations and express the result to the correct number of significant figures.
    a. $6.022 \times 10^{23} \times 1.05 \times 10^2$
    b. $\dfrac{6.6262 \times 10^{-34} \times 2.998 \times 10^8}{2.54 \times 10^{-9}}$
    c. $1.285 \times 10^{-2} + 1.24 \times 10^{-3} + 1.879 \times 10^{-1}$
    d. $1.285 \times 10^{-2} - 1.24 \times 10^{-3}$
    e. $\dfrac{(1.00866 - 1.00728)}{6.02205 \times 10^{23}}$
    f. $\dfrac{9.875 \times 10^2 - 9.795 \times 10^2}{9.875 \times 10^2} \times 100$ (100 is exact)
    g. $\dfrac{9.42 \times 10^2 + 8.234 \times 10^2 + 1.625 \times 10^3}{3}$ (3 is exact)

19. Complete the following conversions:
    a. 1 km = _____ m = _____ mm = _____ pm
    b. 1 g = _____ kg = _____ mg = _____ ng
    c. 1 mL = _____ L = _____ dm^3 = _____ cm^3
    d. 1 mg = _____ kg = _____ g = _____ μg
       = _____ ng = _____ pg = _____ fg
    e. 1 s = _____ ms = _____ ns

20. a. How many kilograms are in one teragram?
    b. How many nanometers are in 6.50×10^2 terameters?
    c. How many kilograms are in 25 femtograms?
    d. How many liters are in 8.0 cubic decimeters?
    e. How many microliters are in one milliliter?
    f. How many picograms are in one microgram?

21. Many atomic dimensions are expressed in angstroms. (1 Å$=1 \times 10^{-8}$ cm). What is the angstrom equal to in terms of the SI units nanometer (nm) and picometer (pm)?

22. Two atoms in a molecule are 134 pm apart. What is the distance in nanometers and angstroms?

23. Perform the following unit conversions:
    a. In the 1987–1988 NBA season, the long and the short of it ranged from 7 ft 6 in tall Manute Bol to 5 ft 2 in tall Tyrone Bogues. What are these basketball players' heights in centimeters and meters? (These heights are $\pm\frac{1}{2}$ in. Use this to calculate the uncertainty of the heights in centimeters. Use this result to determine the number of significant figures to use in your answers.)
    b. The circumference of the earth is 25,000 mi at the equator. What is the circumference in kilometers? in meters?
    c. A rectangular solid measures 1.0 m by 5.6 cm by 2.1 dm. Express its volume in cubic meters, liters, cubic inches, and cubic feet.

24. Convert each of the following expressions to appropriate SI units:
    a. an 18-gal gas tank
    b. an automobile engine with a displacement of 4.00×10^2 in^3
    c. a $\frac{1}{4}$-in (0.25) diameter tube
    d. a 14,110-ft elevation above sea level, the height of Pikes Peak in Colorado
    e. a 198-lb man
    f. a speed of 45 mi/h

25. Use the following exact conversion factors to do the stated conversions:

$$6 \text{ ft} = 1 \text{ fathom}$$
$$100 \text{ fathoms} = 1 \text{ cable length}$$
$$10 \text{ cable lengths} = 1 \text{ nautical mile}$$
$$3 \text{ nautical miles} = 1 \text{ league}$$

a. 928 miles = _____ leagues = _____ km
b. 1.0 cable length = _____ km = _____ cm
c. The "Green Monster," as the left field wall in Boston's Fenway Park is called, is 315 ft from home plate down the left field line and 37 ft high. What are these distances in meters? How far from home plate is the "Green Monster" in cable lengths? How high is it in fathoms?

26. Use the following exact conversion factors to perform the stated calculations:

$$5\tfrac{1}{2} \text{ yards} = 1 \text{ rod}$$
$$40 \text{ rods} = 1 \text{ furlong}$$
$$8 \text{ furlongs} = 1 \text{ mile}$$

a. The Kentucky Derby race is 1.25 miles. How long is the race in rods, furlongs, meters, and kilometers?
b. A marathon race is 26 miles, 385 yards. What is this distance in rods, furlongs, meters, and kilometers?

27. According to *The Sporting News*, the fastest recorded fastball was thrown by Nolan Ryan and had a velocity of 100.8 mi/h.
a. Calculate this velocity in meters per second.
b. How long would it take for this pitch to travel the 60 ft 6 in from the mound to home plate?

28. Science fiction often uses nautical analogies to describe space travel. If the starship *U.S.S. Enterprise* is traveling at warp factor 1.71, what is its speed in knots? (Warp 1.71 = 5.00 times the speed of light; speed of light = 3.00×10^8 m/s; 1 knot = 2000 yd/h, exactly.)

29. Precious metals and gems are measured in troy weights in the English system:

$$24 \text{ grains} = 1 \text{ pennyweight (exact)}$$
$$20 \text{ pennyweight} = 1 \text{ troy ounce (exact)}$$
$$12 \text{ troy ounces} = 1 \text{ troy pound (exact)}$$
$$1 \text{ grain} = 0.0648 \text{ grams}$$
$$1 \text{ carat} = 0.200 \text{ grams}$$

a. The most common English unit of mass is the pound avoirdupois (the pound discussed in Chapter 1). What is one troy pound in kilograms and in pounds?
b. What is the mass of a troy ounce of gold in grams and in carats?
c. The density of gold is 19.3 g/cm³. What is the volume of a troy pound of gold?

30. Apothocaries (druggists) use the following set of measures in the English system:

$$20 \text{ grains ap} = 1 \text{ scruple (exact)}$$
$$3 \text{ scruples} = 1 \text{ dram ap (exact)}$$
$$8 \text{ dram ap} = 1 \text{ oz ap (exact)}$$
$$1 \text{ dram ap} = 3.888 \text{ g}$$

a. Is an apothocary grain the same as a troy grain? (See Exercise 29.)
b. 1 oz ap = _____ oz troy
c. An aspirin tablet contains 5.00×10^2 mg of active ingredient. How many grains ap of active ingredient does it contain? How many scruples?
d. What is the mass of 1 scruple in grams?

31. The long ton is equal to 2240 lb (exactly). The metric tonne is equal to 1000 kg (exactly). What is the mass of a long ton in kilograms and in metric tonnes?

32. The speed of light is 3.00×10^8 m/s. How far will a beam of light travel in 1.00 ns?

Temperature

33. A person has a temperature of 102.5°F. What is this temperature on the Celsius scale? on the Kelvin scale?

34. If the temperature in a room is 74°F, what is this temperature on the Celsius scale? on the Kelvin scale?

35. Many chemical quantities are specified as being measured at 25°C. What is this temperature on the Fahrenheit scale? on the Kelvin scale?

36. Helium boils at about 4 K. What is this temperature in °F? in °C?

37. A thermometer gives a reading of 20.6°C ± 0.1°C. What is the temperature in °F? What is the uncertainty?

38. A thermometer gives a reading of 96.1°F ± 0.2°F. What is the temperature in °C? What is the uncertainty?

Density

39. The density of aluminum is 2.70 g/cm^3. Express this value in units of kilograms per cubic meter and pounds per cubic foot.

40. The density of water is 1.0 g/cm^3. Express this value in kilograms per cubic meter and pounds per cubic foot.

41. The diameter of a hydrogen nucleus is 1.0×10^{-3} pm and its mass is 1.67×10^{-24} g. What is the density of the nucleus in grams per cubic centimeter?

42. Hydrogen gas (H_2) at 0°C and 1 atmosphere (atm) pressure has a density of 0.045 g/L. What is the density in grams per cubic centimeter? in kilograms per cubic meter?

43. Diamonds are measured in carats, and 1 carat = 0.200 g. The density of diamond is 3.51 g/cm^3. What is the volume of a 5.0-carat diamond?
$\frac{4}{3}\pi r^3$ — volume of a sphere

44. The volume of a diamond is found to be 2.8 mL. What is the mass of the diamond in carats? (See Exercise 43.)

45. In each of the following pairs, which has the greater mass? (See Table 1.5.)
    a. 1.0 kg of feathers or 1.0 kg of lead
    b. 1.0 mL of mercury or 1.0 mL of water
    c. 19.32 mL of water or 1.00 mL of gold
    d. 75 mL of copper or 1.0 L of benzene

46. In each of the following pairs, which has the greater volume?
    a. 1.0 kg of feathers or 1.0 kg of lead
    b. 100 g of gold or 100 g of water
    c. 1.0 L of copper or 1.0 L of mercury

Classification and Separation of Matter

47. What are some of the differences between a solid, a liquid, and a gas?

48. What is the difference between homogeneous and heterogeneous matter? Classify each of the following as homogeneous or heterogeneous.
    a. soil
    b. the atmosphere
    c. a carbonated soft drink
    d. gasoline
    e. gold
    f. a solution of ethanol and water

49. Classify each of the following as a mixture or a pure substance.
    a. water   d. iron   g. wine
    b. blood   e. brass   h. leather
    c. the oceans   f. uranium   i. table salt (NaCl)

50. Of the pure substances in Exercise 49, which are elements, and which are compounds?

Additional Exercises

51. Perform the indicated mathematical operations and express each result to the correct number of significant figures.
    a. 3.894×2.16
    b. $2.96 + 8.1 + 5.0214$
    c. $485 \div 9.231$
    d. 2.46×2
    e. $9.146 - 9.137$
    f. $2.17 + 4.32 + 401.278 + 21.826$

52. Chemists often give the composition of a mixture as mass per unit volume. For example, if 1.5 g of table sugar is dissolved in 5.0 mL of water, we say there is 1.5 g/5.0 mL = 0.30 g/mL of sugar in the solution. Express 0.30 g/mL in each of the following units.
    a. mg/mL   c. μg/mL   e. μg/μL
    b. kg/m^3 d. ng/mL

53. A star is estimated to have a mass of 2×10^{36} kg. Assuming it to be a sphere of average radius 6.96×10^5 km, calculate the average density of the star in units of
    a. kg/km^3 b. kg/m^3 c. g/cm^3

54. In the opening scenes of the movie *Raiders of the Lost Ark*, Indiana Jones tries to remove a gold idol from a booby-trapped pedestal. He replaces the idol with a bag of sand of approximately equal volume. (Density of gold = 19.32 g/cm^3; density of sand $\approx$ 3 g/cm^3.)
    a. Did he have a reasonable chance of not activating the mass-sensitive booby trap?
    b. In a later scene he and an unscrupulous guide play catch with the idol. Assume that the volume of the idol is about

1.0 L. If it were solid gold, what mass would the idol have? Is playing catch with it plausible?

55. An automobile achieves a gas mileage of 36.1 mi/gal. How many kilometers can it travel on 1.0 L of gasoline?

56. According to the *Official Rules of Baseball,* a baseball must have a circumference not more than 9.25 in or less than 9.00 in and a mass not more than 5.25 oz or less than 5.00 oz. What range of densities can a baseball be expected to have? Express this range as a single number with an accompanying uncertainty limit.

57. Assume that the following numbers are known to ± 1 in the last digit. Perform the following divisions and estimate the maximum uncertainty in each result. That is, determine the largest and smallest number that could occur for each case. (See Appendix 1.5.)
   a. $103 \div 101$
   b. $101 \div 99$
   c. $99 \div 101$
   Considering your calculated error limits, to how many significant figures should each result be expressed? Do any of these constitute an exception to the rule for division listed in Section 1.5? Rationalize any discrepancies.

58. The chemist in Sample Exercise 1.13 did some further experiments. She found that the pipet used to measure the volume of the cleaner is accurate to ± 0.03 cm^3. The mass measurement is accurate to ± 0.002 g. Are these measurements sufficiently precise for the chemist to distinguish between isopropyl alcohol and ethanol?

59. In Shakespeare's *Richard III,* the First Murderer says:

   ''Take that, and that! [*Stabs Clarence*]
   If that is not enough, I'll drown you in the malmsey butt within!''

   Given that 1 butt = 126 gal, in how many liters of malmsey (a foul brew similar to mead) was the unfortunate Clarence about to be drowned?

60. Although the preferred SI unit of area is the square meter, land is often measured in the metric system in hectares (ha). One hectare is equal to 10,000 m^2. In the English system of measure, land is often measured in acres (1 acre = 160 rod^2). Use these exact conversions and those given in Exercise 26 to calculate:
   a. 1 ha = _____ km^2
   b. the area of a 5.5-acre plot of land in hectares, square meters, and square kilometers.
   c. A lot with dimensions 120 ft by 75 ft is to be sold for $6500. What is the price per acre? What is the price per hectare?
   d. A plot of land is 27 ft wide by 1.4 furlongs long. What is the area in square feet, square rods, acres, square meters, and hectares?

61. On the distant planet of Majipoor, the smallest monetary unit is the weight. The monetary scale is

   100 weights = 1 crown
   20 crowns = 1 royal

   (Assume all numbers are exact.)
   a. A horse costs 85 crowns. How much does the horse cost in royals and weights? How many horses can be purchased for 50 royals? How much of the 50 royals would be left after purchasing the horses?
   b. Haigus hides cost 13 crowns per bundle. A bundle contains 25 haigus hides. What is the cost of a single haigus hide in weights? What is the cost of 288 bundles of haigus hides in royals?

62. The mass and volume of an object were measured and found to be 16.50 g ± 0.02 g and 15.5 cm^3 ± 0.2 cm^3, respectively. Calculate the density with appropriate error limits. (See Appendix 1.5.)

63. The density of an irregularly shaped object was determined as follows. The mass of the object was found to be 28.90 g ± 0.03 g. A graduated cylinder was partially filled with water. The reading of the level of the water was 6.4 cm^3 ± 0.1 cm^3. The object was dropped in the cylinder, and the level of the water rose to 9.8 cm^3 ± 0.1 cm^3. What is the density of the object with appropriate error limits? (See Appendix 1.5.)

64. A rectangular block has dimensions 29 mm $\times$ 35 mm $\times$ 100. mm. The mass of the block is 615.0 g ± 0.2 g. What are the volume and density of the block? What is the uncertainty in the volume and density? Assume that the dimensions of the block are known to ± 1 mm.

65. The world record for the hundred meter dash is 9.86 s. What is the corresponding average speed in units of m/s, km/h, ft/s, and mi/h? At this speed, how long would it take to run 1.00×10^2 yards?

66. If the amount of mercury in a polluted lake is 0.4 μg Hg/mL, what is the total mass in kilograms of mercury in the lake? (The lake has a surface area of 100 mi^2 and an average depth of 20 ft.)

67. Express 0 K in °F.

68. A 16-oz container of baking soda costs 65¢. What is the cost of the baking soda per gram and per kilogram?

69. Two spherical objects have the same mass. One floats on water; the other sinks. Which object has the greater diameter? Explain your answer.

70. The density of osmium (the densest metal) is 22.57 g/cm^3. What is the mass of a block of osmium with dimensions 5.00 cm $\times$ 4.00 cm $\times$ 2.50 cm? What volume would be occupied by 1.00 kg of osmium?

71. One metal object is a cube with edges of 3.00 cm and a mass of 140.4 g. A second metal object is a sphere with radius 1.42 cm and a mass of 61.6 g. Are these objects made of the same or different metals? Assume that the calculated densities are accurate to $\pm 1.00\%$.

Challenge Problems

72. Many times errors are expressed in terms of percentage. The percent error is the absolute value of the difference of the true value and the experimental value, divided by the true value, and multiplied by 100.

$$\text{Percent error} = \frac{|\text{true value} - \text{experimental value}|}{\text{true value}} \times 100$$

Calculate the percent error for the following measurements.
a. The density of an aluminum block determined in an experiment was 2.64 g/cm³. (True value 2.70 g/cm³.)
b. The experimental determination of iron in iron ore was 16.48%. (True value 16.12%.)
c. A balance measured the mass of a 1.000-g standard as 0.9981 g.

73. A rule of thumb in designing experiments is to avoid using a result that is the small difference between two large measured quantities. In terms of uncertainties in measurement, why is this good advice?

74. A person weighed 15 pennies on a balance and recorded the following masses:

3.112 g	3.109 g	3.059 g
2.467 g	3.079 g	2.518 g
3.129 g	2.545 g	3.050 g
3.053 g	3.054 g	3.072 g
3.081 g	3.131 g	3.064 g

Curious about the results, he looked at the dates on each penny. Two of the light pennies were minted in 1983 and one in 1982. The dates on the 12 heavier pennies ranged from 1970 to 1982. Two of the 12 heavier pennies were minted in 1982.
a. Do you think the Bureau of the Mint changed the way they made pennies? Explain.
b. The person calculated the average mass of the 12 heavy pennies. He expressed this average as 3.0828 g ± 0.0482 g. What is wrong with the numbers in this result, and how should the value be expressed?

75. On October 21, 1982, the Bureau of the Mint changed the composition of pennies (see Exercise 74). Instead of an alloy of 95% Cu and 5% Zn by mass, a core of 99.2% Zn and 0.8% Cu with a thin shell of copper was adopted. The overall composition of the new penny was 97.6% Zn and 2.4% Cu by mass. Does this account for the difference in mass among the pennies in Exercise 74, assuming that each type of penny is the same size? (Density of Cu = 8.96 g/cm³; density of Zn = 7.14 g/cm³.)

76. Ethylene glycol is the main component in automobile antifreeze. To monitor the temperature of an auto cooling system, you intend to use a meter that reads from 0 to 100. You devise a new temperature scale based on the approximate melting and boiling points of a typical antifreeze solution (−45°C and 115°C). You wish these points to correspond to 0°A and 100°A, respectively.
a. Derive an expression for converting between °A and °C.
b. Derive an expression for converting between °F and °A.
c. At what temperature would your thermometer and a Celsius thermometer give the same numerical reading?
d. Your thermometer reads 86°A. What is the temperature in °C and in °F?
e. What is a temperature of 45°C in °A?

77. Confronted with the box shown in the diagram, you wish to discover something about its internal workings. You have no tools and cannot open the box. You pull on rope B, and it moves rather freely. When you pull on rope A, rope C appears to be pulled slightly into the box. When you pull on rope C, rope A almost disappears into the box.*

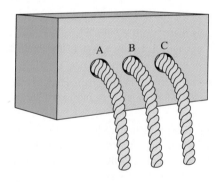

a. Based on these observations, construct a model for the interior mechanism of the box.
b. What further experiments could you do to refine your model?

*From Yoder, Suydam, and Snavely, *Chemistry* (New York: Harcourt Brace Jovanovich, 1975), pp. 9–11.

Marathon Problem*

78. A cylindrical bar of gold that is 1.5 in high and 0.25 in in diameter has a mass of 23.1984 g, as determined on an analytical balance. An empty graduated cylinder is weighed on a triple-beam balance and has a mass of 73.47 g. After pouring a small amount of a liquid into the graduated cylinder, the mass is 79.16 g. When the gold cylinder is placed in the graduated cylinder (the liquid covers the top of the gold cylinder), the volume indicated on the graduated cylinder is 8.5 mL.

Assume that the temperatures of the gold bar and the liquid are 86°F. If the density of the liquid decreases by 1.0% for each 10°C rise in temperature (over the range 0 to 50°C), determine

a. the density of the gold at 86°F.

b. the density of the liquid at 40°F.

Note: Parts (a) and (b) can be answered independently.

*This Marathon Problem is taken from an article, ''The Use of 'Marathon' Problems as Effective Vehicles for the Presentation of General Chemistry Lectures,'' by James H. Burness, that originally appeared in *Journal of Chemical Education,* **1991,** *68,* 920.

CHAPTER 2

Atoms, Molecules, and Ions

W here does one start in learning chemistry? Clearly we must consider some essential vocabulary and something about the origins of the science before we can proceed very far. Thus, while Chapter 1 provided background on the fundamental ideas and procedures of science in general, Chapter 2 covers the specific chemical background necessary for understanding the material in the next few chapters. The coverage of these topics is necessarily brief at this point. We will develop these ideas more fully as it becomes appropriate to do so. A major goal of this chapter is to present the systems for naming chemical compounds to provide you with the vocabulary necessary to understand this book and to pursue your laboratory studies.

Because chemistry is concerned first and foremost with chemical changes, we will proceed as quickly as possible to a study of chemical reactions (Chapters 3 and 4). However, before we can discuss reactions, we must consider some fundamental ideas about atoms and how they combine.

CONTENTS

< This figure, entitled "Molecular Man," was crafted of 28 individual molecules at the IBM Research Division's Almaden Research Center in San Jose. The scientists position individual atoms and molecules to create and study very small structures. Each of the gold-colored peaks in the "Molecular Man" is an image of a carbon monoxide molecule (the molecules are spaced about 4.8 Å apart). "Molecular Man" measures 50 Å (200 billionths of an inch) head-to-toe and 25 Å hand-to-hand. More than 20,000 of the figures, linked hand-to-hand, would be needed to span the width of a single human hair.

2.1 *The Early History of Chemistry*

Purpose

- To give a brief account of early chemical discoveries.

The Alchemists, an oil on slate painting by Jan van der Straet in 1570.

Chemistry has been important since ancient times. The processing of natural ores to produce metals for ornaments and weapons and the use of embalming fluids are two applications of chemical phenomena that were utilized prior to 1000 B.C.

The Greeks were the first to try to explain why chemical changes occur. By about 400 B.C. they had proposed that all matter was composed of four fundamental substances: fire, earth, water, and air. The Greeks also considered the question of whether matter is continuous, and thus infinitely divisible into smaller pieces, or composed of small, indivisible particles. Supporters of the latter position were Demokritos* of Abdera (*c.*460–*c.*370 B.C.) and Leucippos, who used the term *atomos* (which later became **atoms**) to describe these ultimate particles. However, because the Greeks had no experiments to test their ideas, no definitive conclusion could be reached about the divisibility of matter.

The next 2000 years of chemical history were dominated by a pseudoscience called **alchemy.** Alchemists were often mystics and fakes who were obsessed with the idea of turning cheap metals into gold. However, this period also saw important advances: the alchemists discovered several elements and learned to prepare the mineral acids.

The foundations of modern chemistry were laid in the sixteenth century with the development of systematic metallurgy (extraction of metals from ores) by a German, Georg Bauer (1494–1555), and the medicinal application of minerals by a Swiss alchemist/physician known as Paracelsus [full name: Philippus Theophrastus Bombastus von Hohenheim (1493–1541)].

The first "chemist" to perform truly quantitative experiments was Robert Boyle (1627–1691), who carefully measured the relationship between the pressure and volume of air. When Boyle published his book *The Skeptical Chymist* in 1661, the quantitative sciences of physics and chemistry were born. In addition to his results on the quantitative behavior of gases, Boyle's other major contribution to chemistry consisted of his ideas about the chemical elements. Boyle held no preconceived notion about the number of elements. In his view a substance was an element unless it could be broken down into two or more simpler substances. As Boyle's experimental definition of an element became generally accepted, the list of known elements began to grow, and the Greek system of four elements finally died. Although Boyle was an excellent scientist, he was not always right. For example, he clung to the alchemists' views that metals were not true elements and that a way would eventually be found to change one metal into another.

The phenomenon of combustion evoked intense interest in the seventeenth and eighteenth centuries. The German chemist Georg Stahl (1660–1734) suggested that a substance he called "phlogiston" flowed out of the burning material. Stahl postulated that a substance burning in a closed container eventually stopped burning because the air in the container became saturated with phlogiston. Oxygen gas, discovered by Joseph Priestley (1733–1804),† an English clergyman and scientist

*Democritus is an alternate spelling.

†Oxygen gas was actually first observed by the Swedish chemist Karl W. Scheele (1742–1786), but because his results were published after Priestley's, the latter is commonly credited with the discovery of oxygen.

(Fig. 2.1), was found to support vigorous combustion and was thus supposed to be low in phlogiston. In fact, oxygen was originally called "dephlogisticated air."

2.2 Fundamental Chemical Laws

Purpose

- To describe and illustrate the laws of conservation of mass, definite proportion, and multiple proportions.

By the late eighteenth century, combustion had been studied extensively; the gases carbon dioxide, nitrogen, hydrogen, and oxygen had been discovered; and the list of elements continued to grow. However, it was Antoine Lavoisier (1743–1794), a French chemist (Fig. 2.2), who finally explained the true nature of combustion, thus clearing the way for the tremendous progress that was made near the end of the eighteenth century. Lavoisier, like Boyle, regarded measurement as the essential operation of chemistry. His experiments, in which he carefully weighed

Figure 2.1

The Priestley Medal is the highest honor given by the American Chemical Society. It is named for Joseph Priestley, who was born in England on March 13, 1733. He performed many important scientific experiments, among them the discovery that a gas later identified as carbon dioxide could be dissolved in water to produce *seltzer*. Also, as a result of meeting Benjamin Franklin in London in 1766, Priestley became interested in electricity and was the first to observe that graphite was an electrical conductor. However, his greatest discovery occurred in 1774 when he isolated oxygen by heating mercuric oxide.

Because of his nonconformist political views, he was forced to leave England. He died in the United States in 1804.

Figure 2.2

Antoine Lavoisier was born in Paris on August 26, 1743. Although Lavoisier's father wanted his son to follow him into the legal profession, young Lavoisier was fascinated by science. From the beginning of his scientific career, Lavoisier recognized the importance of accurate measurements. His careful weighings showed that mass was conserved in chemical reactions and that combustion involves reaction with oxygen. Also, he wrote the first modern chemistry textbook. It is not surprising that Lavoisier is often called the father of modern chemistry.

To help support his scientific work, Lavoisier invested in a private tax-collecting firm and married the daughter of one of the company executives. His connection to the tax collectors proved fatal, for radical French revolutionaries demanded his execution, which occurred on the guillotine on May 8, 1794.

the reactants and products of various reactions, suggested that *mass is neither created nor destroyed.* Lavoisier's discovery of this **law of conservation of mass** was the basis for the developments in chemistry in the nineteenth century.

Lavoisier's quantitative experiments showed that combustion involved oxygen (which Lavoisier named), not phlogiston. He also discovered that life was supported by a process that also involved oxygen and was similar in many ways to combustion. In 1789 Lavoisier published the first modern chemistry textbook, *Elementary Treatise on Chemistry,* in which he presented a unified picture of the chemical knowledge assembled up to that time. Unfortunately, in the same year the text was published, the French Revolution broke out. Lavoisier, who had been associated with collecting taxes for the government, was executed on the guillotine as an enemy of the people in 1794.

After 1800 chemistry was dominated by scientists who, following Lavoisier's lead, performed careful weighing experiments to study the course of chemical reactions and to determine the composition of various chemical compounds. One of these chemists, a Frenchman, Joseph Proust (1754–1826), showed that *a given compound always contains exactly the same proportion of elements by mass.* For example, Proust found that the substance copper carbonate is always 5.3 parts copper to 4 parts oxygen to 1 part carbon (by mass). The principle of the constant composition of compounds, originally called ''Proust's law,'' is now known as the **law of definite proportion.**

Proust's discovery stimulated John Dalton (1766–1844), an English schoolteacher (Fig. 2.3), to think about atoms as the particles that might compose elements. Dalton reasoned that if elements were composed of tiny individual particles, a given compound should always contain the same combination of these atoms. This concept explained why the same relative masses of elements were always found in a given compound.

But Dalton discovered another principle that convinced him even more of the existence of atoms. He noted, for example, that carbon and oxygen form two different compounds that contain different relative amounts of carbon and oxygen, as shown by the following data:

	Mass of Oxygen that Combines with 1 g of Carbon
Compound I	1.33 g
Compound II	2.66 g

Dalton noted that compound II contains twice as much oxygen per gram of carbon as compound I, a fact that could be easily explained in terms of atoms. Compound I might be CO, and compound II might be CO_2.* This principle, which was found to apply to compounds of other elements as well, became known as the **law of multiple proportions:** *when two elements form a series of compounds, the ratios of the masses of the second element that combine with 1 gram of the first element can always be reduced to small whole numbers.*

*Subscripts are used to show the numbers of atoms present. The number 1 is understood (not written). The symbols for the elements and the writing of chemical formulas will be illustrated further in Sections 2.6 and 2.7.

Oxygen is from the French *oxygène,* meaning "generator of acid," because it was initially considered to be an integral part of all acids.

Figure 2.3

John Dalton (1766–1844), an Englishman, began teaching at a Quaker school when he was 12. His fascination with science included an intense interest in meteorology, which led to an interest in the gases of the air and their ultimate components, atoms. Dalton is best known for his atomic theory, in which he postulated that the fundamental differences among atoms are their masses. He was the first to prepare a table of relative atomic weights.

Dalton was a humble man with several apparent handicaps: he was not articulate and he was color-blind, a terrible problem for a chemist. In spite of these disadvantages, he helped to revolutionize the science of chemistry.

To make sure the significance of this observation is clear, in Sample Exercise 2.1 we will consider data for a series of compounds consisting of nitrogen and oxygen.

Sample Exercise 2.1

The following data were collected for several compounds of nitrogen and oxygen:

	Mass of Nitrogen that Combines with 1 g of Oxygen
Compound *A*	1.750 g
Compound *B*	0.8750 g
Compound *C*	0.4375 g

Show how these data illustrate the law of multiple proportions.

Solution

For the law of multiple proportions to hold, the ratios of the masses of nitrogen combining with 1 gram of oxygen in each pair of compounds should be small whole numbers. We therefore compute the ratios as follows:

$$\frac{A}{B} = \frac{1.750}{0.875} = \frac{2}{1}$$

$$\frac{B}{C} = \frac{0.875}{0.4375} = \frac{2}{1}$$

$$\frac{A}{C} = \frac{1.750}{0.4375} = \frac{4}{1}$$

These results support the law of multiple proportions.

The significance of the data in Sample Exercise 2.1 is that compound *A* contains twice as much nitrogen (N) per gram of oxygen (O) as does compound *B* and that compound *B* contains twice as much nitrogen per gram of oxygen as does compound *C*. In terms of the numbers of atoms combining, any of the following formulas can explain these data:

Compound *A*	N_2O	NO	N_4O_2
Compound *B*	NO or	NO_2 or	N_2O_2
Compound *C*	NO_2	NO_4	N_2O_4

In fact, an infinite number of other possibilities exists. Dalton could not deduce absolute formulas from the available data on relative masses. However, the data on the composition of compounds in terms of the relative masses of the elements supported his hypothesis that each element consisted of a certain type of atom and that compounds were formed from specific combinations of atoms.

2.3 Dalton's Atomic Theory

Purpose

- To describe Dalton's theory of atoms and show the significance of Gay-Lussac's experiments.

These statements are a modern paraphrase of Dalton's ideas.

In 1808 Dalton published *A New System of Chemical Philosophy*, in which he presented his theory of atoms:

1. *Each element is made up of tiny particles called atoms.*

2. *The atoms of a given element are identical; the atoms of different elements are different in some fundamental way or ways.*

3. *Chemical compounds are formed when atoms combine with each other. A given compound always has the same relative numbers and types of atoms.*

4. *Chemical reactions involve reorganization of the atoms—changes in the way they are bound together. The atoms themselves are not changed in a chemical reaction.*

It is instructive to consider Dalton's reasoning on the relative masses of the atoms of the various elements. In Dalton's time water was known to be composed of the elements hydrogen and oxygen, with 8 grams of oxygen present for every 1 gram of hydrogen. If the formula for water were OH, an oxygen atom would have to have 8 times the mass of a hydrogen atom. However, if the formula for water were H_2O (two atoms of hydrogen for every oxygen atom), this would mean that each atom of oxygen is 16 times as massive as *each* atom of hydrogen (since the ratio of the mass of one oxygen to that of *two* hydrogens is 8 to 1). Because the formula for water was not then known, Dalton could not specify the relative masses of oxygen and hydrogen unambiguously. To solve the problem, Dalton made a fundamental assumption: he decided that nature would be as simple as possible. This assumption led him to conclude that the formula for water should be OH. He thus assigned hydrogen a mass of 1 and oxygen a mass of 8.

Joseph Louis Gay-Lussac, a French physicist and chemist, was remarkably versatile. Although he is now primarily known for his studies on the combining of volumes of gases, Gay-Lussac was instrumental in the studies of many of the other properties of gases. Some of Gay-Lussac's motivation to learn about gases arose from his passion for ballooning. In fact, he made ascents to heights of over four miles to collect air samples, setting altitude records that stood for about 50 years. Gay-Lussac also was the codiscoverer of boron and the developer of a process for manufacturing sulfuric acid. As chief assayer of the French mint, Gay-Lussac developed many techniques for chemical analysis and invented many types of glassware now used routinely in labs. Gay-Lussac spent his last twenty years as a lawmaker in the French government.

Using similar reasoning for other compounds, Dalton prepared the first table of **atomic masses** (called **atomic weights** by chemists, since mass is often determined by comparison to a standard mass—a process called **weighing**). Many of the masses were later proved to be wrong because of Dalton's incorrect assumptions about the formulas of certain compounds, but the construction of a table of masses was an important step forward.

Although not recognized as such for many years, the keys to determining absolute formulas for compounds were provided in the experimental work of the French chemist Joseph Gay-Lussac (1778–1850) and by the hypothesis of an Italian chemist named Amadeo Avogadro (1776–1856). In 1809 Gay-Lussac performed experiments in which he measured (under the same conditions of temperature and pressure) the volumes of gases that reacted with each other. For example, Gay-Lussac found that 2 volumes of hydrogen react with 1 volume of oxygen to form 2 volumes of gaseous water and that 1 volume of hydrogen reacts with 1 volume of chlorine to form 2 volumes of hydrogen chloride. These results are represented schematically in Fig. 2.4.

In 1811 Avogadro interpreted these results by proposing that *at the same temperature and pressure, equal volumes of different gases contain the same number of*

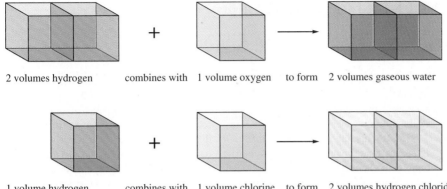

2 volumes hydrogen   combines with 1 volume oxygen   to form   2 volumes gaseous water

1 volume hydrogen   combines with 1 volume chlorine   to form   2 volumes hydrogen chloride

Figure 2.4

A representation of some of Gay-Lussac's experimental results on combining gas volumes.

particles. This assumption (called **Avogadro's hypothesis**) makes sense if the distances between the particles in a gas are very great compared with the sizes of the particles. Under these conditions, the volume of a gas is determined by the number of molecules present, not by the size of the individual particles.

If Avogadro's hypothesis is correct, Gay-Lussac's result,

2 volumes of hydrogen react with 1 volume of oxygen

$\rightarrow$ 2 volumes of water vapor

can be expressed as follows:

2 molecules* of hydrogen react with 1 molecule of oxygen

$\rightarrow$ 2 molecules of water

These observations can best be explained by assuming that gaseous hydrogen, oxygen, and chlorine are all composed of diatomic (two-atom) molecules: H_2, O_2, and Cl_2, respectively. Gay-Lussac's results can then be represented as shown in Fig. 2.5. (Note that this reasoning suggests that the formula for water is H_2O, not OH as Dalton believed.)

Unfortunately, Avogadro's interpretations were not accepted by most chemists, and a half-century of confusion followed, in which many different assumptions were made about formulas and atomic masses.

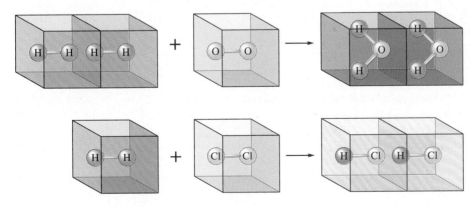

Figure 2.5

A representation of combining gases at the molecular level. The spheres represent atoms in the molecules.

---

*A **molecule** is a collection of atoms (see Sec. 2.6).

◀ **CHEMICAL IMPACT** ▶

Berzelius, Selenium, and Silicon

Jöns Jakob Berzelius (see figure) was probably the best experimental chemist of his generation and, given the crudeness of his laboratory equipment, maybe the best of all time. Unlike Lavoisier, who could afford to buy the best laboratory equipment available, Berzelius worked with minimal equipment in very plain surroundings. One of Berzelius's students described the Swedish chemist's workplace: ''The laboratory consisted of two ordinary rooms with the very simplest arrangements; there were neither furnaces nor hoods, neither water system nor gas. Against the walls stood some closets with the chemicals, in the middle the mercury trough and the blast lamp table. Beside this was the sink consisting of a stone water holder with a stopcock and a pot standing under it. [Next door in the kitchen] stood a small heating furnace.''

In these simple facilities Berzelius performed more than 2000 experiments over a 10-year period to determine accurate atomic masses for the 50 elements then known. His success can be seen from the data in the table below. These remarkably accurate values attest to his experimental skills and patience.

Besides his table of atomic masses, Berzelius made many other major contributions to chemistry. The most important of these was the invention of a simple set of symbols for the elements along with a system for writing the formulas of compounds to replace the awkward symbolic representations of the alchemists. Although some chemists, including Dalton, objected to the new system, it was gradually adopted and forms the basis of the system we use today.

In addition to these accomplishments, Berzelius also discovered the elements cerium, thorium, selenium, and silicon. Of these elements, selenium and silicon are particularly important in today's world. Berzelius discovered selenium in 1817 in connection with his studies of sulfuric acid. For years selenium's toxicity has been known, but only recently have we become aware that it may have a positive effect on human health. Studies have shown that trace amounts of selenium in the diet may protect people from heart disease and cancer. One study based on data from 27 countries showed an inverse relationship between the cancer death rate and the selenium content of soil in a particular region (low cancer death rate in areas with high selenium content). Another research paper reported an inverse relationship between the selenium content of the blood and the incidence of breast cancer in women. Selenium is also found in the heart muscle and may play an important role in proper heart function. Because of these and other studies, selenium's reputation has improved, and many scientists are now studying its function in the human body.

Jöns Jakob Berzelius (1779–1848).

Comparison of Several of Berzelius's Atomic Masses with the Modern Values

	Atomic Mass	
Element	Berzelius's Value	Current Value
Chlorine	35.41	35.45
Copper	63.00	63.55
Hydrogen	1.00	1.01
Lead	207.12	207.2
Nitrogen	14.05	14.01
Oxygen	16.00	16.00
Potassium	39.19	39.10
Silver	108.12	107.87
Sulfur	32.18	32.06

The Alchemists' Symbols for Some Common Elements and Compounds

Substance	Alchemists' Symbol
Silver	☽
Lead	♄
Tin	♃
Platinum	☽⊙
Sulfuric acid	+⊕
Alcohol	↮
Sea salt	⊙

Silicon is the second most abundant element in the earth's crust, exceeded only by oxygen. As we will see in Chapter 10, compounds involving silicon bonded to oxygen make up most of the earth's sand, rock, and soil. Berzelius prepared silicon in its pure form in 1824 by heating silicon tetrafluoride (SiF_4) with potassium metal. Today, silicon forms the basis for the modern microelectronics industry centered near San Francisco in a place that has come to be known as "Silicon Valley." The technology of the silicon chip (see figure) with its printed circuits has transformed computers from room-sized monsters with thousands of unreliable vacuum tubes to desktop and notebook-sized units with trouble-free "solid-state" circuitry.

See E. J. Holmyard, *Alchemy* (New York: Penguin Books, 1968).

A silicon chip.

During the nineteenth century, painstaking measurements were made of the masses of various elements that combined to form compounds. From these experiments a list of relative atomic masses could be determined. One of the chemists involved in contributing to this list was a Swede named Jöns Jakob Berzelius (1779–1848), who discovered the elements cerium, selenium, silicon, and thorium and developed the modern symbols for the elements used in writing the formulas of compounds.

2.4 Early Experiments to Characterize the Atom

Purpose

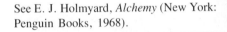

• To summarize the experiments that characterized the structure of the atom.

On the basis of the work of Dalton, Gay-Lussac, Avogadro, and others, chemistry was beginning to make sense. The concept of atoms was clearly a good idea. Inevitably, scientists began to wonder about the nature of the atom. What is an atom made of, and how do the atoms of the various elements differ?

The Electron

The first important experiments that led to an understanding of the composition of the atom were done by the English physicist J. J. Thomson (Fig. 2.6), who studied

Figure 2.6

J. J. Thomson (1856–1940) was an English physicist at Cambridge University. He received the Nobel Prize in physics in 1906.

Source of electrical potential

Stream of negative particles (electrons)

(−)

Metal electrode

Partially evacuated glass tube

(+)

Metal electrode

Figure 2.7

A cathode-ray tube. The fast-moving electrons excite the gas in the tube, causing a glow between the electrodes. The green color in the photo is due to the response of the screen (coated with zinc sulfide) to the electron beam.

electrical discharges in partially evacuated tubes called **cathode-ray tubes** (Fig. 2.7) during the period from 1898 to 1903. Thomson found that when high voltage was applied to the tube, a "ray" he called a **cathode ray** (because it emanated from the negative electrode, or cathode) was produced. Because this ray was produced at the negative electrode and was repelled by the negative pole of an applied electric field (see Fig. 2.8), Thomson postulated that the ray was a stream of negatively charged particles, now called **electrons.** From experiments in which he measured the deflection of the beam of electrons in a magnetic field, Thomson determined the *charge-to-mass ratio* of an electron:

$$\frac{e}{m} = -1.76 \times 10^8 \text{ C/g}$$

where e represents the charge on the electron in coulombs (C) and m represents the electron mass in grams.

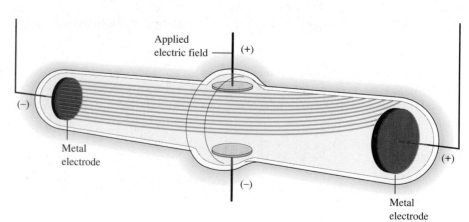

Applied electric field

(+)

(−)

Metal electrode

(−)

(+)

Metal electrode

Figure 2.8

Deflection of cathode rays by an applied electric field.

One of Thomson's primary goals in his cathode-ray tube experiments was to gain an understanding of the structure of the atom. He reasoned that since electrons could be produced from electrodes made of various types of metals, *all* atoms must contain electrons. Since atoms were known to be electrically neutral, Thomson further assumed that atoms also must contain some positive charge. Thomson postulated that an atom consisted of a diffuse cloud of positive charge with the negative electrons embedded randomly in it. This model, shown in Fig. 2.9, is often called the **plum pudding model** because the electrons are like raisins dispersed in a pudding (the positive charge cloud), as in plum pudding, a favorite English dessert.*

In 1909 Robert Millikan (1868–1953), working at the University of Chicago, performed very clever experiments involving charged oil drops. These experiments allowed him to determine the magnitude of the electron charge (see Fig. 2.10). With this value and the charge-to-mass ratio determined by Thomson, Millikan was able to calculate the mass of the electron as 9.11×10^{-31} kilogram.

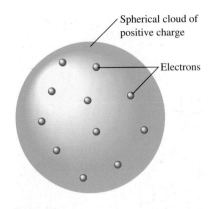

Figure 2.9

The plum pudding model of the atom.

Radioactivity

In the late nineteenth century scientists discovered that certain elements produce high-energy radiation. For example, in 1896 the French scientist Henri Becquerel found accidentally that a piece of a mineral containing uranium could produce its image on a photographic plate in the absence of light. He attributed this phenomenon to a spontaneous emission of radiation by the uranium, which he called **radioactivity.** Studies in the early twentieth century demonstrated three types of radioactive emission: gamma (γ) rays, beta (β) particles, and alpha (α) particles. A γ ray is high-energy "light"; a β particle is a high-speed electron; and an α particle has a 2+ charge, that is, a charge twice that of the electron and with the opposite sign. The mass of an α particle is 7300 times that of the electron. More modes of radioactivity are now known, and we will discuss them in Chapter 21. Here we will consider only α particles because they were used in some crucial early experiments.

The Nuclear Atom

In 1911 Ernest Rutherford (Fig. 2.11), who performed many of the pioneering experiments to explore radioactivity, carried out an experiment to test Thomson's

Figure 2.10

A schematic representation of the apparatus Millikan used to determine the charge on the electron. The fall of charged oil droplets due to gravity can be halted by adjusting the voltage across the two plates. The voltage and the mass of an oil drop can then be used to calculate the charge on the oil drop. Millikan's experiments showed that the charge on an oil drop is always a whole-number multiple of the electron charge.

---

*Although J. J. Thomson is generally given credit for this model, the idea was apparently first suggested by the English mathematician and physicist William Thomson (better known as Lord Kelvin and not related to J. J. Thomson).

Figure 2.11

Ernest Rutherford (1871–1937) was born on a farm in New Zealand. In 1895 he placed second in a scholarship competition to attend Cambridge University but was awarded the scholarship when the winner decided to stay home and get married. As a scientist in England, Rutherford did much of the early work on characterizing radioactivity. He named the α and β particles and the γ ray and coined the term *half-life* to describe an important attribute of radioactive elements. His experiments on the behavior of α particles striking thin metal foils led him to postulate the nuclear atom. He also invented the name *proton* for the nucleus of the hydrogen atom. He received the Nobel Prize in chemistry in 1908.

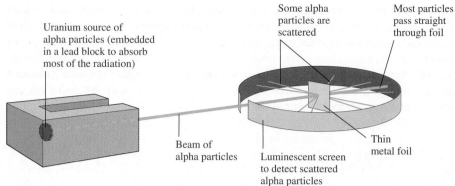

Figure 2.12

Rutherford's experiment on α-particle bombardment of metal foil.

plum pudding model. The experiment involved directing α particles at a thin sheet of metal foil, as illustrated in Fig. 2.12. Rutherford reasoned that if Thomson's model were accurate, the massive α particles should crash through the thin foil like cannonballs through gauze, as shown in Fig. 2.13(a). He expected the α particles to travel through the foil with, at the most, very minor deflections in their paths. The results of the experiment were very different from those Rutherford anticipated. Although most of the α particles passed straight through, many of the particles were deflected at large angles, as shown in Fig. 2.13(b), and some were reflected, never hitting the detector. This outcome was a great surprise to Rutherford. (He wrote that this result was comparable to shooting a howitzer at a piece of paper and having the shell reflected back.)

Rutherford knew from these results that the plum pudding model for the atom could not be correct. The large deflections of the α particles could only be caused by a center of concentrated positive charge that contains most of the atom's mass, as illustrated in Fig. 2.13(b). Most of the α particles pass directly through the foil

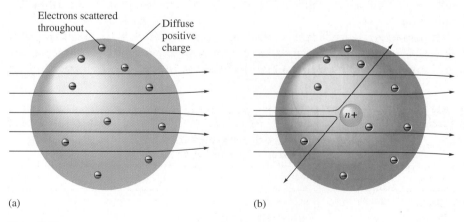

Figure 2.13

(a) The expected results of the metal foil experiment if Thomson's model were correct. (b) Actual results.

because the atom is mostly open space. The deflected α particles are those which had a "close encounter" with the massive positive center of the atom, and the few reflected α particles are those which made a "direct hit" on the much more massive positive center.

In Rutherford's mind these results could only be explained in terms of a **nuclear atom**—an atom with a dense center of positive charge (the **nucleus**) with electrons moving around the nucleus at a distance that is large relative to the nuclear radius.

2.5 The Modern View of Atomic Structure: An Introduction

Purpose

• To describe features of subatomic particles.

• To explain the use of the symbol $^A_Z X$ to describe a given atom.

In the years since Thomson and Rutherford, a great deal has been learned about atomic structure. Because much of this material will be covered in detail in later chapters, only an introduction will be given here. The simplest view of the atom is that it consists of a tiny nucleus (with a diameter of about 10^{-13} cm) and electrons that move about the nucleus at an average distance of about 10^{-8} cm from it (see Fig. 2.14).

As we will see later, the chemistry of an atom mainly results from its electrons. For this reason, chemists can be satisfied with a relatively crude nuclear model. The nucleus is assumed to contain **protons,** which have a positive charge equal in magnitude to the electron's negative charge, and **neutrons,** which have virtually the same mass as a proton but no charge. The masses and charges of the electron, proton, and neutron are shown in Table 2.1.

Two striking things about the nucleus are its small size compared with the overall size of the atom and its extremely high density. The tiny nucleus accounts for almost all the atom's mass. Its great density is dramatically demonstrated by the fact that a piece of nuclear material about the size of a pea would have a mass of 250 million tons!

An important question to consider at this point is, *"If all atoms are composed of these same components, why do different atoms have different chemical properties?"* The answer to this question lies in the number and the arrangement of the

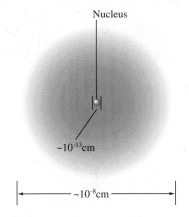

Nucleus

~10^{-13}cm

~10^{-8}cm

Figure 2.14

A nuclear atom viewed in cross section.

The forces that bind the positively charged protons in the nucleus will be discussed in Chapter 21.

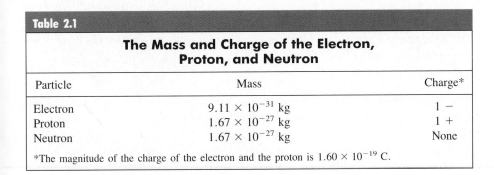

Table 2.1		
The Mass and Charge of the Electron, Proton, and Neutron		
Particle	Mass	Charge*
Electron	9.11×10^{-31} kg	1 −
Proton	1.67×10^{-27} kg	1 +
Neutron	1.67×10^{-27} kg	None
*The magnitude of the charge of the electron and the proton is 1.60×10^{-19} C.		

Nucleus

{ 11 protons
  12 neutrons

11 electrons

$^{23}_{11}$Na

Nucleus

{ 11 protons
  13 neutrons

11 electrons

$^{24}_{11}$Na

Figure 2.15

Two isotopes of sodium. Both have eleven protons and eleven electrons, but they differ in the number of neutrons in their nuclei.

The chemistry of an atom arises from its electrons.

electrons. The electrons comprise most of the atomic volume and thus are the parts that "intermingle" when atoms combine to form molecules. Therefore, the number of electrons possessed by a given atom greatly affects its ability to interact with other atoms. As a result, the atoms of different elements, which have different numbers of protons and electrons, show different chemical behavior.

A sodium atom has 11 protons in its nucleus. Since atoms have no net charge, the number of electrons must equal the number of protons. Therefore, a sodium atom has 11 electrons moving around its nucleus. It is *always* true that a sodium atom has 11 protons and 11 electrons. However, each sodium atom also has neutrons in its nucleus, and different types of sodium atoms exist that have different numbers of neutrons. For example, consider the sodium atoms represented in Fig. 2.15. These two atoms are **isotopes,** or *atoms with the same number of protons but different numbers of neutrons*. Note that the symbol for one particular type of sodium atom is written

Mass number ⟶ ^A_ZX ← Element symbol
Atomic number ⟶

Mass number ⟶ $^{23}_{11}$Na ← Element symbol
Atomic number ⟶

where the **atomic number** Z (number of protons) is written as a subscript and the **mass number** A (the total number of protons and neutrons) is written as a superscript. (The particular atom represented here is called "sodium twenty-three." It has 11 electrons, 11 protons, and 12 neutrons.) Because the chemistry of an atom is due to its electrons, isotopes show almost identical chemical properties. In nature most elements are mixtures of isotopes.

Sample Exercise 2.2

Write the symbol for the atom that has an atomic number of 9 and a mass number of 19. How many electrons and how many neutrons does this atom have?

Solution

The atomic number 9 means the atom has 9 protons. This element is called **fluorine,** symbolized by F. The atom is represented as

$$^{19}_{9}F$$

and is called "fluorine nineteen." Since the atom has 9 protons, it also must have 9 electrons to achieve electrical neutrality. The mass number gives the total number of protons and neutrons, which means that this atom has 10 neutrons.

2.6 Molecules and Ions

Purpose

- To introduce basic ideas of bonding in molecules.
- To show various ways of representing molecules.

From a chemist's viewpoint, the most interesting characteristic of an atom is its ability to combine with other atoms to form compounds. It was John Dalton who first recognized that chemical compounds are collections of atoms, but he could not determine the structure of atoms or their means for binding to each other. During the twentieth century we have learned that atoms have electrons and that these electrons participate in bonding one atom to another. We will discuss bonding thoroughly in Chapters 8 and 9; here we will introduce some simple bonding ideas that will be useful in the next few chapters.

The forces that hold atoms together in compounds are called **chemical bonds.** One way that atoms can form bonds is by *sharing electrons*. These bonds are called **covalent bonds,** and the resulting collection of atoms is called a **molecule.** Molecules can be represented in several different ways. The simplest method is the **chemical formula,** in which the symbols for the elements are used to indicate the types of atoms present and subscripts are used to indicate the relative numbers of atoms. For example, the formula for carbon dioxide is CO_2, meaning that each molecule contains 1 atom of carbon and 2 atoms of oxygen.

Examples of molecules that contain covalent bonds are hydrogen (H_2), water (H_2O), oxygen (O_2), ammonia (NH_3), and methane (CH_4). More information about a molecule is given by its **structural formula,** in which the individual bonds are shown (indicated by lines). Structural formulas may or may not indicate the actual shape of the molecule. For example, water might be represented as

$$H—O—H \quad \text{or} \quad \overset{O}{\underset{H \quad H}{\diagup \diagdown}}$$

The structure on the right shows the actual shape of the water molecule. Scientists know from experimental evidence that the molecule looks like this. (We will study the shapes of molecules further in Chapter 8.) Other examples of structural formulas are

$$\underset{\text{Ammonia}}{H—\overset{H}{\underset{H}{\overset{|}{N}}} \quad \text{or} \quad H \overset{N}{\underset{H}{\diagup \diagdown}} H} \qquad \underset{\text{Methane}}{H—\overset{H}{\underset{H}{\overset{|}{C}}}—H \quad \text{or} \quad H \overset{\overset{H}{|}{C}}{\underset{H}{\diagup \diagdown}} H}$$

In the actual structures on the right the central atom and the solid lines are understood to be in the plane of the paper. Atoms connected to the central atom by dashed

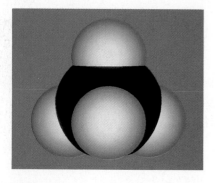

Figure 2.16

Space-filling model of methane. This type of model shows both the relative sizes of the atoms in the molecule and their spatial relationships.

lines are behind the plane of the paper, and atoms connected to the central atom by wedges are in front of the plane of the page.

In a compound composed of molecules, the individual molecules move around as independent units. For example, a molecule of methane gas is represented in Fig. 2.16 using **space-filling models.** These models show the relative sizes of the atoms as well as their relative orientation in the molecule. Fig. 2.17 shows other examples. **Ball-and-stick models** are also used to represent molecules. The ball-and-stick structure of methane is shown in Fig. 2.18.

A second type of chemical bond results from attractions among ions. An **ion** is an atom or group of atoms that has a net positive or negative charge. The best known ionic compound is common table salt, or sodium chloride, which forms when neutral chlorine and sodium react.

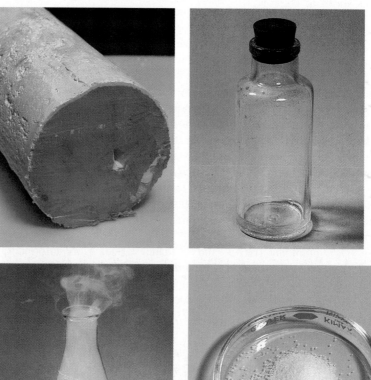

(upper left) Sodium metal is soft enough to be cut easily with a knife. (upper right) Chlorine is a green gas. (lower left) When sodium and chlorine are combined, they react vigorously (lower center) to form sodium chloride (lower right).

To see how ions are formed, consider what happens when an electron is transferred from a sodium atom to a chlorine atom (the neutrons in the nuclei will be ignored):

Neutral sodium
atom (Na)

Sodium ion
(Na$^+$)

Minus 1
electron

11+ → 11+

11 electrons → 10 electrons

Figure 2.17
Space-filling models of various molecules.

With one electron stripped off, the sodium, with its 11 protons and only 10 electrons, now has a net 1+ charge—it has become a *positive ion*. A positive ion is called a **cation.** The sodium ion is written as Na$^+$, and the process can be represented in shorthand form as

$$Na \rightarrow Na^+ + e^-$$

If an electron is added to chlorine,

Neutral chlorine
atom (Cl)

Chloride ion
(Cl$^-$)

Plus 1
electron

17+ → 17+

17 electrons → 18 electrons

Figure 2.18
Ball-and-stick model of methane.

the 18 electrons produce a net 1− charge; the chlorine has become an *ion with a negative charge*—an **anion.** The chloride ion is written as Cl$^-$, and the process is represented as

$$Cl + e^- \rightarrow Cl^-$$

Because anions and cations have opposite charges, they attract each other. This *force of attraction between oppositely charged ions* is called **ionic bonding.** Sodium metal and chlorine gas (a green gas composed of Cl$_2$ molecules) react to form solid sodium chloride, which contains many Na$^+$ and Cl$^-$ ions packed together, as shown in Fig. 2.19(a). The solid forms the beautiful colorless cubic crystals shown in Fig. 2.19(b).

Na$^+$ is usually called the **sodium ion** rather than the sodium cation. Also Cl$^-$ is called the **chloride ion** rather than the chloride anion. In general, when a specific ion is referred to; the word **ion** rather than cation or anion is used.

Cl$^-$ Na$^+$ Cl$^-$

Na$^+$ Cl$^-$ Na$^+$

Cl$^-$ Na$^+$ Cl$^-$

Na$^+$ Cl$^-$ Na$^+$

(a)

(b)

Figure 2.19

(a) The arrangement of sodium ions (Na$^+$) and chloride ions (Cl$^-$) in the ionic compound sodium chloride. (b) Sodium chloride forms cubic crystals.

Figure 2.20

Ball-and-stick models of the ammonium ion (NH_4^+) and the nitrate ion (NO_3^-).

Gold is one of only a few metals that occur naturally as a free element, sometimes in spectacular form. The largest gold nugget ever mined in Colorado (found near Breckenridge) weighs 13 pounds.

A solid consisting of oppositely charged ions is called an **ionic solid,** or a **salt.** Ionic solids can consist of simple ions, as in sodium chloride, or of **polyatomic (many atom) ions,** as in ammonium nitrate (NH_4NO_3), which contains ammonium ions (NH_4^+) and nitrate ions (NO_3^-). The ball-and-stick models of these ions are shown in Fig. 2.20.

2.7 An Introduction to the Periodic Table

Purpose

- To introduce various features of the periodic table.

In a room where chemistry is taught or practiced, a chart called the **periodic table** is almost certain to be found hanging on the wall. This chart shows all the known elements and gives a good deal of information about each. As our study of chemistry progresses, the usefulness of the periodic table will become more obvious. This section will simply introduce it to you.

A simplified version of the periodic table is shown in Fig. 2.21. The letters in the boxes are the symbols for the elements; these abbreviations are based on the current element names or the original names* (see Table 2.2). The number shown above each symbol is the **atomic number** (number of protons) for that element. For example, carbon (C) has atomic number 6, and lead (Pb) has atomic number 82. Most of the elements are **metals.** Metals have characteristic physical properties such as efficient conduction of heat and electricity, malleability (they can be hammered into thin sheets), ductility (they can be pulled into wires), and (often) a lustrous appearance. Chemically, metals tend to *lose* electrons to form positive ions. For example, copper is a typical metal. It is lustrous (although it tarnishes readily); it is an excellent conductor of electricity (it is widely used in electrical wires); and it is

Table 2.2

The Symbols for the Elements that Are Based on the Original Names

Current Name	Original Name	Symbol
Antimony	Stibium	Sb
Copper	Cuprum	Cu
Iron	Ferrum	Fe
Lead	Plumbum	Pb
Mercury	Hydragyum	Hg
Potassium	Kalium	K
Silver	Argentum	Ag
Sodium	Natrium	Na
Tin	Stannum	Sn
Tungsten	Wolfram	W

*See David W. Ball, "Elemental Etymology: What's in a Name?" *Journal of Chemical Education* **62** (1985): 787.

Figure 2.21

The periodic table. Although rutherfordium and hahnium have been proposed as names for elements 104 and 105, an attempt is being made to name the elements after 103 systematically, using a letter abbreviation for each number. In this system the symbol for element 104 is Unq, and for 105 is Unp. The systematic symbols are shown for elements 106–109.

readily formed into various shapes, such as pipes for water systems. Copper is also found in many salts, such as the beautifully blue copper sulfate, in which copper is present as Cu^{2+} ions. Copper is a member of the transition metals—the metals shown in the center of the periodic table.

The relatively few **nonmetals** appear in the upper right-hand corner of the table (to the right of the heavy line in Fig. 2.21), except hydrogen, a nonmetal that resides in the upper left-hand corner. The nonmetals lack the physical properties that characterize the metals. Chemically, they tend to *gain* electrons in reactions with metals to form negative ions. Nonmetals often bond to each other by forming

Metals tend to form positive ions; nonmetals tend to form negative ions.

Elements in the same vertical column in the periodic table form a group (or family) and generally have similar properties.

Three members of the halogen family: chlorine (green), iodine (purple), and bromine (reddish-brown).

Another format of the periodic table will be discussed in Section 7.11.

covalent bonds. For example, chlorine is a typical nonmetal. Under normal conditions it exists as Cl_2 molecules; it reacts with metals to form salts containing Cl^- ions (NaCl, for example); and it forms covalent bonds with nonmetals (for example, hydrogen chloride gas, HCl).

The periodic table is arranged so that elements in the same vertical columns (called **groups** or **families**) have *similar chemical properties*. For example, all the **alkali metals,** members of Group 1A—lithium (Li), sodium (Na), potassium (K), rubidium (Rb), cesium (Cs), and francium (Fr)—are very active elements that readily form ions with a 1+ charge when they react with nonmetals. The members of Group 2A—beryllium (Be), magnesium (Mg), calcium (Ca), strontium (Sr), barium (Ba), and radium (Ra)—are called the **alkaline earth metals.** They all form ions with a 2+ charge when they react with nonmetals. The **halogens,** the members of Group 7A—fluorine (F), chlorine (Cl), bromine (Br), iodine (I), and astatine (At)—all form diatomic molecules. Fluorine, chlorine, bromine, and iodine all react with metals to form salts containing ions with a 1− charge (F^-, Cl^-, Br^-, and I^-). The members of Group 8A—helium (He), neon (Ne), argon (Ar), krypton (Kr), xenon (Xe), and radon (Rn)—are known as the **noble gases.** They all exist under normal conditions as monatomic (single-atom) gases and have little chemical reactivity.

Note from Fig. 2.21 that alternate sets of symbols are used to denote the groups. The symbols 1A through 8A are the traditional designations, whereas the numbers 1 to 18 have been suggested recently. In this text the 1A to 8A designations will be used.

The horizontal rows of elements in the periodic table are called **periods.** Horizontal row one is called the **first period** (it contains H and He); row two is called the **second period** (elements Li through Ne); and so on.

We will learn much more about the periodic table as we continue with our study of chemistry. Meanwhile, when an element is introduced in this text, you should always note its position on the periodic table.

2.8 Naming Simple Compounds

Purpose

- To demonstrate how to name compounds given their formulas and to write formulas given their names.

The systematic naming of organic compounds will be discussed in Chapter 22.

When chemistry was an infant science, there was no system for naming compounds. Names such as sugar of lead, blue vitrol, quicklime, Epsom salts, milk of magnesia, gypsum, and laughing gas were coined by early chemists. Such names are called **common names.** As chemistry grew, it became clear that using common names for compounds would lead to unacceptable chaos. Nearly five million chemical compounds are currently known. Memorizing common names for these compounds would be an impossible task.

The solution, of course, is to adopt a *system* for naming compounds in which the name tells something about the composition of the compound. After learning the system, a chemist given a formula should be able to name the compound, or given a name should be able to construct the compound's formula. In this section we will specify the most important rules for naming compounds other than organic compounds (those based on chains of carbon atoms).

We will begin with the systems for naming inorganic **binary compounds**—compounds composed of two elements—which we classify into various types for easier recognition. We will consider both ionic and covalent compounds.

Binary Ionic Compounds (Type I)

Binary ionic compounds contain a positive ion (cation) always written first in the formula and a negative ion (anion). In naming these compounds, the following rules apply:

1. The cation is always named first and the anion second.

2. A monatomic (meaning one-atom) cation takes its name from the name of the element. For example, Na^+ is called sodium in the names of compounds containing this ion.

   A monatomic cation has the same name as its parent element.

3. A monatomic anion is named by taking the root of the element name and adding *-ide*. Thus the Cl^- ion is called chloride.

Some common monatomic cations and anions and their names are given in Table 2.3.

The rules for naming binary ionic compounds are illustrated by the following examples:

In formulas of ionic compounds, simple ions are represented by the element symbol: Cl means Cl^-, Na means Na^+, etc.

Compound	Ions Present	Name
NaCl	Na^+, Cl^-	Sodium chloride
KI	K^+, I^-	Potassium iodide
CaS	Ca^{2+}, S^{2-}	Calcium sulfide
Li_3N	Li^+, N^{3-}	Lithium nitride
CsBr	Cs^+, Br^-	Cesium bromide
MgO	Mg^{2+}, O^{2-}	Magnesium oxide

Table 2.3

Common Monatomic Cations and Anions

Cation	Name	Anion	Name
H^+	Hydrogen	H^-	Hydride
Li^+	Lithium	F^-	Fluoride
Na^+	Sodium	Cl^-	Chloride
K^+	Potassium	Br^-	Bromide
Cs^+	Cesium	I^-	Iodide
Be^{2+}	Beryllium	O^{2-}	Oxide
Mg^{2+}	Magnesium	S^{2-}	Sulfide
Ca^{2+}	Calcium	N^{3-}	Nitride
Ba^{2+}	Barium	P^{3-}	Phosphide
Al^{3+}	Aluminum		
Ag^+	Silver		

Sample Exercise 2.3

Name each binary compound.

a. CsF   **b.** $AlCl_3$ **c.** LiH

Solution

a. CsF is cesium fluoride.
b. $AlCl_3$ is aluminum chloride.
c. LiH is lithium hydride.

Notice that, in each case, the cation is named first, and then the anion is named.

Binary Ionic Compounds (Type II)

Type II binary ionic compounds contain a metal that can form more than one type of cation.

Table 2.4

Common Type II Cations

Ion	Systematic Name
Fe^{3+}	Iron(III) *iv*
Fe^{2+}	Iron(II) *ous,*
Cu^{2+}	Copper(II) *iv*
Cu^{+}	Copper(I) *ous*
Co^{3+}	Cobalt(III)
Co^{2+}	Cobalt(II)
Sn^{4+}	Tin(IV)
Sn^{2+}	Tin(II)
Pb^{4+}	Lead(IV)
Pb^{2+}	Lead(II)
Hg^{2+}	Mercury(II)
Hg_2^{2+}*	Mercury(I)

*Note that mercury(I) ions always occur bound together to form Hg_2^{2+} ions.

A compound must be electrically neutral.

In the binary ionic compounds considered above (Type I), the metal present forms only a single type of cation. That is, sodium forms only Na^+, calcium forms only Ca^{2+}, and so on. However, as we will see in more detail later in the text, there are many metals that form more than one type of positive ion and thus form more than one type of ionic compound with a given anion. For example, the compound $FeCl_2$ contains Fe^{2+} ions, and the compound $FeCl_3$ contains Fe^{3+} ions. In a case such as this, the *charge on the metal ion must be specified*. The systematic names for these two iron compounds are iron(II) chloride and iron(III) chloride, respectively, where the *Roman numeral indicates the charge of the cation*.

Another system for naming these ionic compounds that is seen in the older literature was used for metals that form only two ions. *The ion with the higher charge has a name ending in -ic, and the one with the lower charge has a name ending in -ous.* In this system, for example, Fe^{3+} is called the ferric ion, and Fe^{2+} is called the ferrous ion. The names for $FeCl_3$ and $FeCl_2$ are then ferric chloride and ferrous chloride, respectively. In this text we will use the system that employs Roman numerals. Table 2.4 lists the systematic names for many common Type II cations.

Sample Exercise 2.4

Give the systematic name of each of the following compounds.

a. CuCl   **b.** HgO   **c.** Fe_2O_3 **d.** MnO_2 **e.** $PbCl_2$

Solution

All these compounds include a metal that can form more than one type of cation; thus we must first determine the charge on each cation. This can be done by recognizing that a compound must be electrically neutral; that is, the positive and negative charges must exactly balance.

a. In CuCl, for example, since the anion is Cl^-, the cation must be Cu^+. The name is copper(I) chloride, where the Roman numeral I indicates the 1+ charge on Cu^+.

b. In HgO, since the anion is oxide, O^{2-}, the mercury cation must be Hg^{2+} to give a net charge of zero as required. Thus the name is mercury(II) oxide.

c. In Fe_2O_3, the three O^{2-} ions carry a total charge of $6-$, so the two iron cations must carry a total charge of $6+$. Thus each iron ion is Fe^{3+}, and the name is iron(III) oxide.

d. In the compound MnO_2, the cation has a $4+$ charge, and the name is manganese(IV) oxide.

e. In $PbCl_2$ the cation has a $2+$ charge, so the name is lead(II) chloride.

Note that the use of a Roman numeral in a systematic name is required only in cases where more than one ionic compound forms between a given pair of elements. This case most commonly occurs for compounds containing transition metals, which often form more than one cation. *Elements that form only one cation do not need to be identified by a Roman numeral.* Common metals that do not require Roman numerals are the Group 1A elements, which form only $1+$ ions; the Group 2A elements, which form only $2+$ ions; and aluminum, which forms only Al^{3+}. The element silver deserves special mention at this point. In virtually all its compounds silver is found as the Ag^+ ion. Therefore, although silver is a transition metal (and can potentially form ions other than Ag^+), silver compounds are usually named without a Roman numeral. Thus AgCl is typically called silver chloride rather than silver(I) chloride, although the latter name is technically correct.

As shown in Sample Exercise 2.4, when a metal ion is present that forms more than one type of cation, the charge on the metal ion must be determined by balancing the positive and negative charges of the compound. To do this you must be able to recognize the common cations and anions and know their charges (see Tables 2.3 and 2.5).

A compound containing a transition metal must have a Roman numeral in its name.

A close-up photo of copper(II) sulfate crystals.

Sample Exercise 2.5

Give the systematic name of each of the following compounds.

a. $CoBr_2$ **b.** $CaCl_2$ **c.** Al_2O_3 **d.** $CrCl_3$

Solution

Compound	Name	Comment
a. $CoBr_2$	Cobalt(II) bromide	Cobalt is a transition metal; the compound name must have a Roman numeral. The two Br^- ions must be balanced by a Co^{2+} ion.
b. $CaCl_2$	Calcium chloride	Calcium, an alkaline earth metal, forms only the Ca^{2+} ion. A Roman numeral is not necessary.
c. Al_2O_3	Aluminum oxide	Aluminum forms only Al^{3+}. A Roman numeral is not necessary.
d. $CrCl_3$	Chromium(III) chloride	Chromium is a transition metal. The compound name must have a Roman numeral. $CrCl_3$ contains Cr^{3+}.

◀ **C H E M I C A L   I M P A C T** ▶

Buckminsterfullerene: A New Form of Carbon

A favorite chemistry exam question—What are the forms of elemental carbon?—now has a new answer: diamond, graphite, and buckminsterfullerene. Buckminsterfullerene? This fascinating new form of elemental carbon containing C_{60} molecules was first identified by R. E. Smalley of Rice University, H. F. Kroto of University of Sussex, England, and their collaborators. It has now been synthesized in large quantities using techniques developed by a team of physicists at the University of Arizona.

The structure of the C_{60} molecule resembles a soccer ball. It is an approximately spherical molecule with the carbon atoms arranged at the 60 vertices of 32 interconnecting pentagons (12) and hexagons (20). This molecule gets its name from the work of Buckminster Fuller, who proposed geodesic domes with frameworks similar to the arrangement of the carbon atoms in C_{60}.

Buckminsterfullerene was first synthesized in large quantities in the lab of Don-

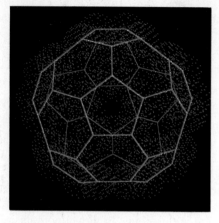

A computer simulation of the electron distribution in buckminsterfullerene. Each vertex represents a carbon atom.

ald R. Huffman of the University of Arizona by vaporizing carbon from pure graphite electrodes in an atmosphere of helium gas at a pressure of 100 torr. This process was a team effort with Wolfgang

Krätschmer of the Max Planck Institute for Nuclear Physics in Germany. The soot that forms in this environment is about 5% C_{60} by mass. The scientists have also found significant quantities of another "fullerene" in this soot that consists of C_{70} molecules. The C_{70} molecule is similar to the spherical C_{60} molecule except that the extra carbon atoms lead to an egg-shaped structure.

The discovery of fullerenes has led to a flurry of activity in labs around the world as chemists rush to characterize this new substance. Already scientists have produced the C_{60}^{-} and C_{60}^{2-} anions and have prepared C_{60} molecules with various substituents added. It's safe to say that a new branch of chemistry has been founded.

For further reading, see R. M. Baum, "Research on Buckminsterfullerene Continues to Proliferate," *Chemical and Engineering News*, June 10(1991): 31.

The following flow chart is useful when you are naming binary ionic compounds:

Ionic Compounds with Polyatomic Ions

We have not yet considered ionic compounds that contain polyatomic ions. For example, the compound ammonium nitrate, NH_4NO_3, contains the polyatomic ions NH_4^{+} and NO_3^{-}. Polyatomic ions are assigned special names that *must be memo-*

Polyatomic ion formulas must be memorized.

Various chromium compounds dissolved in water. From left to right: $CrCl_2$, $K_2Cr_2O_7$, $Cr(NO_3)_3$, $CrCl_3$, K_2CrO_4.

rized in order to name the compounds containing them. The most important polyatomic ions and their names are listed in Table 2.5.

Note in Table 2.5 that several series of anions contain an atom of a given element and different numbers of oxygen atoms. These anions are called **oxyanions.** When there are two members in such a series, the name of the one with the smaller number of oxygen atoms ends in *-ite* and the name of the one with the larger number ends in *-ate,* for example, sulfite (SO_3^{2-}) and sulfate (SO_4^{2-}). When more than two oxyanions make up a series, *hypo-* (less than) and *per-* (more than) are used as prefixes to name the members of the series with the fewest and the most oxygen atoms, respectively. The best example involves the oxyanions containing chlorine, as shown in Table 2.5.

Table 2.5			
Common Polyatomic Ions			
Ion	Name	Ion	Name
Hg_2^{2+}	Mercury(I)	NCS^-	Thiocyanate
NH_4^+	Ammonium	CO_3^{2-}	Carbonate
NO_2^-	Nitrite	HCO_3^-	Hydrogen carbonate
NO_3^-	Nitrate		(bicarbonate is a widely
SO_3^{2-}	Sulfite		used common name)
SO_4^{2-}	Sulfate	ClO^-	Hypochlorite
HSO_4^-	Hydrogen sulfate	ClO_2^-	Chlorite
	(bisulfate is a widely	ClO_3^-	Chlorate
	used common name)	ClO_4^-	Perchlorate
OH^-	Hydroxide	$C_2H_3O_2^-$	Acetate
CN^-	Cyanide	MnO_4^-	Permanganate
PO_4^{3-}	Phosphate	$Cr_2O_7^{2-}$	Dichromate
HPO_4^{2-}	Hydrogen phosphate	CrO_4^{2-}	Chromate
$H_2PO_4^-$	Dihydrogen phosphate	O_2^{2-}	Peroxide
		$C_2O_4^{2-}$	Oxalate

Sample Exercise 2.6

Give the systematic name of each of the following compounds.

a. Na_2SO_4 **b.** KH_2PO_4 **c.** $Fe(NO_3)_3$ **d.** $Mn(OH)_2$
e. Na_2SO_3 **f.** Na_2CO_3 **g.** $NaHCO_3$ **h.** $CsClO_4$
i. $NaOCl$ **j.** Na_2SeO_4 **k.** $KBrO_3$

Solution

Compound	Name	Comment
a. Na_2SO_4	Sodium sulfate	
b. KH_2PO_4	Potassium dihydrogen phosphate	
c. $Fe(NO_3)_3$	Iron(III) nitrate	Transition metal—name must contain a Roman numeral. Fe^{3+} ion balances three NO_3^- ions.
d. $Mn(OH)_2$	Manganese(II) hydroxide	Transition metal—name must contain a Roman numeral. Mn^{2+} ion balances two OH^- ions.
e. Na_2SO_3	Sodium sulfite	
f. Na_2CO_3	Sodium carbonate	
g. $NaHCO_3$	Sodium hydrogen carbonate	Often called sodium bicarbonate.
h. $CsClO_4$	Cesium perchlorate	
i. $NaOCl$	Sodium hypochlorite	
j. Na_2SeO_4	Sodium selenate	Atoms in the same group, like sulfur and selenium, often form similar ions that are named similarly. Thus SeO_4^{2-} is selenate, like SO_4^{2-} (sulfate).
k. $KBrO_3$	Potassium bromate	As above, BrO_3^- is bromate, like ClO_3^- (chlorate).

Binary Compounds
(Type III; Covalent—Contain Two Nonmetals)

In binary covalent compounds the element names follow the same rules as for binary ionic compounds.

Binary covalent compounds are formed between *two nonmetals*. Although these compounds do not contain ions, they are named very similarly to binary ionic compounds.

In the naming of binary covalent compounds, the following rules apply:

1. The first element in the formula is named first, using the full element name.

2. The second element is named as if it were an anion.

3. Prefixes are used to denote the numbers of atoms present. These prefixes are given in Table 2.6.

4. The prefix *mono-* is never used for naming the first element. For example, CO is called carbon monoxide, *not* monocarbon monoxide.

To see how these rules apply, we will now consider the names of the several covalent compounds formed by nitrogen and oxygen:

Compound	Systematic Name	Common Name
N_2O	Dinitrogen monoxide	Nitrous oxide
NO	Nitrogen monoxide	Nitric oxide
NO_2	Nitrogen dioxide	
N_2O_3	Dinitrogen trioxide	
N_2O_4	Dinitrogen tetroxide	
N_2O_5	Dinitrogen pentoxide	

Table 2.6	
Prefixes Used to Indicate Number in Chemical Names	
Prefix	Number Indicated
mono-	1
di-	2
tri-	3
tetra-	4
penta-	5
hexa-	6
hepta-	7
octa-	8
nona-	9
deca-	10

Notice from the preceding examples that to avoid awkward pronunciations, we often drop the final *o* or *a* of the prefix when the element begins with a vowel. For example, N_2O_4 is called dinitrogen tetroxide, *not* dinitrogen tetra*o*xide, and CO is called carbon monoxide, *not* carbon mon*o*oxide.

Some compounds are always referred to by their common names. The two best examples are water and ammonia. The systematic names for H_2O and NH_3 are never used.

Sample Exercise 2.7

Name each of the following compounds.

a. PCl_5 **b.** PCl_3 **c.** SF_6 **d.** SO_3 **e.** SO_2 **f.** CO_2

Solution

Compound	Name
a. PCl_5	Phosphorus pentachloride
b. PCl_3	Phosphorus trichloride
c. SF_6	Sulfur hexafluoride
d. SO_3	Sulfur trioxide
e. SO_2	Sulfur dioxide
f. CO_2	Carbon dioxide

The rules for naming binary compounds are summarized in Fig. 2.22. Notice that prefixes to indicate the number of atoms are used only in Type III binary compounds (those containing two nonmetals). An overall strategy for naming compounds is summarized in Fig. 2.23.

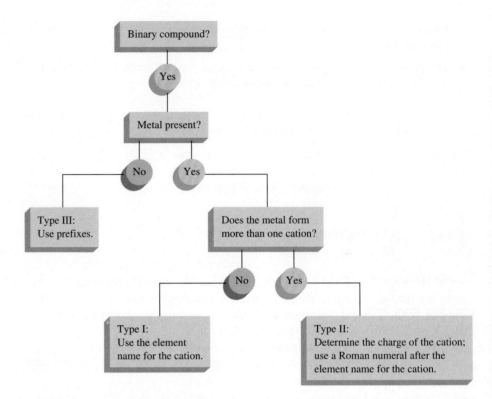

Figure 2.22

A flow chart for naming binary compounds.

Sample Exercise 2.8

Give the systematic name for each of the following compounds.

a. P_4O_{10} **b.** Nb_2O_5 **c.** Li_2O_2 **d.** $Ti(NO_3)_4$

Solution

Compound	Name	Comment
a. P_4O_{10}	Tetraphosphorus decaoxide	Binary covalent compound (Type III), so prefixes are used. The *a* in *deca-* is sometimes dropped.
b. Nb_2O_5	Niobium(V) oxide	Type II binary compound containing Nb^{5+} and O^{2-} ions. Niobium is a transition metal and requires a Roman numeral.
c. Li_2O_2	Lithium peroxide	Type I binary compound containing the Li^+ and O_2^{2-} (peroxide) ions.
d. $Ti(NO_3)_4$	Titanium(IV) nitrate	Not a binary compound. Contains the Ti^{4+} and NO_3^- ions. Titanium is a transition metal and requires a Roman numeral.

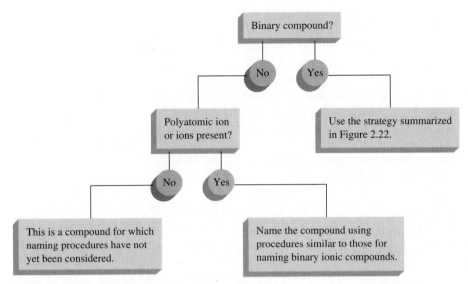

Figure 2.23

Overall strategy for naming chemical compounds.

Formulas from Names

So far we have started with the chemical formula of a compound and decided on its systematic name. The reverse process is also important. For example, given the name calcium hydroxide, we can write the formula as $Ca(OH)_2$ because we know that calcium only forms Ca^{2+} ions and that, since hydroxide is OH^-, two of these anions will be required to give a neutral compound. Similarly, the name iron(II) oxide implies the formula FeO, since the Roman numeral II indicates the presence of Fe^{2+}, which is balanced by one oxide ion, O^{2-}.

Sample Exercise 2.9

Given the following systematic names, write the formula for each compound.

a. Vanadium(V) fluoride   **b.** Dioxygen difluoride
c. Rubidium peroxide   **d.** Gallium oxide

Solution

Name	Chemical Formula	Comment
a. Vanadium(V) fluoride	VF_5	The compound contains V^{5+} ions and requires five F^- ions for charge balance.
b. Dioxygen difluoride	O_2F_2	The prefix *di-* indicates two of each atom.
c. Rubidium peroxide	Rb_2O_2	Since rubidium is in Group 1A, it forms only 1+ ions. Thus two Rb^+ ions are needed to balance the 2− charge on the peroxide ion (O_2^{2-}).
d. Gallium oxide	Ga_2O_3	Since gallium is in Group 3A, like aluminum, it forms 3+ ions. Two Ga^{3+} ions are required to balance the charge on three O^{2-} ions.

Acids

Acids can be recognized by the hydrogen that appears first in the formula.

When dissolved in water, certain molecules produce a solution containing free H^+ ions (protons). These substances, **acids,** will be discussed in detail in Chapters 4, 14, and 15. Here we will simply present the rules for naming acids.

An acid can be viewed as a molecule with one or more H^+ ions attached to an anion. The rules for naming acids depend on whether or not the anion contains oxygen. If the *anion does not contain oxygen,* the acid is named with the prefix *hydro-* and the suffix *-ic.* For example, when gaseous HCl is dissolved in water, it forms hydrochloric acid. Similarly, HCN and H_2S dissolved in water are called hydrocyanic and hydrosulfuric acids, respectively.

When the *anion contains oxygen,* the acid name is formed from the root name of the anion with a suffix of *-ic* or *-ous,* depending on the name of the anion.

1. If the anion name ends in *-ate,* the *-ate* is replaced by *-ic* (or sometimes *-ric*). For example, H_2SO_4 contains the sulfate anion (SO_4^{2-}) and is called sulfuric acid; H_3PO_4 contains the phosphate anion (PO_4^{3-}) and is called phosphoric acid; and $HC_2H_3O_2$ contains the acetate ion ($C_2H_3O_2^-$) and is called acetic acid.

2. If the anion has an *-ite* ending, the *-ite* is replaced by *-ous.* For example, H_2SO_3, which contains sulfite (SO_3^{2-}), is named sulfurous acid; and HNO_2, which contains nitrite (NO_2^-), is named nitrous acid.

The application of these rules can be seen in the names of the acids of the oxyanions of chlorine:

Acid	Anion	Name
$HClO_4$	Perchlor*ate*	Perchlor*ic* acid
$HClO_3$	Chlor*ate*	Chlor*ic* acid
$HClO_2$	Chlor*ite*	Chlor*ous* acid
$HClO$	Hypochlor*ite*	Hypochlor*ous* acid

The names of the most important acids are given in Tables 2.7 and 2.8. An overall strategy for naming acids is shown in Fig. 2.24.

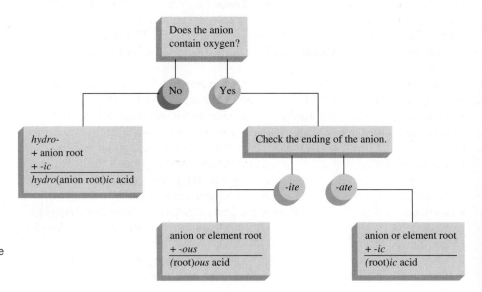

Figure 2.24

A flow chart for naming acids. An acid is best considered as one or more H^+ ions attached to an anion.

Table 2.7	
Names of Acids* that Do Not Contain Oxygen	
Acid	Name
HF	Hydrofluoric acid
HCl	Hydrochloric acid
HBr	Hydrobromic acid
HI	Hydroiodic acid
HCN	Hydrocyanic acid
H_2S	Hydrosulfuric acid

*Note that these acids are aqueous solutions containing these substances.

Table 2.8	
Names of Some Oxygen-Containing Acids	
Acid	Name
HNO_3	Nitric acid
HNO_2	Nitrous acid
H_2SO_4	Sulfuric acid
H_2SO_3	Sulfurous acid
H_3PO_4	Phosphoric acid
$HC_2H_3O_2$	Acetic acid

F O R   R E V I E W

Summary

Three fundamental laws formed the basis for early chemistry: the law of conservation of mass (matter can neither be created nor destroyed), the law of definite proportion (a given compound always contains exactly the same proportion of elements by mass), and the law of multiple proportions (if two elements A and B form a series of compounds, the ratios of the masses of A that combine with 1 gram of B can always be represented by small whole numbers). Dalton accounted for these laws in his atomic theory. He postulated that all elements are composed of atoms; that all atoms of a given element are identical; that chemical compounds are formed when atoms combine; and that the atoms themselves are not changed in a chemical reaction but the way they are grouped (bound together) is changed.

Atoms consist of a dense nucleus containing protons and neutrons, surrounded by electrons that occupy a very large volume relative to the size of the nucleus. Electrons have a relatively small mass (1/1840 of the proton mass) and a negative charge. Protons have a positive charge equal in magnitude (but opposite in sign) to that on the electron. A neutron has virtually the same mass as a proton but no charge.

Isotopes are atoms with the same number of protons (thus constituting the same element) but different numbers of neutrons. That is, isotopes have the same atomic number but different mass numbers (total numbers of neutrons and protons).

Atoms can combine to form molecules by sharing electrons to form covalent bonds. A molecule can be described by a chemical formula showing the numbers and types of atoms involved, a structural formula (showing which atoms are joined to each other), or by ball-and-stick or space-filling models that show the exact positions of the atoms in space. When an atom loses one or more electrons, it forms a positive ion called a cation. If an atom gains electrons, it becomes a negatively charged anion. The interaction of oppositely charged ions to form an ionic compound is called ionic bonding.

The periodic table arranges the elements in order of increasing atomic number, and elements having similar chemical properties fall into vertical columns, or groups. Most of the elements are metals, which tend to form cations in ionic compounds with nonmetals. Nonmetals tend to form anions when they react with metals.

Compounds are named using systems of rules. These rules vary depending on the type of compound being named. For binary ionic compounds (those which contain a metal and a nonmetal), the metal is named first, followed by a name derived from the root name of the nonmetal. In a compound (Type I) containing a metal that always forms the same cation (sodium always forms Na^+, magnesium always forms Mg^{2+}, and so on), the name of the metal is sufficient. In a compound (Type II) that contains a metal that can form more than one cation (iron can form Fe^{2+} and Fe^{3+} and so on), the metal name is followed by a Roman numeral that indicates the cation charge.

Polyatomic ions have special names that must be memorized along with their net charges. In compounds containing polyatomic ions, the cation name is given first, followed by the anion name. For Type III binary covalent compounds (those which contain two nonmetals), the first element is named using the entire element name and the second element is named as if it were an anion. Prefixes are used to indicate the numbers of atoms present.

Suggested Reading

1. Isaac Asimov, *A Short Story of Chemistry* (New York: Anchor Books, Doubleday and Co., Inc., 1965).

2. Robert P. Crease and Charles C. Mann, *The Second Creation*, Chapters 1 and 2 (New York: Macmillan Publishing Co., 1986).

3. Enid S. Lipeles, "The Chemical Contributions of Amadeo Avogadro," *J. Chem. Ed.* **60** (1983): 127.

4. Sir William Roscoe, *John Dalton and the Rise of Modern Chemistry*, 1896.

Key Terms

Section 2.2
law of conservation of mass
law of definite proportion
law of multiple proportions

Section 2.3
atomic masses
atomic weights
Avogadro's hypothesis

Section 2.4
cathode ray
electron
radioactivity
nuclear atom
nucleus

Section 2.5
proton
neutron

isotopes
atomic number
mass number

Section 2.6
chemical bond
covalent bond
molecule
chemical formula
structural formula
space-filling model
ball-and-stick model
ion
cation
anion
ionic bond
polyatomic ion

Section 2.7
periodic table
metal
nonmetal
group (family)
period
alkali metals
alkaline earth metals
halogens
noble gases

Section 2.8
binary compounds
binary ionic compounds
oxyanions
binary covalent compound
acid

A blue question or exercise number indicates that the answer to that question or exercise appears at the back of this book and a solution appears in the Solutions Guide.

Questions

1. The vitamin niacin (nicotinic acid, $C_6H_5NO_2$) can be isolated from a variety of natural sources such as liver, yeast, milk, and whole grain. It also can be synthesized from commercially available materials. Which source of nicotinic acid, from a nutritional view, is best for use in a multivitamin tablet? Why?

2. Use Dalton's atomic theory to account for each of the following.
   a. The law of conservation of mass
   b. The law of definite proportion
   c. The law of multiple proportions

3. What refinements had to be made in Dalton's atomic theory to account for Gay-Lussac's results on the combining volumes of gases?

4. One of the best indications of a useful theory is that it raises more questions for further experimentation than it originally answered. Does this apply to Dalton's atomic theory? Give examples.

5. Dalton assumed that all atoms of the same element were identical in all their properties. Explain why this assumption is not valid.

6. What evidence led to the conclusion that cathode rays had a negative charge?

7. Is there a difference between a cathode ray and a β particle?

8. What discoveries were made by J. J. Thomson, Henri Becquerel, and Lord Rutherford? How did Dalton's model of the atom have to be modified to account for these discoveries?

9. What is the distinction between atomic number and mass number? Between mass number and atomic mass?

10. Distinguish between the terms *family* and *period* in connection with the periodic table. For which of these terms is the term *group* also used?

11. When hydrogen is burned in oxygen to form water, the composition of the water formed does not depend on the amount of oxygen. Interpret this in terms of the law of definite proportions.

12. The two most reactive families of elements are the halogens and the alkali metals. How do they differ in their reactivities?

Exercises

In this section similar exercises are paired.

Development of the Atomic Theory

13. When mixtures of gaseous H_2 and gaseous Cl_2 react, a product forms that has the same properties regardless of the relative amounts of H_2 and Cl_2 used.
    a. How is this result interpreted in terms of the law of definite proportion?
    b. When a volume of H_2 reacts with an equal volume of Cl_2 at the same temperature and pressure, what volume of product having the formula HCl is formed?

14. A reaction of 1 liter of chlorine gas (Cl_2) with 3 liters of fluorine gas (F_2) yields 2 liters of a gaseous product. All gas volumes are at the same temperature and pressure. What is the formula of the gaseous product?

15. Several compounds containing only sulfur (S) and fluorine (F) are known. Three of them have the following compositions:
    i. 1.188 g of F for every 1.000 g of S
    ii. 2.375 g of F for every 1.000 g of S
    iii. 3.563 g of F for every 1.000 g of S

    How do these data illustrate the law of multiple proportions?

16. Hydrazine, ammonia, and hydrogen azide all contain only nitrogen and hydrogen. The mass of hydrogen that combines with 1.00 g of nitrogen for each compound is 1.44×10^{-1} g, 2.16×10^{-1} g, and 2.40×10^{-2} g, respectively. Show how these data illustrate the law of multiple proportions.

17. Early tables of atomic weights (masses) were generated by measuring the mass of a substance that reacts with 1 g of oxygen. Given the following data and taking the atomic mass of hydrogen as 1.00, generate a table of relative atomic masses for oxygen, sodium, and magnesium.

Element	Mass that Combines with 1.00 g Oxygen	Assumed Formula
Hydrogen	0.1260 g	HO
Sodium	2.8750 g	NaO
Magnesium	1.5000 g	MgO

How do your values compare with those in the periodic table? How do you account for any differences?

18. The mass of beryllium that combines with 1.000 g of oxygen to form beryllium oxide is 0.5633 g. When atomic masses were first being measured, it was thought that the formula of beryllium oxide was Be_2O_3. What would be the atomic mass of beryllium if this were the case?

The Nature of the Atom

19. From the information in this chapter on the mass of the proton, the mass of the electron, and the sizes of the nucleus and the atom, calculate the densities of a hydrogen nucleus and a hydrogen atom.

20. If you wanted to make an accurate scale model of the hydrogen atom and decided that the nucleus would have a diameter of 1 mm, what would be the diameter of the entire model?

21. In an experiment it was found that the total charge on an oil drop was 5.93×10^{-18} C. How many negative charges does the drop contain?

22. A chemist in a galaxy far, far away performed the Millikan oil drop experiment and got the following results for the charges on various drops. Use these data to calculate the charge of the electron in zirkombs.

2.56×10^{-12} zirkombs	7.68×10^{-12} zirkombs
3.84×10^{-12} zirkombs	5.12×10^{-12} zirkombs

23. What are the symbols of the following elements: gold, silver, mercury, potassium, iron, antimony, tungsten?

24. What are the symbols of the following metals: sodium, beryllium, manganese, chromium, uranium?

25. What are the symbols of the following nonmetals: fluorine, chlorine, bromine, sulfur, oxygen, phosphorus?

26. What are the symbols of the following elements: titanium, selenium, plutonium, nitrogen, and silicon?

27. Give the names of the metals that correspond to the following symbols: Sn, Pt, Co, Ni, Mg, Ba, K.

28. Give the names of the nonmetals that correspond to the following symbols: As, I, Xe, He, C, Si.

29. List the noble gas elements. Which of the noble gases has only radioactive isotopes? (This situation is indicated on most periodic tables by parentheses around the mass of the element. See inside front cover.)

30. Which lanthanide element and which transition element have only radioactive isotopes? (See Exercise 29.)

31. In the periodic table, how many elements are found in
a. the second period?
b. the third period?
c. the fourth period?
d. Group 5A?

32. In the periodic table, how many elements are found in
a. Group 2A?
b. the "oxygen family"?
c. the nickel group?
d. Group 8A?

33. Give the number of protons and neutrons in the nucleus of each of the following atoms:
a. $^{238}_{94}Pu$ c. $^{52}_{24}Cr$ e. $^{60}_{27}Co$
b. $^{65}_{29}Cu$ d. $^{4}_{2}He$ f. $^{54}_{24}Cr$

34. Using the periodic table, give the number of protons and neutrons in the nucleus of each of the following atoms:
a. ^{15}N c. ^{207}Pb e. ^{107}Ag
b. ^{3}H d. ^{151}Eu f. ^{109}Ag

35. An atom has 9 protons and 10 neutrons in the nucleus. What is its symbol?

36. Identify each of the following elements:
a. $^{31}_{15}X$ c. $^{39}_{19}X$
b. $^{127}_{53}X$ d. $^{173}_{70}X$

37. What is the symbol for an ion with 63 protons, 60 electrons, and 88 neutrons?

38. An ion contains 50 protons, 68 neutrons, and 48 electrons. What is its symbol?

39. What is the symbol of an ion with 16 protons, 18 neutrons, and 18 electrons?

40. What is the symbol for an ion that has 16 protons, 16 neutrons, and 18 electrons?

41. Complete the following table:

Symbol	Number of protons in nucleus	Number of neutrons in nucleus	Number of electrons	Net charge
	33	42		3+
$^{128}_{52}Te^{2-}$			54	
	16	16	16	
	81	123		1+
$^{195}_{78}Pt$				

42. Complete the following table:

Symbol	Number of protons in nucleus	Number of neutrons in nucleus	Number of electrons	Net charge
$^{238}_{92}U$				
	20	20		2+
	23	28	20	
$^{89}_{39}Y$				
	35	44	36	
	15	16		3−

43. Classify the following elements as metals or nonmetals:
Mg   Si   Rn
Ti   Ge   Eu
Au   B   Am
Bi   At   Br

44. The distinction between metals and nonmetals is really not a clear one. Some elements, called **metalloids,** are intermediate in their properties. Which elements in Exercise 43 would you reclassify as metalloids? What other elements in the periodic table would you expect to be metalloids?

45. Which of the following sets of elements are all in the same group in the periodic table?
a. Fe, Ru, Os   c. Sn, As, S
b. Rh, Pd, Ag   d. Se, Te, Po

46. Which of the following sets of elements are all in the same group in the periodic table?
a. N, P, O   c. Rb, Sn
b. C, Si, Ge   d. Mg, Ca

47. Consider the elements of Group 4A (the ''carbon family''): C, Si, Ge, Sn, and Pb. What is the trend in metallic character as one goes down this group?

48. What is the trend in metallic character going from left to right across a period in the periodic table?

49. Would you expect each of the following atoms to gain or lose electrons when forming ions? What ion is the most likely in each case?
a. Na   d. I
b. Sr   e. Al
c. Ba   f. S

50. Would you expect each of the following atoms to gain or lose electrons when forming ions? What ion is the most likely in each case?
a. B   d. N
b. Cs   e. O
c. Se   f. Mg

Nomenclature

51. Name each of the following compounds:
a. CrO_3 c. Al_2O_3 e. SeO_3 g. PCl_3
b. Cr_2O_3 d. SeO_2 f. NI_3 h. SF_2

52. Name each of the following compounds:
a. NiO c. CeO_2 e. Ag_2S g. NaH
b. Fe_2O_3 d. Ce_2O_3 f. MnO_2 h. H_2S

53. Name each of the following compounds:
   a. NaCl
   b. $MgCl_2$
   c. RbBr
   d. CsF
   e. AlI_3
   f. HI
   g. NO
   h. NF_3
   i. N_2F_4
   j. N_2Cl_2
   k. SiF_4
   l. H_2Se

54. Name each of the following compounds:
   a. $KClO_4$
   b. $Ca_3(PO_4)_2$
   c. $Al_2(SO_4)_3$
   d. $Pb(NO_3)_2$
   e. $BaSO_3$
   f. $NaNO_2$
   g. $KMnO_4$
   h. $K_2Cr_2O_7$
   i. $AuCl_3$
   j. HIO_2
   k. TiO_2
   l. NiS

55. Name each of the following compounds:
   a. HNO_3
   b. HNO_2
   c. H_3PO_4
   d. H_3PO_3
   e. $NaHSO_4$
   f. $Ca(HSO_3)_2$
   g. $NaBrO_3$
   h. $Fe(IO_4)_3$
   i. $Ru(NO_3)_3$
   j. V_2O_5
   k. $PtCl_4$
   l. $FePO_4$

56. Name each of the following compounds:
   a. CuI
   b. CuI_2
   c. CoI_2
   d. Na_2CO_3
   e. $NaHCO_3$
   f. S_4N_4
   g. SF_6
   h. NaOCl
   i. $BaCrO_4$
   j. $Ce(NO_3)_4$

57. Write the formula for each of the following compounds:
   a. Cesium bromide
   b. Barium sulfate
   c. Ammonium chloride
   d. Chlorine monoxide
   e. Silicon tetrachloride
   f. Chlorine trifluoride
   g. Beryllium oxide
   h. Magnesium fluoride

58. Write the formula for each of the following compounds:
   a. Ammonium hydrogen phosphate
   b. Mercury(I) sulfide
   c. Silicon dioxide
   d. Sodium sulfite
   e. Aluminum hydrogen sulfate
   f. Nitrogen trichloride
   g. Hydrobromic acid
   h. Bromous acid
   i. Perbromic acid
   j. Potassium hydrogen sulfide
   k. Calcium iodide
   l. Cesium perchlorate

59. Write the formula for each of the following compounds:
   a. Sulfur difluoride
   b. Sulfur hexafluoride
   c. Sodium dihydrogen phosphate
   d. Lithium nitride
   e. Chromium(III) carbonate
   f. Tin(II) fluoride
   g. Ammonium acetate
   h. Ammonium hydrogen sulfate
   i. Cobalt(III) nitrate
   j. Mercury(I) chloride
   k. Potassium chlorate
   l. Sodium hydride

60. Write the formula for each of the following compounds:
   a. Sodium hydroxide
   b. Aluminum hydroxide
   c. Hydrogen cyanide
   d. Sodium peroxide
   e. Copper(II) acetate
   f. Carbon tetrafluoride
   g. Lead(II) oxide
   h. Lead(IV) oxide
   i. Lead dioxide (common name)
   j. Copper(I) bromide
   k. Germanium dioxide
   l. Gallium arsenide

Additional Exercises

61. Insulin, a complex protein molecule produced by the pancreas in all vertebrates, is a hormone that regulates carbohydrate metabolism. Inability to produce sufficient insulin results in diabetes mellitus. Diabetes is treated by prescribing injections of insulin. Given the law of definite proportion, would you expect any differences in chemical activity between human insulin extracted from pancreatic tissue and human insulin produced by genetically engineered bacteria? Explain.

62. How many protons, neutrons, and electrons are present in each of the following atoms or ions?
   a. $^{24}_{12}Mg$
   b. $^{24}_{12}Mg^{2+}$
   c. $^{59}_{27}Co^{2+}$
   d. $^{59}_{27}Co^{3+}$
   e. $^{59}_{27}Co$
   f. $^{79}_{34}Se$
   g. $^{79}_{34}Se^{2-}$
   h. $^{63}_{28}Ni$
   i. $^{59}_{28}Ni^{2+}$

63. The formulas and common names for several substances are given below. Give the systematic names for these substances.
   a. Sugar of lead $Pb(C_2H_3O_2)_2$
   b. Blue vitrol $CuSO_4$
   c. Quicklime   CaO
   d. Epsom salts $MgSO_4$
   e. Milk of magnesia $Mg(OH)_2$
   f. Gypsum $CaSO_4$
   g. Laughing gas N_2O

64. Identify each of the following elements:
   a. A noble gas with 54 protons in the nucleus.
   b. A member of the same family as oxygen whose 2− ion contains 36 electrons.
   c. A member of the alkaline earth metal family whose 2+ ion contains 18 electrons.
   d. A transition metal with 42 protons in the nucleus.
   e. A radioactive element with 94 protons and 94 electrons.

65. Chlorine has two natural isotopes: $^{37}_{17}Cl$ and $^{35}_{17}Cl$. Hydrogen reacts with chlorine to form the compound HCl. Would a given amount of hydrogen react with different masses of the two chlorine isotopes? Does this conflict with the law of definite proportion? Why or why not?

Challenge Problems

66. The elements in one of the groups in the periodic table are often called the **coinage metals.** Identify the elements in this group based on your own experience.

67. Predict the formula and name of a binary compound formed from each of the following pairs of elements:

a. Ba and O   e. B and O
b. Li and H   f. O and F
c. In and F   g. Al and H
d. As and S   h. In and P

68. Technetium (Tc) was the first synthetically produced element. Technetium (the word comes from the Greek word for artificial) was first produced by Perries and Segré in 1937 in Berkeley, California, by bombarding a molybdenum plate with ^2H nuclei. Elemental technetium is produced from ammonium pertechnetate. How many protons and neutrons are in the nuclei of ^{98}Tc and ^{99}Tc? What is the formula of ammonium pertechnetate?

69. The early alchemists used to do an experiment in which water was boiled for several days in a sealed glass container. Eventually, some solid residue would appear in the bottom of the flask, which was interpreted to mean that some of the water in the flask had been converted into "earth". When Lavoisier repeated this experiment, he found that the water weighed the same before and after heating and the mass of the flask plus the solid residue equaled the original mass of the flask. Were the alchemists correct? Explain what really happened. (This experiment is described in the article by A. F. Scott, in *Scientific American,* January 1984.)

70. Elements in the same family often form oxyanions of the same general formula. The anions are named in a similar fashion. What are the names of the oxyanions of selenium and tellurium: SeO_4^{2-}, SeO_3^{2-}, TeO_4^{2-}, TeO_3^{2-}?

71. By analogy to phosphorus compounds, name the following: Na_3AsO_4, H_3AsO_4, $Mg_3(SbO_4)_2$.

a) Barium oxide
BaO
Lithium
LiH

◀ CHAPTER 3 ▶

Stoichiometry

Chemical reactions have a profound effect on our lives. There are many examples: food is converted to energy in the human body; nitrogen and hydrogen are combined to form ammonia, which is used as a fertilizer; fuels and plastics are produced from petroleum; the starch in plants is synthesized from carbon dioxide and water using energy from sunlight; human insulin is produced in laboratories by bacteria; cancer is induced in humans by substances from our environment; and so on, in a seemingly endless list. The central activity of chemistry is to understand chemical changes such as these, and the study of reactions occupies a central place in this book. We will examine why reactions occur, how fast they occur, and the specific pathways they follow.

In this chapter we will consider the quantities of materials consumed and produced in chemical reactions. This area of study is called **chemical stoichiometry** (pronounced stoy·kē·om′·etry). To understand chemical stoichiometry, you must first understand the concept of relative atomic masses.

< Sodium hydrogen carbonate ($NaHCO_3$) reacts vigorously with hydrochloric acid to produce carbon dioxide gas.

3.1 Atomic Masses

Purpose

• To describe the modern atomic mass scale and explain how atomic masses are determined experimentally.

As we saw in Chapter 2, the first quantitative information about atomic masses came from the work of Dalton, Gay-Lussac, Lavoisier, Avogadro, and Berzelius. By observing the proportions in which elements combine to form various compounds, nineteenth-century chemists calculated relative atomic masses. The modern system of atomic masses, instituted in 1961, is based on ^{12}C ("carbon twelve") as the standard. In this system, *^{12}C is assigned a mass of exactly 12 atomic mass units* (amu), and the masses of all other atoms are given relative to this standard.

The most accurate method currently available for comparing the masses of atoms involves the use of the **mass spectrometer.** In this instrument, diagrammed in Fig. 3.1, atoms or molecules are passed into a beam of high-speed electrons. The high-speed electrons knock electrons off the atoms or molecules being analyzed and change them into positive ions. An applied electric field then accelerates these ions into a magnetic field. Because an accelerating ion produces its own magnetic field, an interaction with the applied magnetic field occurs, which tends to change the path of the ion. The amount of path deflection for each ion depends on its mass—the most massive ions are deflected the smallest amount—which causes the ions to separate, as shown in Fig. 3.1. A comparison of the positions where the ions hit the detector plate gives very accurate values of their relative masses. For example, when ^{12}C and ^{13}C are analyzed in a mass spectrometer, the ratio of their masses is found to be

$$\frac{\text{Mass } ^{13}C}{\text{Mass } ^{12}C} = 1.0836129$$

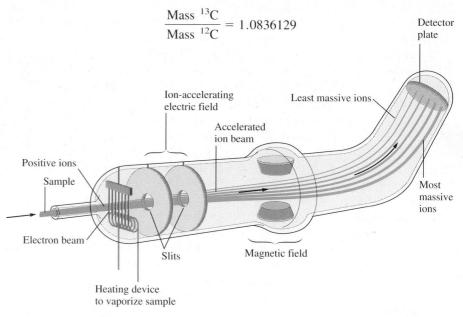

Figure 3.1

Schematic diagram of a mass spectrometer.

Since the atomic mass unit is defined such that the mass of ^{12}C is *exactly* 12 atomic mass units, then on this same scale,

$$\text{Mass of } {}^{13}C = (1.0836129)(12 \text{ amu}) = 13.003355 \text{ amu}$$

↑
Exact number
by definition

The masses of other atoms can be determined in a similar fashion.

The mass for each element is given in the table inside the front cover of this book. This value, even though it is actually a mass, is (for historical reasons) often called the atomic weight for each element.

Look at the value of the atomic mass of carbon given in this table. You might expect to see 12, since we said the system of atomic masses is based on ^{12}C. However, the number given for carbon is not 12 but 12.01. Why? The reason for this apparent discrepancy is that the carbon found on earth (natural carbon) is a mixture of the isotopes ^{12}C, ^{13}C, and ^{14}C. All three isotopes have six protons, but they have six, seven, and eight neutrons, respectively. Because natural carbon is a mixture of isotopes, the atomic mass we use for carbon is an *average value* reflecting the average of the isotopes composing it.

The average atomic mass for carbon is computed as follows. It is known that natural carbon is composed of 98.89% ^{12}C atoms and 1.11% ^{13}C atoms. The amount of ^{14}C is negligibly small at this level of precision. Using the masses of ^{12}C (exactly 12 amu) and ^{13}C (13.003355 amu), we can calculate the average atomic mass for natural carbon as follows:

98.89% of 12 amu + 1.11% of 13.0034 amu =
$$(0.9889)(12 \text{ amu}) + (0.0111)(13.0034 \text{ amu}) = 12.01 \text{ amu}$$

This average atomic mass has traditionally been called the atomic weight of carbon. In this text we will call the average mass for an element the **average atomic mass** or, simply, the **atomic mass** for that element.

Even though natural carbon does not contain a single atom with mass 12.01, for stoichiometric purposes, we can consider carbon to be composed of only one type of atom with a mass of 12.01. This enables us to count atoms of natural carbon by weighing a sample of carbon. We will illustrate this concept by considering how we could count jelly beans by weighing them. For example, it is much easier to weigh out 3000 grams of jelly beans (with an average mass of 3 grams per jelly bean) than to count out 1000 of them. Note that none of the jelly beans has to have a mass of 3 grams for this method to work; only the *average* mass must be 3 grams. We extend this same principle to counting atoms. For natural carbon with an average mass of 12.01 atomic mass units, to obtain 1000 atoms would require weighing out 12,010 atomic mass units of natural carbon (a mixture of ^{12}C and ^{13}C).

As in the case of carbon, the mass for each element listed in the table inside the front cover of the book is an average value based on the isotopic composition of the naturally occurring element. For instance, the mass listed for hydrogen (1.008) is the average mass for natural hydrogen, which is a mixture of ^{1}H and ^{2}H (deuterium). *No atom of hydrogen actually has the mass 1.008.*

In addition to being useful for determining accurate mass values for individual atoms, the mass spectrometer is also used to determine the isotopic composition of a natural element. For example, when a sample of natural neon is injected into a

Most elements occur in nature as mixtures of isotopes; thus atomic weights (masses) are usually average values.

3000 grams of jelly beans.

Figure 3.2

(a) Neon gas glowing in a discharge tube. The relative intensities of the signals recorded when natural neon is injected into a mass spectrometer, represented in terms of (b) "peaks" and (c) a bar graph. The relative areas of the peaks are 0.9092 (^{20}Ne), 0.00257 (^{21}Ne), and 0.0882 (^{22}Ne); natural neon is therefore 90.92% ^{20}Ne, 0.257% ^{21}Ne, and 8.82% ^{22}Ne.

(a)

(b)

(c)

mass spectrometer, the mass spectrum shown in Fig. 3.2 is obtained. The areas of the "peaks" or the heights of the bars indicate the relative abundances of $^{20}_{10}Ne$, $^{21}_{10}Ne$, and $^{22}_{10}Ne$ atoms.

Sample Exercise 3.1

When a sample of natural copper is vaporized and injected into a mass spectrometer, the results shown in Fig. 3.3 are obtained. Use these data to compute the average mass of natural copper. (The mass values for ^{63}Cu and ^{65}Cu are 62.93 amu and 64.93 amu, respectively.)

Solution

As shown by the graph, of every 100 atoms of natural copper, 69.09 are ^{63}Cu and 30.91 are ^{65}Cu. Thus the mass of 100 atoms of natural copper is

$$(69.09 \text{ atoms})\left(62.93 \frac{\text{amu}}{\text{atom}}\right) + (30.91 \text{ atoms})\left(64.93 \frac{\text{amu}}{\text{atom}}\right) = 6355 \text{ amu}$$

The *average mass* of a copper atom is

$$\frac{6355 \text{ amu}}{100 \text{ atoms}} = 63.55 \text{ amu/atom}$$

This mass value is used in doing calculations involving the reactions of copper and is the value given in the table inside the front cover of this book.

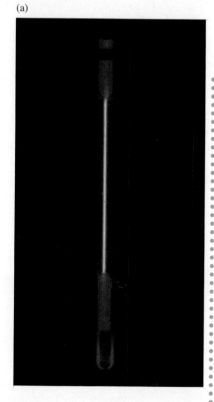

Figure 3.3

Mass spectrum of natural copper.

3.2 The Mole

Purpose

- To explain the importance of the mole concept.
- To show how to convert among moles, mass, and number of particles for a given sample.

Because samples of matter typically contain so many atoms, a unit of measure called the mole has been established for use in counting atoms. For our purposes, it is most convenient to define the **mole** (abbreviated mol) as *the number equal to the number of carbon atoms in exactly 12 grams of pure ^{12}C*. Techniques such as mass spectrometry, which count atoms very precisely, have been used to determine this number as 6.02214×10^{23} (6.022×10^{23} will be sufficient for our purposes). This number is called **Avogadro's number** to honor his contributions to chemistry. *One mole of something consists of 6.022×10^{23} units of that substance.* Just as a dozen eggs is 12 eggs, a mole of eggs is 6.022×10^{23} eggs.

The magnitude of the number 6.022×10^{23} is very difficult to imagine. To give you some idea, 1 mole of seconds represents a span of time 4 million times as long as the earth has already existed, and 1 mole of marbles is enough to cover the entire earth to a depth of 50 miles! However, since atoms are so tiny, a mole of atoms or molecules is a perfectly manageable quantity to use in a reaction (see Fig. 3.4).

How do we use the mole in chemical calculations? Recall that Avogadro's number is defined as the number of atoms in exactly 12 grams of ^{12}C. This means that 12 grams of ^{12}C contain 6.022×10^{23} atoms. It also means that a 12.01-gram sample of natural carbon contains 6.022×10^{23} atoms (a mixture of ^{12}C, ^{13}C, and ^{14}C atoms, with an average atomic mass of 12.01). Since the ratio of the masses of the samples (12 g/12.01 g) is the same as the ratio of the masses of the individual components (12 amu/12.01 amu), the two samples contain the *same number* of atoms (6.022×10^{23}).

To be sure this point is clear, think of oranges with an average mass of 0.5 pound each and grapefruit with an average mass of 1.0 pound each. Any two sacks for which the sack of grapefruit weighs twice as much as the sack of oranges will contain the same number of pieces of fruit. The same idea extends to atoms. Compare natural carbon (average mass of 12.01) and natural helium (average mass of 4.003). A sample of 12.01 grams of natural carbon contains the same number of atoms as 4.003 grams of natural helium. Both samples contain 1 mole of atoms (6.022×10^{23}). Table 3.1 gives more examples that illustrate this basic idea.

The SI definition of the mole is the amount of a substance that contains as many entities as there are in exactly 12 g of carbon-12.

Avogadro's number is 6.022×10^{23}. One mole of anything is 6.022×10^{23} units of that substance.

Figure 3.4

Proceeding clockwise from the top, samples containing one mole each of copper, iron, iodine, sulfur, aluminum, and (in the center) mercury.

Table 3.1		
Comparison of 1-Mole Samples of Various Elements		
Element	Number of Atoms Present	Mass of Sample (g)
Aluminum	6.022×10^{23}	26.98
Copper	6.022×10^{23}	63.55
Iron	6.022×10^{23}	55.85
Sulfur	6.022×10^{23}	32.06
Iodine	6.022×10^{23}	126.9
Mercury	6.022×10^{23}	200.6

The mass of 1 mole of an element is equal to its atomic mass in grams.

Thus the mole is defined such that a sample of a natural element with a mass equal to the element's atomic mass expressed in grams contains 1 mole of atoms. This definition also fixes the relationship between the atomic mass unit and the gram. Since 6.022×10^{23} atoms of carbon (each with a mass of 12 amu) have a mass of 12 g, then

$$(6.022 \times 10^{23} \text{ atoms})\left(\frac{12 \text{ amu}}{\text{atom}}\right) = 12 \text{ g}$$

and

$$6.022 \times 10^{23} \text{ amu} = 1 \text{ g}$$

$\uparrow$
Exact
number

This relationship can be used to derive the unit factor needed to convert between atomic mass units and grams.

◀ **C H E M I C A L   I M P A C T** ▶

Elemental Analysis Catches Elephant Poachers

In an effort to combat the poaching of elephants by controlling illegal exports of ivory, scientists are now using the isotopic composition of ivory trinkets and elephant tusks to identify the region of Africa where the elephant lived. Using a mass spectrometer, scientists analyze the ivory for the relative amounts of ^{12}C, ^{13}C, ^{14}N, ^{15}N, ^{86}Sr, and ^{87}Sr to determine the diet of the elephant and thus its place of origin. For example, because grasses use a different photosynthetic pathway to produce glucose than do trees, grasses have a slightly different $^{13}C/^{12}C$ ratio from that of trees. They have different ratios because each time a carbon atom is added in going from simpler to more complex compounds, the more massive ^{13}C is disfavored relative to ^{12}C because it reacts more slowly. Because trees use more steps to build up glucose, they end up with a smaller $^{13}C/^{12}C$ ratio in their leaves relative to grasses, and this difference is then reflected in the tissues of elephants. Thus scientists can tell whether a particular tusk came from a savanna-dwelling elephant (grass-eating) or from a tree-browsing elephant.

Similarly, because the ratios of $^{15}N/^{14}N$ and $^{87}Sr/^{86}Sr$ in elephant tusks also vary depending on the region of Africa the elephant inhabits, they can also be used to trace the elephant's origin. In fact, using these techniques, scientists have reported being able to discriminate between elephants living only about 100 miles apart.

There is now international concern about the dwindling elephant populations in Africa—their numbers have decreased by 40% over the past decade. This concern has led to bans in the export of ivory from many countries in Africa. However, a few nations still allow ivory to be exported. Thus, to enforce the trade restrictions, the origin of a given piece of ivory must be established. It is hoped that the "isotope signature" of the ivory can be used for this purpose.

Sample Exercise 3.2

Americium is an element that does not occur naturally. It can be made in very small amounts in a device known as a particle accelerator. Compute the mass in grams of a sample of americium containing six atoms.

Solution

From the table inside the front cover of the book, we note that one americium atom has a mass of 243 amu. Thus the mass of six atoms is

$$6 \text{ atoms} \times 243 \frac{\text{amu}}{\text{atom}} = 1.46 \times 10^3 \text{ amu}$$

Using the relationship

$$6.022 \times 10^{23} \text{ amu} = 1 \text{ g}$$

we write the conversion factor for converting atomic mass units to grams:

$$\frac{1 \text{ g}}{6.022 \times 10^{23} \text{ amu}}$$

The mass of six americium atoms in grams is

$$1.46 \times 10^3 \text{ amu} \times \frac{1 \text{ g}}{6.022 \times 10^{23} \text{ amu}} = 2.42 \times 10^{-21} \text{ g}$$

To do chemical calculations, you must understand what the mole means and how to determine the number of moles in a given mass of a substance. These procedures are illustrated in Sample Exercises 3.3 and 3.4.

Sample Exercise 3.3

Aluminum (Al) is a metal with a high strength-to-mass ratio and a high resistance to corrosion; thus it is often used for structural purposes. Compute both the number of moles of atoms and the number of atoms in a 10.0-g sample of aluminum.

Solution

The mass of 1 mole (6.022×10^{23} atoms) of aluminum is 26.98 g. The sample we are considering has a mass of 10.0 g. Since the mass is less than 26.98 g, this sample contains less than 1 mole of aluminum atoms. We can calculate the number of moles of aluminum atoms in 10.0 g as follows:

$$10.0 \text{ g Al} \times \frac{1 \text{ mol Al}}{26.98 \text{ g Al}} = 0.371 \text{ mol Al}$$

The number of atoms in 10.0 g (0.371 mol) of aluminum is

$$0.371 \text{ mol Al} \times \frac{6.022 \times 10^{23} \text{ atoms}}{1 \text{ mol Al}} = 2.23 \times 10^{23} \text{ atoms}$$

(top) Pure aluminum. (bottom) Aluminum alloys are used for many high-quality bicycle components, such as this chain wheel.

Sample Exercise 3.4

A silicon chip used in an integrated circuit of a microcomputer has a mass of 5.68 mg. How many silicon (Si) atoms are present in this chip?

Solution

The strategy for doing this problem is to convert from milligrams of silicon to grams of silicon, then to moles of silicon, and finally to atoms of silicon:

$$5.68 \text{ mg Si} \times \frac{1 \text{ g Si}}{1000 \text{ mg Si}} = 5.68 \times 10^{-3} \text{ g Si}$$

$$5.68 \times 10^{-3} \text{ g Si} \times \frac{1 \text{ mol Si}}{28.09 \text{ g Si}} = 2.02 \times 10^{-4} \text{ mol Si}$$

$$2.02 \times 10^{-4} \text{ mol Si} \times \frac{6.022 \times 10^{23} \text{ atoms}}{1 \text{ mol Si}} = 1.22 \times 10^{20} \text{ atoms}$$

Always check to see if your answer is sensible.

It always makes sense to think about whether your answer is reasonable as you do a calculation. In Sample Exercise 3.4, 5.68 mg of silicon is clearly much less than 1 mol of silicon (which has a mass of 28.08 g), so the final answer of 1.22×10^{20} atoms (compared with 6.022×10^{23} atoms) is at least in the right direction. Paying careful attention to units and making sure the answer is reasonable can help you detect an inverted conversion factor or a number that was incorrectly entered in your calculator.

Sample Exercise 3.5

Cobalt (Co) is a metal that is added to steel to improve its resistance to corrosion. Calculate both the number of moles in a sample of cobalt containing 5.00×10^{20} atoms and the mass of the sample.

Solution

Note that the sample of 5.00×10^{20} atoms of cobalt is less than 1 mole (6.022×10^{23} atoms) of cobalt. What fraction of a mole it represents can be determined as follows:

$$5.00 \times 10^{20} \text{ atoms Co} \times \frac{1 \text{ mol Co}}{6.022 \times 10^{23} \text{ atoms Co}} = 8.30 \times 10^{-4} \text{ mol Co}$$

Since the mass of 1 mole of cobalt atoms is 58.93 g, the mass of 5.00×10^{20} atoms can be determined as follows:

$$8.30 \times 10^{-4} \text{ mol Co} \times \frac{58.93 \text{ g Co}}{1 \text{ mol Co}} = 4.89 \times 10^{-2} \text{ g Co}$$

3.3 Molar Mass

Purpose

- To show how to calculate values for molar mass.
- To show how to convert among molar mass, moles, and number of particles in a given sample.

A chemical compound is, ultimately, a collection of atoms. For example, methane (the major component of natural gas) consists of molecules that each contain one carbon and four hydrogen atoms (CH_4). How can we calculate the mass of 1 mole of methane; that is, what is the mass of 6.022×10^{23} CH_4 molecules? Since each CH_4 molecule contains one carbon atom and four hydrogen atoms, 1 mole of CH_4 molecules contains 1 mole of carbon atoms and 4 moles of hydrogen atoms. The mass of 1 mole of methane can be found by summing the masses of carbon and hydrogen present:

$$
\begin{aligned}
\text{Mass of 1 mol C} &= 12.01\ \text{g} \\
\text{Mass of 4 mol H} &= \underline{4 \times 1.008\ \text{g}} \\
\text{Mass of 1 mol } CH_4 &= 16.04\ \text{g}
\end{aligned}
$$

Note that in this case, the term 12.01 limits the number of significant figures.

Because 16.04 g represents the mass of 1 mole of methane molecules, it makes sense to call it the *molar mass* for methane. Thus the **molar mass** of a substance is *the mass in grams of one mole of the compound.* Traditionally, the term **molecular weight** has been used for this quantity. However, we will use molar mass exclusively in this text. The molar mass of a known substance is obtained by summing the masses of the component atoms as we did for methane.

A substance's molar mass is the mass in grams of 1 mole of the substance.

◀ **CHEMICAL IMPACT** ▶

Measuring the Masses of Large Molecules or Making Elephants Fly

When a chemist produces a new molecule, one crucial property for making a positive identification is the molecule's mass. There are many ways to determine the molar mass of a compound, but one of the fastest and most accurate methods involves mass spectrometry. This method requires that the substance be put into the gas phase and ionized. The deflection that the resulting ion exhibits as it is accelerated through a magnetic field can be used to obtain a very precise value of its mass. One drawback of this method is that it is difficult to use with large molecules because they are difficult to vaporize. That is, substances that contain large molecules typically have very high boiling points, and these molecules are often damaged when they are vaporized at such

high temperatures. A case in point involves proteins, an extremely important class of large biological molecules that are quite fragile at high temperatures. Typical methods used to obtain the masses of protein molecules are slow and tedious.

Mass spectrometry has not previously been used to obtain protein masses, because proteins decompose at the temperatures necessary to vaporize them. However, a new technique called "matrix-assisted laser desorption" has been developed that allows mass spectrometric determination of protein molar masses. In this technique, the large "target" molecule is embedded in a matrix of smaller molecules. The matrix is then placed in a mass spectrometer and blasted with a laser beam, which causes its disintegration.

Disintegration of the matrix frees the large target molecule, which is then swept into the mass spectrometer. One researcher involved in this project likened this method to an elephant on top of a tall building: "The elephant must fly if the building is suddenly turned into fine grains of sand."

This technique allows scientists to determine the mass of huge molecules. So far researchers have measured proteins with masses up to 350,000 daltons (1 dalton is the mass of a hydrogen atom). This method, which makes mass spectrometry a routine tool for the determination of protein masses, probably will be extended to even larger molecules such as DNA and could be a revolutionary development in the characterization of biomolecules.

Sample Exercise 3.6

Juglone, a dye known for centuries, is produced from the husks of black walnuts. It is also a natural herbicide (weed killer) that kills off competitive plants around the black walnut tree but does not affect grass and other noncompetitive plants. The formula for juglone is $C_{10}H_6O_3$.

a. Calculate the molar mass of juglone.
b. A sample of 1.56×10^{-2} g of pure juglone was extracted from black walnut husks. How many moles of juglone does this sample represent?

Solution

a. The molar mass is obtained by summing the masses of the component atoms. In 1 mole of juglone there are 10 moles of carbon atoms, 6 moles of hydrogen atoms, and 3 moles of oxygen atoms:

$$
\begin{array}{lll}
10\ C: & 10 \times 12.01\ g = & 120.1\ \ g \\
6\ H: & 6 \times 1.008\ g = & 6.048\ g \\
3\ O: & 3 \times 16.00\ g = & \underline{48.00\ \ g} \\
\multicolumn{2}{r}{\text{Mass of 1 mol } C_{10}H_6O_3 =} & 174.1\ \ \ g
\end{array}
$$

The mass of 1 mole of juglone is 174.1 g, which is the molar mass.

b. The mass of 1 mole of this compound is 174.1 g; thus 1.56×10^{-2} g is much less than a mole. The exact fraction of a mole can be determined as follows:

$$
1.56 \times 10^{-2}\ \text{g juglone} \times \frac{1\ \text{mol juglone}}{174.1\ \text{g juglone}} = 8.96 \times 10^{-5}\ \text{mol juglone}
$$

Sample Exercise 3.7

Calcium carbonate ($CaCO_3$), also called calcite, is the principal mineral found in limestone, marble, chalk, pearls, and the shells of marine animals such as clams.

a. Calculate the molar mass of calcium carbonate.
b. A certain sample of calcium carbonate contains 4.86 moles. What is the mass in grams of this sample? What is the mass of the CO_3^{2-} ions present?

Solution

a. Calcium carbonate is an ionic compound composed of Ca^{2+} and CO_3^{2-} ions. In 1 mole of calcium carbonate there are 1 mole of Ca^{2+} ions and 1 mole of CO_3^{2-} ions. The molar mass is calculated by summing the masses of the components:

$$
\begin{array}{lll}
1\ Ca^{2+}: & 1 \times 40.08\ g = & 40.08\ g \\
1\ CO_3^{2-}: & & \\
1\ C: & 1 \times 12.01\ g = & 12.01\ g \\
3\ O: & 3 \times 16.00\ g = & \underline{48.00\ g} \\
\multicolumn{2}{r}{\text{Mass of 1 mol } CaCO_3 =} & 100.09\ g
\end{array}
$$

Thus the mass of 1 mole of $CaCO_3$ (1 mol Ca^{2+} plus 1 mol CO_3^{2-}) is 100.09 g. This is the molar mass.

b. The mass of 1 mole of $CaCO_3$ is 100.09 g. The sample contains nearly 5 moles, or close to 500 g. The exact amount is determined as follows:

$$4.86 \text{ mol } CaCO_3 \times \frac{100.09 \text{ g } CaCO_3}{1 \text{ mol } CaCO_3} = 486 \text{ g } CaCO_3$$

To find the mass of carbonate ions (CO_3^{2-}) present in this sample, we must realize that 4.86 moles of $CaCO_3$ contains 4.86 moles of Ca^{2+} ions and 4.86 moles of CO_3^{2-} ions. The mass of 1 mole of CO_3^{2-} ions is

$$\begin{aligned}
1 \text{ C:} \quad & 1 \times 12.01 = 12.01 \text{ g} \\
3 \text{ O:} \quad & 3 \times 16.00 = \underline{48.00 \text{ g}} \\
\text{Mass of 1 mol } CO_3^{2-} = {} & 60.01 \text{ g}
\end{aligned}$$

Thus the mass of 4.86 moles of CO_3^{2-} ions is

$$4.86 \text{ mol } CO_3^{2-} \times \frac{60.01 \text{ g } CO_3^{2-}}{1 \text{ mol } CO_3^{2-}} = 292 \text{ g } CO_3^{2-}$$

Sample Exercise 3.8

Isopentyl acetate ($C_7H_{14}O_2$), the compound responsible for the scent of bananas, can be produced commercially. Interestingly, bees release about 1 μg (1×10^{-6} g) of this compound when they sting. The resulting scent attracts other bees to join the attack. How many molecules of isopentyl acetate are released in a typical bee sting? How many atoms of carbon are present?

Solution

Since we are given a mass of isopentyl acetate and want to find the number of molecules, we must first compute the molar mass:

$$7 \text{ mol C} \times 12.01 \frac{\text{g}}{\text{mol}} = 84.07 \text{ g C}$$

$$14 \text{ mol H} \times 1.008 \frac{\text{g}}{\text{mol}} = 14.11 \text{ g H}$$

$$2 \text{ mol O} \times 16.00 \frac{\text{g}}{\text{mol}} = \frac{32.00 \text{ g O}}{130.18 \text{ g}}$$

This means that 1 mole of isopentyl acetate (6.022×10^{23} molecules) has a mass of 130.18 g.

To find the number of molecules released in a sting, we must first determine the number of moles of isopentyl acetate in 1×10^{-6} g:

$$1 \times 10^{-6} \text{ g } C_7H_{14}O_2 \times \frac{1 \text{ mol } C_7H_{14}O_2}{130.18 \text{ g } C_7H_{14}O_2} = 8 \times 10^{-9} \text{ mol } C_7H_{14}O_2$$

Since 1 mole is 6.022×10^{23} units, we can determine the number of molecules:

$$8 \times 10^{-9} \text{ mol } C_7H_{14}O_2 \times \frac{6.022 \times 10^{23} \text{ molecules}}{1 \text{ mol } C_7H_{14}O_2} = 5 \times 10^{15} \text{ molecules}$$

To determine the number of carbon atoms present, we must multiply the number of molecules by 7, since each molecule of isopentyl acetate contains seven carbon atoms:

$$5 \times 10^{15} \text{ molecules} \times \frac{7 \text{ carbon atoms}}{\text{molecule}} = 4 \times 10^{16} \text{ carbon atoms}$$

NOTE:

In keeping with our practice of always showing the correct number of significant figures, we have rounded after each step. However, if extra digits are carried throughout this problem, the final answer rounds to 3×10^{16}.

To show the correct number of significant figures in each calculation, we round after each step. In your calculations always carry extra significant figures through to the end; then round.

3.4 Percent Composition of Compounds

Purpose

- To demonstrate the calculation of the mass percent of a given element in a compound.

There are two common ways of describing the composition of a compound: in terms of the numbers of its constituent atoms and in terms of the percentages (by mass) of its elements. We can obtain the mass percents of the elements from the formula of the compound by comparing the mass of each element present in 1 mole of the compound to the total mass of 1 mole of the compound.

For example, for ethanol, which has the formula C_2H_5OH, the mass of each element present and the molar mass are obtained as follows:

$$\text{Mass of C} = 2 \text{ mol} \times 12.01 \frac{\text{g}}{\text{mol}} = 24.02 \text{ g}$$

$$\text{Mass of H} = 6 \text{ mol} \times 1.008 \frac{\text{g}}{\text{mol}} = 6.048 \text{ g}$$

$$\text{Mass of O} = 1 \text{ mol} \times 16.00 \frac{\text{g}}{\text{mol}} = \underline{16.00 \text{ g}}$$

$$\text{Mass of 1 mol } C_2H_5OH = 46.07 \text{ g}$$

The **mass percent** (often called the **weight percent**) of carbon in ethanol can be computed by comparing the mass of carbon in 1 mole of ethanol to the total mass of 1 mole of ethanol and multiplying the result by 100:

$$\text{Mass percent of C} = \frac{\text{mass of C in 1 mol } C_2H_5OH}{\text{mass of 1 mol } C_2H_5OH} \times 100$$

$$= \frac{24.02 \text{ g}}{46.07 \text{ g}} \times 100 = 52.14\%$$

The mass percents of hydrogen and oxygen in ethanol are obtained in a similar manner:

$$\text{Mass percent of H} = \frac{\text{mass of H in 1 mol C}_2\text{H}_5\text{OH}}{\text{mass of 1 mol C}_2\text{H}_5\text{OH}} \times 100$$

$$= \frac{6.048 \text{ g}}{46.07 \text{ g}} \times 100 = 13.13\%$$

$$\text{Mass percent of O} = \frac{\text{mass of O in 1 mol C}_2\text{H}_5\text{OH}}{\text{mass of 1 mol C}_2\text{H}_5\text{OH}} \times 100$$

$$= \frac{16.00 \text{ g}}{46.07 \text{ g}} \times 100 = 34.73\%$$

Notice that the percentages add up to 100.00%; this provides a check that the calculations are correct.

Sample Exercise 3.9

Carvone is a substance that occurs in two forms having different arrangements of the atoms but the same molecular formula ($C_{10}H_{14}O$) and mass. One type of carvone gives caraway seeds their characteristic smell, and the other type is responsible for the smell of spearmint oil. Compute the mass percent of each element in carvone.

Solution

The masses of the elements in 1 mole of carvone are

$$\text{Mass of C in 1 mol} = 10 \text{ mol} \times 12.01\frac{\text{g}}{\text{mol}} = 120.1 \text{ g}$$

$$\text{Mass of H in 1 mol} = 14 \text{ mol} \times 1.008\frac{\text{g}}{\text{mol}} = 14.11 \text{ g}$$

$$\text{Mass of O in 1 mol} = 1 \text{ mol} \times 16.00\frac{\text{g}}{\text{mol}} = \underline{16.00 \text{ g}}$$

$$\text{Mass of 1 mol C}_{10}\text{H}_{14}\text{O} = 150.2 \text{ g}$$

Next we find the fraction of the total mass contributed by each element and convert it to a percentage:

$$\text{Mass percent of C} = \frac{120.1 \text{ g C}}{150.2 \text{ g C}_{10}\text{H}_{14}\text{O}} \times 100 = 79.96\%$$

$$\text{Mass percent of H} = \frac{14.11 \text{ g H}}{150.2 \text{ g C}_{10}\text{H}_{14}\text{O}} \times 100 = 9.394\%$$

$$\text{Mass percent of O} = \frac{16.00 \text{ g O}}{150.2 \text{ g C}_{10}\text{H}_{14}\text{O}} \times 100 = 10.65\%$$

CHECK:

Sum the individual mass percent values—they should total to 100% within round-off errors. In this case, the percentages add up to 100.00%.

Although Fleming is commonly given credit for the discovery of penicillin, there is good evidence that penicillium mold extracts were used in the nineteenth century by Lord Joseph Lister to cure infections.

Penicillin is isolated from a mold that can be grown in large quantities in fermentation tanks.

Sample Exercise 3.10

Penicillin, the first of a now large number of antibiotics (antibacterial agents), was discovered accidentally by the Scottish bacteriologist Alexander Fleming in 1928, but he was never able to isolate it as a pure compound. This and similar antibiotics have saved millions of lives that might have been lost to infections. Penicillin F has the formula $C_{14}H_{20}N_2SO_4$. Compute the mass percent of each element.

Solution

The molar mass of penicillin F is computed as follows:

$$C: \quad 14 \text{ mol} \times 12.01 \frac{g}{mol} = 168.1 \text{ g}$$

$$H: \quad 20 \text{ mol} \times 1.008 \frac{g}{mol} = 20.16 \text{ g}$$

$$N: \quad 2 \text{ mol} \times 14.01 \frac{g}{mol} = 28.02 \text{ g}$$

$$S: \quad 1 \text{ mol} \times 32.07 \frac{g}{mol} = 32.07 \text{ g}$$

$$O: \quad 4 \text{ mol} \times 16.00 \frac{g}{mol} = \underline{64.00 \text{ g}}$$

$$\text{Mass of 1 mol } C_{14}H_{20}N_2SO_4 = 312.4 \text{ g}$$

$$\text{Mass percent of C} = \frac{168.1 \text{ g C}}{312.4 \text{ g } C_{14}H_{20}N_2SO_4} \times 100 = 53.81\%$$

$$\text{Mass percent of H} = \frac{20.16 \text{ g H}}{312.4 \text{ g } C_{14}H_{20}N_2SO_4} \times 100 = 6.453\%$$

$$\text{Mass percent of N} = \frac{28.02 \text{ g N}}{312.4 \text{ g } C_{14}H_{20}N_2SO_4} \times 100 = 8.969\%$$

$$\text{Mass percent of S} = \frac{32.07 \text{ g S}}{312.4 \text{ g } C_{14}H_{20}N_2SO_4} \times 100 = 10.27\%$$

$$\text{Mass percent of O} = \frac{64.00 \text{ g O}}{312.4 \text{ g } C_{14}H_{20}N_2SO_4} \times 100 = 20.49\%$$

CHECK:

The percentages add up to 99.99%.

3.5 Determining the Formula of a Compound

Purpose

- To demonstrate the calculation of the empirical formula of a compound.
- To show how to obtain the molecular formula, given the empirical formula and the molar mass.

Furnace

CO$_2$, H$_2$O, O$_2$, and other gases

O$_2$

Sample

O$_2$ and other gases

H$_2$O absorber
such as Mg (ClO$_4$)$_2$

CO$_2$ absorber
such as NaOH

Figure 3.5

A schematic diagram of the combustion device used to analyze substances for carbon and hydrogen. The sample is burned in the presence of excess oxygen, which converts all of its carbon to carbon dioxide and all of its hydrogen to water. These products are collected by absorption using appropriate materials, and their amounts are determined by measuring the increase in masses of the absorbents.

When a new compound is prepared, one of the first items of interest is the formula of the compound. This is most often determined by taking a weighed sample of the compound and either decomposing it into its component elements or reacting it with oxygen to produce substances such as CO_2, H_2O and N_2, which are then collected and weighed. A device for doing this type of analysis is shown in Fig. 3.5. The results of such analyses provide the mass of each type of element in the compound, which can be used to determine the mass percent of each element.

We will see how information of this type can be used to compute the formula of a compound. Suppose a substance has been prepared that is composed of carbon, hydrogen, and nitrogen. When 0.1156 gram of this compound is reacted with oxygen, 0.1638 gram of carbon dioxide (CO_2) and 0.1676 gram of water (H_2O) are collected. Assuming that all the carbon in the compound is converted to CO_2, we can determine the mass of carbon originally present in the 0.1156-gram sample. To do this, we must use the fraction (by mass) of carbon in CO_2. The molar mass of CO_2 is

$$\text{C:} \quad 1 \text{ mol} \times 12.01 \frac{\text{g}}{\text{mol}} = 12.01 \text{ g}$$

$$\text{O:} \quad 2 \text{ mol} \times 16.00 \frac{\text{g}}{\text{mol}} = \underline{32.00 \text{ g}}$$

$$\text{Molar mass of } CO_2 = 44.01 \text{ g/mol}$$

The fraction of carbon present by mass is

$$\frac{\text{Mass of C}}{\text{Total mass of } CO_2} = \frac{12.01 \text{ g C}}{44.01 \text{ g } CO_2}$$

Ball-and-stick model of CO_2.

This factor can now be used to determine the mass of carbon in 0.1638 gram of CO_2:

$$0.1638 \text{ g } CO_2 \times \frac{12.01 \text{ g C}}{44.01 \text{ g } CO_2} = 0.04470 \text{ g C}$$

Remember that this carbon originally came from the 0.1156-gram sample of unknown compound. Thus the mass percent of carbon in this compound is

$$\frac{0.04470 \text{ g C}}{0.1156 \text{ g compound}} \times 100 = 38.67\% \text{ C}$$

The same procedure can be used to find the mass percent of hydrogen in the unknown compound. We assume that all the hydrogen present in the original 0.1156 gram of compound was converted to H_2O. The molar mass of H_2O is 18.02 grams, and the fraction of hydrogen by mass in H_2O is

$$\frac{\text{Mass of H}}{\text{Mass of } H_2O} = \frac{2.016 \text{ g H}}{18.02 \text{ g } H_2O}$$

Ball-and-stick model of H_2O.

Therefore, the mass of hydrogen in 0.1676 gram of H_2O is

$$0.1676 \text{ g } H_2O \times \frac{2.016 \text{ g H}}{18.02 \text{ g } H_2O} = 0.01875 \text{ g H}$$

And the mass percent of hydrogen in the compound is

$$\frac{0.01875 \text{ g H}}{0.1156 \text{ g compound}} \times 100 = 16.22\% \text{ H}$$

The unknown compound contains only carbon, hydrogen, and nitrogen. So far we have determined that it is 38.67% carbon and 16.22% hydrogen. The remainder must be nitrogen:

$$100.00\% - (\underset{\%\ C}{38.67\%} + \underset{\%\ H}{16.22\%}) = 45.11\% \text{ N}$$

We have determined that the compound contains 38.67% carbon, 16.22% hydrogen, and 45.11% nitrogen. Next we use these data to obtain the formula.

Since the formula of a compound indicates the *numbers* of atoms in the compound, we must convert the masses of the elements to numbers of atoms. The easiest way to do this is to work with 100.00 grams of the compound. In the present case, 38.67% carbon by mass means 38.67 grams of carbon per 100.00 grams of compound; 16.22% hydrogen means 16.22 grams of hydrogen per 100.00 grams of compound; and so on. To determine the formula, we must calculate the number of carbon atoms in 38.67 grams of carbon, the number of hydrogen atoms in 16.22 grams of hydrogen, and the number of nitrogen atoms in 45.11 grams of nitrogen. We can do this as follows:

$$38.67 \text{ g C} \times \frac{1 \text{ mol C}}{12.01 \text{ g C}} = 3.220 \text{ mol C}$$

$$16.22 \text{ g H} \times \frac{1 \text{ mol H}}{1.008 \text{ g H}} = 16.09 \text{ mol H}$$

$$45.11 \text{ g N} \times \frac{1 \text{ mol N}}{14.01 \text{ g N}} = 3.219 \text{ mol N}$$

Thus 100.00 grams of this compound contains 3.220 moles of carbon atoms, 16.09 moles of hydrogen atoms, and 3.219 moles of nitrogen atoms.

We can find the smallest *whole-number ratio* of atoms in this compound by dividing each of the mole values above by the smallest of the three:

$$\text{C:} \quad \frac{3.220}{3.219} = 1.000 = 1$$

$$\text{H:} \quad \frac{16.09}{3.219} = 4.998 = 5$$

$$\text{N:} \quad \frac{3.219}{3.219} = 1.000 = 1$$

Thus the formula might well be CH_5N. However, it also could be $C_2H_{10}N_2$ or $C_3H_{15}N_3$, and so on—that is, some multiple of the smallest whole-number ratio. Each of these alternatives also has the correct relative numbers of atoms. That is, any molecule that can be represented as $(CH_5N)_n$, where n is an integer, has the

$P_4 = (P)_4$

$S_8 = (S)_8$

$C_6H_{12}O_6 = (CH_2O)_6$

Figure 3.6
Examples of substances whose empirical and molecular formulas differ. Notice that molecular formula = (empirical formula)$_x$ where x is an integer.

empirical formula CH_5N. To be able to specify the exact formula of the molecule involved, the **molecular formula,** we must know the molar mass.

Suppose we know that this compound with empirical formula CH_5N has a molar mass of 31.06 g/mol. How do we determine which of the possible choices represents the molecular formula? Since the molecular formula is always a whole-number multiple of the empirical formula, we must first find the empirical formula mass for CH_5N:

Molecular formula = (empirical formula)$_n$, where n is an integer.

$$
\begin{aligned}
&\text{1 C:} \quad 1 \times 12.01 \text{ g} = 12.01 \text{ g} \\
&\text{5 H:} \quad 5 \times 1.008 \text{ g} = 5.040 \text{ g} \\
&\text{1 N:} \quad 1 \times 14.01 \text{ g} = \underline{14.01 \text{ g}} \\
&\text{Formula mass of } CH_5N = 31.06 \text{ g/mol}
\end{aligned}
$$

This is the same as the known molar mass of the compound. Thus in this case the empirical formula and the molecular formula are the same; this substance consists of molecules with the formula CH_5N. It is quite common for the empirical and molecular formulas to be different; some examples where this is the case are shown in Fig. 3.6.

Sample Exercise 3.11

Determine the empirical and molecular formulas for a compound that gives the following analysis (in mass percents):

71.65% Cl   24.27% C   4.07% H

The molar mass is known to be 98.96 g/mol.

Solution

First, we convert the mass percents to masses in grams. In 100.00 g of this compound there are 71.65 g of chlorine, 24.27 g of carbon, and 4.07 g of hydrogen. We use these masses to compute the moles of atoms present:

$$71.65 \, \cancel{g \, Cl} \times \frac{1 \text{ mol Cl}}{35.45 \, \cancel{g \, Cl}} = 2.021 \text{ mol Cl}$$

$$24.27 \, \cancel{g \, C} \times \frac{1 \text{ mol C}}{12.01 \, \cancel{g \, C}} = 2.021 \text{ mol C}$$

$$4.07 \, \cancel{g \, H} \times \frac{1 \text{ mol H}}{1.008 \, \cancel{g \, H}} = 4.04 \text{ mol H}$$

Dividing each mole value by 2.021 (the smallest number of moles present), we obtain the empirical formula $ClCH_2$.

To determine the molecular formula, we must compare the empirical formula mass to the molar mass. The empirical formula mass is 49.48 g/mol (confirm this). The molar mass is known to be 98.96 g/mol.

$$\frac{\text{Molar mass}}{\text{Empirical formula mass}} = \frac{98.96 \text{ g/mol}}{49.48 \text{ g/mol}} = 2$$

$$\text{Molecular formula} = (ClCH_2)_2 = Cl_2C_2H_4$$

This substance is composed of molecules with the formula $Cl_2C_2H_4$.

Notice that the method we employ here allows us to determine the molecular formula of a compound but not its structural formula. The compound $Cl_2C_2H_4$ is called dichloroethane. There are two forms of this compound, shown in Fig. 3.7. The form in (b) was formerly used as an additive in leaded gasoline.

Figure 3.7

The two forms of dichloroethane.

Sample Exercise 3.12

A white powder is analyzed and found to contain 43.64% phosphorus and 56.36% oxygen by mass. The compound has a molar mass of 283.88 g/mol. What are the compound's empirical and molecular formulas?

Solution

In 100.00 g of this compound there are 43.64 g of phosphorus and 56.36 g of oxygen. In terms of moles, in 100.00 g of the compound we have

$$43.64 \, \cancel{g \, P} \times \frac{1 \text{ mol P}}{30.97 \, \cancel{g \, P}} = 1.409 \text{ mol P}$$

$$56.36 \, \cancel{g \, O} \times \frac{1 \text{ mol O}}{16.00 \, \cancel{g \, O}} = 3.523 \text{ mol O}$$

Dividing both mole values by the smaller one gives

$$\frac{1.409}{1.409} = 1 \text{ P} \quad \text{and} \quad \frac{3.523}{1.409} = 2.5 \text{ O}$$

This yields the formula $PO_{2.5}$. Since compounds must contain whole numbers of atoms, the empirical formula should contain only whole numbers. To obtain the simplest set of whole numbers, we multiply both numbers by 2 to give the empirical formula P_2O_5.

To obtain the molecular formula, we must compare the empirical formula mass to the molar mass. The empirical formula mass for P_2O_5 is 141.94.

$$\frac{\text{Molar mass}}{\text{Empirical formula mass}} = \frac{283.88}{141.94} = 2$$

The molecular formula is $(P_2O_5)_2$, or P_4O_{10}.

The structural formula of this interesting compound is given in Fig. 3.8.

Figure 3.8

The structure of P_4O_{10}. Note that the oxygen atoms act as "bridges" between the phosphorus atoms. This compound has a great affinity for water and is often used as a desiccant, or drying agent.

In Sample Exercises 3.11 and 3.12 we found the molecular formula by comparing the empirical formula mass to the molar mass. There is an alternate way to obtain the molecular formula. For example, in Sample Exercise 3.11 we know the molar mass of the compound is 98.96 g/mol. This means that 1 mole of the compound weighs 98.96 grams. Since we also know the mass percentages of each element, we can compute the mass of each element present in 1 mole of compound:

Chlorine: $\dfrac{71.65 \text{ g Cl}}{100.0 \text{ g compound}} \times \dfrac{98.96 \text{ g}}{\text{mol}} = \dfrac{70.90 \text{ g Cl}}{\text{mol compound}}$

Carbon: $\dfrac{24.27 \text{ g C}}{100.0 \text{ g compound}} \times \dfrac{98.96 \text{ g}}{\text{mol}} = \dfrac{24.02 \text{ g C}}{\text{mol compound}}$

Hydrogen: $\dfrac{4.07 \text{ g H}}{100.0 \text{ g compound}} \times \dfrac{98.96 \text{ g}}{\text{mol}} = \dfrac{4.03 \text{ g H}}{\text{mol compound}}$

Now we can compute moles of atoms present per mole of compound:

Chlorine: $\dfrac{70.90 \text{ g Cl}}{\text{mol compound}} \times \dfrac{1 \text{ mol Cl}}{35.45 \text{ g Cl}} = \dfrac{2.000 \text{ mol Cl}}{\text{mol compound}}$

Carbon: $\dfrac{24.02 \text{ g C}}{\text{mol compound}} \times \dfrac{1 \text{ mol C}}{12.01 \text{ g C}} = \dfrac{2.000 \text{ mol C}}{\text{mol compound}}$

Hydrogen: $\dfrac{4.03 \text{ g H}}{\text{mol compound}} \times \dfrac{1 \text{ mol H}}{1.008 \text{ g H}} = \dfrac{4.00 \text{ mol H}}{\text{mol compound}}$

Thus 1 mole of the compound contains 2 mol Cl atoms, 2 mol C atoms, and 4 mol H atoms, and the molecular formula is $Cl_2C_2H_4$, as obtained in Sample Exercise 3.11.

Sample Exercise 3.13

Caffeine, a stimulant found in coffee, tea, and chocolate, contains 49.48% carbon, 5.15% hydrogen, 28.87% nitrogen, and 16.49% oxygen, by mass and has a molar mass of 194.2 g/mol. Determine the molecular formula of caffeine.

Solution

We will first determine the mass of each element in 1 mole (194.2 g) of caffeine:

$$\frac{49.48 \text{ g C}}{100.0 \text{ g caffeine}} \times \frac{194.2 \text{ g}}{\text{mol}} = \frac{96.09 \text{ g C}}{\text{mol caffeine}}$$

$$\frac{5.15 \text{ g H}}{100.0 \text{ g caffeine}} \times \frac{194.2 \text{ g}}{\text{mol}} = \frac{10.0 \text{ g H}}{\text{mol caffeine}}$$

$$\frac{28.87 \text{ g N}}{100.0 \text{ g caffeine}} \times \frac{194.2 \text{ g}}{\text{mol}} = \frac{56.07 \text{ g N}}{\text{mol caffeine}}$$

$$\frac{16.49 \text{ g O}}{100.0 \text{ g caffeine}} \times \frac{194.2 \text{ g}}{\text{mol}} = \frac{32.02 \text{ g O}}{\text{mol caffeine}}$$

Now we will convert to moles:

Carbon: $\dfrac{96.09 \text{ g C}}{\text{mol caffeine}} \times \dfrac{1 \text{ mol C}}{12.01 \text{ g C}} = \dfrac{8.001 \text{ mol C}}{\text{mol caffeine}}$

Hydrogen: $\dfrac{10.0 \text{ g H}}{\text{mol caffeine}} \times \dfrac{1 \text{ mol H}}{1.008 \text{ g H}} = \dfrac{9.92 \text{ mol H}}{\text{mol caffeine}}$

Nitrogen: $\dfrac{56.07 \text{ g N}}{\text{mol caffeine}} \times \dfrac{1 \text{ mol N}}{14.01 \text{ g N}} = \dfrac{4.002 \text{ mol N}}{\text{mol caffeine}}$

Oxygen: $\dfrac{32.02 \text{ g O}}{\text{mol caffeine}} \times \dfrac{1 \text{ mol O}}{16.00 \text{ g O}} = \dfrac{2.001 \text{ mol O}}{\text{mol caffeine}}$

Rounding the numbers to integers gives the molecular formula for caffeine: $C_8H_{10}N_4O_2$.

The methods for obtaining empirical and molecular formulas are summarized as follows:

Empirical Formula Determination

- Since mass percentage gives the number of grams of a particular element per 100 grams of compound, base the calculation on 100 grams of compound. Each percent will then represent the mass in grams of that element.
- Determine the number of moles of each element present in 100 grams of compound using the atomic masses of the elements present.
- Divide each value of the number of moles by the smallest of the values. If each resulting number is a whole number (after appropriate rounding), these numbers represent the subscripts of the elements in the empirical formula.
- If the numbers obtained in the previous step are not whole numbers, multiply each number by an integer so that the results are all whole numbers.

Numbers very close to whole numbers, such as 9.92 and 1.08, should be rounded to whole numbers. Numbers such as 2.25, 4.33, and 2.72 should not be rounded to whole numbers.

Molecular Formula Determination

Method One

- Obtain the empirical formula.

- Compute the mass corresponding to the empirical formula.
- Calculate the ratio

$$\frac{\text{Molar mass}}{\text{Empirical formula mass}}$$

- The integer from the previous step represents the number of empirical formula units in one molecule. When the empirical formula subscripts are multiplied by this integer, the molecular formula results. This procedure is summarized by the equation:

$$\text{Molecular formula} = (\text{empirical formula}) \times \frac{\text{molar mass}}{\text{empirical formula mass}}$$

Method Two

- Using the mass percentages and the molar mass, determine the mass of each element present in one mole of compound.
- Determine the number of moles of each element present in one mole of compound.
- The integers from the previous step represent the subscripts in the molecular formula.

3.6 *Chemical Equations*

Purpose

- To identify the characteristics of a chemical reaction and the information given by a chemical equation.

Chemical Reactions

A chemical change involves a reorganization of the atoms in one or more substances. For example, when the methane (CH_4) in natural gas combines with oxygen (O_2) in the air and burns, carbon dioxide (CO_2) and water (H_2O) are formed. This process is represented by a **chemical equation** with the **reactants** (here methane and oxygen) on the left side of an arrow and the **products** (carbon dioxide and water) on the right side:

$$\underset{\text{Reactants}}{CH_4 + O_2} \rightarrow \underset{\text{Products}}{CO_2 + H_2O}$$

Notice that the atoms have been reorganized. *Bonds have been broken, and new ones have been formed.* It is important to recognize that *in a chemical reaction, atoms are neither created nor destroyed. All atoms present in the reactants must be accounted for among the products.* In other words, there must be the same number of each type of atom on the product side and on the reactant side of the arrow. Making sure that this rule is obeyed is called **balancing a chemical equation** for a reaction.

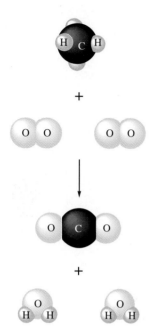

Figure 3.9

The reaction between methane and oxygen to give water and carbon dioxide. Note that no atoms have been gained or lost in the reaction. The reaction simply reorganizes the groupings of atoms.

Hydrochloric acid reacts with solid sodium hydrogen carbonate to produce gaseous carbon dioxide.

The equation (shown above) for the reaction between CH_4 and O_2 is not balanced. As we will see in the next section, the equation can be balanced to produce

$$CH_4 + 2O_2 \rightarrow CO_2 + 2H_2O$$

This reaction is shown more graphically in Fig. 3.9. We can check that the equation is balanced by comparing the number of each type of atom on both sides:

$$CH_4 + 2O_2 \rightarrow CO_2 + 2H_2O$$

1 C 4 H   1 C   4 H

4 O   2 O   2 O

To summarize our check, we have

Reactants	Products
1 C	1 C
4 H	4 H
4 O	4 O

The Meaning of a Chemical Equation

The chemical equation for a reaction gives two important types of information: the nature of the reactants and products and the relative numbers of each.

The reactants and products in a specific reaction must be identified by experiment. Besides specifying the compounds involved in the reaction, the equation often gives the **physical states** of the reactants and products:

State	Symbol
Solid	(s)
Liquid	(l)
Gas	(g)
Dissolved in water (in aqueous solution)	(aq)

For example, when hydrochloric acid in aqueous solution is added to solid sodium hydrogen carbonate, the products carbon dioxide gas, liquid water, and sodium chloride (which dissolves in the water) are formed:

$$HCl(aq) + NaHCO_3(s) \rightarrow CO_2(g) + H_2O(l) + NaCl(aq)$$

The relative numbers of reactants and products in a reaction are indicated by the **coefficients** in the balanced equation. (The coefficients can be determined because we know that the same number of each type of atom must occur on both sides of the equation.) For example, the balanced equation

$$CH_4(g) + 2O_2(g) \rightarrow CO_2(g) + 2H_2O(g)$$

can be interpreted in several equivalent ways, as shown in Table 3.2. Note that the total mass is 80 grams for both reactants and products. We expect the mass to remain constant, since chemical reactions involve only a rearrangement of atoms. Atoms, and therefore mass, are conserved in a chemical reaction.

From this discussion you can see that a balanced chemical equation gives you a great deal of information.

3.7 Balancing Chemical Equations

Purpose

• To show how to write a balanced equation to describe a chemical reaction.

An unbalanced chemical equation is of limited use. Whenever you see an equation, you should ask yourself whether or not it is balanced. The principle that lies at the heart of the balancing process is that atoms are conserved in a chemical reaction. The same number of each type of atom must be found among the reactants and products. It is also important to recognize that the identity of the reactants and products of a reaction are determined by experimental observation. For example, when liquid ethanol is burned in the presence of sufficient oxygen gas, the products are always carbon dioxide and water. When the equation for this reaction is balanced, the *identities* of the reactants and products must not be changed. *The formulas of the compounds must never be changed in balancing a chemical equation.* That is, the subscripts in a formula cannot be changed, nor can atoms be added or subtracted from a formula.

Most chemical equations can be balanced by inspection, that is, by trial and error. It is always best to start with the most complicated molecules (those containing the greatest number of atoms). For example, consider the reaction of ethanol with oxygen, given by the unbalanced equation

In balancing equations, start with the most complicated molecule.

$$C_2H_5OH(l) + O_2(g) \rightarrow CO_2(g) + H_2O(g)$$

The most complicated molecule here is C_2H_5OH. We will begin by balancing the products that contain the atoms in C_2H_5OH. Since C_2H_5OH contains two carbon atoms, we place the coefficient 2 before the CO_2 to balance the carbon atoms:

$$C_2H_5OH(l) + O_2(g) \rightarrow 2CO_2(g) + H_2O(g)$$
2 C atoms 2 C atoms

Since C_2H_5OH contains six hydrogen atoms, the hydrogen atoms can be balanced by placing a 3 before the H_2O:

$$C_2H_5OH(l) + O_2(g) \rightarrow 2CO_2(g) + 3H_2O(g)$$
$$\underset{(5\,+\,1)\ H}{} \qquad\qquad\qquad\qquad \underset{(3\,\times\,2)\ H}{}$$

Last, we balance the oxygen atoms. Note that the right side of the preceding equation contains seven oxygen atoms, whereas the left side has only three. We can correct this by putting a 3 before the O_2 to produce the balanced equation:

$$C_2H_5OH(l) + 3O_2(g) \rightarrow 2CO_2(g) + 3H_2O(g)$$
$$\underbrace{\underset{1\ O}{}\qquad\underset{6\ O}{}}_{7\ O} \qquad \underbrace{\underset{(2\,\times\,2)\ O}{}\quad\underset{3\ O}{}}_{7\ O}$$

Now we check:

$$C_2H_5OH(l) + 3O_2(g) \rightarrow 2CO_2(g) + 3H_2O(g)$$

2 C atoms	2 C atoms
6 H atoms	6 H atoms
7 O atoms	7 O atoms

The equation is balanced.

WRITING AND BALANCING THE EQUATION FOR A CHEMICAL REACTION

STEP 1
Determine what reaction is occurring. What are the reactants, the products, and the physical states involved?

STEP 2
Write the *unbalanced* equation that summarizes the reaction described in Step 1.

STEP 3
Balance the equation by inspection, starting with the most complicated molecule(s). Determine what coefficients are necessary so that the same number of each type of atom appears on both reactant and product sides. Do not change the identities (formulas) of any of the reactants or products.

Sample Exercise 3.14

Chromate and dichromate compounds are carcinogens (cancer-inducing agents) and should be handled very carefully.

Chromium compounds exhibit a variety of bright colors. When solid ammonium dichromate, $(NH_4)_2Cr_2O_7$, a vivid orange compound, is ignited, a spectacular reaction occurs, as shown in the two photographs. Although the reaction is actually somewhat more complex, let's assume here that the products are solid chromium(III) oxide, nitrogen gas (consisting of N_2 molecules), and water vapor. Balance the equation for this reaction.

Solution

STEP 1
From the description given, the reactant is solid ammonium dichromate, $(NH_4)_2Cr_2O_7(s)$, and the products are nitrogen gas, $N_2(g)$, water vapor, $H_2O(g)$, and solid chromium(III) oxide, $Cr_2O_3(s)$. The formula for chromium(III) oxide can

be determined by recognizing that the Roman numeral III means that Cr^{3+} ions are present. For a neutral compound, the formula must then be Cr_2O_3, since each oxide ion is O^{2-}.

STEP 2

The unbalanced equation is

$$(NH_4)_2Cr_2O_7(s) \rightarrow Cr_2O_3(s) + N_2(g) + H_2O(g)$$

STEP 3

Note that nitrogen and chromium are balanced (two nitrogen atoms and two chromium atoms on each side), but hydrogen and oxygen are not. A coefficient of 4 for H_2O balances the hydrogen atoms:

$$(NH_4)_2Cr_2O_7(s) \rightarrow Cr_2O_3(s) + N_2(g) + 4H_2O(g)$$
$$(4 \times 2)\ H \qquad\qquad\qquad\qquad (4 \times 2)\ H$$

Note that in balancing the hydrogen we also have balanced the oxygen, since there are seven oxygen atoms in the reactants and in the products.

CHECK:

$$2\ N,\ 8\ H,\ 2\ Cr,\ 7\ O \rightarrow 2\ N,\ 8\ H,\ 2\ Cr,\ 7\ O$$
$$\text{Reactant} \qquad\qquad\qquad \text{Product}$$
$$\text{atoms} \qquad\qquad\qquad\quad \text{atoms}$$

The equation is balanced.

Decomposition of ammonium dichromate.

Sample Exercise 3.15

Propane (C_3H_8), a liquid at 25°C under high pressure, is often used as a fuel in rural areas where there is no natural gas pipeline. When liquid propane is released from its storage tank, the pressure on it is lowered and it changes to a gas. Propane gas reacts with oxygen gas (a combustion reaction) in a furnace to produce gaseous carbon dioxide and water vapor. Balance the equation for this reaction.

Solution

The reactants are propane and oxygen; the products are carbon dioxide and water. All are in the gaseous state. Thus the unbalanced equation for the reaction is

$$C_3H_8(g) + O_2(g) \rightarrow CO_2(g) + H_2O(g)$$

We start with C_3H_8 because it is the most complicated molecule. Since C_3H_8 contains three carbon atoms per molecule, a coefficient of 3 is needed for CO_2:

$$C_3H_8(g) + O_2(g) \rightarrow 3CO_2(g) + H_2O(g)$$

Also, each C_3H_8 molecule contains eight hydrogen atoms, so a coefficient of 4 is required for H_2O:

$$C_3H_8(g) + O_2(g) \rightarrow 3CO_2(g) + 4H_2O(g)$$

The final element to be balanced is oxygen. Note that the left side of the equation

Propane burns readily in the presence of oxygen, giving this characteristic blue flame.

now has two oxygen atoms, and the right side has ten. We can balance the oxygen using a coefficient of 5 for O_2:

$$C_3H_8(g) + 5O_2(g) \rightarrow 3CO_2(g) + 4H_2O(g)$$

CHECK: 3 C, 8 H, 10 O → 3 C, 8 H, 10 O

Reactant   Product

atoms   atoms

The Ostwald process is described in Section 19.2.

Sample Exercise 3.16

At 1000°C, ammonia gas, $NH_3(g)$, reacts with oxygen gas to form gaseous nitric oxide, $NO(g)$, and water vapor. This reaction is the first step in the commercial production of nitric acid by the Ostwald process. Balance the equation for this reaction.

Solution

The unbalanced equation for the reaction is

$$NH_3(g) + O_2(g) \rightarrow NO(g) + H_2O(g)$$

Because all the molecules in this equation are of about equal complexity, where we start in balancing it is rather arbitrary. Let's begin by balancing the hydrogen. A coefficient of 2 for NH_3 and a coefficient of 3 for H_2O give six atoms of hydrogen on both sides:

$$2NH_3(g) + O_2(g) \rightarrow NO(g) + 3H_2O(g)$$

The nitrogen can be balanced with a coefficient of 2 for NO:

$$2NH_3(g) + O_2(g) \rightarrow 2NO(g) + 3H_2O(g)$$

Finally, note that there are two atoms of oxygen on the left and five on the right. The oxygen can be balanced with a coefficient of $\frac{5}{2}$ for O_2:

$$2NH_3(g) + \frac{5}{2}O_2(g) \rightarrow 2NO(g) + 3H_2O(g)$$

However, the usual custom is to have whole-number coefficients. We simply multiply the entire equation by 2.

$$4NH_3(g) + 5O_2(g) \rightarrow 4NO(g) + 6H_2O(g)$$

CHECK:

There are 4 N, 12 H, and 10 O on both sides, so the equation is balanced.

3.8 Stoichiometric Calculations: Amounts of Reactants and Products

Purpose

• To show how to calculate the masses of reactants and products using the chemical equation.

◀ **CHEMICAL IMPACT** ▶

Sulfuric Acid: The Most Important Chemical

More sulfuric acid (H_2SO_4) is produced in the world than any other chemical. About 45 million tons (4.5×10^{10} kilograms) is manufactured annually in the United States. Sulfuric acid is used in the production of fertilizers, explosives, petroleum products, detergents, dyes, insecticides, drugs, plastics, steel, storage batteries, and many other materials. The largest amount of sulfuric acid is used in the production of phosphate fertilizers. In this process, calcium phosphate, $Ca_3(PO_4)_2$, in phosphate rock, which cannot be used by plants because of its insolubility in ground water, is converted to forms that will dissolve in water, thus making the phosphate available to plants. This reaction can be represented as

$$Ca_3(PO_4)_2(s) + 3H_2SO_4(aq) \rightarrow$$
$$3CaSO_4(s) + 2H_3PO_4(aq)$$

The resulting mixture of $CaSO_4$ and H_3PO_4 (phosphoric acid) is dried, pulverized, and spread on fields, where the phosphate is dissolved by rainfall.

Sulfuric acid is produced by a sequence of three simple reactions.

1. The combustion of sulfur to form sulfur dioxide:

$$S(s) + O_2(g) \rightarrow SO_2(g)$$

2. The conversion of sulfur dioxide to sulfur trioxide:

$$2SO_2(g) + O_2(g) \rightarrow 2SO_3(g)$$

3. The combination of sulfur trioxide with water:

$$SO_3(g) + H_2O(l) \rightarrow H_2SO_4(aq)$$

More than 90% of sulfuric acid is produced commercially by the **contact process.** This name was coined because the sulfur dioxide and oxygen molecules react in *contact* with the surface of solid vanadium(V) oxide (V_2O_5).

Because gaseous sulfur trioxide reacts so violently with water, it is absorbed during the production process by a sulfuric acid solution rather than by pure water. The sulfur trioxide is added to a flowing solution of sulfuric acid to which water is constantly added to keep the concentration at 98% sulfuric acid by mass. This is the substance sold as *concentrated sulfuric acid.*

One remarkable property of sulfuric acid is its great affinity for water. For example, when it is mixed with sugar, it dehydrates the sugar (takes the water out) and forms a column of black carbon (see Fig. 3.10). Because of this high affinity for water, sulfuric acid is often used as a drying agent in the production of explosives, dyes, detergents, and various anhydrous (water-free) materials.

The violence with which sulfuric acid and water combine makes the dilution of concentrated sulfuric acid potentially hazardous. The addition of water to the con-

Figure 3.10

Sulfuric acid is a powerful dehydrating (water-removing) agent. For example, sulfuric acid reacts with table sugar to produce a column of carbon.

centrated acid produces a vigorous reaction, which often causes acid droplets to spew in all directions. For obvious reasons, this must be avoided. *Always add the acid to water when diluting* so that any accidental splattering will involve dilute acid rather than concentrated acid.

As we have seen in previous sections of this chapter, the coefficients in chemical equations represent *numbers* of molecules, not masses of molecules. However, when a reaction is to be run in a laboratory or chemical plant, the amounts of substances needed cannot be determined by counting molecules directly. Counting is always done by weighing. In this section we will see how chemical equations can be used to determine the *masses* of reacting chemicals.

To develop the principles for dealing with the stoichiometry of reactions, we will again consider the reaction of propane with oxygen to produce carbon dioxide and water (see Sample Exercise 3.15). We will consider the question: "What mass of oxygen will react with 96.1 grams of propane?" In doing stoichiometry, the first thing we must do is *write the balanced chemical equation* for the reaction. In this

Before doing any calculations involving a chemical reaction, be sure the equation for the reaction is balanced.

case the balanced equation is

$$C_3H_8(g) + 5O_2(g) \rightarrow 3CO_2(g) + 4H_2O(g)$$

This equation means that 1 mole of C_3H_8 reacts with 5 moles of O_2 to produce 3 moles of CO_2 and 4 moles of H_2O. To use this equation to find the masses of reactants and products, we must be able to convert between masses and moles of substances. Thus we must first ask: *"How many moles of propane are present in 96.1 grams of propane?"* The molar mass of propane to three significant figures is 44.1 (that is, $3 \times 12.01 + 8 \times 1.008$). The moles of propane can be calculated as follows:

$$96.1 \text{ g } C_3H_8 \times \frac{1 \text{ mol } C_3H_8}{44.1 \text{ g } C_3H_8} = 2.18 \text{ mol } C_3H_8$$

Next we must take into account the fact that each mole of propane reacts with 5 moles of oxygen. The best way to do this is to use the balanced equation to construct a **mole ratio.** In this case we want to convert from moles of propane to moles of oxygen. From the balanced equation we see that 5 moles of O_2 is required for each mole of C_3H_8, so the appropriate ratio is

$$\frac{5 \text{ mol } O_2}{1 \text{ mol } C_3H_8}$$

Multiplying the number of moles of C_3H_8 by this factor gives the number of moles of O_2 required:

$$2.18 \text{ mol } C_3H_8 \times \frac{5 \text{ mol } O_2}{1 \text{ mol } C_3H_8} = 10.9 \text{ mol } O_2$$

Notice that the mole ratio is set up so that the moles of C_3H_8 cancel out, and the units that result are moles of O_2.

Since the original question asked for the mass of oxygen needed to react with 96.1 grams of propane, the 10.9 moles of O_2 must be converted to *grams*. Since the molar mass of O_2 is 32.0 g/mol,

$$10.9 \text{ mol } O_2 \times \frac{32.0 \text{ g } O_2}{1 \text{ mol } O_2} = 349 \text{ g } O_2$$

Therefore, 349 grams of oxygen is required to burn 96.1 grams of propane.

This example can be extended by asking: "What mass of carbon dioxide is produced when 96.1 grams of propane is combusted with oxygen?" In this case we must convert between moles of propane and moles of carbon dioxide. This can be accomplished by looking at the balanced equation, which shows that 3 moles of CO_2 is produced for each mole of C_3H_8 reacted. The mole ratio needed to convert from moles of propane to moles of carbon dioxide is

$$\frac{3 \text{ mol } CO_2}{1 \text{ mol } C_3H_8}$$

The conversion is

$$2.18 \text{ mol } C_3H_8 \times \frac{3 \text{ mol } CO_2}{1 \text{ mol } C_3H_8} = 6.54 \text{ mol } CO_2$$

Then, using the molar mass of CO_2 (44.0 g/mol), we calculate the mass of CO_2 produced:

$$6.54 \; \text{mol CO}_2 \times \frac{44.0 \text{ g CO}_2}{1 \text{ mol CO}_2} = 288 \text{ g CO}_2$$

We will now summarize the sequence of steps needed to carry out stoichiometric calculations.

96.1 g C_3H_8 $\dfrac{1 \text{ mol } C_3H_8}{44.1 \text{ g } C_3H_8}$ ⟩ 2.18 mol C_3H_8 $\dfrac{3 \text{ mol } CO_2}{1 \text{ mol } C_3H_8}$ ⟩ 6.54 mol CO_2

$\dfrac{44.0 \text{ g } CO_2}{1 \text{ mol } CO_2}$ ⟩ 288 g CO_2

THE STEPS FOR CALCULATING MASSES OF REACTANTS AND PRODUCTS IN CHEMICAL REACTIONS

STEP 1
Balance the equation for the reaction.

STEP 2
Convert the known mass of the reactant or product to moles of that substance.

STEP 3
Use the balanced equation to set up the appropriate mole ratios.

STEP 4
Use the appropriate mole ratios to calculate the number of moles of the desired reactant or product.

STEP 5
Convert from moles back to grams if required by the problem.

Sample Exercise 3.17

Solid lithium hydroxide is used in space vehicles to remove exhaled carbon dioxide from the living environment by forming solid lithium carbonate and liquid water. What mass of gaseous carbon dioxide can be absorbed by 1.00 kg of lithium hydroxide?

Solution

STEP 1
Using the description of the reaction, we can write the unbalanced equation:

$$LiOH(s) + CO_2(g) \rightarrow Li_2CO_3(s) + H_2O(l)$$

The balanced equation is

$$2LiOH(s) + CO_2(g) \rightarrow Li_2CO_3(s) + H_2O(l)$$

In the space shuttle, exhaled carbon dioxide is removed from the air by using lithium hydroxide. In this photo, an astronaut opens the stowage area for lithium hydroxide canisters in the space shuttle Columbia. Note that two canisters are floating about.

STEP 2

We convert the given mass of LiOH to moles, using the molar mass of LiOH $(6.941 + 16.00 + 1.008 = 23.95$ g/mol):

$$1.00 \text{ kg LiOH} \times \frac{1000 \text{ g LiOH}}{1 \text{ kg LiOH}} \times \frac{1 \text{ mol LiOH}}{23.95 \text{ g LiOH}} = 41.8 \text{ mol LiOH}$$

STEP 3

Since we want to determine the amount of CO_2 that reacts with the given amount of LiOH, the appropriate mole ratio is

$$\frac{1 \text{ mol } CO_2}{2 \text{ mol LiOH}}$$

STEP 4

We calculate the moles of CO_2 needed to react with the given mass of LiOH using this mole ratio:

$$41.8 \text{ mol LiOH} \times \frac{1 \text{ mol } CO_2}{2 \text{ mol LiOH}} = 20.9 \text{ mol } CO_2$$

STEP 5

Next we calculate the mass of CO_2, using its molar mass (44.0 g/mol):

$$20.9 \text{ mol } CO_2 \times \frac{44.0 \text{ g } CO_2}{1 \text{ mol } CO_2} = 9.20 \times 10^2 \text{ g } CO_2$$

Thus 920. g of $CO_2(g)$ will be absorbed by 1.00 kg of LiOH(s).

Sample Exercise 3.18

Baking soda ($NaHCO_3$) is often used as an antacid. It neutralizes excess hydrochloric acid secreted by the stomach:

$$NaHCO_3(s) + HCl(aq) \rightarrow NaCl(aq) + H_2O(l) + CO_2(aq)$$

Milk of magnesia, which is an aqueous suspension of magnesium hydroxide, is also used as an antacid:

$$Mg(OH)_2(s) + 2HCl(aq) \rightarrow 2H_2O(l) + MgCl_2(aq)$$

Which is the more effective antacid per gram, $NaHCO_3$ or $Mg(OH)_2$?

Solution

To answer the question, we must determine the amount of HCl neutralized per gram of $NaHCO_3$ and per gram of $Mg(OH)_2$. Using the molar mass of $NaHCO_3$ (84.01 g/mol), we can determine the moles of $NaHCO_3$ in 1.00 g of $NaHCO_3$:

$$1.00 \text{ g } NaHCO_3 \times \frac{1 \text{ mol } NaHCO_3}{84.01 \text{ g } NaHCO_3} = 1.19 \times 10^{-2} \text{ mol } NaHCO_3$$

Antacids contain bases for neutralizing excess stomach acid.

Next we determine the moles of HCl using the mole ratio 1 mol HCl/1 mol $NaHCO_3$:

$$1.19 \times 10^{-2} \text{ mol NaHCO}_3 \times \frac{1 \text{ mol HCl}}{1 \text{ mol NaHCO}_3} = 1.19 \times 10^{-2} \text{ mol HCl}$$

Thus 1.00 g of $NaHCO_3$ will neutralize 1.19×10^{-2} mol HCl.

Using the molar mass of $Mg(OH)_2$ (58.32 g/mol), we determine the moles of $Mg(OH)_2$ in 1.00 g:

$$1.00 \text{ g Mg(OH)}_2 \times \frac{1 \text{ mol Mg(OH)}_2}{58.32 \text{ g Mg(OH)}_2} = 1.71 \times 10^{-2} \text{ mol Mg(OH)}_2$$

To determine the moles of HCl that will react with this amount of $Mg(OH)_2$, we use the mole ratio 2 mol HCl/1 mol $Mg(OH)_2$:

$$1.71 \times 10^{-2} \text{ mol Mg(OH)}_2 \times \frac{2 \text{ mol HCl}}{1 \text{ mol Mg(OH)}_2} = 3.42 \times 10^{-2} \text{ mol HCl}$$

Thus 1.00 g of $Mg(OH)_2$ will neutralize 3.42×10^{-2} mol HCl. It is a better antacid per gram than $NaHCO_3$.

3.9 Calculations Involving a Limiting Reactant

Purpose

- To show how to recognize the limiting reactant.
- To demonstrate the use of the limiting reactant in stoichiometric calculations.

When chemicals are mixed together to undergo a reaction, they are often mixed in **stoichiometric quantities,** that is, in exactly the correct amounts so that all reactants "run out" (are used up) at the same time. To clarify this concept, let's consider the production of hydrogen for use in the manufacture of ammonia by the **Haber process.** Ammonia, a very important fertilizer itself and a starting material for other fertilizers, is made by combining nitrogen (from the air) with hydrogen according to the equation:

The details of the Haber process are discussed in Section 19.2.

$$N_2(g) + 3H_2(g) \rightarrow 2NH_3(g)$$

The hydrogen is produced from the reaction of methane with water vapor:

$$CH_4(g) + H_2O(g) \rightarrow 3H_2(g) + CO(g)$$

What mass of water is required to react *exactly* with 2.50×10^3 kilograms of methane? That is, how much water will just consume all the 2.50×10^3 kilograms of methane, leaving no methane or water remaining? Using the principles developed in the last section, we can calculate that if 2.50×10^3 kilograms of methane is mixed with 2.81×10^3 kilograms of water, both reactants will "run out" at the same time. The reactants have been mixed in stoichiometric quantities.

If, on the other hand, 2.50×10^3 kilograms of methane is mixed with 3.00×10^3 kilograms of water, the methane will be consumed before the water runs out.

The water will be in *excess*. In this case the quantity of products formed will be determined by the quantity of methane present. Once the methane is consumed, no more products can be formed, even though some water still remains. In this situation the amount of methane *limits* the amount of products that can be formed. This brings us to the concept of the **limiting reactant** (or **limiting reagent**), which is the reactant that is consumed first and which therefore limits the amounts of products that can be formed. In any stoichiometry calculation involving a chemical reaction, it is essential to determine which reactant is limiting in order to calculate correctly the amounts of products that will be formed.

Suppose 25.0 kilograms of nitrogen and 5.00 kilograms of hydrogen are mixed and reacted to form ammonia. How do we calculate the mass of ammonia produced when this reaction is run to completion (until one of the reactants is completely consumed).

To solve this problem, we must use the balanced equation

$$N_2(g) + 3H_2(g) \rightarrow 2NH_3(g)$$

to determine whether nitrogen or hydrogen is the limiting reactant and then to determine the amount of ammonia that is formed. We first calculate the moles of reactants present:

$$25.0 \text{ kg N}_2 \times \frac{1000 \text{ g N}_2}{1 \text{ kg N}_2} \times \frac{1 \text{ mol N}_2}{28.0 \text{ g N}_2} = 8.93 \times 10^2 \text{ mol N}_2$$

$$5.00 \text{ kg H}_2 \times \frac{1000 \text{ g H}_2}{1 \text{ kg H}_2} \times \frac{1 \text{ mol H}_2}{2.016 \text{ g H}_2} = 2.48 \times 10^3 \text{ mol H}_2$$

Since 1 mol N_2 reacts with 3 mol H_2, the number of moles of H_2 that will react exactly with 8.93×10^2 mol N_2 is

$$8.93 \times 10^2 \text{ mol N}_2 \times \frac{3 \text{ mol H}_2}{1 \text{ mol N}_2} = 2.68 \times 10^3 \text{ mol H}_2$$

Thus 8.93×10^2 mol N_2 requires 2.68×10^3 mol H_2 to react completely. However, in this case, only 2.48×10^3 mol H_2 is present. This means that the hydrogen will be consumed before the nitrogen. Thus hydrogen is the *limiting reactant* in this particular situation, and we must use the amount of hydrogen to compute the quantity of ammonia formed:

Always determine which reactant is limiting.

$$2.48 \times 10^3 \text{ mol H}_2 \times \frac{2 \text{ mol NH}_3}{3 \text{ mol H}_2} = 1.65 \times 10^3 \text{ mol NH}_3$$

Converting moles to kilograms gives

$$1.65 \times 10^3 \text{ mol NH}_3 \times \frac{17.0 \text{ g NH}_3}{1 \text{ mol NH}_3} = 2.80 \times 10^4 \text{ g NH}_3 = 28.0 \text{ kg NH}_3$$

Note that to determine the limiting reactant, we could have started instead with the given amount of hydrogen and calculated the moles of nitrogen required:

$$2.48 \times 10^3 \text{ mol H}_2 \times \frac{1 \text{ mol N}_2}{3 \text{ mol H}_2} = 8.27 \times 10^2 \text{ mol N}_2$$

Thus 2.48×10^3 mol H_2 requires 8.27×10^2 mol N_2. Since 8.93×10^2 mol N_2 is actually present, the nitrogen is in excess. The hydrogen will run out first, and thus again we find that hydrogen limits the amount of ammonia formed.

A related, but simpler way to determine which reactant is limiting is to compare the mole ratio of the substances required by the balanced equation to the mole ratio of reactants actually present. For example, in this case the mole ratio of H_2 to N_2 required by the balanced equation is

$$\frac{3 \text{ mol } H_2}{1 \text{ mol } N_2}$$

That is, $\qquad \dfrac{\text{mol } H_2}{\text{mol } N_2} \text{ (required)} = \dfrac{3}{1} = 3$

In this experiment, we have 2.48×10^3 mol H_2 and 8.93×10^2 mol N_2. Thus the ratio

$$\frac{\text{mol } H_2}{\text{mol } N_2} \text{ (actual)} = \frac{2.48 \times 10^3}{8.93 \times 10^2} = 2.78$$

Since 2.78 is less than 3, the actual mole ratio of H_2 to N_2 is too small, and H_2 must be limiting. If the actual H_2 to N_2 mole ratio had been greater than 3, then the H_2 would have been in excess and the N_2 would be limiting.

Sample Exercise 3.19

Nitrogen gas can be prepared by passing gaseous ammonia over solid copper(II) oxide at high temperatures. The other products of the reaction are solid copper and water vapor. If a sample containing 18.1 g of NH_3 is reacted with 90.4 g of CuO, which is the limiting reactant? How many grams of N_2 will be formed?

Solution

From the description of the problem, we can obtain the following balanced equation:

$$2NH_3(g) + 3CuO(s) \rightarrow N_2(g) + 3Cu(s) + 3H_2O(g)$$

Next, we must compute the moles of NH_3 (molar mass = 17.03 g/mol) and of CuO (molar mass = 79.55 g/mol):

$$18.1 \text{ g } NH_3 \times \frac{1 \text{ mol } NH_3}{17.03 \text{ g } NH_3} = 1.06 \text{ mol } NH_3$$

$$90.4 \text{ g } CuO \times \frac{1 \text{ mol } CuO}{79.55 \text{ g } CuO} = 1.14 \text{ mol } CuO$$

To determine the limiting reactant, we use the mole ratio for CuO and NH_3:

$$1.06 \text{ mol } NH_3 \times \frac{3 \text{ mol } CuO}{2 \text{ mol } NH_3} = 1.59 \text{ mol } CuO$$

Thus 1.59 mol CuO is required to react with 1.06 mol NH_3. Since only 1.14 mol CuO is actually present, the amount of CuO is limiting; CuO will run out before

NH_3 does. We can verify this conclusion by comparing the mole ratio of CuO and NH_3 required by the balanced equation

$$\frac{\text{mol CuO}}{\text{mol NH}_3} \text{ (required)} = \frac{3}{2} = 1.5$$

to the mole ratio actually present

$$\frac{\text{mol CuO}}{\text{mol NH}_3} \text{ (actual)} = \frac{1.14}{1.06} = 1.08$$

Since the actual ratio is too small (smaller than 1.5), CuO is the limiting reactant.

Because CuO is the limiting reactant, we must use the amount of CuO to calculate the amount of N_2 formed. From the balanced equation, the mole ratio between CuO and N_2 is

$$\frac{1 \text{ mol N}_2}{3 \text{ mol CuO}}$$

$$1.14 \text{ mol CuO} \times \frac{1 \text{ mol N}_2}{3 \text{ mol CuO}} = 0.380 \text{ mol N}_2$$

Using the molar mass of N_2 (28.0 g/mol), we can calculate the mass of N_2 produced:

$$0.380 \text{ mol N}_2 \times \frac{28.0 \text{ g N}_2}{1 \text{ mol N}_2} = 10.6 \text{ g N}_2$$

The amount of a product formed when the limiting reactant is completely consumed is called the **theoretical yield** of that product. In Sample Exercise 3.19, 10.6 grams of nitrogen represents the theoretical yield. This is the *maximum amount* of nitrogen that can be produced from the quantities of reactants used. Actually, the amount of product predicted by the theoretical yield is seldom obtained because of side reactions (other reactions that involve one or more of the reactants or products) and other complications. The **actual yield** of product is often given as a percentage of the theoretical yield. This is called the **percent yield:**

$$\frac{\text{Actual yield}}{\text{Theoretical yield}} \times 100 = \text{percent yield}$$

For example, if the reaction considered in Sample Exercise 3.19 actually gave 6.63 grams of nitrogen instead of the predicted 10.6 grams, the percent yield of nitrogen would be

$$\frac{6.63 \text{ g N}_2}{10.6 \text{ g N}_2} \times 100 = 62.5\%$$

Percent yield is important as an indicator of the efficiency of a particular laboratory or industrial reaction.

Methanol is used as a fuel in Indianapolis-type racing cars.

Sample Exercise 3.20

Methanol (CH_3OH), also called methyl alcohol, is the simplest alcohol. It is used as a fuel in race cars and is a potential replacement for gasoline. Methanol can be manufactured by combination of gaseous carbon monoxide and hydrogen. Suppose 68.5 kg CO(g) is reacted with 8.60 kg H_2(g). Calculate the theoretical yield of methanol. If 3.57×10^4 g CH_3OH is actually produced, what is the percent yield of methanol?

Solution

First, we must find out which reactant is limiting. The balanced equation is

$$2H_2(g) + CO(g) \rightarrow CH_3OH(l)$$

Next, we must calculate the moles of reactants:

$$68.5 \ \text{kg CO} \times \frac{1000 \ \text{g CO}}{1 \ \text{kg CO}} \times \frac{1 \ \text{mol CO}}{28.02 \ \text{g CO}} = 2.44 \times 10^3 \ \text{mol CO}$$

$$8.60 \ \text{kg H}_2 \times \frac{1000 \ \text{g H}_2}{1 \ \text{kg H}_2} \times \frac{1 \ \text{mol H}_2}{2.016 \ \text{g H}_2} = 4.27 \times 10^3 \ \text{mol H}_2$$

To determine which reactant is limiting, we compare the mole ratio of H_2 and CO required by the balanced equation

$$\frac{\text{mol H}_2}{\text{mol CO}} \ (\text{required}) = \frac{2}{1} = 2$$

to the actual mole ratio

$$\frac{\text{mol H}_2}{\text{mol CO}} \ (\text{actual}) = \frac{4.27 \times 10^3}{2.44 \times 10^3} = 1.75$$

Since the actual mole ratio of H_2 to CO is smaller than the required ratio, *H_2 is limiting*. We therefore must use the amount of H_2 and the mole ratio between H_2 and CH_3OH to determine the maximum amount of methanol that can be produced:

$$4.27 \times 10^3 \ \text{mol H}_2 \times \frac{1 \ \text{mol CH}_3\text{OH}}{2 \ \text{mol H}_2} = 2.14 \times 10^3 \ \text{mol CH}_3\text{OH}$$

Using the molar mass of CH_3OH (32.04 g/mol), we can calculate the theoretical yield in grams:

$$2.14 \times 10^3 \ \text{mol CH}_3\text{OH} \times \frac{32.04 \ \text{g CH}_3\text{OH}}{1 \ \text{mol CH}_3\text{OH}} = 6.86 \times 10^4 \ \text{g CH}_3\text{OH}$$

Thus, from the amounts of reactants given, the maximum amount of CH_3OH that can be formed is 6.86×10^4 g. This is the *theoretical yield*.

The percent yield is

$$\frac{\text{Actual yield (grams)}}{\text{Theoretical yield (grams)}} \times 100 = \frac{3.57 \times 10^4 \ \text{g CH}_3\text{OH}}{6.86 \times 10^4 \ \text{g CH}_3\text{OH}} \times 100 = 52.0\%$$

STEPS FOR SOLVING A STOICHIOMETRY PROBLEM INVOLVING MASSES OF REACTANTS AND PRODUCTS

STEP 1
Write and balance the equation for the reaction.

STEP 2
Convert the known masses of substances to moles.

STEP 3

Determine which reactant is limiting.

STEP 4

Using the amount of the limiting reactant and the appropriate mole ratios, compute the number of moles of the desired product.

STEP 5

Convert from moles to grams, using the molar mass.

Sample Exercise 3.21

Potassium chromate, a bright yellow solid, is produced by the reaction of solid chromite ore ($FeCr_2O_4$) with solid potassium carbonate and gaseous oxygen at high temperatures. The other products of the reaction are solid iron(III) oxide and gaseous carbon dioxide. In a particular experiment, 169 kg chromite ore, 298 kg potassium carbonate, and 75.0 kg oxygen were sealed in a reaction vessel and reacted at a high temperature. The amount of potassium chromate obtained was 194 kg. Calculate the percent yield of potassium chromate.

Solution

STEP 1

The unbalanced equation, which can be written from the preceding description of the reaction, is

$$FeCr_2O_4(s) + K_2CO_3(s) + O_2(g) \rightarrow K_2CrO_4(s) + Fe_2O_3(s) + CO_2(g)$$

The balanced equation is

$$4FeCr_2O_4(s) + 8K_2CO_3(s) + 7O_2(g) \rightarrow 8K_2CrO_4(s) + 2Fe_2O_3(s) + 8CO_2(g)$$

STEP 2

The numbers of moles of the various reactants are

$$169 \text{ kg FeCr}_2O_4 \times \frac{1000 \text{ g FeCr}_2O_4}{1 \text{ kg FeCr}_2O_4} \times \frac{1 \text{ mol FeCr}_2O_4}{223.84 \text{ g FeCr}_2O_4}$$
$$= 7.55 \times 10^2 \text{ mol FeCr}_2O_4$$

$$298 \text{ kg K}_2CO_3 \times \frac{1000 \text{ g K}_2CO_3}{1 \text{ kg K}_2CO_3} \times \frac{1 \text{ mol K}_2CO_3}{138.21 \text{ g K}_2CO_3}$$
$$= 2.16 \times 10^3 \text{ mol K}_2CO_3$$

$$75.0 \text{ kg O}_2 \times \frac{1000 \text{ g O}_2}{1 \text{ kg O}_2} \times \frac{1 \text{ mol O}_2}{32.00 \text{ g O}_2} = 2.34 \times 10^3 \text{ mol O}_2$$

STEP 3

Now we must determine which of the three reactants is limiting. To do this, we will compare the mole ratios of reactants required by the balanced equation to the actual mole ratios. For the reactants K_2CO_3 and $FeCr_2O_4$ the required mole ratio is

$$\frac{\text{mol K}_2CO_3}{\text{mol FeCr}_2O_4} \text{ (required)} = \frac{8}{4} = 2$$

Chromite ore shown with metallic chromium.

whereas the actual mole ratio is

$$\frac{\text{mol } K_2CO_3}{\text{mol } FeCr_2O_4} \text{ (actual)} = \frac{2.16 \times 10^3}{7.55 \times 10^2} = 2.86$$

Since the actual mole ratio is greater than that required, the K_2CO_3 is in excess compared to $FeCr_2O_4$. Thus either $FeCr_2O_4$ or O_2 must be limiting. To determine which of these will limit the amounts of products, we compare the required mole ratio

$$\frac{\text{mol } O_2}{\text{mol } FeCr_2O_4} \text{ (required)} = \frac{7}{4} = 1.75$$

to the actual mole ratio

$$\frac{\text{mol } O_2}{\text{mol } FeCr_2O_4} \text{ (actual)} = \frac{2.34 \times 10^3}{7.55 \times 10^2} = 3.10$$

Since the actual mole ratio of O_2 to $FeCr_2O_4$ exceeds what is required, the O_2 is in excess of the $FeCr_2O_4$. Thus $FeCr_2O_4$ is the limiting reagent. Since this is the first case we have considered that involves three reactants, we will verify this conclusion by calculating the amounts (in moles) of K_2CO_3 and O_2 required by the amount of $FeCr_2O_4$ present:

$$7.55 \times 10^2 \text{ mol } FeCr_2O_4 \times \frac{8 \text{ mol } K_2CO_3}{4 \text{ mol } FeCr_2O_4} = 1.51 \times 10^3 \text{ mol } K_2CO_3 \text{ required}$$

Compare to 2.16×10^3 mol K_2CO_3 present

$$7.55 \times 10^2 \text{ mol } FeCr_2O_4 \times \frac{7 \text{ mol } O_2}{4 \text{ mol } FeCr_2O_4} = 1.32 \times 10^3 \text{ mol } O_2 \text{ required}$$

Compare to 2.34×10^3 mol O_2 present

STEP 4

Thus more K_2CO_3 and O_2 are present than required. These reactants are in excess, so $FeCr_2O_4$ is the limiting reactant. We must use the amount of $FeCr_2O_4$ to calculate the maximum amount of K_2CrO_4 that can be formed:

$$7.55 \times 10^2 \text{ mol } FeCr_2O_4 \times \frac{8 \text{ mol } K_2CrO_4}{4 \text{ mol } FeCr_2O_4} = 1.51 \times 10^3 \text{ mol } K_2CrO_4$$

STEP 5

Using the molar mass of K_2CrO_4, we can determine the mass:

$$1.51 \times 10^3 \text{ mol } K_2CrO_4 \times \frac{194.19 \text{ g } K_2CrO_4}{1 \text{ mol } K_2CrO_4} = 2.93 \times 10^5 \text{ g } K_2CrO_4$$

This mass represents the theoretical yield of K_2CrO_4. The actual yield was 194 kg, or 1.94×10^5 g. Thus the percent yield is

$$\frac{1.94 \times 10^5 \text{ g } K_2CrO_4}{2.93 \times 10^5 \text{ g } K_2CrO_4} \times 100 = 66.2\%$$

FOR REVIEW

Summary

Stoichiometry deals with the quantities of materials consumed and produced in chemical reactions. It is, in effect, chemical arithmetic. The average atomic mass for each element is obtained by computing the average of the masses of the naturally occurring isotopes. All atomic masses are based on a mass scale that assigns exactly 12 atomic mass units to a ^{12}C atom.

A mole is a unit of measure equal to the number of carbon atoms in exactly 12 grams of pure ^{12}C. This number has been determined experimentally to be 6.02214×10^{23}, which is called Avogadro's number. One mole of any substance contains Avogadro's number of units. One mole of an element has a mass equal to the element's atomic mass in grams.

The molar mass (molecular weight) of a compound is the mass in grams of one mole of the compound and is computed by summing the average masses of its constituent atoms.

Percent composition represents the mass percent of each element in a compound:

$$\text{Mass percent} = \frac{\text{mass of element in 1 mole of substance}}{\text{mass of 1 mole of substance}} \times 100$$

The empirical formula is the simplest whole-number ratio of the various types of atoms in a compound and can be derived from the percent composition of the compound. The molecular formula is the exact formula of a molecule of a substance and is always an integer multiple of the empirical formula.

In a chemical reaction, atoms are neither created nor destroyed; they are merely reorganized. All atoms present in the reactants must be accounted for among the products. A chemical equation represents the chemical reaction showing reactants on the left side of an arrow and products on the right. A balanced equation gives the relative numbers of reactant and product molecules.

Amounts of reactants consumed and products formed can be calculated from the balanced equation for a reaction by using the mole ratios relating the reactants and products. The limiting reactant (reagent) is the one that is consumed first and thus determines how much product can be formed.

The theoretical yield of a product is the maximum amount that can be produced from a given amount of the limiting reactant. The actual yield, the amount of product actually obtained in a given experiment, is always less than the theoretical yield. The actual yield is usually represented as a percent yield: the percentage of the theoretical yield actually obtained.

Key Terms

chemical stoichiometry

Section 3.1
mass spectrometer
average atomic mass

Section 3.2
mole
Avogadro's number

Section 3.3
molar mass

Section 3.5
empirical formula
molecular formula

Section 3.6
chemical equation

reactants
products
balancing a chemical equation

Section 3.8
mole ratio

Section 3.9
stoichiometric quantities

Haber process
limiting reactant
theoretical yield
percent yield

A blue question or exercise number indicates that the answer to that question or exercise appears at the back of the book and a solution appears in the Solutions Guide.

Questions

1. The atomic mass of boron (B) is given in the periodic table as 10.81, yet no single atom of boron has a mass of 10.81 amu. Explain.

2. The listed atomic mass of chromium is 52.00 amu. Does this mean that chromium can have only a single isotope with mass 52.00 amu? Explain.

3. What is the difference between the empirical and molecular formulas of a compound? Can they ever be the same? Explain.

4. Why is the actual yield of a reaction often less than the theoretical yield?

Exercises

In this section similar exercises are paired.

Atomic Masses and the Mass Spectrometer

5. The element magnesium (Mg) has three stable isotopes with the following masses and abundances:

Isotope	Mass (amu)	Abundance
^{24}Mg	23.9850	78.99%
^{25}Mg	24.9858	10.00%
^{26}Mg	25.9826	11.01%

Calculate the average atomic mass (the atomic weight) of magnesium from these data.

6. Assume that element Uus is synthesized and that it has the following stable isotopes:

^{284}Uus (283.4 amu)   34.60%
^{285}Uus (284.7 amu)   21.20%
^{288}Uus (287.8 amu)   44.20%

What is the value of the average atomic mass for Uus that would be listed on the periodic table?

7. The element europium exists in nature as two isotopes: ^{151}Eu has a mass of 150.9196 amu, and ^{153}Eu has a mass of 152.9209 amu. The average atomic mass of europium is 151.96 amu. Calculate the relative abundance of the two europium isotopes.

8. The element silver (Ag) has two naturally occurring isotopes: ^{109}Ag and ^{107}Ag with a mass of 106.905 amu. Silver consists of 51.82% ^{107}Ag and has an average atomic mass of 107.868 amu. Calculate the mass of ^{109}Ag.

9. The mass spectrum of bromine (Br_2) consists of three peaks with the following characteristics:

Mass (amu)	Relative size
157.84	0.2534
159.84	0.5000
161.84	0.2466

How do you interpret these data?

10. Naturally occurring tellurium (Te) has the following isotopic abundances:

Isotope	Abundance	Mass (amu)
^{120}Te	0.09%	119.90
^{122}Te	2.46%	121.90
^{123}Te	0.87%	122.90
^{124}Te	4.61%	123.90
^{125}Te	6.99%	124.90
^{126}Te	18.71%	125.90
^{128}Te	31.79%	127.90
^{130}Te	34.48%	129.91

Draw the mass spectrum of H_2Te, assuming that the only hydrogen isotope present is ^{1}H (mass 1.008).

11. Only one isotope of this element occurs in nature. One atom of this isotope has a mass of 9.123×10^{-23} g. Identify the element and give its atomic mass.

12. An element consists of 90.51% of an isotope with a mass of 19.992 amu, 0.27% of an isotope with a mass of 20.994 amu, and 9.22% of an isotope with a mass of 21.990 amu. Calculate the average atomic mass and identify the element.

Moles and Molar Masses

13. Calculate the number of moles of each element present in 1.0 mol of each of the following substances:
    a. NH_3
    b. N_2H_4
    c. $(NH_4)_2Cr_2O_7$

14. Give the number of moles of each element present in 1.0 mol of each of the following:
    a. $CoCl_2 \cdot 6H_2O$ (the $\cdot 6H_2O$ indicates 6 water molecules)
    b. $Ca_3(PO_4)_2$
    c. Na_2HPO_4

15. How many atoms of each element are present in 1.0 mol of each of the substances in Exercise 13?

16. How many atoms of each element are present in 1.0 mol of each of the substances in Exercise 14?

17. How many grams of each element are present in 1.0 mol of each of the substances in Exercise 13?

18. How many grams of each element are present in 1.0 mol of each of the substances in Exercise 14?

19. How many moles of each element are present in 1.0 g of each of the substances in Exercise 13?

20. How many moles of each element are present in 1.0 g of each of the substances in Exercise 14?

21. How many atoms of each element are present in 1.0 g of each of the substances in Exercise 13?

22. How many atoms of each element are present in 1.0 g of each of the substances in Exercise 14?

23. Aluminum metal is produced by passing an electric current through a solution of aluminum oxide (Al_2O_3) dissolved in molten cryolite (Na_3AlF_6). Calculate the molar masses of Al_2O_3 and Na_3AlF_6.

24. The Freons are a class of compounds containing carbon, chlorine, and fluorine. While they have many valuable uses, they have been shown to be responsible for depletion of the ozone in the upper atmosphere. In 1991 two replacement compounds for the Freons have gone into production: HFC-134a (CH_2FCF_3) and HCFC-124 ($CHClFCF_3$). Calculate the molar masses of these two compounds.

25. Ascorbic acid, or vitamin C ($C_6H_8O_6$), is an essential vitamin. It cannot be stored by the body and must be present in the diet. What is the molar mass of ascorbic acid? Vitamin C tablets are often taken as a dietary supplement. If a typical tablet contains 500.0 mg of vitamin C, how many moles and how many molecules of vitamin C does it contain?

26. The molecular formula of acetylsalicylic acid (aspirin), one of the most commonly used pain relievers, is $C_9H_8O_4$.
    a. Calculate the molar mass of aspirin.
    b. A typical aspirin tablet contains 500. mg of $C_9H_8O_4$. How many moles of $C_9H_8O_4$ molecules and how many molecules of acetylsalicylic acid are in a 500.-mg tablet?

27. How many moles are represented by each of these samples?
    a. 100 molecules (exactly) of H_2O
    b. 100.0 g H_2O
    c. 500 atoms (exactly) of Fe
    d. 500.0 g Fe
    e. 150 molecules (exactly) of O_2

28. How many moles are represented by each of these samples?
    a. 150.0 g Fe_2O_3
    b. 10.0 mg NO_2
    c. 1.0 femtomoles of NO_2
    d. 1.5×10^{16} molecules of BF_3
    e. 2.6 mg BF_3

29. Determine the mass in grams of the following:
    a. 3.00×10^{20} N_2 molecules
    b. 3.00×10^{-3} mol N_2
    c. 1.5×10^2 mol N_2
    d. A single N_2 molecule
    e. 2.00×10^{-15} mol N_2
    f. 18.0 picomoles of N_2
    g. 5.0 nanomoles of N_2

30. How many atoms of carbon are present in 1.0 g of each of the following?
    a. CH_4O
    b. CH_3CO_2H
    c. Na_2CO_3
    d. $C_6H_{12}O_6$
    e. $C_{12}H_{22}O_{11}$
    f. $CHCl_3$

31. Aspartame is an artificial sweetener that is 160 times sweeter than sucrose (table sugar) when dissolved in water. It is marketed as Nutra-Sweet. The molecular formula of aspartame is $C_{14}H_{18}N_2O_5$.
    a. Calculate the molar mass of aspartame.
    b. How many moles of molecules are present in 10.0 g aspartame?
    c. Calculate the mass in grams of 1.56 mol aspartame?
    d. How many molecules are in 5.0 mg aspartame?
    e. How many atoms of nitrogen are in 1.2 g aspartame?
    f. What is the mass in grams of 1.0×10^9 molecules of aspartame?
    g. What is the mass in grams of one molecule of aspartame?

32. Dimethylnitrosamine, $(CH_3)_2N_2O$, is a carcinogenic (cancer-causing) substance that may be formed in foods, beverages, or gastric juices from the reaction of nitrite ion (used as a food preservative) with other substances.
    a. What is the molar mass of dimethylnitrosamine?
    b. How many moles of $(CH_3)_2N_2O$ molecules are present in 250 mg dimethylnitrosamine?
    c. What is the mass of 0.050 mol dimethylnitrosamine?
    d. How many atoms of hydrogen are in 1.0 mol dimethylnitrosamine?
    e. What is the mass of 1.0×10^6 molecules of dimethylnitrosamine?
    f. What is the mass in grams of one molecule of dimethylnitrosamine?

Percent Composition

33. Calculate the percent composition by mass of the substances listed in Exercise 15 in Chapter 2.

34. Calculate the percent composition by mass of the substances in Exercise 16 in Chapter 2.

35. In 1987 the first substance to act as a superconductor at a temperature above that of liquid nitrogen (77 K) was discovered. The approximate formula of this substance is $YBa_2Cu_3O_7$. Calculate the percent composition by mass of this material.

36. There are several important compounds that contain only nitrogen and oxygen. Calculate the mass percent of nitrogen in each of the following:
    a. NO, a gas formed by the reaction of N_2 with O_2 in internal combustion engines
    b. NO_2, a brown gas mainly responsible for the brownish color of photochemical smog
    c. N_2O_4, a colorless liquid used as a fuel in space shuttles
    d. N_2O, a colorless gas sometimes used as an anesthetic by dentists (known as laughing gas)

37. Arrange the following substances in order of the increasing percent of phosphorus.
    a. Na_3PO_4 c. P_4O_{10}
    b. PH_3 d. $(NPCl_2)_3$

38. Arrange the substances in Exercise 36 in order of the increasing percent of nitrogen.

39. Vitamin B_{12}, cyanocobalamin, is essential for human nutrition. It is concentrated in animal tissue but not in higher plants. Although nutritional requirements for the vitamin are quite low, people who abstain completely from animal products may develop a deficiency anemia. Cyanocobalamin is the form used in vitamin supplements. It contains 4.34% cobalt by mass. Calculate the molar mass of cyanocobalamin, assuming that there is one atom of cobalt in every molecule of cyanocobalamin.

40. Hemoglobin is the protein that transports oxygen in mammals. Hemoglobin is 0.342% Fe by mass, and each hemoglobin molecule contains four iron atoms. Calculate the molar mass of hemoglobin.

41. Photocells utilize a semiconducting material that produces an electric current or a change in resistance on exposure to light. Compounds of cadmium (Cd) combined with an element from Group 6A of the periodic table are used in many common photocells. Calculate the mass percent of Cd in CdS, CdSe, and CdTe.

42. The first binary compounds containing a noble gas element were prepared at the Argonne National Laboratories near Chicago in 1962. The first compound prepared was XeF_4. Two other xenon fluorides, XeF_2 and XeF_6, are also known. Calculate the mass percent of fluorine in each of these three compounds.

43. Calculate the percent composition by mass of the following compounds that are important starting materials for synthetic polymers:
    a. $C_3H_4O_2$ (acrylic acid, from which acrylic plastics are made)
    b. $C_4H_6O_2$ (methyl acrylate, from which Plexiglas is made)
    c. C_3H_3N (acrylonitrile, from which Orlon is made)

44. Calculate the percent composition of the elements by mass for aluminum oxide, cryolite, HFC-134a, and HCFC-124 (compounds mentioned in Exercises 23 and 24).

Empirical and Molecular Formulas

45. Calculate the empirical formula for each of the substances listed in Exercise 15 in Chapter 2.

46. Calculate the empirical formula for each of the substances listed in Exercise 16 in Chapter 2.

47. Determine the molecular formulas to which the following empirical formulas and molar masses pertain:
    a. SNH (188.35 g/mol)   c. CoC_4O_4 (341.94 g/mol)
    b. $NPCl_2$ (347.64 g/mol) d. SN (184.32 g/mol)

48. Give the empirical formula for each of the following compounds (for which the common names are given):
    a. Vitamin C, $C_6H_8O_6$ d. Phosphorus pentoxide, P_4O_{10}
    b. Benzene, C_6H_6 e. Glucose, $C_6H_{12}O_6$
    c. Acetylene, C_2H_2 f. Acetic acid, $HC_2H_3O_2$

49. Express the composition of each of the following compounds as the mass percents of its elements:
    a. Formaldehyde, CH_2O
    b. Glucose, $C_6H_{12}O_6$
    c. Acetic acid, $HC_2H_3O_2$

50. Considering your answer to Exercise 49, which type of formula, empirical or molecular, can be obtained from elemental analysis that gives percent composition?

51. A compound that contains only carbon, hydrogen, and oxygen is 48.38% C and 8.12% H by mass. What is the empirical formula of this substance?

52. A compound containing only sulfur and nitrogen is 69.6% S by mass; the molar mass is 184 g/mol. What are the empirical and molecular formulas of the compound?

53. The active ingredient in photographic fixer solution contains sodium, sulfur, and oxygen. Analysis of a sample shows that the sample contains 0.979 g Na, 1.365 g S, and 1.021 g O. What is the empirical formula of this substance?

54. A sample of urea contains 1.121 g N, 0.161 g H, 0.480 g C, and 0.640 g O. What is the empirical formula of urea?

55. A compound that contains only nitrogen and oxygen is 30.4% N by mass; the molar mass of the compound is 92 g/mol. What is the empirical formula of the compound? What is the molecular formula of the compound?

56. One of the most commonly used white pigments in paint is a compound of titanium and oxygen that contains 59.9% Ti by mass. Calculate the empirical formula of this compound.

57. A compound contains only carbon, hydrogen, nitrogen, and oxygen. Combustion of 0.157 g of the compound produced 0.213 g CO_2 and 0.0310 g H_2O. In another experiment, it is found that 0.103 g of the compound produces 0.0230 g NH_3. What is the empirical formula of the compound? *Hint:* Combustion involves reacting with excess O_2. Assume that all the carbon ends up in CO_2 and all the hydrogen ends up in H_2O. Also assume that all the nitrogen ends up in the NH_3 in the second experiment.

58. A compound contains only carbon, hydrogen, and oxygen. Combustion of 10.68 mg of the compound yields 16.01 mg CO_2 and 4.37 mg H_2O. The molar mass of the compound is 176.1 g/mol. What are the empirical and molecular formulas of the compound?

Balancing Chemical Equations

59. Balance the equations for the following reactions that occur during steel production in a blast furnace:
a. $Fe_2O_3 + CO \rightarrow Fe_3O_4 + CO_2$
b. $Fe_3O_4 + CO \rightarrow FeO + CO_2$

60. Balance the following equations:
a. $Ca(OH)_2(aq) + H_3PO_4(aq) \rightarrow H_2O(l) + Ca_3(PO_4)_2(s)$
b. $Al(OH)_3(s) + HCl(aq) \rightarrow AlCl_3(aq) + H_2O(l)$
c. $AgNO_3(aq) + H_2SO_4(aq) \rightarrow Ag_2SO_4(s) + HNO_3(aq)$

61. Balance the following equations representing combustion reactions:
a. $C_{12}H_{22}O_{11}(s) + O_2(g) \rightarrow CO_2(g) + H_2O(g)$
b. $C_6H_6(l) + O_2(g) \rightarrow CO_2(g) + H_2O(g)$
c. $Fe(s) + O_2(g) \rightarrow Fe_2O_3(s)$
d. $C_4H_{10}(g) + O_2(g) \rightarrow CO_2(g) + H_2O(g)$
e. $FeO(s) + O_2(g) \rightarrow Fe_2O_3(s)$

62. Balance the following equations:
a. $Cr(s) + S_8(s) \rightarrow Cr_2S_3(s)$
b. $NaHCO_3(s) \xrightarrow{\text{Heat}} Na_2CO_3(s) + CO_2(g) + H_2O(g)$
c. $KClO_3(s) \xrightarrow{\text{Heat}} KCl(s) + O_2(g)$
d. $Eu(s) + HF(g) \rightarrow EuF_3(s) + H_2(g)$

63. Balance the following equations:
a. $Cu(s) + AgNO_3(aq) \rightarrow Ag(s) + Cu(NO_3)_2(aq)$
b. $Zn(s) + HCl(aq) \rightarrow ZnCl_2(aq) + H_2(g)$
c. $Au_2S_3(s) + H_2(g) \rightarrow Au(s) + H_2S(g)$
d. $Ca(s) + H_2O(l) \rightarrow Ca(OH)_2(aq) + H_2(g)$

64. Give the balanced equation for each of the following chemical reactions;
a. $HNO_3(l) + P_4O_{10}(s) \rightarrow (HPO_3)_3(l) + N_2O_5(g)$
b. Solid iron(III) sulfide reacts with gaseous hydrogen chloride to form solid iron(III) chloride and hydrogen sulfide gas.
c. Carbon disulfide liquid reacts with ammonia gas to produce hydrogen sulfide gas and solid ammonium thiocyanate (NH_4SCN).

65. Silicon is produced for the chemical and electronics industries by the following reactions. Give the balanced equation for each reaction.
a. $SiO_2(s) + C(s) \xrightarrow[\text{arc furnace}]{\text{Electric}} Si(s) + CO(g)$
b. Silicon tetrachloride is reacted with very pure magnesium, producing silicon and magnesium chloride.
c. $Na_2SiF_6(s) + Na(s) \rightarrow Si(s) + NaF(s)$

66. Phosphorus occurs naturally in the form of fluorapatite, $CaF_2 \cdot 3Ca_3(PO_4)_2$, the dot indicating 1 part CaF_2 to 3 parts $Ca_3(PO_4)_2$. This mineral is reacted with an aqueous solution of sulfuric acid in the preparation of a fertilizer. The products are phosphoric acid, hydrogen fluoride, and gypsum, $CaSO_4 \cdot 2H_2O$. Write and balance the chemical equation describing this process.

67. Lead hydrogen arsenate, an inorganic insecticide still used against the potato beetle, is a product in the following reaction:

$Pb(NO_3)_2(aq) + H_3AsO_4(aq) \rightarrow PbHAsO_4(s) + HNO_3(aq)$

Balance this equation.

68. The electrolysis of concentrated brine solutions is an important source of NaOH, H_2, and Cl_2 for the chemical industry. The reaction is

$NaCl(aq) + H_2O(l)$

$\xrightarrow{\text{Electricity}} Cl_2(g) + H_2(g) + NaOH(aq)$

Balance this equation.

Reaction Stoichiometry

69. Calculate the masses of Cr_2O_3, N_2, and H_2O produced from 10.8 g $(NH_4)_2Cr_2O_7$ in an ammonium dichromate volcano reaction as described in Sample Exercise 3.14.

70. Over the years, the thermite reaction has been used for welding railroad rails, in incendiary bombs, and to ignite solid-fuel rocket motors. The reaction is

$$Fe_2O_3(s) + 2Al(s) \rightarrow 2Fe(l) + Al_2O_3(s)$$

What masses of iron(III) oxide and aluminum must be used to produce 15.0 g iron? What is the maximum mass of aluminum oxide that could be produced?

71. The reusable booster rockets of the U.S. space shuttle employ a mixture of aluminum and ammonium perchlorate for fuel. A possible equation for this reaction is

$$3Al(s) + 3NH_4ClO_4(s)$$
$$\rightarrow Al_2O_3(s) + AlCl_3(s) + 3NO(g) + 6H_2O(g)$$

What mass of NH_4ClO_4 should be used in the fuel mixture for every kilogram of Al?

72. Nitric acid is produced commercially by the Ostwald process, represented by the following equations:

$$4NH_3(g) + 5O_2(g) \rightarrow 4NO(g) + 6H_2O(g)$$
$$2NO(g) + O_2(g) \rightarrow 2NO_2(g)$$
$$3NO_2(g) + H_2O(l) \rightarrow 2HNO_3(aq) + NO(g)$$

What mass of NH_3 must be used to produce 1.0×10^6 kg HNO_3 by the Ostwald process, assuming 100% yield in each reaction?

73. One of the major commercial uses of sulfuric acid is the production of phosphoric acid and calcium sulfate. The reaction is

$$Ca_3(PO_4)_2(s) + 3H_2SO_4(aq) \rightarrow 3CaSO_4(s) + 2H_3PO_4(aq)$$

What mass of concentrated sulfuric acid (98% H_2SO_4 by mass) must be used to react completely with 1.0×10^2 g $Ca_3(PO_4)_2$?

74. One of relatively few reactions that takes place directly between two solids at room temperature is

$$Ba(OH)_2 \cdot 8H_2O(s) + NH_4SCN(s)$$
$$\rightarrow Ba(SCN)_2(s) + H_2O(l) + NH_3(g)$$

In this equation, the $\cdot 8H_2O$ in $Ba(OH)_2 \cdot 8H_2O$ indicates the presence of eight water molecules. This compound is called barium hydroxide octahydrate.
a. Balance the equation.
b. What mass of ammonium thiocyanate (NH_4SCN) must be used if it is to react completely with 6.5 g barium hydroxide octahydrate?
c. What masses of the three products would be produced in the reaction of part b?

75. Elixirs such as Alka-Seltzer use the reaction of sodium bicarbonate with citric acid in aqueous solution to produce a fizz:

$$3NaHCO_3(aq) + C_6H_8O_7(aq)$$
$$\rightarrow 3CO_2(g) + 3H_2O(l) + Na_3C_6H_5O_7(aq)$$

a. What mass of $C_6H_8O_7$ should be used for every 1.0×10^2 mg $NaHCO_3$?
b. What mass of $CO_2(g)$ could be produced from such a mixture?

76. Aspirin ($C_9H_8O_4$) is synthesized by reacting salicylic acid ($C_7H_6O_3$) with acetic anhydride ($C_4H_6O_3$). The balanced equation is

$$C_7H_6O_3 + C_4H_6O_3 \rightarrow C_9H_8O_4 + HC_2H_3O_2$$

a. What mass of acetic anhydride is needed to completely consume 1.00×10^2 g salicylic acid?
b. What is the maximum mass of aspirin (the theoretical yield) that could be produced in this reaction?

Limiting Reactants and Percent Yield

77. Consider the reaction

$$Mg(s) + I_2(s) \rightarrow MgI_2(s)$$

Identify the limiting reagent in each of the reaction mixtures below:
a. 100 atoms of Mg and 100 molecules of I_2
b. 150 atoms of Mg and 100 molecules of I_2
c. 200 atoms of Mg and 300 molecules of I_2
d. 0.16 mol Mg and 0.25 mol I_2
e. 0.14 mol Mg and 0.14 mol I_2
f. 0.12 mol Mg and 0.08 mol I_2
g. 6.078 g Mg and 63.455 g I_2
h. 1.00 g Mg and 2.00 g I_2
i. 1.00 g Mg and 20.00 g I_2

78. Consider the reaction

$$2H_2(g) + O_2(g) \rightarrow 2H_2O(g)$$

Identify the limiting reagent in each of the reaction mixtures given below:
a. 50 molecules of H_2 and 25 molecules of O_2
b. 100 molecules of H_2 and 40 molecules of O_2
c. 100 molecules of H_2 and 100 molecules of O_2
d. 0.50 mol H_2 and 0.75 mol O_2
e. 0.80 mol H_2 and 0.75 mol O_2
f. 1.0 g H_2 and 0.25 mol O_2
g. 5.00 g H_2 and 56.00 g O_2

79. When copper is heated with an excess of sulfur, copper(I) sulfide is formed. In a given experiment, 1.50 g copper was heated with excess sulfur to yield 1.76 g copper(I) sulfide. What is the theoretical yield? What was the percent yield?

80. Aluminum burns in bromine, producing aluminum bromide:

$$2Al(s) + 3Br_2(l) \rightarrow 2AlBr_3(s)$$

In a certain experiment, 6.0 g aluminum was reacted with an excess of bromine to yield 50.3 g aluminum bromide. Calculate the theoretical and percent yields for this experiment.

81. When a mixture of silver metal and sulfur is heated, silver sulfide is formed:

$$16Ag(s) + S_8(s) \xrightarrow{\text{Heat}} 8Ag_2S(s)$$

a. What mass of Ag_2S is produced from a mixture of 2.0 g Ag and 2.0 g S_8?
b. What mass of which reactant is left unreacted?

82. Ammonia is produced from the reaction of nitrogen and hydrogen according to the following balanced equation:

$$N_2(g) + 3H_2(g) \rightarrow 2NH_3(g)$$

a. What is the maximum mass of ammonia that can be produced from a mixture of 1.00×10^3 g N_2 and 5.00×10^2 g H_2?
b. What mass of which starting material would remain unreacted?

83. Anthraquinone ($C_{14}H_8O_2$), an important intermediate in the dye industry, is produced from the reaction of benzene (C_6H_6) with phthalic anhydride ($C_8H_4O_3$), followed by dehydration with sulfuric acid. The overall reaction is

$$C_8H_4O_3(s) + C_6H_6(l) \rightarrow C_{14}H_8O_2(s) + H_2O(l)$$

a. What mass of benzene reacts completely with 2.00×10^3 g phthalic anhydride?
b. What masses of anthraquinone and of water are produced assuming 100% yield?
c. If 1.96×10^3 g anthraquinone is actually obtained, what is the percent yield of the reaction?

84. A student prepared aspirin in a laboratory experiment using the reaction in Exercise 76. The student reacted 1.50 g salicylic acid with 2.00 g acetic anhydride. The yield was 1.50 g aspirin. Calculate the theoretical yield and the percent yield for this experiment.

Additional Exercises

85. Calculate the molar mass for each of the following substances:
a. $Cu(H_2O)_6Cl_2$
b. $NaBrO_3$
c. $(C_2F_4)_{500}$ (the polymer Teflon), which is made of the unit

$$\begin{array}{cc} \text{F} & \text{F} \\ | & | \\ -\text{C}-\text{C}- \\ | & | \\ \text{F} & \text{F} \end{array}$$

d. H_3PO_4
e. $CaCO_3$

86. Chloral hydrate ($C_2H_3Cl_3O_2$) is a drug formerly used as a sedative and hypnotic. It is the compound used to make ''Mickey Finns'' in detective stories.
a. Calculate the molar mass of chloral hydrate.
b. How many moles of $C_2H_3Cl_3O_2$ molecules are in 500.0 g chloral hydrate?
c. What is the mass in grams of 2.0×10^{-2} mol chloral hydrate?
d. How many chlorine atoms are in 5.0 g chloral hydrate?

e. What mass of chloral hydrate would contain 1.0 g Cl?
f. What is the mass of exactly 500 molecules of chloral hydrate?

87. Automobile safety glass is made by laminating a sheet of polyvinylbutyral between two thin sheets of glass. Polyvinylbutyral has the general formula (the fragment shown is called a monomer unit)

$$\begin{array}{c} \left[\begin{array}{c} -\text{CHCH}_2\text{CHCH}_2- \\ | \qquad | \\ \text{O} \qquad \text{O} \\ \diagdown \quad \diagup \\ \text{CH} \\ | \\ \text{CH}_2\text{CH}_2\text{CH}_3 \end{array} \right]_n \end{array}$$

If the average molar mass of a sample of polyvinylbutyral is 100,000 g/mol, what is the average number of monomer units present in the molecule?

88. Write a balanced equation that describes each of the following reactions:
a. Pure indium metal reacts with oxygen gas to form solid indium(III) oxide.

b. The fermentation of fruit juice to produce wine involves the conversion of glucose ($C_6H_{12}O_6$) to ethanol (C_2H_6O) and carbon dioxide (CO_2).

c. Potassium metal reacts with water to produce aqueous potassium hydroxide and hydrogen gas.

d. Barium oxide reacts with nitric acid to produce barium nitrate and water.

89. a. Write the balanced equation for the combustion of isooctane (C_8H_{18}) to produce water vapor and carbon dioxide gas.

b. Assuming gasoline is 100.% isooctane, with a density of 0.692 g/mL, what is the theoretical yield of carbon dioxide produced by the combustion of 1.2×10^{10} gal gasoline (the approximate annual consumption of gasoline in the United States)?

90. A confiscated white substance, suspected of being cocaine, was purified by a forensic chemist and subjected to elemental analysis. Combustion of a 50.86-mg sample yielded 150.0 mg CO_2 and 46.05 mg H_2O. Analysis for nitrogen showed that the compound contained 9.39% N by mass. The formula of cocaine is $C_{17}H_{21}NO_4$. Can the forensic chemist conclude that the suspected compound is cocaine?

91. Cumene is a compound containing only carbon and hydrogen that is used in the production of acetone and phenol in the chemical industry. Combustion of 47.6 mg cumene produces 156.8 mg CO_2 and 42.8 mg water. The molar mass of cumene is between 115 and 125 g/mol. Determine the empirical and molecular formulas.

92. Indium oxide contains 4.784 g indium for every gram of oxygen. In 1869 when Mendeleev first presented his version of the periodic table, he proposed that the formula of indium oxide was In_2O_3. Before that time it was thought that the formula was InO. What values for the atomic mass of indium are obtained assuming these two formulas?

93. A compound composed of only antimony and oxygen is 83.53% Sb by mass. The molar mass is between 550 and 600 g/mol. Calculate the empirical and molecular formulas of the compound.

94. Commercial brass, an alloy of Zn and Cu, reacts with hydrochloric acid as follows:

$$Zn(s) + 2HCl(aq) \rightarrow ZnCl_2(aq) + H_2(g)$$

(Cu does not react with HCl.) When 0.5065 g of a certain brass alloy is reacted with excess HCl, 0.0985g $ZnCl_2$ is eventually isolated.

a. What is the composition of the brass by mass?

b. How could this result be checked without changing the above procedure?

95. Terephthalic acid is an important chemical used in the manufacture of polyesters and plasticizers. It contains only C, H, and O. Combustion of 19.81 mg terephthalic acid produces 41.98 mg CO_2 and 6.45 mg H_2O. The molar mass of terephthalic acid is 166 g/mol. Calculate the empirical and molecular formulas for terephthalic acid.

96. The compound cisplatin, $Pt(NH_3)_2Cl_2$, is widely used as an antitumor agent.

a. Calculate the elemental percent composition by mass for cisplatin.

b. Cisplatin is synthesized as follows:

$$K_2PtCl_4(aq) + 2NH_3(aq) \rightarrow Pt(NH_3)_2Cl_2(s) + 2KCl(aq)$$

What mass of cisplatin can be made from 65 g K_2PtCl_4 and sufficient NH_3? What mass of KCl is also produced?

97. Consider the reaction

$$4Al(s) + 3O_2(g) \rightarrow 2Al_2O_3(s)$$

Identify the limiting reagent in each of the following reaction mixtures:

a. 1.0 mol Al and 1.0 mol O_2

b. 2.0 mol Al and 4.0 mol O_2

c. 0.50 mol Al and 0.75 mol O_2

d. 64.75 g Al and 115.21 g O_2

e. 75.89 g Al and 112.25 g O_2

f. 51.28 g Al and 118.22 g O_2

98. Bromine (Br_2) is produced by reacting seawater with chlorine (Cl_2).

$$2Br^-(aq) + Cl_2(aq) \rightarrow Br_2(aq) + 2Cl^-(aq)$$

What mass of Cl_2 is needed to produce 1.0 kg Br_2?

99. Calcium oxide, or lime, is produced by the thermal decomposition of limestone:

$$CaCO_3(s) \xrightarrow{\text{Heat}} CaO(s) + CO_2(g)$$

What mass of CaO can be produced from 2.00×10^3 kg limestone?

100. Consider the following unbalanced equation:

$$Ca_3(PO_4)_2(s) + H_2SO_4(aq) \rightarrow CaSO_4(s) + H_3PO_4(aq)$$

What masses of calcium sulfate and phosphoric acid can be produced from the reaction of 1.0 kg calcium phosphate with 1.0 kg concentrated sulfuric acid (98% H_2SO_4 by mass)?

101. Impure nickel can be purified by first forming the compound $Ni(CO)_4$, which is then decomposed by heating to yield very pure nickel. Metallic nickel reacts directly with gaseous carbon monoxide as follows:

$$Ni(s) + 4CO(g) \rightarrow Ni(CO)_4(g)$$

Other metals present do not react. If 94.2 g of a metal mixture produces 98.4 g $Ni(CO)_4$, what is the mass percent of nickel in the original sample?

102. Mercury and bromine will react with each other to produce mercury(II) bromide:

$$Hg(l) + Br_2(l) \rightarrow HgBr_2(s)$$

a. What mass of $HgBr_2$ can be produced from the reaction of 10.0 g Hg and 9.00 g Br_2? What mass of which reagent is left unreacted?

b. What mass of $HgBr_2$ can be produced from the reaction of 5.00 mL mercury (density = 13.5 g/mL) and 5.00 mL bromine (density = 3.2 g/mL)?

103. Hexamethylenediamine ($C_6H_{16}N_2$) is one of the starting materials for the production of nylon. It can be prepared from adipic acid ($C_6H_{10}O_4$) by the following overall reaction:

$$C_6H_{10}O_4(l) + 2NH_3(g) + 4H_2(g) \rightarrow C_6H_{16}N_2(l) + 4H_2O(l)$$

a. What mass of hexamethylenediamine can be produced from 1.00×10^3 g adipic acid?

b. What is the percent yield if 765 g hexamethylenediamine is made from 1.00×10^3 g adipic acid?

Challenge Problems

104. In the spring of 1984 concern arose over the presence of ethylene dibromide, or EDB, in grains and cereals. EDB has the molecular formula $C_2H_4Br_2$ and until 1984 was commonly used a plant fumigant. The federal limit for EDB in finished cereal products is 30.0 parts per billion (ppb), where 1.0 ppb = 10^{-9} g EDB for every 1.0 g sample. How many molecules of EDB are in 1.0 lb flour if 30.0 ppb EDB is present?

105. When aluminum metal is heated with an element from Group 6A of the periodic table, an ionic compound forms. When the experiment is performed with an unknown Group 6A element, the product is 18.56% Al by mass. What is the formula of the compound?

106. A salt contains only barium and one of the halide ions. A 0.158-g sample of the salt was dissolved in water, and an excess of sulfuric acid was added to form barium sulfate ($BaSO_4$), which was filtered, dried, and weighed. Its mass was found to be 0.124 g. What is the formula of the barium halide?

107. Hydrogen cyanide is produced industrially from the reaction of gaseous ammonia, oxygen, and methane:

$$2NH_3(g) + 3O_2(g) + 2CH_4(g) \rightarrow 2HCN(g) + 6H_2O(g)$$

If 5.00×10^3 kg each of NH_3, O_2, and CH_4 are reacted, what mass of HCN and of H_2O would be produced, assuming 100% yield?

108. The production capacity for acrylonitrile (C_3H_3N) in the United States is over 2 billion pounds per year. Acrylonitrile, the building block for polyacrylonitrile fibers and a variety of plastics, is produced from gaseous propylene, ammonia, and oxygen:

$$2C_3H_6(g) + 2NH_3(g) + 3O_2(g) \rightarrow 2C_3H_3N(g) + 6H_2O(g)$$

a. Assuming 100% yield, what mass of acrylonitrile can be produced from a mixture of 5.00×10^2 g propylene, 5.00×10^2 g ammonia, and 1.00×10^3 g oxygen?

b. What mass of water is produced, and what masses of which starting materials are left in excess?

109. An element X forms both a dichloride (XCl_2) and a tetrachloride (XCl_4). Treatment of 10.00 g XCl_2 with excess chlorine forms 12.55 g XCl_4. Calculate the atomic mass of X, and identify X.

110. Lanthanum was reacted with hydrogen in a given experiment to produce the nonstoichiometric compound $LaH_{2.90}$. Assuming that the compound contains H^-, La^{2+}, and La^{3+}, calculate the fraction of La^{2+} and La^{3+} present.

111. A 1.500-g sample of a mixture containing only Cu_2O and CuO was treated with hydrogen to produce 1.252 g pure copper metal. Calculate the percentage composition (by mass) of the mixture.

Marathon Problem*

112. From the information below, determine the mass of substance C that will be formed if 45.0 grams of substance A reacts with 23.0 grams of substance B. (Assume that the reaction between A and B goes to completion.)

a. Substance A is a gray solid that consists of an alkaline earth metal and carbon (37.5% by mass). It reacts with substance B to produce substances C and D. Forty million trillion formula units of A have a mass of 4.26 milligrams.

b. 47.9 grams of substance B contains 5.36 grams of hydrogen and 42.5 grams of oxygen.

c. When 10.0 grams of C is burned in excess oxygen, 33.8 grams of carbon dioxide and 6.92 grams of water are produced. A mass spectrum of substance C shows a parent molecular ion with a mass-to-charge ratio of 26.

d. Substance D is the hydroxide of the metal in substance A.

*This Marathon Problem was developed by James H. Burness of Penn State University, York Campus.

CHAPTER 4

Types of Chemical Reactions and Solution Stoichiometry

CONTENTS

M uch of the chemistry that affects each of us occurs among substances dissolved in water. For example, virtually all the chemistry that makes life possible occurs in an aqueous environment. Also, various medical tests involve aqueous reactions, depending heavily on analyses of blood and other body fluids. In addition to the common tests for sugar, cholesterol, and iron, analyses for specific chemical markers allow detection of many diseases before obvious symptoms occur.

Aqueous chemistry is also important in our environment. In recent years, contamination of the groundwater by substances such as chloroform and nitrates has been widely publicized. Water is essential for life, and the maintenance of an ample supply of clean water is crucial to all civilization.

To understand the chemistry that occurs in such diverse places as the human body, the atmosphere, the groundwater, the oceans, the local water treatment plant, your hair as you shampoo it, and so on, we must understand how substances dissolved in water react with each other.

However, before we can understand solution reactions, we need to discuss the nature of solutions in which water is the dissolving medium, or **solvent.** These solutions are called **aqueous solutions.** In this chapter we will study the nature of materials after they are dissolved in water and various types of reactions that occur among these substances. You will see that the procedures developed in Chapter 3 to deal with chemical reactions work very well for reactions that take place in aqueous solutions. To understand the types of reactions that occur in aqueous solutions, we must first explore the types of species present. This requires an understanding of the nature of water.

< Potassium metal reacts so vigorously with water that a flame is produced. The reaction also produces hydroxide ions that cause the indicator in the water to turn pink.

4.1 Water, the Common Solvent

Purpose

• To show why the polar nature of water makes it an effective solvent.

Water is one of the most important substances on earth. It is essential for sustaining the reactions that keep us alive, but it also affects our lives in many indirect ways. Water helps moderate the earth's temperature; it cools automobile engines, nuclear power plants, and many industrial processes; it provides a means of transportation on the earth's surface and a medium for the growth of a myriad of creatures we use as food; and much more.

One of the most valuable properties of water is its ability to dissolve many different substances. For example, salt disappears when you sprinkle it into the water used to cook vegetables, as does sugar when you add it to your iced tea. In each case the "disappearing" substance is obviously still present—you can taste it. What happens when a solid dissolves? To understand this process, we need to consider the nature of water. Liquid water consists of a collection of H_2O molecules. An individual H_2O molecule is "bent" or V-shaped, with an H—O—H angle of approximately 105 degrees:

$$H \overset{105°}{\underset{O}{\longleftrightarrow}} H$$

The O—H bonds in the water molecule are covalent bonds formed by electron sharing between the oxygen and hydrogen atoms. However, the electrons of the bond are not shared equally between these atoms. For reasons we will discuss in later chapters, oxygen has a greater attraction for electrons than does hydrogen. If the electrons were shared equally between the two atoms, both would be electrically neutral because, on average, the number of electrons around each would equal the number of protons in that nucleus. However, because the oxygen atom has a greater attraction for electrons, the shared electrons tend to spend more time close to the oxygen than to either of the hydrogens. Thus the oxygen atom gains a slight excess of negative charge, and the hydrogen atoms become slightly positive. This is shown in Fig. 4.1, where δ (delta) indicates a *partial* charge *(less than one unit of charge)*. Because of this unequal charge distribution, water is said to be a **polar molecule.** It is this polarity that gives water its great ability to dissolve compounds.

A schematic of an ionic solid dissolving in water is shown in Fig. 4.2. Note that the "positive ends" of the water molecules are attracted to the negatively charged anions and that the "negative ends" are attracted to the positively charged cations. This process is called **hydration.** The hydration of its ions tends to cause a salt to "fall apart" in the water, or to dissolve. The strong forces present among the positive and negative ions of the solid are replaced by strong water–ion interactions.

It is very important to recognize that when ionic substances (salts) dissolve in water, they break up into the *individual* cations and anions. For instance, when ammonium nitrate (NH_4NO_3) dissolves in water, the resulting solution contains NH_4^+ and NO_3^- ions moving around independently. This process can be represented as

$$NH_4NO_3(s) \xrightarrow{H_2O(l)} NH_4^+(aq) + NO_3^-(aq)$$

where (*aq*) designates that the ions are hydrated by unspecified numbers of water molecules.

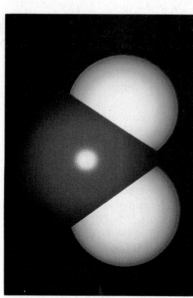

Figure 4.1

(a) The water molecule is polar.
(b) A space-filling model of the water molecule.

Figure 4.2

Polar water molecules interact with the positive and negative ions of a salt, assisting in the dissolving process.

The solubility of ionic substances in water varies greatly. For example, sodium chloride is quite soluble in water, whereas silver chloride (contains Ag^+ and Cl^- ions) is only very slightly soluble. The differences in the solubilities of ionic compounds in water typically depend on the relative attractions of the ions for each other (these forces hold the solid together) and the attractions of the ions for water molecules (which cause the solid to disperse [dissolve] in water). Solubility is a complex

Figure 4.3

(a) The ethanol molecule contains a polar O—H bond similar to those in the water molecule.
(b) The polar water molecule interacts strongly with the polar O—H bond in ethanol. This is a case of "like dissolving like."

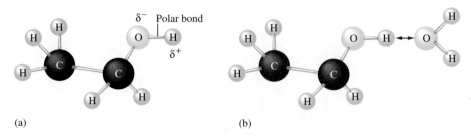

(a)   (b)

topic that we will explore in much more detail in Chapter 11. However, the most important thing to remember at this point is that when an ionic solid does dissolve in water, the ions become hydrated and are dispersed (move around independently).

Water also dissolves many nonionic substances. Ethanol (C_2H_5OH), for example, is very soluble in water. Wine, beer, and mixed drinks are aqueous solutions of ethanol and other substances. Why is ethanol so soluble in water? The answer lies in the structure of the alcohol molecules, which is shown in Fig. 4.3(a). The molecule contains a polar O—H bond like those in water, which makes it very compatible with water. The interaction of water with ethanol is represented in Fig. 4.3(b).

Many substances do not dissolve in water. Pure water will not, for example, dissolve animal fat, because fat molecules are nonpolar and do not interact effectively with polar water molecules. In general, polar and ionic substances are expected to be more soluble in water than nonpolar substances. "Like dissolves like" is a useful rule for predicting solubility. We will explore the basis for this generalization when we discuss the details of solution formation in Chapter 11.

4.2 The Nature of Aqueous Solutions: Strong and Weak Electrolytes

Purpose

• To characterize strong electrolytes, weak electrolytes, and nonelectrolytes.

As we discussed in Chapter 2, a solution is a homogeneous mixture. It is the same throughout (the first sip of a cup of coffee is the same as the last), but its composition can be varied by changing the amount of dissolved substances (one can make weak or strong coffee). In this section we will consider what happens when a substance, the **solute,** is dissolved in liquid water, the **solvent.**

One useful property for characterizing a solution is its **electrical conductivity,** its ability to conduct an electric current. This characteristic can be checked conveniently by using an apparatus like the one shown in Fig. 4.4. If the solution in the container conducts electricity, the bulb lights. Pure water is not an electrical conductor. However, some aqueous solutions conduct current very efficiently, and the bulb shines very brightly; these solutions contain **strong electrolytes.** Other solutions conduct only a small current, and the bulb glows dimly; these solutions contain **weak electrolytes.** Some solutions permit no current to flow, and the bulb remains unlit; these solutions contain **nonelectrolytes.**

An electrolyte is a substance that when dissolved in water produces a solution that can conduct electricity.

Power source

(a)   (b)   (c)

Figure 4.4

Electrical conductivity of aqueous solutions. The circuit will be completed and will allow current to flow only when there are charge carriers (ions) in the solution. (a) Strong electrolyte in solution. (b) Weak electrolyte in solution. (c) Nonelectrolyte in solution.

The basis for the conductivity properties of solutions was first correctly identified by Svante Arrhenius (1859–1927), then a Swedish graduate student in physics, who carried out research on the nature of solutions at the University of Uppsala in the early 1880s. Arrhenius came to believe that the conductivity of solutions arose from the presence of ions, an idea that was at first scorned by the majority of the scientific establishment. However, in the late 1890s when atoms were found to contain charged particles, the ionic theory suddenly made sense and became widely accepted.

As Arrhenius postulated, the extent to which a solution can conduct an electric current depends directly on the number of ions present. Some materials, such as sodium chloride, readily produce ions in aqueous solution and are thus strong electrolytes. Other substances, such as acetic acid, produce relatively few ions when dissolved in water and are weak electrolytes. A third class of materials, such as sugar, form virtually no ions when dissolved in water and are nonelectrolytes.

Strong Electrolytes

Strong electrolytes are substances that are completely ionized when they are dissolved in water. We will consider several classes of strong electrolytes: (1) soluble salts, (2) strong acids, and (3) strong bases.

As shown in Fig. 4.2, a salt consists of an array of cations and anions that separate and become hydrated when the salt dissolves. For example, when $BaCl_2$ dissolves in water, it produces hydrated Ba^{2+} and Cl^- ions in the solution. Virtually no $BaCl_2$ units are present. Thus $BaCl_2$ is a strong electrolyte.

One of Arrhenius's most important discoveries concerned the nature of acids. Acidity was first associated with the sour taste of citrus fruits. In fact, the word *acid* comes directly from the Latin word *acidus,* meaning ''sour.'' The mineral acids sulfuric acid (H_2SO_4) and nitric acid (HNO_3), so named because they were originally obtained by the treatment of minerals, were discovered around 1300.

Although acids were known for hundreds of years before the time of Arrhenius, no one had recognized their essential nature. In his studies of solutions, Arrhenius found that when the substances HCl, HNO$_3$, and H$_2$SO$_4$ were dissolved in water, they behaved as strong electrolytes. He postulated that this was the result of ionization reactions in water, for example:

$$HCl \xrightarrow{\text{H}_2\text{O}} H^+(aq) + Cl^-(aq)$$

$$HNO_3 \xrightarrow{\text{H}_2\text{O}} H^+(aq) + NO_3^-(aq)$$

$$H_2SO_4 \xrightarrow{\text{H}_2\text{O}} H^+(aq) + HSO_4^-(aq)$$

Thus Arrhenius proposed that an *acid is a substance that produces H$^+$ ions (protons) when it is dissolved in water.*

Studies of conductivity show that when HCl, HNO$_3$, and H$_2$SO$_4$ are placed in water, *virtually every molecule* dissociates to give ions. These substances are strong electrolytes and are thus called **strong acids.** All three are very important chemicals, and much more will be said about them as we proceed. However, at this point the following facts are important:

> Sulfuric acid, nitric acid, and hydrochloric acid are aqueous solutions and should be written in chemical equations as H$_2$SO$_4$(*aq*), HNO$_3$(*aq*), and HCl(*aq*), respectively, although they often appear without the (*aq*) symbol.

> A strong acid is one that completely dissociates into its ions. Thus if 100 molecules of HCl are dissolved in water, 100 H$^+$ ions and 100 Cl$^-$ ions are produced. Virtually no HCl molecules exist in aqueous solution.

> Sulfuric acid is a special case. The formula H$_2$SO$_4$ indicates that this acid can produce two H$^+$ ions per molecule when dissolved in water. However, only the first H$^+$ ion is completely dissociated. The second H$^+$ ion can be pulled off under certain conditions, which we will discuss later. Thus an aqueous solution of H$_2$SO$_4$ contains mostly H$^+$ ions and HSO$_4^-$ ions.

Another important class of strong electrolytes consists of the **strong bases,** soluble compounds containing the hydroxide ion (OH$^-$) that completely dissociate when dissolved in water. Solutions containing bases have a bitter taste and a slippery feel. The most common basic solutions are those produced when solid sodium

The Arrhenius definition of an acid is a substance that produces H$^+$ ions in solution.

Perchloric acid, HClO$_4$(aq), is another strong acid.

Strong electrolytes dissociate completely in aqueous solution.

(left) A hydrochloric acid solution freely conducts electricity. The bulb glows brightly. (right) An acetic acid solution is a weak conductor of electricity. The bulb glows dimly.

◀ **CHEMICAL IMPACT** ▶

Arrhenius, a Man with Solutions

Science is a human endeavor, subject to human frailties and governed by personalities, politics, and prejudices. One of the best illustrations of the often bumpy path of the advancement of scientific knowledge is the story of Swedish chemist Svante Arrhenius.

When Arrhenius began studies toward his doctorate at the University of Uppsala around 1880, he chose to investigate the passage of electricity through solutions, a mystery that had baffled scientists for a century. The first experiments had been done in the 1770s by Cavendish, who compared the conductivity of salt solutions with that of rain water using his own physiologic reaction to the electric shocks he received! Arrhenius had an array of instruments to measure electric current, but the process of carefully weighing, measuring, and recording data from a multitude of experiments was a tedious one.

After his long series of experiments was performed, Arrhenius quit his laboratory bench and returned to his country home to try to formulate a model that could account for his data. He wrote, "I got the idea in the night of the 17th of May in the year 1883, and I could not sleep that night until I had worked through the whole problem." His idea was that ions were responsible for conducting electricity through a solution.

Back at Uppsala, Arrhenius took his doctoral dissertation containing the new theory to his advisor, Professor Cleve, an eminent chemist and the discoverer of the elements holmium and thulium. Cleve's uninterested response was what Arrhenius had expected. It was in keeping with Cleve's resistance to new ideas—he had

Svante August Arrhenius

not even accepted Mendeleev's periodic table, introduced 10 years earlier.

It is a long-standing custom that before a doctoral degree is granted, the dissertation must be defended before a panel of professors. Although this procedure is still followed at most universities today, the problems are usually worked out in private with the evaluating professors before the actual defense. However, when Arrhenius did it, the dissertation defense was an open debate, which could be rancorous and humiliating. Knowing that it would be unwise to antagonize his professors, Arrhenius downplayed his convictions about his new theory as he defended his dissertation. His diplomacy paid off: he was awarded his degree, albeit reluctantly, because the professors still did not believe his model and considered him to be a marginal scientist, at best.

Such a setback could have ended his scientific career, but Arrhenius was a crusader; he was determined to see his theory triumph. He promptly embarked on a po-

litical campaign, enlisting the aid of several prominent scientists, to get his theory accepted.

Ultimately, the ionic theory triumphed. Arrhenius's fame spread, and honors were heaped on him, culminating in the Nobel Prize in chemistry in 1903. Not one to rest on his laurels, Arrhenius turned to new fields, including astronomy; he formulated a new theory that the solar system may have come into being through the collision of stars. His exceptional versatility led him to study the use of serums to fight disease, energy resources and conservation, and the origin of life.

Additional insight on Arrhenius and his scientific career can be obtained from his address on receiving the Willard Gibbs Award. See *Journal of the American Chemical Society* **36** (1912): 353.

hydroxide (NaOH) or potassium hydroxide (KOH) is dissolved in water to produce ions, as follows:

$$NaOH(s) \xrightarrow{\text{H}_2\text{O}} Na^+(aq) + OH^-(aq)$$

$$KOH(s) \xrightarrow{\text{H}_2\text{O}} K^+(aq) + OH^-(aq)$$

Weak Electrolytes

Weak electrolytes are substances that exhibit a small degree of ionization in water. That is, they produce relatively few ions when dissolved in water. The most common weak electrolytes are weak acids and weak bases.

The main acidic component of vinegar is acetic acid ($HC_2H_3O_2$). The formula is written to indicate that acetic acid has two chemically distinct types of hydrogen atoms. Formulas for acids are often written with the acidic hydrogen atom or atoms (any that will produce H^+ ions in solution) listed first. If any nonacidic hydrogens are present, they are written later in the formula. Thus the formula $HC_2H_3O_2$ indicates one acidic and three nonacidic hydrogen atoms. The dissociation reaction for acetic acid in water can be written as follows:

$$HC_2H_3O_2(aq) \underset{\text{H}_2\text{O}}{\rightleftharpoons} H^+(aq) + C_2H_3O_2^-(aq)$$

Acetic acid is very different from the strong acids because only about 1% of its molecules dissociate in aqueous solutions at typical concentrations. For example, in a solution containing 0.1 mole of $HC_2H_3O_2$ per liter, for every 100 molecules of $HC_2H_3O_2$ originally dissolved in water, approximately 99 molecules of $HC_2H_3O_2$ remain intact. That is, only one molecule out of every 100 dissociates (to produce one H^+ ion and one $C_2H_3O_2^-$).

Because acetic acid is a weak electrolyte, it is called a **weak acid.** Any acid, such as acetic acid, that *dissociates only to a slight extent in aqueous solutions is called a weak acid.* In Chapter 14 we will explore the subject of weak acids in detail.

The most common weak base is ammonia (NH_3). When ammonia is dissolved in water, it reacts as follows:

$$NH_3(aq) + H_2O(l) \rightarrow NH_4^+(aq) + OH^-(aq)$$

The solution is *basic* because OH^- ions are produced. Ammonia is called a **weak base** because *the resulting solution is a weak electrolyte;* that is, very few ions are formed. In fact, in a solution containing 0.1 mole of NH_3 per liter, for every 100 molecules of NH_3 originally dissolved, only one NH_4^+ ion and one OH^- ion are produced; 99 molecules of NH_3 remain unreacted.

Nonelectrolytes

Nonelectrolytes are substances that dissolve in water but do not produce any ions. An example of a nonelectrolyte is ethanol (see Fig. 4.3 for the structural formula). When ethanol dissolves, entire C_2H_5OH molecules are dispersed in the water. Since the molecules do not break up into ions, the resulting solution does not conduct an electric current. Another common nonelectrolyte is table sugar (sucrose, $C_{12}H_{22}O_{11}$), which is very soluble in water but which produces no ions when it dissolves. The sucrose molecules remain intact.

Weak electrolytes dissociate only to a small extent in aqueous solution.

4.3 *The Composition of Solutions*

Purpose

- To define molarity and demonstrate calculations involving the compositions of solutions.

Chemical reactions often take place when two solutions are mixed. To perform stoichiometric calculations in such cases, we must know two things: (1) the *nature of the reaction*, which depends on the exact forms the chemicals take when dissolved, and (2) the *amounts of chemicals* present in the solutions, usually expressed as concentrations.

The concentration of a solution can be described in many different ways, as we will see in Chapter 11. At this point we will consider only the most commonly used expression of concentration, **molarity** (*M*), which is defined as *moles of solute per volume of solution in liters:*

$$M = \text{molarity} = \frac{\text{moles of solute}}{\text{liters of solution}}$$

A solution that is 1.0 molar (written as 1.0 *M*) contains 1.0 mole of solute per liter of solution.

Sample Exercise 4.1

Calculate the molarity of a solution prepared by dissolving 11.5 g of solid NaOH in enough water to make 1.50 L of solution.

Solution

To find the molarity of the solution, we first compute the number of moles of solute using the molar mass of NaOH (40.00 g/mol)

$$11.5 \text{ g NaOH} \times \frac{1 \text{ mol NaOH}}{40.00 \text{ g NaOH}} = 0.288 \text{ mol NaOH}$$

Then we divide by the volume of the solution in liters:

$$\text{Molarity} = \frac{\text{mol solute}}{\text{L solution}} = \frac{0.288 \text{ mol NaOH}}{1.50 \text{ L solution}} = 0.192 \ M \text{ NaOH}$$

Sample Exercise 4.2

Calculate the molarity of a solution prepared by dissolving 1.56 g of gaseous HCl in enough water to make 26.8 mL of solution.

Solution

First, we calculate the number of moles of HCl (molar mass = 36.46 g/mol):

$$1.56 \text{ g } \cancel{\text{HCl}} \times \frac{1 \text{ mol HCl}}{36.46 \text{ g } \cancel{\text{HCl}}} = 4.28 \times 10^{-2} \text{ mol HCl}$$

Next, we must change the volume of the solution to liters:

$$26.8 \cancel{\text{ mL}} \times \frac{1 \text{ L}}{1000 \cancel{\text{ mL}}} = 2.68 \times 10^{-2} \text{ L}$$

Finally, we divide the moles of solute by the liters of solution:

$$\text{Molarity} = \frac{4.28 \times 10^{-2} \text{ mol HCl}}{2.68 \times 10^{-2} \text{ L solution}} = 1.60 \ M \text{ HCl}$$

It is important to realize that the conventional description of a solution's concentration may not accurately reflect the true composition of the solution. Solution concentration is always given in terms of the form of the solute *before* it dissolves. For example, when a solution is described as being 1.0 M NaCl, this means that the solution was prepared by dissolving 1.0 mole of solid NaCl in enough water to make 1.0 liter of solution; it does not mean that the solution contains 1.0 mole of NaCl units. Actually, the solution contains 1.0 mole of Na^+ ions and 1.0 mole of Cl^- ions. This situation is further illustrated in Sample Exercise 4.3.

Sample Exercise 4.3

Give the concentration of each type of ion in the following solutions:

a. 0.50 M $Co(NO_3)_2$ **b.** 1 M $Fe(ClO_4)_3$

Solution

a. When solid $Co(NO_3)_2$ dissolves, the cobalt(II) cation and the nitrate anions separate:

$$Co(NO_3)_2(s) \xrightarrow{\text{H}_2\text{O}} Co^{2+}(aq) + 2NO_3^-(aq)$$

For each mole of $Co(NO_3)_2$ that is dissolved, the solution contains 1 mol Co^{2+} ions and 2 mol NO_3^- ions. Thus a solution that is 0.50 M $Co(NO_3)_2$ contains 0.50 M Co^{2+} and (2×0.50) M NO_3^- or 1.0 M NO_3^-.

b. When solid $Fe(ClO_4)_3$ dissolves, the iron(III) cation and the perchlorate anions separate:

$$Fe(ClO_4)_3(s) \xrightarrow{\text{H}_2\text{O}} Fe^{3+}(aq) + 3ClO_4^-(aq)$$

Thus a solution that is described as 1 M $Fe(ClO_4)_3$ actually contains 1 M Fe^{3+} ions and 3 M ClO_4^- ions.

An aqueous solution of $Co(NO_3)_2$.

Often chemists need to determine the number of moles of solute present in a given volume of a solution of known molarity. The procedure for doing this is easily derived from the definition of molarity. If we multiply the molarity of a solution by the volume (in liters) of a particular sample of the solution, we get the moles of solute present in that sample:

$$\text{Liters of solution} \times \text{molarity} = \underline{\text{liters of solution}} \times \frac{\text{moles of solute}}{\underline{\text{liters of solution}}}$$

$$= \text{moles of solute}$$

$$M = \frac{\text{moles of solute}}{\text{liters of solution}}$$

This procedure is demonstrated in Sample Exercises 4.4 through 4.7.

Sample Exercise 4.4

How many moles of Ag^+ ions are present in 25 mL of a 0.75 M $AgNO_3$ solution?

Solution

To solve this problem, we must first recognize that 0.75 M $AgNO_3$ contains 0.75 M Ag^+ ions and 0.75 M NO_3^- ions. To find the moles of Ag^+ in 25 mL of a 0.75 M Ag^+ solution, we must express the volume in liters:

$$25 \text{ mL} \times \frac{1 \text{ L}}{1000 \text{ mL}} = 2.5 \times 10^{-2} \text{ L}$$

Then we must multiply the volume in liters by the molarity:

$$2.5 \times 10^{-2} \text{ L solution} \times \frac{0.75 \text{ mol Ag}^+}{\text{L solution}} = 1.9 \times 10^{-2} \text{ mol Ag}^+$$

Sample Exercise 4.5

Calculate the number of moles of Cl^- ions in 1.75 L of 1.0×10^{-3} M $ZnCl_2$.

Solution

When solid $ZnCl_2$ dissolves, it produces ions as follows:

$$ZnCl_2(s) \xrightarrow{H_2O} Zn^{2+}(aq) + 2Cl^-(aq)$$

Thus a 1.0×10^{-3} M $ZnCl_2$ solution contains 1.0×10^{-3} M Zn^{2+} ions and 2.0×10^{-3} M Cl^- ions. To calculate the moles of Cl^- ions in 1.75 L of the 1.0×10^{-3} M $ZnCl_2$ solution, we must multiply the volume times the molarity:

$$1.75 \text{ L solution} \times 2.0 \times 10^{-3} \text{ } M \text{ Cl}^- = 1.75 \text{ L solution} \times \frac{2.0 \times 10^{-3} \text{ mol Cl}^-}{\text{L solution}}$$

$$= 3.5 \times 10^{-3} \text{ mol Cl}^-$$

Sample Exercise 4.6

Formalin is an aqueous solution of formaldehyde (HCHO). At high concentrations it is used as a preservative for biologic specimens. How many grams of formaldehyde are contained in 2.5 L of 12.3 M formalin?

Solution

We must first determine the number of moles of formaldehyde in 2.5 L of 12.3 M formalin. Remember that volume of solution (in liters) times molarity yields moles of solute. In this case, the volume of solution is 2.5 L, and the molarity is 12.3 mol HCHO per liter of solution.

$$2.5 \text{ L solution} \times \frac{12.3 \text{ mol HCHO}}{\text{L solution}} = 31 \text{ mol HCHO}$$

Next, using the molar mass of HCHO (30.0 g/mol), we convert 31 mol HCHO to grams:

$$31 \text{ mol HCHO} \times \frac{30.0 \text{ g HCHO}}{1 \text{ mol HCHO}} = 9.3 \times 10^2 \text{ g HCHO}$$

Thus 2.5 L of 12.3 M formalin contains 9.3×10^2 g formaldehyde.

Sample Exercise 4.7

Typical blood serum is about 0.14 M NaCl. What volume of blood contains 1.0 mg NaCl?

Solution

We must first determine the number of moles represented by 1.0 mg NaCl (molar mass = 58.45 g/mol):

$$1.0 \text{ mg NaCl} \times \frac{1 \text{ g NaCl}}{1000 \text{ mg NaCl}} \times \frac{1 \text{ mol NaCl}}{58.45 \text{ g NaCl}} = 1.7 \times 10^{-5} \text{ mol NaCl}$$

Next, we must determine what volume of 0.14 M NaCl solution contains 1.7×10^{-5} mol NaCl. There is some volume, call it V, that when multiplied by the molarity of this solution will yield 1.7×10^{-5} mol NaCl, that is:

$$V \times \frac{0.14 \text{ mol NaCl}}{\text{L solution}} = 1.7 \times 10^{-5} \text{ mol NaCl}$$

We want to solve for the volume:

$$V = \frac{1.7 \times 10^{-5} \text{ mol NaCl}}{\dfrac{0.14 \text{ mol NaCl}}{\text{L solution}}} = 1.2 \times 10^{-4} \text{ L solution}$$

Thus 0.12 mL of blood contains 1.7×10^{-5} mol NaCl or 1.0 mg NaCl.

Volume marker
(calibration mark)

Wash bottle

Weighed amount
of solute

(a)   (b)   (c)   (d)

Figure 4.5

Steps involved in the preparation
of a standard solution. (a) A
weighed amount of a substance
(the solute) is put into the
volumetric flask, and (b) a small
quantity of water is added.
(c) The solid is dissolved in the
water by gently swirling the flask
(*with the stopper in place*).
(d) More water is added, until the
level of the solution just reaches
the mark etched on the neck of
the flask.

A **standard solution** is a *solution whose concentration is accurately known.*
Standard solutions, often used in chemical analysis, can be prepared as shown in
Fig. 4.5 and in Sample Exercise 4.8.

Sample Exercise 4.8

To analyze the alcohol content of a certain wine, a chemist needs 1.00 L of an
aqueous 0.200 M $K_2Cr_2O_7$ (potassium dichromate) solution. How much solid
$K_2Cr_2O_7$ must be weighed out to make this solution?

Solution

We must first determine the moles of $K_2Cr_2O_7$ required:

$$1.00 \text{ L solution} \times \frac{0.200 \text{ mol } K_2Cr_2O_7}{\text{L solution}} = 0.200 \text{ mol } K_2Cr_2O_7$$

Winemaking has become a
science as well as an art.

This amount can be converted to grams using the molar mass of $K_2Cr_2O_7$ (294.18 g/mol).

$$0.200 \ \cancel{\text{mol } K_2Cr_2O_7} \times \frac{294.18 \ \text{g } K_2Cr_2O_7}{\cancel{\text{mol } K_2Cr_2O_7}} = 58.8 \ \text{g } K_2Cr_2O_7$$

Thus, to make 1.00 L of 0.200 M $K_2Cr_2O_7$, the chemist must weigh out 58.8 g $K_2Cr_2O_7$, transfer it to a 1.00-L volumetric flask, and add distilled water to the mark on the flask.

Dilution

To save time and space in the laboratory, routinely used solutions are often purchased or prepared in concentrated form (called **stock solutions**). Water is then added to achieve the molarity desired for a particular solution. This process is called **dilution.** For example, the common acids are purchased as concentrated solutions and diluted as needed. A typical dilution calculation involves determining how much water must be added to an amount of stock solution to achieve a solution of the desired concentration. The key to doing these calculations is to remember that:

Moles of solute after dilution = moles of solute before dilution

because only water (no solute) is added to accomplish the dilution.

For example, suppose we need to prepare 500. mL of 1.00 M acetic acid ($HC_2H_3O_2$) from a 17.4 M stock solution of acetic acid. What volume of the stock solution is required? The first step is to determine the number of moles of acetic acid in the final solution by multiplying the volume by the molarity (remembering that the volume must be changed to liters):

$$500. \ \cancel{\text{mL solution}} \times \frac{1 \ \cancel{\text{L solution}}}{1000 \ \cancel{\text{mL solution}}} \times \frac{1.00 \ \text{mol } HC_2H_3O_2}{\cancel{\text{L solution}}}$$
$$= 0.500 \ \text{mol } HC_2H_3O_2$$

Thus we need to use a volume of 17.4 M acetic acid that contains 0.500 mol $HC_2H_3O_2$. That is,

$$V \times \frac{17.4 \ \text{mol } HC_2H_3O_2}{\text{L solution}} = 0.500 \ \text{mol } HC_2H_3O_2$$

Solving for V gives

$$V = \frac{0.500 \ \cancel{\text{mol } HC_2H_3O_2}}{\dfrac{17.4 \ \cancel{\text{mol } HC_2H_3O_2}}{\text{L solution}}} = 0.0287 \ \text{L or } 28.7 \ \text{mL solution}$$

Thus, to make 500 mL of a 1.00 M acetic acid solution, we can take 28.7 mL of 17.4 M acetic acid and dilute it to a total volume of 500 mL with distilled water.

A dilution procedure typically involves two types of glassware: a pipet and a volumetric flask. A **pipet** is a device for accurately measuring and transferring a given volume of solution. There are two common types of pipets: *volumetric (or transfer) pipets* and *measuring pipets,* as shown in Fig. 4.6. Volumetric pipets come in specific sizes, such as 5 mL, 10 mL, 25 mL, and so on. Measuring pipets are used to measure volumes for which a volumetric pipet is not available. For example, we would use a measuring pipet as shown in Fig. 4.7 to deliver 28.7 mL of

Dilution with water does not alter the numbers of moles of solute present.

Calibration mark

(a)   (b)

Figure 4.6

(a) A measuring pipet is graduated and can be used to measure various volumes of liquid accurately. (b) A volumetric (transfer) pipet is designed to measure one volume accurately. When filled to the mark, it delivers the volume indicated on the pipet.

Rubber bulb

500 mL

(a)   (b)   (c)

Figure 4.7
(a) A measuring pipet is used to transfer 28.7 mL of 17.4 M acetic acid solution to a volumetric flask. (b) Water is added to the flask to the calibration mark. (c) The resulting solution is 1 M acetic acid.

17.4 M acetic acid into a 500-mL volumetric flask and then add water to the mark to perform the dilution described above.

Sample Exercise 4.9

What volume of 16 M sulfuric acid must be used to prepare 1.5 L of a 0.10 M H_2SO_4 solution?

Solution

We must first determine the moles of H_2SO_4 in 1.5 L of 0.10 M H_2SO_4:

$$1.5 \text{ L solution} \times \frac{0.10 \text{ mol } H_2SO_4}{\text{L solution}} = 0.15 \text{ mol } H_2SO_4$$

Next, we must find the volume of 16 M H_2SO_4 that contains 0.15 mol H_2SO_4:

$$V \times \frac{16 \text{ mol } H_2SO_4}{\text{L solution}} = 0.15 \text{ mol } H_2SO_4$$

Solving for V gives

$$V = \frac{0.15 \text{ mol } H_2SO_4}{\dfrac{16 \text{ mol } H_2SO_4}{1 \text{ L solution}}} = 9.4 \times 10^{-3} \text{ L or } 9.4 \text{ mL solution}$$

Thus, to make 1.5 L of 0.10 M H_2SO_4 using 16 M H_2SO_4, we must take 9.4 mL of the concentrated acid and dilute it with water to 1.5 L. The correct way to do this is to add the 9.4 mL of acid to about 1 L of distilled water and then dilute to 1.5 L by adding more water.

In diluting an acid, "Do what you oughta, always add acid to water."

As noted above, the central idea in performing the calculations associated with dilutions is to recognize that the moles of solute are not changed by the dilution. Another way to express this condition is by the following equation:

$$M_1V_1 = M_2V_2$$

where M_1 and V_1 represent the molarity and volume of the original solution (before dilution) and M_2 and V_2 represent the molarity and volume of the diluted solution. This equation makes sense because

$$M_1 \times V_1 = \text{mol solute before dilution}$$
$$= \text{mol solute after dilution} = M_2 \times V_2$$

Repeat Sample Exercise 4.9 using the equation $M_1V_1 = M_2V_2$. Note that in doing so

$$M_1 = 16\ M \qquad M_2 = 0.10\ M \qquad V_2 = 1.5\ \text{L}$$

and V_1 is the unknown quantity sought. The equation $M_1V_1 = M_2V_2$ always holds for a dilution. This equation will be easy for you to remember if you understand where it comes from.

4.4 Types of Chemical Reactions

Purpose

- To introduce several types of solution reactions.

Although we have considered many reactions so far in this text, we have examined only a tiny fraction of the millions of possible chemical reactions. In order to make sense of all these reactions, we need some system for grouping reactions into classes. Although there are many different ways to do this, we will use the system most commonly used by practicing chemists:

Types of Solution Reactions

- Precipitation reactions
- Acid–base reactions
- Oxidation–reduction reactions

Virtually all reactions can be put into one of these classes. We will define and illustrate each type in the following sections.

4.5 Precipitation Reactions

Purpose

- To show how to predict whether a solid will form in a solution reaction.

When two solutions are mixed, an insoluble substance sometimes forms; that is, a solid forms and separates from the solution. Such a reaction is called a **precipitation reaction,** and the solid that forms is called a **precipitate.** For example, a precipitation reaction occurs when an aqueous solution of potassium chromate, $K_2CrO_4(aq)$, which is yellow, is added to a colorless aqueous solution containing barium nitrate, $Ba(NO_3)_2(aq)$. As shown in Fig. 4.8, when these solutions are mixed, a yellow solid forms. What is the equation that describes this chemical change? To write the equation, we must know the identities of the reactants and products. The reactants have already been described: $K_2CrO_4(aq)$ and $Ba(NO_3)_2(aq)$. Is there some way we can predict the identities of the products? In particular, what is the yellow solid?

The best way to predict the identity of this solid is to think carefully about what products are possible. To do this, we need to know what species are present in the solution after the two reactant solutions are mixed. First, let's think about the nature of each reactant solution. The designation $Ba(NO_3)_2(aq)$ means that barium nitrate (a white solid) has been dissolved in water. Notice that barium nitrate contains the Ba^{2+} and NO_3^- ions. *Remember: In virtually every case, when a solid containing ions dissolves in water, the ions separate* and move around independently. That is, $Ba(NO_3)_2(aq)$ does not contain $Ba(NO_3)_2$ units; it contains separated Ba^{2+} and NO_3^- ions.

When ionic compounds dissolve in water, the resulting solution contains the separated ions.

Similarly, since solid potassium chromate contains the K^+ and CrO_4^{2-} ions, an aqueous solution of potassium chromate (which is prepared by dissolving solid K_2CrO_4 in water) contains these separated ions.

We can represent the mixing of $K_2CrO_4(aq)$ and $Ba(NO_3)_2(aq)$ in two ways. First, we can write:

$$K_2CrO_4(aq) + Ba(NO_3)_2(aq) \rightarrow \text{products}$$

However, a much more accurate representation is:

$$\underbrace{2K^+(aq) + CrO_4^{2-}(aq)}_{\substack{\text{The ions in} \\ K_2CrO_4(aq)}} + \underbrace{Ba^{2+}(aq) + 2NO_3^-(aq)}_{\substack{\text{The ions in} \\ Ba(NO_3)_2(aq)}} \rightarrow \text{products}$$

Thus the mixed solution contains the ions:

$$K^+, \quad CrO_4^{2-}, \quad Ba^{2+}, \quad NO_3^-$$

How can some or all of these ions combine to form a yellow solid? This is not an easy question to answer. In fact, predicting the products of a chemical reaction is one of the hardest things a beginning chemistry student is asked to do. Even an experienced chemist, when confronted with a new reaction, is often not sure what will happen. The chemist tries to think of the various possibilities, considers the likelihood of each possibility, and then makes a prediction (an educated guess). Only after identifying each product *experimentally* is the chemist sure what reaction has taken place. However, an educated guess is very useful because it provides a place to start. It tells us what kinds of products we are most likely to find. We already know some things that will help us predict the products of the above reaction.

1. When ions form a solid compound, the compound must have a zero net charge. Thus the products of this reaction must contain *both anions and cations.* For example, K^+ and Ba^{2+} could not combine to form the solid, nor could CrO_4^{2-} and NO_3^-.

Figure 4.8

When yellow aqueous potassium chromate is added to a colorless barium nitrate solution, yellow barium chromate precipitates.

2. Most ionic materials contain only two types of ions: one type of cation and one type of anion [for example, NaCl, KOH, Na_2SO_4, K_2CrO_4, $Co(NO_3)_2$, NH_4Cl, Na_2CO_3].

The possible combinations of a given cation and a given anion from the list of ions K^+, CrO_4^{2-}, Ba^{2+}, and NO_3^- are

$$K_2CrO_4, \qquad KNO_3, \qquad BaCrO_4, \qquad Ba(NO_3)_2$$

Which of these possibilities is most likely to represent the yellow solid? We know it's not K_2CrO_4 or $Ba(NO_3)_2$. They are the reactants. They were present (dissolved) in the separate solutions that were mixed. The only real possibilities for the solid that formed are

$$KNO_3 \qquad \text{and} \qquad BaCrO_4$$

To decide which of these most likely represents the yellow solid, we need more facts. An experienced chemist knows that the K^+ ion and the NO_3^- ion are both colorless. Thus if the solid is KNO_3, it should be white not yellow. On the other hand, the CrO_4^{2-} ion is yellow [note in Fig. 4.8 that $K_2CrO_4(aq)$ is yellow]. Thus the yellow solid is almost certainly $BaCrO_4$. Further tests show that this is the case.

So far we have determined that one product of the reaction between $K_2CrO_4(aq)$ and $Ba(NO_3)_2(aq)$ is $BaCrO_4(s)$, but what happened to the K^+ and NO_3^- ions? The answer is that these ions are left dissolved in the solution; KNO_3 does not form a solid when the K^+ and NO_3^- ions are present in this much water. In other words, if we took solid KNO_3 and put it in the same quantity of water as is present in the mixed solution, it would dissolve. Thus, when we mix $K_2CrO_4(aq)$ and $Ba(NO_3)_2(aq)$, $BaCrO_4(s)$ forms, but KNO_3 is left behind in solution [we write it as $KNO_3(aq)$]. Thus the equation for this precipitation reaction is

$$K_2CrO_4(aq) + Ba(NO_3)_2(aq) \rightarrow BaCrO_4(s) + 2KNO_3(aq)$$

As long as water is present, the KNO_3 remains dissolved. However, if we removed the solid $BaCrO_4$ and then evaporated the water, white solid KNO_3 would be obtained; the K^+ and NO_3^- ions assemble themselves into solid KNO_3 when the water is removed.

Now let's consider another example. When an aqueous solution of silver nitrate is added to an aqueous solution of potassium chloride, a white precipitate forms. We can represent what we know so far as

$$AgNO_3(aq) + KCl(aq) \rightarrow \text{unknown white solid}$$

Remembering that when ionic substances dissolve in water, the ions separate, we can write

$$\underbrace{Ag^+, \quad NO_3^-}_{\substack{\text{In silver} \\ \text{nitrate} \\ \text{solution}}} + \underbrace{K^+, \quad Cl^-}_{\substack{\text{In potassium} \\ \text{chloride} \\ \text{solution}}} \rightarrow \underbrace{Ag^+, \quad NO_3^-, \quad K^+, \quad Cl^-}_{\substack{\text{Combined solution,} \\ \text{before reaction}}} \rightarrow \text{white solid}$$

Since we know the white solid must contain both positive and negative ions, the possible compounds that can be assembled from this collection of ions are:

$$AgNO_3, \qquad KCl, \qquad AgCl, \qquad KNO_3$$

Since $AgNO_3$ and KCl are the substances dissolved in the two reactant solutions, we know that they do not represent the white solid product. Therefore, the only real

possibilities are

$$AgCl \quad \text{and} \quad KNO_3$$

From the first example considered, we know that KNO_3 is quite soluble in water. Thus solid KNO_3 will not form when the reactant solids are mixed. The product must be $AgCl(s)$ (which can be proved by experiment to be true). The equation for the reaction now can be written

$$AgNO_3(aq) + KCl(aq) \rightarrow AgCl(s) + KNO_3(aq)$$

Figure 4.9 shows the result of mixing aqueous solutions of $AgNO_3$ and KCl.

Notice that in these two examples we had to apply both concepts (solids must have a zero net charge) and facts (KNO_3 is very soluble in water, the CrO_4^{2-} is yellow, and so on). Doing chemistry requires both understanding ideas and remembering key information. Predicting the identity of the solid product in a precipitation reaction requires knowledge of the solubilities of common ionic substances. As an aid in predicting the products of precipitation reactions, some simple solubility rules are given in Table 4.1. You should memorize these rules.

The phrase *slightly soluble* used in the solubility rules in Table 4.1 means that the tiny amount of solid that dissolves is not noticeable. The solid appears to be insoluble to the naked eye. Thus the terms *insoluble* and *slightly soluble* are often used interchangeably.

Note that the information in Table 4.1 allows us to predict that AgCl is the white solid formed when solutions of $AgNO_3$ and KCl are mixed. Rules 1 and 2 indicate that KNO_3 is soluble, and Rule 3 states that AgCl is insoluble.

When solutions containing ionic substances are mixed, it will be helpful in determining the products if you think in terms of *ion interchange*. For example, in the preceding discussion we considered the results of mixing $AgNO_3(aq)$ and $KCl(aq)$. In determining the products, we took the cation from one reactant and combined it with the anion of the other reactant:

$$Ag^+ \quad + \quad NO_3^- \quad + \quad K^+ \quad + \quad Cl^- \quad \rightarrow$$

Possible
solid
products

Figure 4.9

Precipitation of silver chloride by mixing solutions of silver nitrate and potassium chloride. The K^+ and NO_3^- ions remain in solution.

Table 4.1
Simple Rules for the Solubility of Salts in Water

1. Most nitrate (NO_3^-) salts are soluble.
2. Most salts containing the alkali metal ions (Li^+, Na^+, K^+, Cs^+, Rb^+) and the ammonium ion (NH_4^+) are soluble.
3. Most chloride, bromide, and iodide salts are soluble. Notable exceptions are salts containing the ions Ag^+, Pb^{2+}, and Hg_2^{2+}.
4. Most sulfate salts are soluble. Notable exceptions are $BaSO_4$, $PbSO_4$, $HgSO_4$, and $CaSO_4$.
5. Most hydroxide salts are only slightly soluble. The important soluble hydroxides are NaOH and KOH. The compounds $Ba(OH)_2$, $Sr(OH)_2$, and $Ca(OH)_2$ are marginally soluble.
6. Most sulfide (S^{2-}), carbonate (CO_3^{2-}), chromate (CrO_4^{2-}), and phosphate (PO_4^{3-}) salts are only slightly soluble.

The solubility rules in Table 4.1 allow us to predict whether either product forms as a solid.

The key to dealing with the chemistry of an aqueous solution is first to *focus on the actual components of the solution before any reaction occurs* and then to figure out how these components will react with each other. Sample Exercise 4.10 illustrates this process for three different reactions.

To begin, focus on the ions in solution before any reaction occurs.

Sample Exercise 4.10

Using the solubility rules in Table 4.1, predict what will happen when the following pairs of solutions are mixed.

a. $KNO_3(aq)$ and $BaCl_2(aq)$
b. $Na_2SO_4(aq)$ and $Pb(NO_3)_2(aq)$
c. $KOH(aq)$ and $Fe(NO_3)_3(aq)$

Solution

a. $KNO_3(aq)$ stands for an aqueous solution obtained by dissolving solid KNO_3 in water to form a solution containing the hydrated ions $K^+(aq)$ and $NO_3^-(aq)$. Likewise, $BaCl_2(aq)$ is a solution formed by dissolving solid $BaCl_2$ in water to produce $Ba^{2+}(aq)$ and $Cl^-(aq)$. When these two solutions are mixed, the resulting solution contains the ions K^+, NO_3^-, Ba^{2+}, and Cl^-. All ions are hydrated, but the (aq) is omitted for simplicity. To look for possible solid products, combine the cation from one reactant with the anion from the other:

$$K^+ \quad + \quad NO_3^- \quad + \quad Ba^{2+} \quad + \quad Cl^- \quad \rightarrow$$

Possible
solid
products

Note from Table 4.1 that the rules predict that both KCl and $Ba(NO_3)_2$ are soluble in water. Thus no precipitate forms when $KNO_3(aq)$ and $BaCl_2(aq)$ are mixed. All the ions remain dissolved in solution. No chemical reaction occurs.

b. Using the same procedures as in part a, we find that the ions present in the combined solution before any reaction occurs are Na^+, SO_4^{2-}, Pb^{2+}, and NO_3^-. The possible salts that could form precipitates are

$$Na^+ \quad + \quad SO_4^{2-} \quad + \quad Pb^{2+} \quad + \quad NO_3^- \quad \rightarrow$$

The compound $NaNO_3$ is soluble, but $PbSO_4$ is insoluble (see Rule 4 in Table 4.1). When these solutions are mixed, $PbSO_4$ will precipitate from the solution. The balanced equation is

$$Na_2SO_4(aq) + Pb(NO_3)_2(aq) \rightarrow PbSO_4(s) + 2NaNO_3(aq)$$

c. The combined solution (before any reaction occurs) contains the ions K^+, OH^-, Fe^{3+}, and NO_3^-. The salts that might precipitate are KNO_3 and $Fe(OH)_3$. The solubility rules in Table 4.1 indicate that both K^+ and NO_3^- salts are soluble.

Lead sulfate is a white solid.

However, $Fe(OH)_3$ is only slightly soluble (Rule 5) and hence will precipitate. The balanced equation is

$$3KOH(aq) + Fe(NO_3)_3(aq) \rightarrow Fe(OH)_3(s) + 3KNO_3(aq)$$

4.6 *Describing Reactions in Solution*

Purpose

- To describe reactions in solution by molecular, complete ionic, and net ionic equations.

Solid $Fe(OH)_3$ forms when aqueous KOH and $Fe(NO_3)_3$ are mixed.

In this section we will consider the types of equations used to represent reactions in solution. For example, when we mix aqueous potassium chromate with aqueous barium nitrate, a reaction occurs to form a precipitate ($BaCrO_4$) and dissolved potassium nitrate. So far we have written the **molecular equation** for this reaction:

$$K_2CrO_4(aq) + Ba(NO_3)_2(aq) \rightarrow BaCrO_4(s) + 2KNO_3(aq)$$

Although the molecular equation shows the reactants and products of the reaction, it does not give a very clear picture of what actually occurs in solution. As we have seen, aqueous solutions of potassium chromate, barium nitrate, and potassium nitrate contain individual ions, not molecules as implied by the molecular equation. Thus the **complete ionic equation**

$$2K^+(aq) + CrO_4^{2-}(aq) + Ba^{2+}(aq) + 2NO_3^-(aq)$$
$$\rightarrow BaCrO_4(s) + 2K^+(aq) + 2NO_3^-(aq)$$

better represents the actual forms of the reactants and products in solution. *In a complete ionic equation, all substances that are strong electrolytes are represented as ions.*

The complete ionic equation reveals that only some of the ions participate in the reaction. The K^+ and NO_3^- ions are present in solution both before and after the reaction. The ions that do not participate directly in the reaction are called **spectator ions.** The ions that participate in this reaction are the Ba^{2+} and CrO_4^{2-} ions, which combine to form solid $BaCrO_4$:

$$Ba^{2+}(aq) + CrO_4^{2-}(aq) \rightarrow BaCrO_4(s)$$

This equation, called the **net ionic equation,** includes only those solution components directly involved in the reaction. Chemists usually write the net ionic equation for a reaction in solution because it gives the actual forms of the reactants and products and only includes the species that undergo a change.

A strong electrolyte is a substance that completely breaks apart into ions when dissolved in water.

Net ionic equations include only those components which undergo changes in the reaction.

Three Types of Equations Are Used to Describe Reactions in Solution:

- The **molecular equation** gives the overall reaction stoichiometry but not necessarily the actual forms of the reactants and products in solution.
- The **complete ionic equation** represents as ions all reactants and products that are strong electrolytes.
- The **net ionic equation** includes only those solution components undergoing a change. Spectator ions are not included.

Sample Exercise 4.11

For each of the following reactions, write the molecular equation, the complete ionic equation, and the net ionic equation.

a. Aqueous potassium chloride is added to aqueous silver nitrate to form a silver chloride precipitate plus aqueous potassium nitrate.

b. Aqueous potassium hydroxide is mixed with aqueous iron(III) nitrate to form a precipitate of iron(III) hydroxide and aqueous potassium nitrate.

Solution

a. Molecular Equation

$$KCl(aq) + AgNO_3(aq) \rightarrow AgCl(s) + KNO_3(aq)$$

Complete Ionic Equation (*Remember:* any ionic compound dissolved in water will be present as the separated ions.)

$$K^+(aq) + Cl^-(aq) + Ag^+(aq) + NO_3^-(aq) \rightarrow AgCl(s) + K^+(aq) + NO_3^-(aq)$$

| Spectator ion | | Spectator ion | Solid, not written as separate ions | Spectator ion | Spectator ion |

Canceling the spectator ions

$$\cancel{K^+}(aq) + Cl^-(aq) + Ag^+(aq) + \cancel{NO_3^-}(aq) \rightarrow AgCl(s) + \cancel{K^+}(aq) + \cancel{NO_3^-}(aq)$$

gives the following net ionic equation.

Net Ionic Equation

$$Cl^-(aq) + Ag^+(aq) \rightarrow AgCl(s)$$

b. Molecular Equation

$$3KOH(aq) + Fe(NO_3)_3(aq) \rightarrow Fe(OH)_3(s) + 3KNO_3(aq)$$

Complete Ionic Equation

$$3K^+(aq) + 3OH^-(aq) + Fe^{3+}(aq) + 3NO_3^-(aq)$$
$$\rightarrow Fe(OH)_3(s) + 3K^+(aq) + 3NO_3^-(aq)$$

Net Ionic Equation

$$3OH^-(aq) + Fe^{3+}(aq) \rightarrow Fe(OH)_3(s)$$

4.7 Stoichiometry of Precipitation Reactions

Purpose

• To demonstrate stoichiometric calculations involving precipitation reactions.

In Chapter 3 we covered the principles of chemical stoichiometry: the procedures for calculating quantities of reactants and products involved in a chemical reaction. Recall that in performing these calculations we first convert all quantities to moles and then use the coefficients of the balanced equation to assemble the appropriate mole ratios. In cases where reactants are mixed we must determine which reactant is limiting, since the reactant that is consumed first will limit the amounts of products formed. *These same principles apply to reactions that take place in solutions.* However, there are two points about solution reactions that need special emphasis. The first is that it is sometimes difficult to tell immediately what reaction will occur when two solutions are mixed. Usually we must do some thinking about the various possibilities and then decide what probably will happen. The first step in this process *always* should be to write down the species that are actually present in the solution, as we did in Section 4.5. The second special point about solution reactions is that to obtain the moles of reactants we must use the volume of the solution and its molarity. This procedure was covered in Section 4.3.

We will introduce stoichiometric calculations for reactions in solution in Sample Exercise 4.12.

$$1.50 L \times \frac{1\ mol}{1 L}\ ;\ mol$$

Sample Exercise 4.12

Calculate the mass of solid NaCl that must be added to 1.50 L of a 0.100 *M* AgNO$_3$ solution to precipitate all the Ag$^+$ ions in the form of AgCl.

Solution

When added to the AgNO$_3$ solution (which contains Ag$^+$ and NO$_3^-$ ions), the solid NaCl dissolves to yield Na$^+$ and Cl$^-$ ions. Thus the mixed solution contains the ions

$$Ag^+, \quad NO_3^-, \quad Na^+, \quad Cl^-$$

Note from Table 4.1 that NaNO$_3$ is soluble and AgCl is insoluble. Therefore, solid AgCl forms according to the following net ionic equation:

$$Ag^+(aq) + Cl^-(aq) \rightarrow AgCl(s)$$

In this case we must add enough Cl$^-$ ions to react with all the Ag$^+$ ions present. Thus we must calculate the moles of Ag$^+$ ions present in 1.50 L of a 0.100 *M* AgNO$_3$ solution (remember that a 0.100 *M* AgNO$_3$ solution contains 0.100 *M* Ag$^+$ ions and 0.100 *M* NO$_3^-$ ions):

$$1.50\ L \times \frac{0.100\ mol\ Ag^+}{L} = 0.150\ mol\ Ag^+$$

Because Ag$^+$ and Cl$^-$ react in a 1:1 ratio, 0.150 mol Cl$^-$ ions and thus 0.150 mol NaCl is required. We calculate the mass of NaCl required as follows:

$$0.150\ mol\ NaCl \times \frac{58.45\ g\ NaCl}{mol\ NaCl} = 8.77\ g\ NaCl$$

Notice from Sample Exercise 4.12 that the procedures for doing stoichiometric calculations for solution reactions are very similar to those for other types of reactions. It is useful to think in terms of the following steps for reactions in solution.

STOICHIOMETRY FOR REACTIONS IN SOLUTION

STEP 1
Identify the species present in the combined solution, and determine what reaction occurs.

STEP 2
Write the balanced net ionic equation for the reaction.

STEP 3
Calculate the moles of reactants.

STEP 4
Determine which reactant is limiting.

STEP 5
Calculate the moles of product or products, as required.

STEP 6
Convert to grams or other units, as required.

Sample Exercise 4.13

When aqueous solutions of Na_2SO_4 and $Pb(NO_3)_2$ are mixed, $PbSO_4$ precipitates. Calculate the mass of $PbSO_4$ formed when 1.25 L of 0.0500 M $Pb(NO_3)_2$ and 2.00 L of 0.0250 M Na_2SO_4 are mixed.

Solution

STEP 1

Identify the species present in the combined solution, and determine what reaction occurs. When the aqueous solutions of Na_2SO_4 (containing Na^+ and SO_4^{2-} ions) and $Pb(NO_3)_2$ (containing Pb^{2+} and NO_3^- ions) are mixed, the resulting solution contains the ions Na^+, SO_4^{2-}, Pb^{2+}, and NO_3^-. Since $NaNO_3$ is soluble and $PbSO_4$ is insoluble (see Rule 4 in Table 4.1), solid $PbSO_4$ will form.

STEP 2

Write the balanced net ionic equation for the reaction. The net ionic equation is

$$Pb^{2+}(aq) + SO_4^{2-}(aq) \rightarrow PbSO_4(s)$$

STEP 3

Calculate the moles of reactants. Since 0.0500 M $Pb(NO_3)_2$ contains 0.0500 M Pb^{2+} ions, we can calculate the moles of Pb^{2+} ions in 1.25 L of this solution as follows:

$$1.25 \, L \times \frac{0.0500 \text{ mol } Pb^{2+}}{L} = 0.0625 \text{ mol } Pb^{2+}$$

The 0.0250 M Na_2SO_4 solution contains 0.0250 M SO_4^{2-} ions, and the number of moles of SO_4^{2-} ions in 2.00 L of this solution is

$$2.00 \, L \times \frac{0.0250 \text{ mol } SO_4^{2-}}{L} = 0.0500 \text{ mol } SO_4^{2-}$$

STEP 4

Determine which reactant is limiting. Because Pb^{2+} and SO_4^{2-} react in a $1:1$ ratio, the amount of SO_4^{2-} will be limiting (0.0500 mol SO_4^{2-} is less than 0.0625 mol Pb^{2+}).

STEP 5

Calculate the moles of product. Since the Pb^{2+} ions are present in excess, only 0.0500 mol of solid $PbSO_4$ will be formed.

STEP 6

Convert to grams of product. The mass of $PbSO_4$ formed can be calculated using the molar mass of $PbSO_4$ (303.3 g/mol):

$$0.0500 \text{ mol } PbSO_4 \times \frac{303.3 \text{ g } PbSO_4}{1 \text{ mol } PbSO_4} = 15.2 \text{ g } PbSO_4$$

4.8 Acid–Base Reactions

Purpose

- To show how to perform calculations involved in acid–base volumetric analysis.

Earlier in this chapter we considered Arrhenius's concept of acids and bases: An acid is a substance that produces H^+ ions when dissolved in water, and a base is a substance that produces OH^- ions. Although these ideas are fundamentally correct, it is convenient to have a more general definition of a base, which includes substances that do not contain OH^- ions. Such a definition was provided by Johannes N. Brønsted (1879–1947) and Thomas M. Lowry (1874–1936), who defined acids and bases as follows:

An **acid** is a proton donor.

A **base** is a proton acceptor.

The Brønsted-Lowry concept of acids and bases will be discussed in detail in Chapter 14.

How do we know when to expect an acid–base reaction? One of the most difficult tasks for someone inexperienced in chemistry is to predict what reaction might occur when two solutions are mixed. With precipitation reactions, we found that the best way to deal with this problem is to focus on the species actually present in the mixed solution. This also applies to acid–base reactions. For example, when an aqueous solution of hydrogen chloride (HCl) is mixed with an aqueous solution of sodium hydroxide (NaOH), the combined solution contains the ions H^+, Cl^-, Na^+ and OH^-. The separated ions are present because HCl is a strong acid and NaOH is a strong base. How can we predict what reaction occurs, if any? First, will NaCl precipitate? From Table 4.1 we can see that NaCl is soluble in water and thus will not precipitate. Therefore, the Na^+ and Cl^- ions are spectator ions. On the other hand, because water is a nonelectrolyte, large quantities of H^+ and OH^- ions cannot coexist in solution. They react to form H_2O molecules:

$$H^+(aq) + OH^-(aq) \rightarrow H_2O(l)$$

This is the net ionic equation for the reaction that occurs when aqueous solutions of HCl and NaOH are mixed.

Next, consider mixing an aqueous solution of acetic acid ($HC_2H_3O_2$) with an aqueous solution of potassium hydroxide (KOH). In our earlier discussion of conductivity we said that an aqueous solution of acetic acid is a weak electrolyte. This tells us that acetic acid does not dissociate into ions to any great extent. In fact, in 0.1 M $HC_2H_3O_2$ approximately 99% of the $HC_2H_3O_2$ molecules remain undissociated. However, when solid KOH is dissolved in water, it dissociates completely to produce K^+ and OH^- ions. Therefore, in the solution formed by mixing aqueous solutions of $HC_2H_3O_2$ and KOH, *before any reaction occurs,* the principal species are $HC_2H_3O_2$, K^+, and OH^-. What reaction will occur? A possible precipitation reaction could occur between K^+ and OH^-. However, we know that KOH is soluble, so precipitation does not occur. Another possibility is a reaction involving the hydroxide ion (a proton acceptor) and some proton donor. Is there a source of protons in the solution? The answer is yes—the $HC_2H_3O_2$ molecules. The OH^- ion has such a strong affinity for protons that it can strip them from the $HC_2H_3O_2$ molecules. The net ionic equation for this reaction is

$$OH^-(aq) + HC_2H_3O_2(aq) \rightarrow H_2O(l) + C_2H_3O_2{}^-(aq)$$

This reaction illustrates a very important general principle: *The hydroxide ion is such a strong base that for purposes of stoichiometric calculations it can be assumed to react completely with any weak acid that we will encounter.* Of course, OH^- ions also react completely with the H^+ ions in solutions of strong acids.

We will now deal with the stoichiometry of acid–base reactions in aqueous solutions. The procedure is fundamentally the same as that used previously for precipitation reactions.

PERFORMING CALCULATIONS FOR ACID–BASE REACTIONS

STEP 1
List the species present in the combined solution *before any reaction occurs,* and decide what reaction will occur.

STEP 2
Write the balanced net ionic equation for this reaction.

STEP 3
Calculate the moles of reactants. For reactions in solution, use the volumes of the original solutions and their molarities.

STEP 4
Determine the limiting reactant where appropriate.

STEP 5
Calculate the moles of the required reactant or product.

STEP 6
Convert to grams or volume (of solution), as required.

An acid–base reaction is often called a **neutralization reaction.** When just enough base is added to react exactly with the acid in a solution, we say the acid has been *neutralized.*

Sample Exercise 4.14

What volume of a 0.100 M HCl solution is needed to neutralize 25.0 mL of 0.350 M NaOH?

Solution

STEP 1

List the species present in the combined solution before any reaction occurs, and decide what reaction will occur. The species present in the mixed solutions before any reaction occurs are

$$\underbrace{H^+, \quad Cl^-,}_{\text{From } HCl(aq)} \qquad \underbrace{Na^+, \quad OH^-}_{\text{From } NaOH(aq)}$$

What reaction will occur? The two possibilities are

$$Na^+(aq) + Cl^-(aq) \rightarrow NaCl(s)$$
$$H^+(aq) + OH^-(aq) \rightarrow H_2O(l)$$

Since we know that NaCl is soluble, the first reaction does not take place (Na^+ and Cl^- are spectator ions). However, as we have seen before, the reaction of the H^+ and OH^- ions to form H_2O does occur.

STEP 2

Write the balanced net ionic equation. The balanced net ionic equation for this reaction is

$$H^+(aq) + OH^-(aq) \rightarrow H_2O(l)$$

STEP 3

Calculate the moles of reactants. The number of moles of OH^- ions in the 25.0-mL sample of 0.350 M NaOH is

$$25.0 \text{ mL NaOH} \times \frac{1 \text{ L}}{1000 \text{ mL}} \times \frac{0.350 \text{ mol } OH^-}{\text{L NaOH}} = 8.75 \times 10^{-3} \text{ mol } OH^-$$

STEP 4

Determine the limiting reactant. This problem requires the addition of just enough H^+ ions to react exactly with the OH^- ions present. Thus we need not be concerned with determining a limiting reactant.

STEP 5

Calculate the moles of reactant needed. Since H^+ and OH^- ions react in a $1:1$ ratio, 8.75×10^{-3} mol H^+ ions is required to neutralize the OH^- ions present.

STEP 6

Convert to volume required. The volume V of 0.100 M HCl required to furnish 8.75×10^{-3} mol H^+ ions can be calculated as follows:

$$V \times \frac{0.100 \text{ mol } H^+}{\text{L}} = 8.75 \times 10^{-3} \text{ mol } H^+$$

Solving for V gives

$$V = \frac{8.75 \times 10^{-3} \text{ mol } H^+}{\dfrac{0.100 \text{ mol } H^+}{\text{L}}} = 8.75 \times 10^{-2} \text{ L}$$

Thus 8.75×10^{-2} L (87.5 mL) of 0.100 M HCl is required to neutralize 25.0 mL of 0.350 M NaOH.

Sample Exercise 4.15

In a certain experiment, 28.0 mL of 0.250 M HNO_3 and 53.0 mL of 0.320 M KOH are mixed. Calculate the amount of water formed in the resulting reaction. What is the concentration of H^+ or OH^- ions in excess after the reaction goes to completion?

Solution

The species available for reaction are

$$\underbrace{H^+, \quad NO_3^-,}_{\substack{\text{From } HNO_3 \\ \text{solution}}} \quad \underbrace{K^+, \quad OH^-}_{\substack{\text{From KOH} \\ \text{solution}}}$$

Since KNO_3 is soluble, K^+ and NO_3^- are spectator ions, so the net ionic equation is

$$H^+(aq) + OH^-(aq) \rightarrow H_2O(l)$$

We next compute the amounts of H^+ and OH^- ions present:

$$28.0 \text{ mL HNO}_3 \times \frac{1 \text{ L}}{1000 \text{ mL}} \times \frac{0.250 \text{ mol } H^+}{\text{L HNO}_3} = 7.00 \times 10^{-3} \text{ mol } H^+$$

$$53.0 \text{ mL KOH} \times \frac{1 \text{ L}}{1000 \text{ mL}} \times \frac{0.320 \text{ mol } OH^-}{\text{L KOH}} = 1.70 \times 10^{-2} \text{ mol } OH^-$$

Since H^+ and OH^- react in a 1 : 1 ratio, the limiting reactant is H^+. This means that 7.00×10^{-3} mol H^+ ions will react with 7.00×10^{-3} mol OH^- ions to form 7.00×10^{-3} mol H_2O.

The amount of OH^- ions in excess is obtained from the following difference:

$$\text{Original amount} - \text{amount consumed} = \text{amount in excess}$$

$$1.70 \times 10^{-2} \text{ mol } OH^- - 7.00 \times 10^{-3} \text{ mol } OH^- = 1.00 \times 10^{-2} \text{ mol } OH^-$$

The volume of the combined solution is the sum of the individual volumes:

$$\text{Original volume of } HNO_3 + \text{original volume of KOH} = \text{total volume}$$

$$28.0 \text{ mL} + 53.0 \text{ mL} = 81.0 \text{ mL} = 8.10 \times 10^{-2} \text{ L}$$

Thus the molarity of OH^- ions in excess is

$$\frac{\text{mol } OH^-}{\text{L solution}} = \frac{1.00 \times 10^{-2} \text{ mol } OH^-}{8.10 \times 10^{-2} \text{ L}} = 0.123 \text{ } M \text{ } OH^-$$

Acid–Base Titrations

Volumetric analysis is a technique for determining the amount of a certain substance by doing a titration. A **titration** involves delivery (from a buret) of a mea sured volume of a solution of known concentration (the **titrant**) into a solution containing the substance being analyzed (the **analyte**). The titrant contains a substance that reacts in a known manner with the analyte. The point in the titration where enough titrant has been added to react exactly with the analyte is called the **equivalence point** or the **stoichiometric point.** This point is often marked by an **indicator,** a substance added at the beginning of the titration that changes color at (or very near) the equivalence point. The point where the indicator *actually* changes color is called the **endpoint** of the titration. The goal is to choose an indicator such that the endpoint (where the indicator changes color) occurs exactly at the equivalence point (where just enough titrant has been added to react with all the analyte).

The following requirements must be met for a titration to be successful:

1. The exact reaction between titrant and analyte must be known (and rapid).

2. The stoichiometric (equivalence) point must be marked accurately.

3. The volume of titrant required to reach the stoichiometric point must be known accurately.

When the analyte is a base or an acid, the required titrant is a strong acid or strong base, respectively. This procedure is called an **acid–base titration.** An indicator very commonly used for acid–base titrations is phenolphthalein, which is colorless in an acidic solution and pink in a basic solution. Thus, when an acid is titrated with a base, the phenolphthalein remains colorless until after the acid is consumed and the first drop of excess base is added. In this case, the endpoint (the solution changes from colorless to pink) occurs approximately one drop of base beyond the stoichiometric point. This type of titration is illustrated in Fig. 4.10.

We will deal with acid–base titrations only briefly here but will return to the topic of titrations and indicators in more detail in Chapter 15. The titration of an acid with a standard solution containing hydroxide ions is illustrated in Sample Exercise 4.17. In Sample Exercise 4.16 we show how to determine accurately the concentration of a sodium hydroxide solution. This procedure is called **standardizing the solution.**

Ideally, the endpoint and stoichiometric point should coincide.

(a) (b) (c)

Figure 4.10

The titration of an acid with a base. (a) The titrant (the base) is in the buret, and the beaker contains the acid solution along with a small amount of indicator. (b) As base is added drop by drop to the acid solution in the beaker during the titration, the indicator changes color, but the color disappears on mixing. (c) The stoichiometric (equivalence) point is marked by a permanent indicator color change. The volume of base added is the difference between the final and initial buret readings.

Sample Exercise 4.16

A student carries out an experiment to standardize (determine the exact concentration of) a sodium hydroxide solution. To do this, the student weighs out a 1.3009-g sample of potassium hydrogen phthalate ($KHC_8H_4O_4$, often abbreviated KHP). KHP (molar mass 204.22 g/mol) has one acidic hydrogen. The student dissolves the KHP in distilled water, adds phenolphthalein as an indicator, and titrates the resulting solution with the sodium hydroxide solution to the phenolphthalein endpoint. The difference between the final and initial buret readings indicates that 41.20 mL of the sodium hydroxide solution is required to react exactly with the 1.3009 g KHP. Calculate the concentration of the sodium hydroxide solution.

Solution

$KHC_8H_4O_4$ dissolves in water to give the K^+ and $HC_8H_4O_4^-$ ions. The net ionic acid–base reaction between aqueous sodium hydroxide (containing Na^+ and OH^- ions) and KHP is

$$HC_8H_4O_4^-(aq) + OH^-(aq) \rightarrow H_2O(l) + C_8H_4O_4^{2-}(aq)$$

Since the reaction exhibits 1:1 stoichiometry, we know that 41.20 mL of the sodium hydroxide solution must contain exactly the same number of moles of OH^- as there are moles of $HC_8H_4O_4^-$ in 1.3009 g $KHC_8H_4O_4$.

We calculate the moles of $KHC_8H_4O_4$ in the usual way:

$$1.3009 \text{ g } \cancel{KHC_8H_4O_4} \times \frac{1 \text{ mol } KHC_8H_4O_4}{204.22 \text{ g } \cancel{KHC_8H_4O_4}} = 6.3701 \times 10^{-3} \text{ mol } KHC_8H_4O_4$$

This means that 6.3701×10^{-3} mol OH^- must be added to react with the 6.3701×10^{-3} mol $HC_8H_4O_4^-$. Thus 41.20 mL (4.120×10^{-2} L) of the sodium hydroxide solution must contain 6.3701×10^{-3} mol OH^- (and Na^+), and the concentration of the sodium hydroxide solution is

$$\text{Molarity of NaOH} = \frac{\text{mol NaOH}}{\text{L solution}} = \frac{6.3701 \times 10^{-3} \text{ mol NaOH}}{4.120 \times 10^{-2} \text{ L}}$$
$$= 0.1546 \ M$$

This standard sodium hydroxide solution can now be used in other experiments (see Sample Exercise 4.17).

Sample Exercise 4.17

An environmental chemist analyzed the effluent (the released waste material) from an industrial process known to produce the compounds carbon tetrachloride (CCl_4) and benzoic acid ($HC_7H_5O_2$), a weak acid that has one acidic hydrogen atom per molecule. A sample of this effluent weighing 0.3518 g was shaken with water, and the resulting aqueous solution required 10.59 mL of 0.1546 M NaOH for neutralization. Calculate the mass percent of $HC_7H_5O_2$ in the original sample.

Solution

In this case, the sample was a mixture containing CCl_4 and $HC_7H_5O_2$, and it was titrated with OH^- ions. Clearly CCl_4 is not an acid (it contains no hydrogen atoms), so we can assume it does not react with OH^- ions. However, $HC_7H_5O_2$ is an acid that donates one H^+ ion per molecule to react with an OH^- ion as follows:

$$HC_7H_5O_2(aq) + OH^-(aq) \rightarrow H_2O(l) + C_7H_5O_2^-(aq)$$

Although $HC_7H_5O_2$ is a weak acid, the OH^- ion is such a strong base that we can assume that each OH^- ion added will react with a $HC_7H_5O_2$ molecule until all the benzoic acid is consumed.

We must first determine the number of moles of OH^- ions required to react with all the $HC_7H_5O_2$:

$$10.59 \text{ mL NaOH} \times \frac{1 \text{ L}}{1000 \text{ mL}} \times \frac{0.1546 \text{ mol OH}^-}{\text{L NaOH}} = 1.637 \times 10^{-3} \text{ mol OH}^-$$

This number is also the number of moles of $HC_7H_5O_2$ present. The number of grams of the acid is calculated using its molar mass (122.12 g/mol):

$$1.637 \times 10^{-3} \text{ mol HC}_7\text{H}_5\text{O}_2 \times \frac{122.12 \text{ g HC}_7\text{H}_5\text{O}_2}{1 \text{ mol HC}_7\text{H}_5\text{O}_2} = 0.1999 \text{ g HC}_7\text{H}_5\text{O}_2$$

The mass percent of $HC_7H_5O_2$ in the original sample is

$$\frac{0.1999 \text{ g}}{0.3518 \text{ g}} \times 100 = 56.82\%$$

In doing problems involving titrations, you must first decide what reaction is occurring. Sometimes this seems difficult because the titration solution contains several components. *The key to success is to first write down all the components in the solution and focus on the chemistry of each one.* We have been emphasizing this approach in dealing with the reactions between ions in solution. Make it a habit to write down the components of solutions before trying to decide what reaction(s) might take place as you attempt the end-of-chapter problems involving titrations.

The first step in the analysis of a complex solution is to write down the components and focus on the chemistry of each one.

4.9 Oxidation–Reduction Reactions

Purpose

- To characterize oxidation–reduction reactions.
- To describe how to assign oxidation states.
- To identify oxidizing and reducing agents.

We have seen that many important substances are ionic. Sodium chloride, for example, can be formed by the reaction of elemental sodium and chlorine:

$$2Na(s) + Cl_2(g) \rightarrow 2NaCl(s)$$

In this reaction an electron is transferred from a sodium atom to a chlorine atom, yielding a Na^+ ion and a Cl^- ion. *Reactions like this one, in which one or more*

◀ **CHEMICAL IMPACT** ▶

State-of-the-Art Analysis

The real world of chemical analysis is often quite different from what students do in the typical university laboratory. In the real world, chemical analysis must be done quickly, accurately, economically, and often outside the laboratory setting. Analytical accuracy is crucial. A career can hinge on accuracy when a drug test is involved, and sometimes accuracy is truly a life-or-death matter, as in the screening of air travelers' luggage for explosives.

Chemical analysis can turn up in unexpected places. Modern engines in automobiles have been made much more fuel efficient and less polluting by the inclusion of a sensor to analyze the oxygen (O_2) concentration in the exhaust gases. The signal from this sensor is sent to the computer that controls engine function so that instantaneous adjustments can be made in spark timing and air–fuel mixtures.

The automated screening of luggage for explosives is a very difficult and important analysis problem. The method being developed for luggage screening is called **thermal neutron analysis** (TNA), in which the substance to be analyzed is bombarded with neutrons. When nuclei in the sample absorb neutrons, they release gamma rays that are characteristic of a specific nucleus. For example, after the nucleus of a nitrogen atom absorbs a neutron, it emits a gamma ray that is unique to nitrogen, whereas an oxygen atom would produce a different gamma ray unique to oxygen, and so on. Thus when a sample is bombarded by neutrons and the resulting gamma rays are analyzed by a detector connected to a computer, the atoms present in the sample can be specified. In an airport the luggage passes through the TNA instrument on a conveyor belt, where it is bombarded by neutrons from californium-252. The detector is set up to look for unusually large quantities of nitrogen, because most chemical explosives are based on nitrogen compounds. Although this system is still under development, the Federal Aviation Administration is optimistic that it will work.

Analytical chemists have always admired the supersensitive natural detection devices built into organisms as part of elaborate control systems used to regulate the levels of various crucial chemicals, such as enzymes, hormones, and neurotransmitters. Because these "biosensors" are so sensitive, chemists are now attaching them to their instruments. For example, the sensory hairs from Hawaiian red swimming crabs can be connected to electrical analyzers and used to detect hormones at concentrations lower than 10^{-12} M. Also, slices from the tissues of pineapple cores can be used to detect hydrogen peroxide at levels of $\approx 10^{-6}$ M.

Another state-of-the-art detection system contains a surface acoustic wave (SAW) device, which is based on a piezoelectric crystal whose resonant frequency is sensitive to tiny changes in its mass—it can sense a change of 10^{-10} g/cm^2. In one use of this device as a detector, it was coated with a thin film of zeolite, a silicate mineral. Zeolite has intricate passages of a very uniform size. Thus it can act as a "molecular sieve," allowing only molecules of a certain size to pass through onto the detector, where their accumulation changes the mass and therefore alters the detector frequency. This sensor has been used to detect amounts of methyl alcohol (CH_3OH) as low as 10^{-9} g.

The face of chemical analysis is changing rapidly. In fact, although wet chemical analyses (titrations, for example) are still quite important in the chemical industry, increasingly these routine analyses are done by robots, which not only perform the analyses automatically but also send the results to a computer for interpretation.

---

electrons are transferred, are called **oxidation–reduction reactions** *or* **redox reactions.**

Many important chemical reactions involve oxidation and reduction. In fact, most reactions used for energy production are redox reactions. In humans, the oxidation of sugars, fats, and proteins provides the energy necessary for life. Combustion reactions, which provide most of the energy to power our civilization, also involve oxidation and reduction. An example is the reaction of methane with oxygen:

$$CH_4(g) + 2O_2(g) \rightarrow CO_2(g) + 2H_2O(g) + \text{energy}$$

Even though none of the reactants or products in this reaction is ionic, the reaction is still assumed to involve a transfer of electrons from carbon to oxygen. To explain this, we must introduce the concept of oxidation states.

Oxidation States

The concept of **oxidation states** (also called **oxidation numbers**) provides a way to keep track of electrons in oxidation–reduction reactions, particularly redox reactions involving covalent substances. Recall that electrons are shared by atoms in covalent bonds. The oxidation states of atoms in covalent compounds are obtained by arbitrarily assigning the electrons (which are actually shared) to particular atoms. We do this as follows: For a covalent bond between two identical atoms, the electrons are split equally between the two. In cases where two different atoms are involved (and the electrons are thus shared unequally), the shared electrons are assigned completely to the atom that has the stronger attraction for electrons. For example, recall from the discussion of the water molecule in Section 4.1 that oxygen has a greater attraction for electrons than does hydrogen. Therefore, in assigning the oxidation state of oxygen and hydrogen in H_2O, we assume that the oxygen atom actually possesses all the electrons. Recall that a hydrogen atom has one electron. Thus, in water, oxygen has formally ''taken'' the electrons from two hydrogen atoms. This gives the oxygen an *excess* of two electrons (its oxidation state is -2) and leaves each hydrogen with no electrons (the oxidation state of each hydrogen is thus $+1$).

We define the **oxidation states** (or **oxidation numbers**) of the atoms in a covalent compound as the imaginary charges the atoms would have if the shared electrons were divided equally between identical atoms bonded to each other or, for different atoms, were all assigned to the atom in each bond that has the greater attraction for electrons. Of course, for ionic compounds containing monatomic ions, the oxidation states of the ions are equal to the ion charges.

These considerations lead to a series of rules for assigning oxidation states that are summarized in Table 4.2. Application of these simple rules allows the assignment of oxidation states in most compounds. The principles are illustrated by Sample Exercise 4.18.

Oxidation of copper metal by nitric acid. The copper atoms lose two electrons to form Cu^{2+} ions, which give a deep green color that becomes turquoise when diluted with water.

Table 4.2
Rules for Assigning Oxidation States
1. The oxidation state of an atom in an element is 0. For example, the oxidation state of each atom in the substances $Na(s)$, $O_2(g)$, $O_3(g)$, and $Hg(l)$ is 0.
2. The oxidation state of a monatomic ion is the same as its charge. For example, the oxidation state of the Na^+ ion is $+1$ and of the Cl^- ion is -1.
3. Oxygen is assigned an oxidation state of -2 in its covalent compounds, such as CO, CO_2, SO_2, and SO_3. An exception to this rule occurs in peroxides (compounds containing the O_2^{2-} group), where each oxygen is assigned an oxidation state of -1. The best-known example of a peroxide is hydrogen peroxide (H_2O_2).
4. In its covalent compounds with nonmetals, hydrogen is assigned an oxidation state of $+1$. For example, in the compounds HCl, NH_3, H_2O, and CH_4, hydrogen is assigned an oxidation state of $+1$.
5. In its compounds, fluorine is always assigned an oxidation state of -1.
6. The sum of the oxidation states must be zero for an electrically neutral compound. For an ion, the sum of the oxidation states must equal the charge of the ion. For example, the sum of the oxidation states for the hydrogen and oxygen atoms in water is 0; the sum of the oxidation states for the carbon and oxygen atoms in CO_3^{2-} is -2; and the sum of oxidation states for the nitrogen and hydrogen atoms in NH_4^+ is $+1$.

Although these rules do not cover every possible case, they will be sufficient for our purposes.

It is worthwhile to note at this point that the convention is to write actual charges on ions as $n+$ or $n-$, the number being written *before* the plus or minus sign. On the other hand, oxidation states (not actual charges) are written $+n$ or $-n$, the number being written *after* the plus or minus sign.

Sample Exercise 4.18

Assign oxidation states to all atoms in the following.

a. CO_2 **b.** SF_6 **c.** NO_3^-

Solution

a. Since we have a specific rule for the oxidation state of oxygen, we will assign its value first. The oxidation state of oxygen is -2. The oxidation state of the carbon atom can be determined by recognizing that since CO_2 has no charge, the sum of the oxidation states for oxygen and carbon must be zero. Since each oxygen is -2 and there are two oxygen atoms, the carbon atom must be assigned an oxidation state of $+4$:

$$CO_2$$
$$+4 \qquad -2 \text{ for each oxygen}$$

We can check the assigned oxidation states by noting that when the number of atoms is taken into account, the sum is zero as required:

$$1(+4) + 2(-2) = 0$$
$$\text{No. of C} \qquad \text{No. of O}$$
$$\text{atoms} \qquad \text{atoms}$$

b. Since we have no rule for sulfur, we first assign the oxidation state of each fluorine as -1. The sulfur must then be assigned an oxidation state of $+6$ to balance the total of -6 from the fluorine atoms:

$$SF_6$$
$$+6 \qquad -1 \text{ for each fluorine}$$

CHECK: $+6 + 6(-1) = 0$

c. Oxygen has an oxidation state of -2. Because the sum of the oxidation states of the three oxygens is -6 and the net charge on the NO_3^- ion is $1-$, the nitrogen must have an oxidation state of $+5$:

$$NO_3^-$$
$$+5 \qquad -2 \text{ for each oxygen}$$

CHECK: $+5 + 3(-2) = -1$

Note that in this case the sum must be -1 (the overall charge on the ion).

We need to make one more point about oxidation states, and this can be illustrated by the compound Fe_3O_4, which is the main component in magnetite, an iron ore that accounts for the reddish color of many types of rocks and soils. To determine the oxidation states in Fe_3O_4, we first assign each oxygen atom its usual oxidation state of -2. The three iron atoms must yield a total of $+8$ to balance the total of -8 from the four oxygens. This means that each iron atom has an oxidation state of $+\frac{8}{3}$. A noninteger value for oxidation state may seem strange because charge is expressed in whole numbers. However, although they are rare, noninteger oxidation states do occur because of the rather arbitrary way that electrons are divided up by the rules in Table 4.2. For Fe_3O_4, for example, the rules assume that all the iron atoms are equal, when in fact this compound can best be viewed as containing four O^{2-} ions, two Fe^{3+} ions, and one Fe^{2+} ion per formula unit. (Note that the "average" charge on iron works out to be $\frac{8}{3}+$, which is equal to the oxidation state we determined above.) Noninteger oxidation states should not intimidate you. They are used in the same way as integer oxidation states—for keeping track of electrons.

Magnetite is a magnetic ore containing Fe_3O_4. Note that the compass needles point toward the ore.

The Characteristics of Oxidation–Reduction Reactions

Oxidation–reduction reactions are characterized by a transfer of electrons. In some cases, the transfer occurs in a literal sense to form ions, such as in the reaction

$$2Na(s) + Cl_2(g) \rightarrow 2NaCl(s)$$

However, sometimes the transfer is less obvious. For example, consider the combustion of methane (the oxidation state for each atom is given):

$$CH_4(g) + 2O_2(g) \rightarrow CO_2(g) + 2H_2O(g)$$

Oxidation
state: -4 $+1$ 0 $+4$ -2 $+1$ -2
         (each H)   (each O) (each H)

Note that the oxidation state for oxygen in O_2 is 0 because it is in elemental form. In this reaction there are no ionic compounds, but we can still describe the process in terms of a transfer of electrons. Note that carbon undergoes a change in oxidation state from -4 in CH_4 to $+4$ in CO_2. Such a change can be accounted for by a loss of eight electrons (the symbol e^- stands for an electron):

$$CH_4 \rightarrow CO_2 + 8e^-$$
$$-4 \qquad +4$$

On the other hand, each oxygen changes from an oxidation state of 0 in O_2 to -2 in H_2O and CO_2, signifying a gain of two electrons per atom. Since four oxygen atoms are involved, this is a gain of eight electrons:

$$2O_2 + 8e^- \rightarrow CO_2 + 2H_2O$$
$$0 \qquad\qquad 4(-2) = -8$$

No change occurs in the oxidation state of hydrogen, and it is not formally involved in the electron-transfer process.

With this background, we can now define some important terms. **Oxidation** is an *increase* in oxidation state (a loss of electrons). **Reduction** is a *decrease* in oxida-

Oxidation is an increase in oxidation state. Reduction is a decrease in oxidation state.

tion state (a gain of electrons). Thus in the reaction

$$2Na(s) + Cl_2(g) \rightarrow 2NaCl(s)$$

$$\begin{array}{cccc} \uparrow & \uparrow & \uparrow & \uparrow \\ 0 & 0 & +1 & -1 \end{array}$$

sodium is oxidized and chlorine is reduced. In addition, Cl_2 is called the **oxidizing agent (electron acceptor)** and Na is called the **reducing agent (electron donor).**

Concerning the reaction

$$CH_4(g) + 2O_2(g) \rightarrow CO_2(g) + 2H_2O(g)$$

$$\begin{array}{cccccc} \uparrow \nwarrow & \uparrow & \uparrow \nwarrow & \uparrow \uparrow \\ -4 \; +1 & 0 & +4 \; -2 & +1 \; -2 \end{array}$$

we can say the following:

Carbon is oxidized because there has been an increase in its oxidation state (carbon has formally lost electrons).

Oxygen is reduced because there has been a decrease in its oxidation state (oxygen has formally gained electrons).

CH_4 is the reducing agent.

O_2 is the oxidizing agent.

Note that when the oxidizing or reducing agent is named, the *whole compound* is specified, not just the element that undergoes the change in oxidation state.

A helpful mnemonic device is OIL RIG (Oxidation *Involves Loss*; Reduction *Involves Gain*). Another common mnemonic is LEO says GER. (*Loss of Electrons, Oxidation; Gain of Electrons, Reduction*).

An oxidizing agent is reduced and a reducing agent is oxidized in a redox reaction.

Sample Exercise 4.19

When powdered aluminum metal is mixed with pulverized iodine crystals and a drop of water is added to help the reaction get started, the resulting reaction produces a great deal of energy. The mixture bursts into flames, and a purple smoke of I_2 vapor is produced from the excess iodine. The equation for the reaction is

$$2Al(s) + 3I_2(s) \rightarrow 2AlI_3(s)$$

For this reaction, identify the atoms that are oxidized and reduced, and specify the oxidizing and reducing agents.

A mixture of finely ground aluminum and iodine reacts vigorously to form aluminum iodide after a drop of water is added. The purple cloud is excess iodine vaporized by the heat of the reaction.

Solution

The first step is to assign oxidation states:

$$2Al(s) + 3I_2(s) \rightarrow 2AlI_3(s)$$

     ↑   ↑   ↑ ↖

     0   0   +3 −1 (each I)

  Free elements   AlI$_3$(s) is a salt that
                  contains Al^{3+} and I$^-$ ions

Since each aluminum atom changes its oxidation state from 0 to +3 (an increase in oxidation state), aluminum is *oxidized*. On the other hand, the oxidation state of each iodine atom decreases from 0 to −1, and iodine is *reduced*. Since Al furnishes electrons for the reduction of iodine, it is the *reducing agent;* I$_2$ is the *oxidizing agent*.

Sample Exercise 4.20

Metallurgy, the process of producing a metal from its ore, always involves oxidation–reduction reactions. In the metallurgy of galena (PbS), the principal lead-containing ore, the first step is the conversion of lead sulfide to its oxide (a process called **roasting**):

$$2PbS(s) + 3O_2(g) \rightarrow 2PbO(s) + 2SO_2(g)$$

The oxide is then treated with carbon monoxide to produce the free metal:

$$PbO(s) + CO(g) \rightarrow Pb(s) + CO_2(g)$$

For each reaction, identify the atoms that are oxidized and reduced, and specify the oxidizing and reducing agents.

Solution

For the first reaction, we can assign the following oxidation states:

$$2PbS(s) + 3O_2(g) \rightarrow 2PbO(s) + 2SO_2(g)$$

    ↗↑   ↑   ↑↖   ↑↖

  +2 −2   0   +2 −2 +4 −2 (each O)

The oxidation state for the sulfur atom increases from −2 to +4. Thus sulfur is oxidized. The oxidation state for each oxygen atom decreases from 0 to −2. Oxygen is reduced. The oxidizing agent (that accepts the electrons) is O$_2$, and the reducing agent (that donates electrons) is PbS.

For the second reaction we have

$$PbO(s) + CO(g) \rightarrow Pb(s) + CO_2(g)$$

   ↑↖   ↑↖   ↑   ↑↖

 +2 −2 +2 −2   0   +4 −2 (each O)

Lead is reduced (its oxidation state decreases from +2 to 0), and carbon is oxidized (its oxidation state increases from +2 to +4). PbO is the oxidizing agent, and CO is the reducing agent.

◀ **CHEMICAL IMPACT** ▶

Aging: Does It Involve Oxidation?

Although aging is supposed to bring wisdom, almost no one wants to get old. Along with wisdom, aging brings wrinkles, loss of physical strength, and greater susceptibility to disease.

Why do we age? No one knows for certain, but many scientists think that oxidation plays a major role. The oxygen molecule and other oxidizing agents in the body apparently can extract single electrons from the large molecules that make up cell membranes, thus making them very reactive. Subsequently, these activated molecules can link up, changing the properties of the cell membrane. At some point enough of these reactions have occurred that the body's immune system comes to view the changed cell as an ''enemy'' and destroys it. This is particularly detrimental to the organism when the cells involved are irreplaceable. Nerve cells, for example, fall into this category. They rarely regenerate in an adult.

The body has defenses against oxidation, such as vitamin E, a well-known antioxidant. Studies have shown that red blood cells age much faster than normal when they are deficient in vitamin E. Based on studies such as these, some have suggested large doses of vitamin E as a preventative against aging, but there is no solid evidence that this practice has any impact on aging.

Another protective antioxidant found in our bodies is superoxide dismutase (SOD), which protects us from the superoxide ion O_2^-, a powerful oxidizing agent that is particularly damaging to vital enzymes. The importance of SOD in opposing the aging process is indicated from the results of a study by Dr. Richard Cutler at the Gerontology Research Center of the National Institutes of Health in Baltimore that showed a strong correlation between the life span of a dozen mammalian species and their levels of SOD. Human SOD is now being produced by the techniques of biotechnology in amounts that will enable scientists to carefully study its effects on aging and on various diseases such as rheumatoid arthritis and muscular dystrophy. Although SOD is available in health food stores in forms to be taken orally, this practice is useless because the SOD is digested (broken down into simpler substances) before it can reach the bloodstream.

Oxidation is only one possible cause for aging. Research continues on many fronts to try to discover why we get ''older'' as time passes.

For more information on the aging process, see Morton Rothstein, ''Biochemical Studies of Aging,'' *Chemical and Engineering News* (August 11, 1986): 26.

4.10 Balancing Oxidation–Reduction Equations

Purpose

- To describe the half-reaction method for balancing oxidation–reduction reactions.

Oxidation–reduction reactions in aqueous solutions are often complicated, which means that it can be difficult to balance their equations by simple inspection. In this section we will discuss a special technique for balancing the equations of redox reactions that occur in aqueous solutions. This is called the **half-reaction method.**

The Half-Reaction Method for Balancing Oxidation–Reduction Reactions in Aqueous Solutions

For oxidation–reduction reactions that occur in aqueous solution, it is useful to separate the reaction into two **half-reactions:** one involving oxidation and the other involving reduction. For example, consider the unbalanced equation for the oxidation–reduction reaction between cerium(IV) ion and tin(II) ion:

$$Ce^{4+}(aq) + Sn^{2+}(aq) \rightarrow Ce^{3+}(aq) + Sn^{4+}(aq)$$

This reaction can be separated into a half-reaction involving the substance being *reduced*,

$$Ce^{4+}(aq) \rightarrow Ce^{3+}(aq)$$

and one involving the substance being *oxidized*,

$$Sn^{2+}(aq) \rightarrow Sn^{4+}(aq)$$

The general procedure is to balance the equations for the half-reactions separately and then to add them to obtain the overall balanced equation. The half-reaction method for balancing oxidation–reduction equations differs slightly depending on whether the reaction takes place in acidic or basic solution.

STEPS IN THE HALF-REACTION METHOD FOR BALANCING EQUATIONS FOR OXIDATION–REDUCTION REACTIONS OCCURRING IN ACIDIC SOLUTION

STEP 1
Write separate equations for the oxidation and reduction half-reactions.

STEP 2
For each half-reaction,
a. Balance all the elements except hydrogen and oxygen.
b. Balance oxygen using H_2O.
c. Balance hydrogen using H^+.
d. Balance the charge using electrons.

STEP 3
If necessary, multiply one or both balanced half-reactions by an integer to equalize the number of electrons transferred in the two half-reactions.

STEP 4
Add the half-reactions and cancel identical species.

STEP 5
Check that the elements and charges are balanced.

We will illustrate this method by balancing the equation for the reaction between permanganate and iron(II) ions in acidic solution:

$$MnO_4^-(aq) + Fe^{2+}(aq) \xrightarrow{\text{Acid}} Fe^{3+}(aq) + Mn^{2+}(aq)$$

This reaction can be used to analyze iron ore for its iron content.

STEP 1
Identify and write equations for the half-reactions. The oxidation states for the half-reaction involving the permanganate ion show that manganese is reduced:

$$MnO_4^- \rightarrow Mn^{2+}$$
$$\begin{array}{cc} \uparrow\ \uparrow & \uparrow \\ +7\ -2\ \text{(each O)} & +2 \end{array}$$

This is the *reduction half-reaction.* The other half-reaction involves the oxidation of iron(II) to iron(III) ion and is the *oxidation half-reaction:*

$$Fe^{2+} \rightarrow Fe^{3+}$$
$$\begin{array}{cc} \uparrow & \uparrow \\ +2 & +3 \end{array}$$

STEP 2

Balance each half-reaction. For the reduction reaction, we have

$$MnO_4^-(aq) \rightarrow Mn^{2+}(aq)$$

a. The manganese is balanced.
b. We balance oxygen by adding $4H_2O$ to the right side of the equation:

$$MnO_4^-(aq) \rightarrow Mn^{2+}(aq) + 4H_2O(l)$$

c. Next we balance hydrogen by adding $8H^+$ to the left side:

$$8H^+(aq) + MnO_4^-(aq) \rightarrow Mn^{2+}(aq) + 4H_2O(l)$$

d. All the elements have been balanced, but we need to balance the charge using electrons. At this point we have the following overall charges for reactants and products in the reduction half-reaction:

$$\underbrace{8H^+(aq) + \underset{8+ \quad\quad 1-}{MnO_4^-(aq)}}_{7+} \rightarrow \underbrace{Mn^{2+}(aq) + 4H_2O(l)}_{2+ \quad\quad 0}$$
$$2+$$

We can equalize the charges by adding five electrons to the left side:

$$\underbrace{5e^- + 8H^+(aq) + MnO_4^-(aq)}_{2+} \rightarrow \underbrace{Mn^{2+}(aq) + 4H_2O(l)}_{2+}$$

Both the *elements* and the *charges* are now balanced, so this represents the balanced reduction half-reaction. The fact that five electrons appear on the reactant side of the equation makes sense, since five electrons are required to reduce MnO_4^- (Mn has an oxidation state of $+7$) to Mn^{2+} (Mn has an oxidation state of $+2$).

For the oxidation reaction

$$Fe^{2+}(aq) \rightarrow Fe^{3+}(aq)$$

the elements are balanced, and we must simply balance the charge:

$$\underbrace{Fe^{2+}(aq)}_{2+} \rightarrow \underbrace{Fe^{3+}(aq)}_{3+}$$

One electron is needed on the right side to give a net $2+$ charge on both sides:

$$\underbrace{Fe^{2+}(aq)}_{2+} \rightarrow \underbrace{Fe^{3+}(aq) + e^-}_{2+}$$

STEP 3

The number of electrons gained in the reduction half-reaction must equal the number of electrons lost in the oxidation half-reaction.

Equalize the electron transfer in the two half-reactions. Since the reduction half-reaction involves a transfer of five electrons and the oxidation half-reaction involves a transfer of only one electron, the oxidation half-reaction must be multiplied by 5:

$$5Fe^{2+}(aq) \rightarrow 5Fe^{3+}(aq) + 5e^-$$

STEP 4

Add the half-reactions. The half-reactions are added to give

$$5e^- + 5Fe^{2+}(aq) + MnO_4^-(aq) + 8H^+(aq)$$
$$\rightarrow 5Fe^{3+}(aq) + Mn^{2+}(aq) + 4H_2O(l) + 5e^-$$

Note that the electrons cancel (as they must) to give the final balanced equation:

$$5Fe^{2+}(aq) + MnO_4^-(aq) + 8H^+(aq) \rightarrow 5Fe^{3+}(aq) + Mn^{2+}(aq) + 4H_2O(l)$$

STEP 5

Check that elements and charges are balanced.

Elements balance: 5 Fe, 1 Mn, 4 O, 8 H $\rightarrow$ 5 Fe, 1 Mn, 4 O, 8 H

Charges balance: $5(2+) + (1-) + 8(1+) = 17+ \rightarrow 5(3+) + (2+) + 0 = 17+$

The equation is balanced.

Sample Exercise 4.21

Potassium dichromate ($K_2Cr_2O_7$) is a bright orange compound that can be reduced to a blue-violet solution of Cr^{3+} ions. Under certain conditions, $K_2Cr_2O_7$ reacts with ethyl alcohol (C_2H_5OH) as follows:

$$H^+(aq) + Cr_2O_7^{2-}(aq) + C_2H_5OH(l) \rightarrow Cr^{3+}(aq) + CO_2(g) + H_2O(l)$$

Balance this equation using the half-reaction method.

Solution

STEP 1

The reduction half-reaction is

$$Cr_2O_7^{2-}(aq) \rightarrow Cr^{3+}(aq)$$

Chromium is reduced from an oxidation state of $+6$ in $Cr_2O_7^{2-}$ to one of $+3$ in Cr^{3+}.

The oxidation half-reaction is

$$C_2H_5OH(l) \rightarrow CO_2(g)$$

Carbon is oxidized from an oxidation state of -2 in C_2H_5OH to $+4$ in CO_2.

STEP 2

Balancing all elements except hydrogen and oxygen in the first half-reaction, we have

$$Cr_2O_7^{2-}(aq) \rightarrow 2Cr^{3+}(aq)$$

Balancing oxygen using H_2O, we have

$$Cr_2O_7^{2-}(aq) \rightarrow 2Cr^{3+}(aq) + 7H_2O(l)$$

Balancing hydrogen using H^+, we have

$$14H^+(aq) + Cr_2O_7^{2-}(aq) \rightarrow 2Cr^{3+}(aq) + 7H_2O(l)$$

Balancing the charge using electrons, we have

$$6e^- + 14H^+(aq) + Cr_2O_7^{2-}(aq) \rightarrow 2Cr^{3+}(aq) + 7H_2O(l)$$

Next, we turn to the oxidation half-reaction

$$C_2H_5OH(l) \rightarrow CO_2(g)$$

Balancing carbon, we have

$$C_2H_5OH(l) \rightarrow 2CO_2(g)$$

Balancing oxygen using H_2O, we have

$$C_2H_5OH(l) + 3H_2O(l) \rightarrow 2CO_2(g)$$

Balancing hydrogen using H^+, we have

$$C_2H_5OH(l) + 3H_2O(l) \rightarrow 2CO_2(g) + 12H^+(aq)$$

Balancing the charge using electrons, we have

$$C_2H_5OH(l) + 3H_2O(l) \rightarrow 2CO_2(g) + 12H^+(aq) + 12e^-$$

STEP 3

In the reduction half-reaction there are 6 electrons on the left-hand side, and there are 12 electrons on the right-hand side of the oxidation half-reaction. Thus we multiply the reduction half-reaction by 2 to give

$$12e^- + 28H^+(aq) + 2Cr_2O_7^{2-}(aq) \rightarrow 4Cr^{3+}(aq) + 14H_2O(l)$$

STEP 4

Adding the half-reactions and canceling identical species, we have

Reduction Half-Reaction
$$12e^- + 28H^+(aq) + 2Cr_2O_7^{2-}(aq) \rightarrow 4Cr^{3+}(aq) + 14H_2O(l)$$

Oxidation Half-Reaction
$$C_2H_5OH(l) + 3H_2O(l) \rightarrow 2CO_2(g) + 12H^+(aq) + 12e^-$$
$$\overline{16H^+(aq) + 2Cr_2O_7^{2-}(aq) + C_2H_5OH(l) \rightarrow 4Cr^{3+} + 11H_2O(l) + 2CO_2(g)}$$

STEP 5

Check that elements and charges are balanced.

Elements balance: 22H, 4Cr, 15O, 2C $\rightarrow$ 22H, 4Cr, 15O, 2C
Charges balance: $+16 + 2(-2) + 0 = +12 \rightarrow 4(+3) + 0 + 0 = +12$

Oxidation–reduction reactions can occur in basic solutions (the reactions involve OH^- ions) as well as in acidic solution (the reactions involve H^+ ions). The half-reaction method for balancing equations is slightly different for the two cases.

THE HALF-REACTION METHOD FOR BALANCING EQUATIONS FOR OXIDATION–REDUCTION REACTIONS OCCURRING IN BASIC SOLUTION

STEP 1

Use the half-reaction method as specified for acidic solutions to obtain the final balanced equation *as if H^+ ions were present.*

STEP 2

To both sides of the equation obtained above, add a number of OH^- ions that is equal to the number of H^+ ions. (We want to eliminate H^+ by forming H_2O.)

STEP 3
Form H_2O on the side containing both H^+ and OH^- ions, and eliminate the number of H_2O molecules that appear on both sides of the equation.

STEP 4
Check that elements and charges are balanced.
   We will illustrate how this method is applied in Sample Exercise 4.22.

Sample Exercise 4.22

Silver is sometimes found in nature as large nuggets; more often it is found mixed with other metals and their ores. An aqueous solution containing cyanide ion is often used to extract the silver using the following reaction that occurs in basic solution:

$$Ag(s) + CN^-(aq) + O_2(g) \xrightarrow{\text{Basic}} Ag(CN)_2^-(aq)$$

Balance this equation using the half-reaction method.

Solution

STEP 1

Balance the equation as if H^+ ions were present. Balance the oxidation half-reaction:

$$CN^-(aq) + Ag(s) \rightarrow Ag(CN)_2^-(aq)$$

Balance carbon and nitrogen:

$$2CN^-(aq) + Ag(s) \rightarrow Ag(CN)_2^-(aq)$$

Balance the charge:

$$2CN^-(aq) + Ag(s) \rightarrow Ag(CN)_2^-(aq) + e^-$$

Balance the reduction half-reaction:

$$O_2(g) \rightarrow$$

Balance oxygen:

$$O_2(g) \rightarrow 2H_2O(l)$$

Balance hydrogen:

$$O_2(g) + 4H^+(aq) \rightarrow 2H_2O(l)$$

Balance the charge:

$$4e^- + O_2(g) + 4H^+(aq) \rightarrow 2H_2O(l)$$

Multiply the balanced oxidation half-reaction by 4:

$$8CN^-(aq) + 4Ag(s) \rightarrow 4Ag(CN)_2^-(aq) + 4e^-$$

Add the half-reactions, and cancel identical species:

Oxidation Half-Reaction

$$8CN^-(aq) + 4Ag(s) \rightarrow 4Ag(CN)_2^-(aq) + 4e^-$$

Reduction Half-Reaction

$$4e^- + O_2(g) + 4H^+(aq) \rightarrow 2H_2O(l)$$

$$8CN^-(aq) + 4Ag(s) + O_2(g) + 4H^+(aq) \rightarrow 4Ag(CN)_2^-(aq) + 2H_2O(l)$$

STEP 2

Add OH^- ions to both sides of balanced equation to eliminate the H^+ ions. We need to add $4OH^-$ to each side:

$$8CN^-(aq) + 4Ag(s) + O_2(g) + \underbrace{4H^+(aq) + 4OH^-(aq)}_{4H_2O(l)}$$

$$\rightarrow 4Ag(CN)_2^-(aq) + 2H_2O(l) + 4OH^-(aq)$$

STEP 3

Eliminate as many H_2O molecules as possible.

$$8CN^-(aq) + 4Ag(s) + O_2(g) + 2H_2O(l) \rightarrow 4Ag(CN)_2^-(aq) + 4OH^-(aq)$$

STEP 4

Check that elements and charges are balanced.

Elements balance: 8C, 8N, 4Ag, 4O, 4H $\rightarrow$ 8C, 8N, 4Ag, 4O, 4H

Charges balance: $8(1-) + 0 + 0 + 0 = 8- \rightarrow 4(1-) + 4(1-) = 8-$

4.11 Simple Oxidation–Reduction Titrations

Purpose

- To learn to do the calculations associated with oxidation–reduction titrations.

Oxidation–reduction reactions are commonly used as the basis for volumetric analytical procedures. For example, a reducing substance can be titrated with a solution of a strong oxidizing agent, or vice versa. Three of the most frequently used oxidizing agents are aqueous solutions of potassium permanganate ($KMnO_4$), potassium dichromate ($K_2Cr_2O_7$), and cerium hydrogen sulfate [$Ce(HSO_4)_4$].

Figure 4.11
Solid potassium permanganate.

Sample Exercise 4.23

Cerium (IV) ion is a strong oxidizing agent that accepts one electron to produce cerium(III) ion:

$$Ce^{4+}(aq) + e^- \rightarrow Ce^{3+}(aq)$$

A solution containing an unknown concentration of Sn^{2+} ions was titrated with a solution containing Ce^{4+} ions, which oxidize the Sn^{2+} ions to Sn^{4+} ions. In one titration, 1.00 L of the unknown solution required 46.45 mL of a 0.1050 *M* Ce^{4+} solution to reach the stoichiometric point. Calculate the concentration of Sn^{2+} ions in the unknown solution.

Solution

The unbalanced equation for the titration reaction is

$$Ce^{4+}(aq) + Sn^{2+}(aq) \rightarrow Ce^{3+}(aq) + Sn^{4+}(aq)$$

The balanced equation is

$$2Ce^{4+}(aq) + Sn^{2+}(aq) \rightarrow 2Ce^{3+}(aq) + Sn^{4+}(aq)$$

We can obtain the number of moles of Ce^{4+} ions from the volume and molarity of the Ce^{4+} solution used as the titrant:

$$46.45 \text{ mL} \times \frac{1 \text{ L}}{1000 \text{ mL}} \times \frac{0.1050 \text{ mol } Ce^{4+}}{\text{L}} = 4.877 \times 10^{-3} \text{ mol } Ce^{4+}$$

The number of moles of Sn^{2+} ions can be obtained by applying the appropriate mole ratio from the balanced equation:

$$4.877 \times 10^{-3} \text{ mol } Ce^{4+} \times \frac{1 \text{ mol } Sn^{2+}}{2 \text{ mol } Ce^{4+}} = 2.439 \times 10^{-3} \text{ mol } Sn^{2+}$$

This value represents the quantity of Sn^{2+} ions in 1.00 L of solution. Thus the concentration of Sn^{2+} in the unknown solution is

$$\text{Molarity} = \frac{\text{mol } Sn^{2+}}{\text{L solution}} = \frac{2.439 \times 10^{-3} \text{ mol } Sn^{2+}}{1.00 \text{ L}} = 2.44 \times 10^{-3} M$$

Another strong oxidizing agent, the permanganate ion (MnO_4^-), can undergo several different reactions. The one that occurs in acid solution is the most commonly used:

$$MnO_4^-(aq) + 8H^+(aq) + 5e^- \rightarrow Mn^{2+}(aq) + 4H_2O(l)$$

Permanganate has the advantage of being its own indicator—the MnO_4^- ion is intensely purple, and the Mn^{2+} ion is almost colorless. A typical titration using permanganate is illustrated in Fig. 4.11. As long as some reducing agent remains in the solution being titrated, the solution remains colorless (assuming all other species present are colorless), since the purple MnO_4^- ion being added is converted to the essentially colorless Mn^{2+} ion. However, when all the reducing agent has been consumed, the next drop of permanganate titrant will turn the solution being titrated light purple (pink). Thus the endpoint (where the color change indicates the titration should stop) occurs approximately one drop beyond the stoichiometric point (the actual point at which all the reducing agent has been consumed).

Sample Exercise 4.24 describes a typical volumetric analysis using permanganate.

Sample Exercise 4.24

Iron ores contain iron oxide minerals, which often contain a mixture of Fe^{2+} and Fe^{3+} ions. Such an ore can be analyzed for its iron content by dissolving it in acidic solution, reducing all the iron to Fe^{2+} ions, and then titrating with a standard solution of potassium permanganate. In the resulting solution, MnO_4^- is reduced to

Mn^{2+} and Fe^{2+} is oxidized to Fe^{3+}. A sample of iron ore weighing 0.3500 g was dissolved in acidic solution, and all the iron was reduced to Fe^{2+}. Then the solution was titrated with a 1.621×10^{-2} M $KMnO_4$ solution. The titration required 41.56 mL of the permanganate solution to reach the pink endpoint. Determine the mass percent of iron in the iron ore.

Solution

First we write the unbalanced equation for the reaction:

$$H^+(aq) + MnO_4^-(aq) + Fe^{2+}(aq) \rightarrow Fe^{3+}(aq) + Mn^{2+}(aq) + H_2O(l)$$

Using the half-reaction method, we obtain the balanced equation:

$$8H^+(aq) + MnO_4^-(aq) + 5Fe^{2+}(aq) \rightarrow 5Fe^{3+}(aq) + Mn^{2+}(aq) + 4H_2O(l)$$

The number of moles of MnO_4^- ion required in the titration is found from the volume and concentration of permanganate solution used:

$$41.56 \; \cancel{mL} \times \frac{1 \; \cancel{L}}{1000 \; \cancel{mL}} \times \frac{1.621 \times 10^{-2} \; mol \; MnO_4^-}{\cancel{L}}$$

$$= 6.737 \times 10^{-4} \; mol \; MnO_4^-$$

The balanced equation shows that five times as much Fe^{2+} as MnO_4^- is required:

$$6.737 \times 10^{-4} \; \cancel{mol \; MnO_4^-} \times \frac{5 \; mol \; Fe^{2+}}{1 \; \cancel{mol \; MnO_4^-}} = 3.368 \times 10^{-3} \; mol \; Fe^{2+}$$

This means that the 0.3500-g sample of iron ore contained 3.368×10^{-3} mol iron. The mass of iron present is

$$3.368 \times 10^{-3} \; \cancel{mol \; Fe} \times \frac{55.85 \; g \; Fe}{1 \; \cancel{mol \; Fe}} = 0.1881 \; g \; Fe$$

The mass percent of iron in the iron ore is

$$\frac{0.1881 \; \cancel{g}}{0.3500 \; \cancel{g}} \times 100 = 53.74\%$$

FOR REVIEW

Summary

Many important chemical reactions occur in aqueous solutions. Water is a good solvent for ionic solids because the polar water molecules interact with the ions. This assists in the dissolving process. One characteristic property of a solution is its electrical conductivity. Solutions of strong electrolytes conduct current easily because there is 100% dissociation to ions. Weak electrolytes dissociate only to a small extent and their solutions exhibit low conductivity. Nonelectrolytes produce no ions when they dissolve and conduct no current.

The Arrhenius definition regards an acid as a substance that produces H^+ ions (protons) in solution; a base is a substance that produces OH^- ions. The Brønsted–

Lowry concept defines an acid as a proton donor and a base as a proton acceptor. A strong acid dissociates completely in water, and a weak acid dissociates only very slightly.

One means of describing solution concentration is molarity:

$$\text{Molarity } (M) = \frac{\text{moles of solute}}{\text{liters of solution}}$$

Since molarity relates the volume of the solution and the moles of solute, it allows the principles of stoichiometry to be applied to reactions in solution. A standard solution is one in which the molarity is accurately known. When a solution is diluted, only solvent is added, which means that

moles of solute after dilution = moles of solute before dilution

which leads to the relationship

$$M_1V_1 = M_2V_2$$

Three types of equations describe reactions in solution: molecular equations, which show reactants and products as if they were molecules; complete ionic equations, in which all reactants and products that are strong electrolytes are represented as ions; and net ionic equations, in which only those solution components undergoing a change are represented. Spectator ions (those ions remaining unchanged in a reaction) are not included in the net ionic equation.

General rules concerning solubility help to predict the outcomes of precipitation reactions.

Volumetric analysis involves the titration of a solution containing the substance to be determined. One type of volumetric analysis utilizes neutralization (acid–base) reactions; the unknown concentration of an acid is determined by titration with a base of known concentration (or vice versa). The point in the titration where just enough titrant has been added to react exactly with the substance being determined is called the stoichiometric (equivalence) point.

Oxidation–reduction (redox) reactions involve a transfer of electrons. One method for keeping track of electrons is to use oxidation states for atoms in compounds. A series of rules is used to assign these oxidation states. Oxidation is an increase in oxidation state (a loss of electrons). Reduction is a decrease in oxidation state (a gain of electrons). An oxidizing agent accepts electrons, and a reducing agent donates electrons.

Equations for oxidation–reduction reactions occurring in aqueous solution can be balanced using the half-reaction method, which splits a reaction into two parts (the oxidation half-reaction and the reduction half-reaction). The balanced equation can be used to carry out the stoichiometric calculations for an oxidation–reduction titration.

Key Terms

aqueous solution

Section 4.1

polar molecule
hydration
solubility

Section 4.2

solute

solvent
electrical conductivity
strong electrolyte
weak electrolyte
nonelectrolyte
acid
strong acid
strong base

weak acid
weak base

Section 4.3

molarity
standard solution
dilution

Section 4.5

precipitation reaction
precipitate

Section 4.6

molecular equation
complete ionic equation
spectator ions

net ionic equation

Section 4.7

gravimetric analysis

Section 4.8

neutralization reaction
titration
volumetric analysis

titrant	oxidation state
analyte	oxidation
stoichiometric (equivalence) point	reduction
indicator	oxidizing agent
endpoint	reducing agent
Section 4.9	*Section 4.10*
oxidation–reduction (redox) reaction	half-reactions

A blue question or exercise number indicates that the answer to that question or exercise appears at the back of this book and a solution appears in the Solutions Guide.

Questions

1. Distinguish between the terms *slightly soluble* and *weak electrolyte*.

2. How would you determine experimentally whether a substance is a strong or a weak electrolyte?

Exercises

In this section similar exercises are paired.

Aqueous Solutions: Strong and Weak Electrolytes

3. Show how each of the following strong electrolytes "breaks up" into its component ions upon dissolving in water.
   a. NaBr
   b. $MgCl_2$
   c. $Al(NO_3)_3$
   d. $(NH_4)_2SO_4$
   e. HI
   f. $FeSO_4$
   g. $KMnO_4$
   h. $HClO_4$
   i. $NH_4C_2H_3O_2$ (ammonium acetate)

4. Show how each of the following strong acids or strong bases "breaks up" into its component ions upon dissolving in water.
   a. HCl
   b. HNO_3
   c. $Ca(OH)_2$
   d. KOH

5. Calcium chloride is a strong electrolyte and is used to "salt" streets in the winter to melt ice and snow. Write a reaction to show how this substance breaks apart when it dissolves in water.

6. Commercial cold packs and hot packs are available for treating athletic injuries. Both types contain a pouch of water and a dry chemical. When the pack is struck, the pouch of water breaks, dissolving the chemical, and the solution becomes either hot or cold. Many hot packs use magnesium sulfate, and many cold packs use ammonium nitrate. Write reactions to show how these strong electrolytes break apart when they dissolve in water.

Solution Concentration: Molarity

7. Describe how you would prepare 1.0 L of each of the following solutions.
   a. 0.10 *M* NaCl from solid NaCl
   b. 0.10 *M* NaCl from a 2.5 *M* stock solution
   c. 0.20 *M* $NaIO_3$ from solid $NaIO_3$
   d. 0.010 *M* $NaIO_3$ from a 0.20 *M* stock solution
   e. 0.050 *M* potassium hydrogen phthalate ($KHC_8H_4O_4$, abbreviated KHP) from solid potassium hydrogen phthalate
   f. 0.040 *M* KHP from a 0.50 *M* stock solution

8. How would you prepare 1.00 L of a 0.50 *M* solution of each of the following?
   a. H_2SO_4 from "concentrated" (18 *M*) sulfuric acid
   b. HCl from "concentrated" (12 *M*) reagent
   c. $NiCl_2$ from the salt $NiCl_2 \cdot 6H_2O$
   d. HNO_3 from "concentrated" (16 *M*) reagent
   e. Sodium carbonate from the pure solid

9. Calculate the molarity of each of these solutions.
   a. A 5.623-g sample of $NaHCO_3$ is dissolved in enough water to make 250.0 mL of solution.
   b. A 184.6-mg sample of $K_2Cr_2O_7$ is dissolved in enough water to make 500.0 mL of solution.
   c. A 0.1025-g sample of copper metal is dissolved in 35 mL of concentrated HNO_3 to form Cu^{2+} ions and then water is added to make a total volume of 200.0 mL. (Calculate the molarity of Cu^{2+}.)

10. Calculate the molarity of each of the following solutions.
    a. A 16.45-g sample of NaCl is dissolved in enough water to make 1.000 L of solution.
    b. An 853.5-mg sample of KIO_3 is dissolved in enough water to make 250.0 mL of solution.
    c. A 0.4508-g sample of iron is dissolved in a small amount of concentrated nitric acid forming Fe^{3+} ions in solution and is diluted to a total volume of 500.0 mL. (Calculate the molarity of Fe^{3+}.)

11. Calculate the concentration of all ions present in each of the following solutions of strong electrolytes.
    a. 0.15 M $CaCl_2$
    b. 0.26 M $Al(NO_3)_3$
    c. 0.25 M $K_2Cr_2O_7$
    d. 2.0×10^{-3} M $Al_2(SO_4)_3$

12. Calculate the concentration of all ions present in each of the following solutions of strong electrolytes.
    a. 0.100 g of $MgCl_2$ in 100.0 mL of solution
    b. 55.1 mg NH_4Br in 500.0 mL of solution
    c. 5.47 g Na_2S in 1.00 L of solution
    d. 0.208 g $AlCl_3$ in 250.0 mL of solution

13. A solution is prepared by dissolving 10.8 g ammonium sulfate in enough water to make 100.0 mL of stock solution. A 10.00-mL sample of this stock solution is added to 50.00 mL of water. Calculate the concentration of ammonium ions and sulfate ions in the final solution.

14. A solution of ethanol (C_2H_5OH) in water is prepared by dissolving 10.0 mL ethanol (density 0.79 g/cm^3) in enough water to make 250.0 mL of solution. What is the molarity of the ethanol in this solution?

15. The World Health Organization lists the maximum desirable concentrations of Mg^{2+} and Ca^{2+} in drinking water as 30. and 75 mg/L, respectively. The maximum permissible concentrations are 1250 and 200. mg/L for the same ions. Calculate all four of these concentrations in moles per liter. (Recall that a decimal point makes trailing zeros count as significant digits.)

16. Disodium aurothiomalate ($Na_2C_4H_3O_4SAu$) has the trade name Myocrisin and is used in the treatment of rheumatoid arthritis. Patients receive weekly intramuscular injections consisting of 50.0 mg Myocrisin in 0.500 mL of solution. During treatment, blood serum levels of gold can reach levels as high as 300.0 μg gold per 100.0 mL serum. Calculate these two concentrations of Myocrisin in terms of molarity.

17. A solution is prepared by dissolving 0.5842 g oxalic acid ($H_2C_2O_4$) in enough water to make 100.0 mL of solution. A 10.00-mL aliquot (portion) of this solution is then diluted to a final volume of 250.0 mL. What is the final molarity of the oxalic acid solution?

18. A stock solution containing Mn^{2+} ions was prepared by dissolving 1.584 g pure manganese metal in nitric acid and diluting to a final volume of 1.00 L. The following solutions were then prepared by dilution:

    For solution A, 50.00 mL of stock solution was diluted to 1000.0 mL.

    For solution B, 10.00 mL of solution A was diluted to 250.0 mL.

    For solution C, 10.00 mL of solution B was diluted to 500.0 mL.

    Calculate the concentrations of the stock solution and solutions A, B, and C.

Precipitation Reactions

19. Predict the products and write the balanced molecular equation, complete ionic equation, and the net ionic equation for each of the following.
    a. $BaCl_2(aq) + Na_2SO_4(aq) \rightarrow$
    b. $Pb(NO_3)_2(aq) + HCl(aq) \rightarrow$
    c. $AgNO_3(aq) + Na_3PO_4(aq) \rightarrow$
    d. $NaOH(aq) + Fe(NO_3)_3(aq) \rightarrow$

20. Predict the products and write the balanced molecular equation, complete ionic equation, and the net ionic equation for each of the following.
    a. $CuCl_2(aq) + Na_2S(aq) \rightarrow$
    b. $NiSO_4(aq) + KOH(aq) \rightarrow$
    c. $KOH(aq) + NaNO_3(aq) \rightarrow$
    d. $NaOH(aq) + MnSO_4(aq) \rightarrow$

21. Write net ionic equations for each of the following.
    a. $AgNO_3(aq) + KI(aq) \rightarrow$
    b. $CuSO_4(aq) + Na_2S(aq) \rightarrow$
    c. $CoCl_2(aq) + NaOH(aq) \rightarrow$
    d. $NiCl_2(aq) + HNO_3(aq) \rightarrow$

22. Write the net ionic equation for each of the following.
    a. $AgNO_3(aq) + BaCl_2(aq) \rightarrow$
    b. $FeSO_4(aq) + K_2S(aq) \rightarrow$
    c. $NaOH(aq) + K_2SO_4(aq) \rightarrow$
    d. $Hg_2(NO_3)_2(aq) + HCl(aq) \rightarrow$

23. Write net ionic equations for the reaction, if any, that occurs when aqueous solutions of the following are mixed.
    a. Ammonium sulfate and barium nitrate
    b. Lead(II) nitrate and sodium chloride
    c. Sodium phosphate and potassium nitrate
    d. Sodium bromide and hydrochloric acid
    e. Copper(II) chloride and sodium hydroxide

24. Write net ionic equations for the reaction, if any, that occurs when aqueous solutions of the following are mixed.
    a. Iron(III) nitrate and sodium hydroxide
    b. Cadmium chloride and sodium sulfide (cadmium only forms Cd^{2+} ions)
    c. Silver nitrate and rubidium bromide
    d. Copper(II) chloride and calcium hydroxide

25. A lake may be polluted with Pb^{2+} ions. What precipitation reaction might you use to test for the presence of Pb^{2+}?

26. A sample may contain any or all of the following ions: Hg_2^{2+}, Ba^{2+}, and Mn^{2+}. No precipitate formed when an aqueous solution of NaCl or Na_2SO_4 was added to the sample solution. A precipitate formed when the sample solution was made basic with NaOH. Which ion or ions are present in the sample solution?

27. What mass of solid AgBr is produced when 100.0 mL of 0.150 M $AgNO_3$ is added to 20.0 mL of 1.00 M NaBr?

28. What mass of barium sulfate is produced when 100.0 mL of a 0.100 M solution of barium chloride is mixed with 100.0 mL of a 0.100 M solution of iron(III) sulfate?

29. What volume of 0.100 M NaOH is required to precipitate all of the nickel(II) ions from 150.0 mL of 0.250 M Ni $(NO_3)_2$?

30. What volume of 0.204 M HCl is required to precipitate all the silver ions from 50.0 mL of a 0.0500 M solution of $AgNO_3$?

Acid–Base Reactions

31. Write the balanced molecular, complete ionic, and net ionic equations for each of the following acid–base reactions.
    a. $HClO_4(aq) + Mg(OH)_2(s) \rightarrow$
    b. $HCN(aq) + NaOH(aq) \rightarrow$
    c. $HCl(aq) + NaOH(aq) \rightarrow$

32. Write the balanced molecular, complete ionic, and net ionic equations for each of the following acid–base reactions.
    a. $HNO_3(aq) + Al(OH)_3(s) \rightarrow$
    b. $HC_2H_3O_2(aq) + KOH(aq) \rightarrow$
    c. $Ca(OH)_2(aq) + HCl(aq) \rightarrow$

33. Write the balanced molecular, complete ionic, and net ionic equations for the reactions that occur when the following are mixed.
    a. Potassium hydroxide (aqueous) and nitric acid
    b. Barium hydroxide (aqueous) and hydrochloric acid
    c. Perchloric acid [$HClO_4(aq)$] and solid iron(III) hydroxide

34. Write the balanced molecular, complete ionic, and net ionic equations for the reactions that occur when the following are mixed.
    a. Solid silver hydroxide and hydrobromic acid
    b. Aqueous strontium hydroxide and hydroiodic acid
    c. Solid iron(III) hydroxide and nitric acid

35. What volume of each of the following acids will react completely with 50.00 mL of 0.200 M NaOH?
    a. 0.100 M HCl
    b. 0.200 M H_3PO_4 (3 acidic hydrogens)
    c. 0.150 M HNO_3
    d. 0.200 M $HC_2H_3O_2$ (1 acidic hydrogen)

36. What volume of each of the following bases will react completely with 25.00 mL of 0.200 M HCl?
    a. 0.100 M NaOH
    b. 0.0500 M $Ba(OH)_2$
    c. 0.250 M KOH

37. A solution is prepared by dissolving 15 g NaOH in 150 mL of 0.25 M nitric acid. Will the final solution be acidic, basic, or neutral? Calculate the concentrations of all the ions present in the solution after the reaction has occurred.

38. Hydrochloric acid (75 mL of 0.25 M) is added to 225 mL of 0.055 M $Ba(OH)_2$ solution. What is the concentration of the excess H^+ or OH^- ions left in this solution?

39. A 25.00-mL sample of hydrochloric acid solution requires 24.16 mL of 0.106 M sodium hydroxide for complete neutralization. What is the concentration of the original hydrochloric acid solution?

40. A 50.00-mL sample of aqueous $Ca(OH)_2$ requires 34.66 mL of 0.0980 M nitric acid for neutralization. Calculate the concentration of the original solution of calcium hydroxide.

Oxidation–Reduction Reactions

41. Assign oxidation states for all atoms in each of the following compounds.
    a. $KMnO_4$
    b. NiO_2
    c. $K_4Fe(CN)_6$ (Fe only)
    d. $(NH_4)_2HPO_4$
    e. P_4O_6
    f. Fe_3O_4
    g. $XeOF_4$
    h. SF_4
    i. CO
    j. $Na_2C_2O_4$

42. Assign oxidation states for all atoms in each of the following compounds.
    a. UO_2^{2+}
    b. As_2O_3
    c. $NaBiO_3$
    d. As_4
    e. $HAsO_2$
    f. $Mg_2P_2O_7$
    g. $Na_2S_2O_3$
    h. Hg_2Cl_2
    i. $Ca(NO_3)_2$

43. Assign the oxidation state for chlorine in each of the following anions: OCl^-, ClO_2^-, ClO_3^-, and ClO_4^-.

44. Assign the oxidation state for nitrogen in each of the following.
    a. Li_3N
    b. NH_3
    c. N_2H_4
    d. NO
    e. N_2O
    f. NO_2
    g. NO_2^-
    h. NO_3^-
    i. N_2

45. Specify which of the following are oxidation–reduction reactions, and identify the oxidizing agent, the reducing agent, the substance being oxidized, and the substance being reduced.
    a. $CH_4(g) + 2O_2(g) \rightarrow CO_2(g) + 2H_2O(g)$
    b. $Zn(s) + 2HCl(aq) \rightarrow ZnCl_2(aq) + H_2(g)$
    c. $Cr_2O_7^{2-}(aq) + 2OH^-(aq) \rightarrow 2CrO_4^{2-}(aq) + H_2O(l)$
    d. $O_3(g) + NO(g) \rightarrow O_2(g) + NO_2(g)$
    e. $2H_2O_2(l) \rightarrow 2H_2O(l) + O_2(g)$
    f. $2CuCl(aq) \rightarrow CuCl_2(aq) + Cu(s)$

46. Specify which of the following are oxidation–reduction reactions, and identify the oxidizing agent, the reducing agent, the substance being oxidized, and the substance being reduced.
    a. $Cu(s) + 2Ag^+(aq) \rightarrow 2Ag(s) + Cu^{2+}(aq)$
    b. $HCl(g) + NH_3(g) \rightarrow NH_4Cl(s)$
    c. $SiCl_4(l) + 2H_2O(l) \rightarrow 4HCl(aq) + SiO_2(s)$
    d. $SiCl_4(l) + 2Mg(s) \rightarrow 2MgCl_2(s) + Si(s)$
    e. $Al(OH)_4^-(aq) \rightarrow AlO_2^-(aq) + 2H_2O(l)$

47. Balance the following oxidation–reduction reactions that occur in acidic solution.
    a. $Zn(s) + HCl(aq) \rightarrow Zn^{2+}(aq) + H_2(g)$
    b. $I^-(aq) + ClO^-(aq) \rightarrow I_3^-(aq) + Cl^-(aq)$
    c. $As_2O_3(s) + NO_3^-(aq) \rightarrow H_3AsO_4(aq) + NO(g)$
    d. $Br^-(aq) + MnO_4^-(aq) \rightarrow Br_2(l) + Mn^{2+}(aq)$
    e. $CH_3OH(aq) + Cr_2O_7^{2-}(aq) \rightarrow CH_2O(aq) + Cr^{3+}(aq)$

48. Balance the following oxidation–reduction reactions that occur in acidic solution using the half-reaction method.
    a. $Cu(s) + HNO_3(aq) \rightarrow Cu^{2+}(aq) + NO(g)$
    b. $Cr_2O_7^{2-}(aq) + Cl^-(aq) \rightarrow Cr^{3+}(aq) + Cl_2(g)$
    c. $Pb(s) + PbO_2(s) + H_2SO_4(aq) \rightarrow PbSO_4(s)$
    d. $Mn^{2+}(aq) + NaBiO_3(s) \rightarrow Bi^{3+}(aq) + MnO_4^-(aq)$
    e. $H_3AsO_4(aq) + Zn(s) \rightarrow AsH_3(g) + Zn^{2+}(aq)$

49. Balance the following oxidation–reduction reactions that occur in basic solution.
    a. $Al(s) + MnO_4^-(aq) \rightarrow MnO_2(s) + Al(OH)_4^-(aq)$
    b. $Cl_2(g) \rightarrow Cl^-(aq) + ClO^-(aq)$
    c. $NO_2^-(aq) + Al(s) \rightarrow NH_3(g) + AlO_2^-(aq)$

50. Balance the following oxidation–reduction reactions that occur in basic solution.
    a. $Cr(s) + CrO_4^{2-}(aq) \rightarrow Cr(OH)_3(s)$
    b. $MnO_4^-(aq) + S^{2-}(aq) \rightarrow MnS(s) + S(s)$
    c. $CN^-(aq) + MnO_4^-(aq) \rightarrow CNO^-(aq) + MnO_2(s)$

51. Chlorine gas was first prepared in 1774 by C. W. Scheele by oxidizing hydrochloric acid with manganese(IV) oxide. The reaction is

    $NaCl(aq) + H_2SO_4(aq) + MnO_2(s)$
    $\rightarrow Na_2SO_4(aq) + MnCl_2(aq) + H_2O(l) + Cl_2(g)$

    Balance this equation.

52. Gold metal will not dissolve in either concentrated nitric acid or concentrated hydrochloric acid. It will dissolve, however, in aqua regia, a mixture of the two concentrated acids. The products of the reaction are the $AuCl_4^-$ ion and gaseous NO. Write a balanced equation for the dissolution of gold in aqua regia.

53. A solution of permanganate was standardized by titration with oxalic acid ($H_2C_2O_4$). It required 28.97 mL of the permanganate solution to react completely with 0.1058 g of oxalic acid. The unbalanced equation for the reaction is

$$MnO_4^-(aq) + H_2C_2O_4(aq) \xrightarrow{\text{Acid}} Mn^{2+}(aq) + CO_2(g)$$

Calculate the molarity of the permanganate solution.

54. What mass of CO_2 is produced from the reaction of 0.500 g oxalic acid with 50.00 mL of a 0.0200 M $KMnO_4$ solution in acidic solution? (See Exercise 53.)

55. A 50.00-mL sample of solution containing Fe^{2+} ions is titrated with a 0.0216 M $KMnO_4$ solution. It required 20.62 mL of the $KMnO_4$ solution to oxidize all the Fe^{2+} ions to Fe^{3+} ions by the reaction

$$MnO_4^-(aq) + Fe^{2+}(aq)$$
$$\xrightarrow{\text{Acid}} Mn^{2+}(aq) + Fe^{3+}(aq) \text{ (Unbalanced)}$$

a. What was the concentration of Fe^{2+} ions in the sample solution?

b. What volume of 0.0150 M $K_2Cr_2O_7$ solution would it take to do the same titration? The reaction is

$$Cr_2O_7^{2-}(aq) + Fe^{2+}(aq)$$
$$\xrightarrow{\text{Acid}} Cr^{3+}(aq) + Fe^{3+}(aq) \text{ (Unbalanced)}$$

56. The iron content of iron ore can be determined by titration with standard $KMnO_4$ solution. The iron ore is dissolved in HCl, and all the iron is reduced to Fe^{2+} ions. This solution is then titrated with $KMnO_4$ solution, producing Fe^{3+} and Mn^{2+} ions in acidic solution. If it required 41.95 mL of 0.0205 M $KMnO_4$ to titrate a solution made from 0.6128 g iron ore, what is the mass percent of iron in the iron ore?

Additional Exercises

57. Calcium metal will react with water as follows:

$$Ca(s) + 2H_2O(l) \rightarrow Ca(OH)_2(aq) + H_2(g)$$

What is the molarity of hydroxide ions in the solution formed when 4.25 g calcium metal is dissolved in enough water to make a final volume of 225 mL?

58. The Ostwald process for the commercial production of nitric acid involves the following three steps:

$$4NH_3(g) + 5O_2(g) \rightarrow 4NO(g) + 6H_2O(g)$$
$$2NO(g) + O_2(g) \rightarrow 2NO_2(g)$$
$$3NO_2(g) + H_2O(l) \rightarrow 2HNO_3(aq) + NO(g)$$

a. Which reactions in the Ostwald process are oxidation–reduction reactions?

b. Identify each oxidizing agent and reducing agent.

c. How much nitric oxide (NO) can be produced from a mixture of 5.0×10^6 g ammonia and 5.0×10^7 g O_2?

59. One of the classical methods for the determination of the manganese content in steel is to convert all the manganese to the deeply colored permanganate ion and then to measure the absorption of light. The steel is dissolved in nitric acid, producing the manganese(II) ion and nitrogen dioxide gas. This solution is then reacted with an acidic solution containing periodate ion; the products are the permanganate and iodate ions. Write balanced chemical equations for both these steps.

60. A piece of copper metal (1.50 g) is placed in 250 mL of a 0.20 M $AgNO_3$ solution. Will all the copper dissolve in this solution? The net ionic equation is

$$Cu(s) + 2Ag^+(aq) \rightarrow 2Ag(s) + Cu^{2+}(aq)$$

61. During the developing process, silver bromide is removed from photographic film by the fixer. The major component of the fixer is sodium thiosulfate. The net ionic equation for the reaction is

$$AgBr(s) + 2S_2O_3^{2-}(aq) \rightarrow Ag(S_2O_3)_2^{3-}(aq) + Br^-(aq)$$

What mass of AgBr can be dissolved by 1.00 L of 0.200 M $Na_2S_2O_3$?

62. A 100.0-mL aliquot of 0.200 M aqueous potassium hydroxide is mixed with 100.0 mL of 0.200 M aqueous magnesium nitrate.

a. Write a balanced chemical equation for any reaction that occurs.

b. What precipitate forms?

c. What mass of precipitate is produced?

63. The aluminum ion content of a substance can be determined by reaction with a solution of 8-hydroxyquinoline (C_9H_7NO) to produce a precipitate. The net ionic equation is

$$Al^{3+}(aq) + 3C_9H_7NO(aq) \rightarrow Al(C_9H_6NO)_3(s) + 3H^+(aq)$$

A mass of 0.1248 g Al(C$_9$H$_6$NO)$_3$ was obtained by precipitating all the Al^{3+} from a solution prepared by dissolving 1.8571 g of a mineral. What is the mass percent of aluminum in the mineral?

64. The thallium (present as Tl$_2$SO$_4$) in a 9.486-g pesticide sample was precipitated as thallium(I) iodide. Calculate the percentage of Tl$_2$SO$_4$ in the sample if 0.1824 g TlI was recovered.

65. A 10.00-mL sample of vinegar, an aqueous solution of acetic acid (HC$_2$H$_3$O$_2$), is titrated with 0.5062 *M* NaOH, and 16.58 mL is required to reach the equivalence point.
   a. What is the molarity of the acetic acid?
   b. If the density of the vinegar is 1.006 g/cm^3, what is the mass percent of acetic acid in the vinegar?

66. A 50.00-mL sample of an ammonia solution is analyzed by titration with HCl. The reaction is

$$NH_3(aq) + H^+(aq) \rightarrow NH_4^+(aq)$$

It took 39.47 mL of 0.0984 *M* HCl to titrate (react completely with) the ammonia. What is the concentration of the original ammonia solution?

67. The concentration of a certain sodium hydroxide solution was determined by using the solution to titrate a sample of potassium hydrogen phthalate (KHP), an acid with one acidic hydrogen and a molar mass of 204.22 g/mol. In the titration, 20.46 mL of the sodium hydroxide solution was required to react with 0.1082 g KHP. Calculate the molarity of the sodium hydroxide.

68. Lead chromate (PbCrO$_4$) is used as a pigment in paints and is commonly called chrome yellow. What mass of chrome yellow is produced when 100.0 mL of 0.4100 *M* sodium chromate is mixed with 100.0 mL of 0.3200 *M* lead(II) nitrate?

69. Rust stains can be removed by washing a surface with a dilute solution of oxalic acid (H$_2$C$_2$O$_4$). The reaction is

$$Fe_2O_3(s) + 6H_2C_2O_4(aq)$$
$$\rightarrow 2Fe(C_2O_4)_3{}^{3-}(aq) + 3H_2O(l) + 6H^+(aq)$$

   a. Is this an oxidation–reduction reaction?
   b. What mass of rust can be removed by 1.0 L of a 0.14 *M* solution of oxalic acid?

70. What mass of Fe(OH)$_3$ would be produced by reacting 75.0 mL of 0.105 *M* Fe(NO$_3$)$_3$ with 125 mL of 0.150 *M* NaOH?

71. You are given a compound that is either iron(II) sulfate or iron(III) sulfate. How could you determine the identity of the compound using a dilute solution of potassium permanganate?

72. The legal definition of intoxication in some states is a blood alcohol (C$_2$H$_5$OH) level of 0.1% by mass or higher. In a given case, 35.48.mL of 0.05182 *M* K$_2$Cr$_2$O$_7$ was required to titrate a 50.02-g sample of blood.
   a. Assuming that only C$_2$H$_5$OH reacts with K$_2$Cr$_2$O$_7$, was the

person from whom this blood was taken legally intoxicated? (See Sample Exercise 4.21.)
   b. What would be your answer to part a if instead it required 48.02 mL of the same K$_2$Cr$_2$O$_7$ dichromate solution to titrate 48.91 g blood?

73. Stibnite (Sb$_2$S$_3$) is the most important ore containing antimony. A 0.506-g sample of ore was chemically treated to produce antimony(III) ions in solution. The antimony(III) was oxidized to antimony(V) by adding 25.00 mL of 0.0233 *M* KMnO$_4$ solution. The excess KMnO$_4$ was titrated with 0.0843 *M* Fe^{2+}; 2.58 mL was required, producing Fe^{3+}(*aq*) and Mn^{2+}(*aq*). All reactions were carried out in acidic solutions. Calculate the mass percent of Sb$_2$S$_3$ in the sample.

74. Saccharin (C$_7$H$_5$NO$_3$S) is sometimes dispensed in tablet form. Ten tablets with a total mass of 0.5894 g were dissolved in water. They were oxidized to convert all the sulfur to sulfate ion, which was precipitated by adding an excess of barium chloride solution. The mass of BaSO$_4$ obtained was 0.5032 g. What is the average mass of saccharin per tablet? What is the average mass percent of saccharin in the tablets?

75. Chlorisondiamine (C$_{14}$H$_{18}$Cl$_6$N$_2$) is a drug used in the treatment of hypertension. A 1.28-g sample of a medication containing the drug was treated to destroy the organic material and to release all the chlorine as chloride ion. When the filtered solution containing chloride ion was treated with an excess of silver nitrate, 0.104 g silver chloride was recovered. Calculate the mass percent of chlorisondiamine in the medication, assuming the drug is the only source of chloride.

76. The zinc in a 1.200-g sample of foot powder was precipitated as ZnNH$_4$PO$_4$. Strong heating of the precipitate yielded 0.4089 g Zn$_2$P$_2$O$_7$. Calculate the mass percent of zinc in the sample of foot powder.

Challenge Problems

77. Balance the following equations by the half-reaction method.
   a. Fe(*s*) + HCl(*aq*) $\rightarrow$ HFeCl$_4$(*aq*) + H$_2$(*g*)
   b. IO$_3{}^-$(*aq*) + I$^-$(*aq*) $\xrightarrow{\text{Acid}}$ I$_3{}^-$(*aq*)
   c. Cr(NCS)$_6{}^{4-}$(*aq*) + Ce^{4+}(*aq*) $\xrightarrow{\text{Acid}}$
      Cr^{3+}(*aq*) + Ce^{3+}(*aq*) + NO$_3{}^-$(*aq*) + CO$_2$(*g*) + SO$_4{}^{2-}$(*aq*)
   d. CrI$_3$(*s*) + Cl$_2$(*g*)
      $\xrightarrow{\text{Base}}$ CrO$_4{}^{2-}$(*aq*) + IO$_4{}^-$(*aq*) + Cl$^-$(*aq*)
   e. Fe(CN)$_6{}^{4-}$(*aq*) + Ce^{4+}(*aq*) $\xrightarrow{\text{Base}}$
      Ce(OH)$_3$(*s*) + Fe(OH)$_3$(*s*) + CO$_3{}^{2-}$(*aq*) + NO$_3{}^-$(*aq*)
   f. Fe(OH)$_2$(*s*) + H$_2$O$_2$(*aq*) $\xrightarrow{\text{Base}}$ Fe(OH)$_3$(*s*)

78. Complete and balance each acid–base reaction.
   a. H$_3$PO$_4$(*aq*) + NaOH(*aq*) $\rightarrow$
      Contains three acidic hydrogens
   b. Al(OH)$_3$(*s*) + H$_2$SO$_4$(*aq*) $\rightarrow$

c. $H_2Se(aq) + Ba(OH)_2(s) \rightarrow$
   Contains two acidic hydrogens
d. $H_2C_2O_4(aq) + NaOH(aq) \rightarrow$
   Contains two acidic hydrogens

79. One of the harmful effects of acid rain is the deterioration of structures and statues made of marble or limestone, both essentially calcium carbonate. The reaction of calcium carbonate with sulfuric acid yields carbon dioxide, water, and calcium sulfate. Since calcium sulfate is soluble in water, part of the object is washed away by the rain. Write a balanced chemical equation for the reaction of sulfuric acid with calcium carbonate.

80. A solution contains an unknown concentration of citric acid $(H_3C_6H_5O_7)$, which has three acidic hydrogens. It takes 41.28 mL of 0.250 M sodium hydroxide to titrate (react completely with) 10.00 mL of the citric acid solution. The reaction is

$$H_3C_6H_5O_7(aq) + 3NaOH(aq) \rightarrow 3H_2O(l) + Na_3C_6H_5O_7(aq)$$

What is the molarity of the original citric acid solution?

81. A 10.00-mL sample of sulfuric acid from an automobile battery requires 35.08 mL of 2.12 M sodium hydroxide solution for complete neutralization. What is the molarity of the sulfuric acid? The reaction is

$$H_2SO_4(aq) + 2NaOH(aq) \rightarrow 2H_2O(l) + Na_2SO_4(aq)$$

82. Some of the substances commonly used in stomach antacids are MgO, $Mg(OH)_2$, and $Al(OH)_3$.
   a. Write a balanced equation for the neutralization of hydrochloric acid by each of these substances.
   b. Which of these substances will neutralize the greatest amount of 0.1 M HCl per gram?

83. A 0.500-L sample of H_2SO_4 solution was analyzed by taking a 100.0-mL portion (aliquot) and adding 50.0 mL of 0.213 M NaOH. After the reaction occurred, an excess of OH^- ions remained in the solution. The excess base required 13.21 mL of 0.103 M HCl for neutralization. Calculate the molarity of the original sample of H_2SO_4.

84. Carminic acid, a naturally occurring red pigment extracted from the cochineal insect, contains only carbon, hydrogen, and oxygen. It was commonly used as a dye in the first half of the nineteenth century. It is 53.66% C and 4.09% H by mass. A titration required 18.02 mL of 0.0406 M NaOH to neutralize 0.3602 g carminic acid. Assuming that there is only one acidic hydrogen per molecule, what is the molecular formula of carminic acid?

85. Triiodide ions are generated in solution by the following reaction in acidic solution:

$$IO_3^-(aq) + I^-(aq) \rightarrow I_3^-(aq)$$

Triiodide ion is determined by titration with a sodium thiosulfate $(Na_2S_2O_3)$ solution. The products are iodide ion and tet-

rathionate ion $(S_4O_6^{2-})$.
   a. Balance the equation for the reaction of IO_3^- with I^- ions.
   b. Write and balance the equation for the reaction of $S_2O_3^{2-}$ with I_3^- in acidic solution.
   c. A 25.00-mL sample of a 0.0100 M solution of KIO_3 is reacted with an excess of KI. It requires 32.04 mL of $Na_2S_2O_3$ solution to titrate the I_3^- ions present. What is the molarity of the $Na_2S_2O_3$ solution?
   d. How would you prepare 500.0 mL of the KIO_3 solution in part c using pure, dry KIO_3?

86. In most of its ionic compounds, cobalt is either Co(II) or Co(III). One such compound, containing chloride ion and waters of hydration, was analyzed, and the following results were obtained. A 0.256-g sample of the compound was dissolved in water, and excess silver nitrate was added. The silver chloride was filtered, dried, and weighed, and it had a mass of 0.308 g. A second sample of 0.416 g of the compound was dissolved in water, and an excess of sodium hydroxide was added. The hydroxide salt was filtered and heated in a flame, forming cobalt(III) oxide. The mass of cobalt(III) oxide formed was 0.145 g.
   a. What is the percent composition, by mass, of the compound?
   b. Assuming the compound contains one cobalt atom per formula unit, what is the molecular formula?
   c. Write balanced equations for the three reactions described.

87. A mixture contains only NaCl and $Fe(NO_3)_3$. A 0.456-g sample of the mixture is dissolved in water, and an excess of NaOH is added, producing a precipitate of $Fe(OH)_3$. The precipitate is filtered, dried, and weighed. Its mass is 0.107 g. Calculate the following.
   a. The mass of iron in the sample
   b. The mass of $Fe(NO_3)_3$ in the sample
   c. The mass percent of $Fe(NO_3)_3$ in the sample

88. A sample is a mixture of KCl and KBr. When 0.1024 g of the sample is dissolved in water and reacted with excess silver nitrate, 0.1889 g solid is obtained. What is the composition by mass percent of the original mixture?

89. You are given a solid that is a mixture of Na_2SO_4 and K_2SO_4. A 0.205-g sample of the mixture is dissolved in water. An excess of an aqueous solution of $BaCl_2$ is added. The $BaSO_4$ that is formed is filtered, dried, and weighed. Its mass is 0.298 g. What mass of SO_4^{2-} ion is in the sample? What is the mass percent of SO_4^{2-} ion in the sample? What are the percent compositions by mass of Na_2SO_4 and K_2SO_4 in the sample?

90. The units of parts per million (ppm) and parts per billion (ppb) are commonly used by environmental chemists. In general, 1 ppm means 1 part of solution for every 10^6 parts of solution. Mathematically, by mass

$$ppm = \frac{\mu g \text{ solute}}{g \text{ solution}} = \frac{mg \text{ solute}}{kg \text{ solution}}$$

In the case of very dilute aqueous solutions, a concentration of 1.0 ppm is equal to 1.0 μg of solute per 1.0 mL, which equals 1.0 g solution. Parts per billion is defined in a similar fashion. Calculate the molarity of each of the following aqueous solutions.

a. 5.0 ppb Hg in H_2O
b. 1.0 ppb $CHCl_3$ in H_2O
c. 10.0 ppm As in H_2O
d. 0.10 ppm DDT ($C_{14}H_9Cl_5$) in H_2O

91. a. A 150-mg sample of Na_2CO_3 is dissolved in H_2O to give 1.0 L of solution. What is the concentration of Na^+ in parts per million?

b. A 2.5-mg sample of dioctyl phthalate ($C_{24}H_{38}O_4$), a plasticizer, is dissolved in H_2O to give 500.0 mL of solution. What is the concentration of dioctyl phthalate in parts per billion? (See Exercise 90 for definitions.)

92. A standard is prepared for the analysis of fluoxymesterone ($C_{20}H_{29}FO_3$), an anabolic steroid. A stock solution is prepared by dissolving 10.0 mg fluoxymesterone in a total volume of 500.0 mL. A 100.0-μL aliquot (portion) of this solution is diluted to a final volume of 100.0 mL. Calculate the concentration of the final solution in parts per billion and in terms of molarity. (See Exercise 90 for definitions.)

93. In the spectroscopic analysis of many substances, a series of standard solutions of known concentration are measured in order to generate a calibration curve. How would you prepare standard solutions containing 10.0, 25.0, 50.0, 75.0, and 100. ppm of copper from a commercially produced 1000.0-ppm solution? Assume that each solution has a final volume of 100.0 mL.

94. A solution is prepared by dissolving 0.150 ±0.003 g NaCl in a volumetric flask. The volume of the flask is 100.0 ±0.5 mL. What is the molarity of NaCl in the solution? What is the range of values for the molarity of NaCl? Express this as a value ± the uncertainty. (See Appendix 1.5.)

95. It took 25.06 ±0.05 mL of a sodium hydroxide solution to titrate a 0.4016-g sample of KHP (see Exercise 67). Calculate the concentration and uncertainty in the concentration of the sodium hydroxide solution. (See Appendix 1.5.) Neglect any uncertainty in the mass.

96. You wish to prepare 1 L of a 0.02 M potassium iodate solution. You require that the final concentration be within 1% of 0.02 M and that the concentration must be known accurately

to the fourth decimal place. How would you prepare this solution? Specify the glassware you would use, the accuracy needed for the balance, and the ranges of acceptable masses of KIO_3 that can be used.

97. You have a stock solution that is 0.200 M HCl. Which of the following procedures would give a final solution that is most accurately 1.00 × 10^{-4} M HCl? Why? A 10.00-mL portion (aliquot) of the stock solution is diluted to 200.0 mL using a volumetric pipet and flask, followed by two 10:1 dilutions using volumetric pipet and flask. Assume that all volume measurements are accurate to ±.01 mL. A 0.050-mL aliquot of the stock solution is diluted to a final volume of 100.0 mL. Assume the 0.050 mL aliquot can be measured to ±1 μL.

Marathon Problem*

98. The formate ion, $(CHO_2)^-$, forms ionic compounds with many metal ions. Assume that 9.7416 g $M(CHO_2)_2$ (where M represents the atomic symbol for a particular metal) is dissolved in water. When a solution of 0.200 M sodium sulfate is added, a white precipitate forms. The sodium sulfate solution is added until no more precipitate forms; then a few milliliters are added in excess. The precipitate is filtered, dried, and weighed. It has a mass of 9.9389 g. The filtrate is saved for further use.

A potassium permanganate solution is standardized by dissolving 0.9234 g sodium oxalate in dilute sulfuric acid and then titrating with the potassium permanganate solution. The principal products of the reaction are manganese(II) ion and carbon dioxide gas. The titration requires 18.55 mL of the potassium permanganate solution to reach the endpoint, which is indicated by the first permanent, but barely perceptible, pink color of the permanganate ion.

The filtrate from the original reaction is diluted by pouring it into a 250-mL volumetric flask, diluting to the mark with water, and then mixing thoroughly. An aliquot consisting of 10.00 mL of this diluted solution is pipetted into a 125-mL Erlenmeyer flask, approximately 25 mL of water is added, and the solution is made basic. What volume of the standard permanganate solution will be needed to titrate this solution to the equivalence point? The principal products of the reaction are carbonate ion and manganese(IV) oxide. Identify M.

*This Marathon Problem is taken from an article "The Use of 'Marathon' Problems as Effective Vehicles for the Presentation of General Chemistry Lectures," by James H. Burness that originally appeared in *Journal of Chemical Education*, **1991**, *68*, 921.

◄ CHAPTER 5 ►

Gases

M atter exists in three distinct physical states: gas, liquid, and solid. Although relatively few substances exist in the gaseous state under typical conditions, gases are very important. For example, we live immersed in a gaseous solution. The earth's atmosphere is a mixture of gases that consists mainly of elemental nitrogen (N_2) and oxygen (O_2). The atmosphere both supports life and acts as a waste receptacle for the exhaust gases that accompany many industrial processes. The chemical reactions of these waste gases in the atmosphere lead to various types of pollution, including smog and acid rain. The gases in the atmosphere also shield us from harmful radiation from the sun and keep the earth warm by reflecting heat radiation back toward the earth. In fact, there is now great concern that an increase in atmospheric carbon dioxide, a product of the combustion of fossil fuels, is causing a dangerous warming of the earth.

In this chapter we will look carefully at the properties of gases. First we will see how measurements of gas properties lead to various types of laws—statements that show how the properties are related to each other. Then we will construct a model to explain why gases behave as they do. This model will show how the behavior of the individual particles of a gas lead to the observed properties of the gas itself (a collection of many, many particles).

The study of gases provides an excellent example of the scientific method in action. It illustrates how observations lead to natural laws, which in turn can be accounted for by models.

CONTENTS

◄ A half-size model of a balloon its designers hope will circumnavigate the earth. The upper helium-filled balloon is made of a special type of polyethylene (the polymer used for sandwich bags). The lower balloon is made from polyethylene with an ultrahigh molar mass and contains air that will be used as ballast—air will be pumped into and out of the lower balloon to vary the mass, and thus the altitude, of the double balloon with its pressurized gondola.

5.1 Pressure

Purpose

- To demonstrate atmospheric pressure and explain how barometers work.
- To define the various units of pressure.

A gas uniformly fills any container, is easily compressed, and mixes completely with any other gas. One of the most obvious properties of a gas is that it exerts pressure on its surroundings. For example, when you blow up a balloon, the air inside pushes against the elastic sides of the balloon and keeps it firm.

As mentioned above, the gases most familiar to us form the earth's atmosphere. The pressure exerted by this gaseous mixture that we call air can be dramatically demonstrated by the experiment shown in Fig. 5.1. A small volume of water is placed in a metal can and the water is boiled, which fills the can with steam. The can is then sealed and allowed to cool. Why does the can collapse as it cools? It is the atmospheric pressure that crumples the can. When the can is cooled after being sealed so that no air can flow in, the water vapor (steam) condenses to a very small volume of liquid water. As a gas, the water filled the can, but when it is condensed to a liquid, the liquid does not come close to filling the can. The H_2O molecules formerly present as a gas are now collected in a very small volume of liquid, and there are very few molecules of gas left to exert pressure outward and counteract the air pressure. As a result, the pressure exerted by the gas molecules in the atmosphere smashes the can.

A device to measure atmospheric pressure, the **barometer,** was invented in 1643 by an Italian scientist named Evangelista Torricelli (1608–1647), who had been a student of Galileo. Torricelli's barometer is constructed by filling a glass tube with liquid mercury and inverting it in a dish of mercury, as shown in Fig. 5.2. Notice that a large quantity of mercury stays in the tube. In fact, at sea level the height of this column of mercury averages 760 mm. Why does this mercury stay in the tube, seemingly in defiance of gravity? Figure 5.2 illustrates how the pressure exerted by

As a gas, water occupies 1200 times as much space as it does as a liquid at 25°C and atmospheric pressure.

Soon after Torricelli died, a German physicist named Otto von Guericke invented an air pump. In a famous demonstration for the King of Prussia in 1663, Guericke placed two hemispheres together, pumped the air out of the resulting sphere through a valve, and showed that teams of horses could not pull the hemispheres apart. Then, after secretly opening the air valve, Guericke easily separated the hemispheres by hand. The King of Prussia was so impressed that he awarded Guericke a lifetime pension!

Figure 5.1

The pressure exerted by the gases in the atmosphere can be demonstrated by boiling water in a large metal can (a) and then turning off the heat and sealing the can. As the can cools, the water vapor condenses, lowering the gas pressure inside the can. This causes the can to crumple (b).

(a)

(b)

the atmospheric gases on the surface of mercury in the dish keeps the mercury in the tube.

Atmospheric pressure results from the mass of the air being pulled toward the center of the earth by gravity—in other words, it results from the weight of the air. Changing weather conditions cause the atmospheric pressure to vary, so the height of the column of Hg supported by the atmosphere at sea level varies; it is not always 760 mm. The meteorologist who says a "low" is approaching means that the atmospheric pressure is going to decrease. This condition often occurs in conjunction with a storm.

Atmospheric pressure also varies with altitude. For example, when Torricelli's experiment is done in Breckenridge, Colorado (elevation 9600 feet), the atmosphere supports a column of mercury only about 520 mm high because the air is "thinner." That is, there is less air pushing down on the earth's surface at Breckenridge than at sea level.

Units of Pressure

Because instruments used for measuring pressure, such as the **manometer** (Fig. 5.3), often contain mercury, the most commonly used units for pressure are based

$h = 760$ mm Hg for standard atmosphere

Figure 5.2

A torricellian barometer. The tube, completely filled with mercury, is inverted in a dish of mercury. Mercury flows out of the tube until the pressure of the column of mercury (shown by black arrow) "standing on the surface" of the mercury in the dish is equal to the pressure of the air (shown by yellow arrows) on the rest of the surface of the mercury in the dish.

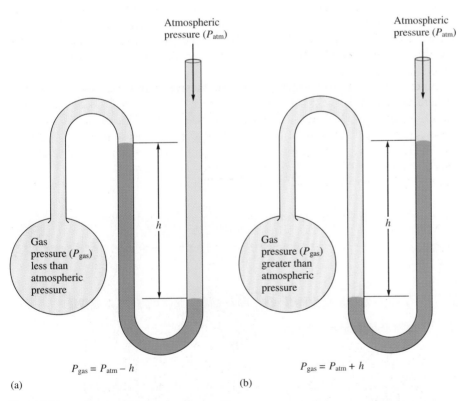

(a)

(b)

$$P_{gas} = P_{atm} - h$$

$$P_{gas} = P_{atm} + h$$

Figure 5.3

A simple manometer, a device for measuring the pressure of a gas in a container. The pressure of the gas is given by h (the difference in mercury levels) in units of torr (equivalent to mm Hg). (a) Gas pressure = atmospheric pressure − h. (b) Gas pressure = atmospheric pressure + h.

Mercury is used to measure pressure because of its high density. By way of comparison, the column of water required to measure a given pressure would be 13.5 times as high as a mercury column used for the same purpose.

on the height of the mercury column (in millimeters) that the gas pressure can support. The unit **mm Hg** (millimeter of mercury) is often called the **torr** in honor of Torricelli. The terms *torr* and *mm Hg* are used interchangeably by chemists. A related unit for pressure is the **standard atmosphere** (abbreviated atm):

$$1 \text{ standard atmosphere} = 1 \text{ atm} = 760 \text{ mm Hg} = 760 \text{ torr}$$

However, since pressure is defined as force per unit area,

$$\text{Pressure} = \frac{\text{force}}{\text{area}}$$

the fundamental units of pressure involve units of force divided by units of area. In the SI system, the unit of force is the newton (N) and the unit of area is meters squared (m^2). (For a review of the SI system, see Chapter 1.) Thus the unit of pressure in the SI system is newtons per meter squared (N/m^2) and is called the **pascal** (Pa). In terms of pascals, the standard atmosphere is

$$1 \text{ standard atmosphere} = 101,325 \text{ Pa}$$

Thus 1 atmosphere is about 10^5 pascals. Since the pascal is so small, and since it is not commonly used in the United States, we will use it sparingly in this book. However, converting from torrs or atmospheres to pascals is straightforward, as shown in Sample Exercise 5.1.

$1 \text{ atm} = 760 \text{ mm Hg}$
$= 760 \text{ torr}$
$= 101,325 \text{ Pa}$
$= 29.92 \text{ in Hg}$
$= 14.7 \text{ lb/in}^2$

Sample Exercise 5.1

The pressure of a gas is measured as 49 torr. Represent this pressure in both atmospheres and pascals.

Solution

$$49 \text{ torr} \times \frac{1 \text{ atm}}{760 \text{ torr}} = 6.4 \times 10^{-2} \text{ atm}$$

$$6.4 \times 10^{-2} \text{ atm} \times \frac{101,325 \text{ Pa}}{1 \text{ atm}} = 6.5 \times 10^3 \text{ Pa}$$

5.2 The Gas Laws of Boyle, Charles, and Avogadro

Purpose

• To describe certain laws that relate the volume, pressure, and temperature of a gas and to do calculations involving these laws.

In this section we will consider several mathematical laws that relate the properties of gases. These laws derive from experiments involving careful measurements of the relevant gas properties. From these experimental results, the mathematical relationships among the properties can be discovered. These relationships are often represented pictorially by means of graphs (plots).

We will take an historical approach to these laws to give you some perspective on the scientific method in action.

Boyle's Law

The first quantitative experiments on gases were performed by an Irish chemist, Robert Boyle (1627–1691). Using a J-shaped tube closed at one end (Fig. 5.4), which he reportedly set up in the multistory entryway of his house, Boyle studied the relationship between the pressure of the trapped gas and its volume. Representative values from Boyle's experiments are given in Table 5.1. These data show that the product of the pressure and volume for the trapped air sample is constant within the accuracies of Boyle's measurements (note the third column in Table 5.1). This behavior can be represented by the equation

$$PV = k$$

which is called **Boyle's law** and where k is a constant for a given sample of air at a specific temperature.

It is convenient to represent the data in Table 5.1 by using two different plots. The first type of plot, P versus V, forms a curve called a **hyperbola** shown in Fig. 5.5(a) on p. 188. Looking at this plot, note that as the pressure drops by about half (from 58.8 to 29.1), the volume doubles (from 24.0 to 48.0). In other words, there is an *inverse relationship* between pressure and volume. The second type of plot can be obtained by rearranging Boyle's law to give

$$V = \frac{k}{P} = k\frac{1}{P}$$

which is the equation for a straight line of the type

$$y = mx + b$$

where m represents the slope and b the intercept of the straight line. In this case, $y = V$, $x = 1/P$, $m = k$, and $b = 0$. Thus a plot of V versus $1/P$ using Boyle's data gives a straight line with an intercept of zero, as shown in Fig. 5.5(b).

Figure 5.4

A J-tube similar to the one used by Boyle.

Boyle's law: $V \propto 1/P$ at constant temperature.

Graphing is reviewed in Appendix 1.3.

Table 5.1		
Actual Data from Boyle's Experiment		
Volume (in^3)	Pressure (in Hg)	Pressure × Volume (in Hg × in^3)
117.5	12.0	14.1×10^2
87.2	16.0	14.0×10^2
70.7	20.0	14.1×10^2
58.8	24.0	14.1×10^2
44.2	32.0	14.1×10^2
35.3	40.0	14.1×10^2
29.1	48.0	14.0×10^2

(a) V (in³)

(b)

Figure 5.5

Plotting Boyle's data from Table 5.1. (a) A plot of P versus V shows that the volume doubles as the pressure is halved. (b) A plot of V versus $1/P$ gives a straight line. The slope of this line equals the value of the constant k.

Boyle's law also can be written as

$$P_1 V_1 = P_2 V_2$$

In the three centuries since Boyle carried out his studies, the sophistication of measuring techniques has increased tremendously. The results of highly accurate measurements show that Boyle's law holds precisely only at very low pressures. Measurements at higher pressures reveal that PV is not constant but varies as the pressure is varied. Results for several gases at pressures below 1 atm are shown in Fig. 5.6. Note the very small changes that occur in the product PV as the pressure is changed at these low pressures. Such changes become more significant at much higher pressures, where the complex nature of the dependence of PV on pressure becomes more obvious. We will discuss these deviations and the reasons for them in detail in Section 5.8. *A gas that strictly obeys Boyle's law is called an ideal gas.* We will describe the characteristics of an ideal gas more completely in Section 5.3.

One common use of Boyle's law is to predict the new volume of a gas when the pressure is changed (at constant temperature), or vice versa. Because deviations from Boyle's law are so slight at pressures close to 1 atm, in our calculations we will assume that gases obey Boyle's law (unless stated otherwise).

Sample Exercise 5.2

Sulfur dioxide (SO_2), a gas that plays a central role in the formation of acid rain, is found in the exhaust of automobiles and power plants. Consider a 1.53-L sample of gaseous SO_2 at a pressure of 5.6×10^3 Pa. If the pressure is changed to 1.5×10^4 Pa at a constant temperature, what will be the new volume of the gas?

Solution

We can solve this problem using Boyle's law,

$$PV = k$$

which also can be written as

$$P_1 V_1 = k = P_2 V_2 \quad \text{or} \quad P_1 V_1 = P_2 V_2$$

where the subscripts 1 and 2 represent two states (conditions) of the gas (both at the same temperature). In this case,

$$P_1 = 5.6 \times 10^3 \text{ Pa} \qquad P_2 = 1.5 \times 10^4 \text{ Pa}$$
$$V_1 = 1.53 \text{ L} \qquad V_2 = ?$$

We can solve the preceding equation for V_2:

$$V_2 = \frac{P_1 V_1}{P_2} = \frac{5.6 \times 10^3 \cancel{\text{Pa}} \times 1.53 \text{ L}}{1.5 \times 10^4 \cancel{\text{Pa}}} = 0.57 \text{ L}$$

The new volume will be 0.57 L.

The fact that the volume descreases in Sample Exercise 5.2 makes sense because the pressure was increased. *To help eliminate errors, make it a habit to check whether an answer to a problem makes physical sense.*

We mentioned before that Boyle's law is only approximately true for real gases. To determine the significance of the deviations, studies of the effect of changing pressure on the volume of a gas are often done, as shown in Sample Exercise 5.3.

Sample Exercise 5.3

In a study to see how closely gaseous ammonia obeys Boyle's law, several volume measurements were made at various pressures, using 1.0 mol NH_3 gas at a temperature of 0°C. Using the results listed below, calculate the Boyle's law constant for NH_3 at the various pressures.

Experiment	Pressure (atm)	Volume (L)
1	0.1300	172.1
2	0.2500	89.28
3	0.3000	74.35
4	0.5000	44.49
5	0.7500	29.55
6	1.000	22.08

Solution

To determine how closely NH_3 gas follows Boyle's law under these conditions, we calculate the value of k (in L · atm) for each set of values:

Experiment	1	2	3	4	5	6
$k = PV$	22.37	22.32	22.31	22.24	22.16	22.08

Although the deviations from true Boyle's law behavior are quite small at these low pressures, note that the value of k changes regularly in one direction as the pressure is increased. Thus to calculate the "ideal" value of k for NH_3, we can plot PV versus P, as shown in Fig. 5.7, and extrapolate (extend the line beyond the experimental points) back to zero pressure, where, for reasons we will discuss later, a gas behaves most ideally. The value of k obtained by this extrapolation is 22.41 L · atm. Notice that this is the same value obtained from similar plots for the gases CO_2, O_2, and Ne at 0°C, as shown in Fig. 5.6.

Figure 5.6

A plot of PV versus P for several gases at pressures below 1 atm. An ideal gas is expected to have a constant value of PV, as shown by the dotted line. Carbon dioxide shows the largest change in PV, and this change is actually quite small: PV changes from about 22.39 L atm at 0.25 atm to 22.26 L atm at 1.00 atm. Thus Boyle's law is a good approximation at these relatively low pressures.

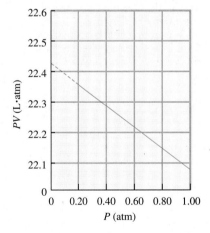

Figure 5.7

A plot of PV versus P for 1 mol of ammonia. The dashed line shows the extrapolation of the data to zero pressure to give the "ideal" value of PV of 22.41 L atm.

Charles's Law

In the century following Boyle's findings, scientists continued to study the properties of gases. One of these scientists was a French physicist, Jacques Charles (1746–1823), who was the first person to fill a balloon with hydrogen gas and who made the first solo balloon flight. Charles found in 1787 that the volume of a gas at constant pressure increases *linearly* with the temperature of the gas. That is, a plot of the volume of a gas (at constant pressure) versus its temperature (°C) gives a straight line. This behavior is shown for several gases in Fig. 5.8 on p. 190. A very

Figure 5.8

Plots of V versus T (°C) for several gases. The solid lines represent experimental measurements on gases. The dashed lines represent extrapolation of the data into regions where these gases would become liquids or solids. Note that the samples of the various gases contain different numbers of moles.

Figure 5.9

Plots of V versus T as in Fig. 5.8, except here the Kelvin scale is used for temperature.

interesting feature of these plots is that the volumes of all the gases extrapolate to zero at the same temperature, -273.2°C. On the Kelvin temperature scale this point is defined as 0 K, which leads to the following relationship between the Kelvin and Celsius scales:

$$K = °C + 273$$

When the volumes of the gases shown in Fig. 5.8 are plotted versus temperature on the Kelvin scale, the plots in Fig. 5.9 result. In this case, the volume of each gas is *directly proportional to temperature* and extrapolates to zero when the temperature is 0 K. This behavior is represented by the equation known as **Charles's law,**

Charles's law: $V \propto T$ (expressed in K) at constant pressure.

$$V = bT$$

where T is in Kelvins and b is a proportionality constant.

Before we illustrate the uses of Charles's law, let us consider the importance of 0 K. At temperatures below this point, the extrapolated volumes would become negative. The fact that a gas cannot have a negative volume suggests that 0 K has a special significance. In fact, 0 K is called **absolute zero,** and there is much evidence to suggest that this temperature cannot be attained. Temperatures of approximately 0.000001 K have been produced in laboratories, but 0 K has never been reached.

Sample Exercise 5.4

A sample of gas at 15°C and 1 atm has a volume of 2.58 L. What volume will this gas occupy at 38°C and 1 atm?

Solution

Charles's law, which describes the dependence of the volume of a gas on temperature at constant pressure, can be used to solve this problem. Charles's law in the form $V = bT$ can be rearranged to

$$\frac{V}{T} = b$$

An equivalent statement is

Charles's law also can be written as

$$\frac{V_1}{T_1} = \frac{V_2}{T_2}$$

$$\frac{V_1}{T_1} = b = \frac{V_2}{T_2}$$

where the subscripts 1 and 2 represent two states for a given sample of gas at constant pressure. In this case, we are given the following (note that the temperature values *must* be changed to the Kelvin scale):

$$T_1 = 15°C + 273 = 288 \text{ K} \qquad T_2 = 38°C + 273 = 311 \text{ K}$$
$$V_1 = 2.58 \text{ L} \qquad V_2 = ?$$

Solving for V_2 gives

$$V_2 = \left(\frac{T_2}{T_1}\right) V_1 = \left(\frac{311 \cancel{K}}{288 \cancel{K}}\right) 2.58 \text{ L} = 2.79 \text{ L}$$

CHECK: The new volume is greater than the initial volume, which makes physical sense because the gas will expand as it is heated.

Avogadro's Law

In Chapter 2 we noted that in 1811 the Italian chemist Avogadro postulated that equal volumes of gases at the same temperature and pressure contain the same number of "particles." This observation is called **Avogadro's law,** which is illustrated by Fig. 5.10. Stated mathematically, Avogadro's law is

$$V = an$$

where V is the volume of the gas, n is the number of moles of gas particles, and a is a proportionality constant. This equation states that *for a gas at constant temperature and pressure, the volume is directly proportional to the number of moles of gas.* This relationship is obeyed closely by gases at low pressures.

Sample Exercise 5.5

Suppose we have a 12.2-L sample containing 0.50 mol oxygen gas (O_2) at a pressure of 1 atm and a temperature of 25°C. If all this O_2 were converted to ozone (O_3) at the same temperature and pressure, what would be the volume of the ozone?

Solution

The balanced equation for the reaction is

$$3O_2(g) \rightarrow 2O_3(g)$$

To calculate the moles of O_3 produced, we must use the appropriate mole ratio:

$$0.50 \cancel{\text{ mol } O_2} \times \frac{2 \text{ mol } O_3}{3 \cancel{\text{ mol } O_2}} = 0.33 \text{ mol } O_3$$

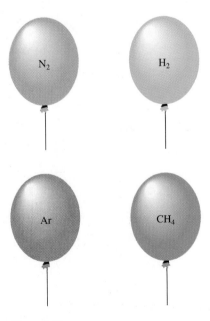

Figure 5.10

These balloons each hold 1.0 L of gas at 25°C and 1 atm. Each balloon contains 0.041 mol of gas, or 2.5×10^{22} molecules.

Avogadro's law states that $V = an$, which can be rearranged to give

$$\frac{V}{n} = a$$

Since a is a constant, an alternative representation is

$$\frac{V_1}{n_1} = a = \frac{V_2}{n_2}$$

where V_1 is the volume of n_1 moles of O_2 gas and V_2 is the volume of n_2 moles of O_3 gas. In this case we have

$$n_1 = 0.50 \text{ mol} \qquad n_2 = 0.33 \text{ mol}$$
$$V_1 = 12.2 \text{ L} \qquad V_2 = ?$$

Solving for V_2 gives

$$V_2 = \left(\frac{n_2}{n_1}\right) V_1 = \left(\frac{0.33 \text{ mol}}{0.50 \text{ mol}}\right) 12.2 \text{ L} = 8.1 \text{ L}$$

CHECK: Note that the volume decreases, as it should, since fewer moles of gas molecules will be present after O_2 is converted to O_3.

Avogadro's law also can be written as

$$\frac{V_1}{n_1} = \frac{V_2}{n_2}$$

5.3 The Ideal Gas Law

Purpose

• To define the ideal gas law.
• To show how to do calculations involving the ideal gas law.

We have considered three laws that describe the behavior of gases as revealed by experimental observations:

$$\textit{Boyle's law:} \qquad V = \frac{k}{P} \qquad \text{(at constant } T \text{ and } n\text{)}$$

$$\textit{Charles's law:} \qquad V = bT \qquad \text{(at constant } P \text{ and } n\text{)}$$

$$\textit{Avogadro's law:} \qquad V = an \qquad \text{(at constant } T \text{ and } P\text{)}$$

These relationships, which show how the volume of a gas depends on pressure, temperature, and number of moles of gas present, can be combined as follows:

$$V = R\left(\frac{Tn}{P}\right)$$

$$R = 0.08206 \, \frac{\text{L} \cdot \text{atm}}{\text{K} \cdot \text{mol}}$$

where R is the combined proportionality constant called the **universal gas constant.** When the pressure is expressed in atmospheres and the volume in liters, R has the value 0.08206 L · atm/K · mol. The preceding equation can be rearranged to the more familiar form of the **ideal gas law:**

$$PV = nRT$$

The ideal gas law is an *equation of state* for a gas, where the state of the gas is its condition at a given time. A particular *state* of a gas is described by its pressure, volume, temperature, and number of moles. Knowledge of any three of these properties is enough to completely define the state of a gas, since the fourth property can then be determined from the equation for the ideal gas law.

It is important to recognize that the ideal gas law is an empirical equation—it is based on experimental measurements of the properties of gases. A gas that obeys this equation is said to behave *ideally*. The ideal gas equation is best regarded as a limiting law—it expresses behavior that real gases *approach* at low pressures and high temperatures. Therefore, an ideal gas is a hypothetical substance. However, most gases obey the ideal gas equation closely enough at pressures below 1 atm that only minimal errors result from assuming ideal behavior. Unless you are given information to the contrary, you should assume ideal gas behavior when solving problems involving gases in this text.

The ideal gas law can be used to solve a variety of problems. Sample Exercise 5.6 demonstrates one type, where you are asked to find one property characterizing the state of a gas, given the other three.

The ideal gas law applies best at pressures smaller than 1 atm.

Sample Exercise 5.6

A sample of hydrogen gas (H_2) has a volume of 8.56 L at a temperature of 0°C and a pressure of 1.5 atm. Calculate the moles of H_2 molecules present in this gas sample.

Solution

Solving the ideal gas law for n gives

$$n = \frac{PV}{RT}$$

In this case $P = 1.5$ atm, $V = 8.56$ L, $T = 0°C + 273 = 273$ K, and $R = 0.08206$ L · atm/K · mol. Thus

$$n = \frac{(1.5 \text{ atm})(8.56 \text{ L})}{\left(0.08206 \dfrac{\text{L} \cdot \text{atm}}{\text{K} \cdot \text{mol}}\right)(273 \text{ K})} = 0.57 \text{ mol}$$

The ideal gas law is also used to calculate the changes that will occur when the conditions of the gas are changed.

The reaction of zinc with hydrochloric acid to produce bubbles of hydrogen gas.

Sample Exercise 5.7

Suppose we have a sample of ammonia gas with a volume of 3.5 L at a pressure of 1.68 atm. The gas is compressed to a volume of 1.35 L at a constant temperature. Use the ideal gas law to calculate the final pressure.

Solution

The basic assumption we make when using the ideal gas law to describe a change in state for a gas is that the equation applies equally well to both the initial and the final states. In dealing with a change in state, we always *place the variables that change on one side of the equal sign and the constants on the other*. In this case the pressure and volume change, and the temperature and the number of moles remain constant (as does R, by definition). Thus we write the ideal gas law as

$$PV = nRT$$

Change Remain constant

Since n and T remain the same in this case, we can write $P_1V_1 = nRT$ and $P_2V_2 = nRT$. Combining these gives

$$P_1V_1 = nRT = P_2V_2 \quad \text{or} \quad P_1V_1 = P_2V_2$$

We are given $P_1 = 1.68$ atm, $V_1 = 3.5$ L, and $V_2 = 1.35$ L. Solving for P_2 thus gives

$$P_2 = \left(\frac{V_1}{V_2}\right)P_1 = \left(\frac{3.5\,\cancel{L}}{1.35\,\cancel{L}}\right) 1.68 \text{ atm} = 4.4 \text{ atm}$$

CHECK: Does this answer make sense? The volume decreased (at constant temperature), so the pressure should increase, as the result of the calculation indicates. Note that the calculated final pressure is 4.4 atm. Most gases do not behave ideally above 1 atm. Therefore, we might find that if we *measured* the pressure of this gas sample, the observed pressure would differ slightly from 4.4 atm.

Sample Exercise 5.8

A sample of methane gas that has a volume of 3.8 L at 5°C is heated to 86°C at constant pressure. Calculate its new volume.

Solution

To solve this problem, we take the ideal gas law and segregate the changing variables and the constants by placing them on opposite sides of the equation. In this case, volume and temperature change, and the number of moles and pressure (and, of course, R) remain constant. Thus $PV = nRT$ becomes

$$\frac{V}{T} = \frac{nR}{P}$$

which leads to

$$\frac{V_1}{T_1} = \frac{nR}{P} \quad \text{and} \quad \frac{V_2}{T_2} = \frac{nR}{P}$$

Combining these gives

$$\frac{V_1}{T_1} = \frac{nR}{P} = \frac{V_2}{T_2} \quad \text{or} \quad \frac{V_1}{T_1} = \frac{V_2}{T_2}$$

We are given

$$T_1 = 5°C + 273 = 278 \text{ K} \qquad T_2 = 86°C + 273 = 359 \text{ K}$$
$$V_1 = 3.8 \text{ L} \qquad\qquad\qquad V_2 = ?$$

Thus
$$V_2 = \frac{T_2 V_1}{T_1} = \frac{(359 \cancel{K})(3.8 \text{ L})}{278 \cancel{K}} = 4.9 \text{ L}$$

CHECK: Is the answer sensible? In this case the temperature increased (at constant pressure), so the volume should increase. Thus the answer makes sense.

The problem in Sample Exercise 5.8 could be described as a "Charles's law problem," whereas the problem in Sample Exercise 5.7 might be called a "Boyle's law problem." In both cases, however, we started with the ideal gas law. The real advantage of using the ideal gas law is that it applies to virtually any problem dealing with gases and is easy to remember.

Sample Exercise 5.9

A sample of diborane gas (B_2H_6), a substance that bursts into flame when exposed to air, has a pressure of 345 torr at a temperature of $-15°C$ and a volume of 3.48 L. If conditions are changed so that the temperature is 36°C and the pressure is 468 torr, what will be the volume of the sample?

Solution

Since, for this sample, pressure, temperature, and volume all change while the number of moles remains constant, we use the ideal gas law in the form

$$\frac{PV}{T} = nR$$

which leads to

$$\frac{P_1 V_1}{T_1} = nR = \frac{P_2 V_2}{T_2} \qquad \text{or} \qquad \frac{P_1 V_1}{T_1} = \frac{P_2 V_2}{T_2}$$

Then
$$V_2 = \frac{T_2 P_1 V_1}{T_1 P_2}$$

We have

$$P_1 = 345 \text{ torr} \qquad\qquad P_2 = 468 \text{ torr}$$
$$T_1 = -15°C + 273 = 258 \text{ K} \qquad T_2 = 36°C + 273 = 309 \text{ K}$$
$$V_1 = 3.48 \text{ L} \qquad\qquad\qquad V_2 = ?$$

Thus
$$V_2 = \frac{(309 \cancel{K})(345 \cancel{\text{torr}})(3.48 \text{ L})}{(258 \cancel{K})(468 \cancel{\text{torr}})} = 3.07 \text{ L}$$

Since the equation used in Sample Exercise 5.9 involves a *ratio* of pressures, it was unnecessary to convert pressures to units of atmospheres. The units of torrs cancel. (You will obtain the same answer by inserting $P_1 = \frac{345}{760}$ and $P_2 = \frac{468}{760}$ into the equation.) However, temperature *must always* be converted to the Kelvin scale; since this conversion involves *addition* of 273, the conversion factor does not cancel. Be careful.

One of the many other types of problems dealing with gases that can be solved using the ideal gas law is illustrated in Sample Exercise 5.10.

Always convert the temperature to the Kelvin scale when applying the ideal gas law.

Sample Exercise 5.10

A sample containing 0.35 mol argon gas at a temperature of 13°C and a pressure of 568 torr is heated to 56°C and a pressure of 897 torr. Calculate the change in volume that occurs.

Solution

We use the ideal gas law to find the volume for each set of conditions:

State 1	State 2
$n_1 = 0.35$ mol	$n_2 = 0.35$ mol
$P_1 = 568 \text{ torr} \times \dfrac{1 \text{ atm}}{760 \text{ torr}} = 0.747$ atm	$P_2 = 897 \text{ torr} \times \dfrac{1 \text{ atm}}{760 \text{ torr}} = 1.18$ atm
$T_1 = 13°C + 273 = 286$ K	$T_2 = 56°C + 273 = 329$ K

Solving the ideal gas law for volume gives

$$V_1 = \frac{n_1 R T_1}{P_1} = \frac{(0.35 \text{ mol})(0.08206 \text{ L} \cdot \text{atm/K} \cdot \text{mol})(286 \text{ K})}{(0.747 \text{ atm})} = 11 \text{ L}$$

and

$$V_2 = \frac{n_2 R T_2}{P_2} = \frac{(0.35 \text{ mol})(0.08206 \text{ L} \cdot \text{atm/K} \cdot \text{mol})(329 \text{ K})}{(1.18 \text{ atm})} = 8.0 \text{ L}$$

Thus, in going from state 1 to state 2, the volume changes from 11 L to 8.0 L. The change in volume, ΔV (Δ is the Greek capital letter delta), is then

$$\Delta V = V_2 - V_1 = 8.0 \text{ L} - 11 \text{ L} = -3 \text{ L}$$

The *change* in volume is negative because the volume decreases. Note that for this problem (unlike Sample Exercise 5.9) the pressures must be converted from torrs to atmospheres, as required by the atmosphere part of the units for R, since each volume was found separately and the conversion factor does not cancel.

Argon glowing in a discharge tube.

5.4 *Gas Stoichiometry*

Purpose

- To define the molar volume for an ideal gas.
- To define STP.
- To show how to do stoichiometric calculations for reactions involving gases.
- To show how to calculate molar mass from gas density.

Suppose we have 1 mole of an ideal gas at 0°C (273.2 K) and 1 atm. From the ideal gas law, the volume of the gas is given by

$$V = \frac{nRT}{P} = \frac{(1.000 \text{ mol})(0.08206 \text{ L} \cdot \text{atm}/\text{K} \cdot \text{mol})(273.2 \text{ K})}{1.000 \text{ atm}} = 22.42 \text{ L}$$

This volume of 22.42 liters is the **molar volume** of an ideal gas (at 0°C and 1 atm). The measured molar volumes of several gases are listed in Table 5.2. Note that the molar volumes of some of the gases are very close to the ideal value, while others deviate significantly. Later in this chapter we will discuss some of the reasons for the deviations.

The conditions 0°C and 1 atm, called **standard temperature and pressure** (abbreviated **STP**), are common reference conditions for the properties of gases. For example, the molar volume of an ideal gas is 22.42 liters at STP (see Fig. 5.11).

When 273.15 K is used in this calculation, the molar volume obtained is 22.41 L in Sample Exercise 5.3.

STP: 0°C and 1 atm

Table 5.2	
Molar Volumes for Various Gases at 0°C and 1 atm	
Gas	Molar Volume (L)
Oxygen (O_2)	22.397
Nitrogen (N_2)	22.402
Hydrogen (H_2)	22.433
Helium (He)	22.434
Argon (Ar)	22.397
Carbon dioxide (CO_2)	22.260
Ammonia (NH_3)	22.079

32 g of O_2
(1 mole)

2 g of H_2
(1 mole)

17 g of NH_3
(1 mole)

Figure 5.11
A mole of any gas occupies a volume of approximately 22.4 L at STP.

Sample Exercise 5.11

A sample of nitrogen gas has a volume of 1.75 L at STP. How many moles of N_2 are present?

Solution

We could solve this problem using the ideal gas equation, but we can take a shortcut by using the molar volume of an ideal gas at STP. Since 1 mole of an ideal gas at STP has a volume of 22.42 L, 1.75 L of N_2 at STP will contain less than 1 mole. We can find how many moles using the ratio of 1.75 L to 22.42 L:

$$1.75 \text{ L } N_2 \times \frac{1 \text{ mol } N_2}{22.42 \text{ L } N_2} = 7.81 \times 10^{-2} \text{ mol } N_2$$

Many chemical reactions involve gases. By assuming ideal behavior for these gases, we can carry out stoichiometric calculations if the pressure, volume, and temperature of the gases are known.

Sample Exercise 5.12

Quicklime (CaO) is produced by the thermal decomposition of calcium carbonate ($CaCO_3$). Calculate the volume of CO_2 at STP produced from the decomposition of 152 g $CaCO_3$ by the reaction

$$CaCO_3(s) \rightarrow CaO(s) + CO_2(g)$$

Solution

We employ the same strategy we used in the stoichiometry problems earlier in this book. That is, we compute the number of moles of $CaCO_3$ consumed and the number of moles of CO_2 produced. The moles of CO_2 can then be converted to volume using the molar volume of an ideal gas.

Using the molar mass of $CaCO_3$ (100.09 g/mol), we can calculate the number of moles of $CaCO_3$:

$$152 \text{ g } CaCO_3 \times \frac{1 \text{ mol } CaCO_3}{100.09 \text{ g } CaCO_3} = 1.52 \text{ mol } CaCO_3$$

Since each mole of $CaCO_3$ produces a mole of CO_2, 1.52 mol CO_2 will be formed. We can compute the volume of CO_2 at STP by using the molar volume:

$$1.52 \text{ mol } CO_2 \times \frac{22.42 \text{ L } CO_2}{1 \text{ mol } CO_2} = 34.1 \text{ L } CO_2$$

Thus the decomposition of 152 g $CaCO_3$ produces 34.1 L CO_2 at STP.

When lime (CaO) is heated to incandescence with a hot flame, it gives an intense, bright light. Such lights were used by 1800s' theaters to spotlight actors, originating the phrase "in the limelight."

Note that in Sample Exercise 5.12 the final step involved calculation of the volume of gas from the number of moles. Since the conditions were specified as STP, we were able to use the molar volume of a gas at STP. If the conditions of a problem are different from STP, the ideal gas law must be used to compute the volume.

Remember that the molar volume of an ideal gas is 22.42 L when measured at STP.

Sample Exercise 5.13

A sample of methane gas having a volume of 2.80 L at 25°C and 1.65 atm was mixed with a sample of oxygen gas having a volume of 35.0 L at 31°C and 1.25 atm. The mixture was then ignited to form carbon dioxide and water. Calculate the volume of CO_2 formed at a pressure of 2.50 atm and a temperature of 125°C.

Solution

From the description of the reaction, the unbalanced equation is

$$CH_4(g) + O_2(g) \rightarrow CO_2(g) + H_2O(g)$$

which can be balanced to give

$$CH_4(g) + 2O_2(g) \rightarrow CO_2(g) + 2H_2O(g)$$

Next, we must find the limiting reactant, which requires calculating the numbers of moles of each reactant. We convert the given volumes of methane and oxygen to moles using the ideal gas law as follows:

$$n_{CH_4} = \frac{PV}{RT} = \frac{(1.65 \text{ atm})(2.80 \text{ L})}{(0.08206 \text{ L} \cdot \text{atm/K} \cdot \text{mol})(298 \text{ K})} = 0.189 \text{ mol}$$

$$n_{O_2} = \frac{PV}{RT} = \frac{(1.25 \text{ atm})(35.0 \text{ L})}{(0.08206 \text{ L} \cdot \text{atm/K} \cdot \text{mol})(304 \text{ K})} = 1.75 \text{ mol}$$

In the balanced equation for the combustion reaction, 1 mol CH_4 requires 2 mol O_2. Thus the moles of O_2 required by 0.189 mol CH_4 can be calculated as follows:

$$0.189 \text{ mol } CH_4 \times \frac{2 \text{ mol } O_2}{1 \text{ mol } CH_4} = 0.378 \text{ mol } O_2$$

Since 1.75 mol O_2 is available, O_2 is in excess. The limiting reactant is CH_4. The number of moles of CH_4 available must be used to calculate the number of moles of CO_2 produced:

$$0.189 \text{ mol } CH_4 \times \frac{1 \text{ mol } CO_2}{1 \text{ mol } CH_4} = 0.189 \text{ mol } CO_2$$

Since the conditions stated are not STP, we must use the ideal gas law to calculate the volume:

$$V = \frac{nRT}{P}$$

In this case $n = 0.189$ mol, $T = 125°C + 273 = 398$ K, $P = 2.50$ atm, and $R = 0.08206$ L · atm/K · mol. Thus

$$V = \frac{(0.189 \text{ mol})(0.08206 \text{ L} \cdot \text{atm/K} \cdot \text{mol})(398 \text{ K})}{2.50 \text{ atm}} = 2.47 \text{ L}$$

This represents the volume of CO_2 produced under these conditions.

Molar Mass of a Gas

One very important use of the ideal gas law is in the calculation of the molar mass (molecular weight) of a gas from its measured density. To see the relationship between gas density and molar mass, consider that the number of moles of gas n can be expressed as

$$n = \frac{\text{grams of gas}}{\text{molar mass}} = \frac{\text{mass}}{\text{molar mass}} = \frac{m}{\text{molar mass}}$$

Substitution into the ideal gas equation gives

$$P = \frac{nRT}{V} = \frac{(m/\text{molar mass})RT}{V} = \frac{m(RT)}{V(\text{molar mass})}$$

$$\text{Density} = \frac{\text{mass}}{\text{volume}}$$

$$PV = nRT$$

$$PV = \frac{m}{\text{molar mass}} \times RT$$

However, m/V is the gas density d in units of grams per liter. Thus

$$P = \frac{dRT}{\text{molar mass}}$$

or $\qquad\qquad$ Molar mass $= \dfrac{dRT}{P}$ $\qquad\qquad\qquad$ (5.1)

Thus, if the density of a gas at a given temperature and pressure is known, its molar mass can be calculated.

Sample Exercise 5.14

The density of a gas was measured at 1.50 atm and 27°C and found to be 1.95 g/L. Calculate the molar mass of the gas.

Solution

Using Equation (5.1), we calculate the molar mass as follows:

$$\text{Molar mass} = \frac{dRT}{P} = \frac{\left(1.95\frac{\text{g}}{\text{L}}\right)\left(0.08206\frac{\text{L} \cdot \text{atm}}{\text{K} \cdot \text{mol}}\right)(300 \text{ K})}{1.50 \text{ atm}} = 32.0 \text{ g/mol}$$

CHECK: These are the units expected for molar mass.

You could memorize the equation involving gas density and molar mass, but it is better simply to remember the ideal gas equation, the definition of density, and the relationship between number of moles and molar mass. You can then derive the appropriate equation when you need it. This approach ensures that you understand the concepts and means one less equation to memorize.

5.5 Dalton's Law of Partial Pressures

Purpose

- To state the relationship between partial pressures and total pressure and between partial pressure and mole fraction.

5.0 L at 20°C

0.50 mol H_2

$P_{H_2} = 2.4$ atm

Among the experiments that led John Dalton to propose the atomic theory were his studies of mixtures of gases. In 1803 Dalton summarized his observations as follows: *For a mixture of gases in a container, the total pressure exerted is the sum of the pressures that each gas would exert if it were alone.* This statement, known as **Dalton's law of partial pressures** can be expressed as follows:

$$P_{\text{TOTAL}} = P_1 + P_2 + P_3 + \cdots$$

where the subscripts refer to the individual gases (gas 1, gas 2, etc.). The symbols P_1, P_2, P_3, and so on represent each **partial pressure;** that is, the pressure that a particular gas would exert if it were alone in the container.

Assuming that each gas behaves ideally, the partial pressure of each gas can be calculated from the ideal gas law:

$$P_1 = \frac{n_1 RT}{V}, \qquad P_2 = \frac{n_2 RT}{V}, \qquad P_3 = \frac{n_3 RT}{V}, \qquad \cdots$$

5.0 L at 20°C

1.25 mol He

$P_{He} = 6.0$ atm

The total pressure of the mixture P_{TOTAL} can be represented as

$$P_{\text{TOTAL}} = P_1 + P_2 + P_3 + \cdots = \frac{n_1 RT}{V} + \frac{n_2 RT}{V} + \frac{n_3 RT}{V} + \cdots$$

$$= (n_1 + n_2 + n_3 + \cdots)\left(\frac{RT}{V}\right)$$

$$= n_{\text{TOTAL}}\left(\frac{RT}{V}\right)$$

5.0 L at 20°C

1.25 mol He
+0.50 mol H_2
_____
1.75 mol gas

$P_{\text{Total}} = 8.4$ atm

Figure 5.12

The partial pressure of each gas in a mixture of gases in a container depends on the number of moles of that gas. The total pressure is the sum of the partial pressures and depends on the total moles of gas particles present, no matter what they are.

where n_{TOTAL} is the sum of the numbers of moles of the various gases. Thus, for a mixture of ideal gases, it is the *total number of moles of particles* that is important, not the identity or composition of the individual gas particles. This idea is illustrated in Fig. 5.12.

This important observation indicates some fundamental characteristics of an ideal gas. The fact that the pressure exerted by an ideal gas is not affected by the identity (composition) of the gas particles reveals two things about ideal gases: (1) the volume of the individual gas particle must not be important, and (2) the forces among the particles must not be important. If these factors were important, the pressure exerted by the gas would depend on the nature of the individual particles. These observations will strongly influence the model that we will eventually construct to explain ideal gas behavior.

Sample Exercise 5.15

Mixtures of helium and oxygen are used in scuba diving tanks to help prevent "the bends." For a particular dive, 46 L O_2 at 25°C and 1.0 atm and 12 L He at 25°C and 1.0 atm were pumped into a tank with a volume of 5.0 L. Calculate the partial pressure of each gas and the total pressure in the tank at 25°C.

Solution

The first step is to calculate the number of moles of each gas using the ideal gas law in the form:

$$n = \frac{PV}{RT}$$

$$n_{O_2} = \frac{(1.0 \text{ atm})(46 \text{ L})}{(0.08206 \text{ L} \cdot \text{atm/K} \cdot \text{mol})(298 \text{ K})} = 1.9 \text{ mol}$$

$$n_{He} = \frac{(1.0 \text{ atm})(12 \text{ L})}{(0.08206 \text{ L} \cdot \text{atm/K} \cdot \text{mol})(298 \text{ K})} = 0.49 \text{ mol}$$

The tank containing the mixture has a volume of 5.0 L, and the temperature is 25°C. We can use these data and the ideal gas law to calculate the partial pressure of each gas:

$$P = \frac{nRT}{V}$$

$$P_{O_2} = \frac{(1.9 \text{ mol})(0.08206 \text{ L} \cdot \text{atm/K} \cdot \text{mol})(298 \text{ K})}{5.0 \text{ L}} = 9.3 \text{ atm}$$

$$P_{He} = \frac{(0.49 \text{ mol})(0.08206 \text{ L} \cdot \text{atm/K} \cdot \text{mol})(298 \text{ K})}{5.0 \text{ L}} = 2.4 \text{ atm}$$

The total pressure is the sum of the partial pressures:

$$P_{\text{TOTAL}} = P_{O_2} + P_{He} = 9.3 \text{ atm} + 2.4 \text{ atm} = 11.7 \text{ atm}$$

At this point we need to define the **mole fraction:** *the ratio of the number of moles of a given component in a mixture to the total number of moles in the mixture.* The Greek lowercase letter chi (χ) is used to symbolize the mole fraction. For example, for a given component in a mixture, the mole fraction χ_1 is

$$\chi_1 = \frac{n_1}{n_{\text{TOTAL}}} = \frac{n_1}{n_1 + n_2 + n_3 + \cdots}$$

From the ideal gas equation we know that the number of moles of a gas is directly proportional to the pressure of the gas, since

$$n = P\left(\frac{V}{RT}\right)$$

That is, for each component in the mixture,

$$n_1 = P_1\left(\frac{V}{RT}\right), \qquad n_2 = P_2\left(\frac{V}{RT}\right), \qquad \cdots$$

Therefore, we can represent the mole fraction in terms of pressures:

$$\chi_1 = \frac{n_1}{n_{\text{TOTAL}}} = \frac{\overbrace{P_1(V/RT)}^{n_1}}{\underbrace{P_1(V/RT)}_{n_1} + \underbrace{P_2(V/RT)}_{n_2} + \underbrace{P_3(V/RT)}_{n_3} + \cdots}$$

$$= \frac{(V/RT)P_1}{(V/RT)(P_1 + P_2 + P_3 + \cdots)}$$

$$= \frac{P_1}{P_1 + P_2 + P_3 + \cdots} = \frac{P_1}{P_{\text{TOTAL}}}$$

In fact, the mole fraction of each component in a mixture of ideal gases is directly related to its partial pressure:

$$\chi_2 = \frac{n_2}{n_{\text{TOTAL}}} = \frac{P_2}{P_{\text{TOTAL}}}$$

Sample Exercise 5.16

The partial pressure of oxygen was observed to be 156 torr in air with an atmospheric pressure of 743 torr. Calculate the mole fraction of O_2 present.

Solution

The mole fraction of O_2 can be calculated from the equation

$$\chi_{O_2} = \frac{P_{O_2}}{P_{\text{TOTAL}}} = \frac{156 \text{ torr}}{743 \text{ torr}} = 0.210$$

Note that mole fraction has no units.

◄ **CHEMICAL IMPACT** ►

The Chemistry of Air Bags

Most experts agree that air bags represent a very important advance in automobile safety. These bags, which are stored in the auto's steering wheel or dash, are designed to inflate rapidly (within about 40 ms) in the event of a crash, cushioning the front seat occupants against impact. The bags then deflate immediately to allow vision and movement after the crash. Air bags are activated when a severe deceleration (an impact) causes a steel ball to compress a spring and electrically ignite a detonator cap, which, in turn, causes sodium azide (NaN_3) to decompose explosively, forming sodium and nitrogen gas:

$$2NaN_3(s) \rightarrow 2Na(s) + 3N_2(g)$$

This system works very well and requires a relatively small amount of sodium azide [100 g yields 56 L $N_2(g)$ at 25°C].

When a vehicle containing air bags reaches the end of its useful life, the sodium azide present in the activators must be given proper disposal. Sodium azide, besides being explosive, has a toxicity roughly equal to that of sodium cyanide. It also forms hydrazoic acid (HN_3), a toxic and explosive liquid, when treated with acid.

The air bag represents an application of chemistry that will undoubtedly save thousands of lives in the years ahead.

The expression for the mole fraction,

$$\chi_1 = \frac{P_1}{P_{\text{TOTAL}}}$$

can be rearranged to give

$$P_1 = \chi_1 \times P_{\text{TOTAL}}$$

That is, *the partial pressure of a particular component of a gaseous mixture is the mole fraction of that component times the total pressure.*

Sample Exercise 5.17

The mole fraction of nitrogen in the air is 0.7808. Calculate the partial pressure of N_2 in air when the atmospheric pressure is 760. torr.

Solution

The partial pressure of N_2 can be calculated as follows:

$$P_{N_2} = \chi_{N_2} \times P_{\text{TOTAL}} = 0.7808 \times 760.\ \text{torr} = 593\ \text{torr}$$

A mixture of gases results whenever a gas is collected by displacement of water. For example, Fig. 5.13 shows the collection of oxygen gas produced by the decomposition of solid potassium chlorate. In this situation, the gas in the bottle is a mixture of water vapor and the oxygen being collected. Water vapor is present because molecules of water escape from the surface of the liquid and collect in the space above the liquid. Molecules of water also return to the liquid. When the rate

Vapor pressure will be discussed in detail in Chapter 10. A table of water vapor pressure values is given in Section 10.8.

Figure 5.13

The production of oxygen by thermal decomposition of $KClO_3$. The MnO_2 is mixed with the $KClO_3$ to make the reaction faster.

of escape equals the rate of return, the number of water molecules in the vapor state remains constant, and thus the pressure of water vapor remains constant. This pressure, which depends on temperature, is called the **vapor pressure of water.**

Sample Exercise 5.18

A sample of solid potassium chlorate ($KClO_3$) was heated in a test tube (see Fig. 5.13) and decomposed by the following reaction:

$$2KClO_3(s) \rightarrow 2KCl(s) + 3O_2(g)$$

The oxygen produced was collected by displacement of water at 22°C at a total pressure of 754 torr. The volume of the gas collected was 0.650 L, and the vapor pressure of water at 22°C is 21 torr. Calculate the partial pressure of O_2 in the gas collected and the mass of $KClO_3$ in the sample that was decomposed.

Solution

First we find the partial pressure of O_2 from Dalton's law of partial pressures:

$$P_{TOTAL} = P_{O_2} + P_{H_2O} = P_{O_2} + 21 \text{ torr} = 754 \text{ torr}$$

Thus $\qquad\qquad P_{O_2} = 754 \text{ torr} - 21 \text{ torr} = 733 \text{ torr}$

Now we use the ideal gas law to find the number of moles of O_2:

$$n_{O_2} = \frac{P_{O_2}V}{RT}$$

In this case,

$$P_{O_2} = 733 \text{ torr} = \frac{733 \text{ torr}}{760 \text{ torr/atm}} = 0.964 \text{ atm}$$

$$V = 0.650 \text{ L}$$

$$T = 22°C + 273 = 295 \text{ K}$$

$$R = 0.08206 \text{ L} \cdot \text{atm/K} \cdot \text{mol}$$

Thus $\quad n_{O_2} = \dfrac{(0.964 \text{ atm})(0.650 \text{ L})}{(0.08206 \text{ L} \cdot \text{atm/K} \cdot \text{mol})(295 \text{ K})} = 2.59 \times 10^{-2} \text{ mol}$

Next we will calculate the moles of $KClO_3$ needed to produce this quantity of O_2. From the balanced equation for the decomposition of $KClO_3$, we have a mole ratio of 2 mol $KClO_3$/3 mol O_2. The moles of $KClO_3$ can be calculated as follows:

$$2.59 \times 10^{-2} \text{ mol O}_2 \times \frac{2 \text{ mol KClO}_3}{3 \text{ mol O}_2} = 1.73 \times 10^{-2} \text{ mol KClO}_3$$

Using the molar mass of $KClO_3$ (122.6 g/mol), we calculate the grams of $KClO_3$:

$$1.73 \times 10^{-2} \text{ mol KClO}_3 \times \frac{122.6 \text{ g KClO}_3}{1 \text{ mol KClO}_3} = 2.12 \text{ g KClO}_3$$

Thus the original sample contained 2.12 g $KClO_3$.

◀ **C H E M I C A L   I M P A C T** ▶

Scuba Diving

Oxygen is essential to our existence, but surprisingly, it can be harmful under certain circumstances. At sea level the partial pressure of this life-sustaining gas is 0.21 atmosphere,* and in each normal breath we inhale about 0.02 mole of O_2 molecules. Our bodies operate very effectively under these conditions, but the situation changes if we subject ourselves to greater pressures—for example, by diving in deep water. A scuba diver at a depth of 100 feet experiences approximately 4 atmospheres of pressure, and at 300 feet the pressure is about 10 atmospheres. This increased pressure affects the ear canals and squeezes the lungs, but a more serious effect involves the increased partial pressure of oxygen in air breathed at these pressures. Elevated concentrations of oxygen are actually quite harmful for reasons that are not well understood. The symptoms of oxygen poisoning include confusion, impaired vision and hearing, and nausea. Clearly, it is possible to get too much of a good thing.

At a depth of 300 feet under the ocean's surface, the partial pressure of oxygen is about 2 atmospheres (0.21 × 10 atmospheres) for a diver inhaling compressed air. This is much too high, so the oxygen must be diluted by another gas. Although it might seem to be an ideal candidate, nitrogen cannot be used. At elevated pressures, a large quantity of nitrogen dissolves in the blood, producing nitrogen narcosis, often called "rapture of the deep," which has an effect not unlike that from imbibing too many martinis. The increased solubility of nitrogen in blood at high pressures is also responsible for an agonizing condition called "the bends," which results when a diver makes too rapid an ascent. The diver's joints become locked in a bent position—hence the name. Just as a bottle of soda fizzes when the pressure inside the bottle is released by opening the cap, the excess dissolved nitrogen in the bloodstream forms bubbles that can stop blood flow and impair the nervous system.

Helium is the diluting agent most often used in scuba tanks. It is inert, and its solubility in blood is much lower than that of oxygen or nitrogen. However, it has the effect of raising the pitch of the human voice, producing a "Donald Duck" effect. This effect occurs because the pitch of the voice depends on the density of the gas surrounding the vocal cords: lower density yields a higher pitch. Because the mass of a He atom is much smaller than the masses of N_2 and O_2, the density of helium gas is much lower than that of air.

Scuba divers.

*This result is obtained from Dalton's law. Since the mole fraction of O_2 in air is 0.21, the partial pressure of O_2 is 0.21 × 1 atm = 0.21 atm.

5.6 The Kinetic Molecular Theory of Gases

Purpose

- To present the basic postulates of the kinetic molecular theory.
- To define temperature.
- To show how to calculate and use root mean square velocity.

We have so far considered the behavior of gases from an experimental point of view. Based on observations from different types of experiments, we know that at pressures of less than 1 atm most gases closely approach the behavior described by the ideal gas law. Now we want to construct a model to explain this behavior.

Before we do this, let's briefly review the scientific method. Recall that a law is a way of generalizing behavior that has been observed in many experiments. Laws are very useful, since they allow us to predict the behavior of similar systems. For example, if a chemist prepares a new gaseous compound, a measurement of the gas density at known pressure and temperature can provide a reliable value for the compound's molar mass.

However, although laws summarize observed behavior, they do not tell us *why* nature behaves in the observed fashion. This is the central question for scientists. To try to answer this question, we construct theories (build models). The models in chemistry consist of speculations about what the individual atoms or molecules (microscopic particles) might be doing to cause the observed behavior of the macroscopic systems (collections of very large numbers of atoms and molecules).

A model is considered successful if it explains the observed behavior in question and predicts correctly the results of future experiments. It is important to understand that a model can never be proved absolutely true. In fact, *any model is an approximation* by its very nature and is bound to fail at some point. Models range from the simple to the extraordinarily complex. We use simple models to predict approximate behavior and more complicated models to account very precisely for observed quantitative behavior. In this text we will stress simple models that provide an approximate picture of what might be happening and that fit the most important experimental results.

An example of this type of model is the **kinetic molecular theory,** a simple model that attempts to explain the properties of an ideal gas. This model is based on speculations about the behavior of the individual gas particles (atoms or molecules). The postulates of the kinetic molecular theory as they relate to the particles of an ideal gas can be stated as follows:

1. The particles are so small compared with the distances between them that *the volume of the individual particles can be assumed to be negligible* (zero).

2. *The particles are in constant motion. The collisions of the particles with the walls of the container are the cause of the pressure exerted by the gas.*

3. *The particles are assumed to exert no forces on each other;* they are assumed neither to attract nor to repel each other.

4. *The average kinetic energy of a collection of gas particles is assumed to be directly proportional to the Kelvin temperature of the gas.*

Of course, the molecules in a real gas have finite volumes and do exert forces on each other. Thus *real gases* do not conform to these assumptions. However, we will see that these postulates do indeed explain *ideal gas* behavior.

The true test of a model is how well its predictions fit the experimental observations. The postulates of the kinetic molecular model picture an ideal gas as consisting of particles having no volume and no attractions for each other, and the model assumes that the gas produces pressure on its container by collisions with the walls. To test the validity of this model, we need to consider the question: "When we apply the principles of physics to a collection of these gas particles, can we derive an expression for pressure that agrees with the ideal gas law?" The answer is, "Yes, we can." As shown in detail in Appendix 2, we can apply the definitions of

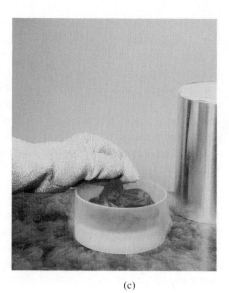

(a)

(b)

(c)

(a) A balloon filled with air at room temperature. (b) The balloon is dipped into liquid nitrogen at 77 K. (c) The balloon collapses as the molecules inside slow down due to the decreased temperature. Slower molecules produce a lower pressure.

Kinetic energy (KE) given by the equation KE = $\frac{1}{2}mu^2$ is the energy due to the motion of a particle. We will discuss this further in Section 6.1.

velocity, momentum, force, and pressure to the collection of particles in an ideal gas and *derive* the following expression for pressure:

$$P = \frac{2}{3}\left[\frac{nN_A(\frac{1}{2}\overline{mu^2})}{V}\right]$$

where P is the pressure of the gas, n is the number of moles of gas, N_A is Avogadro's number, m is the mass of each particle, $\overline{u^2}$ is the average of the square of the velocities of the particles, and V is the volume of the container.

The quantity $\frac{1}{2}\overline{mu^2}$ represents the average kinetic energy of a single gas particle. If the average kinetic energy of an individual particle is multiplied by N_A, the number of particles in a mole, we get the average kinetic energy for a mole of gas particles:

$$(KE)_{avg} = N_A(\tfrac{1}{2}\overline{mu^2})$$

Using this definition, we can rewrite the expression for pressure as

$$P = \frac{2}{3}\left[\frac{n(KE)_{avg}}{V}\right] \qquad \text{or} \qquad \frac{PV}{n} = \frac{2}{3}(KE)_{avg}$$

The fourth postulate of the kinetic molecular theory is that the average kinetic energy of the particles in the gas sample is directly proportional to the temperature in Kelvins. Thus, since $(KE)_{avg} \propto T$, we can write

$$\frac{PV}{n} = \frac{2}{3}(KE)_{avg} \propto T \qquad \text{or} \qquad \frac{PV}{n} \propto T$$

Note that this expression has been *derived* from the assumptions of the kinetic molecular theory. How does it compare to the ideal gas law—the equation obtained from experiment? Compare the ideal gas law,

$$\frac{PV}{n} = RT \qquad \text{From experiment}$$

with the result from the kinetic molecular theory,

$$\frac{PV}{n} \propto T \qquad \text{From theory}$$

These expressions have exactly the same form if R, the universal gas constant, is considered the proportionality constant in the second case.

The agreement between the ideal gas law and the predictions of the kinetic molecular theory gives us confidence in the validity of the model. The characteristics we have assumed for ideal gas particles must agree, at least under certain conditions, with their actual behavior.

The Meaning of Temperature

We have seen from the kinetic molecular theory that the Kelvin temperature indicates the average kinetic energy of the gas particles. The exact relationship between temperature and average kinetic energy can be obtained by combining the equations:

$$\frac{PV}{n} = RT = \frac{2}{3}(\text{KE})_{\text{avg}}$$

which yields the expression

$$(\text{KE})_{\text{avg}} = \frac{3}{2}RT$$

This is a very important relationship. It summarizes the meaning of the Kelvin temperature of a gas: the Kelvin temperature is an index of the random motions of the particles of a gas, with higher temperature meaning greater motion. (As we will see in Chapter 10, temperature is an index of the random motions in solids and liquids as well as in gases.)

Root Mean Square Velocity

In the equation from the kinetic molecular theory, the average velocity of the gas particles is a special kind of average. The symbol $\overline{u^2}$ means the average of the *squares* of the particle velocities. The square root of $\overline{u^2}$ is called the **root mean square velocity** and is symbolized by u_{rms}:

$$u_{\text{rms}} = \sqrt{\overline{u^2}}$$

We can obtain an expression for u_{rms} from the equations

$$(\text{KE})_{\text{avg}} = N_A(\tfrac{1}{2}m\overline{u^2}) \qquad \text{and} \qquad (\text{KE})_{\text{avg}} = \frac{3}{2}RT$$

Combination of these equations gives

$$N_A(\tfrac{1}{2}m\overline{u^2}) = \frac{3}{2}RT \qquad \text{or} \qquad \overline{u^2} = \frac{3RT}{N_A m}$$

Taking the square root of both sides of the last equation produces

$$\sqrt{\overline{u^2}} = u_{\text{rms}} = \sqrt{\frac{3RT}{N_A m}}$$

In this expression m represents the mass in kilograms of a single gas particle. When N_A, the number of particles in a mole, is multiplied by m, the product is the mass of a *mole* of gas particles in *kilograms*. We will call this quantity M. Substituting M for $N_A m$ in the equation for u_{rms}, we obtain

$$u_{rms} = \sqrt{\frac{3RT}{M}}$$

Before we can use this equation, we need to consider the units for R. So far we have used 0.08206 L $\cdot$ atm/K $\cdot$ mol as the value of R. But to obtain the desired units (meters per second) for u_{rms}, R must be expressed in different units. As we will see in more detail in Chapter 6, the energy unit most often used in the SI system is the joule (J). A **joule** is defined as a kilogram meter squared per second squared (kg $\cdot$ m^2/s^2). When R is converted to include the unit of joules, it has the value 8.3145 J/K $\cdot$ mol. When R in these units is used in the expression $\sqrt{3RT/M}$, u_{rms} is obtained in the units of meters per second as desired.

$R = 0.08206 \dfrac{\text{L} \cdot \text{atm}}{\text{K} \cdot \text{mol}}$

$R = 8.3145 \dfrac{\text{J}}{\text{K} \cdot \text{mol}}$

Sample Exercise 5.19

Calculate the root mean square velocity for the atoms in a sample of helium gas at 25°C.

Solution

The formula for root mean square velocity is

$$u_{rms} = \sqrt{\frac{3RT}{M}}$$

In this case $T = 25°C + 273 = 298$ K, $R = 8.3145$ J/K $\cdot$ mol, and M is the mass of a mole of helium in kilograms:

$$M = 4.00\frac{\text{g}}{\text{mol}} \times \frac{1 \text{ kg}}{1000 \text{ g}} = 4.00 \times 10^{-3} \text{ kg/mol}$$

Thus
$$u_{rms} = \sqrt{\frac{3\left(8.3145\dfrac{\text{J}}{\text{K} \cdot \text{mol}}\right)(298 \text{ K})}{4.00 \times 10^{-3}\dfrac{\text{kg}}{\text{mol}}}} = \sqrt{1.86 \times 10^6 \frac{\text{J}}{\text{kg}}}$$

Since the units of J are kg $\cdot$ m^2/s^2, this expression becomes

$$\sqrt{1.86 \times 10^6 \frac{\text{kg} \cdot \text{m}^2}{\text{kg} \cdot \text{s}^2}} = 1.36 \times 10^3 \text{ m/s}$$

Note that the resulting units (m/s) are appropriate for velocity.

So far we have said nothing about the range of velocities actually found in a gas sample. In a real gas there are large numbers of collisions between particles. For example, as we will see in the next section, when an odorous gas such as ammonia is released in a room, it takes some time for the odor to permeate the air. This delay results from collisions between the NH_3 molecules and the O_2 and N_2 molecules in the air, which greatly slow the mixing process.

If the path of a particular gas particle could be monitored, it would look very erratic, something like that shown in Fig. 5.14. The average distance a particle travels between collisions in a particular gas sample is called the **mean free path.** It is typically a very small distance (1×10^{-7} m for O_2 at STP). One effect of the many collisions among gas particles is to produce a large range of velocities as the particles collide and exchange kinetic energy. Although u_{rms} for oxygen gas at STP is approximately 500 meters per second, the majority of O_2 molecules do not have this velocity. The actual distribution of molecular velocities for oxygen gas at STP is shown in Fig. 5.15. This figure shows the relative number of gas molecules having each particular velocity.

We are also interested in the effect of *temperature* on the velocity distribution in a gas. Figure 5.16 shows the velocity distribution for nitrogen gas at three temperatures. Note that as the temperature is increased, the curve peak moves toward higher values and the range of velocities becomes much larger. The peak of the curve reflects the most probable velocity (the velocity found most often as we sample the movement of the various particles in the gas). Because the kinetic energy increases with temperature, it makes sense that the peak of the curve should move to higher values as the temperature of the gas is increased.

5.7 Effusion and Diffusion

Purpose

- To describe effusion and diffusion.
- To show the relationship between effusion and molar mass.

We have seen that the postulates of the kinetic molecular theory, when combined with the appropriate physical principles, produce an equation that successfully fits the experimentally observed behavior of gases as they approach ideal behavior. Two phenomena involving gases provide further tests of this model.

Diffusion is the term used to describe the mixing of gases. When a small amount of pungent-smelling ammonia is released at the front of a classroom, it takes some time before everyone in the room can smell it, because time is required for the ammonia to mix with the air. The rate of diffusion is the rate of the mixing of gases. **Effusion** is the term used to describe the passage of a gas through a tiny orifice into an evacuated chamber, as shown in Fig. 5.17. The rate of effusion measures the speed at which the gas is transferred into the chamber.

Figure 5.14

Path of one particle in a gas. Any given particle will continuously change its course as a result of collisions with other particles, as well as with the walls of the container.

Figure 5.15

A plot of the relative number of O_2 molecules that have a given velocity at STP.

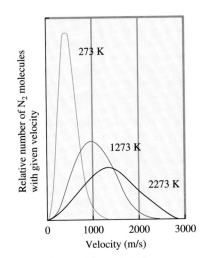

Figure 5.16

A plot of the relative number of N_2 molecules that have a given velocity at three temperatures. Note that as the temperature increases, both the average velocity (reflected by the curve's peak) and the spread of velocities increase.

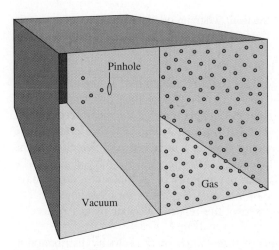

Figure 5.17

The effusion of a gas into an evacuated chamber. The rate of effusion (the rate at which the gas is transferred across the barrier through the pin hole) is inversely proportional to the square root of the mass of the gas molecules.

Effusion

Thomas Graham (1805–1869), a Scottish chemist, found experimentally that the rate of effusion of a gas is inversely proportional to the square root of the mass of its particles. Stated in another way, the relative rates of effusion of two gases at the same temperature and pressure are given by the inverse ratio of the square roots of the masses of the gas particles:

$$\frac{\text{Rate of effusion for gas 1}}{\text{Rate of effusion for gas 2}} = \frac{\sqrt{M_2}}{\sqrt{M_1}}$$

where M_1 and M_2 represent the molar masses of the gases. This equation is called **Graham's law of effusion.**

In Graham's law the units for molar mass can be g/mol or kg/mol, since the units cancel in the ratio $\sqrt{M_2}/\sqrt{M_1}$.

Sample Exercise 5.20

Calculate the ratio of the effusion rates of hydrogen gas (H_2) and uranium hexafluoride (UF_6), a gas used in the enrichment process to produce fuel for nuclear reactors (see Fig. 5.18).

Solution

First, we need to compute the molar masses: molar mass of $H_2 = 2.016$ g/mol, and molar mass of $UF_6 = 352.02$ g/mol. Using Graham's law,

$$\frac{\text{Rate of effusion for } H_2}{\text{Rate of effusion for } UF_6} = \frac{\sqrt{M_{UF_6}}}{\sqrt{M_{H_2}}} = \sqrt{\frac{352.02}{2.016}} = 13.2$$

The effusion rate of the very light H_2 molecules is about 13 times that of the massive UF_6 molecules.

Figure 5.18

Individual diffusion chambers in the gaseous diffusion plant at Oak Ridge National Laboratory in Tennessee.

Does the kinetic molecular model for gases correctly predict the relative effusion rates of gases summarized by Graham's law? To answer this question, we must recognize that the effusion rate for a gas depends directly on the average velocity of its particles. The faster the gas particles are moving, the more likely they are to pass through the effusion orifice. This reasoning leads to the following *prediction* for two gases at the same temperature (T):

$$\frac{\text{Effusion rate for gas 1}}{\text{Effusion rate for gas 2}} = \frac{u_{rms} \text{ for gas 1}}{u_{rms} \text{ for gas 2}} = \frac{\sqrt{\dfrac{3RT}{M_1}}}{\sqrt{\dfrac{3RT}{M_2}}} = \frac{\sqrt{M_2}}{\sqrt{M_1}}$$

This equation is identical to Graham's law. Thus the kinetic molecular model does fit the experimental results for the effusion of gases.

Diffusion

Diffusion is frequently illustrated by the lecture demonstration represented in Fig. 5.19 on p. 214, in which two cotton plugs soaked in ammonia and hydrochloric acid are simultaneously placed at the ends of a long tube. A white ring of ammonium chloride (NH_4Cl) forms where the NH_3 and HCl molecules meet several minutes later:

$$NH_3(g) + HCl(g) \rightarrow NH_4Cl(s)$$
White solid

As a first approximation we might expect that the distances traveled by the two gases are related to the relative velocities of the gas molecules:

$$\frac{\text{Distance traveled by } NH_3}{\text{Distance traveled by } HCl} = \frac{u_{rms} \text{ for } NH_3}{u_{rms} \text{ for } HCl} = \sqrt{\frac{M_{HCl}}{M_{NH_3}}} = \sqrt{\frac{36.5}{17}} = 1.5$$

However, careful experiments show that this prediction is not borne out, indicating that a quantitative analysis of diffusion requires a more complex analysis.

Figure 5.19

(left) When HCl(g) and NH$_3$(g) meet in the tube, a white ring of NH$_4$Cl(s) forms. (right) A demonstration of the relative diffusion rates of NH$_3$ and HCl molecules through air. Two cotton plugs, one dipped in HCl(aq) and one dipped in NH$_3$(aq), are simultaneously inserted into the ends of the tube. Gaseous NH$_3$ and HCl vaporizing from the cotton plugs diffuse toward each other and, where they meet, react to form NH$_4$Cl(s).

The diffusion of the gases through the tube is surprisingly slow in light of the fact that the velocities of HCl and NH$_3$ molecules at 25°C are about 450 and 660 meters per second, respectively. Why does it take several minutes for the NH$_3$ and HCl molecules to meet? The answer is that the tube contains air and thus the NH$_3$ and HCl molecules undergo many collisions with O$_2$ and N$_2$ molecules as they travel through the tube. Because so many collisions occur when gases mix, diffusion is quite complicated to describe theoretically.

5.8 Real Gases

Purpose

* To describe how real gases deviate from ideal behavior.
* To show how van der Waals's equation allows for real conditions.

An ideal gas is a hypothetical concept. No gas *exactly* follows the ideal gas law, although many gases come very close at low pressures and/or high temperatures. Thus ideal gas behavior can best be thought of as the behavior *approached by **real gases*** under certain conditions.

We have seen that a very simple model, the kinetic molecular theory, by making some rather drastic assumptions (no interparticle interactions and zero volume for the gas particles), successfully explains ideal behavior. However, it is important that we examine real gas behavior to see how it differs from that predicted by the ideal gas law and to determine what modifications are needed in the kinetic molecular theory to explain the observed behavior. Since a model is an approximation and will inevitably fail, we must be ready to learn from such failures. In fact, we often learn more about nature from the failures of our models than from their successes.

We will examine the experimentally observed behavior of real gases by measuring pressure, volume, temperature, and number of moles for a gas and noting how the quantity PV/nRT depends on pressure. Plots of PV/nRT versus P are shown for several gases in Fig. 5.20. For an ideal gas, PV/nRT equals 1 under all conditions, but notice that for real gases, PV/nRT approaches 1 only at very low pressures (typically below 1 atm). To illustrate the effect of temperature, PV/nRT is plotted

Figure 5.20

Plots of PV/nRT versus P for several gases (200 K). Note the significant deviations from ideal behavior ($PV/nRT = 1$). The behavior is close to ideal only at low pressures (less than 1 atm).

versus P for nitrogen gas at several temperatures in Fig. 5.21. Note that the behavior of the gas appears to become more nearly ideal as the temperature is increased. The most important conclusion to be drawn from these figures is that a real gas typically exhibits behavior that is closest to ideal behavior at *low pressures* and *high temperatures*.

How can we modify the assumptions of the kinetic molecular theory to fit the behavior of real gases? An equation for real gases was developed in 1873 by Johannes van der Waals (1837–1923), a physics professor at the University of Amsterdam who in 1910 received a Nobel Prize for his work. To follow his analysis, we start with the ideal gas law,

$$P = \frac{nRT}{V}$$

Remember that this equation describes the behavior of a hypothetical gas consisting of volumeless entities that do not interact with each other. In contrast, a real gas consists of atoms or molecules that have finite volumes. Therefore, the volume available to a given particle in a real gas is less than the volume of the container because the gas particles themselves take up some of the space. To account for this discrepancy, van der Waals represented the actual volume as the volume of the container V minus a correction factor for the volume of the molecules nb, where n is the number of moles of gas and b is an empirical constant (one determined by fitting the equation to the experimental results). Thus the volume *actually available* to a given gas molecule is given by the difference $V - nb$.

This modification of the ideal gas equation leads to the equation

$$P' = \frac{nRT}{V - nb}$$

The volume of the gas particles has now been taken into account.

The next step is to allow for the attractions that occur among the particles in a real gas. The effect of these attractions is to make the observed pressure P_{obs} smaller than it would be if the gas particles did not interact:

$$P_{obs} = (P' - \text{correction factor}) = \left(\frac{nRT}{V - nb} - \text{correction factor} \right)$$

This effect can be understood using the following model. When gas particles come close together, attractive forces occur, which cause the particles to hit the wall with slightly less force than they would in the absence of these interactions (see Fig. 5.22 on p. 216).

The size of the correction factor depends on the concentration of gas molecules defined in terms of moles of gas particles per liter (n/V). The higher the concentration, the more likely a pair of gas particles will be close enough to attract each other. For large numbers of particles, the number of interacting *pairs* of particles depends on the square of the number of particles and thus on the square of the concentration, or $(n/V)^2$. This can be justified as follows: in a gas sample containing N particles, there are $N - 1$ partners available for each particle, as shown in Fig. 5.23 on p. 216. Since the $1 \cdots 2$ pair is the same as the $2 \cdots 1$ pair, this analysis counts each pair twice. Thus, for N particles, there are $N(N - 1)/2$ pairs. If N is a very large number, $N - 1$ approximately equals N, giving $N^2/2$ possible pairs. Thus the pressure, corrected for the attractions of the particles, has the form

$$P_{obs} = P' - a \left(\frac{n}{V} \right)^2$$

Figure 5.21

Plots of PV/nRT versus P for nitrogen gas at three temperatures. Note that, although nonideal behavior is evident in each case, the deviations are smaller at the higher temperatures.

P' is corrected for the finite volume of the particles. The attractive forces have not yet been taken into account.

The attractive forces among molecules will be discussed in Chapter 10.

We have now corrected for both the finite volume and the attractive forces of the particles.

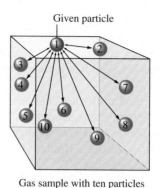

Gas sample with ten particles

Figure 5.22

(a) Gas at low concentration—relatively few interactions between particles. The indicated gas particle exerts a pressure on the wall close to that predicted for an ideal gas. (b) Gas at high concentration—many more interactions between particles. The indicated gas particle exerts a much lower pressure on the wall than would be expected in the absence of interactions.

Figure 5.23

Illustration of pairwise interactions among gas particles. In a sample with 10 particles, each particle has 9 possible partners, to give $10(9)/2 = 45$ distinct pairs. The factor of $\frac{1}{2}$ arises because when particle 1 is the particle of interest we count the ① ⋯ ② pair, and when particle ② is the particle of interest we count the ② ⋯ ① pair. However ① ⋯ ② and ② ⋯ ① are the same pair that we have counted twice. Therefore we must divide by 2 to get the actual number of pairs.

where a is a proportionality constant (which includes the factor of $\frac{1}{2}$ from $N^2/2$). The value of a for a given real gas can be determined from observing the actual behavior of that gas. Inserting the corrections for both the volume of the particles and the attractions of the particles gives the equation

$$P_{obs} = \frac{nRT}{V - nb} - a\left(\frac{n}{V}\right)^2$$

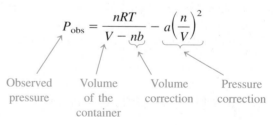

Observed pressure   Volume of the container   Volume correction   Pressure correction

This equation can be rearranged to give the **van der Waals equation:**

$$\left[P_{obs} + a\left(\frac{n}{V}\right)^2\right] \times \underbrace{(V - nb)}_{} = nRT$$

$$\underbrace{\text{Corrected pressure}}_{P_{ideal}} \quad \underbrace{\text{Corrected volume}}_{V_{ideal}}$$

P_{obs} is usually called just P.

The values of the weighting factors a and b are determined for a given gas by fitting experimental behavior. That is, a and b are varied until the best fit of the observed pressure is obtained under all conditions. The values of a and b for various gases are given in Table 5.3.

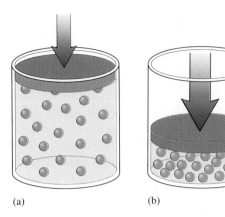

(a)   (b)

Figure 5.24
The volume taken up by the gas particles themselves is less important at (a) large container volumes (low pressure) than at (b) small container volumes (high pressure).

	Table 5.3	
	Values of the van der Waals Constants for Some Common Gases	
Gas	$a\left(\dfrac{\text{atm} \cdot \text{L}^2}{\text{mol}^2}\right)$	$b\left(\dfrac{\text{L}}{\text{mol}}\right)$
He	0.0341	0.0237
Ne	0.211	0.0171
Ar	1.35	0.0322
Kr	2.32	0.0398
Xe	4.19	0.0511
H_2	0.244	0.0266
N_2	1.39	0.0391
O_2	1.36	0.0318
Cl_2	6.49	0.0562
CO_2	3.59	0.0427
CH_4	2.25	0.0428
NH_3	4.17	0.0371
H_2O	5.46	0.0305

Experimental studies indicate that the changes van der Waals made in the basic assumptions of the kinetic molecular theory corrected the major flaws in the model. First, consider the effects of volume. For a gas at low pressure (large volume), the volume of the container is very large compared with the volumes of the gas particles. That is, in this case the volume available to the gas is essentially equal to the volume of the container, and the gas behaves ideally. On the other hand, for a gas at high pressure (small container volume), the volume of the particles becomes significant so that the volume available to the gas is significantly less than the container volume. These cases are illustrated in Fig. 5.24. Note from Table 5.3 that the volume correction constant b generally increases with the size of the gas molecule, which gives further support to these arguments.

The fact that a real gas tends to behave more ideally at high temperatures also can be explained in terms of the van der Waals model. At high temperatures the particles are moving so rapidly that the effects of interparticle interactions are not very important.

The corrections to the kinetic molecular theory that van der Waals found necessary to explain real gas behavior make physical sense, which makes us confident that we understand the fundamentals of gas behavior at the particle level. This is significant because so much important chemistry takes place in the gas phase. In fact, the mixture of gases called the atmosphere is vital to our existence. In the next section we consider some of the important reactions that occur in the atmosphere.

5.9 *Chemistry in the Atmosphere*

Purpose
- To characterize the composition of the atmosphere.
- To describe some of the chemistry of air pollution.

The most important gases to us are those in the **atmosphere** that surrounds the earth's surface. The principal components are N_2 and O_2, but many other important gases, such as H_2O and CO_2, are also present. The average composition of the earth's atmosphere near sea level, with the water vapor removed, is shown in Table 5.4. Because of gravitational effects, the composition of the earth's atmosphere is not constant: heavier molecules tend to be near the earth's surface, and light mole-

Table 5.4	
Atmospheric Composition Near Sea Level (Dry Air)*	
Component	Mole Fraction
N_2	0.78084
O_2	0.20948
Ar	0.00934
CO_2	0.000345
Ne	0.00001818
He	0.00000524
CH_4	0.00000168
Kr	0.00000114
H_2	0.0000005
NO	0.0000005
Xe	0.000000087

*The atmosphere contains various amounts of water vapor depending on conditions.

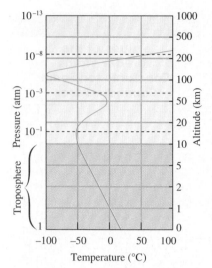

Figure 5.25

The variation of temperature and pressure with altitude. Note that the pressure steadily decreases with altitude, but the temperature increases and decreases.

The Aurora Borealis over Alaska.

The OH radical has no charge [it has one fewer electron than the hydroxide ion (OH⁻)].

cules tend to migrate to higher altitudes, with some eventually escaping into space. The atmosphere is a highly complex and dynamic system, but for convenience we divide it into several layers based on the way the temperature changes with altitude. (The lowest layer, called the **troposphere,** is shown in Fig. 5.25.) Note that in contrast to the complex temperature profile of the atmosphere, the pressure decreases in a regular way with increasing altitude.

The chemistry occurring in the higher levels of the atmosphere is mostly determined by the effects of high-energy radiation and particles from the sun and other sources in space. In fact, the upper atmosphere serves as an important shield to prevent this high-energy radiation from reaching the earth, where it would damage the relatively fragile molecules sustaining life. In particular, the ozone in the upper atmosphere helps prevent high-energy ultraviolet radiation from penetrating to the earth. Intensive research is in progress to determine the natural factors that control the ozone concentration and how it is affected by chemicals released into the atmosphere.

The chemistry occurring in the troposphere, the layer of atmosphere closest to the earth's surface, is strongly influenced by human activities. Millions of tons of gases and particulates are released into the troposphere by our highly industrial civilization. Actually, it is amazing that the atmosphere can absorb so much material with relatively small permanent changes (so far).

Significant changes, however, are occurring. Severe **air pollution** is found around many large cities, and it is probable that long-range changes in our planet's weather are taking place. We will discuss some of the long-range effects of pollution in Chapter 6. In this section we will deal with short-term, localized effects of pollution.

The two main sources of pollution are transportation and the production of electricity. The combustion of petroleum in vehicles produces CO, CO_2, NO, and NO_2, along with unburned molecules from petroleum. When this mixture is trapped close to the ground in stagnant air, reactions occur producing chemicals that are potentially irritating and harmful to living systems.

The complex chemistry of polluted air appears to center around the nitrogen oxides (NO_x). At the high temperatures found in the gasoline and diesel engines of cars and trucks, N_2 and O_2 react to form a small quantity of NO that is emitted into the air with the exhaust gases (see Fig. 5.26). This NO is immediately oxidized in air to NO_2, which, in turn, absorbs energy from sunlight and breaks up into nitric oxide and free oxygen atoms:

$$NO_2(g) \xrightarrow{\text{Radiant energy}} NO(g) + O(g)$$

Oxygen atoms are very reactive and can combine with O_2 to form *ozone:*

$$O(g) + O_2(g) \rightarrow O_3(g)$$

Ozone is also very reactive and can react directly with other pollutants, or the ozone can absorb light and break up to form an energetically excited O_2 molecule (O_2^*) and an energetically excited oxygen atom (O^*). The latter species readily reacts with a water molecule to form two hydroxyl radicals (OH):

$$O^* + H_2O \rightarrow 2OH$$

The hydroxyl radical is a very reactive oxidizing agent. For example, OH can react with NO_2 to form nitric acid:

$$OH + NO_2 \rightarrow HNO_3$$

The OH radical also can react with the unburned hydrocarbons in the polluted air to produce chemicals that cause the eyes to water and burn and are harmful to the respiratory system.

The end product of this whole process is often referred to as **photochemical smog,** so-called because light is required to initiate some of the reactions. The production of photochemical smog can be understood more clearly by examining as a group the reactions discussed above:

$$NO_2(g) \rightarrow NO(g) + O(g)$$
$$O(g) + O_2(g) \rightarrow O_3(g)$$
$$\underline{NO(g) + \tfrac{1}{2}O_2(g) \rightarrow NO_2(g)}$$
Net reaction:
$$\tfrac{3}{2}O_2(g) \rightarrow O_3(g)$$

Note that the NO_2 molecules assist in the formation of ozone without being themselves used up. The ozone formed then leads to the formation of OH and other pollutants.

We can observe this process by analyzing polluted air at various times during a day (see Fig. 5.26). As people drive to work between 6 and 8 a.m., the amounts of NO, NO_2, and unburned molecules from petroleum increase. Later, as the decomposition of NO_2 occurs, the concentration of ozone and other pollutants builds up. Current efforts to combat the formation of photochemical smog are focused on cutting down the amounts of molecules from unburned fuel in automobile exhaust and designing engines that produce less nitric oxide (see Fig. 5.27).

The other major source of pollution results from burning coal to produce electricity. Much of the coal found in the Midwest contains significant quantities of sulfur, which, when burned, produces sulfur dioxide:

$$S \text{ (in coal)} + O_2(g) \rightarrow SO_2(g)$$

A further oxidation reaction occurs when sulfur dioxide is changed to sulfur trioxide in the air*:

$$2SO_2(g) + O_2(g) \rightarrow 2SO_3(g)$$

The production of sulfur trioxide is significant because it can combine with droplets of water in the air to form sulfuric acid:

$$SO_3(g) + H_2O(l) \rightarrow H_2SO_4(aq)$$

Sulfuric acid is very corrosive to both living things and building materials. Another result of this type of pollution is **acid rain** (see Fig. 5.28 on p. 221). In many parts of the northeastern United States and southeastern Canada, acid rain has caused some freshwater lakes to become too acidic to support any life.

The problem of sulfur dioxide pollution is made more complicated by the energy crisis. As petroleum supplies dwindle and the price increases, our dependence on coal will grow. As supplies of low-sulfur coal are used up, high-sulfur coal will be utilized. One way to use high-sulfur coal without further harming the air quality is to remove the sulfur dioxide from the exhaust gas by means of a system called a **scrubber** before it is emitted from the power plant stack. A common method of scrubbing is to blow powdered limestone ($CaCO_3$) into the combustion chamber, where it is decomposed to lime and carbon dioxide:

$$CaCO_3(s) \rightarrow CaO(s) + CO_2(g)$$

*This reaction is very slow unless solid particles are present. See Chapter 12 for a discussion.

Although represented here as O_2, the actual oxidant for NO is OH or an organic peroxide such as CH_3COO, formed by oxidation of organic pollutants.

Figure 5.26

Concentration (in molecules per million molecules of "air") for some smog components versus time of day. After P. A. Leighton, "Photochemistry of Air Pollution" in *Physical Chemistry: A Series of Monographs,* ed. Eric Hutchinson and P. Van Rysselberghe, Vol. IX, New York: Academic Press, 1961.

Figure 5.27

Our various modes of transportation produce large amounts of nitrogen oxides, which facilitate the formation of photochemical smog.

◀ **CHEMICAL IMPACT** ▶

Acid Rain: A Growing Problem

Rainwater, even in pristine wilderness areas, is slightly acidic, because some of the carbon dioxide present in the atmosphere dissolves in the raindrops to produce H^+ ions by the following reaction:

$$H_2O(l) + CO_2(g) \rightarrow H^+(aq) + HCO_3^-(aq)$$

This process produces only very small concentrations of H^+ ions in the rainwater. However, gases such as NO_2 and SO_2, which are by-products of energy use, can produce significantly higher H^+ concentrations. Nitrogen dioxide reacts with water to give a mixture of nitrous acid and nitric acid

$$2NO_2(g) + H_2O(l) \rightarrow HNO_2(aq) + HNO_3(aq)$$

Sulfur dioxide is oxidized to sulfur trioxide, which then reacts with water to form sulfuric acid:

$$2SO_2(g) + O_2(g) \rightarrow 2SO_3(g)$$
$$SO_3(g) + H_2O(l) \rightarrow H_2SO_4(aq)$$

The damage caused by the acid formed in polluted air is a growing worldwide problem. Lakes are dying in Norway, the forests are under stress in Germany, and buildings and statues are deteriorating all over the world.

For example, the Field Museum in Chicago contains more white Georgia marble than any other structure in the world. But nearly 70 years of exposure to the elements has taken such a toll on it that the building has recently undergone a multimillion-dollar renovation to replace the damaged marble with freshly quarried material.

What is the chemistry of the deterioration of marble by sulfuric acid? Marble is produced by geologic processes at high temperatures and pressures from limestone, a sedimentary rock formed by slow deposition of calcium carbonate from the shells of marine organisms. Limestone

The damaging effects of acid rain can be seen by comparing these photos of a decorative statue on the Field Museum in Chicago. The first photo was taken c. 1920, the second in 1990.

and marble are chemically identical ($CaCO_3$) but differ in physical properties; limestone is composed of smaller particles of calcium carbonate and is thus more porous and more workable. Although both limestone and marble are used for buildings, marble can be polished to a higher sheen and is often preferred for decorative purposes.

Both marble and limestone react with sulfuric acid to form calcium sulfate. The process can be represented most simply as

$$CaCO_3(s) + H_2SO_4(aq) \rightarrow Ca^{2+}(aq) + SO_4^{2-}(aq) + H_2O(l) + CO_2(g)$$

In this equation the calcium sulfate is represented by separate hydrated ions because calcium sulfate is quite water soluble and dissolves in rainwater. Thus, in areas bathed by rainwater, the marble slowly dissolves away.

In areas of the building protected from the rain, the calcium sulfate can form the mineral gypsum ($CaSO_4 \cdot 2H_2O$). The $\cdot 2H_2O$ in the formula of gypsum indicates the presence of two water molecules (called **waters of hydration**) for each $CaSO_4$ formula unit in the solid. The smooth surface of the marble is thus replaced by a thin layer of gypsum, a more porous material that binds soot and dust.

What can be done to protect limestone and marble structures from this kind of damage? Of course, one approach is to lower sulfur dioxide emissions from power plants (see Fig. 5.29). In addition, scientists are experimenting with coatings to protect marble from the acidic atmosphere. However, a coating can do more harm than good unless it "breathes." If moisture trapped beneath the coating freezes, the expanding ice can fracture the marble. Needless to say, it is difficult to find a coating that will allow water to pass but not acid—but the search continues.

For more information on this topic, see A. Elena Charola, "Acid Rain Effects on Stone Monuments," *J. Chem. Ed.* **64**(1987): 436.

The lime then combines with the sulfur dioxide to form calcium sulfite:

$$CaO(s) + SO_2(g) \rightarrow CaSO_3(s)$$

To remove the calcium sulfite and any remaining unreacted sulfur dioxide, an aqueous suspension of lime is injected into the combustion chamber and the stack to produce a *slurry* (a thick suspension), as shown in Fig. 5.29.

Unfortunately, there are many problems associated with scrubbing. The systems are complicated and expensive and consume a great deal of energy. The large quantities of calcium sulfite produced in the process present a disposal problem. With a typical scrubber, approximately 1 ton of calcium sulfite per year is produced per person served by the power plant. Since no use has yet been found for this calcium sulfite, it is usually buried in a landfill. As a result of these difficulties, air pollution by sulfur dioxide continues to be a major problem, one that is expensive in terms of damage to the environment and human health as well as in monetary terms.

Figure 5.28
Trees in North Carolina damaged by acid rain.

Figure 5.29
A schematic diagram of the process for scrubbing sulfur dioxide from stack gases in power plants.

FOR REVIEW

Summary

Of the three states of matter, the gaseous state is the most easily understood experimentally and theoretically. A gas can be described quantitatively by specifying four properties: volume, pressure, temperature, and the amount of gas present.

Atmospheric pressure is measured with a barometer, and in the laboratory, gas pressure is usually measured with a manometer. Both devices employ columns filled with mercury, and the most commonly used units of pressure are based on the height of such a column in millimeters: 1 mm Hg equals 1 torr; 1 standard atmosphere equals 760 torr. In the SI system, the unit of pressure is the pascal ($1 \ N/m^2$).

Early experiments on the behavior of gases dealt with the relationship among the four characteristic properties. Boyle's law states that the volume of a given amount of a gas is inversely proportional to its pressure (at constant temperature). Charles's law states that for a given amount of gas at a constant pressure, the volume is directly proportional to the temperature in Kelvins. At a temperature of $-273.2°C$

(0 K), the volume of a gas extrapolates to zero, and this temperature is called absolute zero. Avogadro's law states that equal volumes of gases at the same temperature and pressure contain the same number of particles.

These three laws can be combined into the ideal gas law:

$$PV = nRT$$

where R is called the universal gas constant (0.08206 L · atm/K · mol). This equation allows calculation of any one of the characteristic properties, given the other three. The ideal gas law describes the limiting behavior approached by real gases at low pressures and high temperatures.

The molar volume (22.42 liters) is the volume of an ideal gas at STP (standard temperature and pressure) or 0°C and 1 atmosphere.

The pressure of a gaseous mixture is described by Dalton's law of partial pressures, which states that the total pressure of a mixture of gases in a container is the sum of the pressures that each gas would exert if it were alone (its partial pressure), that is,

$$P_{\text{TOTAL}} = P_1 + P_2 + P_3 + \cdots$$

The mole fraction of a given component in a mixture of gases can be calculated from the ratio of the partial pressure of that component to the total gas pressure.

The kinetic molecular theory of gases is a theoretical model constructed to account for ideal gas behavior. This model assumes that the volume of the gas particles is zero, that there are no interactions between particles, and that the particles are in constant motion, colliding with the container walls to produce pressure. In addition, this model shows that the average kinetic energy of the gas particles is directly proportional to the Kelvin temperature of the gas.

The root mean square velocity for the particles in a gas can be calculated from the temperature and the molar mass of the gas. Within any gas sample there is a range of velocities, since the gas particles collide and exchange kinetic energy. An increase in temperature increases the average velocity of the gas particles. The relative rates of diffusion, the mixing of gases, and effusion, the passage of a gas through a small orifice into an empty chamber, are inversely proportional to the square roots of the atomic or molar masses of the gases in question.

Real gases behave ideally only at high temperatures and low pressures. The van der Waals equation is a modification of the ideal gas equation that takes into consideration that real gas particles take up volume and interact with each other.

Key Terms

Section 5.1
barometer
manometer
mm Hg
torr
standard atmosphere
pascal

Section 5.2
Boyle's law
ideal gas
Charles's law

absolute zero
Avogadro's law

Section 5.3
universal gas constant
ideal gas law

Section 5.4
molar volume
standard temperature and pressure (STP)

Section 5.5
Dalton's law of partial pressures

partial pressure
mole fraction

Section 5.6
kinetic molecular theory
root mean square velocity
joule

Section 5.7
diffusion
effusion
Graham's law of effusion

Section 5.8
real gas
van der Waals equation

Section 5.9
atmosphere
air pollution
photochemical smog
acid rain

Questions

1. Rationalize the following observations:
   a. Aerosol cans will explode if heated.
   b. You can drink through a soda straw.
   c. A thin-walled can will collapse when the air inside is removed by a vacuum pump.

2. Why do manufacturers produce different types of tennis balls for high and low elevations?

3. Show how Boyle's law and Charles's law are special cases of the ideal gas law.

4. Using the postulates of the kinetic molecular theory, give molecular interpretations of Boyle's law, Charles's law, and Dalton's law of partial pressures.

Exercises

In this section similar exercises are paired.

Pressure

5. Atmospheric pressures announced during weather forecasts are typically given in inches of mercury. Calculate the value of one standard atmosphere in inches of mercury.

6. A gauge on a compressed gas cylinder reads 2200 psi (pounds per square inch; 1 atm = 14.7 psi). Express this pressure in each of the following units:
   a. Standard atmospheres
   b. Megapascals (MPa)
   c. Torr

7. A sealed-tube manometer (as shown below) can be used to measure pressures below atmospheric pressure. The tube above the mercury is evacuated. When there is a vacuum in the flask, the mercury levels in both arms of the U-tube are equal. If a gaseous sample is introduced into the flask, the mercury levels are different. The difference h is a measure of the pressure of the gas inside the flask. If h is equal to 6.5 cm, calculate the pressure in the flask in torr, pascals, and atmospheres.

8. Freon-12 (CF_2Cl_2) is commonly used as the refrigerant in central home air conditioners. The system is initially charged to a pressure of 70. psi. Express this pressure in each of the following units (remember that 1 atm = 14.7 psi):
   a. mm Hg   d. kPa
   b. atm   e. MPa
   c. Pa

h

Gas

9. A diagram for an open-tube manometer is shown below.

Atmosphere

If the flask is open to the atmosphere, the mercury levels are equal. For each of the following situations where a gas is contained in the flask, calculate the pressure in the flask in torr, atmospheres, and pascals.

Atmosphere (760. torr)   Atmosphere (760. torr)

Flask   Flask

140 mm   175 mm

a.   b.

c. Calculate the pressures in the flask in parts a and b (in torr) if the atmospheric pressure is 635 torr.

10. a. If the open-tube manometer in Exercise 9 contains a non-volatile silicone oil (density = 1.30 g/cm^3) instead of mercury, what are the pressures in the flask as shown in parts a and b in torr, atmospheres, and pascals?

b. What advantage would there be in using a less dense fluid than mercury in a manometer used to measure relatively small differences in pressure?

Gas Laws

11. Complete the following table for an ideal gas:

	P (atm)	V(L)	n(mol)	T
a.	5.00	—	2.00	155°C
b.	0.300	2.00	—	155 K
c.	4.47	25.0	2.01	—
d.	—	2.25	10.5	75°C

12. Complete the following table for an ideal gas:

	P	V	n	T
a.	875 torr	275 mL	0.0105 mol	—
b.	—	0.100 L	0.200 mol	38°C
c.	2.50 atm	—	3.00 mol	565°C
d.	688 torr	986 mL	—	565 K

13. Calculate the value of the universal gas constant R in units of L · Pa/K · mol.

14. Calculate the value of the universal gas constant R in units of m^3 · Pa/K · mol. What other SI unit can replace m^3 · Pa?

15. Consider the flask diagramed below. What are the final partial pressures of H_2 and N_2 after the stopcock between the two flasks is opened? (Assume the final volume is 1.50 L.) What is the total pressure (in torr)?

1.00 L H_2
475 torr

0.50 L N_2
45 kPa

16. If the initial pressures of the H_2 and N_2 in the flasks in Exercise 15 were 360 torr and 240 torr, respectively, what would be the final pressure after the stopcock is opened?

17. A certain flexible weather balloon contains helium gas. Initially, the balloon is at sea level, where the temperature is 25°C and the barometric pressure is 720. torr. The balloon then rises to an altitude of 6000 ft, where the pressure is 605 torr and the temperature is 15°C. What is the change in the volume of the balloon as it ascends from sea level to 6000 ft?

18. An ideal gas is contained in a cylinder with a volume of 5.0×10^2 mL at a temperature of 30.0°C and a pressure of 710. torr. The gas is then compressed to a volume of 25 mL, and the temperature is raised to 820°C. What is the new pressure of the gas?

19. The steel reaction vessel of a bomb calorimeter, which has a volume of 75 mL, is charged with oxygen gas to a pressure of 145 atm at 22°C. Calculate the moles of oxygen in the reaction vessel.

20. A 5.0-L flask contains 0.60 g O_2 at a temperature of 22°C. What is the pressure (in atm) inside the flask?

21. A mixture of 1.00 g H_2 and 1.00 g He exerts a pressure of 0.480 atm. What is the partial pressure of each gas present in the mixture?

22. The partial pressure of $CH_4(g)$ is 0.175 atm and that of $O_2(g)$ is 0.250 atm in a mixture of the two gases.
   a. What is the mole fraction of each gas in the mixture?
   b. If the mixture occupies a volume of 10.5 L at 65°C, calculate the total number of moles of gas in the mixture.
   c. Calculate the number of grams of each gas in the mixture.

23. A balloon is filled to a volume of 7.00×10^2 mL at a temperature of 20.0°C. The balloon is then cooled at constant pressure to a temperature of 1.00×10^2 K. What is the final volume of the balloon?

24. A balloon has a volume of 175 cm³ at 19°C. At what temperature will the volume of the balloon have increased by 25.0% (at constant pressure)?

25. A 2.50-L container is filled with 175 g argon.
   a. If the pressure is 10.0 atm, what is the temperature?
   b. If the temperature is 225 K, what is the pressure?

26. A 2.00-L flask contains helium gas at a pressure of 685 torr and a temperature of 0°C. What would be the pressure in the flask if each of the following occurred?
   a. The temperature is increased to 150.°C.
   b. The temperature is lowered to 77 K.

27. A compressed gas cylinder, at 13.7 MPa and 23°C, is in a room where a fire raises the temperature to 450°C. What is the new pressure in the cylinder?

28. A steel cylinder contains 150 mol argon gas at a temperature of 25°C and a pressure of 7.5 MPa. After some of the argon has been used, the pressure is 2.0 MPa at a temperature of 19°C. What mass of argon remains in the cylinder?

29. A sample of nitrogen gas was collected over water at 20.°C and a total pressure of 1.00 atm. A total volume of 2.50×10^2 mL was collected. What mass of nitrogen was collected? (At 20.°C the vapor pressure of water is 17.5 torr.)

30. A sample of oxygen gas is collected over water at 25°C and a total pressure of 641 torr. The volume of gas collected is 500.0 mL. What mass of oxygen is collected? (At 25°C the vapor pressure of water is 23.8 torr.)

125.

Gas Density, Molar Mass, and Reaction Stoichiometry

31. Silicon tetrachloride ($SiCl_4$) and trichlorosilane ($SiHCl_3$) are both starting materials for the production of electronics-grade silicon. Calculate the densities of pure $SiCl_4$ and pure $SiHCl_3$ vapor at 85°C and 758 torr.

32. Calculate the density of ammonia gas at 27°C and 635 torr.

33. A compound contains only nitrogen and hydrogen and is 87.4% nitrogen by mass. A gaseous sample of the compound has a density of 0.977 g/L at 710. torr and 100°C. What is the molecular formula of the compound?

34. A compound has the empirical formula CHCl. A 256-mL flask, at 373 K and 750 torr, contains 0.80 g of the gaseous compound. Give the molecular formula.

35. In a recent year, production of ammonia in the United States totaled 27.37×10^9 lb (*Chemical & Engineering News,* May 7, 1984). Assuming 100% yield, calculate the volumes of N_2 and H_2 measured at STP required to produce this much ammonia by the reaction

$$N_2(g) + 3H_2(g) \rightarrow 2NH_3(g)$$

36. Urea (H_2NCONH_2) is used extensively as a nitrogen source in fertilizers. It is produced commercially from the reaction of ammonia and carbon dioxide:

$$2NH_3(g) + CO_2(g) \xrightarrow[\text{Pressure}]{\text{Heat}} H_2NCONH_2(s) + H_2O(g)$$

Ammonia is added to an evacuated 5.0-L flask, to a pressure of 9.0 atm, at a temperature of 23°C. Carbon dioxide is added to the ammonia, to give a total pressure of 14.0 atm. The flask is then heated. What mass of urea is produced in this reaction, assuming 100% yield?

37. Calculate the volume of O_2, at STP, required for the complete combustion of 125 g octane (C_8H3_{18}) to CO_2 and H_2O.

38. The method used by Joseph Priestley to obtain oxygen made use of the thermal decomposition of mercuric oxide:

$$2HgO(s) \xrightarrow{\text{Heat}} 2Hg(l) + O_2(g)$$

What volume of oxygen gas, measured at 30°C and 725 torr, can be produced from the complete decomposition of 4.1 g mercuric oxide?

39. Hydrogen cyanide is prepared commercially by the reaction of methane, $CH_4(g)$, ammonia, $NH_3(g)$, and oxygen, $O_2(g)$, at high temperature. The other product is gaseous water.
   a. Write a chemical equation for the reaction.
   b. What volume of $HCN(g)$ can be obtained from 20.0 L $CH_4(g)$, 20.0 L $NH_3(g)$, and 20.0 L $O_2(g)$? The volumes of all gases are measured at the same temperature and pressure.

40. Consider the first step in the industrial production of nitric acid:

$$4NH_3(g) + 5O_2(g) \rightarrow 4NO(g) + 6H_2O(g)$$

   a. What volume of NO, measured at 1.0 atm and 1000.°C, can be produced from 10.0 L NH_3 and excess O_2 measured at the same temperature and pressure?
   b. What volume of O_2 measured at STP is consumed in reacting with 10.0 kg NH_3?
   c. What mass of NO is produced from the reaction of 5.00×10^2 L NH_3, measured at 250.°C and 3.00 atm, with excess O_2?
   d. What mass of H_2O is produced from the reaction of 65 L NH_3 and 75 L O_2, both measured at STP?
   e. How many moles of NO are produced from the mixture in part d?

41. The nitrogen content of organic compounds can be determined by the Dumas method. The compound in question is first reacted by passage over hot $CuO(s)$:

$$\text{Compound} \xrightarrow[\text{CuO}(s)]{\text{Hot}} N_2(g) + CO_2(g) + H_2O(g)$$

The product gas is then passed through a concentrated solution of KOH to remove the CO_2. After passage through the KOH solution, the gas contains N_2 and is saturated with water vapor. In a given experiment a 0.253-g sample of a compound produced 31.8 mL N_2 saturated with water vapor at 25°C and 726 torr. What is the mass percent nitrogen in the compound? (The vapor pressure of water at 25°C is 23.8 torr.)

42. An organic compound contains C, H, N, and O. Combustion of 0.1023 g of the compound yielded 0.2766 g CO_2 and 0.0991 g H_2O. A 0.4831-g sample of the compound was analyzed for nitrogen by the Dumas method. At STP, 27.6 mL of dry N_2 was obtained. In a third experiment, the density of the compound as a gas was found to be 4.02 g/L at 127°C and 256 torr. What are the empirical formula and the molecular formula of the compound?

43. Oxygen gas can be produced in small quantities in the laboratory from the thermal decomposition of potassium chlorate:

$$2KClO_3(s) \xrightarrow{\text{Heat}} 2KCl(s) + 3O_2(g)$$

If 3.7 g $KClO_3$ is heated, what volume of gas will be collected over water at 27°C and 735 torr? (At 27°C the vapor pressure of water is 26.7 torr.)

44. Acetylene gas, $C_2H_2(g)$, can be produced by reacting solid calcium carbide, CaC_2, with water. The products are acetylene and calcium hydroxide. What volume of wet acetylene is collected at 25°C and 715 torr when 5.20 g calcium carbide is reacted with an excess of water? (At 25°C the vapor pressure of water is 23.8 torr.)

Kinetic Molecular Theory and Real Gases

45. Calculate the average kinetic energy of the CH_4 molecules in a sample of CH_4 gas at 273 K and at 546 K.

46. Calculate the average kinetic energy of the N_2 molecules in a sample of N_2 gas at 273 K and at 546 K.

47. Calculate the root mean square velocity of the CH_4 molecules in a sample of CH_4 gas at 273 K and at 546 K.

48. Calculate the root mean square velocity of the N_2 molecules in a sample of N_2 gas at 273 K and at 546 K.

49. Do all the molecules in a 1-mol sample of $CH_4(g)$ have the same energy at 273 K?

50. Do all the molecules in a 1-mol sample of $CH_4(g)$ have the same velocity at 546 K?

51. Consider three identical flasks filled with different gases.

Flask A: CO at 760 torr and 0°C

Flask B: N_2 at 250 torr and 0°C

Flask C: H_2 at 100 torr and 0°C

a. In which flask will the molecules have the greatest average kinetic energy?
b. In which flask will the molecules have the greatest root mean square velocity?

52. Consider a 1.0-L container of neon gas at STP. Will the average kinetic energy, root mean square velocity, frequency of collisions of gas molecules with the walls of the container, and energy of impact of gas molecules with the container increase, decrease, or remain the same under each of the following conditions:
a. The temperature is increased to 100°C.
b. The temperature is decreased to 50°C.
c. The volume is decreased to 0.5 L.
d. The number of moles of neon is doubled.

53. The diffusion rate of an unknown gas is measured and found to be 31.50 mL/min. Under identical experimental conditions, the diffusion rate of O_2 is found to be 30.50 mL/min. If the choices are CH_4, CO, NO, CO_2, and NO_2, what is the identity of the unknown gas?

54. The rate of diffusion of a particular gas was measured and found to be 24.0 mL/min. Under the same conditions, the rate of diffusion of pure methane (CH_4) gas is 47.8 mL/min. What is the molar mass of the unknown gas?

55. Calculate the pressure exerted by 0.5000 mol N_2 in a 1.000-L container at 25.0°C
    a. using the ideal gas law.
    b. using the van der Waals equation.
    c. Compare the results.

56. Calculate the pressure exerted by 0.5000 mol N_2 in a 10.00-L container at 25.0°C
    a. using the ideal gas law.
    b. using the van der Waals equation.
    c. Compare the results.
    d. Compare the results with those in Exercise 55.

Atmosphere Chemistry

57. Use the data in Table 5.4 to calculate the partial pressure of NO in dry air assuming that the total pressure is 1.0 atm. Assuming a temperature of 0°C, calculate the number of molecules of NO per cubic centimeter.

58. Use the data in Table 5.4 to calculate the partial pressure of He in dry air assuming that the total pressure is 1.0 atm. Assuming a temperature of 25°C, calculate the number of He atoms per cubic centimeter.

59. A 10.0-L sample of air was collected at an altitude of 1.00×10^2 km. What would be the volume of the sample at STP? (See Fig. 5.25.)

60. A 1.0-L sample of air is collected at 25°C at sea level (1.00 atm). What volume would this sample of air have at an altitude of 15 km?

61. Write reactions to show how nitric and sulfuric acids are produced in the atmosphere.

62. Write reactions to show how the nitric and sulfuric acids in acid rain react with marble and limestone. (Both marble and limestone are primarily calcium carbonate.)

Additional Exercises

63. Draw a qualitative graph to show how the first property varies with the second in each of the following (assume 1 mol of an ideal gas):
    a. PV versus V with constant T
    b. P versus T with constant V
    c. T versus V with constant P
    d. P versus V with constant T
    e. P versus $1/V$ with constant T
    f. PV/T versus P

64. At 0°C, a 1.0-L flask contains 5.0×10^{-2} mol N_2, 1.5×10^2 mg O_2, and NH_3 at a concentration of 5.0×10^{18} molecules/cm^3. What is the partial pressure of each gas, and what is the total pressure in the flask?

65. A container is filled with an ideal gas to a pressure of 40.0 atm at 0°C.
    a. What will be the pressure in the container if it is heated to 45°C?
    b. At what temperature would the pressure be 1.50×10^2 atm?
    c. At what temperature would the pressure be 25.0 atm?

66. A piece of solid carbon dioxide, with a mass of 7.8 g, is placed in a 4.0-L otherwise empty container at 27°C. What is the pressure in the container after all the carbon dioxide vaporizes? If 7.8 g solid carbon dioxide were placed in the same container but it already contained air at 740 torr, what would be the partial pressure of carbon dioxide and the total pressure in the container after the carbon dioxide vaporizes?

67. Helium is collected over water at 25°C and 1.0 atm total pressure. What total volume of "wet" gas must be collected in order to obtain 0.586 g He? (At 25°C the vapor pressure of water is 23.8 torr.)

68. Nitrous oxide (N_2O) can be produced by the thermal decomposition of ammonium nitrate:

$$NH_4NO_3(s) \xrightarrow{\text{Heat}} N_2O(g) + 2H_2O(l)$$

What volume of N_2O, collected over water, at a total pressure of 94 kPa and 22°C, can be produced from the thermal decomposition of 2.6 g NH_4NO_3? (The vapor pressure of water at 22°C is 21 torr.)

69. At STP, 1.0 L Br_2 reacts completely with 3.0 L F_2, producing 2.0 L of a product. What is the formula of the product? (All substances are gases.)

70. In the "Méthode Champenoise," grape juice is fermented in a wine bottle to produce sparkling wine. The reaction is

$$C_6H_{12}O_6(aq) \rightarrow 2C_2H_5OH(aq) + 2CO_2(g)$$

Fermentation of 750. mL grape juice (density = 1.0 g/cm^3) is allowed to take place in a bottle with a total volume of 825 mL until 12% by volume is ethanol (C_2H_5OH). Assuming that the CO_2 is insoluble in H_2O (actually, a wrong assumption), what would be the pressure of CO_2 inside the wine bottle at 25°C? (The density of ethanol is 0.79 g/cm^3.)

71. A compressed gas cylinder contains 5.00×10^2 g argon gas with a pressure of 2050. psi at a temperature of 18°C. Some argon is then released from the cylinder. How much gas remains in the cylinder if the pressure is 980. psi at a temperature of 26°C?

72. Consider the three flasks in the diagram below. Assuming the connecting tubes have negligible volume, what is the partial pressure of each gas and the total pressure when all the stopcocks are opened?

1.0 L	1.0 L	2.0 L
180 torr	0.45 atm	25 kPa

73. One of the chemical controversies of the nineteenth century concerned the element beryllium (Be). Berzelius originally claimed that beryllium was a trivalent element (forming Be^{3+} ions) and that it gave an oxide with the formula Be_2O_3. This resulted in a calculated atomic weight of 13.5 for beryllium. In formulating his periodic table, Mendeleev proposed that beryllium was divalent (forming Be^{2+} ions) and that it gave an oxide with the formula BeO. This assumption gives an atomic weight of 9.0. In 1894, A. Combes (*Comptes Rendus* 1894, p. 1221) reacted beryllium with the anion $C_5H_7O_2^-$ and measured the density of the gaseous product. Combes's data for two different experiments are as follows:

	I	II
Mass	0.2022 g	0.2224 g
Volume	22.6 cm^3	26.0 cm^3
Temperature	13°C	17°C
Pressure	765.2 mm Hg	764.6 mm Hg

If beryllium is a divalent metal, the molecular formula of the product will be $Be(C_5H_7O_2)_2$; if it is trivalent, the formula will be $Be(C_5H_7O_2)_3$. Show how Combes's data help to confirm that beryllium is a divalent metal.

74. A 1.00-L container is evacuated until the pressure is 1.00×10^{-6} torr at 22°C. How many molecules of gas remain in the container? How many molecules are there per cubic centimeter?

75. A compound contains only C, H, and N. It is 58.51% C and 7.37% H by mass. Helium effuses through a porous frit 3.20 times as fast as the compound does. Determine the empirical and molecular formulas of this compound.

76. A compound contains only C, H, and N. A chemist analyzes it by doing the following experiments:

   i. Complete combustion of 35.0 mg of the compound produced 33.5 mg CO_2 and 41.1 mg H_2O.
   ii. A 65.2-mg sample of the compound was analyzed for nitrogen by the Dumas method, giving 35.6 mL N_2 at 740. torr and 25°C.
   iii. The effusion rate of the compound as a gas was measured and found to be 24.6 mL/min. The effusion rate of argon gas, under identical conditions, is 26.4 mL/min.

   What is the formula of the compound?

77. A 15.0-L tank is filled with H_2 to a pressure of 2.00×10^2 atm. How many balloons (each 2.00 L) can be inflated to a pressure of 1.00 atm from the tank? Assume that there is no temperature change and that the tank cannot be emptied below 1.00 atm pressure.

78. Consider the following diagram:

   Container A (with porous walls) is filled with air at STP. It is then inserted into a large enclosed container (B) which is then flushed with $H_2(g)$. What will happen to the pressure inside container A? Explain your answer.

79. Without looking at tables of values, which of the following gases would you expect to have the largest value of the van der Waals constant b: H_2, N_2, CH_4, C_2H_6, or C_3H_8?

80. From the values in Table 5.3 for the van der Waals constant a for the gases H_2, CO_2, N_2, and CH_4, predict which of these gas molecules show the strongest intermolecular attractions.

Challenge Problems

81. Derive a linear relationship between gas density and temperature, and use it to estimate the value of absolute zero temperature (in °C to the nearest 0.1°C) from an air sample whose density is 1.2930 g/L at 0.0°C and 0.9460 g/L at 100.0°C. Assume that air obeys the ideal gas law and that the pressure is held constant.

82. One way of separating oxygen isotopes is by gaseous diffusion of carbon monoxide. Calculate the relative rates of diffusion of $^{12}C^{16}O$, $^{12}C^{17}O$, and $^{12}C^{18}O$. Name some advantages and disadvantages of separating oxygen isotopes by gaseous diffusion of carbon dioxide instead of carbon monoxide.

83. It took 4.5 minutes for 1.0 L helium to effuse through a porous barrier. How long will it take for 1.0 L Cl_2 gas to effuse under identical conditions?

84. Using values of the van der Waals constants for NH_3 from Table 5.3, show how much of its deviation from ideal behavior can be accounted for by the van der Waals equation. Use the data for pressure and volume given in Sample Exercise 5.3.

85. We state that the ideal gas law tends to hold best at low pressures and high temperatures. Show how the van der Waals equation simplifies to the ideal gas law under these conditions.

86. A bicycle tire is filled with air to a pressure of 610 kPa at a temperature of 19°C. Riding the bike on asphalt on a hot day increases the temperature of the tire to 58°C. The volume of the tire increases by 4.0%. What is the new pressure in the bicycle tire?

87. A hot-air balloon is filled with air to a volume of 4.00×10^3 m^3 at 745 torr and 21°C. The air in the balloon is then heated to 62°C, and the balloon expands to a volume of 4.20×10^3 m^3. What is the ratio of the number of moles of air in the heated balloon to the original number of moles of air in the balloon? *Hint:* Openings in the balloon allow air to flow in and out. Thus the pressure in the balloon is always the same as that of the atmosphere.

88. The total mass that can be lifted by a balloon is given by the difference between the mass of air displaced by the balloon and the mass of the gas inside the balloon. Consider a hot-air balloon that approximates a sphere 5.0 m in diameter and contains air heated to 65°C. The surrounding air temperature is 21°C. The pressure in the balloon is equal to the atmospheric pressure, which is 745 torr.
    a. What total mass can the balloon lift? Assume that the average molar mass of air is 29.0 g/mol. (*Hint:* Heated air is less dense than cool air.)
    b. If the balloon is filled with enough helium at 21°C and 745 torr to achieve the same volume as in part a, what total mass can the balloon lift?
    c. What mass could the hot-air balloon in part a lift if it were on the ground in Denver, Colorado, where a typical atmospheric pressure is 630. torr?

89. Xenon and fluorine react to form binary compounds when a mixture of the two gases is heated to 400°C in a nickel reaction vessel. A 100.0-mL nickel container is filled with xenon and fluorine to partial pressures of 1.24 atm and 10.10 atm, respectively, at a temperature of 25°C. The reaction vessel is heated to 400°C and then cooled to a temperature at which F_2 is a gas and the xenon fluorides are nonvolatile solids. The

remaining F_2 gas is transferred to another 100.0-mL nickel container where the pressure of F_2 at 25°C is 7.62 atm. Assuming all the xenon has reacted, what is the formula of the product?

90. Discrepancies in the experimental values of the molar mass of nitrogen provided some of the first evidence for the existence of the noble gases. If pure nitrogen is collected from the decomposition of ammonium nitrite:

$$NH_4NO_2(s) \xrightarrow{\text{Heat}} N_2(g) + 2H_2O(g)$$

its measured molar mass is 28.01 g/mol. If O_2, CO_2, and H_2O are removed from air, the remaining gas has an average molar mass of 28.15 g/mol. Assuming that this discrepancy is solely the result of contamination with argon, calculate the ratio of moles of Ar to moles of N_2 in air.

91. An important process for the production of acrylonitrile (C_3H_3N) is given by the following reaction:

$$2C_3H_6(g) + 2NH_3(g) + 3O_2(g) \rightarrow 2C_3H_3N(g) + 6H_2O(g)$$

A 150.-L reactor is charged to the following partial pressures at 25°C:

$$P_{C_3H_6} = 0.50 \text{ MPa}$$
$$P_{NH_3} = 0.80 \text{ MPa}$$
$$P_{O_2} = 1.50 \text{ MPa}$$

What mass of acrylonitrile can be produced from this mixture (MPa = 10^6 Pa)?

92. The oxides of Group 2A metals (symbolized by M here) react with carbon dioxide according to the following reaction:

$$MO(s) + CO_2(g) \rightarrow MCO_3(s)$$

A 2.85-g sample containing only MgO and CuO is placed in a 3.0-L container. The container is filled with CO_2 to a pressure of 740 torr, at 20.°C. After the reaction has gone to completion, the pressure inside the flask is 390 torr, also at 20.°C. What is the mass percent of MgO in the mixture? Assume that only the MgO reacts with CO_2.

93. Atmospheric scientists often use mixing ratios to express the concentrations of trace compounds in air. Mixing ratios are often expressed as ppmv (parts per million volume):

$$\text{ppmv of } X = \frac{\text{vol. of } X \text{ at STP}}{\text{total vol. of air at STP}} \times 10^6$$

On a recent autumn day, the concentration of carbon monoxide in the air in downtown Denver, Colorado, reached 3.0×10^2 ppmv. The atmospheric pressure at that time was 628 torr, and the temperature was 0°C.
    a. What was the partial pressure of CO?
    b. What was the concentration of CO in molecules per cubic meter?

c. What was the concentration of CO in molecules per cubic centimeter?

94. In a particular urban area, the NO_2 concentration reached a maximum value of 0.2 ppm by volume. (See Exercise 93.) Assume that this concentration exists to an altitude of 5.0×10^3 ft over an area of 5.0 mi by 10.0 mi. Assuming 1.0 atm pressure and 0°C temperature, calculate the total mass of NO_2 in the atmosphere over this city.

95. Trace organic compounds in the atmosphere are first concentrated and then measured by gas chromatography. In the concentration step, several liters of air are pumped through a tube containing a porous substance that traps organic compounds. The tube is then connected to a gas chromatograph and heated to release the trapped compounds. The organic compounds are separated in the column, and the amounts are measured. In an analysis for benzene and toluene in air, a 2.0-L sample of air, at 748 torr and 23°C, was passed through the trap. The gas chromatography analysis showed that this air sample contained 101 ng benzene (C_6H_6) and 274 ng toluene (C_7H_8). Calculate the mixing ratio (see Exercise 93) and number of molecules per cubic centimeter for both benzene and toluene.

96. Formaldehyde (CH_2O) is sometimes released from foamed insulation currently being used in homes. The federal standard for the allowable amount of CH_2O in air is 1.0 ppbv (parts per billion volume; similar to ppmv as defined in Exercise 93). How many molecules per cubic centimeter is this at STP? If the concentration of formaldehyde in a room is 1.0 ppbv, what total mass of formaldehyde is present at STP if the room measures 18 ft × 24 ft × 8 ft?

Marathon Problem*

97. An empty glass container has a mass of 658.57 g. It has a mass of 659.45 g after it has been filled with nitrogen gas at a pressure of 790. torr and a temperature of 15°C. When the container is evacuated and refilled with a certain element (A) at a pressure of 745 torr and a temperature of 26°C, it has a mass of 660.6 g.

Compound B, a gaseous organic compound that consists of 85.6% carbon and 14.4% hydrogen by mass, is placed in a stainless steel vessel (10.68 L) with excess oxygen gas. The vessel is placed in a constant-temperature bath at 22°C. The pressure in the vessel is 11.98 atm. In the bottom of the vessel is a container that is packed with Ascarite and a desiccant. Ascarite is asbestos impregnated with sodium hydroxide; it quantitatively absorbs carbon dioxide:

$$2NaOH(s) + CO_2(g) \rightarrow Na_2CO_3(s) + H_2O(l)$$

The desiccant is anhydrous magnesium perchlorate, which quantitatively absorbs the water produced by the combustion reaction as well as the water produced by the above reaction. Neither the Ascarite nor the desiccant react with compound B or oxygen. The total mass of the container with the Ascarite and desiccant is 765.3 g.

The reaction is initiated by a spark. The pressure immediately rises, then begins to decrease, and finally reaches a steady value of 6.02 atm. The stainless steel vessel is carefully opened, and the mass of the container inside the vessel is found to be 846.7 g. A and B react quantitatively in a 1:1 mole ratio to form one mole of the single product, gas C.

1. How many grams of C will be produced if 10.0 L of A and 8.6 L of B (each at STP) are reacted by opening a stopcock connecting the two samples?

2. What will be the total pressure in the system?

*This Marathon Problem was developed by James H. Burness of Penn State University, York Campus.

CHAPTER 6

Thermochemistry

Energy is the essence of our very existence as individuals and as a society. The food that we eat furnishes the energy to live, work, and play, just as the coal and oil consumed by manufacturing and transportation systems power our modern industrialized civilization.

Huge quantities of carbon-based fossil fuels have been available for the taking. This abundance of fuels has led to a world society with a voracious appetite for energy, consuming millions of barrels of petroleum every day. We are now dangerously dependent on the dwindling supplies of oil, and this dependence is an important source of tension among nations in today's world. In an incredibly short time we have moved from a period of ample and cheap supplies of petroleum to one of high prices and uncertain supplies. If our present standard of living is to be maintained, we must find alternatives to petroleum. To do this, we need to know the relationship between chemistry and energy, which we explore in this chapter.

There are additional problems with fossil fuels. The waste products from burning fossil fuels significantly affect our environment. For example, when a carbon-based fuel is burned, the carbon reacts with oxygen to form carbon dioxide, which is released into the atmosphere. Although much of this carbon dioxide is consumed in various natural processes such as photosynthesis and the formation of carbonate minerals, the amount of carbon dioxide in the atmosphere is steadily increasing. This increase is significant because atmospheric carbon dioxide absorbs heat radiated from the earth's surface and radiates it back toward the earth. Since this is an important mechanism for controlling the earth's temperature, many scientists fear that an increase in the concentration of carbon dioxide will warm the earth, causing significant changes in climate. In addition, impurities in the fossil fuels react with components of the air to produce air pollution. We discussed some aspects of this problem in Chapter 5.

In this chapter we will cover the fundamental concepts of energy and take a brief look at the practical aspects of energy supply and pollution. Additional theoretical aspects of energy will be presented in Chapter 16.

CONTENTS

< The glow of the flame from a burning match results from the release of excess energy as visible light by the products of the combustion reaction. Note the complex structure of the flame.

6.1 The Nature of Energy

Purpose

- To describe the energy flow between a system and its surroundings.
- To discuss the first law of thermodynamics.
- To show how to calculate the work that results from changing the volume of a gas at constant pressure.

Although the concept of energy is quite familiar, energy itself is rather difficult to define precisely. We will define **energy** as the *capacity to do work or to produce heat*. In this chapter we will concentrate specifically on the heat transfer that accompanies chemical processes.

One of the most important characteristics of energy is that it is conserved. The **law of conservation of energy** states that *energy can be converted from one form to another but can be neither created nor destroyed*. That is, the energy of the universe is constant. Energy can be classified as either potential energy or kinetic energy. **Potential energy** is energy due to position or composition. For example, water behind a dam has potential energy that can be converted to work when the water flows down through turbines, thereby creating electricity. Attractive and repulsive forces also lead to potential energy. The energy released when gasoline is burned results from differences in attractive forces between the nuclei and electrons in the reactants and products. The **kinetic energy** of an object is energy due to the motion of the object and depends on the mass of the object m and its velocity v: $KE = \frac{1}{2}mv^2$.

Energy can be converted from one form to another. For example, consider the two balls in Fig. 6.1(a). Ball A, because of its higher position initially, has more potential energy than ball B. When A is released, it moves down the hill and strikes B. Eventually, the arrangement shown in Fig. 6.1(b) is achieved. What has happened in going from the initial to the final arrangement? The potential energy of A has decreased, but since energy is conserved, all the energy lost by A must be accounted for. How is this energy distributed?

Initially, the potential energy of A is changed to kinetic energy as the ball rolls down the hill. Part of this kinetic energy is then transferred to B, causing it to be raised to a higher final position. Thus the potential energy of B has been increased. However, since the final position of B is lower than the original position of A, some of the energy is still unaccounted for. Both balls in their final positions are at rest, so the missing energy cannot be due to their motions. What has happened to the remaining energy?

The answer lies in the interaction between the hill's surface and the ball. As ball A rolls down the hill, some of its kinetic energy is transferred to the surface of the hill as heat. This transfer of energy is called **frictional heating.** The temperature of the hill increases very slightly as the ball rolls down.

Before we proceed further, it is important to recognize that heat and temperature are decidedly different. As we saw in Chapter 5, **temperature** is a property that reflects the random motions of the particles in a particular substance. **Heat,** on the other hand, involves the *transfer* of energy between two objects due to a temperature difference. Heat is not a substance contained by an object, although we often talk of heat as if this were true.

Note that in going from the initial to the final arrangements in Fig. 6.1, ball B gains potential energy because work was done by ball A on B. **Work** is defined as

The total energy content of the universe is constant.

A ——— Held in place

B

(a) Initial

B

A

(b) Final

Figure 6.1

(a) In the initial positions, ball A has a higher potential energy than ball B. (b) After A has rolled down the hill, the potential energy lost by A has been converted to random motions of the components of the hill (frictional heating) and to the increase in the potential energy of B.

Heat involves a transfer *of energy.*

force acting over a distance. Work is required to raise B from its original position to its final one. Part of the original energy stored as potential energy in A has been transferred through work to B, thereby increasing B's potential energy. Thus there are two ways to transfer energy: through work and through heat.

In rolling to the bottom of the hill shown in Fig. 6.1, ball A will always lose the same amount of potential energy. However, the way that this energy transfer is divided between work and heat depends on the specific conditions—the **pathway.** For example, the surface of the hill might be so rough that the energy of A is expended completely through frictional heating; A is moving so slowly when it hits B that it cannot move B to the next level. In this case, no work is done. Regardless of the condition of the hill's surface, the *total energy* transferred will be constant. However, the amounts of heat and work will differ. Energy change is independent of the pathway; however, work and heat are both dependent on the pathway.

This brings us to a very important concept: the **state function** or **state property.** A state function refers to a property of the system that depends only on its *present state*. A state function (property) does not depend in any way on the system's past (or future). In other words, the value of a state function does not depend on how the system arrived at the present state; it depends only on the characteristics of the present state. This leads to a very important characteristic of a state function: a change in this function (property) in going from one state to another state is independent of the particular pathway taken between the two states.

Of the functions considered in our present example, energy is a state function, but work and heat are not state functions.

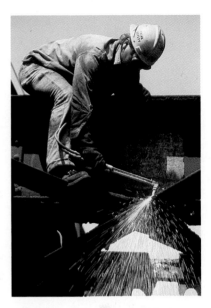

A worker cutting steel with the flame from an oxyacetylene torch.

Energy is a state function; work and heat are not.

Chemical Energy

The ideas we have just illustrated using mechanical examples also apply to chemical systems. The combustion of methane, for example, is used to heat many homes in the United States:

$$CH_4(g) + 2O_2(g) \rightarrow CO_2(g) + 2H_2O(g) + \text{energy (heat)}$$

To discuss this reaction, we divide the universe into two parts: the system and the surroundings. The **system** is the part of the universe on which we wish to focus attention; the **surroundings** include everything else in the universe. In this case we define the system as the reactants and products of the reaction. The surroundings consist of the reaction container (a furnace, for example), the room, and anything else other than the reactants and products.

When a reaction results in the evolution of heat, it is said to be **exothermic** (*exo*- is a prefix meaning "out of"); that is, energy flows *out of the system*. For example, in the combustion of methane, energy flows out of the system as heat. Reactions that absorb energy from the surroundings are said to be **endothermic.** When the heat flow is *into a system,* the process is endothermic. For example, the formation of nitric oxide from nitrogen and oxygen is endothermic:

$$N_2(g) + O_2(g) + \text{energy (heat)} \rightarrow 2NO(g)$$

Where does the energy, released as heat, come from in an exothermic reaction? The answer lies in the difference in potential energies between the products and the reactants. Which has lower potential energy, the reactants or the products? We know that total energy is conserved and that energy flows from the system into the surroundings in an exothermic reaction. This means that *the energy gained by the*

Figure 6.2

The combustion of methane releases the quantity of energy $\Delta(PE)$ to the surroundings via heat flow. This is an exothermic process.

surroundings must be equal to the energy lost by the system. In the combustion of methane, the energy content of the system decreases, which means that 1 mole of CO_2 and 2 moles of H_2O molecules (the products) possess less potential energy than do 1 mole of CH_4 and 2 moles of O_2 molecules (the reactants). The heat flow into the surroundings results from a lowering of the potential energy of the reaction system. This always holds true. *In any exothermic reaction some of the potential energy stored in the chemical bonds is being converted to thermal energy (random kinetic energy) via heat.*

The energy diagram for the combustion of methane is shown in Fig. 6.2, where $\Delta(PE)$ represents the *change* in potential energy stored in the bonds of the products as compared with the bonds of the reactants. In other words, this quantity represents the difference between the energy required to break the bonds in the reactants and the energy released when the bonds in the products are formed. In an exothermic process, the bonds in the products are stronger (on average) than those of the reactants. That is, more energy is released by forming the new bonds in the products than is consumed to break the bonds in the reactants. The net result is that the quantity of energy $\Delta(PE)$ is transferred to the surroundings through heat.

Figure 6.3

The energy diagram for the reaction of nitrogen and oxygen to form nitric oxide. This is an endothermic process: heat [equal in magnitude to $\Delta(PE)$] flows into the system from the surroundings.

For an endothermic reaction, the situation is reversed, as shown in Fig. 6.3. Energy that flows into the system as heat is used to increase the potential energy of the system. In this case the products have higher potential energy (weaker bonds on average) than the reactants.

The study of energy and its interconversions is called **thermodynamics.** The law of conservation of energy is often called the **first law of thermodynamics** and is stated as follows: *the energy of the universe is constant.*

The **internal energy** E of a system can be defined most precisely as the sum of the kinetic and potential energies of all the "particles" in the system. The internal energy of a system can be changed by a flow of work, heat, or both. That is,

$$\Delta E = q + w$$

where ΔE represents the change in the system's internal energy, q represents heat, and w represents work.

Thermodynamic quantities always consist of two parts: a *number,* giving the magnitude of the change, and a *sign,* indicating the direction of the flow. *The sign reflects the system's point of view.* For example, if a quantity of energy flows *into* the system via heat (an endothermic process), q is equal to $+x$, where the *positive* sign indicates that the *system's energy is increasing.* On the other hand, when energy flows *out of* the system via heat (an exothermic process), q is equal to $-x$, where the *negative* sign indicates that the *system's energy is decreasing.*

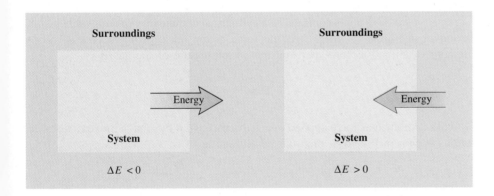

In this text the same conventions also apply to the flow of work. If the system does work on the surroundings (energy flows out of the system), w is negative. If the surroundings do work on the system (energy flows into the system), w is positive. We define work from the system's point of view to be consistent for all thermodynamic quantities. That is, in this convention the signs of both q and w reflect what happens to the system; thus we use $\Delta E = q + w$.

In this text we *always* take the system's point of view. This convention is not followed in every area of science. For example, engineers are in the business of designing machines to do work, that is, to make the system (the machine) transfer energy to its surroundings through work. Consequently, engineers define work from the surroundings' point of view. In their convention, work that flows out of the system is treated as positive because the energy of the surroundings has increased. The first law of thermodynamics is then written $\Delta E = q - w'$, where w' signifies work from the surroundings' point of view.

The convention in this text is to take the system's point of view; $q = -x$ denotes an exothermic process, and $q = +x$ denotes an endothermic one.

The joule (J) is the fundamental SI unit for energy:

$$J = \frac{kg \cdot m^2}{s^2}$$

One kilojoule (kJ) = 10^3 J.

Sample Exercise 6.1

Calculate ΔE for a system undergoing an endothermic process in which 15.6 kJ of heat flows and where 1.4 kJ of work is done on the system.

Solution

We use the equation

$$\Delta E = q + w$$

where $q = +15.6$ kJ, since the process is endothermic, and $w = +1.4$ kJ, since work is done on the system. Thus

$$\Delta E = 15.6 \text{ kJ} + 1.4 \text{ kJ} = 17.0 \text{ kJ}$$

The system has gained 17.0 kJ of energy.

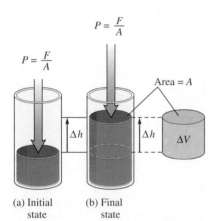

Figure 6.4

(a) The piston, moving a distance Δh against a pressure P, does work on the surroundings.
(b) Since the volume of a cylinder is the area of the base times its height, the change in volume of the gas is given by $\Delta h \times A = \Delta V$.

A common type of work associated with chemical processes is work done by a gas (through *expansion*) or work done to a gas (through *compression*). For example, in an automobile engine, the heat from the combustion of the gasoline expands the gases in the cylinder to push back the piston, and this motion is then translated into the motion of the car.

Suppose we have a gas confined to a cylindrical container with a movable piston as shown in Fig. 6.4, where F is the force acting on a piston of area A. Since pressure is defined as force per unit area, the pressure of the gas is

$$P = \frac{F}{A}$$

Work is defined as force applied over a distance, so if the piston moves a distance Δh, as shown in Fig. 6.4, then the work done is

$$\text{Work} = \text{force} \times \text{distance} = F \times \Delta h$$

Since $P = F/A$ or $F = P \times A$, then

$$\text{Work} = F \times \Delta h = P \times A \times \Delta h$$

Since the volume of a cylinder equals the area of the piston times the height of the cylinder (Fig. 6.4), the change in volume ΔV resulting from the piston moving a distance Δh is

$$\Delta V = \text{final volume} - \text{initial volume} = A \times \Delta h$$

Substituting $\Delta V = A \times \Delta h$ into the expression for work gives

$$\text{Work} = P \times A \times \Delta h = P\Delta V$$

This gives us the *magnitude* (size) of the work required to expand a gas ΔV against a pressure P.

What about the sign of the work? The gas (the system) is expanding, moving the piston against the pressure. Thus the system is doing work on the surroundings, so from the system's point of view the sign of the work should be negative.

For an *expanding* gas, ΔV is a positive quantity because the volume is increasing. Thus ΔV and w must have opposite signs, which leads to the equation

$$w = -P\Delta V$$

Note that for a gas expanding against an external pressure P, w is a negative quantity as required, since work flows out of the system. When a gas is *compressed*, ΔV is a negative quantity (the volume decreases), which makes w a positive quantity (work flows into the system).

Sample Exercise 6.2

Calculate the work associated with the expansion of a gas from 46 L to 64 L at a constant external pressure of 15 atm.

Solution

For a gas at constant pressure,

$$w = -P\Delta V$$

In this case $P = 15$ atm and $\Delta V = 64 - 46 = 18$ L. Hence

$$w = -15 \text{ atm} \times 18 \text{ L} = -270 \text{ L} \cdot \text{atm}$$

Note that since the gas expands, it does work on its surroundings. Energy flows out of the gas, so w is a negative quantity.

For an ideal gas, work can occur only when its volume changes. Thus, if a gas is heated at constant volume, the pressure increases but no work occurs.

In dealing with "*PV* work," keep in mind that the P in $P\Delta V$ always refers to the external pressure—the pressure that causes a compression or that resists an expansion.

Sample Exercise 6.3

A balloon is being inflated to its full extent by heating the air inside it. In the final stages of this process, the volume of the balloon changes from 4.00×10^6 L to 4.50×10^6 L by the addition of 1.3×10^8 J of energy as heat. Assuming that the balloon expands against a constant pressure of 1.0 atm, calculate ΔE for the process. (To convert between L · atm and J, use 1 L · atm = 101.3 J.)

Solution

To calculate ΔE, we use the equation

$$\Delta E = q + w$$

Since the problem states that 1.3×10^8 J of energy is *added* as heat,

$$q = +1.3 \times 10^8 \text{ J}$$

The work done can be calculated from the expression

$$w = -P\Delta V$$

A propane burner is used to heat the air in a hot air balloon.

In this case $P = 1.0$ atm and

$$\Delta V = V_{\text{final}} - V_{\text{initial}}$$
$$= 4.50 \times 10^6 \text{ L} - 4.00 \times 10^6 \text{ L} = 0.50 \times 10^6 \text{ L} = 5.0 \times 10^5 \text{ L}$$

Thus $\qquad w = -1.0 \text{ atm} \times 5.0 \times 10^5 \text{ L} = -5.0 \times 10^5 \text{ L} \cdot \text{atm}$

Note that the negative sign for w makes sense, since the gas is expanding and thus doing work on the surroundings.

To calculate ΔE, we must sum q and w. However, since q is given in units of J and w is given in units of L · atm, we must change the work to units of joules:

$$w = -5.0 \times 10^5 \text{ L} \cdot \text{atm} \times \frac{101.3 \text{ J}}{\text{L} \cdot \text{atm}} = -5.1 \times 10^7 \text{ J}$$

Then $\qquad \Delta E = q + w = (+1.3 \times 10^8 \text{ J}) + (-5.1 \times 10^7 \text{ J}) = 8 \times 10^7 \text{ J}$

Since more energy is added through heating than the gas expends doing work, there is a net increase in the internal energy of the gas in the balloon. Hence ΔE is positive.

6.2 Enthalpy and Calorimetry

Purpose

- To define enthalpy and demonstrate calculations of the change in enthalpy in a chemical reaction.
- To show how a change in enthalpy is measured by calorimetry.

Enthalpy

So far we have discussed the internal energy of a system. A less familiar property of a system is its **enthalpy** H, which is defined as

$$H = E + PV$$

where E is the internal energy of the system, P is the pressure of the system, and V is the volume of the system.

Since internal energy, pressure, and volume are all state functions, *enthalpy is also a state function*. But what exactly is enthalpy? To help answer this question, consider a process carried out at constant pressure and where the only work allowed is pressure–volume work ($w = -P\Delta V$). Under these conditions, the expression

$$\Delta E = q_P + w$$

becomes $\qquad \Delta E = q_P - P\Delta V$

or $\qquad q_P = \Delta E + P\Delta V$

where q_P is the heat at constant pressure.

We will now relate q_P to a change in enthalpy. The definition of enthalpy is $H = E + PV$. Therefore, we can say

$$\text{Change in } H = (\text{change in } E) + (\text{change in } PV)$$

Enthalpy is a state function. A change in enthalpy does not depend on the pathway between two states.

Recall from the previous section that w and $P\Delta V$ have opposite signs:
$$w = -P\Delta V$$

or
$$\Delta H = \Delta E + \Delta(PV)$$

Since P is constant, the change in PV is due only to a change in volume. Thus

$$\Delta(PV) = P\Delta V$$

and
$$\Delta H = \Delta E + P\Delta V$$

This expression is identical to the one we obtained for q_P:

$$q_P = \Delta E + P\Delta V$$

Thus, for a process carried out at constant pressure and where the only work allowed is that from a volume change, we have

$$\Delta H = q_P$$

At constant pressure (where only PV work is allowed), the change in enthalpy ΔH of the system is equal to the energy flow as heat. This means that for a reaction studied at constant pressure, the flow of heat is a measure of the change in enthalpy for the system. For this reason, the terms *heat of reaction* and *change in enthalpy* are used interchangeably for reactions studied at constant pressure.

For a chemical reaction, the enthalpy change is given by the equation

$$\Delta H = H_{products} - H_{reactants}$$

In a case in which the products of a reaction have a greater enthalpy than the reactants, ΔH will be positive. Thus heat will be absorbed by the system, and the reaction is endothermic. On the other hand, if the enthalpy of the products is less than that of the reactants, ΔH will be negative. In this case the overall decrease in enthalpy is achieved by the generation of heat, and the reaction is exothermic.

> $\Delta H = q$ only at constant pressure.

> The change in enthalpy of a system has no easily interpreted meaning except at constant pressure, where ΔH = heat.

> At constant pressure, exothermic means ΔH is negative; endothermic means ΔH is positive.

Sample Exercise 6.4

When 1 mole of methane (CH_4) is burned at constant pressure, 890 kJ of energy is released as heat. Calculate ΔH for a process in which a 5.8-g sample of methane is burned at constant pressure.

Solution

At constant pressure, 890 kJ of energy per mole of CH_4 is produced as heat:

$$q_P = \Delta H = -890 \text{ kJ/mol } CH_4$$

Note that the minus sign indicates an exothermic process. In this case, a 5.8-g sample of CH_4 (molar mass = 16.0 g/mol) is burned. Since this amount is smaller than 1 mole, less than 890 kJ will be released as heat. The actual value can be calculated as follows:

$$5.8 \text{ g } CH_4 \times \frac{1 \text{ mol } CH_4}{16.0 \text{ g } CH_4} = 0.36 \text{ mol } CH_4$$

and
$$0.36 \text{ mol } CH_4 \times \frac{-890 \text{ kJ}}{\text{mol } CH_4} = -320 \text{ kJ}$$

Thus, when a 5.8-g sample of CH_4 is burned at constant pressure,

$$\Delta H = \text{heat flow} = -320 \text{ kJ}$$

Calorimetry

The device used experimentally to determine the heat associated with a chemical reaction is called a **calorimeter. Calorimetry,** the science of measuring heat, is based on observing the temperature change when a body absorbs or discharges energy as heat. Substances respond differently to being heated. One substance might require a great deal of heat energy to raise its temperature by one degree, whereas another will exhibit the same temperature change after absorbing relatively little heat. The **heat capacity** (C) of a substance, which is a measure of this property, is defined as

$$C = \frac{\text{heat absorbed}}{\text{increase in temperature}}$$

When an element or a compound is heated, the energy required will depend on the amount of the substance present (for example, it takes twice as much energy to raise the temperature of two grams of water by one degree than it takes to raise the temperature of one gram of water by one degree). Thus, in defining the heat capacity of a substance, the amount of substance must be specified. If the heat capacity is given *per gram* of substance, it is called the **specific heat capacity,** and its units are J/°C · g or J/K · g. If the heat capacity is given *per mole* of the substance, it is called the **molar heat capacity,** and it has the units J/°C · mol or J/K · mol. The specific heat capacities of some common substances are given in Table 6.1.

Although the calorimeters used for highly accurate work are precision instruments, a very simple calorimeter can be used to examine the fundamentals of calorimetry. All we need are two nested Styrofoam cups with a cover through which a stirrer and thermometer can be inserted, as shown in Fig. 6.5. This device is called a "coffee-cup calorimeter." The outer cup is used to provide extra insulation. The inner cup holds the solution in which the reaction occurs.

The measurement of heat using a simple calorimeter such as that shown in Fig. 6.5 is an example of **constant-pressure calorimetry,** since the pressure (atmospheric pressure) remains constant during the process. Constant-pressure calorimetry is used in determining the changes in enthalpy (heats of reactions) for reactions occurring in solution. Recall that under these conditions, the change in enthalpy equals the heat.

For example, suppose we mix 50.0 mL of 1.0 *M* HCl at 25.0°C with 50.0 mL of 1.0 *M* NaOH also at 25°C in a calorimeter. After the reactants are mixed by stirring, the temperature is observed to increase to 31.9°C. As we saw in Section 4.8, the net

Specific heat capacity: the energy required to raise the temperature of one gram of a substance by one degree Celsius.
Molar heat capacity: the energy required to raise the temperature of one mole of a substance by one degree Celsius.

Thermometer

Styrofoam cover

Styrofoam cups

Stirrer

Figure 6.5

A coffee-cup calorimeter made of two Styrofoam cups.

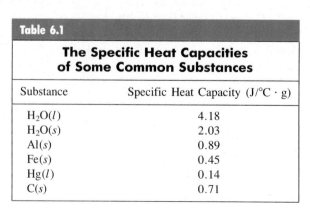

Table 6.1		
The Specific Heat Capacities of Some Common Substances		
Substance	Specific Heat Capacity (J/°C · g)	
$H_2O(l)$	4.18	
$H_2O(s)$	2.03	
Al(s)	0.89	
Fe(s)	0.45	
Hg(l)	0.14	
C(s)	0.71	

ionic equation for this reaction is

$$H^+(aq) + OH^-(aq) \rightarrow H_2O(l)$$

When these reactants (each originally at the same temperature) are mixed, the temperature of the mixed solution is observed to increase. Therefore, the chemical reaction must be releasing energy as heat. This released energy increases the random motions of the solution components, which in turn increases the temperature. The quantity of energy released can be determined from the temperature increase, the mass of solution, and the specific heat capacity of the solution. For an approximate result, we will assume that the calorimeter does not absorb or leak any heat and that the solution can be treated as if it were pure water with a density of 1.0 g/mL.

We also need to know the heat required to raise the temperature of a given amount of water by 1°C. Table 6.1 lists the specific heat capacity of water as 4.18 J/°C · g. This means that 4.18 J of energy is required to raise the temperature of 1 gram of water by 1°C.

From these assumptions and definitions, we can calculate the heat (change in enthalpy) for the neutralization reaction:

Energy released by the reaction
  = energy absorbed by the solution
  = specific heat capacity × mass of solution × increase in temperature
  = $s \times m \times \Delta T$

In this case the increase in temperature (ΔT) = 31.9°C − 25.0°C = 6.9°C, and the mass of solution (m) = 100.0 mL × 1.0 g/mL = 1.0×10^2 g. Thus

$$\text{Energy released} = s \times m \times \Delta T$$

$$= \left(4.18 \frac{J}{°\!\!\!\!C \cdot g\!\!\!/}\right)(1.0 \times 10^2 \, g\!\!\!/)(6.9°\!\!\!\!C\!\!\!/)$$

$$= 2.9 \times 10^3 \, J$$

How much energy would have been released if twice these amounts of solutions had been mixed? The answer is that twice as much energy would have been produced. The heat of a reaction is an **extensive property**; it depends directly on the amount of substance, in this case on the amounts of reactants. In contrast, an **intensive property** is not related to the amount of a substance. For example, temperature is an intensive property.

Enthalpies of reaction are often expressed in terms of moles of reacting substances. The number of moles of H^+ ions consumed in the preceding experiment is

$$50.0 \, mL\!\!\!/ \times \frac{1 \, L\!\!\!/}{1000 \, mL\!\!\!/} \times \frac{1.0 \, mol}{L\!\!\!/} H^+ = 5.0 \times 10^{-2} \, mol \, H^+$$

Thus 2.9×10^3 J heat was released when 5.0×10^{-2} mol H^+ ions reacted, or

$$\frac{2.9 \times 10^3 \, J}{5.0 \times 10^{-2} \, mol \, H^+} = 5.8 \times 10^4 \, J$$

of heat released per 1.0 mol H^+ ions neutralized. Thus the *magnitude* of the enthalpy change per mole for the reaction

$$H^+(aq) + OH^-(aq) \rightarrow H_2O(l)$$

is 58 kJ/mol. Since heat is *evolved*, $\Delta H = -58$ kJ/mol.

If two reactants at the same temperature are mixed and the resulting solution gets warmer, this means the reaction taking place is exothermic. An endothermic reaction cools the solution.

Notice that in this example we mentally keep track of the direction of the energy flow and assign the correct sign at the end of the calculation.

Sample Exercise 6.5

When 1.00 L of 1.00 M $Ba(NO_3)_2$ solution at 25.0°C is mixed with 1.00 L of 1.00 M Na_2SO_4 solution at 25°C in a calorimeter, the white solid $BaSO_4$ forms and the temperature of the mixture increases to 28.1°C. Assuming that the calorimeter absorbs only a negligible quantity of heat, that the specific heat capacity of the solution is 4.18 J/°C · g, and that the density of the final solution is 1.0 g/mL, calculate the enthalpy change per mole of $BaSO_4$ formed.

Solution

The ions present before any reaction occurs are Ba^{2+}, NO_3^-, Na^+, and SO_4^{2-}. The Na^+ and NO_3^- ions are spectator ions, since $NaNO_3$ is very soluble in water and will not precipitate under these conditions. The net ionic equation for the reaction is therefore

$$Ba^{2+}(aq) + SO_4^{2-}(aq) \rightarrow BaSO_4(s)$$

Since the temperature increases, formation of the solid $BaSO_4$ must be exothermic; ΔH will be negative.

Heat evolved by reaction

  = heat absorbed by solution

  = specific heat capacity × mass of solution × increase in temperature

Since 1.00 L of each solution is used, the total solution volume is 2.00 L, and

$$\text{Mass of solution} = 2.00 \, \cancel{L} \times \frac{1000 \, \cancel{mL}}{1 \, \cancel{L}} \times \frac{1.0 \, g}{\cancel{mL}} = 2.0 \times 10^3 \, g$$

$$\text{Temperature increase} = 28.1°C - 25.0°C = 3.1°C$$

$$\text{Heat evolved} = (4.18 \, J/\cancel{°C} \cdot \cancel{g})(2.0 \times 10^3 \, \cancel{g})(3.1 \cancel{°C}) = 2.6 \times 10^4 \, J$$

Thus

$$q = q_P = \Delta H = -2.6 \times 10^4 \, J$$

Since 1.0 L of 1.0 M $Ba(NO_3)_2$ contains 1 mol Ba^{2+} ions and 1.0 L of 1.0 M Na_2SO_4 contains 1.0 mol SO_4^{2-} ions, 1.0 mol solid $BaSO_4$ is formed in this experiment. Thus the enthalpy change per mole of $BaSO_4$ formed is

$$\Delta H = -2.6 \times 10^4 \, J/mol = -26 \, kJ/mol$$

Calorimetry experiments also can be performed at **constant volume.** For example, when a photographic flashbulb flashes, the bulb becomes very hot, because the reaction of the zirconium or magnesium wire with the oxygen inside the bulb is exothermic. The reaction occurs inside the flashbulb, which is rigid and does not change volume. Under these conditions, no work is done (because the volume must change for pressure–volume work to be performed). To study the energy changes in reactions under conditions of constant volume, a ''bomb calorimeter'' (Fig. 6.6) is used. Weighed reactants are placed inside a rigid steel container (the ''bomb'') and ignited. The energy change is determined by measuring the increase in the temperature of the water and other calorimeter parts. For a constant-volume process, the

Figure 6.6

A bomb calorimeter. The reaction is carried out inside a rigid steel "bomb," and the heat evolved is absorbed by the surrounding water and other calorimeter parts. The quantity of energy produced by the reaction can be calculated from the temperature increase.

change in volume ΔV is equal to zero, so work (which is $-P\Delta V$) is also equal to zero. Therefore,

$$\Delta E = q + w = q = q_V \qquad \text{(constant volume)}$$

Suppose we wish to measure the energy of combustion of octane (C_8H_{18}), a component of gasoline. A 0.5269-g sample of octane is placed in a bomb calorimeter known to have a heat capacity of 11.3 kJ/°C. This means that 11.3 kJ of energy is required to raise the temperature of the water and other parts of the calorimeter by 1°C. The octane is ignited in the presence of excess oxygen, and the temperature increase of the calorimeter is 2.25°C. The amount of energy released is calculated as follows:

Energy released by the reaction
    = temperature increase × energy required to change the temperature by 1°C
    = ΔT × heat capacity of calorimeter
    = 2.25°$\cancel{C}$ × 11.3 kJ/°$\cancel{C}$ = 25.4 kJ

This means that 25.4 kJ of energy was released by the combustion of 0.5269 g octane. The number of moles of octane is

$$0.5269 \text{ g octane} \times \frac{1 \text{ mol octane}}{114.2 \text{ g octane}} = 4.614 \times 10^{-3} \text{ mol octane}$$

Since 25.4 kJ of energy was released for 4.614×10^{-3} mol octane, the energy released per mole is

$$\frac{25.4 \text{ kJ}}{4.614 \times 10^{-3} \text{ mol}} = 5.50 \times 10^3 \text{ kJ/mol}$$

Since the reaction is exothermic, ΔE is negative:

$$\Delta E_{\text{combustion}} = -5.50 \times 10^3 \text{ kJ/mol}$$

Note that since no work is done in this case, ΔE is equal to the heat.

$$\Delta E = q + w = q \qquad \text{since } w = 0$$

Thus $q = -5.50 \times 10^3$ kJ/mol.

◀ **CHEMICAL IMPACT** ▶

Firewalking: Magic or Science?

For millennia people have been amazed at the ability of Eastern mystics to walk across beds of glowing coals without any apparent discomfort. Even in the United States, thousands of people have performed feats of firewalking as part of motivational seminars. How is this possible? Do firewalkers have supernatural powers?

Actually, there are good scientific explanations, based on the concepts covered in this chapter, of why firewalking is possible. The first important factor concerns the heat capacity of feet. Because human tissue is mainly composed of water, it has a relatively large specific heat capacity. This means that a large amount of energy must be transferred from the coals to significantly change the temperature of the feet. During the brief contact between feet and coals, there is relatively little time for energy flow so the feet do not reach a high enough temperature to cause damage.

Second, although the surface of the coals has a very high temperature, the red hot layer is very thin. Therefore, the quantity of energy available to heat the feet is smaller than might be expected. This factor points up the difference between temperature and heat. Temperature reflects the *intensity* of the random kinetic energy in a given sample of matter. The amount of energy available for heat flow, on the other hand, depends on the quantity of matter at a given temperature—ten grams of matter at a given temperature contains ten times as much thermal energy

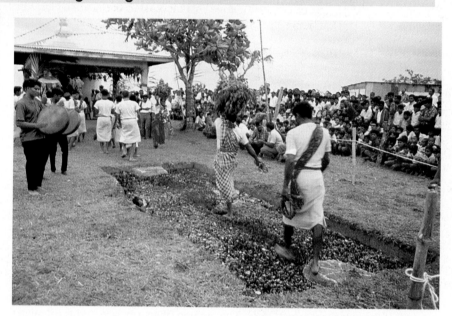

A Hindu firewalking ceremony in the Fiji Islands.

as one gram of the same matter. This is why the tiny spark from a sparkler does not hurt when it hits your hand. The spark has a very high temperature but has so little mass that no significant energy transfer occurs to your hand. This same argument applies to the very thin hot layer on the coals.

A third factor that aids firewalkers is the so-called Leidenfrost effect—the phenomenon that allows water droplets to skate around on a hot griddle for a surprisingly long time. The part of the droplet in contact with the hot surface vaporizes first, providing a gaseous layer that both allows the droplet to skate around and acts as a barrier through which energy does not

readily flow to the rest of the droplet. The perspiration on the feet of the presumably tense firewalker would have the same effect. In addition, because firewalking is often done at night, with moist grass surrounding the bed of coals, the firewalker's feet are probably damp before the walk, providing ample moisture for the Leidenfrost effect to occur.

Thus, although firewalking is an impressive feat, there are several sound scientific reasons why it is possible (with the proper training and a properly prepared bed of coals).

Sample Exercise 6.6

It has been suggested that hydrogen gas obtained by the decomposition of water might be a substitute for natural gas (principally methane). To compare the energies of combustion of these fuels, the following experiment was carried out using a bomb calorimeter with a heat capacity of 11.3 kJ/°C. When a 1.50-g sample of methane gas was burned with excess oxygen in the calorimeter, the temperature increased by 7.3°C. When a 1.15-g sample of hydrogen gas was burned with excess oxygen, the temperature increase was 14.3°C. Calculate the energy of combustion (per gram) for hydrogen and methane.

Hydrogen's potential as a fuel is discussed in Section 6.6.

Solution

We calculate the energy of combustion for methane using the heat capacity of the calorimeter (11.3 kJ/°C) and the observed temperature increase of 7.3°C:

Energy *released* in the combustion of 1.5 g CH_4 = (11.3 kJ/°C)(7.3°C)
= 83 kJ

Energy *released* in the combustion of 1 g CH_4 = $\dfrac{83 \text{ kJ}}{1.5 \text{ g}}$ = 55 kJ/g

Similarly, for hydrogen:

Energy *released* in the combustion of 1.15 g H_2 = (11.3 kJ/°C)(14.3°C)
= 162 kJ

Energy *released* in the combustion of 1 g H_2 = $\dfrac{162 \text{ kJ}}{1.15 \text{ g}}$ = 141 kJ/g

The energy released in the combustion of 1 g hydrogen is approximately 2.5 times that for 1 g methane, indicating that hydrogen gas is a potentially useful fuel.

The direction of energy flow is indicated by words in this example. Using signs to designate the direction of energy flow:

$\Delta E_{combustion} = -55$ kJ/g

for methane and

$\Delta E_{combustion} = -141$ kJ/g

for hydrogen.

6.3 Hess's Law

Purpose

- To discuss the characteristics of enthalpy changes.
- To show how to calculate ΔH for a chemical reaction.

Since enthalpy is a state function, the change in enthalpy in going from some initial state to some final state is independent of the pathway. This means that *in going from a particular set of reactants to a particular set of products, the change in enthalpy is the same whether the reaction takes place in one step or in a series of steps.* This principle is known as **Hess's law** and can be illustrated by examining the oxidation of nitrogen to produce nitrogen dioxide. The overall reaction can be written in one step, where the enthalpy change is represented by ΔH_1.

ΔH is not dependent on the reaction pathway.

$$N_2(g) + 2O_2(g) \rightarrow 2NO_2(g) \qquad \Delta H_1 - 68 \text{ kJ}$$

This reaction also can be carried out in two distinct steps, with enthalpy changes designated by ΔH_2 and ΔH_3:

$$N_2(g) + O_2(g) \rightarrow 2NO(g) \qquad \Delta H_2 = 180 \text{ kJ}$$
$$\underline{2NO(g) + O_2(g) \rightarrow 2NO_2(g) \qquad \Delta H_3 = -112 \text{ kJ}}$$

Net reaction: $\quad N_2(g) + 2O_2(g) \rightarrow 2NO_2(g) \qquad \Delta H_2 + \Delta H_3 = 68 \text{ kJ}$

Note that the sum of the two steps gives the net, or overall, reaction and that

$$\Delta H_1 = \Delta H_2 + \Delta H_3 = 68 \text{ kJ}$$

The principle of Hess's law is shown schematically in Fig. 6.7.

Characteristics of Enthalpy Changes

In order to use Hess's law to compute enthalpy changes for reactions, it is important to understand two characteristics of ΔH for a reaction:

Reversing the direction of a reaction changes the sign of ΔH.

1. If a reaction is reversed, the sign of ΔH is also reversed.

2. The magnitude of ΔH is directly proportional to the quantities of reactants and products in a reaction. If the coefficients in a balanced reaction are multiplied by an integer, the value of ΔH is multiplied by the same integer.

Both these rules follow in a straightforward way from the properties of enthalpy changes. The first rule can be explained by recalling that the *sign* of ΔH indicates the *direction* of the heat flow at constant pressure. If the direction of the reaction is reversed, the direction of the heat flow also will be reversed. To see this, consider the preparation of xenon tetrafluoride, which was the first binary compound made from a noble gas:

$$Xe(g) + 2F_2(g) \rightarrow XeF_4(s) \qquad \Delta H = -251 \text{ kJ}$$

This reaction is exothermic, and 251 kJ of energy flows into the surroundings as heat. On the other hand, if the colorless XeF_4 crystals are decomposed into the elements, according to the equation

$$XeF_4(s) \rightarrow Xe(g) + 2F_2(g)$$

the opposite energy flow occurs because 251 kJ of energy must be added to the system to produce this endothermic reaction. Thus, for this reaction, $\Delta H = +251$ kJ.

Crystals of xenon tetrafluoride, the first reported binary compound containing a noble gas element.

Figure 6.7

The principle of Hess's law. The same change in enthalpy occurs when nitrogen and oxygen react to form nitrogen dioxide, regardless of whether the reaction occurs in one (red) or two (blue) steps.

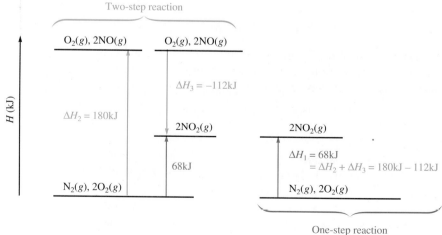

The second rule comes from the fact that ΔH is an extensive property, depending on the amount of substances reacting. For example, since 251 kJ of energy is evolved for the reaction

$$Xe(g) + 2F_2(g) \rightarrow XeF_4(s)$$

then for a preparation involving twice the quantities of reactants and products, or

$$2Xe(g) + 4F_2(g) \rightarrow 2XeF_4(s)$$

twice as much heat would be evolved:

$$\Delta H = 2(-251 \text{ kJ}) = -502 \text{ kJ}$$

Sample Exercise 6.7

Two forms of carbon are *graphite,* the soft, black, slippery material used in "lead" pencils and as a lubricant for locks, and *diamond,* the brilliant, hard gemstone. Using the enthalpies of combustion for graphite (-394 kJ/mol) and diamond (-396 kJ/mol), calculate ΔH for the conversion of graphite to diamond:

$$C_{graphite}(s) \rightarrow C_{diamond}(s)$$

Solution

The combustion reactions are

$$C_{graphite}(s) + O_2(g) \rightarrow CO_2(g) \qquad \Delta H = -394 \text{ kJ}$$
$$C_{diamond}(s) + O_2(g) \rightarrow CO_2(g) \qquad \Delta H = -396 \text{ kJ}$$

Note that if we reverse the second reaction (which means we must change the sign of ΔH) and sum the two reactions, we obtain the desired reaction:

$$C_{graphite}(s) + O_2(g) \rightarrow CO_2(g) \qquad\qquad \Delta H = -394 \text{ kJ}$$
$$\underline{\qquad CO_2(g) \rightarrow C_{diamond}(s) + O_2(g) \qquad \Delta H = -(-396 \text{ kJ})}$$
$$C_{graphite}(s) \rightarrow C_{diamond}(s) \qquad\qquad \Delta H = 2 \text{ kJ}$$

Thus 2 kJ of energy is required to change 1 mol graphite to diamond. This process is endothermic.

Sample Exercise 6.8

Diborane (B_2H_6) is a highly reactive boron hydride, which was once considered as a possible rocket fuel for the U.S. space program. Calculate ΔH for the synthesis of diborane from its elements, according to the equation

$$2B(s) + 3H_2(g) \rightarrow B_2H_6(g)$$

using the following data:

Reaction	ΔH
(a) $2B(s) + \frac{3}{2}O_2(g) \rightarrow B_2O_3(s)$	-1273 kJ
(b) $B_2H_6(g) + 3O_2(g) \rightarrow B_2O_3(s) + 3H_2O(g)$	-2035 kJ
(c) $H_2(g) + \frac{1}{2}O_2(g) \rightarrow H_2O(l)$	-286 kJ
(d) $H_2O(l) \rightarrow H_2O(g)$	44 kJ

Solution

To obtain ΔH for the required reaction, we must somehow combine equations (a), (b), (c), and (d) to produce that reaction and add the corresponding ΔH values. This can best be done by focusing on the reactants and products of the required reaction. The reactants are $B(s)$ and $H_2(g)$, and the product is $B_2H_6(g)$. How can we obtain the correct equation? Reaction (a) has $B(s)$ as a reactant, as needed in the required equation. Thus reaction (a) will be used as it is. Reaction (b) has $B_2H_6(g)$ as a reactant, but this substance is needed as a product. Thus reaction (b) must be reversed, and the sign of ΔH must be changed accordingly. Up to this point we have

$$
\begin{array}{lll}
\text{(a)} & 2B(s) + \tfrac{3}{2}O_2(g) \rightarrow B_2O_3(s) & \Delta H = -1273 \text{ kJ} \\
-\text{(b)} & B_2O_3(s) + 3H_2O(g) \rightarrow B_2H_6(g) + 3O_2(g) & \Delta H = -(-2035 \text{ kJ})
\end{array}
$$

Sum: $B_2O_3(s) + 2B(s) + \tfrac{3}{2}O_2(g) + 3H_2O(g) \rightarrow B_2O_3(s) + B_2H_6(g) + 3O_2(g)$ $\Delta H = 762 \text{ kJ}$

Deleting the species that occur on both sides gives

$$2B(s) + 3H_2O(g) \rightarrow B_2H_6(g) + \tfrac{3}{2}O_2(g) \qquad \Delta H = 762 \text{ kJ}$$

We are closer to the required reaction, but we still need to remove $H_2O(g)$ and $O_2(g)$ and introduce $H_2(g)$ as a reactant. We can do this using reactions (c) and (d). If we multiply reaction (c) and its ΔH value by 3 and add the result to the preceding equation, we have

$$
\begin{array}{lll}
 & 2B(s) + 3H_2O(g) \rightarrow B_2H_6(g) + \tfrac{3}{2}O_2(g) & \Delta H = 762 \text{ kJ} \\
3 \times \text{(c)} & 3[H_2(g) + \tfrac{1}{2}O_2(g) \rightarrow H_2O(l)] & \Delta H = 3(-286 \text{ kJ})
\end{array}
$$

Sum: $2B(s) + 3H_2(g) + \tfrac{3}{2}O_2(g) + 3H_2O(g) \rightarrow B_2H_6(g) + \tfrac{3}{2}O_2(g) + 3H_2O(l)$ $\Delta H = -96 \text{ kJ}$

We can cancel the $\tfrac{3}{2}O_2(g)$ on both sides, but we cannot cancel the H_2O because it is gaseous on one side and liquid on the other. This can be solved by adding reaction (d), multiplied by 3:

$$
\begin{array}{lll}
 & 2B(s) + 3H_2(g) + 3H_2O(g) \rightarrow B_2H_6(g) + 3H_2O(l) & \Delta H = -96 \text{ kJ} \\
3 \times \text{(d)} & 3[H_2O(l) \rightarrow H_2O(g)] & \Delta H = 3(44 \text{ kJ})
\end{array}
$$

$2B(s) + 3H_2(g) + 3H_2O(g) + 3H_2O(l) \rightarrow B_2H_6(g) + 3H_2O(l) + 3H_2O(g)$ $\Delta H = +36 \text{ kJ}$

This gives the reaction required by the problem:

$$2B(s) + 3H_2(g) \rightarrow B_2H_6(g) \qquad \Delta H = +36 \text{ kJ}$$

Thus ΔH for the synthesis of 1 mol diborane from the elements is $+36$ kJ.

HINTS FOR USING HESS'S LAW

Calculations involving Hess's law typically require that several reactions be manipulated and combined to finally give the reaction of interest. In doing this procedure you should work *backward* from the required reaction, using the reactants and products to decide how to manipulate the other given reactions at your disposal. Reverse any reactions as needed to give the required reactants and products, and then multiply reactions to give the correct numbers of reactants and products. This process involves some trial and error, but it can be very systematic if you always allow the final reaction to guide you.

6.4 Standard Enthalpies of Formation

Purpose

- To define standard states.
- To show how to use standard enthalpies of formation to calculate $\Delta H°$ for a reaction.

For a reaction studied under conditions of constant pressure, we can obtain the enthalpy change using a calorimeter. However, this process can be very difficult. In fact, in some cases it is impossible, since certain reactions do not lend themselves to such study. An example is the conversion of solid carbon from its graphite form to its diamond form:

$$C_{graphite}(s) \rightarrow C_{diamond}(s)$$

The value of ΔH for this process cannot be obtained by direct measurement in a calorimeter because the process is much too slow under normal conditions. However, as we saw in Sample Exercise 6.7, ΔH for this process can be calculated from heats of combustion. This is only one example of how useful it is to be able to *calculate* ΔH values for chemical reactions. We will next show how to do this using standard enthalpies of formation.

The **standard enthalpy of formation** ($\Delta H_f°$) of a compound is defined as the *change in enthalpy that accompanies the formation of one mole of a compound from its elements with all substances in their standard states.*

A *degree symbol* on a thermodynamic function, for example, $\Delta H°$, indicates that the corresponding process has been carried out under standard conditions. The **standard state** for a substance is a precisely defined reference state. Because thermodynamic functions often depend on the concentrations (or pressures) of the substances involved, we must use a common reference state to properly compare the thermodynamic properties of two substances. This is especially important because, for most thermodynamic properties, we can only measure *changes* in the property. For example, we have no method for determining absolute values of enthalpy. We can only measure enthalpy changes (ΔH values) by performing heat-flow experiments.

Conventional Definitions of Standard States

For a compound

- The standard state of a gaseous substance is a pressure of exactly 1 atmosphere.
- For a substance present in a solution, the standard state is a concentration of exactly 1 M.
- For a pure substance in a condensed state (liquid or solid), the standard state is the pure liquid or solid.

For an element

- The standard state of an element is the form in which the element exists under conditions of 1 atmosphere and 25°C. (The standard state for oxygen is $O_2(g)$ at a pressure of 1 atmosphere; the standard state for sodium is $Na(s)$; the standard state for mercury is $Hg(l)$, and so on.)

Standard state is *not* the same as the standard temperature and pressure (STP) for a gas (discussed in Section 5.4).

Brown nitrogen dioxide gas.

Several important characteristics of the definition of the enthalpy of formation will become clearer if we again consider the formation of nitrogen dioxide from the elements in their standard states:

$$\tfrac{1}{2}N_2(g) + O_2(g) \rightarrow NO_2(g) \qquad \Delta H_f^\circ = 34 \text{ kJ/mol}$$

Note that the reaction is written so that both elements are in their standard states, and 1 mole of product is formed. Enthalpies of formation are *always* given per mole of product with the product in its standard state.

The formation reaction for methanol is written as

$$C(s) + 2H_2(g) + \tfrac{1}{2}O_2(g) \rightarrow CH_3OH(l) \qquad \Delta H_f^\circ = -239 \text{ kJ/mol}$$

The standard state of carbon is graphite, the standard states for oxygen and hydrogen are the diatomic gases, and the standard state for methanol is the liquid.

The ΔH_f° values for some common substances are shown in Table 6.2. More values are found in Appendix 4. The importance of the tabulated ΔH_f° values is that enthalpies for many reactions can be calculated using these numbers. To see how this is done, we will calculate the standard enthalpy change for the combustion of methane:

$$CH_4(g) + 2O_2(g) \rightarrow CO_2(g) + 2H_2O(l)$$

Enthalpy is a state function, so we can invoke Hess's law and choose *any* convenient pathway from reactants to products and then sum the enthalpy changes along the chosen pathway. A convenient pathway, shown in Fig. 6.8, involves taking the reactants apart to the respective elements in their standard states in reactions (a) and (b) and then forming the products from these elements in reactions (c) and (d). This general pathway will work for any reaction, since atoms are conserved in a chemical reaction.

Note from Fig. 6.8 that reaction (a), where methane is taken apart into its elements:

$$CH_4(g) \rightarrow C(s) + 2H_2(g)$$

is just the reverse of the formation reaction for methane:

$$C(s) + 2H_2(g) \rightarrow CH_4(g) \qquad \Delta H_f^\circ = -75 \text{ kJ/mol}$$

Since reversing a reaction means changing the sign of ΔH but keeping the magnitude the same, ΔH for reaction (a) is $-\Delta H_f^\circ$, or 75 kJ. Thus $\Delta H^\circ_{(a)} = 75$ kJ.

Table 6.2

Standard Enthalpies of Formation for Several Compounds at 25°C

Compound	ΔH_f° (kJ/mol)
$NH_3(g)$	-46
$NO_2(g)$	34
$H_2O(l)$	-286
$Al_2O_3(s)$	-1676
$Fe_2O_3(s)$	-826
$CO_2(g)$	-394
$CH_3OH(l)$	-239
$C_8H_{18}(l)$	-269

Figure 6.8

In this pathway for the combustion of methane, the reactants are first taken apart in reactions (a) and (b) to form the constituent elements in their standard states, which are then used to assemble the products in reactions (c) and (d).

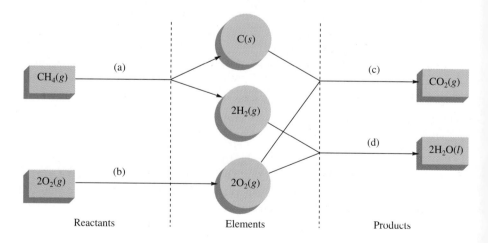

Next we consider reaction (b). Here oxygen is already an element in its standard state, so no change is needed. Thus $\Delta H^\circ_{(b)} = 0$.

The next steps, reactions (c) and (d), use the elements formed in reactions (a) and (b) to form the products. Note that reaction (c) is simply the formation reaction for carbon dioxide:

$$C(s) + O_2(g) \rightarrow CO_2(g) \qquad \Delta H^\circ_f = -394 \text{ kJ/mol}$$

and

$$\Delta H^\circ_{(c)} = \Delta H^\circ_f \text{ for } CO_2(g) = -394 \text{ kJ}$$

Reaction (d) is the formation reaction for water:

$$H_2(g) + \tfrac{1}{2}O_2(g) \rightarrow H_2O(l) \qquad \Delta H^\circ_f = -286 \text{ kJ/mol}$$

However, since 2 moles of water are required in the balanced equation, we must form 2 moles of water from the elements:

$$2H_2(g) + O_2(g) \rightarrow 2H_2O(l)$$

Thus

$$\Delta H^\circ_{(d)} = 2 \times \Delta H^\circ_f \text{ for } H_2O(l) = 2(-286 \text{ kJ}) = -572 \text{ kJ}$$

We have now completed the pathway from the reactants to the products. The change in enthalpy for the reaction is the sum of the ΔH values (including their signs) for the steps:

$$
\begin{aligned}
\Delta H^\circ_{\text{reaction}} &= \Delta H^\circ_{(a)} + \Delta H^\circ_{(b)} + \Delta H^\circ_{(c)} + \Delta H^\circ_{(d)} \\
&= [-\Delta H^\circ_f \text{ for } CH_4(g)] + 0 + [\Delta H^\circ_f \text{ for } CO_2(g)] + [2 \times \Delta H^\circ_f \text{ for } H_2O(l)] \\
&= -(-75 \text{ kJ}) + 0 + (-394 \text{ kJ}) + (-572 \text{ kJ}) \\
&= -891 \text{ kJ}
\end{aligned}
$$

Let's examine carefully the pathway we used in this example. First, the reactants were broken down into the elements in their standard states. This process involved reversing the formation reactions and thus switching the signs of the enthalpies of formation. The products were then constructed from these elements. This involved formation reactions and thus enthalpies of formation. We can summarize this entire process as follows: *The enthalpy change for a given reaction can be calculated by subtracting the enthalpies of formation of the reactants from the enthalpies of formation of the products.* Remember to multiply the enthalpies of formation by integers as required by the balanced equation. This statement can be represented symbolically as follows:

> Subtraction means to reverse the sign and add.

$$\Delta H^\circ_{\text{reaction}} = \Sigma n_p \Delta H^\circ_f(\text{products}) - \Sigma n_r \Delta H^\circ_f(\text{reactants}) \qquad (6.1)$$

where the symbol Σ (sigma) means "to take the sum of the terms," and n_p and n_r represent the moles of each product or reactant, respectively.

Elements are not included in the calculation because elements require no change in form. We have in effect *defined* the enthalpy of formation of an element in its standard state as zero, since we have chosen this as our reference point for calculating enthalpy changes in reactions.

Keep in Mind the Following Key Concepts When Doing Enthalpy Calculations:

- When a reaction is reversed, the magnitude of ΔH remains the same, but its sign changes.
- When the balanced equation for a reaction is multiplied by an integer, the value of ΔH for that reaction must be multiplied by the same integer.

Elements in their standard states are not included in enthalpy calculations using ΔH_f° values.

- The change in enthalpy for a given reaction can be calculated from the enthalpies of formation of the reactants and products:

$$\Delta H^\circ_{\text{reaction}} = \Sigma n_p \Delta H_f^\circ(\text{products}) - \Sigma n_r \, \Delta H_f^\circ(\text{reactants})$$

- Elements in their standard states are not included in the $\Delta H_{\text{reaction}}$ calculations. That is, ΔH_f° for an element in its standard state is zero.

Sample Exercise 6.9

Using the standard enthalpies of formation listed in Table 6.2, calculate the standard enthalpy change for the overall reaction that occurs when ammonia is burned in air to form nitrogen dioxide and water. This is the first step in the manufacture of nitric acid.

$$4NH_3(g) + 7O_2(g) \rightarrow 4NO_2(g) + 6H_2O(l)$$

Solution

We will use the pathway in which the reactants are broken down into elements in their standard states, which are then used to form the products (see Fig. 6.9).

STEP 1

Decomposition of NH$_3$(g) into elements [reaction (a) in Fig. 6.9]. The first step is to decompose 4 moles of NH_3 into N_2 and H_2:

$$4NH_3(g) \rightarrow 2N_2(g) + 6H_2(g)$$

The preceding reaction is 4 times the *reverse* of the formation reaction for NH_3:

$$\tfrac{1}{2}N_2(g) + \tfrac{3}{2}H_2(g) \rightarrow NH_3(g) \qquad \Delta H_f^\circ = -46 \text{ kJ/mol}$$

Thus $\Delta H^\circ_{(a)} = 4 \text{ mol}[-(-46 \text{ kJ/mol})] = 184 \text{ kJ}$

STEP 2

Elemental oxygen [reaction (b) in Fig. 6.9]. Since $O_2(g)$ is an element in its standard state, $\Delta H^\circ_{(b)} = 0$.

We now have the elements $N_2(g)$, $H_2(g)$, and $O_2(g)$, which can be combined to form the products of the overall reaction.

STEP 3

Synthesis of NO$_2$(g) from elements [reaction (c) in Fig. 6.9]. The overall reaction equation has 4 moles of NO_2. Thus the required reaction is 4 times the formation reaction for NO_2:

$$4 \times [\tfrac{1}{2}N_2(g) + O_2(g) \rightarrow NO_2(g)]$$

and $\Delta H^\circ_{(c)} = 4 \times \Delta H_f^\circ \text{ for } NO_2(g)$

From Table 6.2, ΔH_f° for $NO_2(g) = 34$ kJ/mol and

$$\Delta H^\circ_{(c)} = 4 \text{ mol} \times 34 \text{ kJ/mol} = 136 \text{ kJ}$$

STEP 4

Synthesis of H$_2$O(l) from elements [reaction (d) in Fig. 6.9]. Since the overall equation for the reaction has 6 moles of $H_2O(l)$, the required reaction is 6 times the

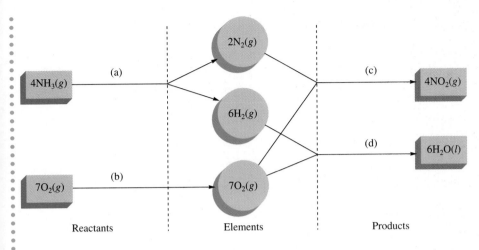

Figure 6.9

A pathway for the combustion of ammonia.

formation reaction for $H_2O(l)$:

$$6 \times [H_2(g) + \tfrac{1}{2}O_2(g) \rightarrow H_2O(l)]$$

and

$$\Delta H^{\circ}_{(d)} = 6 \times \Delta H^{\circ}_f \text{ for } H_2O(l)$$

From Table 6.2, ΔH°_f for $H_2O(l) = -286$ kJ/mol and

$$\Delta H^{\circ}_{(d)} = 6 \text{ mol } (-286 \text{ kJ/mol}) = -1716 \text{ kJ}$$

To summarize, we have done the following:

$$4NH_3(g) \xrightarrow{\Delta H^{\circ}_{(a)}} \left\{ \begin{matrix} 2N_2(g) + 6H_2(g) \\ 7O_2(g) \end{matrix} \right. \left. \begin{matrix} \xrightarrow{\Delta H^{\circ}_{(c)}} 4NO_2(g) \\ \xrightarrow{\Delta H^{\circ}_{(d)}} 6H_2O(l) \end{matrix} \right\}$$

$$7O_2(g) \xrightarrow{\Delta H^{\circ}_{(b)}}$$

Elements in their
standard states

We add the ΔH° values for the steps to get ΔH° for the overall reaction:

$$\begin{aligned} \Delta H^{\circ}_{\text{reaction}} &= \Delta H^{\circ}_{(a)} + \Delta H^{\circ}_{(b)} + \Delta H^{\circ}_{(c)} + \Delta H^{\circ}_{(d)} \\ &= [4 \times -\Delta H^{\circ}_f \text{ for } NH_3(g)] + 0 + [4 \times \Delta H^{\circ}_f \text{ for } NO_2(g)] \\ &\quad + [6 \times \Delta H^{\circ}_f(H_2O(l))] \\ &= [4 \times \Delta H^{\circ}_f \text{ for } NO_2(g)] + [6 \times \Delta H^{\circ}_f \text{ for } H_2O(l)] \\ &\quad - [4 \times \Delta H^{\circ}_f \text{ for } NH_3(g)] \\ &= \Sigma n_p \Delta H^{\circ}_f(\text{products}) - \Sigma n_r \Delta H^{\circ}_f(\text{reactants}) \end{aligned}$$

Remember that elemental reactants and products do not need to be included, since ΔH°_f for an element in its standard state is zero. Note that we have again obtained Equation (6.1). The final solution is

$$\begin{aligned} \Delta H^{\circ}_{\text{reaction}} &= [4 \times (34 \text{ kJ})] + [6 \times (-286 \text{ kJ})] - [4 \times (-46 \text{ kJ})] \\ &= -1396 \text{ kJ} \end{aligned}$$

Now that we have shown the basis for Equation (6.1), we will make direct use of it to calculate ΔH for reactions in succeeding exercises.

The thermite reaction is one of the most energetic chemical reactions known.

Sample Exercise 6.10

Using enthalpies of formation, calculate the standard change in enthalpy for the thermite reaction:

$$2Al(s) + Fe_2O_3(s) \rightarrow Al_2O_3(s) + 2Fe(s)$$

This reaction occurs when a mixture of powdered aluminum and iron(III) oxide is ignited with a magnesium fuse.

Solution

We use Equation (6.1):

$$\Delta H^\circ = \Sigma n_p \Delta H_f^\circ(\text{products}) - \Sigma n_r \Delta H_f^\circ(\text{reactants})$$

where
$$\Delta H_f^\circ \text{ for } Fe_2O_3(s) = -826 \text{ kJ/mol}$$
$$\Delta H_f^\circ \text{ for } Al_2O_3(s) = -1676 \text{ kJ/mol}$$
$$\Delta H_f^\circ \text{ for } Al(s) = \Delta H_f^\circ \text{ for } Fe(s) = 0$$

Thus
$$\Delta H^\circ_{\text{reaction}} = \Delta H_f^\circ \text{ for } Al_2O_3(s) - \Delta H_f^\circ \text{ for } Fe_2O_3(s)$$
$$= -1676 \text{ kJ} - (-826 \text{ kJ}) = -850 \text{ kJ}$$

This reaction is so highly exothermic that the iron produced is initially molten. This process is often used as a lecture demonstration and also has been used in welding massive steel objects such as ships' propellers.

Sample Exercise 6.11

Methanol (CH_3OH) is often used as a fuel in high-performance engines in race cars. Using the data in Table 6.2, compare the standard enthalpy of combustion per gram of methanol with that per gram of gasoline. Gasoline is actually a mixture of compounds, but assume for this problem that gasoline is pure liquid octane (C_8H_{18}).

Solution

The combustion reaction for methanol is

$$2CH_3OH(l) + 3O_2(g) \rightarrow 2CO_2(g) + 4H_2O(l)$$

Using the standard enthalpies of formation from Table 6.2 and Equation (6.1), we have

$$\Delta H^\circ_{\text{reaction}} = 2 \times \Delta H_f^\circ \text{ for } CO_2(g) + 4 \times \Delta H_f^\circ \text{ for } H_2O(l)$$
$$- 2 \times \Delta H_f^\circ \text{ for } CH_3OH(l)$$
$$= 2 \times (-394 \text{ kJ}) + 4 \times (-286 \text{ kJ}) - 2 \times (-239 \text{ kJ})$$
$$= -1454 \text{ kJ}$$

Thus 1454 kJ of heat is evolved when 2 moles of methanol burn. The molar mass of methanol is 32.0 g/mol. This means that 1454 kJ of energy is produced when

64.0 g methanol burns. The enthalpy of combustion per gram of methanol is

$$\frac{-1454 \text{ kJ}}{64.0 \text{ g}} = -22.7 \text{ kJ/g}$$

The combustion reaction for octane is

$$2C_8H_{18}(l) + 25O_2(g) \rightarrow 16CO_2(g) + 18H_2O(l)$$

Using the standard enthalpies of information from Table 6.2 and Equation (6.1), we have

$$\Delta H°_{\text{reaction}} = 16 \times \Delta H°_f \text{ for } CO_2(g) + 18 \times \Delta H°_f \text{ for } H_2O(l)$$
$$- 2 \times \Delta H°_f \text{ for } C_8H_{18}(l)$$
$$= 16 \times (-394 \text{ kJ}) + 18 \times (-286 \text{ kJ}) - 2 \times (-269 \text{ kJ})$$
$$= -1.09 \times 10^4 \text{ kJ}$$

This is the amount of heat evolved when 2 moles of octane burn. Since the molar mass of octane is 114.2 g/mol, the enthalpy of combustion per gram of octane is

$$\frac{-1.09 \times 10^4 \text{ kJ}}{2(114.2 \text{ g})} = -47.8 \text{ kJ/g}$$

The enthalpy of combustion per gram of octane is approximately twice that per gram of methanol. On this basis, gasoline appears to be superior to methanol for use in a racing car, where weight considerations are usually very important. Why then is methanol in fact used in racing cars? The answer is that methanol burns much more smoothly than gasoline in high-performance engines, and this advantage more than compensates for its weight disadvantage.

6.5 *Present Sources of Energy*

Purpose

- To discuss fossil fuels and the effects of their use on climate.

Woody plants, coal, petroleum, and natural gas provide a vast resource of energy that originally came from the sun. By the process of photosynthesis, plants store energy that can be claimed by burning the plants themselves or the decay products that have been converted over millions of years to **fossil fuels.** Although the United States currently depends heavily on petroleum for energy, this dependency is a relatively recent phenomenon, as shown in Fig. 6.10. In this section we discuss some sources of energy and their effects on the environment.*

Petroleum and Natural Gas

Although how they were produced is not completely understood, petroleum and natural gas were most likely formed from the remains of marine organisms that

---

*For a comprehensive treatment of the global energy situation, see "Energy for Planet Earth," a Special Issue of *Scientific American,* September 1990. Also see James Kreiger, "Energy," *Chemical and Engineering News,* June 17, 1991: 18.

Figure 6.10

Energy sources used in the United States.

Table 6.3

Names and Formulas for Some Common Hydrocarbons

Formula	Name
CH_4	Methane
C_2H_6	Ethane
C_3H_8	Propane
C_4H_{10}	Butane
C_5H_{12}	Pentane
C_6H_{14}	Hexane
C_7H_{16}	Heptane
C_8H_{18}	Octane

Table 6.4

Uses of the Various Petroleum Fractions

Petroleum Fraction in Terms of Numbers of Carbon Atoms	Major Uses
C_5-C_{10}	Gasoline
$C_{10}-C_{18}$	Kerosene Jet fuel
$C_{15}-C_{25}$	Diesel fuel Heating oil Lubricating oil
$>C_{25}$	Asphalt

lived approximately 500 million years ago. **Petroleum** is a thick, dark liquid composed mostly of compounds called **hydrocarbons** that contain carbon and hydrogen. (Carbon is unique among elements in the extent to which it can bond to itself to form chains of various lengths.) Table 6.3 gives the formulas and names for several common hydrocarbons. **Natural gas,** usually associated with petroleum deposits, consists mostly of methane, but it also contains significant amounts of ethane, propane, and butane.

The composition of petroleum varies somewhat, but it consists mostly of hydrocarbons having chains that contain from 5 to more than 25 carbons. To be used efficiently, the petroleum must be separated into fractions by boiling. The lighter molecules (having the lowest boiling points) can be boiled off, leaving the heavier ones behind. The commercial uses of various petroleum fractions are shown in Table 6.4.

The petroleum era began when the demand for lamp oil during the Industrial Revolution outstripped the traditional sources: animal fats and whale oil. In response to this increased demand, Edwin Drake drilled the first oil well in 1859 at Titusville, Pennsylvania. The petroleum from this well was refined to produce *kerosene* (fraction $C_{10}-C_{18}$), which served as an excellent lamp oil. *Gasoline* (fraction C_5-C_{10}) had limited use and was often discarded. However this situation soon changed. The development of the electric light decreased the need for kerosene, and the advent of the "horseless carriage" with its gasoline-powered engine signaled the birth of the gasoline age.

As gasoline became more important, new ways were sought to increase the yield of gasoline obtained from each barrel of petroleum. William Burton invented a process at Standard Oil of Indiana called **pyrolytic (high-temperature) cracking.** In this process, the heavier molecules of the kerosene fraction are heated to about 700°C, causing them to break (crack) into the smaller molecules of hydrocarbons in the gasoline fraction. As cars became larger, more efficient internal combustion engines were designed. Because of the uneven burning of the gasoline then available, these engines "knocked," producing unwanted noise and even engine damage. Intensive research to find additives that would promote smoother burning produced tetraethyl lead, $(C_2H_5)_4Pb$, a very effective "antiknock" agent.

The addition of tetraethyl lead to gasoline became a common practice, and by 1960, gasoline contained as much as 3 grams of lead per gallon. As we have discovered so often in recent years, technological advances can produce environmental problems. To prevent air pollution from automobile exhaust, catalytic converters have been added to car exhaust systems. The effectiveness of these converters, however, is destroyed by lead. The use of leaded gasoline also greatly increased the amount of lead in the environment, where it can be ingested by animals and humans. For these reasons, the use of lead in gasoline has been phased out, requiring extensive (and expensive) modifications of engines and of the gasoline refining process.

Coal

Coal was formed from the remains of plants that were buried and subjected to high pressure and heat over long periods of time. Plant materials have a high content of cellulose, a complex molecule whose empirical formula is CH_2O but whose molar mass is around 500,000 g/mol. After the plants and trees that flourished on the earth at various times and places died and were buried, chemical changes gradually lowered the oxygen and hydrogen content of the cellulose molecules. Coal "matures" through four stages: lignite, subbituminous, bituminous, and anthracite. Each stage has a higher carbon-to-oxygen and carbon-to-hydrogen ratio; that is, the relative carbon content gradually increases. Typical elemental compositions of the various coals are given in Table 6.5. The energy available from the combustion of a given mass of coal increases as the carbon content increases. Therefore, anthracite is the most valuable coal, and lignite, the least.

Coal has variable composition depending on both its age and location.

Coal is an important and plentiful fuel in the United States, currently furnishing approximately 20% of our energy. As the supply of petroleum dwindles, the share of the energy supply from coal could increase to as high as 30% by the year 2000. However, coal is expensive and dangerous to mine underground, and the strip mining of fertile farmland in the Midwest or of scenic land in the West causes obvious problems. In addition, the burning of coal, especially high-sulfur coal, yields air pollutants such as sulfur dioxide, which, in turn, can lead to acid rain, as we learned in Chapter 5. However, even if coal were pure carbon, the carbon dioxide produced when it was burned would still have significant effects on the earth's climate.

Coal being strip-mined.

Effects of Carbon Dioxide on Climate

The earth receives a tremendous quantity of radiant energy from the sun, about 30% of which is reflected back into space by the earth's atmosphere. The remaining energy passes through the atmosphere to the earth's surface. Some of this energy is

Table 6.5					
Elemental Composition of Various Types of Coal					
	Mass Percent of Each Element				
Type of Coal	C	H	O	N	S
Lignite	71	4	23	1	1
Subbituminous	77	5	16	1	1
Bituminous	80	6	8	1	5
Anthracite	92	3	3	1	1

absorbed by plants for photosynthesis and some by the oceans to evaporate water, but most of it is absorbed by soil, rock, and water, increasing the temperature of the earth's surface. This energy is in turn radiated from the heated surface mainly as *infrared radiation,* often called *heat radiation.*

The electromagnetic spectrum, including visible and infrared radiation, is discussed in Chapter 7.

The atmosphere, like window glass, is transparent to visible light but does not allow all the infrared radiation to pass back into space. Molecules in the atmosphere, principally H_2O and CO_2, strongly absorb infrared radiation and radiate it back toward the earth, as shown in Fig. 6.11, so a net amount of thermal energy is retained by the earth's atmosphere, causing the earth to be much warmer than it would be without its atmosphere. In a way, the atmosphere acts like the glass of a greenhouse, which is transparent to visible light but absorbs infrared radiation, thus raising the temperature inside the building. This **greenhouse effect** is seen even more spectacularly on Venus, where the dense atmosphere is thought to be responsible for the high surface temperature of that planet.

Thus the temperature of the earth's surface is controlled to a significant extent by the carbon dioxide and water content of the atmosphere. The effect of atmospheric moisture (humidity) is apparent in the Midwest. In summer, when the humidity is high, the heat of the sun is retained well into the night, giving very high nighttime temperatures. On the other hand, in winter, the coldest temperatures always occur on clear nights, when the low humidity allows efficient radiation of energy back into space.

The average temperature of the earth's surface is 288 K. It would be ~255 K without the "greenhouse gases."

The atmosphere's water content is controlled by the water cycle (evaporation and precipitation), and the average remains constant over the years. However, as fossil fuels have been used more extensively, the carbon dioxide concentration has increased by about 16% from 1880 to 1980. Projections indicate that the carbon dioxide content of the atmosphere may be double in the twenty-first century what it was in 1880. This *could* increase the earth's average temperature by as much as 3°C, causing dramatic changes in climate and greatly affecting the growth of food crops.

How well can we predict long-term effects? Because weather has been studied for a period of time that is miniscule compared with the age of the earth, the factors that control the earth's climate in the long range are not clearly understood. For

---

◀ **C H E M I C A L   I M P A C T** ▶

Sulfur-Eating Bacteria Clean Up Coal

Coal is a very important energy resource in the United States. Although enormous quantities of coal are used to produce electricity in the United States every day, tremendous reserves of this fossil fuel remain underground across the country. One major problem is that a great percentage of these reserves have a high sulfur content. Burning high-sulfur coal requires expensive treatment of the exhaust gases to remove the SO_2 that would lead to acid rain and other air pollution problems.

One strategy for dealing with high-sulfur coal is pretreatment to remove the sulfur before the combustion process. The best way to remove the sulfur appears to be by use of bacteria. For example, scientists at the Institute of Gas Technology have used genetic engineering to produce bacteria that selectively remove sulfur from coal without degrading the coal itself. By growing the bacteria under conditions where all nutrients except sulfur are furnished in abundance, the scientists are encouraging the growth of those strains of bacteria which metabolize sulfur most efficiently.

Although the bacterial treatment of coal to remove sulfur is currently not economically feasible, this method shows great promise.

Changes in annual mean temperature between 1958 and 2010–19.

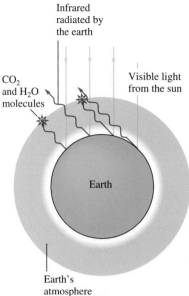

Figure 6.11

The earth's atmosphere is transparent to visible light from the sun. This visible light strikes the earth, and part of it is changed to infrared radiation. This infrared radiation from the earth's surface is strongly absorbed by CO_2, H_2O, and other molecules present in smaller amounts (for example, CH_4 and N_2O) in the atmosphere. In effect, the atmosphere traps some of the energy, acting like the glass in a greenhouse and keeping the earth warmer than it would otherwise be.

example, we do not understand what causes the earth's periodic ice ages. So indeed it is difficult to estimate the impact of the increasing carbon dioxide levels.

In fact, the variation in the earth's average temperature over the last century is somewhat confusing. In the northern latitudes during the last century, the average temperature rose by 0.8°C over a period of 60 years, then cooled by 0.5°C during the next 25 years, and finally warmed by 0.2°C in the succeeding 15 years. Such fluctuations do not match the steady increase in carbon dioxide. However, in southern latitudes and near the equator during the last century, the average temperature showed a steady rise totaling 0.4°C. This figure is in reasonable agreement with the predicted effect of the increasing carbon dioxide concentration over that period. Another significant fact is that the past 10 years constitute the warmest decade on record.

Although the exact relationship between the carbon dioxide concentration in the atmosphere and the earth's temperature is not known at present, one thing is clear: the increase in the atmospheric concentration of carbon dioxide is quite dramatic (see Fig. 6.12). We must consider the implications of this increase as we consider our future energy needs.*

6.6 New Energy Sources

Purpose

• To discuss energy alternatives.

• To compare the available energy of various fuels.

As we search for the energy sources of the future, we need to consider economic, climatic, and supply factors. There are several potential energy sources: the sun

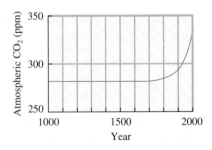

Figure 6.12

The atmospheric CO_2 concentration over the past 1000 years, based on ice core data and direct readings (since 1958). Note the dramatic increase in the past 100 years.

*For a recent review of this topic, see ''Web of Interactions Makes It Difficult to Untangle Global Warming Data'' by Bette Hileman, *Chemical and Engineering News,* April 27, 1992: 7.

A solar-powered car in a race across Australia.

(solar), nuclear processes (fission and fusion), biomass (plants), and synthetic fuels. Direct use of the sun's radiant energy to heat our homes and run our factories and transportation systems seems a sensible long-term goal. But what do we do now? Conservation of fossil fuels is one obvious step, but substitutes for fossil fuels also must be found. We will discuss some alternative sources of energy here. Nuclear power will be considered in Chapter 21.

Coal Conversion

One alternative energy source involves using a traditional fuel—coal—in new ways. Since transportation costs for solid coal are high, more energy-efficient fuels are being developed from coal. One possibility is to produce a gaseous fuel. Substances like coal that contain large molecules have high boiling points and tend to be solids or thick liquids. To convert coal from a solid to a gas therefore requires reducing the size of the molecules; the coal structure must be broken down in a process called *coal gasification*. This is done by treating the coal with oxygen and steam at high temperatures to break many of the carbon–carbon bonds. These bonds are replaced by carbon–hydrogen and carbon–oxygen bonds as the coal fragments react with the water and oxygen. The process is represented in Fig. 6.13. The desired product is a mixture of carbon monoxide and hydrogen called *synthetic gas*, or **syngas,** and methane (CH_4) gas. Since all the components of this product can react with oxygen to release heat in a combustion reaction, this gas is a useful fuel.

One of the most important considerations in designing an industrial process is the efficient use of energy. In coal gasification, some of the reactions are exothermic:

An industrial process must be energy efficient.

$$C(s) + 2H_2(g) \rightarrow CH_4(g) \qquad \Delta H^\circ = -75 \text{ kJ}$$
$$C(s) + \tfrac{1}{2}O_2(g) \rightarrow CO(g) \qquad \Delta H^\circ = -111 \text{ kJ}$$
$$C(s) + O_2(g) \rightarrow CO_2(g) \qquad \Delta H^\circ = -394 \text{ kJ}$$

Other gasification reactions are endothermic, for example:

$$C(s) + H_2O(g) \rightarrow H_2(g) + CO(g) \qquad \Delta H^\circ = 131 \text{ kJ}$$

If such conditions as the rate of feed of coal, air, and steam are carefully controlled, the correct temperature can be maintained in the process without using any external energy source. That is, an energy balance is maintained.

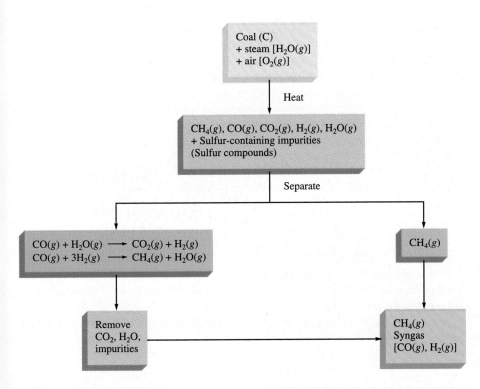

Figure 6.13

Coal gasification. Reaction of coal with a mixture of steam and air breaks down the large hydrocarbon molecules in the coal to smaller gaseous molecules, which can be used as fuels.

As stated earlier, syngas can be used directly as a fuel, but it is also important as a raw material to produce other fuels. For example, syngas can be converted directly to methanol:

$$CO(g) + 2H_2(g) \rightarrow CH_3OH(l)$$

Methanol is used in the production of synthetic fibers and plastics and also can be used as a fuel. In addition, it can be converted directly to gasoline. Approximately half of South Africa's gasoline supply comes from methanol produced from syngas.

In addition to coal gasification, the formation of *coal slurries* is another new use of coal. A slurry is a suspension of fine particles in a liquid, and coal must be pulverized and mixed with water to form a slurry. The slurry can be handled, stored, and burned in ways similar to those used for *residual oil,* a heavy fuel oil from petroleum accounting for almost 15% of U.S. petroleum imports. One hope is that coal slurries might replace solid coal and residual oil as fuels for electricity-generating power plants. However, the water needed for slurries might place an unacceptable burden on water resources, especially in the western states.

Hydrogen as a Fuel

If you have ever seen a lecture demonstration where hydrogen–oxygen mixtures were ignited, or if you have seen a newsfilm or an old photo of the Hindenburg disaster, you have witnessed a demonstration of hydrogen's potential as a fuel. The combustion reaction is

$$H_2(g) + \tfrac{1}{2}O_2(g) \rightarrow H_2O(l) \qquad \Delta H° = -286 \text{ kJ}$$

As we saw in Sample Exercise 6.6, the heat of combustion of $H_2(g)$ per gram is approximately 2.5 times that of natural gas. In addition, hydrogen has a real advantage over fossil fuels in that the only product of hydrogen combustion is water; fossil fuels also produce carbon dioxide. However, even though it appears that hydrogen is a very logical choice as a major fuel for the future, there are three main problems: the cost of production, storage, and transport.

First let's look at the production problem. Although hydrogen is very abundant on earth, virtually none of it exists as the free gas. Currently, the main source of hydrogen gas is from the treatment of natural gas with steam:

$$CH_4(g) + H_2O(g) \rightarrow 3H_2(g) + CO(g)$$

We can calculate ΔH for this reaction using Equation (6.1):

$$\Delta H° = \Sigma n_p \Delta H_f°(\text{products}) - \Sigma n_r \Delta H_f°(\text{reactants})$$
$$= \Delta H_f° \text{ for } CO(g) - \Delta H_f° \text{ for } CH_4(g) - \Delta H_f° \text{ for } H_2O(g)$$
$$= -111 \text{ kJ} - (-75 \text{ kJ}) - (-242 \text{ kJ}) = 206 \text{ kJ}$$

Note that this reaction is highly endothermic; treating methane with steam is not an efficient way to obtain hydrogen for fuel. It would be much more economical to burn the methane directly.

A virtually inexhaustible supply of hydrogen exists in the waters of the world's oceans. However, the reaction

$$H_2O(l) \rightarrow H_2(g) + \tfrac{1}{2}O_2(g)$$

requires 286 kJ of energy per mole of liquid water, and under current circumstances, large-scale production of hydrogen from water is not economically feasible. However, several methods for such production are currently being studied: electrolysis of water, thermal decomposition of water, and biological decomposition of water.

Electrolysis of water involves passing an electric current through it, as shown in Fig. 1.12 in Chapter 1. The present cost of electricity makes the hydrogen produced by electrolysis too expensive to be competitive as a fuel. However, if in the future we develop more efficient sources of electricity, this situation could change.

Thermal decomposition is another method for producing hydrogen from water. This involves heating the water to several thousand degrees, where it spontaneously decomposes into hydrogen and oxygen. However, attaining temperatures in this range would be very expensive even if a practical heat source and a suitable reaction container were available.

In the thermochemical decomposition of water, chemical reactions, as well as heat, are used to "split" water into its components. One such system involves the following reactions (the temperature required for each is given in parentheses):

$$2HI \rightarrow I_2 + H_2 \qquad (425°C)$$
$$2H_2O + SO_2 + I_2 \rightarrow H_2SO_4 + 2HI \qquad (90°C)$$
$$\underline{H_2SO_4 \rightarrow SO_2 + H_2O + \tfrac{1}{2}O_2 \qquad (825°C)}$$
$$\text{Net reaction: } H_2O \rightarrow H_2 + \tfrac{1}{2}O_2$$

Note that the HI is not consumed in the net reaction. Note also that the maximum temperature required is 825°C, a temperature that is feasible if a nuclear reactor is used as a heat source. A current research goal is to find a system for which the required temperatures are low enough that sunlight can be used as the energy source.

Electrolysis will be discussed in Chapter 17.

But what about the organisms that decompose water without the aid of electricity or high temperatures? In the process of photosynthesis, green plants absorb carbon dioxide and water and use them along with energy from the sun to produce the substances needed for growth. Scientists have studied photosynthesis for years, hoping to get answers to humanity's food and energy shortages. At present, much of this research involves attempts to modify the photosynthetic process so that plants will release hydrogen gas from water instead of using the hydrogen to produce complex compounds. Small-scale experiments have shown that under certain conditions plants do produce hydrogen gas, but the yields are far from being commercially useful. At this point the economical production of hydrogen gas remains unrealized.

The storage and transportation of hydrogen also present problems. First, on metal surfaces the H_2 molecule decomposes to atoms. Since the atoms are so small, they can migrate into the metal, causing structural changes that make it brittle. This might lead to a pipeline failure if hydrogen were pumped under high pressure.

A second problem is the relatively small amount of energy that is available *per unit volume* of hydrogen gas. Although the energy available per gram of hydrogen is significantly greater than that per gram of methane, the energy available per given volume of hydrogen is about one-third that available from the same volume of methane. This is demonstrated in Sample Exercise 6.12.

Green plants, such as these wildflowers at the base of Torrey's Peak in Colorado, store energy from the sun.

Sample Exercise 6.12

Compare the energy available from the combustion of a given volume of methane and the same volume of hydrogen at the same temperature and pressure.

Solution

In Sample Exercise 6.6 we calculated the heat released for the combustion of methane and hydrogen: 55 kJ/g CH_4 and 141 kJ/g H_2. We also know from our study of gases that 1 mol $H_2(g)$ has the same volume as 1 mol $CH_4(g)$ at the same temperature and pressure (assuming ideal behavior). Thus, for molar volumes of both gases under the same conditions of temperature and pressure,

$$\frac{\text{Enthalpy of combustion of 1 molar volume of } H_2(g)}{\text{Enthalpy of combustion of 1 molar volume of } CH_4(g)}$$

$$= \frac{\text{enthalpy of combustion per mole of } H_2}{\text{enthalpy of combustion per mole of } CH_4}$$

$$= \frac{(-141 \text{ kJ/g})(2.02 \text{ g } H_2/\text{mol } H_2)}{(-55 \text{ kJ/g})(16.04 \text{ g } CH_4/\text{mol } CH_4)}$$

$$= \frac{-285}{-883} \approx \frac{1}{3}$$

Thus about three times the volume of hydrogen gas is needed to furnish the same energy as a given volume of methane.

Could hydrogen be considered as a potential fuel for automobiles? This is an intriguing question. The internal combustion engines in automobiles can be easily adapted to burn hydrogen. However, the primary difficulty is the storage of enough hydrogen to give an automobile a reasonable range. This is illustrated by Sample Exercise 6.13.

Sample Exercise 6.13

Assuming that the combustion of hydrogen gas provides three times as much energy per gram as gasoline, calculate the volume of liquid H_2 (density = 0.0710 g/mL) required to furnish the energy contained in 80.0 L (about 20 gal) of gasoline (density = 0.740 g/mL). Calculate also the volume that this hydrogen would occupy as a gas at 1.00 atm and 25°C.

Solution

The mass of 80.0 L gasoline is

$$80.0 \ \cancel{L} \times \frac{1000 \ \cancel{mL}}{1 \ \cancel{L}} \times \frac{0.740 \ g}{\cancel{mL}} = 59{,}200 \ g$$

Since H_2 furnishes three times as much energy per gram as gasoline, only a third as much liquid hydrogen is needed to furnish the same energy:

$$\text{Mass of } H_2(l) \text{ needed} = \frac{59{,}200 \ g}{3} = 19{,}700 \ g$$

Since density = mass/volume, then volume = mass/density, and the volume of $H_2(l)$ needed is

$$V = \frac{19{,}700 \ \cancel{g}}{0.0710 \ \cancel{g}/\text{mL}}$$
$$= 2.77 \times 10^5 \ \text{mL} = 277 \ \text{L}$$

Thus 277 L of liquid H_2 is needed to furnish the same energy of combustion as 80.0 L of gasoline.

To calculate the volume that this hydrogen would occupy as a gas at 1.00 atm and 25°C, we use the ideal gas law:

$$PV = nRT$$

In this case $P = 1.00$ atm, $T = 273 + 25°C = 298$ K, and $R = 0.08206$ L · atm/K · mol. Also,

$$n = 19{,}700 \ \cancel{g \ H_2} \times \frac{1 \ \text{mol } H_2}{2.02 \ \cancel{g \ H_2}} = 9.75 \times 10^3 \ \text{mol } H_2$$

Thus

$$V = \frac{nRT}{P} = \frac{(9.75 \times 10^3 \ \cancel{mol})(0.08206 \ \text{L} \cdot \cancel{atm}/\cancel{K} \cdot \cancel{mol})(298 \ \cancel{K})}{1.00 \ \cancel{atm}}$$
$$= 2.38 \times 10^5 \ \text{L} = 238{,}000 \ \text{L}$$

At 1 atm and 25°C, the hydrogen gas needed to replace 20 gal of gasoline occupies a volume of 238,000 L.

◀ **CHEMICAL IMPACT** ▶

Heat Packs

A skier is trapped by a sudden snow-storm. After building a snow cave for protection, she realizes her hands and feet are freezing; she is in danger of frost-bite. Then she remembers the four small packs in her pocket. She removes the plastic cover from each one to reveal a small paper packet. She places one packet in each boot and one in each mitten. Soon her hands and feet are toasty warm.

These "magic" packets of energy contain a mixture of powdered iron, acti-vated carbon, sodium chloride, cellulose (sawdust), and zeolite, all moistened by a little water. The paper cover is permeable to air.

The exothermic reaction that produces the heat is a very common one—the rust-ing of iron. The overall reaction can be represented as

$$4Fe(s) + 3O_2(g) \rightarrow 2Fe_2O_3(s)$$
$$\Delta H^\circ = -1652 \text{ kJ}$$

although in reality it is somewhat more complicated. When the plastic envelope is removed, O_2 molecules penetrate the paper and the reaction begins.

The oxidation of iron by oxygen oc-curs naturally. Any steel surface exposed to the atmosphere inevitably rusts, but this process is quite slow—much too slow to be useful in hot packs. However, if the iron is ground into a fine powder, the re-sulting increase in surface area causes the reaction with oxygen to be fast enough to

A popular brand of portable hot pack.

warm hands and feet. Such packets can produce heat for up to 6 hours.

You can see from Sample Exercise 6.13 that an automobile would need a huge tank to hold enough hydrogen gas (at 1 atm) to have a typical mileage range. Clearly, hydrogen must be stored as a liquid or in some other way. Is this feasible? Because of its very low boiling point (20 K), storage of liquid hydrogen requires a superinsulated container that can withstand high pressures. Storage in this manner would be both expensive and hazardous because of the potential for explosion. Thus storage of hydrogen in the individual automobile as a liquid does not seem practical.

A much better alternative seems to be the use of metals that absorb hydrogen to form solid metal hydrides:

Metal hydrides are discussed in Chapter 18.

$$H_2(g) + M(s) \rightarrow MH_2(s)$$

To use this method of storage, hydrogen gas would be pumped into a tank contain-ing the solid metal in powdered form, where it would be absorbed to form the hydride, whose volume would be little more than that of the metal alone. This hydrogen would then be available for combustion in the engine by release of $H_2(g)$ from the hydride as needed:

$$MH_2(s) \rightarrow M(s) + H_2(g)$$

Several types of solids that absorb hydrogen to form hydrides are being studied for use in hydrogen-powered vehicles. In fact, in 1992 Mazda unveiled a hydrogen-powered car that uses this technology. The 100-hp rotary-engined HR-X can exceed 90 mph and has a range of 120 miles on a tank of hydrogen gas.

Other Energy Alternatives

Many other energy sources are being considered for future use. The western states, especially Colorado, contain huge deposits of *oil shale,* which consists of a complex

◀ **CHEMICAL IMPACT** ▶

Anaerobic Engines: Energy without Oxygen

A fireman frantically tries to rescue a person trapped in a burning building, but his chainsaw dies from a lack of oxygen. This potential tragedy could be averted if the chainsaw were powered by an engine whose fuel did not require oxygen—an anaerobic engine. Such an engine has been suggested by two Canadian scientists* who demonstrated that the compound $(CH_3)_3COOC(CH_3)_3$, called

*H. O. Pritchard and P. Q. E. Clothier, "Anaerobic Operations of an Internal Combustion Engine," *J. Chem. Soc. Chem. Commun.* (1986): 1529.

di-tert-butylperoxide, or DTBP, will decompose exothermically when compressed in the cylinder of an engine, thus providing energy to run the engine without oxygen. The decomposition reaction is

$$(CH_3)_3COOC(CH_3)_3(g)$$
$$\rightarrow C_2H_6(g) + 2(CH_3)_2CO(g)$$

Under conditions where oxygen is plentiful (aerobic conditions), the engine runs normally, with the DTBP fuel reacting with O_2 to produce CO_2 and H_2O. However, when the oxygen supply is se-

verely limited, as in the smoke from a fire, the engine continues to run (although more slowly) from the energy produced by the decomposition of DTBP described by the preceding equation. Thus the DTBP fuel would allow a chainsaw to be used under the conditions encountered at the scene of the fire.

The Canadian scientists have also suggested that large anaerobic engines could be developed to power equipment used in mine rescues and other situations where lack of oxygen would prevent an engine with normal fuel from operating.

carbon-based material called *kerogen* contained in porous rock formations. These deposits have the potential of being a larger energy source than the vast petroleum deposits of the Middle East. The main problem with oil shale is that the trapped fuel is not fluid and cannot be pumped. To recover the fuel, the rock must be heated to a temperature of 250°C or higher to decompose the kerogen to smaller molecules that produce gaseous and liquid products. This process is expensive and yields large quantities of waste rock, which have a negative environmental impact.

Ethanol (C_2H_5OH) is another fuel with the potential to supplement, if not replace, gasoline. The most common method of producing ethanol is fermentation, a process in which sugar is changed to alcohol by the action of yeast. The sugar can come from virtually any source, including fruits and grains, although fuel-grade ethanol would probably come mostly from corn. Car engines can burn pure alcohol or *gasohol,* an alcohol–gasoline mixture (10% ethanol in gasoline), with little modification. Gasohol is now widely available in the United States. The use of pure alcohol as a motor fuel is not feasible in most of the United States because it does not vaporize easily when temperatures are low. However, pure ethanol could be a very practical fuel in warm climates. For example, in Brazil, large quantities of ethanol fuel are being produced for cars.

Methanol (CH_3OH), an alcohol similar to ethanol, which has been used successfully for many years in race cars, is now being evaluated as a motor fuel in California. A major gasoline retailer has agreed to install pumps at 25 locations to dispense a fuel that is 85% methanol and 15% gasoline for use in specially prepared automobiles. The California Energy Commission feels that methanol has great potential for providing a secure, long-term energy supply that would help alleviate air-quality problems. Arizona and Colorado are also considering methanol as a major source of portable energy.

Another potential source of liquid fuels is oil squeezed from seeds *(seed oil).* For example, some farmers in North Dakota, South Africa, and Australia are now using sunflower oil to replace diesel fuel. Oil seeds, found in a wide variety of plants, can be processed to produce an oil composed mainly of carbon and hydrogen, which of

◄ **CHEMICAL IMPACT** ►

Nature Has Hot Plants

The voodoo lily is a beautiful, seductive, and foul-smelling plant. The exotic-looking lily features an elaborate reproductive mechanism—a purple spike that can reach nearly 3 feet in length and is cloaked by a hoodlike leaf. But approach to the plant reveals bad news—it smells terrible!

Despite its antisocial odor, this putrid plant has fascinated biologists for many years because of its ability to generate heat. At the peak of its metabolic activity, the plant's blossom can be as much as 15°C above its ambient temperature. To generate this much heat, the metabolic rate of the plant must be close to that of a flying hummingbird!

What's the purpose of this intense heat production? For a plant faced with limited food supplies in the very competitive tropical climate where it grows, heat production seems like a great waste of energy. The answer to this mystery is that the voodoo lily is pollinated mainly by carrion-loving insects. Thus the lily prepares a malodorous mixture of chemicals characteristic of rotting meat which it then "cooks" off into the surrounding air to attract flesh-feeding beetles and flies. Then, once the insects enter the pollination chamber, the high temperatures there (as high as 110°F) cause the insects to remain very active to better carry out their pollination duties.

The voodoo lily is only one of many thermogenic (heat-producing) plants. These plants are of special interest to biologists because they provide opportunities to study metabolic reactions that are quite subtle in "normal" plants. For example, recent studies have shown that salicylic acid, the active form of aspirin, is probably very important in producing the metabolic bursts in thermogenic plants.

Besides studying the dramatic heat effects in thermogenic plants, biologists are also interested in calorimetric studies of regular plants. For example, very precise calorimeters have been designed that can be used to study the heat produced, and thus the metabolic activities, of clumps of cells no larger than a bread crumb. Several scientists have suggested that a single calorimetric measurement taking just a few minutes on a tiny plant might be useful in predicting the growth rate of the mature plant throughout its lifetime. If true, this would provide a very efficient method for selecting the plants most likely to thrive as adults.

Because the study of the heat production by plants is an excellent way to learn about plant metabolism, this continues to be a "hot" area of research.

course reacts with oxygen to produce carbon dioxide, water, and heat. It is hoped that oil-seed plants can be developed that will thrive under soil and climatic conditions unsuitable for corn and wheat. The main advantage of seed oil as a fuel is that it is renewable. Ideally, fuel would be grown just like food crops.

FOR REVIEW

Summary

Energy can be defined as the capacity to do work or to produce heat. The law of conservation of energy (or the first law of thermodynamics) states that energy can be converted from one form to another, but it cannot be created or destroyed. Heat is a means for the transfer of energy. Chemical reactions can either evolve or absorb heat, depending on whether the potential energy stored in the bonds of the reactant molecules is greater or less than the energy stored in the bonds of the product molecules.

When a reaction evolves heat, it is said to be exothermic; a reaction that absorbs heat from its surroundings is endothermic. Energy is a state function; that is, a change in energy in going from one state to another is independent of the pathway.

Heat flow associated with a chemical reaction is measured by calorimetry, a technique that involves measuring temperature changes when a body absorbs or discharges heat. For a process carried out at constant pressure, the heat flow equals the change in enthalpy (ΔH).

Since enthalpy is a state function, the change in enthalpy in going from a given set of reactants to a given set of products is the same regardless of whether the reaction takes place in one step or in a series of steps (a principle known as Hess's law). We can therefore calculate the enthalpy change for an overall reaction by summing the ΔH values from a series of steps that yield that net reaction. Also, it is often convenient to calculate the $\Delta H°$ value for a reaction from values for the standard enthalpies of formation ($\Delta H_f°$) of the reactants and products. The standard enthalpy of formation is the enthalpy change that accompanies the formation of one mole of a compound from its elements, where all substances are in their standard states. For a given reaction,

$$\Delta H°_{reaction} = \Sigma n_p \Delta H_f°(products) - \Sigma n_r \Delta H_f°(reactants)$$

The practical aspects of energy production from fossil fuels involve problems of supply and environmental impact. The combustion of carbon-based fuels produces carbon dioxide, which is involved, along with atmospheric water, in controlling the surface temperature of the earth. Increased carbon dioxide concentration in the atmosphere may produce gradual global warming due to the greenhouse effect. Alternative fuels, such as syngas from coal, hydrogen from the breakdown of water, and ethanol from the fermentation of sugar, are being studied as replacements for petroleum products.

Key Terms

Section 6.1

energy
law of conservation of energy
potential energy
kinetic energy
heat
work
pathway
state function
system

surroundings
exothermic
endothermic
thermodynamics
first law of thermodynamics
internal energy

Section 6.2

enthalpy
calorimeter
calorimetry

heat capacity
specific heat capacity
molar heat capacity
constant pressure calorimetry
constant volume calorimetry

Section 6.3

Hess's law

Section 6.4

standard enthalpy of formation

standard state

Section 6.5

fossil fuels
petroleum
natural gas
coal
greenhouse effect

Section 6.6

syngas

A blue question or exercise number indicates that the answer to that question or exercise appears at the back of this book and a solution appears in the Solutions Guide.

Questions

1. Explain why ΔH is obtained directly from a coffee-cup calorimeter, whereas ΔE is obtained directly from a bomb calorimeter.

2. Photosynthetic plants use the following reaction to produce glucose, cellulose, etc.:

$$6CO_2(g) + 6H_2O(l) \xrightarrow{\text{Sunlight}} C_6H_{12}O_6(s) + 6O_2(g)$$

How might extensive destruction of forests exacerbate the greenhouse effect?

3. What is a state function? Enthalpy and internal energy are state functions as a direct consequence of the first law of thermodynamics. Explain.

4. Hess's law is really just another statement of the first law of thermodynamics. Explain.

5. What is the purpose for defining standard enthalpies of formation?

6. Explain the advantages and disadvantages of hydrogen as an alternative fuel.

Exercises

In this section similar exercises are paired.

Potential and Kinetic Energy

7. Calculate the kinetic energy of a baseball (mass = 5.25 oz) with a velocity of 1.0×10^2 mi/h.

8. Calculate the kinetic energy of a 1.0×10^{-5}-g object with a velocity of 2.0×10^5 cm/s.

9. Which has the greater kinetic energy, an object with a mass of 2.0 kg and a velocity of 1.0 m/s or an object with a mass of 1.0 kg and a velocity of 2.0 m/s?

10. Consider the accompanying diagram. Ball A is allowed to fall and strike ball B. Assume that all of ball A's energy is transferred to ball B, at point I, and that there is no loss of energy to other sources. What is the kinetic energy and the potential energy of ball B at point II? The potential energy is given by PE = mgz, where m is the mass in kilograms, g is the gravitational constant (9.8 m/s^2), and z is the distance in meters.)

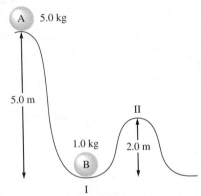

Heat and Work

11. Calculate ΔE for each of the following cases:
    a. $q = +51$ kJ, $w = -15$ kJ
    b. $q = +100.$ kJ, $w = -65$ kJ
    c. $q = -65$ kJ, $w = -20.$ kJ
    d. In which of these cases does the system do work on the surroundings?

12. Calculate ΔE for each of the following:
    a. $q = -47$ kJ, $w = +88$ kJ
    b. $q = +82$ kJ, $w = +47$ kJ
    c. $q = +47$ kJ, $w = 0$
    d. In which of these cases do the surroundings do work on the system?

13. A gas absorbs 45 kJ of heat and does 29 kJ of work. Calculate ΔE.

14. A system releases 125 kJ of heat while 104 kJ of work is done on it. Calculate ΔE.

15. The volume of an ideal gas is decreased from 5.0 L to 5.0 mL at a constant pressure of 2.0 atm. Calculate the work associated with this process.

16. Consider a mixture of air and gasoline vapor in a cylinder with a piston. The original volume is 40. cm^3. If the combustion of this mixture releases 950. J of energy, to what volume will the gases expand against a constant pressure of 650. torr if all the energy of combustion is converted into work to push back the piston?

17. A balloon filled with 39.1 mol helium has a volume of 875 L at 0.0°C and 1.00 atm pressure. The temperature of the balloon is increased to 38.0°C as it expands to a volume of 998 L, the pressure remaining constant. Calculate q, w, and ΔE for the helium in the balloon. (The molar heat capacity for helium gas is 20.8 J/°C · mol.)

18. A balloon contains 313 g He at a pressure of 1.00 atm. The volume of the balloon is 1910 L. The temperature is decreased by 15°C as the volume decreases to 1840 L, the pressure remaining constant. Calculate q, w, and ΔE for the helium in the balloon. (The molar heat capacity of helium gas is 20.8 J/°C · mol.)

Properties of Enthalpy

19. Are the following processes exothermic or endothermic?
    a. When solid KBr is dissolved in water, the solution gets colder.
    b. Natural gas (CH_4) is burned in a furnace.
    c. When concentrated H_2SO_4 is added to water, the solution gets very hot.
    d. Water is boiled in a teakettle.

20. The equation for the fermentation of glucose to alcohol and carbon dioxide is

$$C_6H_{12}O_6 \rightarrow 2C_2H_5OH + 2CO_2$$

The enthalpy change for the reaction is -67 kJ. Is the reaction exothermic or endothermic? Is energy, in the form of heat, absorbed or evolved as the reaction occurs? Calculate the enthalpy change per gram of glucose reacted.

21. For the reaction

$$S(s) + O_2(g) \rightarrow SO_2(g) \qquad \Delta H° = -296 \text{ kJ/mol}$$

    a. How much heat is evolved when 275 g sulfur is burned in excess O_2?
    b. How much heat is evolved when 25 mol sulfur is burned in excess O_2?
    c. How much heat is evolved when 150. g sulfur dioxide is produced?

22. Consider the reaction

$$B_2H_6(g) + 3O_2(g) \rightarrow B_2O_3(s) + 3H_2O(g)$$
$$\Delta H° = -2035 \text{ kJ}$$

Calculate the heat released when each of the following amounts of diborane (B_2H_6) is burned.
    a. 1.0 g
    b. 1.0 kg
    c. 1.0 mol
    d. 1.0×10^2 mol
    e. 2.6×10^{22} molecules
    f. A mixture of 10.0 g B_2H_6 and 10.0 g O_2

Calorimetry and Heat Capacity

23. The specific heat capacity of aluminum is 0.900 J/°C · g.
    a. Calculate the energy needed to raise the temperature of a 8.50×10^2-g block of aluminum from 22.8°C to 94.6°C.
    b. Calculate the molar heat capacity of aluminum.

24. The specific heat capacity of graphite is 0.71 J/°C · g. Calculate the energy required to
    a. Raise the temperature of 1.0 mol graphite by 1.0°C?
    b. Raise the temperature of 850 g graphite by 150°C?
    c. Raise the temperature of 75 kg graphite from 294 K to 348 K?

25. It takes 78.2 J to raise the temperature of 45.6 g lead by 13.3°C. Calculate the specific heat capacity and molar heat capacity of lead.

26. It takes 585 J of energy to raise the temperature of 125.6 g mercury from 20.0°C to 53.5°C. Calculate the specific heat capacity and the molar heat capacity of mercury.

27. A 28.2-g sample of nickel is heated to 99.8°C and placed in a coffee-cup calorimeter containing 150.0 g water at 23.5°C. After the metal cools, the final temperature of metal and water is 25.0°C. Calculate the specific heat capacity of nickel, assuming that no heat escapes to the surroundings or is transferred to the calorimeter.

28. A 46.2-g sample of copper is heated to 95.4°C and then placed in a calorimeter containing 75.0 g water at 19.6°C. The final temperature of the metal and water is 21.8°C. Calculate the specific heat capacity of copper, assuming that all the heat lost by the copper is gained by the water.

29. A coffee-cup calorimeter initially contains 125 g water at 24.2°C. Potassium bromide (10.5 g), also at 24.2°C, is added to the water, and after the KBr dissolves the final temperature is 21.1°C. Calculate the enthalpy change for dissolving the salt in J/g and kJ/mol. Assume that the specific heat capacity of the solution is 4.18 J/°C · g and that no heat is transferred to the surroundings or to the calorimeter.

30. In a coffee-cup calorimeter, 100.0 mL of 1.0 *M* NaOH and 100.0 mL of 1.0 *M* HCl are mixed. Both solutions were originally at 24.6°C. After the reaction, the final temperature is 31.3°C. Assuming that all the solutions have a density of 1.0 g/cm^3 and a specific heat capacity of 4.18 J/°C · g, calculate the enthalpy change for the neutralization of HCl by NaOH. Assume that no heat is lost to the surroundings or to the calorimeter.

31. Camphor ($C_{10}H_{16}O$) has a heat of combustion of 5903.6 kJ/mol. When a sample of camphor with mass 0.1204 g is burned in a bomb calorimeter, the temperature increases by 2.28°C. Calculate the heat capacity of the calorimeter.

32. A 0.1964-g sample of quinone ($C_6H_4O_2$) is burned in a bomb calorimeter that has a heat capacity of 1.56 kJ/°C. The temperature of the calorimeter increases by 3.2°C. Calculate the energy of combustion of quinone per gram and per mole.

33. In a coffee-cup calorimeter, 50.0 mL of 0.100 M $AgNO_3$ and 50.0 mL of 0.100 M HCl are mixed to yield the following reaction:

$$Ag^+(aq) + Cl^-(aq) \rightarrow AgCl(s)$$

The two solutions were initially at 22.6°C, and the final temperature is 23.4°C. Calculate the heat that accompanies this reaction. Assume that the combined solution has a mass of 100.0 g and has a specific heat capacity of 4.18 J/°C · g. Calculate ΔH for the reaction in kJ/mol.

34. Consider the reaction

$$2HCl(aq) + Ba(OH)_2(aq) \rightarrow BaCl_2(aq) + 2H_2O(l)$$
$$\Delta H = -118 \text{ kJ}$$

Calculate the heat when 100.0 mL of 0.500 M HCl is mixed with 300.0 mL of 0.500 M $Ba(OH)_2$. Assuming that the temperature of both solutions was initially 25°C and that the final mixture has a mass of 400.0 g and a specific heat capacity of 4.18 J/°C · g, calculate the final temperature of the mixture.

Hess's Law

35. Given the following data:

$$S(s) + \tfrac{3}{2}O_2(g) \rightarrow SO_3(g) \qquad \Delta H° = -395.2 \text{ kJ}$$
$$2SO_2(g) + O_2(g) \rightarrow 2SO_3(g) \qquad \Delta H° = -198.2 \text{ kJ}$$

calculate $\Delta H°$ for the reaction

$$S(s) + O_2(g) \rightarrow SO_2(g)$$

36. Given the following data:

$$N_2(g) + 2O_2(g) \rightarrow 2NO_2(g) \qquad \Delta H° = 67.7 \text{ kJ}$$
$$N_2(g) + 2O_2(g) \rightarrow N_2O_4(g) \qquad \Delta H° = 9.7 \text{ kJ}$$

calculate $\Delta H°$ for the dimerization of NO_2:

$$2NO_2(g) \rightarrow N_2O_4(g)$$

37. Given the following data:

$$H_2(g) + \tfrac{1}{2}O_2(g) \rightarrow H_2O(l)$$
$$\Delta H° = -285.8 \text{ kJ}$$
$$N_2O_5(g) + H_2O(l) \rightarrow 2HNO_3(l)$$
$$\Delta H° = -76.6 \text{ kJ}$$
$$\tfrac{1}{2}N_2(g) + \tfrac{3}{2}O_2(g) + \tfrac{1}{2}H_2(g) \rightarrow HNO_3(l)$$
$$\Delta H° = -174.1 \text{ kJ}$$

calculate the $\Delta H°$ for the reaction

$$2N_2(g) + 5O_2(g) \rightarrow 2N_2O_5(g)$$

38. Given the following data:

$$C_2H_2(g) + \tfrac{5}{2}O_2(g) \rightarrow 2CO_2(g) + H_2O(l)$$
$$\Delta H° = -1300. \text{ kJ}$$
$$C(s) + O_2(g) \rightarrow CO_2(g)$$
$$\Delta H° = -394 \text{ kJ}$$
$$H_2(g) + \tfrac{1}{2}O_2(g) \rightarrow H_2O(l)$$
$$\Delta H° = -286 \text{ kJ}$$

calculate $\Delta H°$ for the reaction

$$2C(s) + H_2(g) \rightarrow C_2H_2(g)$$

39. Given the following data:

$$2O_3(g) \rightarrow 3O_2(g)$$
$$\Delta H° = -427 \text{ kJ}$$
$$O_2(g) \rightarrow 2O(g)$$
$$\Delta H° = +495 \text{ kJ}$$
$$NO(g) + O_3(g) \rightarrow NO_2(g) + O_2(g)$$
$$\Delta H° = -199 \text{ kJ}$$

calculate $\Delta H°$ for the reaction

$$NO(g) + O(g) \rightarrow NO_2(g)$$

40. The bombardier beetle uses an explosive discharge as a defensive measure. The chemical reaction involved is the oxidation of hydroquinone by hydrogen peroxide to produce quinone and water:

$$C_6H_4(OH)_2(aq) + H_2O_2(aq) \rightarrow C_6H_4O_2(aq) + 2H_2O(l)$$

Calculate $\Delta H°$ for this reaction from the following data:

$$C_6H_4(OH)_2(aq) \rightarrow C_6H_4O_2(aq) + H_2(g)$$
$$\Delta H° = +177.4 \text{ kJ}$$
$$H_2(g) + O_2(g) \rightarrow H_2O_2(aq)$$
$$\Delta H° = -191.2 \text{ kJ}$$
$$H_2(g) + \tfrac{1}{2}O_2(g) \rightarrow H_2O(g)$$
$$\Delta H° = -241.8 \text{ kJ}$$
$$H_2O(g) \rightarrow H_2O(l)$$
$$\Delta H° = -43.8 \text{ kJ}$$

41. Given the following data:

$$O_2(g) + H_2(g) \rightarrow 2OH(g) \quad \Delta H^\circ = +77.9 \text{ kJ}$$
$$O_2(g) \rightarrow 2O(g) \quad \Delta H^\circ = +495 \text{ kJ}$$
$$H_2(g) \rightarrow 2H(g) \quad \Delta H^\circ = +435.9 \text{ kJ}$$

calculate ΔH° for the reaction

$$O(g) + H(g) \rightarrow OH(g)$$

42. Calculate ΔH° for the reaction

$$N_2H_4(l) + O_2(g) \rightarrow N_2(g) + 2H_2O(l)$$

given the following data:

$$2NH_3(g) + 3N_2O(g) \rightarrow 4N_2(g) + 3H_2O(l)$$
$$\Delta H^\circ = -1010. \text{ kJ}$$
$$N_2O(g) + 3H_2(g) \rightarrow N_2H_4(l) + H_2O(l)$$
$$\Delta H^\circ = -317 \text{ kJ}$$
$$2NH_3(g) + \tfrac{1}{2}O_2(g) \rightarrow N_2H_4(l) + H_2O(l)$$
$$\Delta H^\circ = -143 \text{ kJ}$$
$$H_2(g) + \tfrac{1}{2}O_2(g) \rightarrow H_2O(l)$$
$$\Delta H^\circ = -286 \text{ kJ}$$

Standard Enthalpies of Formation

43. Give the definition of the standard enthalpy of formation for a substance. Write separate reactions for the formation of NaCl, H_2O, $C_6H_{12}O_6$, and $PbSO_4$ that have ΔH° values equal to ΔH_f° for each compound.

44. Write reactions for which the enthalpy change will be
a. ΔH_f° for solid aluminum oxide.
b. The standard enthalpy of combustion of liquid ethanol, $C_2H_5OH(l)$.
c. The standard enthalpy of neutralization of sodium hydroxide solution by hydrochloric acid.
d. ΔH_f° for gaseous vinyl chloride, $C_2H_3Cl(g)$.
e. The enthalpy of combustion of liquid benzene, $C_6H_6(l)$.
f. The enthalpy of solution of solid ammonium bromide.

45. Use the values of ΔH_f° in Appendix 4 to calculate ΔH° for the following reactions:
a. $2NH_3(g) + 3O_2(g) + 2CH_4(g) \rightarrow 2HCN(g) + 6H_2O(g)$
b. $Ca_3(PO_4)_2(s) + 3H_2SO_4(l) \rightarrow 3CaSO_4(s) + 2H_3PO_4(l)$
c. $NH_3(g) + HCl(g) \rightarrow NH_4Cl(s)$

46. Use the values of ΔH_f° in Appendix 4 to calculate ΔH° for the following reactions:
a. $C_2H_5OH(l) + 3O_2(g) \rightarrow 2CO_2(g) + 3H_2O(g)$
b. $SiCl_4(l) + 2H_2O(l) \rightarrow SiO_2(s) + 4HCl(aq)$
c. $MgO(s) + H_2O(l) \rightarrow Mg(OH)_2(s)$

47. The Ostwald process for the commercial production of nitric acid from ammonia and oxygen involves the following steps:

$$4NH_3(g) + 5O_2(g) \rightarrow 4NO(g) + 6H_2O(g)$$
$$2NO(g) + O_2(g) \rightarrow 2NO_2(g)$$
$$3NO_2(g) + H_2O(l) \rightarrow 2HNO_3(aq) + NO(g)$$

a. Use the values of ΔH_f° in Appendix 4 to calculate the value of ΔH° for each of the preceding reactions.
b. Write the overall equation for the production of nitric acid by the Ostwald process by combining the preceding equations. (Water is also a product.) Is the overall reaction exothermic or endothermic?

48. Calculate ΔH° for each of the following reactions using the data in Appendix 4:

$$4Na(s) + O_2(g) \rightarrow 2Na_2O(s)$$
$$2Na(s) + 2H_2O(l) \rightarrow 2NaOH(aq) + H_2(g)$$
$$2Na(s) + CO_2(g) \rightarrow Na_2O(s) + CO(g)$$

Use these values to show why a water or carbon dioxide fire extinguisher might not be effective in putting out a sodium fire.

49. The reusable booster rockets of the space shuttle use a mixture of aluminum and ammonium perchlorate as fuel. A possible reaction is

$$3Al(s) + 3NH_4ClO_4(s)$$
$$\rightarrow Al_2O_3(s) + AlCl_3(s) + 3NO(g) + 6H_2O(g)$$

Calculate ΔH° for this reaction.

50. The space shuttle orbiter utilizes the oxidation of methyl hydrazine by dinitrogen tetroxide for propulsion:

$$5N_2O_4(l) + 4N_2H_3CH_3(l)$$
$$\rightarrow 12H_2O(g) + 9N_2(g) + 4CO_2(g)$$

Calculate ΔH° for this reaction.

---

51. Water gas is produced from the reaction of steam with coal:

$$C(s) + H_2O(g) \rightarrow H_2(g) + CO(g)$$

Assuming that coal is pure graphite, calculate $\Delta H°$ for this reaction.

52. Titanium(IV) oxide, one of the most commonly used white paint pigments, is produced by the reaction

$$TiCl_4(g) + 2H_2O(g) \rightarrow TiO_2(s) + 4HCl(g)$$

Calculate $\Delta H°$ for this reaction.

53. Consider the reaction

$$2ClF_3(g) + 2NH_3(g) \rightarrow N_2(g) + 6HF(g) + Cl_2(g)$$
$$\Delta H° = -1196 \text{ kJ}$$

Calculate $\Delta H_f°$ for $ClF_3(g)$.

54. The enthalpy of combustion of ethene gas, $C_2H_4(g)$, is -1411.1 kJ/mol at 298 K. Given the following enthalpies of formation, calculate $\Delta H_f°$ for $C_2H_4(g)$.

$CO_2(g)$	-393.5 kJ/mol
$H_2O(l)$	-285.9 kJ/mol

Energy Consumption and Sources

---

55. Assume that 4.19×10^6 kJ of energy is needed to heat a swimming pool. If this energy is derived from the combustion of methane (CH_4), what volume of methane, measured at STP, must be burned? ($\Delta H°_{\text{combustion}}$ for $CH_4 = -891$ kJ/mol)

56. Ethanol (C_2H_5OH) has been proposed as an alternative fuel. Calculate the enthalpy of combustion per gram of ethanol.

57. Syngas can be burned directly or converted to methanol. Calculate $\Delta H°$ for the reaction

$$CO(g) + 2H_2(g) \rightarrow CH_3OH(l)$$

58. Some automobiles and buses have been equipped to burn propane (C_3H_8). Compare the amounts of energy that can be obtained per gram of $C_3H_8(g)$ and per gram of gasoline, assuming that gasoline is pure octane, $C_8H_{18}(l)$. (See Sample Exercise 6.11.) Look up the boiling point of propane. What disadvantages are there to using propane instead of gasoline as a fuel?

Additional Exercises

---

59. Consider the following reaction:

$$CH_4(g) + 2O_2(g) \rightarrow CO_2(g) + 2H_2O(l)$$
$$\Delta H° = -891 \text{ kJ}$$

Calculate the enthalpy change for each of the following cases:
a. 1.00 g methane is burned in excess oxygen.
b. 1.00×10^3 L methane gas at 740. torr and 25°C is burned in excess oxygen.

60. The reaction vessel of a certain bomb calorimeter, which has a volume of 50.0 mL, is charged with oxygen to a pressure of 125 atm at 22°C. Calculate the maximum mass of benzoic acid ($C_7H_6O_2$) that can be burned in this calorimeter assuming that we want 25 times as much oxygen in the bomb as will be needed for the reaction.

61. High-quality hi-fi power amplifiers generate large amounts of heat. To dissipate the heat and prevent damage to the electronic components, heat-radiating metal fins are used. Would it be better to make these fins out of iron or aluminum? Why? (See Table 6.1 for specific heat capacities.)

62. The combustion of 0.1584 g benzoic acid increases the temperature of a bomb calorimeter by 2.54°C. Calculate the heat capacity of this calorimeter. (The energy released by combustion of benzoic acid is 26.42 kJ/g.) A 0.2130-g sample of vanillin ($C_8H_8O_3$) is then burned in the same calorimeter, and the temperature increases by 3.25°C. What is the energy of combustion per gram of vanillin? Per mole of vanillin?

63. A swimming pool, 10.0 m by 4.0 m, is filled with water to a depth of 3.0 m at a temperature of 20.2°C. How much energy is required to raise the temperature of the water to 30.0°C?

64. In a bomb calorimeter, the reaction vessel is surrounded by water that must be added for each experiment. Since the amount of water is not constant from experiment to experiment, the mass of water must be measured in each case. The heat capacity of the calorimeter is broken down into two parts: the water and the calorimeter components. If a calorimeter contains 1.00 kg water and has a total heat capacity of 10.84 kJ/°C, what is the heat capacity of the calorimeter components?

65. Calculate $\Delta H°$ for the reaction

$$2K(s) + 2H_2O(l) \rightarrow 2KOH(aq) + H_2(g)$$

A 5.00-g chunk of potassium is dropped into 1.00 L water at 24.0°C. What is the final temperature of the water after the preceding reaction occurs? Assume that all the heat is used to raise the temperature of the water. (Never run this reaction. It is very dangerous; it bursts into flame!)

66. Hydrazine (N_2H_4) is used as a fuel in liquid-fueled rockets. Either oxygen [assume $O_2(g)$ for this problem] or dinitrogen tetroxide [$N_2O_4(l)$] can be used as the oxidizing agent. In both cases the products are nitrogen gas and gaseous water. Write balanced equations for the two reactions, and calculate $\Delta H°$ using standard enthalpies of formation. Compare these values to the result in Exercises 49 and 50. Which of the four combinations (per kilogram of the stoichiometric reactant mixture) is the most efficient rocket fuel?

67. The combustion reaction in an oxyacetylene torch is

$$C_2H_2(g) + \tfrac{5}{2}O_2(g) \rightarrow 2CO_2(g) + H_2O(g)$$

Calculate $\Delta H°$ for this reaction. Assume that all the heat generated by this reaction is used to raise the temperature of the carbon dioxide and water present in the flame. What is the maximum temperature of the flame of an oxyacetylene torch? At constant pressure, the molar heat capacities of carbon dioxide gas and water vapor are 37.1 J/°C · mol and 33.6 J/°C · mol, respectively. Assume an initial temperature of 25.0°C.

68. Consider the following changes:
    a. $H_2O(g) \rightarrow H_2O(l)$
    b. $H_2(g) + Cl_2(g) \rightarrow 2HCl(g)$
    c. $2H_2(g) + O_2(g) \rightarrow 2H_2O(g)$
    d. $Xe(g) + F_2(g) \rightarrow XeF_2(s)$
    e. $NiCl_2 \cdot 6H_2O(s) \rightarrow NiCl_2(s) + 6H_2O(g)$
    f. $CO_2(s) \rightarrow CO_2(g)$

    At constant pressure, in which of these changes is work done by the system on the surroundings? By the surroundings on the system? In which of them is no work done?

69. Assume that all the heat in Sample Exercise 6.3 comes from the combustion of propane (C_3H_8). What mass of propane must be burned to furnish this amount of energy?

70. The standard enthalpy of combustion of solid carbon to form carbon dioxide is -393.7 kJ/mol carbon, and the standard enthalpy of combustion of carbon monoxide to form carbon dioxide is -283.3 kJ/mol CO. Use these data to calculate $\Delta H°$ for the reaction

$$2C(s) + O_2(g) \rightarrow 2CO(g)$$

71. Calculate $\Delta H°$ for each of the following reactions, which occur in the atmosphere:
    a. $C_2H_4(g) + O_3(g) \rightarrow CH_3CHO(g) + O_2(g)$
    b. $O_3(g) + NO(g) \rightarrow NO_2(g) + O_2(g)$

c. $SO_3(g) + H_2O(l) \rightarrow H_2SO_4(aq)$
d. $2NO(g) + O_2(g) \rightarrow 2NO_2(g)$

Challenge Problems

72. Consider a gas at an initial pressure of 5.0 atm and an initial volume of 1.0 L that undergoes a change to 2.0 atm and 4.0 L by two different pathways:

Pathway 1

$$\begin{array}{c} P_i = 5.0 \text{ atm} \\ V_i = 1.0 \text{ L} \end{array} \rightarrow \begin{array}{c} P_i = 5.0 \text{ atm} \\ V_f = 4.0 \text{ L} \end{array} \rightarrow \begin{array}{c} P_f = 2.0 \text{ atm} \\ V_f = 4.0 \text{ L} \end{array}$$

Pathway 2

$$\begin{array}{c} P_i = 5.0 \text{ atm} \\ V_i = 1.0 \text{ L} \end{array} \rightarrow \begin{array}{c} P_f = 2.0 \text{ atm} \\ V_i = 1.0 \text{ L} \end{array} \rightarrow \begin{array}{c} P_f = 2.0 \text{ atm} \\ V_f = 4.0 \text{ L} \end{array}$$

These pathways are summarized on the following graph of P versus V:

Calculate the work associated with the two pathways. Is work a state function? Explain.

73. The reaction

$$SO_3(g) + H_2O(l) \rightarrow H_2SO_4(aq)$$

is the last step in the commercial production of sulfuric acid. The enthalpy change for this reaction is -266 kJ. In designing a sulfuric acid plant, is it necessary to provide for heating or cooling the reaction mixture? Explain.

74. A lead bullet with mass 7.8 g and velocity 5.0×10^4 cm/s strikes a 1.00-kg wooden block and becomes embedded in the wood. If both the bullet and the block are initially at 25.0°C, what is the final temperature? Assume that no heat loss occurs to the surroundings and that all the kinetic energy of the bullet is converted to heat. Specific heat capacities: wood, 2.1 J/°C · g; lead, 0.13 J/°C · g.

75. Given the following data:

$$Fe_2O_3(s) + 3CO(g) \rightarrow 2Fe(s) + 3CO_2(g)$$
$$\Delta H° = -23 \text{ kJ}$$

$$3Fe_2O_3(s) + CO(g) \rightarrow 2Fe_3O_4(s) + CO_2(g)$$
$$\Delta H° = -39 \text{ kJ}$$

$$Fe_3O_4(s) + CO(g) \rightarrow 3FeO(s) + CO_2(g)$$
$$\Delta H° = +18 \text{ kJ}$$

calculate $\Delta H°$ for the reaction

$$FeO(s) + CO(g) \rightarrow Fe(s) + CO_2(g)$$

76. On Easter Sunday, April 3, 1983, nitric acid spilled from a tank car near downtown Denver, Colorado. The spill was neutralized with sodium carbonate:

$$2HNO_3(aq) + Na_2CO_3(s)$$
$$\rightarrow 2NaNO_3(aq) + H_2O(l) + CO_2(g)$$

a. Calculate $\Delta H°$ for this reaction. Approximately 2.0×10^4 gal nitric acid was spilled. Assume that the acid was an aqueous solution containing 70.0% HNO_3 by mass with a density of 1.42 g/cm^3. How much sodium carbonate was required for complete neutralization of the spill, and how much heat was evolved? [$\Delta H_f°$ for $NaNO_3(aq) = -467$ kJ/mol.]

b. According to *The Denver Post* for April 4, 1983, authorities feared that dangerous air pollution might occur during the neutralization. Considering the magnitude of $\Delta H°$, what was their major concern?

77. A piece of chocolate cake contains about 400 Calories. A nutritional Calorie is equal to one thousand calories (thermochemical calories), which is equal to 4.184 kJ. How many 8-in-high steps must a 180-lb man climb to expend the 400 Cal from the piece of cake? See Exercise 10 for the formula for potential energy.

Marathon Problem*

78. A sample consisting of 22.7 g of a nongaseous, unstable compound X is placed inside a metal cylinder with a radius of 8.0 cm, and a piston is carefully placed on the surface of the compound so that, for all practical purposes, the distance between the bottom of the cylinder and the piston is zero. (A hole in the piston allows trapped air to escape as the piston is placed on the compound; then this hole is plugged so that nothing inside the cylinder can escape.) The piston-and-cylinder apparatus is carefully placed in 10.00 L of water at 25.00°C. The barometric pressure is 778 torr.

When the compound spontaneously decomposes, the piston moves up, the temperature of the water reaches a maximum of 29.52°C, and then it gradually decreases as the water loses heat to the surrounding air. The distance between the piston and the bottom of the cylinder, at the maximum temperature, is 59.8 cm. Chemical analysis shows that the cylinder contains 0.30 mol carbon dioxide, 0.25 mol liquid water, 0.025 mol oxygen gas, and an undetermined amount of a gaseous element A.

It is known that the enthalpy change for the decomposition of X, according to the reaction described above, is -1893 kJ/mol X. The standard enthalpies of formation for gaseous carbon dioxide and liquid water are -393.5 kJ/mol and -286 kJ/mol, respectively. The heat capacity for water is 4.184 J/°C · g. The conversion factor between L · atm and J can be determined from the two values for the gas constant R, namely, 0.08206 L · atm/mol · K and 8.3145 J/mol · K. The vapor pressure of water at 29.5°C is 31 torr. Assume that the heat capacity of the piston-and-cylinder apparatus is negligible and that the piston has negligible mass.

Given the preceding information, determine

1. The formula for X.

2. The pressure–volume work (in kJ) for the decomposition of the 22.7-g sample of X.

3. The *molar* change in internal energy for the decomposition of X and the approximate standard enthalpy of formation for X.

*This Marathon Problem was developed by James H. Burness of Penn State University, York Campus.

CHAPTER 7

Atomic Structure and Periodicity

In the past 200 years, a great deal of experimental evidence has accumulated to support the atomic model. This theory has proved to be both extremely useful and physically reasonable. When atoms were first suggested by the Greek philosophers Democritus and Leucippus about 400 B.C., the concept was based mostly on intuition. In fact, for the following 20 centuries, no convincing experimental evidence was available to support the existence of atoms. The first real scientific data were gathered by Lavoisier and others from quantitative measurements of chemical reactions. The results of these stoichiometric experiments led John Dalton to propose the first systematic atomic theory. Dalton's theory, although crude, has stood the test of time extremely well.

Once we came to "believe in" atoms, it was logical to ask: What is the nature of an atom? Does an atom have parts, and if so, what are they? In Chapter 2 we considered some of the experiments most important for shedding light on the nature of the atom. Now we will see how the atomic theory has evolved to its present state.

One of the most striking things about the chemistry of the elements is the periodic repetition of properties. There are several groups of elements that show great similarities in chemical behavior. As we saw in Chapter 2, these similarities led to the development of the periodic table of the elements. In this chapter we will see that the modern theory of atomic structure accounts for periodicity in terms of the electron arrangements in atoms.

However, before we examine atomic structure, we must consider the revolution that took place in physics in the first 30 years of the twentieth century. During that time experiments were carried out, the results of which could not be explained by the theories of classical physics developed by Isaac Newton and many others who followed him. A radical new theory

< The computer-enhanced image of the diffraction pattern from a prism.

called **quantum mechanics** was developed to account for the behavior of light and atoms. This "new physics" provides many surprises for humans who are used to the macroscopic world, but it seems to account flawlessly (within the bounds of necessary approximations) for the behavior of matter.

As the first step in our exploration of this revolution in science we will consider the properties of light, more properly called **electromagnetic radiation.**

7.1 Electromagnetic Radiation

Purpose

• To characterize electromagnetic radiation in terms of wavelength, frequency, and speed.

One of the ways that energy travels through space is by **electromagnetic radiation.** The light from the sun, the energy used to cook food in a microwave oven, the X rays used by dentists, and the radiant heat from a fireplace are all examples of electromagnetic radiation. Although these forms of radiant energy seem quite different, they all exhibit the same type of wavelike behavior and travel at the speed of light in a vacuum.

Waves have three primary characteristics: wavelength, frequency, and speed. **Wavelength** (symbolized by the lowercase Greek letter lambda, λ) is the *distance between two consecutive peaks or troughs in a wave,* as shown in Fig. 7.1. The **frequency** (symbolized by the lowercase Greek letter nu, ν) is defined as the *number of waves (cycles) per second that pass a given point in space.* Since all types of

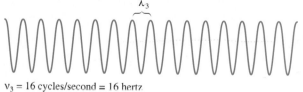

Figure 7.1

The nature of waves. Note that the radiation with the shortest wavelength has the highest frequency.

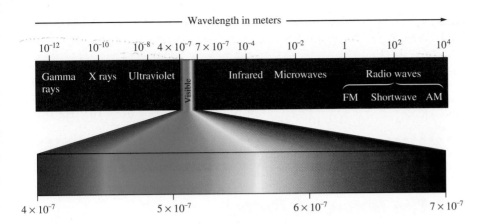

Wavelength in meters

| | | | | | | | | | |

Gamma rays | X rays | Ultraviolet | Visible | Infrared | Microwaves | | Radio waves | | |

FM | Shortwave | AM

4×10^{-7} 5×10^{-7} 6×10^{-7} 7×10^{-7}

Figure 7.2

Classification of electromagnetic radiation. Spectrum adapted by permission from C. W. Keenan, D. C. Kleinfelter, and J. H. Wood, *General College Chemistry*, 6th edition, Harper & Row, Publishers, Inc., 1980.

electromagnetic radiation travel at the speed of light, short-wavelength radiation must have a high frequency. You can see this in Fig. 7.1, where three waves are shown traveling between two points at constant speed. Note that the wave with the shortest wavelength (λ_3) has the highest frequency and the wave with the longest wavelength (λ_1) has the lowest frequency. This implies an inverse relationship between wavelength and frequency, that is, $\lambda \propto 1/\nu$, or

> Wavelength λ and frequency ν are inversely related.

$$\lambda \nu = c$$

where λ is the wavelength in meters, ν is the frequency in cycles per second, and c is the speed of light (2.9979×10^8 m/s). In the SI system, cycles is understood and the unit per second becomes 1/s, or s^{-1}, which is called the **hertz** (abbreviated Hz).

> c = speed of light
> = 2.9979×10^8 m/s

Electromagnetic radiation is classified as shown in Fig. 7.2. Radiation provides an important means of energy transfer. For example, the energy from the sun reaches the earth mainly in the form of visible and ultraviolet radiation, whereas the glowing coals of a fireplace transmit heat energy by infrared radiation. In a microwave oven the water molecules in food absorb microwave radiation, which increases their motions. This energy is then transferred to other types of molecules via collisions, causing an increase in the food's temperature. As we proceed in the study of chemistry, we will consider many of the classes of electromagnetic radiation and the ways in which they affect matter.

Sample Exercise 7.1

The brilliant red colors seen in fireworks are due to the emission of light with wavelengths around 650 nm when strontium salts such as $Sr(NO_3)_2$ and $SrCO_3$ are heated. (This can be easily demonstrated in the lab by dissolving one of these salts in methanol that contains a little water and igniting the mixture in an evaporating dish.) Calculate the frequency of red light of wavelength 6.50×10^2 nm.

Solution

We can convert wavelength to frequency using the equation

$$\lambda \nu = c \quad \text{or} \quad \nu = \frac{c}{\lambda}$$

When a strontium salt is dissolved in methanol (with a little water) and ignited, it gives a brilliant red flame. The red color is produced by emission of light when electrons, excited by the energy of the burning methanol, fall back to their ground states.

where $c = 2.9979 \times 10^8$ m/s. In this case $\lambda = 6.50 \times 10^2$ nm. Changing the wavelength to meters, we have

$$6.50 \times 10^2 \text{ nm} \times \frac{1 \text{ m}}{10^9 \text{ nm}} = 6.50 \times 10^{-7} \text{ m}$$

and

$$\nu = \frac{c}{\lambda} = \frac{2.9979 \times 10^8 \text{ m/s}}{6.50 \times 10^{-7} \text{ m}} = 4.61 \times 10^{14} \text{ s}^{-1} = 4.61 \times 10^{14} \text{ Hz}$$

When alternating current at 110 volts is applied to a dill pickle, a glowing discharge occurs. The current flowing between the electrodes (forks), which is supported by the Na^+ and Cl^- ions present, apparently causes some sodium atoms to form in an excited state. When these atoms relax to the ground state, they emit visible light at 589 nm, producing the yellow glow reminiscent of sodium vapor lamps.

7.2 The Nature of Matter

Purpose

- To introduce the concept of quantized energy.
- To show that light has both wave and particulate properties.
- To describe how diffraction experiments were used to demonstrate the dual nature of all matter.

It is probably fair to say that at the end of the nineteenth century physicists were feeling rather smug. Available theories could explain phenomena as diverse as the motions of the planets and the dispersion of visible light by a prism. Rumor has it that students were being discouraged from pursuing physics as a career because it was felt that all the major problems had been solved, or at least described in terms of the current physical theories.

At the end of the nineteenth century, the idea prevailed that matter and energy were distinct. Matter was thought to consist of particles, whereas energy in the form of light (electromagnetic radiation) was described as a wave. Particles were things that had mass and whose position in space could be specified. Waves were described as massless and delocalized; that is, their position in space could not be specified. It also was assumed that there was no intermingling of matter and light. Everything known before 1900 seemed to fit neatly into this view.

At the beginning of the twentieth century, however, certain experimental results suggested that this picture was incorrect. The first important advance came in 1900 from the German physicist Max Planck (1858–1947). Studying the radiation profiles emitted by solid bodies heated to incandescence, Planck found that the results could not be explained in terms of the physics of his day, which held that matter could absorb or emit any quantity of energy. Planck could only account for these observations by postulating that *energy can be gained or lost only in whole-number multiples* of the quantity $h\nu$, where h is a constant called **Planck's constant,** determined by experiment to have the value 6.626×10^{-34} J · s. That is, the change in energy for a system ΔE can be represented by the equation

Energy can be gained or lost only in integer multiples of $h\nu$.

$$\Delta E = nh\nu$$

Planck's constant = 6.626×10^{-34} J · s.

where n is an integer (1, 2, 3, . . .), h is Planck's constant, and ν is the frequency of the electromagnetic radiation absorbed or emitted.

Planck's result was a real surprise. It had always been assumed that the energy of matter was continuous, which meant that the transfer of any quantity of energy was

◀ **C H E M I C A L I M P A C T** ▶

Solar Polar Bears

The polar bear, a regal beast that has dominated the world's arctic regions for thousands of years, can exist in its incredibly hostile environment partly because its fur is an almost perfect absorber and converter of solar energy.

What color is a polar bear's fur? White, the obvious answer, is incorrect. The hairs on a polar bear are completely colorless and transparent. The bear appears white because of the way the rough inner surfaces of the hollow hairs reflect visible light. The most interesting characteristic of each of these hollow fibers is its ability to act as a solar converter designed to trap ultraviolet light and transmit it to the bear's black skin. In the summer, the sun directly supplies up to 25% of the bear's total energy requirements. This al-lows the polar bear to be very active in pursuing prey while still building up the layers of blubber needed to survive the winter. This ingenious system also en-sures that although the skin of the polar bear is very warm, the outer layers of the fur remain at about the same temperature as the bear's surroundings. Because of the small temperature difference between its fur and the air, the bear loses very little energy through heat leakage to the envi-ronment.

Human society could benefit greatly from polar bear fur as we continue to search for more efficient energy supplies. Clearly, covering our roofs with polar bear pelts is not a viable alternative, but polar bear hair provides an excellent model for possible synthetic optical fibers

A polar bear on Hudson Bay, Canada.

to convert the sun's energy to other en-ergy forms.

possible. Now it seemed clear that energy is in fact **quantized** and can only occur in discrete units of size $h\nu$. Each of these small "packets" of energy is called a **quantum.** A system can transfer energy only in whole *quanta*. Thus energy seems to have particulate properties.

Sample Exercise 7.2

The blue color in fireworks is often achieved by heating copper(I) chloride (CuCl) to about 1200°C. Then the compound emits blue light having a wavelength of 450 nm. What is the increment of energy (the quantum) that is emitted at 4.50×10^2 nm by CuCl?

Solution

The quantum of energy can be calculated from the equation

$$\Delta E = h\nu$$

The frequency ν for this case can be calculated as follows:

$$\nu = \frac{c}{\lambda} = \frac{2.9979 \times 10^8 \text{ m/s}}{4.50 \times 10^{-7} \text{ m}} = 6.66 \times 10^{14} \text{ s}^{-1}$$

So $\Delta E = h\nu = (6.626 \times 10^{-34} \text{ J} \cdot \text{s})(6.66 \times 10^{14} \text{ s}^{-1}) = 4.41 \times 10^{-19} \text{ J}$

A sample of CuCl emitting light at 450 nm can only lose energy in increments of 4.41×10^{-19} J, the size of the quantum in this case.

The next important development in the knowledge of atomic structure came when Albert Einstein (see Fig. 7.3) proposed that electromagnetic radiation is itself quantized. Einstein suggested that electromagnetic radiation can be viewed as a stream of "particles" called **photons.** The energy of each photon is given by the expression

$$E_{\text{photon}} = h\nu = \frac{hc}{\lambda}$$

where h is Planck's constant, ν is the frequency of the radiation, and λ is the wavelength of the radiation.

In a related development, Einstein derived the famous equation

$$E = mc^2$$

in his **special theory of relativity** published in 1905. The main significance of this equation is that *energy has mass*. This is more apparent if we rearrange the equation to the following form:

$$m = \frac{E}{c^2}$$

Mass $\uparrow$ Energy $\leftarrow$ Speed of light

Using this form of the equation, we can calculate the mass associated with a given quantity of energy. For example, we can calculate the apparent mass of a photon. For electromagnetic radiation of wavelength λ, the energy of each photon is given by the expression

$$E_{\text{photon}} = \frac{hc}{\lambda}$$

Then the apparent mass of a photon of light with wavelength λ is given by

$$m = \frac{E}{c^2} = \frac{hc/\lambda}{c^2} = \frac{h}{\lambda c}$$

Note that the mass of a photon depends on its wavelength. The mass of a photon at rest is thought to be zero, although we never observe it at rest.

Figure 7.3

Albert Einstein (1879–1955) was born in Germany. Nothing in his early development suggested genius; even at the age of 9 he did not speak clearly, and his parents feared that he might be handicapped. When asked what profession Einstein should follow, his school principal replied, "It doesn't matter; he'll never make a success of anything." When he was 10, Einstein entered the Luitpold Gymnasium (high school), which was typical of German schools of that time in being harshly disciplinarian. There he developed a deep suspicion of authority and a scepticism that encouraged him to question and doubt—valuable qualities in a scientist. In 1905, while a patent clerk in Switzerland, Einstein published a paper explaining the photoelectric effect via the quantum theory. For this revolutionary thinking he received a Nobel Prize in 1921. Highly regarded by this time, he worked in Germany until 1933, when Hitler's persecution of the Jews forced him to come to the United States. He worked at the Institute for Advanced Studies at Princeton University until his death in 1955.

Einstein was undoubtedly the greatest physicist of our age. Even if someone else had derived the theory of relativity, his other work would have ensured his ranking as the second greatest physicist of his time. Our concepts of space and time were radically changed by ideas he first proposed when he was 26 years old. From then until the end of his life, he attempted unsuccessfully to find a single unifying theory that would explain all physical events.

Does a <u>photon really have mass</u>? The answer *appears to be yes*. In 1922 American physicist Arthur Compton (1892–1962) performed experiments involving collisions of X rays and electrons that showed that photons do exhibit the apparent mass calculated from the preceding equation.

We can summarize the important conclusions from the work of Planck and Einstein as follows:

Energy is quantized. It can occur only in discrete units called quanta.

Electromagnetic radiation, which was previously thought to exhibit only wave properties, seems to show certain characteristics of particulate matter as well. This phenomenon is sometimes referred to as the **dual nature of light** and is illustrated in Fig. 7.4.

Thus light, which was previously thought to be purely wavelike, was found to have certain characteristics of particulate matter. But is the opposite also true? That is, does matter that is normally assumed to be particulate exhibit wave properties? This question was raised in 1923 by a young French physicist named Louis de Broglie (1892–1987). To see how de Broglie supplied the answer to this question, recall that the relationship between mass and wavelength for electromagnetic radiation is $m = h/\lambda c$. For a particle with velocity v, the corresponding expression is

$$m = \frac{h}{\lambda v}$$

Rearranging to solve for λ, we have

$$\lambda = \frac{h}{mv}$$

This equation, called **de Broglie's equation,** allows us to calculate the wavelength for a particle, as shown in Sample Exercise 7.3.

Light as a wave phenomenon

Light as a stream of photons

Figure 7.4

Electromagnetic radiation exhibits wave properties and particulate properties. The energy of each photon of the radiation is related to the wavelength and frequency by the equation $E_{photon} = h\nu = hc/\lambda$.

Do not confuse ν (frequency) with v (velocity).

Sample Exercise 7.3

Compare the wavelength for an electron (mass $= 9.11 \times 10^{-31}$ kg) traveling at a speed of 1.0×10^7 m/s with that for a ball (mass $= 0.10$ kg) traveling at 35 m/s.

Solution

We use the equation $\lambda = h/mv$, where

$$h = 6.626 \times 10^{-34} \text{ J} \cdot \text{s} \quad \text{or} \quad 6.626 \times 10^{-34} \text{ kg} \cdot \text{m}^2/\text{s}$$

since

$$1 \text{ J} = 1 \text{ kg} \cdot \text{m}^2/\text{s}^2$$

For the electron,

$$\lambda_e = \frac{6.626 \times 10^{-34} \frac{\text{kg} \cdot \text{m} \cdot \text{m}}{\text{s}}}{(9.11 \times 10^{-31} \text{ kg})(1.0 \times 10^7 \text{ m/s})} = 7.27 \times 10^{-11} \text{ m}$$

For the ball,

$$\lambda_b = \frac{6.626 \times 10^{-34}\frac{kg \cdot m \cdot m}{s}}{(0.10 \, kg)(35 \, m/s)} = 1.9 \times 10^{-34} \text{ m}$$

Notice from Sample Exercise 7.3 that the wavelength associated with the ball is incredibly short. On the other hand, the wavelength of the electron, although still quite small, happens to be on the same order as the spacing between the atoms in a typical crystal. This is important because, as we will see presently, it provides a means for testing de Broglie's equation.

Diffraction results when light is scattered from a regular array of points or lines. The diffraction of light from the ridges and grooves of a compact disc is shown in the photograph. The colors result because the various wavelengths of visible light are not all scattered in the same way. The colors are "separated," giving the same effect as light passing through a prism. Just as a regular arrnagement of ridges and grooves produces diffraction, so does a regular array of atoms or ions in a crystal. For example, when X rays are directed onto a crystal of sodium chloride, with its regular array of Na^+ and Cl^- ions, the scattered radiation produces a **diffraction pattern** of bright spots and dark areas on a photographic plate, as shown in Fig. 7.5(a). This occurs because the scattered light can interfere constructively (the peaks and troughs of the beams are in phase) to produce a bright spot [Fig. 7.5(b)] or destructively (the peaks and troughs are out of phase) to produce a dark area [Fig. 7.5(c)].

A diffraction pattern can only be explained in terms of waves. Thus this phenomenon provides a test for the postulate that particles such as electrons have wavelengths. As we saw in Sample Exercise 7.3, an electron with a velocity of 10^7 m/s (easily achieved by acceleration of the electron in an electric field) has a wavelength of about 10^{-10} m, which is roughly the distance between the ions in a crystal such as sodium chloride. This is important because diffraction occurs most efficiently when the spacing between the scattering points is about the same as the wavelength of the wave being diffracted. Thus, if electrons really do have an associated wavelength, a crystal should diffract electrons. An experiment to test this idea was carried out in 1927 by C. J. Davisson and L. H. Germer at the Bell Laboratories. When they directed a beam of electrons at a nickel crystal, they observed a diffraction pattern similar to that seen from the diffraction of X rays. This result verified de Broglie's relationship, at least for electrons. Larger chunks of matter, such as balls, have such small wavelengths (see Sample Exercise 7.3) that they are impossible to verify experimentally. However, we believe that all matter obeys de Broglie's equation.

Now we have come full circle. Electromagnetic radiation, which at the turn of the twentieth century was thought to be a pure wave form, was found to possess particulate properties. Conversely, electrons, which were thought to be particles, were found to have a wavelength associated with them. The significance of these results is that matter and energy are not distinct. Energy is really a form of matter, and all matter shows the same types of properties. That is, *all matter exhibits both particulate and wave properties.* Large pieces of matter, such as baseballs, exhibit

(top) Light diffracted by the closely-spaced grooves on a compact disc shows the visible spectrum. (bottom) Prismatic diffraction.

predominantly particulate properties. The associated wavelength is so small that it is not observed. Very small bits of matter, such as photons, while showing some particulate properties, exhibit predominantly wave properties. Pieces of matter with intermediate mass, such as electrons, show clearly both the particulate and wave properties of matter.

7.3 *The Atomic Spectrum of Hydrogen*

Purpose

- To show that the line spectrum of hydrogen demonstrates the quantized nature of the energy of its electron.

As we saw in Chapter 2, key information about the atom came from several experiments carried out in the early twentieth century, in particular Thomson's discovery of the electron and Rutherford's discovery of the nucleus. Another important experiment was the study of the emission of light by excited hydrogen atoms. When a sample of hydrogen gas receives a high-energy spark, the H_2 molecules absorb energy, and some of the H—H bonds are broken. The resulting hydrogen atoms are *excited*; that is, they contain excess energy, which they release by emitting light of various wavelengths to produce what is called the *emission spectrum* of the hydrogen atom.

To understand the significance of the hydrogen emission spectrum, we must first describe the **continuous spectrum** that results when white light is passed through a prism, as shown in Fig. 7.6(a) on p. 288. This spectrum, like the rainbow produced when sunlight is dispersed by raindrops, contains *all* the wavelengths of visible light. In contrast, when the hydrogen emission spectrum in the visible region is passed through a prism, as shown in Fig. 7.6(b), we see only a few lines, each of which corresponds to a discrete wavelength. The hydrogen emission spectrum is called a **line spectrum.**

What is the significance of the line spectrum of hydrogen? It indicates that *only certain energies are allowed for the electron in the hydrogen atom.* In other words, the energy of the electron in the hydrogen atom is *quantized*. This observation ties in perfectly with the postulates of Max Planck discussed in Section 7.2. Changes in energy between discrete energy levels in hydrogen will produce only certain wavelengths of emitted light, as shown in Fig. 7.7 on p. 288. For example, a given change in energy from a high to a lower level would give a wavelength of light that can be calculated from Planck's equation:

$$\Delta E = h\nu = \frac{hc}{\lambda}$$

Change in energy

Frequency of light emitted

Wavelength of light emitted

The discrete line spectrum of hydrogen shows that only certain energies are possible; that is, the electron energy levels are quantized. In contrast, if any energy level were allowed, the emission spectrum would be continuous.

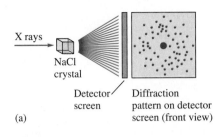

(a)

Detector screen / Diffraction pattern on detector screen (front view)

Constructive interference

Waves in phase (peaks on one wave match peaks on the other wave)

Increased intensity (bright spot)

(b)

Destructive interference

Trough

Peak

Waves out of phase (troughs and peaks coincide)

Decreased intensity (dark spot)

(c)

Figure 7.5

(a) Diffraction occurs when electromagnetic radiation is scattered from a regular array of objects, such as the ions in a crystal of sodium chloride. The large spot in the center is from the main incident beam of X rays. (b) Bright spots in the diffraction pattern result from *constructive interference* of waves. The waves are in phase; that is, their peaks match. (c) Dark areas result from *destructive interference* of waves. The waves are out of phase; the peaks of one wave coincide with the troughs of another wave.

The energy of the electron in the hydrogen atom is quantized.

A rainbow over Vail, Colorado.

Figure 7.6

(a) A continuous spectrum containing all wavelengths of visible light (indicated by the initial letters of the colors of the rainbow). (b) The hydrogen line spectrum contains only a few discrete wavelengths. Spectrum adapted by permission from C. W. Keenan, D. C. Kleinfelter, and J. H. Wood, *General College Chemistry*, 6th edition, Harper & Row, Publishers, Inc., 1980.

(a)

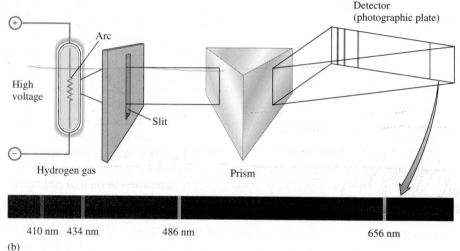

(b)

410 nm   434 nm   486 nm   656 nm

Various energy levels
in the hydrogen atom

Figure 7.7

A change between two discrete energy levels emits a photon of light.

7.4 The Bohr Model

Purpose

• To describe the development of the Bohr model for the hydrogen atom.

In 1913, a Danish physicist named Niels Bohr (1885–1962), aware of the experimental results we have just discussed, developed a **quantum model** for the hydrogen atom. Bohr proposed that the *electron in a hydrogen atom moves around the nucleus only in certain allowed circular orbits*. He calculated the radii for these allowed orbits by using the theories of classical physics and by making some new assumptions.

From classical physics Bohr knew that a particle in motion tends to move in a straight line and can be made to travel in a circle only by application of a force toward the center of the circle. Thus Bohr reasoned that the tendency of the revolv-

◀ **C H E M I C A L   I M P A C T** ▶

Spectra and Space

Every element has a characteristic signature: its unique line spectrum produced by the movement of electrons between quantized energy levels. (The spectrum of hydrogen is shown in Fig. 7.6.) The characteristic spectrum of an element is a sure way to verify its presence (or absence) in a given sample. Spectra are particularly useful for the analyses of extraterrestrial material, since collecting actual samples is so difficult. Although we have directly analyzed rocks from the moon and Mars (at great expense), most of our information about the materials in space comes from the light emitted or absorbed by these materials. For example, we have obtained a detailed knowledge of the composition of the sun and other stars by looking for the characteristic spectral lines of the elements in the light emitted by these sources.

Molecules also have characteristic spectral lines that can be used to identify them. The first spectroscopic observations of a comet were carried out by Giovanni Donati in 1864 when he identified species

An infrared thermogram of the space shuttle Columbia.

such as C_2, $(CN)_2$, C_3, and CH in the Comet Tempel. Since then, using increasingly sensitive instruments, scientists have found more than 60 different molecules in space, including ethanol (C_2H_5OH), carbon monoxide, hydrogen cyanide (HCN), methyl cyanide (CH_3CN), and water.

Electromagnetic radiation is also useful to space scientists in other ways. For example, the microwave radiation that is left over from the postulated "big bang" has yielded an age for the universe of between 15 and 25 billion years. Infrared radiation is especially useful for determining the temperature of space objects. The accompanying photograph is an infrared picture of the shuttle Orbiter Columbia as it returned to earth in 1982, in which the hottest areas appear red and the coolest areas appear violet.

Suggested Reading

P. B. Kelter, W. E. Snyder, and C. S. Buchar, "Using NASA and the Space Program to Help High School and College Students Learn Chemistry," Part II: "The Current State of Chemistry at NASA," *J. Chem. Ed.* **64** (1987): p. 228.

---

ing electron to fly off the atom must be just balanced by its attraction for the positively charged nucleus. But classical physics also decreed that a charged particle under acceleration should radiate energy. Since an electron revolving around the nucleus constantly changes its direction, it is constantly accelerating. Therefore, the electron should emit light and lose energy—and thus be drawn into the nucleus. This, of course, does not correlate with the existence of stable atoms.

Clearly, an atomic model based solely on the theories of classical physics was untenable. Bohr also knew that the correct model had to account for the experimental spectrum of hydrogen, which showed that only certain electron energies were allowed. The experimental data were absolutely clear on this point. Bohr found that his model would fit the experimental results if he assumed that the angular momentum of the electron (angular momentum equals the product of mass, velocity, and orbital radius) could only occur in certain increments. It was not clear why this should be true, but with this assumption, Bohr's model gave hydrogen atom energy levels consistent with the hydrogen emission spectrum. The model is represented pictorially in Fig. 7.8.

Although we will not show the derivation here, the most important equation to come from Bohr's model is the expression for the *energy levels available to the*

Niels Bohr at 37 years of age, photographed in 1922 when he received the Nobel Prize for Physics.

electron in the hydrogen atom:

The J in Equation (7.1) stands for joules.

$$E = -2.178 \times 10^{-18} \text{ J}\left(\frac{Z^2}{n^2}\right) \tag{7.1}$$

in which n is an integer (the larger the value of n, the larger is the orbit radius) and Z is the nuclear charge. Using Equation (7.1), Bohr was able to calculate hydrogen atom energy levels that exactly matched the values obtained by experiment.

The negative sign in Equation (7.1) simply means that the energy of the electron bound to the nucleus is lower than it would be if the electron were at an infinite distance ($n = \infty$) from the nucleus, where there is no interaction and the energy is zero:

$$E = -2.178 \times 10^{-18} \text{ J}\left(\frac{Z^2}{\infty}\right) = 0$$

The energy of the electron in any orbit is negative relative to this reference state.

Equation (7.1) can be used to calculate the change in energy of an electron when the electron changes orbits. For example, suppose an electron in level $n = 6$ of an excited hydrogen atom falls back to level $n = 1$ as the hydrogen atom returns to its lowest possible energy state, its **ground state.** We use Equation (7.1) with $Z = 1$, since the hydrogen nucleus contains a single proton. The energies corresponding to the two states are as follows:

For $n = 6$: $E_6 = -2.178 \times 10^{-18} \text{ J}\left(\frac{1^2}{6^2}\right) = -6.05 \times 10^{-20} \text{ J}$

For $n = 1$: $E_1 = -2.178 \times 10^{-18} \text{ J}\left(\frac{1^2}{1^2}\right) = -2.178 \times 10^{-18} \text{ J}$

Note that for $n = 1$ the electron has a more negative energy than it does for $n = 6$, which means that the electron is more tightly bound in the smallest allowed orbit. The change in energy ΔE when the electron falls from $n = 6$ to $n = 1$ is

$$\Delta E = \text{energy of final state} - \text{energy of initial state}$$
$$= E_1 - E_6 = (-2.178 \times 10^{-18} \text{ J}) - (-6.05 \times 10^{-20} \text{ J})$$
$$= -2.117 \times 10^{-18} \text{ J}$$

The negative sign for the *change* in energy indicates that the atom has *lost* energy and is now in a more stable state. The energy is carried away from the atom by the production (emission) of a photon.

The wavelength of the emitted photon can be calculated from the equation

$$\Delta E = h\left(\frac{c}{\lambda}\right) \quad \text{or} \quad \lambda = \frac{hc}{\Delta E}$$

where ΔE represents the change in energy of the atom, which equals the energy of the emitted photon. We have

$$\lambda = \frac{hc}{\Delta E} = \frac{(6.626 \times 10^{-34} \text{ J}\cdot\text{s})(2.9979 \times 10^8 \text{ m/s})}{2.117 \times 10^{-18} \text{ J}} = 9.383 \times 10^{-8} \text{ m}$$

Note that for this calculation the absolute value of ΔE is used (we have not included the negative sign). In this case we indicate the direction of energy flow by saying that a photon of wavelength 9.383×10^{-8} m has been *emitted* from the hydrogen

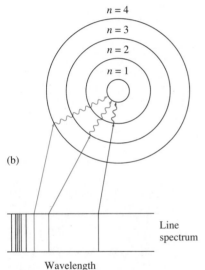

Figure 7.8

Electronic transitions in the Bohr model for the hydrogen atom. (a) An energy-level diagram for electronic transitions. (b) An orbit-transition diagram, which accounts for the experimental spectrum. (Note that the orbits shown are schematic. They are not drawn to scale.) (c) The resulting line spectrum on a photographic plate.

atom. Simply plugging the negative value of ΔE into the equation would produce a negative value for λ, which is physically meaningless.

Sample Exercise 7.4

Calculate the energy required to excite the hydrogen electron from level $n = 1$ to level $n = 2$. Also calculate the wavelength of light that must be absorbed by a hydrogen atom in its ground state to reach this excited state.*

Solution

Using Equation (7.1) with $Z = 1$, we have

$$E_1 = -2.178 \times 10^{-18} \text{ J}\left(\frac{1^2}{1^2}\right) = -2.178 \times 10^{-18} \text{ J}$$

$$E_2 = -2.178 \times 10^{-18} \text{ J}\left(\frac{1^2}{2^2}\right) = -5.445 \times 10^{-19} \text{ J}$$

$$\Delta E = E_2 - E_1 = (-5.445 \times 10^{-19} \text{ J}) - (-2.178 \times 10^{-18} \text{ J}) = 1.633 \times 10^{-18} \text{ J}$$

The positive value for ΔE indicates that the system has gained energy. The wavelength of light that must be *absorbed* to produce this change is

$$\lambda = \frac{hc}{\Delta E} = \frac{(6.626 \times 10^{-34} \text{ J} \cdot \text{s})(2.9979 \times 10^8 \text{ m/s})}{1.633 \times 10^{-18} \text{ J}}$$

$$= 1.216 \times 10^{-7} \text{ m}$$

Note from Fig. 7.2 that the light required to produce the transition from the $n = 1$ to $n = 2$ level in hydrogen lies in the ultraviolet region.

At this time we must emphasize two important points about the Bohr model:

1. The model correctly fits the quantized energy levels of the hydrogen atom and postulates only certain allowed circular orbits for the electron.

2. As the electron becomes more tightly bound, its energy becomes more negative relative to the zero-energy reference state (corresponding to the electron being at infinite distance from the nucleus). As the electron is brought closer to the nucleus, energy is released from the system.

Using Equation (7.1), we can derive a general equation for the electron moving from one level (n_{initial}) to another level (n_{final}):

$$\Delta E = \text{energy of level } n_{\text{final}} - \text{energy of level } n_{\text{initial}}$$

$$= E_{\text{final}} - E_{\text{initial}}$$

$$= (-2.178 \times 10^{-18} \text{ J})\left(\frac{1^2}{n_{\text{final}}^2}\right) - (-2.178 \times 10^{-18} \text{ J})\left(\frac{1^2}{n_{\text{initial}}^2}\right)$$

$$= -2.178 \times 10^{-18} \text{ J}\left(\frac{1}{n_{\text{final}}^2} - \frac{1}{n_{\text{initial}}^2}\right) \tag{7.2}$$

Equation (7.2) can be used to calculate the energy change between *any* two energy levels in a hydrogen atom, as shown in Sample Exercise 7.5.

*After this exercise we will no longer show cancellation marks. However, the same process for canceling units applies throughout this text.

◀ **C H E M I C A L   I M P A C T** ▶

Fireworks

The art of using mixtures of chemicals to produce explosives is an ancient one. Black powder—a mixture of potassium nitrate, charcoal, and sulfur—was being used in China well before 1000 A.D. and has been subsequently used through the centuries in military explosives, in construction blasting, and for fireworks. The du Pont Company, now a major chemical manufacturer, started out as a manufacturer of black powder. In fact, the founder, Eleuthère du Pont, learned the manufacturing technique from none other than Lavoisier.

Before the nineteenth century, fireworks were mainly confined to rockets and loud bangs. Orange and yellow colors came from the presence of charcoal and iron filings. However, with the great advances in chemistry in the nineteenth century, new compounds found their way into fireworks. Salts of copper, strontium, and barium added brilliant colors. Magnesium and aluminum metals gave a dazzling white light. Fireworks, in fact, have changed very little since then.

How do fireworks produce their brilliant colors and loud bangs? Actually, only a handful of different chemicals are responsible for most of the spectacular effects. To produce the noise and flashes, an oxidizer (an oxidizing agent) and a fuel (a reducing agent) are used. A common mixture involves potassium perchlorate ($KClO_4$) as the oxidizer and aluminum and sulfur as the fuel. The perchlorate oxidizes the fuel in a very exothermic reaction, which produces a brilliant flash, due to the aluminum, and a loud report from the rapidly expanding gases produced. For a color effect, an element with a colored emission spectrum is included. Recall that the electrons in atoms can be raised to higher-energy orbitals when the atoms absorb energy. The excited atoms can then release this excess energy by emitting light of specific wavelengths,

A typical aerial shell used in fireworks displays. Time-delayed fuses cause a shell to explode in stages. In this case a red starburst occurs first, followed by a blue starburst, and finally a flash and loud report. From *Chemical & Engineering News*, June 29, 1981, p. 24. Reprinted with permission. Copyright 1981 American Chemical Society.

often in the visible region. In fireworks, the energy to excite the electrons comes from the reaction between the oxidizer and fuel.

Yellow colors in fireworks are due to the 589-nm emission of sodium ions. Red colors come from strontium salts emitting at 606 nm and from 636 to 688 nm. This red color is familiar from highway safety flares. Barium salts give a green color in fireworks, due to a series of emission lines between 505 and 535 nm. A really good blue color, however, is hard to obtain. Copper salts give a blue color, emitting in the 420- to 460-nm region. But difficulties occur because another commonly

used oxidizing agent, potassium chlorate ($KClO_3$), reacts with copper salts to form copper chlorate, a highly explosive compound that is dangerous to store. Paris green, a copper salt containing arsenic, was once used extensively but is now considered to be too toxic.

A typical aerial shell is shown in the diagram. The shell is launched from a mortar (a steel cylinder) using black powder as the propellant. Time-delayed fuses are used to fire the shell in stages. A list of chemicals commonly used in fireworks is given in the table.

Although you might think that the chemistry of fireworks is simple, the

◀ **CHEMICAL IMPACT** ▶

Chemicals Commonly Used in the Manufacture of Fireworks

Oxidizers	Fuels	Special Effects
Potassium nitrate	Aluminum	Red flame: strontium nitrate, strontium carbonate
Potassium chlorate	Magnesium	Green flame: barium nitrate, barium chlorate
Potassium perchlorate	Titanium	Blue flame: copper carbonate, copper sulfate, copper oxide
Ammonium perchlorate	Charcoal	Yellow flame: sodium oxalate, cryolite (Na_3AlF_6)
Barium nitrate	Sulfur	White flame: magnesium, aluminum
Barium chlorate	Antimony sulfide	Gold sparks: iron filings, charcoal
Strontium nitrate	Dextrin	White sparks: aluminum, magnesium, aluminum–magnesium alloy, titanium
	Red gum	Whistle effect: potassium benzoate or sodium salicylate
	Polyvinyl chloride	White smoke: mixture of potassium nitrate and sulfur
		Colored smoke: mixture of potassium chlorate, sulfur, and organic dye

achievement of the vivid white flashes and the brilliant colors requires complex combinations of chemicals. For example, because the white flashes produce high flame temperatures, the colors tend to wash out. Thus oxidizers such as $KClO_4$ are sometimes used with fuels that produce relatively low flame temperatures. An added difficulty, however, is that perchlorates are very sensitive to accidental ignition and are therefore quite hazardous. Another problem arises from the use of sodium salts. Because sodium produces an extremely bright yellow emission, sodium salts cannot be used when other colors are desired. Carbon-based fuels also give a yellow flame that masks other colors, and this limits the use of organic compounds as fuels. You can see that the manufacture of fireworks that produce the desired effects and are also safe to handle requires careful selection of chemicals. And, of course, there is still the dream of a deep blue flame.

A fireworks display over Manhattan.

Sample Exercise 7.5

Calculate the energy required to remove the electron from a hydrogen atom in its ground state.

Solution

Removing the electron from a hydrogen atom in its ground state corresponds to taking the electron from $n_{initial} = 1$ to $n_{final} = \infty$. Thus

$$\Delta E = -2.178 \times 10^{-18} \text{ J} \left(\frac{1}{n_{final}{}^2} - \frac{1}{n_{initial}{}^2} \right)$$

$$= -2.178 \times 10^{-18} \text{ J} \left(\frac{1}{\infty} - \frac{1}{1^2} \right)$$

$$= -2.178 \times 10^{-18} \text{ J}(0 - 1) = 2.178 \times 10^{-18} \text{ J}$$

The energy required to remove the electron from a hydrogen atom in its ground state is 2.178×10^{-18} J.

At first Bohr's model appeared to be very promising. The energy levels calculated by Bohr closely agreed with the values obtained from the hydrogen emission spectrum. However, when Bohr's model was applied to atoms other than hydrogen, it did not work at all. Although some attempts were made to adapt the model using elliptical orbits, it was concluded that Bohr's model is fundamentally incorrect. The model is, however, very important historically, because it showed that the observed quantization of energy in atoms could be explained by making rather simple assumptions. Bohr's model paved the way for later theories. It is important to realize, however, that the current theory of atomic structure is in no way derived from the Bohr model. Electrons do *not* move around the nucleus in circular orbits, as we shall see later in this chapter.

Although Bohr's model fits the energy levels for hydrogen, it is a fundamentally incorrect model for the hydrogen atom.

7.5 The Quantum Mechanical Model of the Atom

Purpose

• To show how standing waves can be used to describe electrons in atoms.
• To describe the Heisenberg uncertainty principle.
• To explain the significance of electron probability distributions.

By the mid-1920s it had become apparent that the Bohr model could not be made to work. A totally new approach was needed. Three physicists were at the forefront of this effort: Werner Heisenberg (1901–1976), Louis de Broglie (1892–1987), and Erwin Schrödinger (1887–1961). The approach they developed became known as **wave mechanics** or, more commonly, **quantum mechanics.** As we have already seen, de Broglie originated the idea that the electron, previously considered to be a particle, also shows wave properties. Pursuing this line of reasoning, Schrödinger, an Austrian physicist, decided to attack the problem of atomic structure by giving emphasis to the wave properties of the electron. To Schrödinger and de Broglie, the electron bound to the nucleus seemed similar to a standing wave, and they began research on a wave mechanical description of the atom.

The most familiar example of standing waves occurs in association with musical instruments such as guitars or violins, where a string attached at both ends vibrates to produce a musical tone. The waves are described as "standing" because they are stationary; the waves do not travel along the length of the string. The motions of the string can be explained as a combination of simple waves of the type shown in Fig. 7.9. The dots in this figure indicate the nodes, or points of zero lateral (sideways) displacement, for a given wave. Note that there are limitations on the allowed wavelengths of the standing wave. Each end of the string is fixed, so there is always a node at each end. This means that there must be a whole number of *half* wavelengths in any of the allowed motions of the string (see Fig. 7.9).

A similar situation results when the electron in the hydrogen atom is imagined to be a standing wave. As shown in Fig. 7.10, only certain circular orbits have a circumference into which a whole number of wavelengths of the standing electron wave will "fit." All other orbits would produce destructive interference of the standing electron wave and are not allowed. This seemed like a possible explanation for the observed quantization of the hydrogen atom, so Schrödinger worked out a model for the hydrogen atom in which the electron was assumed to behave as a standing wave.

It is important to recognize that Schrödinger could not be sure that this idea would work. The test had to be whether or not the model would correctly fit the experimental data on hydrogen and other atoms. The physical principles for describing standing waves were well known in 1925 when Schrödinger decided to treat the electron in this way. His mathematical treatment is too complicated to be detailed here. However, the form of Schrödinger's equation is

$$\hat{H}\psi = E\psi$$

where ψ, called the **wave function,** is a function of the coordinates (x, y, and z) of the electron's position in three-dimensional space and $\hat{H}$ represents a set of mathematical instructions called an **operator.** In this case, the operator contains mathematical terms that produce the total energy of the atom when they are applied to the wave function. E represents the total energy of the atom (the sum of the potential energy due to the attraction between the proton and electron and the kinetic energy of the moving electron). When this equation is analyzed, many solutions are found. Each solution consists of a wave function ψ that is characterized by a particular value of E. A specific wave function is often called an **orbital.**

To illustrate the most important ideas of the quantum (wave) mechanical model of the atom, we will first concentrate on the wave function corresponding to the lowest energy for the hydrogen atom. This wave function is called the $1s$ orbital. The first point of interest is to explore the meaning of the word *orbital.* As we will see, this is not a trivial matter. One thing is clear: an orbital is *not* a Bohr orbit. The electron in the hydrogen $1s$ orbital is not moving around the nucleus in a circular

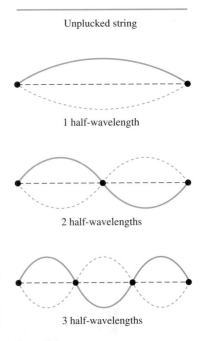

Unplucked string

1 half-wavelength

2 half-wavelengths

3 half-wavelengths

Figure 7.9

The standing waves caused by the vibration of a guitar string fastened at both ends. Each dot represents a node (a point of zero displacement).

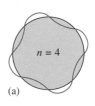

$n = 4$

(a)

$n = 5$

(b)

Mismatch
$n = 4\frac{1}{3}$

(c)

Figure 7.10

The hydrogen electron visualized as a standing wave around the nucleus. The circumference of a particular circular orbit would have to correspond to a whole number of wavelengths, as shown in (a) and (b), or else destructive interference occurs, as shown in (c). This is consistent with the fact that only certain electron energies are allowed; the atom is quantized. (Although this idea encouraged scientists to use a wave theory, it does not mean that the electron really travels in circular orbits.)

orbit. How, then, is the electron moving? The answer is quite surprising: *we do not know*. The wave function gives us no information about the detailed pathway of the electron. This is somewhat disturbing. When we solve problems involving the motions of particles in the macroscopic world, we are able to predict their pathways. For example, when two billiard balls with known velocities collide, we can predict their motions after the collision. However, we cannot predict the electron's motion from the $1s$ orbital function. Does this mean that the theory is wrong? Not necessarily: we have already learned that an electron does not behave much like a billiard ball, so we must examine the situation closely before we discard the theory.

To help us understand the nature of an orbital, we need to consider a principle discovered by Werner Heisenberg, one of the primary developers of quantum mechanics. Heisenberg's mathematical analysis led him to a surprising conclusion: *there is a fundamental limitation to just how precisely we can know both the position and momentum of a particle at a given time*. This is a statement of the **Heisenberg uncertainty principle.** Stated mathematically, the uncertainty principle is

$$\Delta x \cdot \Delta(mv) \geq \frac{h}{4\pi}$$

where Δx is the uncertainty in a particle's position, $\Delta(mv)$ is the uncertainty in a particle's momentum, and h is Planck's constant. Thus the minimum uncertainty in the product $\Delta x \cdot \Delta(mv)$ is $h/4\pi$. What this equation really says is that the more accurately we know a particle's position, the less accurately we can know its momentum, and vice versa. This limitation is so small for large particles such as baseballs or billiard balls that it is unnoticed. However, for a small particle such as the electron, the limitation becomes quite important. Applied to the electron, the uncertainty principle implies that we cannot know the exact motion of the electron as it moves around the nucleus. It is therefore not appropriate to assume that the electron is moving around the nucleus in a well-defined orbit, as in the Bohr model.

The Physical Meaning of a Wave Function

Given the limitations indicated by the uncertainty principle, what then is the physical meaning of a wave function for an electron? That is, what is an atomic orbital? Although the wave function itself has no easily visualized meaning, the square of the function does have a definite physical significance. *The square of the function indicates the probability of finding an electron near a particular point in space.* For example, suppose we have two positions in space, one defined by the coordinates x_1, y_1, and z_1 and the other by the coordinates x_2, y_2, and z_2. The relative probability of finding the electron at positions 1 and 2 is given by substituting the values of x, y, and z for the two positions into the wave function, squaring the function value, and computing the following ratio:

Probability is the likelihood, or odds, that something will occur.

$$\frac{[\psi(x_1, y_1, z_1)]^2}{[\psi(x_2, y_2, z_2)]^2} = \frac{N_1}{N_2}$$

The quotient N_1/N_2 is the ratio of the probabilities of finding the electron at positions 1 and 2. For example, if the value of the ratio N_1/N_2 is 100, the electron is 100 times more likely to be found at position 1 than at position 2. The model gives no information concerning when the electron will be at either position or how it moves between the positions. This vagueness is consistent with the concept of the Heisenberg uncertainty principle.

The square of the wave function is most conveniently represented as a **probability distribution,** in which the intensity of color is used to indicate the probability value near a given point in space. The probability distribution for the hydrogen $1s$ wave function (orbital) is shown in Fig. 7.11(a). The best way to think about this diagram is as a three-dimensional time exposure with the electron as a tiny moving light. The more times the electron visits a particular point, the darker the negative becomes. Thus the darkness of a point indicates the probability of finding an electron at that position. This diagram is also known as an **electron density map;** *electron density* and *electron probability* mean the same thing. When a chemist uses the term *atomic orbital,* he or she is probably picturing an electron density map of this type.

Another way of representing the electron probability distribution for the $1s$ wave function is to calculate the probability at points along a line drawn outward in any direction from the nucleus. The result is shown in Fig. 7.11(b). Note that the probability of finding the electron at a particular position is greatest close to the nucleus and it drops off rapidly as the distance from the nucleus increases. We are also interested in knowing the *total* probability of finding the electron in the hydrogen atom at a particular *distance* from the nucleus. Imagine that the space around the hydrogen nucleus is made up of a series of thin spherical shells (rather like layers in an onion), as shown in Fig. 7.12(a). When the total probability of finding the electron in each spherical shell is plotted versus the distance from the nucleus, the plot in Fig. 7.12(b) is obtained. This graph is called the **radial probability distribution.**

The maximum in the curve occurs because of two opposing effects. The probability of finding an electron at a particular position is greatest near the nucleus, but the volume of the spherical shell increases with distance from the nucleus. Therefore, as we move away from the nucleus, the probability of finding the electron at a given position decreases, but we are summing more positions. Thus the total probability increases to a certain radius and then decreases as the electron probability at each position becomes very small. For the hydrogen $1s$ orbital, the maximum radial probability (the distance at which the electron is most likely to be found) occurs at a distance of 5.29×10^{-2} nm or 0.529 Å from the nucleus. Interestingly, this is exactly the radius of the innermost orbit in the Bohr model. Note that in Bohr's model the electron is assumed to have a circular path and so is *always* found at this distance. In the quantum mechanical model, the specific electron motions are unknown, and this is the *most probable* distance at which the electron is found.

One more characteristic of the hydrogen $1s$ orbital that we must consider is its size. As we can see from Fig. 7.11, the size of this orbital cannot be defined precisely, since the probability never becomes zero (although it drops to an extremely small value at large values of r). So, in fact, the hydrogen $1s$ orbital has no distinct size. However, it is useful to have a definition of relative orbital size. *The*

(a)

Probability (R^2)

Distance from nucleus (r)

(b)

Figure 7.11

(a) The probability distribution for the hydrogen $1s$ orbital in three-dimensional space. (b) The probability of finding the electron at points along a line drawn from the nucleus outward in any direction for the hydrogen $1s$ orbital.

1 Å = 10^{-10} m; the angstrom is most often used as the unit for atomic radius because of its convenient size. Another convenient unit is the picometer:

$$1 \text{ pm} = 10^{-12} \text{ m}$$

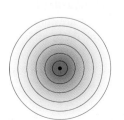

Radial probability ($4\pi r^2 R^2$)

Distance from nucleus (r)

(a)   (b)

Figure 7.12

(a) Cross section of the hydrogen $1s$ orbital probability distribution divided into successive thin spherical shells. (b) The radial probability distribution. A plot of the total probability of finding the electron in each thin spherical shell as a function of distance from the nucleus.

definition most often used by chemists to describe the size of the hydrogen 1s orbital is the radius of the sphere that encloses 90% of the total electron probability. That is, 90% of the time the electron is inside this sphere.

So far we have described only the lowest-energy wave function in the hydrogen atom, the 1s orbital. Hydrogen has many other orbitals, which we will describe in the next section. However, before we proceed, we should summarize what we have said about the meaning of an atomic orbital. An orbital is difficult to define precisely at an introductory level. Technically, an orbital is a wave function. However, it is usually most helpful to picture an orbital as a three-dimensional electron density map. That is, an electron "in" a particular atomic orbital is assumed to exhibit the electron probability indicated by the orbital map.

7.6 Quantum Numbers

Purpose

• To explain the quantum numbers n, ℓ, and m_ℓ.

When we solve the Schrödinger equation for the hydrogen atom, we find many wave functions (orbitals) that satisfy it. Each of these orbitals is characterized by a series of numbers called **quantum numbers,** which describe various properties of the orbital:

The **principal quantum number** (n) has integral values: 1, 2, 3, ... The principal quantum number is related to the size and energy of the orbital. As n increases, the orbital becomes larger and the electron spends more time further from the nucleus. An increase in n also means higher energy, because the electron is less tightly bound to the nucleus, and the energy is less negative.

$n = 1, 2, 3, \ldots$
$\ell = 0, 1, \ldots (n - 1)$
$m_\ell = -\ell, \ldots 0, \ldots +\ell$

The **angular momentum quantum number** (ℓ) has integral values from 0 to $n - 1$ for each value of n. This quantum number is related to the shape of atomic orbitals. The value of ℓ for a particular orbital is commonly assigned a letter: $\ell = 0$ is called s; $\ell = 1$ is called p; $\ell = 2$ is called d; and $\ell = 3$ is called f. This system arises from early spectral studies and is summarized in Table 7.1.

The **magnetic quantum number** (m_ℓ) has integral values between ℓ and $-\ell$, including zero. The value of m_ℓ is related to the orientation of the orbital in space relative to the other orbitals in the atom.

The first four levels of orbitals in the hydrogen atom are listed with their quantum numbers in Table 7.2. Note that each set of orbitals with a given value of ℓ (sometimes called a **subshell**) is designated by giving the value of n and the letter for ℓ. Thus an orbital where $n = 2$ and $\ell = 1$ is symbolized as $2p$. There are three $2p$ orbitals, which have different orientations in space. We will describe these orbitals in the next section.

Sample Exercise 7.6

For principal quantum level $n = 5$, determine the number of allowed subshells (different values of ℓ) and give the designation of each.

Table 7.1

The Angular Momentum Quantum Numbers and Corresponding Letters Used to Designate Atomic Orbitals					
Value of ℓ	0	1	2	3	4
Letter Used	s	p	d	f	g

Table 7.2

Number of Orbitals Per Subshell

$s = 1$
$p = 3$
$d = 5$
$f = 7$
$g = 9$

Quantum Numbers for the First Four Levels of Orbitals in the Hydrogen Atom				
n	ℓ	Orbital Designation	m_ℓ	Number of Orbitals
1	0	$1s$	0	1
2	0	$2s$	0	1
	1	$2p$	$-1, 0, +1$	3
3	0	$3s$	0	1
	1	$3p$	$-1, 0, 1$	3
	2	$3d$	$-2, -1, 0, 1, 2$	5
4	0	$4s$	0	1
	1	$4p$	$-1, 0, 1$	3
	2	$4d$	$-2, -1, 0, 1, 2$	5
	3	$4f$	$-3, -2, -1, 0, 1, 2, 3$	7

Solution

For $n = 5$, the allowed values of ℓ run from 0 to 4 ($n - 1 = 5 - 1$). Thus the subshells and their designations are

$\ell = 0$	$\ell = 1$	$\ell = 2$	$\ell = 3$	$\ell = 4$
$5s$	$5p$	$5d$	$5f$	$5g$

7.7 Orbital Shapes and Energies

Purpose

- To describe the shapes of orbitals designated by s, p, d, and f and to discuss orbital energies.

We have seen that the meaning of an orbital is represented most clearly by a probability distribution. Each orbital in the hydrogen atom has a unique probability distribution. We also saw that another means of representing an orbital is by the

(a)

(b)

Figure 7.13

Two representations of the hydrogen 1s, 2s, and 3s orbitals. (a) The electron probability distribution. (b) The surface that contains 90% of the total electron probability (the size of the orbital, by definition).

n value
↓
$2p_x$ ← orientation in space
↑
ℓ value

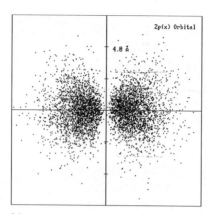

(a)

Figure 7.14

Representation of the 2p orbitals. (a) The electron probability distribution for a 2p orbital. Generated from a program by Robert Allendoerfer on Project SERAPHIM disk PC2402; printed with permission. (b) The boundary surface representations of all three 2p orbitals.

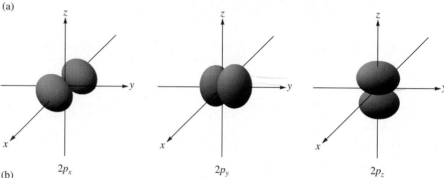

(b) $2p_x$ $2p_y$ $2p_z$

Figure 7.15

A cross section of the electron probability distribution for a 3p orbital.

surface that surrounds 90% of the total electron probability. These two types of representations for the hydrogen 1s, 2s, and 3s orbitals are shown in Fig. 7.13. Note the characteristic spherical shape of each of the s orbitals. Note also that the 2s and 3s orbitals contain areas of high probability separated by areas of zero probability. These latter areas are called **nodal surfaces,** or simply **nodes.** The number of nodes increases as n increases. For s orbitals, the number of nodes is given by $n - 1$. For our purposes, however, we will think of s orbitals only in terms of their overall spherical shape, which becomes larger as the value of n increases.

The two types of representations for the 2p orbitals (there are no 1p orbitals) are shown in Fig. 7.14. Note that the p orbitals are not spherical like s orbitals but have two **lobes** separated by a node at the nucleus. The p orbitals are labeled according to the axis of the xyz coordinate system along which the lobes lie. For example, the 2p orbital with lobes centered along the x axis is called the $2p_x$ orbital.

As you might expect from our discussion of the s orbitals, the 3p orbitals have a more complex probability distribution than that of the 2p orbitals (see Fig. 7.15), but they can still be represented by the same boundary surface shapes. The surfaces just grow larger as the value of n increases.

There are no d orbitals that correspond to principal quantum levels $n = 1$ and $n = 2$. The d orbitals ($\ell = 2$) first occur in level $n = 3$. The five 3d orbitals have the shapes shown in Fig. 7.16. The d orbitals have two different fundamental shapes. Four of the orbitals (d_{xz}, d_{yz}, d_{xy}, and $d_{x^2-y^2}$) have four lobes centered in the plane indicated in the orbital label. Note that d_{xy} and $d_{x^2-y^2}$ are both centered in the xy plane; however, the lobes of the $d_{x^2-y^2}$ lie *along* the x and y axes, while the lobes of d_{xy} lie *between* the axes. The fifth orbital, d_{z^2}, has a unique shape with two lobes along the z axis and a belt centered in the xy plane. The d orbitals for levels $n > 3$ look like the 3d orbitals but have larger lobes.

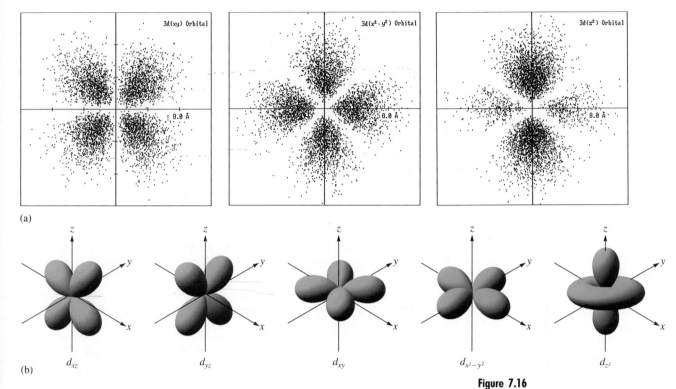

(a)

(b)

d_{xz} d_{yz} d_{xy} $d_{x^2-y^2}$ d_{z^2}

The *f* orbitals first occur in level $n = 4$, and as might be expected, they have shapes even more complex than those of the *d* orbitals. Figure 7.17 shows representations of the 4*f* orbitals ($\ell = 3$) along with their designations. These orbitals are not involved in the bonding in any of the compounds we will consider in this text. Their shapes and labels are simply included for completeness.

So far we have talked about the shapes of the hydrogen atomic orbitals but not about their energies. For the hydrogen atom, the energy of a particular orbital is

Figure 7.16

Representation of the 3*d* orbitals. (a) Electron density plots of selected 3*d* orbitals. Generated from a program by Robert Allendoerfer on Project SERAPHIM disk PC2402; printed with permission. (b) The boundary surfaces of all of the 3*d* orbitals.

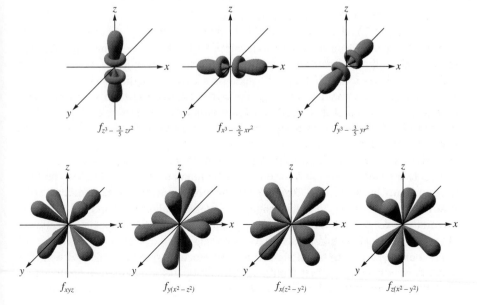

$f_{z^3 - \frac{3}{5}zr^2}$ $f_{x^3 - \frac{3}{5}xr^2}$ $f_{y^3 - \frac{3}{5}yr^2}$

f_{xyz} $f_{y(x^2 - z^2)}$ $f_{x(z^2 - y^2)}$ $f_{z(x^2 - y^2)}$

Figure 7.17

Representation of the 4*f* orbitals in terms of their boundary surfaces.

$3s$ — $3p$ — — — $3d$ — — — — —

E

$2s$ — $2p$ — — —

$1s$ —

Figure 7.18

Orbital energy levels for the hydrogen atom.

determined by its value of n. Thus *all* orbitals with the same value of n have the *same energy*—they are said to be **degenerate.** This is shown in Fig. 7.18, where the energies for the orbitals in the first three quantum levels for hydrogen are shown.

Hydrogen's single electron can occupy any of its atomic orbitals. However, in the lowest energy state, the **ground state,** the electron resides in the $1s$ orbital. If energy is put into the atom, the electron can be transferred to a higher-energy orbital, producing an **excited state.**

A Summary of the Hydrogen Atom

- In the quantum (wave) mechanical model, the electron is viewed as a standing wave. This representation leads to a series of wave functions (orbitals) that describe the possible energies and spatial distributions available to the electron.

- In agreement with the Heisenberg uncertainty principle, the model cannot specify the detailed electron motions. Instead, the square of the wave function represents the probability distribution of the electron in that orbital. This allows us to picture orbitals in terms of probability distributions, or electron density maps.

- The size of an orbital is arbitrarily defined as the surface that contains 90% of the total electron probability.

- The hydrogen atom has many types of orbitals. In the ground state, the single electron resides in the $1s$ orbital. The electron can be excited to higher-energy orbitals if energy is put into the atom.

7.8 Electron Spin and the Pauli Principle

Purpose

- To define electron spin and the electron spin quantum number.
- To explain the Pauli exclusion principle.

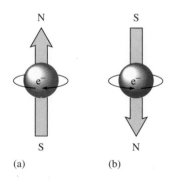

(a)   (b)

Figure 7.19

A picture of the spinning electron. Spinning in one direction, the electron produces the magnetic field oriented as shown in (a). Spinning in the opposite direction, it gives a magnetic field of the opposite orientation, as shown in (b).

The concept of electron spin was developed by Samuel Goudsmit and George Uhlenbeck while they were graduate students at the University of Leyden in the Netherlands. They found that a fourth quantum number (in addition to n, ℓ, and m_ℓ) was necessary to account for the details of the emission spectra of atoms. The spectral data indicate that the electron has a magnetic moment with two possible orientations when the atom is placed in an external magnetic field. Since they knew from classical physics that a spinning charge produces a magnetic moment, it seemed reasonable to assume that the electron could have two spin states, thus producing the two oppositely directed magnetic moments (see Fig. 7.19). The new quantum number adopted to describe this phenomenon, called the **electron spin quantum number** (m_s), can have only one of two values, $+\frac{1}{2}$ and $-\frac{1}{2}$. We can interpret this to mean that the electron can spin in one of two opposite directions, although other interpretations also have been suggested.

For our purposes, the main significance of electron spin is connected with the postulate of Austrian physicist Wolfgang Pauli (1900–1958): *in a given atom no two electrons can have the same set of four quantum numbers* (n, ℓ, m_ℓ, and m_s). This is called the **Pauli exclusion principle.** Since electrons in the same orbital have the same values of n, ℓ, and m_ℓ, this postulate says that they must have different values of m_s. Then, since only two values of m_s are allowed, *an orbital can only hold two electrons, and they must have opposite spins.* This principle will have important consequences as we use the atomic model to account for the electron arrangements of the atoms in the periodic table.

7.9 Polyelectronic Atoms

Purpose

- To show how the quantum mechanical model can be applied to atoms besides hydrogen.

The quantum mechanical model gives a description of the hydrogen atom that agrees very well with experimental data. However, the model would not be very useful if it did not account for the properties of all the other atoms as well.

To see how the model applies to **polyelectronic atoms,** that is, atoms with more than one electron, let's consider helium, which has two protons in its nucleus and two electrons:

There are three energy contributions that must be considered in the description of the helium atom: (1) the kinetic energy of the electrons as they move around the nucleus, (2) the potential energy of attraction between the nucleus and the electrons, and (3) the potential energy of repulsion between the two electrons.

Although the helium atom can be readily described in terms of the quantum mechanical model, the Schrödinger equation that results cannot be solved exactly. The difficulty arises in dealing with the repulsions between the electrons. Since the electron pathways are unknown, the electron repulsions cannot be calculated exactly. This is called the **electron correlation problem.**

The electron correlation problem occurs with all polyelectronic atoms. To treat these systems using the quantum mechanical model, we must make approximations. Most commonly, the approximation used is to treat each electron as if it were moving in a *field of charge that is the net result of the nuclear attraction and the average repulsions of all the other electrons.* To see how this is done, let's consider the neutral helium atom and the He^+ ion:

What energy is required to remove an electron from each of these species? Experiments show that 2372 kJ of energy is required to remove one electron from all the atoms in a mole of helium. Removing the one electron from each ion in a mole of He^+ ions requires 5248 kJ of energy. Thus it takes more than twice as much energy to remove an electron from a He^+ ion as it does from a He atom.

Why such a large difference? In both cases the nucleus has a 2+ charge. However, in the helium atom there are two electrons that exert electron–electron repulsions, while in the He$^+$ ion there is only one electron and thus no electron–electron repulsions. That is, the large difference in the energies required to remove one electron must be due to the electron–electron repulsions in the neutral atom. Each electron in the He atom is much less tightly bound to the nucleus than is the electron in the He$^+$ ion. In other words, the effectiveness of the positively charged nucleus in binding the electrons has been decreased by the repulsions between the electrons. Thus *the effect of the electron repulsions can be thought of as reducing the nuclear charge* to an apparent value of less than 2+ toward a particular electron, as shown below:

Actual He
atom

Hypothetical
He atom

$Z_{eff} = Z -$ effect of electron repulsion.

The *apparent* nuclear charge, or the **effective nuclear charge,** is designated Z_{eff}. For a helium atom Z_{eff}, the charge "felt" by each electron, is less than 2. In general,

$$\text{Effective nuclear charge} = Z_{eff} = Z_{actual} - \text{(effect of electron repulsions)}$$

where $Z_{actual} = Z$, the atomic number (number of protons).

This simplification allows us to treat each electron individually; each electron is viewed as moving under the influence of a positive nuclear charge of Z_{eff}. This simplified atom has one electron, like hydrogen, but with a positive nuclear charge of Z_{eff} instead of 1. We therefore can find the energy and wave function for each helium electron by substituting Z_{eff} in place of $Z = 1$ in the hydrogen wave equations. When we do this, we find that both helium electrons reside in a 1s orbital (but have opposite spin quantum numbers). The orbital is spherical, like that for the hydrogen atom, but smaller because Z_{eff} is larger than 1. The larger nuclear charge draws each of the electrons closer to the nucleus and binds each more tightly than the electron in hydrogen. The increased nuclear charge of the helium atom is more important than the repulsions between the two electrons, so each of the electrons in helium is bound more tightly than the electron in the hydrogen atom.

This same procedure can be used for all polyelectronic atoms. For example, consider the sodium atom, which has 11 protons in its nucleus and 11 electrons. To find the energy and orbital characteristics of each of sodium's electrons, we treat each electron individually and assume that it is influenced by a nuclear charge of Z_{eff}, as illustrated below:

Real sodium atom

Hypothetical one-electron
sodium atom

By treating each electron in turn, we can eventually obtain a complete (although approximate) description of the sodium atom.

The value of this approximation is that we can describe any polyelectronic atom one electron at a time using the mathematical treatment developed for hydrogen.

The orbitals obtained in this type of treatment are *hydrogenlike orbitals* (the same types of orbitals with the same shapes), but their *sizes* and *energies* differ from those of the corresponding hydrogen orbitals. These differences occur because in a polyelectronic atom each electron is attracted by a nuclear charge of Z_{eff} rather than a charge of 1. One especially important difference between polyelectronic atoms and the hydrogen atom is that for hydrogen all orbitals with the same value of *n* have the same energy (are degenerate). This is not the case for polyelectronic atoms, as we will see in Section 7.12.

It is important to understand that in this model each electron in a polyelectronic atom has its own value of Z_{eff}, which can be calculated from the experimental energy required to remove that electron from the atom. We will discuss this procedure in more detail in Section 7.12.

7.10 *The History of the Periodic Table*

Purpose

- To trace the development of the periodic table.

The modern periodic table contains a tremendous amount of useful information. In this section we will discuss the origin of this valuable tool; later we will see how the quantum mechanical model for the atom explains the periodicity of chemical properties. Certainly the greatest triumph of the quantum mechanical model is its ability to account for the arrangement of the elements in the periodic table.

The periodic table was originally constructed to represent the patterns observed in the chemical properties of the elements. As chemistry progressed during the eighteenth and nineteenth centuries, it became evident that the earth is composed of a great many elements with very different properties. Things are much more complicated than the simple model of earth, air, fire, and water suggested by the ancients. At first, the array of elements and properties was bewildering. Gradually, however, patterns were noticed.

The first chemist to recognize patterns was Johann Dobereiner (1780–1849), who found several groups of three elements that have similar properties, for example, chlorine, bromine, and iodine. However, as Dobereiner attempted to expand this model of **triads** (as he called them) to the rest of the known elements, it became clear that it was severely limited.

The next notable attempt was made by the English chemist John Newlands, who in 1864 suggested that elements should be arranged in **octaves,** based on the idea that certain properties seemed to repeat for every eighth element in a way similar to the musical scale, which repeats for every eighth tone. Even though this model managed to group several elements with similar properties, it was not generally successful.

The present form of the periodic table was conceived independently by two chemists: the German Julius Lothar Meyer (1830–1895) and Dmitri Ivanovich Mendeleev (1834–1907), a Russian (Fig. 7.20). Usually Mendeleev is given most of the credit, because it was he who emphasized how useful the table could be in predicting the existence and properties of still unknown elements. For example, in 1872 when Mendeleev first published his table (see Fig. 7.21), the elements gallium, scandium, and germanium were unknown. Mendeleev correctly predicted the

Figure 7.20

Dmitri Ivanovich Mendeleev (1834–1907), born in Siberia as the youngest of 17 children, taught chemistry at the University of St. Petersburg. In 1860 Mendeleev heard the Italian chemist Cannizzaro lecture on a reliable method for determining the correct atomic masses of the elements. This important development paved the way for Mendeleev's own brilliant contribution to chemistry—the periodic table. In 1861 Mendeleev returned to St. Petersburg, where he wrote a book on organic chemistry. Later Mendeleev also wrote a book on inorganic chemistry, and he was struck by the fact that the systematic approach characterizing organic chemistry was lacking in inorganic chemistry. In attempting to systematize inorganic chemistry, he eventually arranged the elements in the form of the periodic table.

Mendeleev was a versatile genius who was interested in many fields of science. He worked on many problems associated with Russia's natural resources, such as coal, salt, and various metals. Being particularly interested in the petroleum industry, he visited the United States in 1876 to study the Pennsylvania oil fields. His interests also included meteorology and hot-air balloons. In 1887 he made an ascent in a balloon to study a total eclipse of the sun.

existence and properties of these elements from gaps in his periodic table. The data for germanium (which Mendeleev called "ekasilicon") are shown in Table 7.3. Note the excellent agreement between the actual values and Mendeleev's predictions, which were based on the properties of other members in the group of elements similar to germanium.

Using his table, Mendeleev also was able to correct several values for atomic masses. For example, the original atomic mass of 76 for indium was based on the assumption that indium oxide had the formula InO. This atomic mass placed indium, which has metallic properties, among the nonmetals. Mendeleev assumed the

TABELLE II

REIHEN	GRUPPE I. — R^2O	GRUPPE II. — RO	GRUPPE III. — R^2O^3	GRUPPE IV. RH^4 RO^2	GRUPPE V. RH^3 R^2O^5	GRUPPE VI. RH^2 RO^3	GRUPPE VII. RH R^2O^7	GRUPPE VIII. — RO^4
1	H = 1							
2	Li = 7	Be = 9,4	B = 11	C = 12	N = 14	O = 16	F = 19	
3	Na = 23	Mg = 24	Al = 27,3	Si = 28	P = 31	S = 32	Cl = 35,5	
4	K = 39	Ca = 40	— = 44	Ti = 48	V = 51	Cr = 52	Mn = 55	Fe = 56, Co = 59, Ni = 59, Cu = 63.
5	(Cu = 63)	Zn = 65	— = 68	— = 72	As = 75	Se = 78	Br = 80	
6	Rb = 85	Sr = 87	?Yt = 88	Zr = 90	Nb = 94	Mo = 96	— = 100	Ru = 104, Rh = 104, Pd = 106, Ag = 108.
7	(Ag = 108)	Cd = 112	In = 113	Sn = 118	Sb = 122	Te = 125	J = 127	
8	Cs = 133	Ba = 137	?Di = 138	?Ce = 140	—	—	—	———
9	(—)							
10	—	—	?Er = 178	?La = 180	Ta = 182	W = 184	—	Os = 195, Ir = 197, Pt = 198, Au = 199.
11	(Au = 199)	Hg = 200	Tl = 204	Pb = 207	Bi = 208	—	—	
12	—	—	—	Th = 231	—	U = 240	—	———

Figure 7.21

Mendeleev's early periodic table, published in 1872. Note the spaces left for missing elements with atomic masses 44, 68, 72, and 100. (From *Annalen der Chemie und Pharmacie*, VIII, Supplementary Volume for 1872, page 511.)

Table 7.3		
Comparison of the Properties of Germanium as Predicted by Mendeleev and as Actually Observed		
Properties of Germanium	Predicted in 1871	Observed in 1886
Atomic weight	72	72.3
Density	5.5 g/cm^3	5.47 g/cm^3
Specific heat	0.31 J/(°C · g)	0.32 J/(°C · g)
Melting point	Very high	960°C
Oxide formula	RO$_2$	GeO$_2$
Oxide density	4.7 g/cm^3	4.70 g/cm^3
Chloride formula	RCl$_4$	GeCl$_4$
bp of chloride	100°C	86°C

Table 7.4		
Predicted Properties of Elements 113 and 114		
Property	Element 113	Element 114
Chemically like	Thallium	Lead
Atomic mass	297	298
Density	16 g/ml	14 g/ml
Melting point	430°C	70°C
Boiling point	1100°C	150°C

atomic mass was probably incorrect and proposed that the formula of indium oxide was really In$_2$O$_3$. Based on this correct formula, indium has an atomic mass of approximately 113, placing the element among the metals. Mendeleev also corrected the atomic masses of beryllium and uranium.

Because of its obvious usefulness, Mendeleev's periodic table was almost universally adopted, and it remains one of the most valuable tools at the chemist's disposal. For example, it is still used to predict the properties of elements yet to be discovered, as shown in Table 7.4.

A current version of the periodic table is shown inside the front cover of this book. The only fundamental difference between this table and that of Mendeleev is that it lists the elements in order by atomic number rather than by atomic mass. The reason for this will become clear later in this chapter as we explore the electron arrangements of the atom. Another recent format of the table is discussed in the following section.

7.11 The Aufbau Principle and the Periodic Table

Purpose

- To explain the aufbau principle.

We can use the quantum mechanical model of the atom to show how the electron arrangements in the hydrogenlike atomic orbitals of the various atoms account for the organization of the periodic table. Our main assumption here is that all atoms have the same type of orbitals as have been described for the hydrogen atom. *As protons are added one by one to the nucleus to build up the elements, electrons are similarly added to these hydrogenlike orbitals.* This is called the **aufbau principle.**

Hydrogen has one electron, which occupies the 1s orbital in its ground state. The configuration for hydrogen is written as 1s^1, which can be represented by the fol-

Aufbau is German for "building up."

lowing **orbital diagram:**

$$1s \quad\quad 2s \quad\quad 2p$$

H: $1s^1$ $\boxed{\uparrow}$ $\boxed{}$ $\boxed{\,|\,\,|\,}$

H (Z = 1)
He (Z = 2)
Li (Z = 3)
Be (Z = 4)
B (Z = 5)
etc.

The arrow represents an electron spinning in a particular direction.

The next element, *helium,* has two electrons. Since two electrons with opposite spins can occupy an orbital, according to the Pauli exclusion principle, the electrons for helium are in the 1s orbital with opposite spins, producing a $1s^2$ configuration:

$$1s \quad\quad 2s \quad\quad 2p$$

He: $1s^2$ $\boxed{\uparrow\downarrow}$ $\boxed{}$ $\boxed{\,|\,\,|\,}$

We will see in Section 7.12 why the 2s orbital is lower in energy than the 2p orbital.

Lithium has three electrons, two of which can go into the 1s orbital before the orbital is filled. Since the 1s orbital is the only orbital for $n = 1$, the third electron will occupy the lowest-energy orbital with $n = 2$, or the 2s orbital, giving a $1s^2 2s^1$ configuration:

$$1s \quad\quad 2s \quad\quad 2p$$

Li: $1s^2 2s^1$ $\boxed{\uparrow\downarrow}$ $\boxed{\uparrow}$ $\boxed{\,|\,\,|\,}$

The next element, *beryllium,* has four electrons, which occupy the 1s and 2s orbitals:

$$1s \quad\quad 2s \quad\quad 2p$$

Be: $1s^2 2s^2$ $\boxed{\uparrow\downarrow}$ $\boxed{\uparrow\downarrow}$ $\boxed{\,|\,\,|\,}$

Boron has five electrons, four of which occupy the 1s and 2s orbitals. The fifth electron goes into the second type of orbital with $n = 2$, the 2p orbitals:

$$1s \quad\quad 2s \quad\quad 2p$$

B: $1s^2 2s^2 2p^1$ $\boxed{\uparrow\downarrow}$ $\boxed{\uparrow\downarrow}$ $\boxed{\uparrow\,|\,\,|\,}$

Since all of the 2p orbitals have the same energy (are degenerate), it does not matter which 2p orbital the electron occupies.

Carbon is the next element and has six electrons. Two electrons occupy the 1s orbital; two occupy the 2s orbital; and two occupy 2p orbitals. Since there are three 2p orbitals with the same energy, the mutually repulsive electrons will occupy *separate* 2p orbitals. This behavior is summarized by **Hund's rule** (named for the German physicist F. H. Hund), which states that *the lowest energy configuration for an atom is the one having the maximum number of unpaired electrons allowed by the Pauli principle in a particular set of degenerate orbitals.* By convention, the unpaired electrons are represented as having parallel spins (with spin "up").

For an atom with unfilled subshells, the lowest energy is achieved by electrons occupying separate orbitals with parallel spins, as far as allowed by the Pauli exclusion principle.

The configuration for carbon could be written $1s^2 2s^2 2p^1 2p^1$ to indicate that the electrons occupy separate 2p orbitals. However, the configuration is usually given as $1s^2 2s^2 2p^2$, and it is understood that the electrons are in different 2p orbitals. The orbital diagram for carbon is

$$1s \quad\quad 2s \quad\quad 2p$$

C: $1s^2 2s^2 2p^2$ $\boxed{\uparrow\downarrow}$ $\boxed{\uparrow\downarrow}$ $\boxed{\uparrow\,|\,\uparrow\,|\,}$

Note that the unpaired electrons in the 2p orbitals are shown with parallel spins.

The configuration for *nitrogen,* which has seven electrons, is $1s^2 2s^2 2p^3$. The three electrons in the $2p$ orbitals occupy separate orbitals with parallel spins:

$$
\begin{array}{cccc}
 & 1s & 2s & 2p \\
\text{N:} \quad 1s^2 2s^2 2p^3 & \boxed{\uparrow\downarrow} & \boxed{\uparrow\downarrow} & \boxed{\uparrow\,|\,\uparrow\,|\,\uparrow}
\end{array}
$$

The configuration for *oxygen,* which has eight electrons, is $1s^2 2s^2 2p^4$. One of the $2p$ orbitals is now occupied by a pair of electrons with opposite spins, as required by the Pauli exclusion principle:

$$
\begin{array}{cccc}
 & 1s & 2s & 2p \\
\text{O:} \quad 1s^2 2s^2 2p^4 & \boxed{\uparrow\downarrow} & \boxed{\uparrow\downarrow} & \boxed{\uparrow\downarrow\,|\,\uparrow\,|\,\uparrow}
\end{array}
$$

The orbital diagrams and electron configurations for *fluorine* (nine electrons) and *neon* (ten electrons) are as follows:

$$
\begin{array}{cccc}
 & 1s & 2s & 2p \\
\text{F:} \quad 1s^2 2s^2 2p^5 & \boxed{\uparrow\downarrow} & \boxed{\uparrow\downarrow} & \boxed{\uparrow\downarrow\,|\,\uparrow\downarrow\,|\,\uparrow} \\
\text{Ne:} \quad 1s^2 2s^2 2p^6 & \boxed{\uparrow\downarrow} & \boxed{\uparrow\downarrow} & \boxed{\uparrow\downarrow\,|\,\uparrow\downarrow\,|\,\uparrow\downarrow}
\end{array}
$$

With neon, the orbitals with $n = 1$ and $n = 2$ are now completely filled.

For *sodium,* the first ten electrons occupy the $1s$, $2s$, and $2p$ orbitals, and the eleventh electron must occupy the first orbital with $n = 3$, the $3s$ orbital. The electron configuration for sodium is $1s^2 2s^2 2p^6 3s^1$. To avoid writing the inner-level electrons, this configuration is often abbreviated as $[\text{Ne}]3s^1$, where [Ne] represents the electron configuration of neon, $1s^2 2s^2 2p^6$.

The next element, *magnesium,* has the configuration $1s^2 2s^2 2p^6 3s^2$, or $[\text{Ne}]3s^2$. Then the next six elements, *aluminum* through *argon,* have configurations obtained by filling the $3p$ orbitals one electron at a time. Figure 7.22 summarizes the electron configurations of the first 18 elements by giving the number of electrons in the type of orbital occupied last.

At this point it is useful to introduce the concept of **valence electrons,** that is, *the electrons in the outermost principal quantum level of an atom.* The valence electrons of the nitrogen atom, for example, are the $2s$ and $2p$ electrons. For the sodium atom, the valence electron is the electron in the $3s$ orbital, and so on. Valence electrons are the most important electrons to chemists because they are involved in bonding, as we will see in the next two chapters. The inner electrons are known as **core electrons.**

[Ne] is shorthand for $1s^2 2s^2 2p^6$.

H $1s^1$									He $1s^2$
Li $2s^1$	Be $2s^2$				B $2p^1$	C $2p^2$	N $2p^3$	O $2p^4$	F $2p^5$	Ne $2p^6$
Na $3s^1$	Mg $3s^2$				Al $3p^1$	Si $3p^2$	P $3p^3$	S $3p^4$	Cl $3p^5$	Ar $3p^6$

Figure 7.22

The electron configurations in the type of orbital occupied last for the first 18 elements.

A vial containing potassium metal.

[Ar] is shorthand for $1s^22s^22p^63s^23p^6$.

Calcium metal.

Note in Fig. 7.22 that a very important pattern is developing: *the elements in the same group (vertical column of the periodic table) have the same valence electron configuration*. Remember that Mendeleev originally placed the elements in groups based on similarities in chemical properties. Now we understand the reason behind these groupings. Elements with the same valence electron configuration show similar chemical behavior.

The element after argon is *potassium*. Since the 3p orbitals are fully occupied in argon, we might expect the next electron to go into a 3d orbital (recall that for $n = 3$ the orbitals are 3s, 3p, and 3d). However, the chemistry of potassium is clearly very similar to that of lithium and sodium, indicating that the last electron in potassium occupies the 4s orbital instead of one of the 3d orbitals, a conclusion confirmed by many types of experiments. The electron configuration of potassium is

$$K: \quad 1s^22s^22p^63s^23p^64s^1 \quad \text{or} \quad [Ar]4s^1$$

The next element is *calcium:*

$$Ca: \quad [Ar]4s^2$$

The next element, *scandium,* begins a series of 10 elements (scandium through zinc) called the **transition metals,** whose configurations are obtained by adding electrons to the five 3d orbitals. The configuration of scandium is

$$Sc: \quad [Ar]4s^23d^1$$

That of *titanium* is

$$Ti: \quad [Ar]4s^23d^2$$

And that of *vanadium* is

$$V: \quad [Ar]4s^23d^3$$

Chromium is the next element. The expected configuration is $[Ar]4s^23d^4$. However, the observed configuration is

$$Cr: \quad [Ar]4s^13d^5$$

The explanation for this configuration of chromium is beyond the scope of this book. In fact, chemists are still disagreeing over the exact cause of this anomaly. Note, however, that the observed configuration has both the 4s and 3d orbitals half-filled. This is a good way to remember the correct configuration.

The next four elements, *manganese* through *nickel,* have the expected configurations:

$$Mn: \quad [Ar]4s^23d^5 \qquad Co: \quad [Ar]4s^23d^7$$
$$Fe: \quad [Ar]4s^23d^6 \qquad Ni: \quad [Ar]4s^23d^8$$

The configuration for *copper* is expected to be $[Ar]4s^23d^9$. However, the observed configuration is

$$Cu: \quad [Ar]4s^13d^{10}$$

In this case, a half-filled 4s orbital and a filled set of 3d orbitals characterize the actual configuration.

Zinc has the expected configuration:

$$Zn: \quad [Ar]4s^23d^{10}$$

The configurations of the transition metals are shown in Fig. 7.23. After that, the next six elements, *gallium* through *krypton,* have configurations that correspond to filling the 4p orbitals (see Fig. 7.23).

Chromium is often used to plate bumpers and hood ornaments, such as this statue of Mercury found on a 1929 Buick.

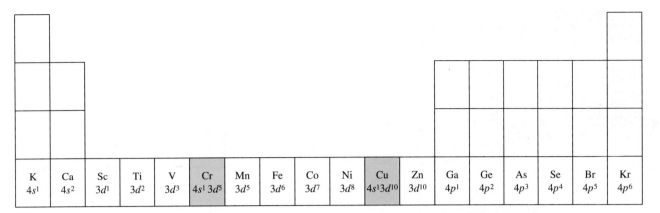

| K $4s^1$ | Ca $4s^2$ | Sc $3d^1$ | Ti $3d^2$ | V $3d^3$ | Cr $4s^1 3d^5$ | Mn $3d^5$ | Fe $3d^6$ | Co $3d^7$ | Ni $3d^8$ | Cu $4s^1 3d^{10}$ | Zn $3d^{10}$ | Ga $4p^1$ | Ge $4p^2$ | As $4p^3$ | Se $4p^4$ | Br $4p^5$ | Kr $4p^6$ |

Figure 7.23

Electron configurations for potassium through krypton. The transition metals (scandium through zinc) have the general configuration $[Ar]4s^2 3d^n$, except for chromium and copper.

The $(n + 1)s$ orbital fills before the nd orbitals.

The entire periodic table is represented in Fig. 7.24 in terms of which orbitals are being filled. The valence electron configurations are given in Fig. 7.25 on p. 312. From these two figures, note the following additional points:

1. The $(n + 1)s$ orbitals always fill before the nd orbitals. For example, the $5s$ orbitals fill in rubidium and strontium before the $4d$ orbitals fill in the second row of transition metals (yttrium through cadmium).

2. After lanthanum, which has the configuration $[Xe]6s^2 5d^1$, a group of 14 elements called the **lanthanide series,** or the **lanthanides,** occurs. This series of elements corresponds to the filling of the seven $4f$ orbitals. Note that sometimes an electron occupies a $5d$ orbital instead of a $4f$ orbital. This occurs because the energies of the $4f$ and $5d$ orbitals are very similar.

Lanthanides are elements in which the $4f$ orbitals are being filled.

3. After actinium, which has the configuration $[Rn]7s^2 6d^1$, a group of 14 elements called the **actinide series,** or the **actinides,** occurs. This series corre-

Actinides are elements in which the $5f$ orbitals are being filled.

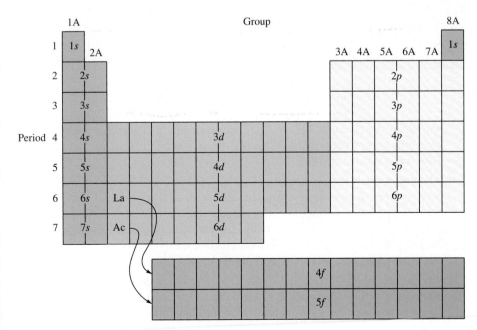

Figure 7.24

The orbitals being filled for elements in various parts of the periodic table. Note that in going along a horizontal row (a period), the $(n + 1)s$ orbital fills before the nd orbital. The group labels indicate the number of valence electrons (ns plus np electrons) for the elements in each group.

Representative Elements | *d*-Transition Elements | Representative Elements | Noble gases

Figure 7.25

The periodic table with atomic symbols, atomic numbers, and partial electron configurations.

The group label tells the total number of valence electrons for that group.

sponds to the filling of the seven $5f$ orbitals. Note that sometimes one or two electrons occupy the $6d$ orbitals instead of the $5f$ orbitals, because these orbitals have very similar energies.

4. The group labels for Groups 1A, 2A, 3A, 4A, 5A, 6A, 7A, and 8A indicate the *total number* of valence electrons for the atoms in these groups. For example, all the elements in Group 5A have the configuration ns^2np^3. (The d electrons fill one period late and are usually not counted as valence electrons.) The meaning of the group labels for the transition metals is not as clear as for the Group A elements, and these will not be used in this text.

5. The groups labeled 1A, 2A, 3A, 4A, 5A, 6A, 7A, and 8A are often called the **main-group,** or **representative, elements.** Remember that every member of these groups has the same valence electron configuration.

1																	18
1 H	2											13	14	15	16	17	**2** He
3 Li	**4** Be											**5** B	**6** C	**7** N	**8** O	**9** F	**10** Ne
11 Na	**12** Mg	3	4	5	6	7	8	9	10	11	12	**13** Al	**14** Si	**15** P	**16** S	**17** Cl	**18** Ar
19 K	**20** Ca	**21** Sc	**22** Ti	**23** V	**24** Cr	**25** Mn	**26** Fe	**27** Co	**28** Ni	**29** Cu	**30** Zn	**31** Ga	**32** Ge	**33** As	**34** Se	**35** Br	**36** Kr
37 Rb	**38** Sr	**39** Y	**40** Zr	**41** Nb	**42** Mo	**43** Tc	**44** Ru	**45** Rh	**46** Pd	**47** Ag	**48** Cd	**49** In	**50** Sn	**51** Sb	**52** Te	**53** I	**54** Xe
55 Cs	**56** Ba	**57** La	**72** Hf	**73** Ta	**74** W	**75** Re	**76** Os	**77** Ir	**78** Pt	**79** Au	**80** Hg	**81** Tl	**82** Pb	**83** Bi	**84** Po	**85** At	**86** Rn
87 Fr	**88** Ra	**89** Ac	**104** Unq	**105** Unp	**106** Unh	**107** Uns	**108**	**109** Une									

Lanthanide series	**58** Ce	**59** Pr	**60** Nd	**61** Pm	**62** Sm	**63** Eu	**64** Gd	**65** Tb	**66** Dy	**67** Ho	**68** Er	**69** Tm	**70** Yb	**71** Lu
Actinide series	**90** Th	**91** Pa	**92** U	**93** Np	**94** Pu	**95** Am	**96** Cm	**97** Bk	**98** Cf	**99** Es	**100** Fm	**101** Md	**102** No	**103** Lr

Figure 7.26

A form of the periodic table recommended by IUPAC.

Recently, the International Union of Pure and Applied Chemistry (IUPAC), a body of scientists organized to standardize scientific conventions, has recommended a new form for the periodic table, which the American Chemical Society has adopted (see Fig. 7.26). In this new version the group number indicates the number of *s*, *p*, and *d* electrons added since the last noble gas. We will not use the new format in this book, but you should be aware that the familiar periodic table may be soon replaced by this or a similar format.

The results considered in this section are very important. We have seen that the quantum mechanical model can be used to explain the arrangement of the elements in the periodic table. This model allows us to understand that the similar chemistry exhibited by the members of a given group arises from the fact that they all have the same valence electron configuration. Only the principal quantum number of the valence orbitals changes in·going down a particular group.

It is important to be able to give the electron configuration for each of the main-group elements. This is most easily done by using the periodic table. If you understand how the table is organized, it is not necessary to memorize the order in which the orbitals fill. Review Figs. 7.24 and 7.25 to make sure that you understand the correspondence between the orbitals and the periods and groups.

Predicting the configurations of the transition metals (3*d*, 4*d*, and 5*d* elements), the lanthanides (4*f* elements), and the actinides (5*f* elements) is somewhat more difficult because there are many exceptions of the type encountered in the first-row transition metals (the 3*d* elements). You should memorize the configurations of chromium and copper, the two exceptions in the first-row transition metals, since these elements are often encountered.

A diagram that is often used to summarize the order in which the orbitals are filled in polyelectronic atoms is shown in Fig. 7.27 on p. 314. Note that this

When an electron configuration is given in this text, the orbitals are listed in the order in which they fill.

Cr: [Ar]$4s^1 3d^5$
Cu: [Ar]$4s^1 3d^{10}$

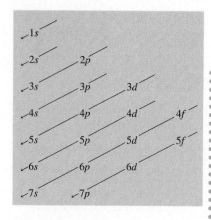

Figure 7.27

A diagram that summarizes the order in which the orbitals fill in polyelectronic atoms.

diagram is generated by listing horizontally the orbitals in a given principal quantum level and then drawing diagonal arrows to show the order of filling.

Sample Exercise 7.7

Give the electron configurations for sulfur (S), cadmium (Cd), hafnium (Hf), and radium (Ra) using the periodic table inside the front cover of this book.

Solution

Sulfur is element 16 and resides in Period 3, where the $3p$ orbitals are being filled (see Fig. 7.28). Since sulfur is the fourth among the "$3p$ elements," it must have four $3p$ electrons. Its configuration is

$$\text{S:} \quad 1s^2 2s^2 2p^6 3s^2 3p^4 \quad \text{or} \quad [\text{Ne}]3s^2 3p^4$$

Cadmium is element 48 and is located in Period 5 at the end of the $4d$ transition metals, as shown in Fig. 7.28. It is the tenth element in the series and thus has 10 electrons in the $4d$ orbitals, in addition to the two electrons in the $5s$ orbital. The configuration is

$$\text{Cd:} \quad 1s^2 2s^2 2p^6 3s^2 3p^6 4s^2 3d^{10} 4p^6 5s^2 4d^{10} \quad \text{or} \quad [\text{Kr}]5s^2 4d^{10}$$

Hafnium is element 72 and is found in Period 6, as shown in Fig. 7.28. Note that it occurs just after the lanthanide series. Thus the $4f$ orbitals are already filled. Hafnium is the second member of the $5d$ transition series and has two $5d$ electrons. The configuration is

$$\text{Hf:} \quad 1s^2 2s^2 2p^6 3s^2 3p^6 4s^2 3d^{10} 4p^6 5s^2 4d^{10} 5p^6 6s^2 4f^{14} 5d^2 \quad \text{or} \quad [\text{Xe}]6s^2 4f^{14} 5d^2$$

Radium is element 88 and is in Period 7 (and Group 2A), as shown in Fig. 7.28. Thus radium has two electrons in the $7s$ orbital, and the configuration is

$$\text{Ra:} \quad 1s^2 2s^2 2p^6 3s^2 3p^6 4s^2 3d^{10} 4p^6 5s^2 4d^{10} 5p^6 6s^2 4f^{14} 5d^{10} 6p^6 7s^2 \quad \text{or} \quad [\text{Rn}]7s^2$$

Figure 7.28

The positions of the elements considered in Sample Exercise 7.7.

7.12 *Further Development of the Polyelectronic Model*

Purpose

- To show how effective nuclear charge varies with position on the periodic table.

The simplest model for polyelectronic atoms views the atom one electron at a time, with each electron moving under the influence of an apparent nuclear charge of Z_{eff}^+. This model results in hydrogenlike orbitals occupied in a way that allows us to explain the patterns observed in the properties of elements—patterns summarized by the periodic table. Although this model greatly oversimplifies the structure of polyelectronic atoms, it is quite useful in a qualitative sense, and we will now consider this model in more detail. By calculating actual values of Z_{eff} and by observing how these values change from element to element, we can "flesh out" and develop the model to explain and predict atomic properties.

In the terms of this polyelectronic model, the energy required to remove an electron from an atom depends mainly on two factors: the effective nuclear charge and the average distance of the electron from the nucleus.

We will use Equation (7.1) to calculate values for Z_{eff}:

$$E = -2.18 \times 10^{-18} \text{ J} \left(\frac{Z^2}{n^2} \right)$$

This expression for the hydrogen energy levels can be derived from the quantum mechanical model, although it originally was derived from the Bohr model. This equation only applies to one-electron species such as H, He^+, Li^{2+}, and so on.

Although this equation originally comes from Bohr's model, which is not physically correct, it also can be derived from the quantum mechanical model. Thus this equation accurately describes the energy levels of one-electron species and is often used to treat systems of this type. For example, Equation (7.1) has been shown to agree with the measured energies for the H atom and the He^+, Li^{2+}, and Be^{3+} ions, all of which have only one electron.

Remember that the energy of a single electron reflects how tightly bound that electron is to the nucleus; the more negative the energy, the more tightly the electron is bound. Given a positive sign, it represents *the quantity of energy required to remove the electron from the gaseous atom or ion,* which is called the **ionization energy.** We will discuss this concept more fully in the next section. To calculate ionization energies, we usually convert Equation (7.1) to express energy per mole of atoms by multiplying by Avogadro's number:

$$E = \left(\frac{6.022 \times 10^{23}}{\text{mol}} \right) (-2.18 \times 10^{-18} \text{ J}) \left(\frac{Z^2}{n^2} \right)$$

$$= -\left(\frac{Z^2}{n^2} \right) (1.31 \times 10^6) \text{ J/mol} = -\left(\frac{Z^2}{n^2} \right) (1310) \text{ kJ/mol}$$

Sample Exercise 7.8

Calculate the ionization energy of the Be^{3+} ion with the electron in its ground state.

Be is $1s^2\,2s^2$; Be^{3+} is $1s^1$.

Solution

The Be^{3+} ion has one electron in the $1s$ orbital ($n = 1$) in its ground state. Since beryllium has four protons in its nucleus ($Z = 4$), the energy of the electron in the $1s$ orbital of Be^{3+} can be calculated using Equation (7.1) as follows:

$$E = -\left(\frac{Z^2}{n^2}\right)(1310)\ \text{kJ/mol} = -\left(\frac{4^2}{1^2}\right)(1310)\ \text{kJ/mol}$$

$$= 2.10 \times 10^4\ \text{kJ/mol}$$

Recall that this energy E is negative because the electron is bound to the nucleus. An equal amount of energy must be applied to remove the electron. Thus the ionization energy is *positive* and is 2.10×10^4 kJ/mol.

Recall that in the simplified model of the polyelectronic atom introduced in Section 7.9 we consider only one electron at a time. We assume that this electron is bound by a positive charge Z_{eff}, where Z_{eff} represents the charge that the electron "feels." Thus Z_{eff} represents the net effect of the attraction of the nuclear charge and the repulsion of the other electrons. In this way we change from a very complicated real atom to a much simpler hypothetical atom:

Real atom   Simplified atom

To calculate the value of Z_{eff} for a particular electron in a polyelectronic atom, we can modify Equation (7.1) by substituting Z_{eff} for Z:

Energy of given electron in polyelectronic atom

$$= -\left(\frac{Z_{\text{eff}}^2}{n^2}\right)(1310)\ \text{kJ/mol} \qquad (7.3)$$

Since this quantity of energy must be furnished to remove the electron, the ionization energy is the *positive* value of Equation (7.3). Thus the ionization energy of a given electron in a polyelectronic atom is:

$$\left(\frac{Z_{\text{eff}}^2}{n^2}\right)(1310)\ \text{kJ/mol} \qquad (7.4)$$

We can see that if the ionization energy of an electron is known from experiment, we can use Equation (7.4) to calculate Z_{eff} for that electron. That is, since ionization energy is a measurable quantity, we have a means of finding values for Z_{eff}. To see how this works, we will calculate the Z_{eff} values for the $1s$ electrons and the $3s$ electron in the sodium atom. The ionization energy for a $1s$ electron is known from experiment to be 1.39×10^5 kJ/mol and for a $3s$ electron is 4.95×10^2 kJ/mol.

For the 1s electron (n = 1),

$$1.39 \times 10^5 \text{ kJ/mol} = \text{ionization energy for a } 1s \text{ electron}$$

$$= \left(\frac{Z_{\text{eff}}^2}{n^2}\right)(1310) \text{ kJ/mol}$$

$$1.39 \times 10^5 \text{ kJ/mol} = Z_{\text{eff}}^2\left(\frac{1310 \text{ kJ/mol}}{1^2}\right)$$

$$Z_{\text{eff}}^2 = \frac{1.39 \times 10^5 \dfrac{\text{kJ}}{\text{mol}}}{1310 \dfrac{\text{kJ}}{\text{mol}}} = 1.06 \times 10^2$$

$$Z_{\text{eff}} = 10.3$$

For the 3s electron (n = 3),

$$4.95 \times 10^2 \text{ kJ/mol} = \text{ionization energy for a } 3s \text{ electron}$$

$$= \left(\frac{Z_{\text{eff}}^2}{n^2}\right)(1310) \text{ kJ/mol}$$

$$4.95 \times 10^2 \text{ kJ/mol} = Z_{\text{eff}}^2\left(\frac{1310 \text{ kJ/mol}}{3^2}\right)$$

$$Z_{\text{eff}}^2 = \frac{(4.95 \times 10^2)(9) \dfrac{\text{kJ}}{\text{mol}}}{1310 \dfrac{\text{kJ}}{\text{mol}}} = 3.40$$

$$Z_{\text{eff}} = 1.84$$

The calculated Z_{eff} value for an electron in a sodium $1s$ orbital is 10.3. Does this value make sense? It does. A $1s$ electron would be significantly affected only by the nucleus and the other $1s$ electron. The outer electrons would not have much effect on it because they are farther out from the nucleus. Thus, for a $1s$ electron, the actual charge of 11 on the sodium nucleus is only slightly reduced (from 11 to 10.3) by electron repulsions between the two $1s$ electrons. Note that since both $1s$ electrons are in an identical environment, each one has a Z_{eff} value of 10.3.

The value of Z_{eff} calculated from Equation (7.4) for the sodium $3s$ electron is 1.84. Let's see how we can use this result to help us understand our model better. The sodium $3s$ valence electron "sees" the nucleus through the 10 inner electrons, whose electron repulsions toward the $3s$ electron effectively reduce the nuclear "pull" on this electron. We say that the inner electrons *screen*, or *shield*, the $3s$ electron from some of the nuclear charge (see Fig. 7.29). If these 10 electrons were completely effective as shielding electrons, the effective nuclear charge would be $11 - 10 = 1$. However, Z_{eff} is calculated to be 1.84. The **shielding** is not totally effective. Why not?

We can understand this by looking at the radial probability distribution for an electron in a $3s$ orbital, shown in Fig. 7.30(a). Note that although the $3s$ electron spends most of the time far from the nucleus, it still has a small but significant probability of being close to the nucleus. We can see that this is so from noting the two inner peaks on the distribution. Therefore, we can say that the $3s$ electron in

Figure 7.29

The $3s$ electron in the sodium atom "sees" the nucleus through a screen of ten inner electrons. Because of this, the effective nuclear charge is much less than the actual nuclear charge of 11.

(a)

(b)

Figure 7.30

(a) The radial probability distribution for an electron in a 3s orbital. Although a 3s electron is mostly found far from the nucleus, there is a small but significant probability (shown by the arrows) of its being found close to the nucleus. The 3s electron penetrates the shield of inner electrons. (b) The radial probability distribution for the 3s, 3p, and 3d orbitals. The arrows indicate that the s orbital (red arrows) allows greater electron penetration than the p orbital (blue arrow) does; the d orbital allows minimal electron penetration.

sodium *penetrates* the 10 core electrons. *This penetration decreases the effectiveness of the shielding and thus increases the value of* Z_{eff} *for the* 3s *electron.* Because of this **penetration effect,** Z_{eff} is 1.84 instead of 1.00, the value it would be if shielding were perfect.

The amount of penetration depends on the orbital type, as we can see from Fig. 7.30(b), which shows the radial probability distributions of the orbitals for $n = 3$. For a given value of n, an electron in the s orbital always penetrates to the greatest extent, followed by one in a p orbital, and then one in a d orbital. Although it is not applicable for $n = 3$, an electron in an f orbital always penetrates least for a given n. This can be summarized as follows:

$$ns > np > nd > nf$$

↑   ↑

Most   Least
penetration   penetration

Orbital Filling Across a Period

Recall that in building up the periodic table of elements we found that for a given value of n, the order of orbital filling is first the ns orbital, then the np orbital, then the $(n + 1)s$ orbital, and then the nd orbital. We can now explain why this happens. Because of the penetration effect, electrons will prefer the ns orbital over the np orbital, and the np orbital over the nd orbital, and so on. In terms of orbital energies,

$$E_{ns} < E_{np} < E_{nd} < E_{nf}$$

Electrons always fill the lowest-energy orbitals first.

The penetration effect also explains why the 4s orbital fills before the 3d orbital. Recall that potassium has the electron configuration $1s^2 2s^2 2p^6 3s^2 3p^6 4s^1$ rather than the expected $1s^2 2s^2 2p^6 3s^2 3p^6 3d^1$. We can explain this by observing that an electron in a 4s orbital penetrates much more than an electron in a 3d orbital does, as shown graphically in Fig. 7.31. Note that although the most probable distance from the nucleus for an electron in a 3d orbital is less than that for an electron in a 4s orbital, the 4s electron has a significant probability of penetrating close to the nucleus. This penetration ability means that the potassium atom in its lowest-energy state has its last electron in the 4s orbital rather than in the 3d orbital.

Next, we want to consider the nature of the orbitals in a polyelectronic atom. How exactly do the hydrogenlike orbitals in these atoms differ from the orbitals of hydrogen? For example, let's compare the 1s orbital in sodium to that in hydrogen. An electron in the 1s orbital of sodium "sees" a positive nuclear charge of about 10.3. How does this large effective nuclear charge affect the nature of the sodium 1s orbitals? Since an electron in a sodium 1s orbital is attracted to the nucleus with a charge 10 times that for a hydrogen 1s electron, the sodium 1s electron will be bound more tightly (it will have lower energy) than the hydrogen 1s electron and

In polyelectronic atoms, only orbitals with the same n and ℓ values are degenerate. In contrast, for the hydrogen atom, all orbitals with the same n value are degenerate.

will have a smaller average distance from the nucleus. Thus the sodium $1s$ orbital is lower in energy and smaller than the hydrogen $1s$ orbital. Both orbitals still have the same spherical shape. The differences are in size and energy.

The nature of electron shielding can best be understood by considering the Z_{eff} values [calculated from Equation (7.4)] for the highest-energy electron in each of the elements hydrogen through sodium, as shown in Fig. 7.32. Note that Z_{eff} for a $1s$ electron increases in going from hydrogen to helium. The two electrons in the $1s$ orbital of helium do not completely shield each other from the nuclear charge. In general, it is true that *electrons in the same type of orbital are not very effective in shielding each other*. On the other hand, the *core electrons closer to the nucleus do provide effective shielding for outer electrons*. For example, note that Z_{eff} decreases in going from helium ($1s^2$) to lithium ($1s^2 2s^1$), because the $1s$ electrons are effective in shielding the electron in the $2s$ orbital.

The increase in Z_{eff} (shown in Fig. 7.32) in going from lithium ($1s^2 2s^1$) to beryllium ($1s^2 2s^2$) is expected, since the $2s$ electrons do not shield each other completely. The decrease in Z_{eff} in going from beryllium ($1s^2 2s^2$) to boron ($1s^2 2s^2 2p^1$) suggests that the electrons in $2s$ effectively shield the $2p$ electron. This is sensible in view of the greater penetration of the $2s$ electrons compared with the $2p$ electron. The $2s$ electrons spend time closer to the nucleus than the $2p$ electron, where they provide effective shielding. The steady increase in Z_{eff} in going from boron ($1s^2 2s^2 2p^1$) to carbon ($1s^2 2s^2 2p^2$) to nitrogen ($1s^2 2s^2 2p^3$) is expected because the $2p$ electrons are not effective in shielding each other from the increasing nuclear charge. The drop in Z_{eff} in going from nitrogen ($1s^2 2s^2 2p^3$) to oxygen ($1s^2 2s^2 2p^4$) can be explained as follows. In nitrogen, each $2p$ electron is in a separate orbital. When the extra electron for oxygen is added, one $2p$ orbital is now doubly occupied. This extra electron repulsion decreases Z_{eff} for the electrons in the doubly occupied orbital, making either of these electrons easier to remove. In going from oxygen ($1s^2 2s^2 2p^4$) to fluorine ($1s^2 2s^2 2p^5$) to neon ($1s^2 2s^2 2p^6$), Z_{eff} increases because in each case the electron being considered is in a doubly occupied orbital. Note that the Z_{eff} values for oxygen, fluorine, and neon are different from those of boron, carbon, and nitrogen by an amount that represents the extra electron repulsion due to the doubly occupied orbital, as shown in Fig. 7.32.

Electrons sharing an orbital do not shield each other as well as core electrons shield outer electrons.

Figure 7.31

Radial probability distributions for the 3d and 4s orbitals. Note that the most probable distance of the electron from the nucleus for the 3d orbital is less than that for the 4s. However, the 4s orbital allows more electron penetration close to the nucleus and thus is preferred over the 3d orbital.

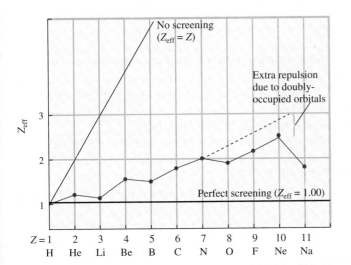

Figure 7.32

Calculated Z_{eff} values for the highest-energy electron in each of the elements hydrogen through sodium. Notice from the graph that Z_{eff} generally increases across a period going from left to right and increases going down a group.

Sample Exercise 7.9

Explain why Z_{eff} for the highest-energy electron on sodium is so much smaller than Z_{eff} for the highest-energy electron on neon.

Solution

Neon has an electron configuration of $1s^2 2s^2 2p^6$; all the $n = 2$ orbitals are filled. Because the $2p$ electrons do not shield each other very effectively, we observe a relatively large value of Z_{eff} for the $2p$ electrons. On the other hand, sodium has an electron configuration of $1s^2 2s^2 2p^6 3s^1$; the highest-energy electron in sodium (the $3s$) is effectively shielded from the nuclear charge by the core electrons. The Z_{eff} value for the $3s$ electron therefore is much smaller than Z_{eff} for the $2p$ electrons in neon. Note, however, that the shielding is not perfect; that is, $Z_{eff} \neq 1$, because the $3s$ electron penetrates the core electrons to some extent.

7.13 Periodic Trends in Atomic Properties

Purpose

- To show general trends in ionization energy, electron affinity, and atomic radius in the periodic table.

We have developed a fairly complete picture of polyelectronic atoms. Although the model is rather crude because the nuclear attractions and electron repulsions are simply lumped together to produce an effective nuclear charge, it is very successful in accounting for the periodic table of elements. Using the concepts of shielding and penetration, we have been able to explain the order of orbital filling and the electron configurations of the atoms. We will next use the model to account for the observed trends in several important atomic properties: ionization energy, electron affinity, and atomic size.

Ionization Energy

As we saw in Section 7.12, ionization energy is the energy required to remove an electron from a gaseous atom or ion:

$$X(g) \rightarrow X^+(g) + e^-$$

where the atom or ion is assumed to be in its ground state.

To introduce some of the characteristics of ionization energy, we will consider the energy required to remove several electrons in succession from aluminum in the gaseous state. The ionization energies are

$$
\begin{aligned}
\text{Al}(g) &\rightarrow \text{Al}^+(g) + e^- & I_1 &= 580 \text{ kJ/mol} \\
\text{Al}^+(g) &\rightarrow \text{Al}^{2+}(g) + e^- & I_2 &= 1815 \text{ kJ/mol} \\
\text{Al}^{2+}(g) &\rightarrow \text{Al}^{3+}(g) + e^- & I_3 &= 2740 \text{ kJ/mol} \\
\text{Al}^{3+}(g) &\rightarrow \text{Al}^{4+}(g) + e^- & I_4 &= 11{,}600 \text{ kJ/mol}
\end{aligned}
$$

Several important points can be illustrated from these results. In a stepwise ionization process, it is always the highest-energy electron (the one bound least tightly) that is removed first. The **first ionization energy** I_1 is the energy required to remove the highest-energy electron of an atom. The first electron removed from the aluminum atom comes from the $3p$ orbital (Al has the electron configuration $[Ne]3s^23p^1$). The second electron comes from the $3s$ orbital (since Al^+ has the configuration $[Ne]3s^2$). Note that the value of I_1 is considerably smaller than the value of I_2, the **second ionization energy.**

This makes sense for several reasons. The primary factor is simply charge. Note that the first electron is removed from a neutral atom (Al), whereas the second electron is removed from a $1+$ ion (Al^+). The increase in positive charge binds the electrons more firmly, and the ionization energy increases. The same trend shows up in the third (I_3) and fourth (I_4) ionization energies, where the electron is removed from the Al^{2+} and Al^{3+} ions, respectively.

The increase in successive ionization energies for an atom also can be interpreted using our simple model for polyelectronic atoms. The increase in ionization energy from I_1 to I_2 makes sense because the first electron is removed from a $3p$ orbital that is higher in energy than the $3s$ orbital from which the second electron is removed. The largest jump in ionization energy by far occurs in going from the third ionization energy (I_3) to the fourth (I_4). This is so because I_4 corresponds to removing a core electron (Al^{3+} has the configuration $1s^22s^22p^6$), and core electrons are bound much more tightly than valence electrons.

Table 7.5 gives the values of ionization energies for all the Period 3 elements. Note the large jump in energy in each case in going from removal of valence electrons to removal of core electrons.

The values of the first ionization energies for the elements in the first six periods of the periodic table are graphed in Fig. 7.33. Note that in general as we go *across a period from left to right, the first ionization energy increases*. This is consistent with our idea that electrons added in the same principal quantum level do not completely shield the increasing nuclear charge caused by the added protons. Thus there is a general increase in both the Z_{eff} and ionization energy values as electrons are added to a given principal quantum level.

Table 7.5

Successive Ionization Energies in Kilojoules per Mole for the Elements in Period 3

Element	I_1	I_2	I_3	I_4	I_5	I_6	I_7
Na	495	4560					
Mg	735	1445	7730	Core electrons*			
Al	580	1815	2740	11,600			
Si	780	1575	3220	4350	16,100		
P	1060	1890	2905	4950	6270	21,200	
S	1005	2260	3375	4565	6950	8490	27,000
Cl	1255	2295	3850	5160	6560	9360	11,000
Ar	1527	2665	3945	5770	7230	8780	12,000

*Note the large jump in ionization energy in going from removal of valence electrons to removal of core electrons.

General decrease ←

General increase →

Figure 7.33

The values of first ionization energy for the elements in the first five periods. In general, ionization energy decreases in going down a group. For example, note the decrease in values for Group 1A and Group 8A. In general, ionization energy increases in going left to right across a period. For example, note the sharp increase going across Period 2 from lithium through neon.

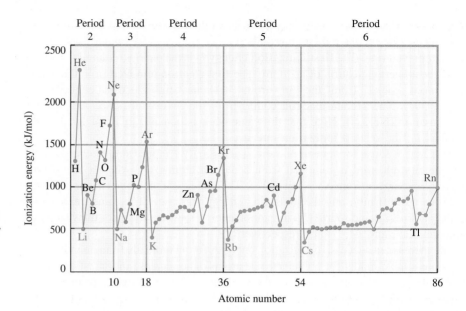

First ionization energy increases across a period and decreases down a group.

Table 7.6

First Ionization Energies for the Alkali Metals and Noble Gases

Atom	I_1 (kJ/mol)
Group 1A	
Li	520
Na	495
K	419
Rb	409
Cs	382
Group 8A	
He	2377
Ne	2088
Ar	1527
Kr	1356
Xe	1176
Rn	1042

On the other hand, *first ionization energy decreases in going down a group.* This can be most clearly seen by focusing on the Group 1A elements (the alkali metals) and the Group 8A elements (the noble gases), as shown in Table 7.6. The main reason for the decrease in ionization energy in going down a group is that the electrons being removed are, on average, farther from the nucleus. As *n* increases, the size of the orbital increases, and the electron is easier to remove.

In Fig. 7.33 we see that there are some discontinuities in ionization energy in going across a period. For example, for Period 2, discontinuities occur in going from beryllium to boron and from nitrogen to oxygen. These exceptions to the normal trend can be explained in terms of how the effective nuclear charge depends on the electron configuration. The decrease in ionization energy in going from beryllium to boron reflects the fact that the electrons in the filled 2*s* orbital provide some shielding for electrons in the 2*p* orbital from the nuclear charge. The decrease in ionization energy in going from nitrogen to oxygen reflects the extra electron repulsions in the doubly occupied oxygen 2*p* orbital.

Sample Exercise 7.10

The first ionization energy for phosphorus is 1060 kJ/mol, and that for sulfur is 1005 kJ/mol. Why?

Solution

Phosphorus and sulfur are neighboring elements in Period 3 of the periodic table and have the following valence electron configurations: phosphorus is $3s^23p^3$, and sulfur is $3s^23p^4$.

Ordinarily, the first ionization energy increases as we go across a period, so we might expect sulfur to have a greater ionization energy than phosphorus. However, in this case the fourth *p* electron in sulfur must be placed in an already occupied orbital. The electron–electron repulsions that result cause this electron to be more easily removed than might be expected.

Sample Exercise 7.11

Consider atoms with the following electron configurations:

$$1s^2 2s^2 2p^6$$
$$1s^2 2s^2 2p^6 3s^1$$
$$1s^2 2s^2 2p^6 3s^2$$

Which atom has the largest first ionization energy, and which one has the smallest second ionization energy? Explain your choices.

Solution

The atom with the largest value of I_1 is the one with the configuration $1s^2 2s^2 2p^6$ (this is the neon atom), because this element is found at the right end of Period 2. Since the $2p$ electrons do not shield each other very effectively, Z_{eff} will be relatively large, and thus I_1 also will be large. The other configurations given include $3s$ electrons. These electrons are effectively shielded by the core electrons and are farther from the nucleus than the $2p$ electrons in neon. Thus I_1 for these atoms will be smaller than for neon.

The atom with the smallest value of I_2 is the one with the configuration $1s^2 2s^2 2p^6 3s^2$ (the magnesium atom). For magnesium, both I_1 and I_2 involve valence electrons. For the atom with the configuration $1s^2 2s^2 2p^6 3s^1$ (sodium), the second electron lost (corresponding to I_2) is a core electron (from a $2p$ orbital).

Electron Affinity

Electron affinity *is the energy change associated with the addition of an electron to a gaseous atom:*

$$X(g) + e^- \rightarrow X^-(g)$$

Because two different conventions have been used, there is a good deal of confusion in the chemical literature about the signs for electron affinity values. Electron affinity has been defined in many textbooks as the energy *released* when an electron is added to a gaseous atom. This convention requires that a positive sign be attached to an exothermic addition of an electron to an atom, which opposes normal thermodynamic conventions. Therefore, in this book we define electron affinity as a *change* in energy, which means that if the addition of the electron is exothermic, the corresponding value for electron affinity will carry a negative sign.

Figure 7.34 shows the electron affinity values for the atoms among the first 20 elements that form stable, isolated, negative ions—that is, the atoms that undergo the addition of an electron as shown above. As expected, all these elements have negative (exothermic) electron affinities. Note that the *more negative* the energy, the greater is the quantity of energy released. Although electron affinities generally become more negative from left to right across a period, there are several exceptions

The sign convention for electron affinity values follows the convention for energy changes used in Chapter 6.

Figure 7.34

The electron affinity values for atoms among the first 20 elements that form stable, isolated X⁻ ions. The lines shown connect adjacent elements. The absence of a line indicates missing elements (He, Be, N, Ne, Mg, Ar, and Ca), whose atoms do not add an electron exothermically and thus do not form stable, isolated X⁻ ions.

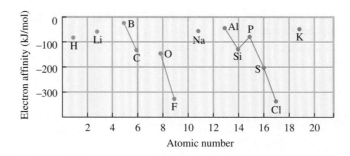

to this rule in each period. The dependence of electron affinity on atomic number can be explained by considering the changes in electron repulsions as a function of electron configurations. For example, the fact that the nitrogen atom does not form a stable, isolated $N^-(g)$ ion, whereas carbon forms $C^-(g)$, reflects the difference in the electron configurations of these atoms. An electron added to nitrogen $(1s^22s^22p^3)$ to form the $N^-(g)$ ion $(1s^22s^22p^4)$ would have to occupy a $2p$ orbital that already contains one electron. The extra repulsion between the electrons in this doubly occupied orbital causes $N^-(g)$ to be unstable. When an electron is added to carbon $(1s^22s^22p^2)$ to form the $C^-(g)$ ion $(1s^22s^22p^3)$, no such extra repulsions occur.

In contrast to the nitrogen atom, the oxygen atom can add one electron to form the stable $O^-(g)$ ion. Presumably oxygen's greater nuclear charge compared with that of nitrogen is sufficient to overcome the repulsion associated with putting a second electron into an already occupied $2p$ orbital. However, it should be noted that a second electron *cannot* be added to an oxygen atom $[O^-(g) + e^- \not\rightarrow O^{2-}(g)]$ to form an isolated oxide ion. This outcome seems strange in view of the many stable oxide compounds (MgO, Fe_2O_3, and so on) that are known. As we will discuss in detail in Chapter 8, the O^{2-} ion is stabilized in ionic compounds by the large attractions that occur among the positive ions and the oxide ions.

When we go down a group, electron affinity should become more positive (less energy released), since the electron is added at increasing distances from the nucleus. Although this is generally the case, the changes in electron affinity in going down most groups are relatively small, and numerous exceptions occur. This behavior is demonstrated by the electron affinities of the Group 7A elements (the halogens) shown in Table 7.7. Note that the range of values is quite small compared with the changes that typically occur across a period. Also note that although chlorine, bromine, and iodine show the expected trend, the energy released when an electron is added to fluorine is smaller than might be expected. This smaller energy release has been attributed to the small size of the $2p$ orbitals. Because the electrons must be very close together in these orbitals, there are unusually large electron–electron repulsions. In the other halogens with their larger orbitals, the repulsions are not as severe.

Atomic Radius

Just as the size of an orbital cannot be specified exactly, neither can the size of an atom. We must make some arbitrary choices to obtain values for **atomic radii.** These values can be obtained by measuring the distances between atoms in chemical compounds. For example, in the bromine molecule the distance between the two

Table 7.7

Electron Affinities of the Halogens

Atom	Electron Affinity (kJ/mol)
F	−327.8
Cl	−348.7
Br	−324.5
I	−295.2

nuclei is known to be 228 pm. The bromine atomic radius is assumed to be half this distance, or 114 pm, as shown in Fig. 7.35. Measurements of this type have led to the values of the atomic radii for the elements shown in Fig. 7.36. These radii are often called **covalent atomic radii** because of the way they are determined (from the distances between atoms in covalent bonds). These values are significantly smaller than might be expected from the 90% electron density volumes of isolated atoms, because when atoms form bonds, their electron "clouds" interpenetrate. However, these values form a self-consistent data set that can be used to discuss the trends in atomic radii.

Note from Fig. 7.36 that the atomic radii decrease in going from left to right across a period. This decrease can be explained in terms of the increasing effective nuclear charge (decreasing shielding) in going from left to right. This means that the valence electrons are drawn closer to the nucleus, decreasing the size of the atom.

Atomic radius increases down a group, because of the increases in the orbital sizes in successive principal quantum levels.

Figure 7.35

The radius of an atom (r) is defined as half the distance between the nuclei in a molecule consisting of identical atoms.

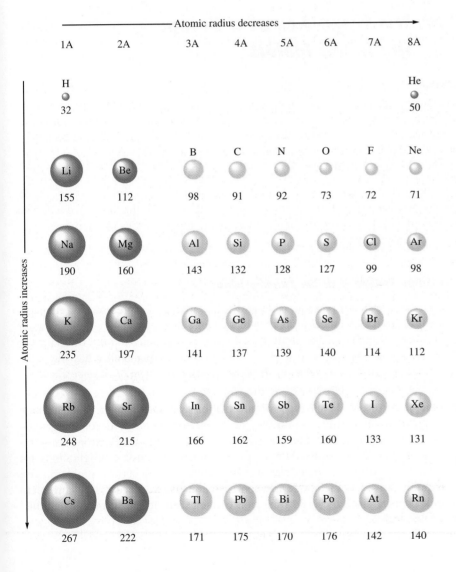

Figure 7.36

Covalent atomic radii (in picometers) for selected atoms. Note that atomic radius decreases going across a period and increases going down a group. The values for the noble gases are estimated, because data from bonded atoms are lacking.

Sample Exercise 7.13

Predict the trend in radius for the following ions: Be^{2+}, Mg^{2+}, Ca^{2+}, and Sr^{2+}.

Solution

All these ions are formed by removing two electrons from an atom of a Group 2A element. In going from beryllium to strontium, we are going down the group, so the sizes increase:

$$Be^{2+} < Mg^{2+} < Ca^{2+} < Sr^{2+}$$

$\uparrow$ $\uparrow$

Smallest radius   Largest radius

7.14 The Properties of a Group: The Alkali Metals

Purpose

- To show what types of information can be obtained from the periodic table.

We have seen that the periodic table originated as a way to portray the systematic properties of the elements. Mendeleev was primarily responsible for first showing its usefulness in correlating and predicting the elemental properties. In this section we will summarize much of the information available from the table. We will also illustrate the usefulness of the table by discussing the properties of a representative group, the alkali metals.

Information Contained in the Periodic Table

1. The essence of the periodic table is that the groups of representative elements exhibit similar chemical properties that change in a regular way. The quantum mechanical model of the atom has allowed us to understand the basis for the similarity of properties in a group—that each group member has the same valence electron configuration. *It is the number and type of valence electrons that primarily determine an atom's chemistry.*

2. One of the most valuable types of information available from the periodic table is the electron configuration of any representative element. If you understand the organization of the table, you will not need to memorize electron configurations for these elements. Although the predicted electron configurations for transition metals are sometimes incorrect, this is not a serious problem. You should, however, memorize the configuration of two exceptions, chromium and copper, since these $3d$ transition elements are found in many important compounds.

Figure 7.37

Special names for groups in the periodic table.

3. As we mentioned in Chapter 2, certain groups in the periodic table have special names. These are summarized in Fig. 7.37. Groups are often referred to by these names, so you should learn them.

4. The most basic division of the elements in the periodic table is into metals and nonmetals. The most important chemical property of a metal atom is the tendency to give up one or more electrons to form a positive ion; metals tend to have low ionization energies. The metallic elements are found on the left side of the table, as shown in Fig. 7.37. The most chemically reactive metals are found on the lower left-hand portion of the table, where the ionization energies are smallest. The most distinctive chemical property of a nonmetal atom is the ability to gain one or more electrons to form an anion when reacting with a metal. Thus nonmetals are elements with large ionization energies and the most negative electron affinities. The nonmetals are found on the right side of the

Metals and nonmetals were first discussed in Chapter 2.

table, with the most reactive ones in the upper right-hand corner, except for the noble gas elements, which are quite unreactive. The division into metals and nonmetals shown in Fig. 7.37 is only approximate. Many elements along the division line exhibit both metallic and nonmetallic properties under certain circumstances. These elements are often called **metalloids,** or sometimes **semimetals.**

The Alkali Metals

The metals of Group 1A, the alkali metals, illustrate very well the relationships among the properties of the elements in a group. Lithium, sodium, potassium, rubidium, cesium, and francium are the most chemically reactive of the metals. We will not discuss francium here because it occurs in nature in only very small quantities. Although hydrogen is found in Group 1A of the periodic table, it behaves as a nonmetal, in contrast to the other members of that group. The fundamental reason for hydrogen's nonmetallic character is its very small size (see Fig. 7.36). The electron in the small $1s$ orbital is bound tightly to the nucleus.

Hydrogen will be discussed further in Chapter 18.

Some important properties of the first five alkali metals are shown in Table 7.8. The data in Table 7.8 show that in going down the group, the first ionization energy decreases and the atomic radius increases. This agrees with the general trends discussed in Section 7.13.

The overall increase in density in going down Group 1A is typical of all groups. This occurs because atomic mass generally increases more rapidly than atomic size. Thus there is more mass per unit volume for each succeeding element.

Other groups will be discussed in Chapters 18 and 19.

The smooth decrease in melting point and boiling point in going down Group 1A is not typical; in most other groups more complicated behavior occurs. Note that the melting point of cesium is only 29°C. Cesium can be melted readily using only the heat from your hand. This is very unusual—metals typically have rather high melting points. For example, tungsten melts at 3410°C. The only other metals with low melting points are mercury (mp -38°C) and gallium (mp 30°C).

Oxidation–reduction reactions were discussed in Chapter 4.

The chemical property most characteristic of a metal is the ability to lose its valence electrons. The Group 1A elements are very reactive. They have low ionization energies and react readily with nonmetals to form ionic solids. A typical example involves the reaction of sodium with chlorine to form sodium chloride:

$$2Na(s) + Cl_2(g) \rightarrow 2NaCl(s)$$

Table 7.8

Properties of Five Alkali Metals

Element	Valence Electron Configuration	Density at 25°C (g/cm³)	mp (°C)	bp (°C)	First Ionization Energy (kJ/mol)	Atomic (covalent) Radius (pm)	Ionic (M⁺) Radius (pm)
Li	$2s^1$	0.53	180	1330	520	155	60
Na	$3s^1$	0.97	98	892	495	190	95
K	$4s^1$	0.86	64	760	419	235	133
Rb	$5s^1$	1.53	39	688	409	248	148
Cs	$6s^1$	1.87	29	690	382	267	169

where sodium chloride contains Na^+ and Cl^- ions. This is an oxidation–reduction reaction in which chlorine oxidizes sodium. In the reactions between metals and nonmetals, it is typical for the nonmetal to behave as the oxidizing agent and the metal to behave as the reducing agent, as shown by the following reactions:

$$2Na(s) + S(s) \rightarrow Na_2S(s)$$
Contains Na^+ and S^{2-} ions

$$6Li(s) + N_2(g) \rightarrow 2Li_3N(s)$$
Contains Li^+ and N^{3-} ions

$$4Na(s) + 2O_2(g) \rightarrow 2Na_2O_2(s)$$
Contains Na^+ and O_2^{2-} ions

For reactions of the types just shown, the relative reducing powers of the alkali metals can be predicted from the first ionization energies listed in Table 7.8. Since it is much easier to remove an electron from a cesium atom than from a lithium atom, cesium should be the better reducing agent. The expected trend in reducing ability is

$$Cs > Rb > K > Na > Li$$

This order is observed experimentally for direct reactions between the solid alkali metals and nonmetals. However, this is not the order of reducing ability found when the alkali metals react in aqueous solution. For example, the reduction of water by an alkali metal is very vigorous and exothermic:

$$2M(s) + 2H_2O(l) \rightarrow H_2(g) + 2M^+(aq) + 2OH^-(aq) + \text{energy}$$

The order of reducing abilities observed for this reaction for the first three group members is

$$Li > K > Na$$

In the gas phase potassium loses an electron more easily than sodium, and sodium more easily than lithium. Thus it is surprising that lithium is the best reducing agent toward water.

This reversal occurs because the formation of the M^+ ions in aqueous solution is strongly influenced by the hydration of these ions by the polar water molecules. The **hydration energy** of an ion represents the change in energy that occurs when water molecules attach to the M^+ ion. The hydration energies for the Li^+, Na^+, and K^+ ions (shown in Table 7.9) indicate that the process is exothermic in each case. However, nearly twice as much energy is released by the hydration of the Li^+ ion as for the K^+ ion. This difference is caused by size effects; the Li^+ ion is much smaller than the K^+ ion, and thus its **charge density** (charge per unit volume) is also much greater. This means that the polar water molecules are more strongly attracted to the small Li^+ ion. Because the Li^+ ion is so strongly hydrated, its formation from the lithium atom occurs more readily than the formation of the K^+ ion from the potassium atom. Although a potassium atom in the gas phase loses its valence electron more readily than a lithium atom in the gas phase, the opposite is true in aqueous solution. This anomaly is an example of the importance of the polarity of the water molecule in aqueous reactions.

There is one more surprise involving the highly exothermic reactions of the alkali metals with water. Experiments show that in water lithium is the best reducing agent, so we might expect that lithium should react the most violently with water. However, this is not true. Sodium and potassium react much more vigorously. Why

Table 7.9

Ion	Hydration Energy (kJ/mol)
Hydration Energies for Li^+, Na^+, and K^+ Ions	
Li^+	−510
Na^+	−402
K^+	−314

Potassium reacts violently with water.

◀ **CHEMICAL IMPACT** ▶

Lithium: Behavior Medicine

More and more people in our society seem to be suffering from the debilitating effects of mania and depression, but the alkali metal lithium can provide help for many. In fact, over 3 million prescriptions for lithium carbonate are filled annually by retail pharmacies.

Although the details are not well understood, the lithium ion seems to alleviate mood disorders by affecting the way that brain cells respond to neurotransmitters, a class of molecules that facilitates the transmission of nerve impulses.

Specifically, it is thought that the lithium ion may interfere with a complex cycle of reactions that relays and amplifies messages carried to the cells by neurotransmitters and hormones. It is theorized that exaggerated forms of behavior, such as mania or depression, arise from the overactivity of this cycle. The fact that lithium inhibits this cycle may be responsible for its moderating effect on behavior.

There is a growing collection of evidence that violent behavior may result at least partially from improper regulation of neurotransmitters and hormones. For example, a study in Finland showed that violent criminals, especially arsonists, often had low levels of serotonin, a common neurotransmitter. Studies are now underway to determine whether lithium might be effective in altering violent behavior.

is this so? The answer lies in the relatively high melting point of lithium. When sodium and potassium react with water, the heat evolved causes them to melt, giving a larger area of contact with water. Lithium, on the other hand, does not melt under these conditions and reacts more slowly. This illustrates the important principle (which we will discuss in detail in Chap. 12) that the energy change for a reaction and the rate at which it occurs are not necessarily related.

In this section we have seen that the trends in atomic properties summarized by the periodic table can be a great help in understanding the chemical behavior of the elements. This fact will be emphasized over and over as we proceed in our study of chemistry.

FOR REVIEW

Summary

Energy can travel through space as electromagnetic radiation, which is characterized by wavelength (λ), frequency (ν), and speed ($c = 2.9979 \times 10^8$ m/s). These three properties are related by the equation $\lambda\nu = c$. Originally, energy was assumed to be continuous, but Planck showed that energy could be lost or gained only in quanta, which are whole-number multiples of $h\nu$ (h is Planck's constant, 6.626×10^{-34} J · s). Einstein postulated that electromagnetic radiation itself can be viewed as a stream of particles called photons, each with energy $h\nu$. Electromagnetic radiation therefore exhibits both wave and particulate properties. The postulate by de Broglie that particles possess wave characteristics was verified by diffraction experiments showing that all matter exhibits the same properties.

A continuous spectrum results from dispersing white light. However, when the emission spectrum produced by excited hydrogen atoms is dispersed, only selected wavelengths are seen, giving a line spectrum. This shows that only certain energies are allowed for the electron in the hydrogen atom.

The Bohr model of the hydrogen atom speculated that the electron in a hydrogen atom moves around the nucleus in certain allowed circular orbits and that the line spectrum was produced when an electron moved from one orbit to another. The Bohr model, however, was shown to be incorrect.

The quantum (wave) mechanical model for the hydrogen atom employs the concept of standing waves. The electron is described by a wave function, often called an orbital, which does not give the exact position for the electron at a given time. This is consistent with the Heisenberg uncertainty principle, which states that it is impossible to know both the position and the momentum of a particle accurately at a given time. However, we can give a physical meaning to the wave function: the square of the function is related to the probability of finding an electron near a particular point in space. Probability distributions (electron density maps) are used to define orbital shapes. Orbitals are characterized by the quantum numbers n, ℓ, and m_ℓ.

Another property of the electron is its spin. An electron appears to spin in two directions, giving rise to two values for the electron spin quantum number (m_s). This concept leads to the Pauli exclusion principle: no two electrons in a given atom can have the same set of four quantum numbers.

Using this principle along with the quantum mechanical model, we can predict the electronic configurations of the atoms in the periodic table. As protons are added one by one to the nucleus to build up the elements, electrons are added to the orbitals. This is called the aufbau principle.

The greatest triumph of the quantum mechanical model is its use to explain the observed periodic properties of the elements as summarized by the periodic table. The chemical properties of an atom are determined by the arrangement of the valence electrons (the electrons in the outermost principal quantum level). Elements in the same group of the periodic table have the same valence electron configurations, which explains why group members show similar chemical properties.

In polyelectronic atoms the repulsions among electrons can be assumed to reduce the actual nuclear charge to an apparent value called the effective nuclear charge (Z_{eff}), which is always less than Z (the atomic number). The ionization energy, the energy required to remove an electron from a gaseous atom or ion, provides a means for calculating Z_{eff}.

The periodic trends in atomic properties such as ionization energy, electron affinity, and atomic radius can be explained in terms of the concepts of shielding and penetration and their influence on the size of Z_{eff}.

Key Terms

Section 7.1
electromagnetic radiation
wavelength
frequency

Section 7.2
Planck's constant
quantization
photon
$E = mc^2$
dual nature of light
diffraction

diffraction pattern

Section 7.3
continuous spectrum
line spectrum

Section 7.4
quantum model
ground state

Section 7.5
standing wave
quantum (wave) mechanical model

wave function
orbital
Heisenberg uncertainty principle
probability distribution
radial probability distribution

Section 7.6
quantum numbers
principal quantum number (n)
angular momentum quantum number (ℓ)
magnetic quantum number (m_ℓ)
subshell

Section 7.7
nodal surface
node
degenerate

Section 7.8
electron spin
electron spin quantum number
Pauli exclusion principle

Section 7.9
polyelectronic atoms
effective nuclear charge

Section 7.11
aufbau principle
Hund's rule
valence electrons
core electrons

transition metals
lanthanide series
actinide series
main-group elements
　(representative elements)

Section 7.12
ionization energy
shielding

penetration effect

Section 7.13
first ionization energy
second ionization energy
electron affinity
atomic radii

Section 7.14
metalloids

A blue question or exercise number indicates that the answer to that question or exercise appears at the back of the book and a solution appears in the Solutions Guide.

Questions

1. What experimental evidence supports the quantum theory for light?

2. What do we mean when we say that something is quantized? In the Bohr model of the hydrogen atom, what is quantized?

3. For what sizes of particles and velocities must one consider quantum effects?

4. Summarize some of the evidence supporting the wave properties of matter.

5. Define each of the following terms.
   a. Photon
   b. Quantum number
   c. Ground state
   d. Excited state

6. In the hydrogen atom, what information do we get from the values of the quantum numbers n, ℓ, and m_ℓ?

7. How do the $2p$ orbitals differ from each other?

8. How do the $2p$ and $3p$ orbitals differ from each other?

9. What is a nodal surface in an atomic orbital?

10. What is the physical significance of the value of ψ^2 at a particular point?

11. Why can we not account exactly for the repulsions among electrons in a polyelectronic atom?

12. We define a spin quantum number, but do we know that an electron literally spins?

13. Explain what we mean when we say that a $4s$ electron is more penetrating than a $3d$ electron.

14. Why do we emphasize the valence electrons in an atom when discussing atomic properties?

15. Many times the claim is made that subshells half filled with electrons are particularly stable. Can you suggest a possible physical basis for this claim?

16. Why do the successive ionization energies of an atom always increase?

17. Scientists use emission spectra to confirm the presence of an element in materials of unknown composition. Why is this possible?

18. Does the minimization of electron–electron repulsions correlate with Hund's rule?

19. In the hydrogen atom, what is the physical significance of the state for which $n = \infty$ and $E = 0$?

20. What is the most important relationship among the elements in the same group in the periodic table?

Exercises

In this section similar exercises are paired.

Light and Matter

21. An FM radio station broadcasts at 99.5 MHz. Calculate the wavelength of the corresponding radio waves.

22. The laser in an audio compact disc player uses light with a wavelength of 7.80×10^2 nm. Calculate the frequency of this light. Calculate the energy of a single photon of this light.

23. Microwave radiation has a wavelength on the order of 1.0 cm. Calculate the frequency and the energy of a single photon of this radiation. Calculate the energy of an Avogadro's number of photons (called an **einstein**) of this radiation.

24. The primary visible emissions from mercury occur at 404.7 and 435.8 nm. Calculate the frequencies of these emissions. Calculate the energy of a single photon and a mole of photons of light with each of these wavelengths.

25. It takes 7.21×10^{-19} J of energy to remove an electron from an iron atom. What is the maximum wavelength of light that can do this?

26. The work function of an element is the energy required to remove an electron from the surface of the solid element. The work function for lithium is 279.7 kJ/mol (that is, it takes 279.7 kJ of energy to remove 1 mole of electrons from 1 mole of Li atoms on the surface of Li metal). What is the maximum wavelength of light that can remove an electron from an atom on the surface of lithium metal?

27. It takes 492 kJ of energy to remove 1 mole of electrons from the atoms on the surface of solid gold. How much energy does it take to remove a single electron from an atom on the surface of solid gold? What is the maximum wavelength of light capable of doing this?

28. It takes 208.4 kJ of energy to remove 1 mole of electrons from the atoms on the surface of rubidium metal. If rubidium metal is irradiated with 254-nm light, what is the maximum kinetic energy a liberated electron can have?

29. The ionization energy of gold is 890.1 kJ/mol. Is light with a wavelength of 225 nm capable of ionizing a gold atom in the gas phase?

30. The ionization energy of sodium is 495 kJ/mol. Will gaseous sodium atoms be ionized by light with wavelength 589 nm?

Hydrogen Atom: The Bohr Model

31. Calculate the wavelength of light emitted when each of the following transitions occur in the hydrogen atom.
    a. $n = 3 \rightarrow n = 2$
    b. $n = 4 \rightarrow n = 2$
    c. $n = 2 \rightarrow n = 1$

32. Calculate the wavelength of light emitted when each of the following transitions occur in the hydrogen atom.
    a. $n = 4 \rightarrow n = 3$
    b. $n = 5 \rightarrow n = 4$
    c. $n = 5 \rightarrow n = 3$

33. Calculate the maximum wavelength of light capable of removing an electron from a hydrogen atom for the energy states characterized by $n = 1$ and $n = 2$.

34. Calculate the maximum wavelength of light capable of removing an electron from a hydrogen atom for the energy states characterized by $n = 4$ and $n = 10$.

35. Using vertical lines, indicate the transitions from Exercise 31 on the energy-level diagram for the hydrogen atom (see Fig. 7.8).

36. Using vertical lines, indicate the transitions that correspond to the transitions in Exercise 32 on the energy-level diagram for the hydrogen atom (see Fig. 7.8).

37. Calculate the longest and shortest wavelengths of light emitted by electrons in the hydrogen atom that begin in the $n = 6$ state and then fall to states with smaller values of n.

38. An excited hydrogen atom emits light with a frequency of 1.141×10^{14} Hz to reach the energy level for which $n = 4$. In what principal quantum level did the electron begin?

Quantum Mechanics, Quantum Numbers, and Orbitals

39. Calculate the de Broglie wavelength for each of the following.
    a. A proton with a velocity 5.0% of the speed of light
    b. An electron with a velocity 15% of the speed of light
    c. The fastest measured pitched baseball (a 5.2-oz baseball with a velocity of 100.8 mi/h)

40. Neutron diffraction is used in determining the structures of molecules.
    a. Calculate the de Broglie wavelength of a neutron moving at 1.00% of the speed of light.
    b. Calculate the velocity of a neutron with a wavelength of 75 pm (1 pm = 10^{-12} m).

41. Calculate the velocities of electrons with de Broglie wavelengths of 1.0×10^2 and 1.0 nm, respectively.

42. What would the value of Planck's constant have to be in order for the wavelength of the baseball in Exercise 39, part c, to be 5.0 cm? 5.0×10^2 nm?

43. From the Heisenberg uncertainty principle, calculate Δx for an electron with $\Delta v = 0.100$ m/s. How does Δx compare with the size of a hydrogen atom?

44. From the Heisenberg uncertainty principle, calculate Δx for a baseball (mass = 145 g) with $\Delta v = 0.100$ m/s. How does Δx compare with the size of a baseball?

45. What are the possible values for the quantum numbers n, ℓ, and m_ℓ?

46. Which of the following orbital designations are incorrect: $1s$, $1p$, $7d$, $9s$, $3f$, $4f$, $2d$?

47. Which of the following sets of quantum numbers are not allowed in the hydrogen atom? For the sets of quantum numbers that are incorrect, state what is wrong in each set.
a. $n = 2$, $\ell = 1$, $m_\ell = -1$
b. $n = 1$, $\ell = 1$, $m_\ell = 0$
c. $n = 8$, $\ell = 7$, $m_\ell = -6$
d. $n = 1$, $\ell = 0$, $m_\ell = 2$

48. Which of the following sets of quantum numbers are not allowed in the hydrogen atom? For the sets of quantum numbers that are incorrect, state what is wrong in each set.
a. $n = 3$, $\ell = 2$, $m_\ell = 2$
b. $n = 4$, $\ell = 3$, $m_\ell = 4$
c. $n = 0$, $\ell = 0$, $m_\ell = 0$
d. $n = 2$, $\ell = -1$, $m_\ell = 1$

Polyelectronic Atoms

49. Calculate the ionization energy (in kJ/mol) for each of the following one-electron species.
a. H   b. He^+ c. Li^{2+}
What are the relative sizes of the $1s$ orbitals in these species?

50. Calculate the ionization energy (in kJ/mol) for each of the following one-electron species.
a. Be^{3+} b. C^{5+} c. Fe^{25+}

51. How many orbitals in an atom can have the designation: $5p$, $3d_{z^2}$, $4d$, $n = 5$, $n = 4$?

52. How many electrons in an atom can have the designation: $1s$, $2p$, $3p_x$, $6f$, $2d_{xy}$?

53. What is the maximum number of electrons in an atom that can have these quantum numbers:
a. $n = 4$
b. $n = 5$, $m_\ell = +1$
c. $n = 5$, $m_s = +\frac{1}{2}$
d. $n = 3$, $\ell = 2$
e. $n = 2$, $\ell = 1$

54. What is the maximum number of electrons in an atom that can have these quantum numbers:
a. $n = 0$, $\ell = 0$, $m_\ell = 0$
b. $n = 2$, $\ell = 1$, $m_\ell = -1$, $m_s = -\frac{1}{2}$
c. $n = 3$
d. $n = 2$, $\ell = 2$
e. $n = 1$, $\ell = 0$, $m_\ell = 0$

55. Write the expected electron configurations for each of the following atoms: Sc, Fe, S, P, Cs, Eu, Pt, Xe, Br, Se.

56. Write the expected electron configurations for each of the following atoms: K, Rb, Fr, Pu, Sb, Os, Pd, Cd, Pb, I.

57. Using Figure 7.25, list elements (ignore the lanthanides and actinides) that have ground state electron configurations that differ from those we would expect from their positions in the periodic table.

58. The electron configurations in Figure 7.25 are for atoms in the gas phase and are determined experimentally. Would you expect the electron configurations to be the same in the solid and liquid states as in the gas phase?

59. Write an electron configuration for each of the following.
a. The smallest halogen atom
b. The alkali metal with only $2p$ and $3p$ electrons
c. The three lightest alkaline earth metals
d. The Group 3A element in the same period as Sn
e. The nonmetallic elements in Group 4A
f. The (as yet undiscovered) noble gas after radon

60. Identify the following elements.
a. An excited state of this element has the electron configuration $1s^2 2s^2 2p^5 3s^1$.
b. The ground-state electron configuration is $[Ne]3s^2 3p^4$.
c. An excited state of this element has the electron configuration $[Kr]5s^2 4d^6 5p^2 6s^1$.
d. The ground-state electron configuration contains three unpaired $6p$ electrons.

61. Give a possible set of values of the four quantum numbers for all the electrons in a boron atom, a carbon atom, a nitrogen atom, and an oxygen atom if each is in the ground state.

62. Give a possible set of values for the four quantum numbers of all the valence electrons in each of the following atoms if each is in its ground state: Al, As, Sb, S, Se.

---

63. A certain oxygen atom has the electron configuration $1s^22s^22p_x^22p_y^2$. How many unpaired electrons are present? Is this an excited state of oxygen? In going from this state to the ground state would energy be released or absorbed?

64. Which of the following electron configurations correspond to an excited state? Identify the atoms and write the ground-state electron configuration where appropriate.
    a. $1s^22s^23p^1$
    b. $1s^22s^22p^6$
    c. $1s^22s^22p^43s^1$
    d. $[Ar]4s^23d^54p^1$
    How many unpaired electrons are present in each of these species?

---

65. How many unpaired electrons are present in the ground-state electron configurations of Sc, Ti, Al, Sn, Te, and Br?

66. How many unpaired electrons are present in each of the following in the ground state: O, O^+, O^-, Fe, Mn, S, F, Ar?

The Periodic Table and Periodic Properties

67. Arrange the following groups of atoms in order of increasing size.
    a. Be, Mg, Ca
    b. Te, I, Xe
    c. Ga, Ge, In

68. Arrange the following groups of atoms in order of increasing size.
    a. As, N, F
    b. S, Cl, F
    c. Cs, Li, K

---

69. Arrange the atoms in Exercise 67 in order of increasing first ionization energy.

70. Arrange the atoms in Exercise 68 in order of increasing first ionization energy.

---

71. Arrange the atoms in Exercise 67 in order of increasing Z_{eff} for the highest-energy electron.

72. Arrange the atoms in Exercise 68 in order of increasing Z_{eff} for the highest-energy electron.

---

73. The first ionization energies of Ge, As, and Se are 0.7622, 0.944, and 0.9409 MJ/mol, respectively. Rationalize these values in terms of electron configurations.

74. The first ionization energies of the so-called coinage metals, Cu, Ag, and Au, are 745.5, 731.0, and 890.1 kJ/mol, respectively. Is this the trend you might have expected? In the *CRC Handbook of Chemistry and Physics,* look up the first ionization energies of the following sets of elements: (Sc, Y, La), (Ti, Zr, Hf), (Fe, Ru, Os), (Ga, In, Tl), and (As, Sb, Bi). Which groups follow the same trend as the coinage metals?

---

75. In each of the following sets, which atom or ion has the smallest radius?
    a. Li, Na, K   d. S, Cl, Kr
    b. P, As   e. Pd, Ni, Cu
    c. O^+, O, O^-

76. In each of the following sets, which atom or ion has the smallest ionization energy?
    a. Cs, Ba, La   d. Tl, Sn, As
    b. Zn, Ga, Ge   e. O, O^-, O^{2-}
    c. Tl, In, Sn

---

77. From the information in Table 7.8, estimate values of the ionization energy and melting point for francium.

78. Predict some of the properties of element 117 (the symbol is Uus, following conventions proposed by the International Union of Pure and Applied Chemistry, or IUPAC).
    a. What will be its electron configuration?
    b. What element will it most resemble chemically?
    c. What will be the formulas of the neutral binary compounds it forms with sodium, magnesium, carbon, and oxygen?
    d. What oxyanions would you expect Uus to form?

---

79. Order the atoms in each of the following sets from the least exothermic electron affinity to the most.
    a. O, S
    b. F, Cl, Br, I

80. Order the atoms in each of the following sets from the least exothermic electron affinity to the most.
    a. N, O, F
    b. B, C, N

81. For each of the following pairs of elements

(Li and K)   (S and Sc)

pick the atom with
a. More favorable (exothermic) electron affinity.
b. Higher ionization energy.
c. Larger size.

82. For each of the following pairs of elements

(B and N)   (F and Cl)

pick the atom with
a. More favorable (exothermic) electron affinity.
b. Higher ionization energy.
c. Larger size.

83. The electron affinity of sodium is -52.9 kJ/mol. In principle, should it be possible to add one electron to $Na(g)$ to form the sodide ion, $Na^-(g)$?

84. Which would have the more negative electron affinity, the oxygen atom or the O^- ion? Explain.

85. Using the element phosphorus as an example, write the equation for a process in which the energy change will correspond to the ionization energy.

86. Using the element phosphorus as an example, write the equation for a process in which the energy change will correspond to the electron affinity.

87. Use data in this chapter to determine
a. The electron affinity of Mg^{2+}.
b. The electron affinity of Al^+.

88. Use data in this chapter to determine
a. The ionization energy of Cl^-.
b. The ionization energy of Cl.
c. The electron affinity of Cl^+.

Alkali and Alkaline Earth Elements

89. Many more anhydrous lithium salts are hygroscopic (readily absorb water) than those of the other alkali metals. Explain.

90. Small daily doses (1 to 2 g) of lithium carbonate taken orally are often given to treat manic depressive psychoses. This dosage maintains the level of lithium ion in the blood at approximately 1×10^{-3} mol/L.
a. What is the formula of lithium carbonate?
b. How many grams of lithium are present per liter of blood in these patients?

91. An ionic compound of potassium and oxygen has the empirical formula KO. Would you expect this compound to be potassium(II) oxide or potassium peroxide? Explain.

92. An ionic compound of magnesium and oxygen has the empirical formula MgO. Would you expect this compound to be magnesium(II) oxide or magnesium(I) peroxide? Explain.

93. Cesium was discovered in natural mineral waters in 1860 by R. W. Bunsen and G. R. Kirchoff using the spectroscope they invented in 1859. The name came from the Latin (*caesius*, "sky blue") because of the prominent blue line observed for this element at 455.5 nm. Calculate the frequency and energy of a photon of this light.

94. The bright yellow light emitted by a sodium vapor lamp consists of two emission lines at 589.0 and 589.6 nm. What are the frequency and the energy of a photon of light at each of these wavelengths? What are the energies in kJ/mol?

95. Give the name and formula of each of the binary compounds formed from the following elements.
a. Li and N
b. Na and Br
c. K and S

96. Give the name and formula of each of the binary compounds formed from the following elements.
a. Li and P
b. Rb and H
c. Na and H

97. Complete and balance the equations for the following reactions.
a. $Li(s) + O_2(g) \rightarrow$
b. $K(s) + S(s) \rightarrow$

98. Complete and balance the equations for the following reactions.
a. $Cs(s) + H_2O(l) \rightarrow$
b. $Na(s) + Cl_2(g) \rightarrow$

Additional Exercises

99. Predict the atomic number of the next alkali metal after francium, and give its ground-state electron configuration.

100. The work function is the energy required to remove an electron from an atom on the surface of a metal. How does this definition differ from that for ionization energy?

101. Photogray lenses incorporate small amounts of silver chloride in the glass of the lens. When light hits the AgCl particles, the following reaction occurs:

$$AgCl \xrightarrow{h\nu} Ag + Cl$$

The silver metal that is formed causes the lenses to darken. The enthalpy change for this reaction is 3.10×10^2 kJ/mol. Assuming all this energy must be supplied by light, what is the maximum wavelength of light that can cause this reaction?

102. On which quantum numbers does the energy of an electron depend in each of the following?
   a. A one-electron atom or ion
   b. An atom or ion with more than one electron

103. How many electrons in an atom can have the following sets of quantum numbers?
   a. $n = 3$
   b. $n = 2$, $\ell = 0$
   c. $n = 2$, $\ell = 2$
   d. $n = 2$, $\ell = 0$, $m_\ell = 0$, $m_s = +\frac{1}{2}$

104. An electron is excited from the $n = 1$ ground state to the $n = 3$ state in a hydrogen atom. Which of the following statements are true? Correct the false statements to make them true.
   a. It takes more energy to ionize the electron from $n = 3$ than from the ground state.
   b. The electron is further from the nucleus on average in the $n = 3$ state than in the $n = 1$ state.
   c. The wavelength of light emitted if the electron drops from $n = 3$ to $n = 2$ will be shorter than the wavelength of light emitted if the electron falls to $n = 1$ from $n = 3$.
   d. The wavelength of light emitted when the electron returns to the ground state from $n = 3$ will be the same as the wavelength of light absorbed to go from $n = 1$ to $n = 3$.
   e. For $n = 3$, the electron is in the first excited state.

105. Are the possible values of ℓ for an electron with $n = 2$ the same as for an electron with $n = 3$?

106. In defining the sizes of orbitals, why must we use an arbitrary value, such as 90% of the probability of finding an electron in that region?

107. Total radial probability distributions for the helium, neon, and argon atoms are shown in the following graph. How can one interpret the shapes of these curves in terms of electron configurations, quantum numbers, and effective nuclear charges?

108. Although no currently known elements contain electrons in g orbitals in the ground state, it is possible that these elements will be found or that electrons in excited states of known elements could be in g orbitals. For g orbitals, the value of ℓ is 4. What is the lowest value of n for which g orbitals could exist? What are the possible values of m_ℓ? How many electrons could a set of g orbitals hold?

109. Which of the following are possible sets of quantum numbers for an electron in an atom? For the sets of quantum numbers that are not possible, state what is wrong with each set.
   a. $n = 1$, $\ell = 0$, $m_\ell = 1$, $m_s = +\frac{1}{2}$
   b. $n = 9$, $\ell = 7$, $m_\ell = -6$, $m_s = -\frac{1}{2}$
   c. $n = 2$, $\ell = 1$, $m_\ell = 0$, $m_s = 0$
   d. $n = 1$, $\ell = 1$, $m_\ell = 1$, $m_s = +\frac{1}{2}$
   e. $n = 3$, $\ell = 2$, $m_\ell = -3$, $m_s = +\frac{1}{2}$
   f. $n = 4$, $\ell = 0$, $m_\ell = 0$, $m_s = -\frac{1}{2}$

110. Using only the periodic table inside the front cover of the text, write the expected electron configurations for
   a. The third element in Group 5A.
   b. Element number 116.
   c. An element with three unpaired $5d$ electrons in the ground state.
   d. Ti, Ni, and Os.

111. In the ground state of antimony, Sb,
   a. How many electrons have $\ell = 1$ as one of their quantum numbers?
   b. How many electrons have $m_\ell = 0$?
   c. How many electrons have $m_\ell = 1$?

112. An ion having a 4+ charge and a mass of 49.9 amu has 2 electrons with principal quantum number $n = 1$, 8 electrons with $n = 2$, and 10 electrons with $n = 3$. Supply as many of the properties for the ion as possible from the information given. *Hint:* In forming ions, the $4s$ electrons are lost before the $3d$ electrons.
   a. The atomic number
   b. Total number of s electrons
   c. Total number of p electrons

d. Total number of d electrons

e. The number of neutrons in the nucleus

f. The mass of 3.01×10^{23} atoms

g. The ground-state electron configuration of the neutral atom

113. Note the successive ionization energies for silicon given in Table 7.5. Would you expect to see any large jumps between successive ionization energies of silicon as you removed all the electrons, one-by-one, beyond those shown in the table?

114. Elements with very large ionization energies also tend to have highly exothermic electron affinities. Explain. Which group of elements would you expect to be an exception to this statement?

115. What role does the repulsion between electrons play in the trend in ionization energies from lithium to neon?

116. Give possible values for the quantum numbers of the valence electrons in an atom of titanium (Ti).

117. The changes in electron affinity as one goes down a group in the periodic table are not nearly as large as the variations in ionization energies. Why?

118. The electron affinities of the elements from aluminum to chlorine are -44, -120, -74, -200.4, and -348.7 kJ/mol, respectively. Rationalize the trend in these values.

119. Three elements have the electron configurations $1s^2 2s^2 2p^6 3s^2 3p^6$, $1s^2 2s^2 2p^6 3s^2$, and $1s^2 2s^2 2p^6 3s^2 3p^6 4s^1$. The first ionization energies of the three elements (not in the same order) are 0.4189, 0.7377, and 1.5205 MJ/mol. The atomic radii are 1.60, 0.94, and 1.97 Å. Identify the three elements, and match the appropriate values of ionization energy and atomic radius to each configuration.

120. The electron affinity for sulfur is more exothermic than that for oxygen. Account for this.

121. Using data from this chapter, calculate the change in energy expected for each of the following processes.

a. $2Cu^+(g) \rightarrow Cu(g) + Cu^{2+}(g)$ (For Cu, $I_1 = 746$ kJ/mol, $I_2 = 1958$ kJ/mol.)

b. $Na^-(g) + Na^+(g) \rightarrow 2Na(g)$ (Electron affinity for Na = -52 kJ/mol.)

c. $Mg^{2+}(g) + K(g) \rightarrow Mg^+(g) + K^+(g)$

d. $Na(g) + Cl(g) \rightarrow Na^+(g) + Cl^-(g)$

e. $Mg(g) + F(g) \rightarrow Mg^+(g) + F^-(g)$

f. $Mg^+(g) + F(g) \rightarrow Mg^{2+}(g) + F^-(g)$

g. $Mg(g) + 2F(g) \rightarrow Mg^{2+}(g) + 2F^-(g)$

122. Write equations corresponding to the following.

a. The fourth ionization energy of Se

b. The electron affinity of S^-

c. The electron affinity of Fe^{3+}

d. The ionization energy of Mg

e. The work function of Mg (See Exercise 100.)

Challenge Problems

123. We expect the atomic radius to increase going down a group in the periodic table. Can you suggest why the atomic radius of hafnium breaks this rule? (See data below.)

Atomic Radii, in pm			
Sc	157	Ti	147.7
Y	169.3	Zr	159.3
La	191.5	Hf	147.6

124. Consider the following ionization energies for aluminum:

$$Al(g) \rightarrow Al^+(g) + e^- \qquad I_1 = 580 \text{ kJ/mol}$$
$$Al^+(g) \rightarrow Al^{2+}(g) + e^- \qquad I_2 = 1815 \text{ kJ/mol}$$
$$Al^{2+}(g) \rightarrow Al^{3+}(g) + e^- \qquad I_3 = 2740 \text{ kJ/mol}$$
$$Al^{3+}(g) \rightarrow Al^{4+}(g) + e^- \qquad I_4 = 11,600 \text{ kJ/mol}$$

a. Account for the trend in the values of the ionization energies.

b. Explain the large increase between I_3 and I_4.

c. Which one of the four ions has the greatest electron affinity? Explain.

d. List the four aluminum ions given above in order of increasing size, and explain your ordering. (*Hint:* Remember that most of the size of an atom or ion is due to its electrons.)

125. Answer the following questions assuming that m_s could have three values rather than two and that the rules for n, ℓ, and m_ℓ are the normal ones.

a. How many electrons would an orbital be able to hold?

b. How many elements would the first and second periods in the periodic table contain?

c. How many elements would be contained in the first transition metal series?

d. How many electrons would the set of $4f$ orbitals be able to hold?

126. Assume that we are in another universe with different physical laws. Electrons in this universe are described by four quantum numbers with meanings similar to those we use. We will call these quantum numbers p, q, r, and s. The rules for these quantum numbers are

$p = 1, 2, 3, 4, 5, \ldots$

q takes on odd integer values and $q \leq p$.

r takes on all even integer values from $-q$ to $+q$. (Zero is considered an even number.)

$s = +\frac{1}{2}$ or $-\frac{1}{2}$.

a. Sketch what the first three periods of the periodic table might look like in this universe.

b. How many electrons can have $p = 3$?

c. How many electrons can have $p = 4$, $q = 3$, $r = 2$?

d. How many electrons can have $p = 4$, $q = 3$?

e. How many electrons can have $p = 3$, $q = 0$, $r = 0$?

f. What are the possible values of q and r for $p = 5$?

g. How many electrons can have $p = 6$?

127. While Mendeleev predicted the existence of several undiscovered elements, he did not predict the existence of the noble gases, the lanthanides, or the actinides. Propose reasons why Mendeleev was not able to predict the existence of the noble gases.

Marathon Problem*

128. From the information below, identify element X.

1. The wavelength of the radio waves sent by an FM station broadcasting at 97.1 MHz is 30 million (3.00×10^7) times greater than the wavelength corresponding to the energy difference between a particular excited state of the hydrogen atom and the ground state.

2. Let V represent the principal quantum number for the valence shell of element X. If an electron in the hydrogen atom falls from shell V to the inner shell corresponding to the excited state mentioned above in part 1, the wavelength of light emitted is the same as the wavelength of an electron moving at a speed of 570. m/s.

3. The number of unpaired electrons for element X is the same as the maximum number of electrons in an atom that can have the quantum number designations $n = 2$, $m_\ell = -1$, and $m_s = -\frac{1}{2}$.

4. Let A represent the principal quantum number for the electron in an excited He^+ ion in which the single electron has the same energy as the electron in the ground state of a hydrogen atom. This value of A also represents the angular momentum quantum number for the subshell containing the unpaired electron(s) for element X.

*This Marathon Problem was developed by James H. Burness of Penn State University, York Campus.

◄ CHAPTER 8 ►

Bonding: General Concepts

As we examine the world around us, we find it to be composed almost entirely of compounds and mixtures of compounds: rocks, coal, soil, petroleum, trees, and human bodies are all complex mixtures of chemical compounds in which different kinds of atoms are bound together. Substances composed of unbound atoms do exist in nature, but they are very rare. Examples are the argon in the atmosphere and the helium mixed with natural gas reserves.

The manner in which atoms are bound together has a profound effect on chemical and physical properties. For example, graphite is a soft, slippery material used as a lubricant in locks, and diamond is one of the hardest materials known, valuable both as a gemstone and in industrial cutting tools. Why do these materials, both composed solely of carbon atoms, have such different properties? The answer, as we will see, lies in the bonding in these substances.

Silicon and carbon are next to each other in Group 4A of the periodic table. From our knowledge of periodic trends, we might expect SiO_2 and CO_2 to be very similar. But SiO_2 is the empirical formula of silica, which is found in sand and quartz, and carbon dioxide is a gas, a product of respiration. Why are they so different? We will be able to answer this question after we have developed models for bonding.

Molecular bonding and structure play the central role in determining the course of all chemical reactions, many of which are vital to our survival. Later in this book we will demonstrate their importance by showing how enzymes facilitate complex chemical reactions, how genetic characteristics are transferred, and how hemoglobin in the blood carries oxygen throughout the body. All of these fundamental biological reactions hinge on the geometric structures of molecules, sometimes depending on very subtle differences in molecular shape to channel the chemical reaction one way rather than another.

◄ Zeolites are aluminosilicate network solids constructed of interconnecting SiO_4 and AlO_4 tetrahedra. Zeolite structures are characterized by the presence of cavities and tunnels. The structure represented here shows a pyridine molecule (C_5H_5N) trapped in a zeolite cavity.

341

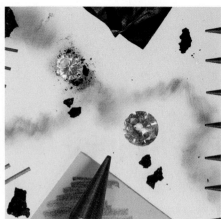

(left) Quartz grows in beautiful, regular crystals. (right) Diamond and graphite.

Many of the world's current problems require fundamentally chemical answers: disease and pollution control, the search for new energy sources, the development of new fertilizers to increase crop yields, the improvement of the protein content in various staple grains, and many more. To understand the behavior of natural materials, we must understand the nature of chemical bonding and the factors that control the structures of compounds. In this chapter we will present various classes of compounds that illustrate the different types of bonds and then develop models to describe the structure and bonding that characterize materials found in nature. Later these models will be useful in understanding chemical reactions.

8.1 Types of Chemical Bonds

Purpose

• To explain why an ionic bond is formed.
• To explain why a covalent bond is formed.
• To introduce the polar covalent bond.

What is a chemical bond? There is no simple and yet complete answer to this question. In Chapter 2 we defined bonds as forces that hold groups of atoms together and make them function as a unit.

There are many types of experiments we can perform to determine the fundamental nature of materials. For example, we can study physical properties such as melting point, hardness, and electrical and thermal conductivity. We can also study solubility characteristics and the properties of the resulting solutions. To determine the charge distribution in a molecule, we can study its behavior in an electric field. We can obtain information about the strength of a bonding interaction by measuring the **bond energy, which is the energy** required to break the bond.

There are several ways in which atoms can interact with one another to form aggregates. We will consider several specific examples to illustrate the various types of chemical bonds.

Earlier, we saw that when solid sodium chloride is dissolved in water, the resulting solution conducts electricity, a fact that helps to convince us that sodium chloride is composed of Na^+ and Cl^- ions. Therefore, when sodium and chlorine react to form sodium chloride, electrons are transferred from the sodium atoms to the chlorine atoms to form Na^+ and Cl^- ions, which then aggregate to form solid sodium chloride. Why does this happen? The best simple answer is that *the system can achieve the lowest possible energy by behaving in this way.* The attraction of a chlorine atom for the extra electron and the very strong mutual attractions of the oppositely charged ions provide the driving forces for the process. The resulting solid sodium chloride is a very sturdy material; it has a melting point of approximately 800°C. The bonding forces that produce this great thermal stability result from the electrostatic attractions of the closely packed, oppositely charged ions. This is an example of **ionic bonding.** Ionic substances are formed when an atom that loses electrons relatively easily reacts with an atom that has a high affinity for electrons. That is, an **ionic compound** results when a metal reacts with a nonmetal.

The energy of interaction between a pair of ions can be calculated using **Coulomb's law** in the form

$$E = 2.31 \times 10^{-19} \text{ J} \cdot \text{nm}\left(\frac{Q_1 Q_2}{r}\right)$$

where E has units of joules, r is the distance between the ion centers in nanometers, and Q_1 and Q_2 are the numerical ion charges.

For example, in solid sodium chloride the distance between the centers of the Na^+ and Cl^- ions is 2.76 Å (0.276 nm), and the ionic energy per pair of ions is

$$E = 2.31 \times 10^{-19} \text{ J} \cdot \text{nm}\left[\frac{(+1)(-1)}{0.276 \text{ nm}}\right] = -8.37 \times 10^{-19} \text{ J}$$

where the negative sign indicates an attractive force. That is, the *ion pair has lower energy than the separated ions.*

Coulomb's law also can be used to calculate the repulsive energy when two like-charged ions are brought together. In this case the calculated value of the energy will have a positive sign.

We have seen that a bonding force develops when two very different types of atoms react to form oppositely charged ions. But how does a bonding force develop between two identical atoms? Let's explore this situation from a very simple point of view by considering the energy terms that result when two hydrogen atoms are brought close together, as shown in Fig. 8.1(a). When hydrogen atoms are brought close together, there are two unfavorable potential energy terms, proton–proton repulsion and electron–electron repulsion, and one favorable term, proton–electron attraction. Under what conditions will the H_2 molecule be favored over the separated hydrogen atoms? That is, what conditions will favor bond formation? The answer lies in the strong tendency in nature for any system to achieve the lowest possible energy. A bond will form (that is, the two hydrogen atoms will exist as a molecular unit) if the system can lower its total energy in the process.

In this case, then, the hydrogen atoms will position themselves so that the system will achieve the lowest possible energy; the system will act to minimize the sum of the positive (repulsive) energy terms and the negative (attractive) energy term. The distance where the energy is minimum is called the **bond length.** The total energy

A bond will form if the energy of the aggregate is lower than that of the separated atoms.

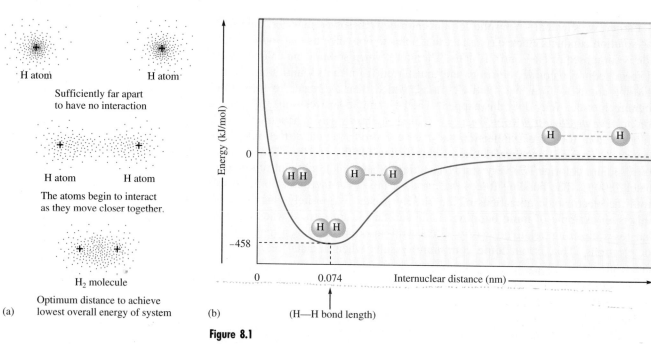

(a) Sufficiently far apart to have no interaction

The atoms begin to interact as they move closer together.

H_2 molecule

Optimum distance to achieve lowest overall energy of system

(b)

(H—H bond length)

Figure 8.1

(a) The interaction of two hydrogen atoms. (b) Energy profile as a function of the distance between the nuclei of the hydrogen atoms. As the atoms approach each other, the energy decreases until the distance reaches 0.074 nm (0.74 Å) and then begins to increase again due to repulsions.

of this system as a function of distance between the hydrogen nuclei is shown in Fig. 8.1(b). Note several important features of this diagram:

Potential energy was discussed in Chapter 6.

> The energy terms involved are the net potential energy that results from the attractions and repulsions among the charged particles and the kinetic energy due to the motions of the electrons.
>
> The zero point of energy is defined with the atoms at infinite separation.
>
> At very short distances the energy rises steeply because of the importance of the repulsive forces when the atoms are very close together.
>
> The bond length is the distance at which the system has minimum energy.

In the H_2 molecule, the electrons reside primarily in the space between the two nuclei, where they are attracted simultaneously by both protons. This positioning is precisely what leads to the stability of the H_2 molecule compared with two separated hydrogen atoms. The potential energy of each electron is lowered because of the increased attractive forces in this area. When we say that a bond is formed between the hydrogen atoms, we mean that the H_2 molecule is more stable than two separated hydrogen atoms by a certain quantity of energy (the bond energy).

We can also think of a bond in terms of forces. The simultaneous attraction of each electron by the two protons generates a force that pulls the protons toward each other and that just balances the proton–proton and electron–electron repulsive forces at the distance corresponding to the bond length.

The type of bonding we encounter in the hydrogen molecule and in many other molecules in which *electrons are shared by nuclei* is called **covalent bonding.**

So far we have considered two extreme types of bonding. In ionic bonding the participating atoms are so different that one or more electrons are transferred to form oppositely charged ions, which then attract each other. In covalent bonding two identical atoms share electrons equally. The bonding results from the mutual attraction of the two nuclei for the shared electrons. Between these extremes are intermediate cases in which the atoms are not so different that electrons are completely transferred but are different enough that unequal sharing results, forming what is called a **polar covalent bond.** An example of this type of bond occurs in the hydrogen fluoride (HF) molecule. When a sample of hydrogen fluoride gas is placed in an electric field, the molecules tend to orient themselves as shown in Fig. 8.2, with the fluoride end closest to the positive pole and the hydrogen end closest to the negative pole. This result implies that the HF molecule has the following charge distribution:

$$\text{H—F}$$
$$\delta+ \;\; \delta-$$

where δ (lowercase delta) is used to indicate a fractional charge. This same effect was noted in Chapter 4, where many of water's unusual properties were attributed to the polar O—H bonds in the H_2O molecule.

The most logical explanation for the development of the partial positive and negative charges on the atoms (bond polarity) in such molecules as HF and H_2O is that the electrons in the bonds are not shared equally. For example, we can account for the polarity of the HF molecule by assuming that the fluorine atom has a stronger attraction for the shared electrons than the hydrogen atom. Likewise, in the H_2O molecule the oxygen atom appears to attract the shared electrons more strongly than the hydrogen atoms do. Because bond polarity has important chemical implications, we find it useful to quantify the ability of an atom to attract shared electrons. In the next section we show how this is done.

Ionic and covalent bonds are the extreme bond types.

(a)

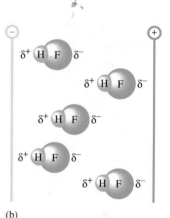

(b)

Figure 8.2

The effect of an electric field on hydrogen fluoride molecules. (a) When no electric field is present the molecules are randomly oriented. (b) When the field is turned on the molecules tend to line up with their negative ends toward the positive pole and their positive ends toward the negative pole.

8.2 Electronegativity

Purpose

• To discuss the nature of bonds in terms of electronegativity.

The different affinities of atoms for the electrons in a bond are described by a property called **electronegativity:** *the ability of an atom in a molecule to attract shared electrons to itself.*

The most widely accepted method for determining values of electronegativity is that of Linus Pauling, an American scientist who has won the Nobel Prizes for both chemistry and peace. To understand Pauling's model, consider a hypothetical molecule HX. The relative electronegativities of the H and X atoms are determined by comparing the measured H—X bond energy with the "expected" H—X bond energy, which is an average of the H—H and X—X bond energies:

$$\text{Expected H—X bond energy} = \frac{\text{H—H bond energy} + \text{X—X bond energy}}{2}$$

The difference (Δ) between the actual (measured) and expected bond energies is

$$\Delta = (\text{H—X})_{act} - (\text{H—X})_{exp}$$

Table 8.1

The Relationship Between Electronegativity and Bond Type

Electronegativity Difference in the Bonding Atoms	Bond Type
Zero	Covalent
Intermediate	Polar covalent
Large	Ionic

Covalent character decreases; Ionic character increases

If H and X have identical electronegativities, $(H—X)_{act}$ and $(H—X)_{exp}$ are the same, and Δ is 0. On the other hand, if X has a greater electronegativity than H, the shared electron(s) will tend to be closer to the X atom. The molecule will be polar, with the following charge distribution:

$$H—X$$
$$\delta+ \quad \delta-$$

Note that this bond can be viewed as having an ionic as well as a covalent component. The attraction between the partially (and oppositely) charged H and X atoms will lead to a greater bond strength. Thus $(H—X)_{act}$ will be larger than $(H—X)_{exp}$. The greater the difference in the electronegativities of the atoms, the greater is the ionic component of the bond and the greater is the value of Δ. Thus the relative electronegativities of H and X can be assigned from the Δ values.

Electronegativity values have been determined by this process for virtually all the elements; the results are given in Fig. 8.3. Note that electronegativity generally increases going from left to right across a period and decreases going down a group for the representative elements. The range of electronegativity values is from 4.0 for fluorine to 0.7 for cesium.

The relationship between electronegativity and bond type is shown in Table 8.1. For identical atoms (an electronegativity difference of zero), the electrons in the bond are shared equally, and no polarity develops. When two atoms with very different electronegativities interact, electron transfer can occur, to form the ions that make up an ionic substance. Intermediate cases give polar covalent bonds with unequal electron sharing.

Sample Exercise 8.1

Order the following bonds according to polarity: H—H, O—H, Cl—H, S—H, and F—H.

(a)

Solution

The polarity of the bond increases as the difference in electronegativity increases. From the electronegativity values in Fig. 8.3, the following variation in bond polarity is expected (the electronegativity value appears in parentheses below each element):

$$H-H < S-H < Cl-H < O-H < F-H$$

(2.1)(2.1) (2.5)(2.1) (3.0)(2.1) (3.5)(2.1) (4.0)(2.1)

Electronegativity difference   0   0.4   0.9   1.4   1.9

Covalent bond $\longrightarrow$ Polar covalent bond

Polarity increases

Figure 8.3

(a) The Pauling electronegativity values. Electronegativity generally increases across a period and decreases down a group. (b) This three-dimensional representation emphasizes the periodic trends.

(a)

(b)

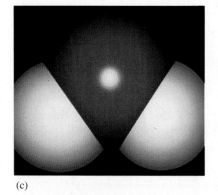

(c)

Figure 8.4

(a) The charge distribution in the water molecule. (b) The water molecule in an electric field. (c) Computer-generated model of the water molecule.

Figure 8.5

(a) The structure and charge distribution of the ammonia molecule. The polarity of the N—H bonds occurs because nitrogen has a greater electronegativity than hydrogen. (b) The dipole moment of the ammonia molecule oriented in an electric field. (c) Computer-generated model of the ammonia molecule.

8.3 *Bond Polarity and Dipole Moments*

Purpose

• To define the relationship between bond polarity and molecular polarity.

We have seen that when hydrogen fluoride is placed in an electric field, the molecules have a preferential orientation (see Fig. 8.2). This follows from the charge distribution in the HF molecule, which has a positive end and a negative end. A molecule such as HF that has a center of positive charge and a center of negative charge is said to be **dipolar,** or to have a **dipole moment.** The dipolar character of a molecule is often represented by an arrow pointing to the negative charge center with the tail of the arrow indicating the positive center of charge:

$$\delta+ \qquad \delta-$$

Of course, any diatomic (two-atom) molecule that has a polar bond also will show a molecular dipole moment. Polyatomic molecules also can exhibit dipolar behavior. For example, because the oxygen atom in the water molecule has a greater electronegativity than the hydrogen atoms, the molecular charge distribution is that shown in Fig. 8.4(a). Because of this charge distribution, the water molecule behaves in an electric field as if it had two centers of charge—one positive and one negative—as shown in Fig. 8.4(b). The water molecule has a dipole moment. The same type of behavior is observed for the NH_3 molecule (Fig. 8.5). Some molecules have polar bonds but do not have a dipole moment. This occurs when the individual bond polarities are arranged in such a way that they cancel each other out. An example is the CO_2 molecule, which is a linear molecule that has the charge distribution shown in Fig. 8.6. In this case the opposing bond polarities cancel out, and the carbon dioxide molecule does not have a dipole moment. There is no preferen-

(a)

(b)

(c)

(a)

(b)

Figure 8.6

(a) The carbon dioxide molecule.
(b) The opposed bond polarities cancel out, and the carbon dioxide molecule has no dipole moment.

Table 8.2				
Types of Molecules with Polar Bonds but No Resulting Dipole Moment				
Type		Cancellation of Polar Bonds	Example	Ball-and-Stick Model
Linear molecules with two identical bonds	B—A—B	⟵—+ +—⟶	CO_2	
Planar molecules with three identical bonds 120 degrees apart	B—A—B B 120°		SO_3	
Tetrahedral molecules with four identical bonds 109.5 degrees apart	B A B B B		CCl_4	

tial way for this molecule to line up in an electric field. (Try to find a preferred orientation to make sure you understand this concept.)

There are many cases besides that of carbon dioxide where the bond polarities oppose and exactly cancel each other. Some common types of molecules with polar bonds but no dipole moment are shown in Table 8.2.

Sample Exercise 8.2

For each of the following molecules, show the direction of the bond polarities and indicate which ones have a dipole moment: HCl, Cl_2, SO_3 (a planar molecule with the oxygen atoms spaced evenly around the central sulfur atom), CH_4 [tetrahedral (see Table 8.2) with the carbon atom at the center], and H_2S (V-shaped with the sulfur atom at the point).

Solution

The HCl molecule: From Fig. 8.3 we can see that the electronegativity of chlorine (3.0) is greater than that of hydrogen (2.1). Thus the chlorine will be partially negative, and the hydrogen will be partially positive. The HCl molecule has a dipole moment:

$$H\text{———}Cl$$
$$\delta+ \qquad \delta-$$
$$\longmapsto\longrightarrow$$

The Cl$_2$ molecule: The two chlorine atoms share the electrons equally. No bond polarity occurs, and the Cl$_2$ molecule has no dipole moment.

The SO$_3$ molecule: The electronegativity of oxygen (3.5) is greater than that of sulfur (2.5). This means that each oxygen will have a partial negative charge, and the sulfur will have a partial positive charge:

$$\begin{array}{c} O\,\delta- \\ | \\ S\,3\delta+ \\ \delta{-}\,O \quad\quad O\,\delta- \end{array}$$

The presence of polar bonds does not always yield a polar molecule.

The bond polarities arranged symmetrically as shown cancel, and the molecule has no dipole moment. This molecule is the second type shown in Table 8.2.

The CH$_4$ molecule: Carbon has a slightly higher electronegativity (2.5) than does hydrogen (2.1). This leads to small partial positive charges on the hydrogen atoms and a small partial negative charge on the carbon:

$$\begin{array}{c} H\,\delta+ \\ | \\ C\,4\delta- \\ \delta{+}\,H \quad H \;\; H\,\delta+ \\ \delta+ \end{array}$$

This case is similar to the third type in Table 8.2, and the bond polarities cancel. The molecule has no dipole moment.

The H$_2$S molecule: Since the electronegativity of sulfur (2.5) is slightly greater than that of hydrogen (2.1), the sulfur will have a partial negative charge and the hydrogen atoms will have a partial positive charge, which can be represented as follows:

$$\begin{array}{c} \delta{+}\,H \quad\quad H\,\delta+ \\ \diagdown \quad \diagup \\ S \\ 2\delta- \end{array}$$

This case is analogous to the water molecule, and the polar bonds result in a dipole moment oriented as shown:

$$\begin{array}{c} H \;\;\overline{+}\;\; H \\ \diagdown\;|\;\diagup \\ \$ \\ \downarrow \end{array}$$

8.4 Ions: Electron Configurations and Sizes

Purpose

- To show how to predict the formulas of ionic compounds.
- To discuss the factors governing ion size.

The description of the electron arrangements in atoms that emerged from the quantum mechanical model has helped a great deal in our understanding of what constitutes a stable compound. In virtually every case the atoms in a stable compound have a noble gas arrangement of electrons. Nonmetallic elements achieve a noble gas electron configuration either by sharing electrons with other nonmetals to form covalent bonds or by taking electrons from metals to form ions. In the second case, the nonmetals form anions and the metals form cations. The generalizations that apply to electron configurations in stable compounds are as follows:

- When *two nonmetals* react to form a covalent bond, they share electrons in a way that completes the valence electron configurations of both atoms. That is, both nonmetals attain noble gas electron configurations.

- When *a nonmetal and a representative-group metal* react to form a binary ionic compound, the ions form so that the valence electron configuration of the nonmetal achieves the electron configuration of the next noble gas atom and the valence orbitals of the metal are emptied. In this way both ions achieve noble gas electron configurations.

These generalizations apply to the vast majority of compounds and are important to remember. We will deal with covalent bonds more thoroughly later, but now we will consider what implications these rules hold for ionic compounds.

Atoms in stable compounds usually have a noble gas electron configuration.

Predicting Formulas of Ionic Compounds

At the beginning of this discussion it should be emphasized that when chemists use the term *ionic compound,* they are usually referring to the solid state of that compound. In the solid state the ions are close together. That is, solid ionic compounds contain a large collection of positive and negative ions packed together in a way that minimizes the $\ominus \cdots \ominus$ and $\oplus \cdots \oplus$ repulsions and maximizes the $\oplus \cdots \ominus$ attractions. This situation stands in contrast to the gas phase of an ionic substance, where the ions are quite far apart on average. In the gas phase, a pair of ions may get close enough to interact, but large collections of ions do not exist. Thus when we speak in this text of the stability of an ionic compound, we are referring to the solid state, where the large attractive forces present among oppositely charged ions tend to stabilize (favor the formation of) the ions. For example, as we mentioned in the previous chapter, the O^{2-} ion is not stable as an isolated, gas-phase species but, of course, is very stable in many solid ionic compounds. That is, $MgO(s)$, which contains Mg^{2+} and O^{2-} ions, is very stable, but the isolated, gas-phase ion pair $Mg^{2+} \cdots O^{2-}$ is not energetically favorable in comparison with the separate neutral gaseous atoms. Thus you should keep in mind that in this section, and in most other cases where we are describing the nature of ionic compounds, the discussion usually refers to the solid state, where many ions are simultaneously interacting.

To illustrate the principles of electron configurations in stable, solid ionic compounds, we will consider the formation of an ionic compound from calcium and

In the solid state of an ionic compound the ions are relatively close together, and many ions are simultaneously interacting:

In the gas phase of an ionic substance the ions would be relatively far apart and would not contain large groups of ions:

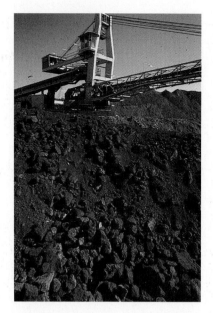

A bauxite mine. Bauxite contains Al_2O_3, the main source of aluminum.

oxygen. We can predict what compound will form by considering the valence electron configurations of the two atoms:

$$Ca: \quad [Ar]4s^2$$
$$O: \quad [He]2s^22p^4$$

From Fig. 8.3 we see that the electronegativity of oxygen (3.5) is much greater than that of calcium (1.0). Because of this large difference, electrons will be transferred from calcium to oxygen to form oxygen anions and calcium cations in the compound. How many electrons are transferred? We can base our prediction on the observation that noble gas configurations are generally the most stable. Note that oxygen needs two electrons to fill its $2s$ and $2p$ valence orbitals and to achieve the configuration of neon ($1s^22s^22p^6$). And by losing two electrons, calcium can achieve the configuration of argon. Two electrons are therefore transferred:

$$Ca + O \rightarrow Ca^{2+} + O^{2-}$$
$$2e^-$$

To predict the formula of the ionic compound, we simply recognize that chemical compounds are always electrically neutral—they have the same quantities of positive and negative charges. In this case we must have equal numbers of Ca^{2+} and O^{2-} ions, and the empirical formula of the compound is CaO.

The same principles can be applied to many other cases. For example, consider the compound formed between aluminum and oxygen. Because aluminum has the configuration $[Ne]3s^23p^1$, it loses three electrons to form the Al^{3+} ion and thus achieves the neon configuration. Therefore, the Al^{3+} and O^{2-} ions form in this case. Since the compound must be electrically neutral, there must be three O^{2-} ions for every two Al^{3+} ions, and the compound has the empirical formula Al_2O_3.

Table 8.3 shows common elements that form ions with noble gas electron configurations in ionic compounds. In losing electrons to form cations, metals in Group 1A lose one electron, those in Group 2A lose two electrons, and those in Group 3A lose three electrons. In gaining electrons to form anions, nonmetals in Group 7A (the halogens) gain one electron, and those in Group 6A gain two electrons. Hydrogen typically behaves as a nonmetal and can gain one electron to form the hydride ion (H^-), which has the electron configuration of helium.

There are some important exceptions to the rules discussed here. For example, tin forms both Sn^{2+} and Sn^{4+} ions, and lead forms both Pb^{2+} and Pb^{4+} ions. Also, bismuth forms Bi^{3+} and Bi^{5+} ions, and thallium forms Tl^+ and Tl^{3+} ions. There are no simple explanations for the behavior of these ions. For now, just note them as

Table 8.3					
Common Ions with Noble Gas Configurations in Ionic Compounds					
Group 1A	Group 2A	Group 3A	Group 6A	Group 7A	Electron Configuration
H^-, Li^+	Be^{2+}				[He]
Na^+	Mg^{2+}	Al^{3+}	O^{2-}	F^-	[Ne]
K^+	Ca^{2+}		S^{2-}	Cl^-	[Ar]
Rb^+	Sr^{2+}		Se^{2-}	Br^-	[Kr]
Cs^+	Ba^{2+}		Te^{2-}	I^-	[Xe]

exceptions to the very useful rule that ions generally adopt noble gas electron configurations in ionic compounds. Our discussion here refers to representative metals. The transition metals exhibit more complicated behavior, forming a variety of ions that will be considered in Chapter 20.

Sizes of Ions

Ion size plays an important role in determining the structure and stability of ionic solids, the properties of ions in aqueous solution, and the biologic effects of ions. As with atoms, it is impossible to define precisely the sizes of ions. Most often, ionic radii are determined from the measured distances between ion centers in ionic compounds. This method, of course, involves as assumption about how the distance should be divided up between the two ions. Thus you will note considerable disagreement among ionic sizes given in various sources. Here we are mainly interested in trends and will be less concerned with absolute ion sizes.

Various factors influence ionic size. We will first consider the relative sizes of an ion and its parent atom. Since a positive ion is formed by removing electrons from a neutral atom, the resulting cation is smaller than its parent atom. The opposite is true for negative ions; the addition of electrons to a neutral atom produces an anion significantly larger than its parent atom.

It is also important to know how the sizes of ions vary depending on the positions of the parent elements in the periodic table. Figure 8.7 shows the sizes of the most important ions (each with a noble gas configuration) and their position in the periodic table. Note that ion size increases down a group. The changes that occur horizontally are complicated because of the change from predominantly metals on the left-hand side of the periodic table to nonmetals on the right-hand side. A given period thus contains both elements that give up electrons to form cations and ones that accept electrons to form anions.

One trend worth noting involves the relative sizes of a set of **isoelectronic ions**—*ions containing the same number of electrons*. Consider the ions O^{2-}, F^-, Na^+, Mg^{2+}, and Al^{3+}. Each of these ions has the neon electron configuration. How do the sizes of these ions vary? In general, there are two important facts to consider in predicting the relative sizes of ions: the number of electrons and the number of protons. Since these ions are isoelectronic, the number of electrons is 10 in each case. Electron repulsions should therefore be about the same in all cases. However, the number of protons increases from 8 to 13 as we go from the O^{2-} ion to the Al^{3+} ion. Thus, in going from O^{2-} to Al^{3+}, the 10 electrons experience a greater attraction as the positive charge on the nucleus increases. This causes the ions to become smaller. You can confirm this by looking at Fig. 8.7. In general, for a series of isoelectronic ions, the size decreases as the nuclear charge Z increases.

For isoelectronic ions, size decreases as Z increases.

Sample Exercise 8.3

Arrange the ions Se^{2-}, Br^-, Rb^+, and Sr^{2+} in order of decreasing size.

Solution

This is an isoelectronic series of ions with the krypton electron configuration. Since these ions all have the same number of electrons, their sizes will depend on the nuclear charge. The Z values are 34 for Se^{2-}, 35 for Br^-, 37 for Rb^+, and 38 for

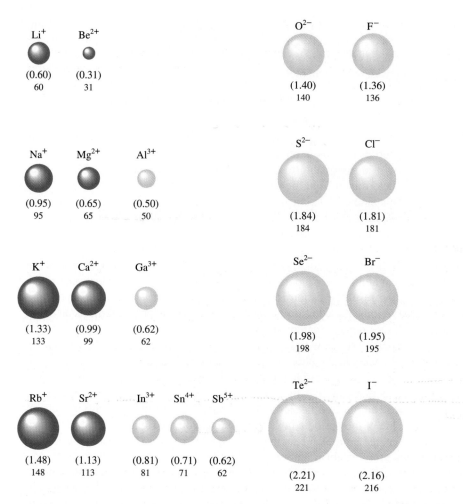

Figure 8.7

Sizes of ions related to positions of the elements in the periodic table. Note that size generally increases down a group. Also note that in a series of isoelectronic ions, size decreases with increasing atomic number. The ionic radii are given in units of angstroms (in parentheses) and picometers.

Sr^{2+}. Since the nuclear charge is greatest for Sr^{2+}, it is the smallest of these ions. The Se^{2-} ion is largest:

$$Se^{2-} > Br^- > Rb^+ > Sr^{2+}$$

↑ Largest ↑ Smallest

Sample Exercise 8.4

Choose the largest ion in each of the following groups.

a. Li^+, Na^+, K^+, Rb^+, Cs^+ **b.** Ba^{2+}, Cs^+, I^-, Te^{2-}

Solution

a. The ions are all from Group 1A elements. Since size increases down a group (the ion with the greatest number of electrons is largest), Cs^+ is the largest ion.

b. This is an isoelectronic series of ions, all of which have the xenon electron configuration. The ion with the smallest nuclear charge is largest:

$$Te^{2-} > I^- > Cs^+ > Ba^{2+}$$
$$Z = 52 \quad Z = 53 \quad Z = 55 \quad Z = 56$$

8.5 Formation of Binary Ionic Compounds

Purpose

• To define lattice energy and show how it can be calculated.

In this section we will introduce the factors that influence the stability and the structures of solid binary ionic compounds. We know that metals and nonmetals react by transferring electrons to form cations and anions that are mutually attractive. The resulting ionic solid forms because the aggregated oppositely charged ions have a lower energy than the original elements. Just how strongly the ions attract each other in the solid state is indicated by the **lattice energy**—*the change in energy that takes place when separated gaseous ions are packed together to form an ionic solid:*

$$M^+(g) + X^-(g) \rightarrow MX(s)$$

The lattice energy is often defined as the energy *released* when an ionic solid forms from its ions. However, in this book the sign of an energy term is always determined from the system's point of view: negative if the process is exothermic; positive if endothermic. Thus lattice energy has a negative sign.

The structures of ionic solids will be discussed in detail in Chapter 10.

We can illustrate the energy changes involved in the formation of an ionic solid by considering the formation of solid lithium fluoride from its elements:

$$Li(s) + \tfrac{1}{2}F_2(g) \rightarrow LiF(s)$$

To see the energy terms associated with this process, we take advantage of the fact that energy is a state function and break this reaction into steps, the sum of which gives the overall reaction.

STEP 1

Sublimation of solid lithium. Sublimation involves taking a substance from the solid state to the gaseous state:

$$Li(s) \rightarrow Li(g)$$

The enthalpy of sublimation for $Li(s)$ is 161 kJ/mol.

STEP 2

Ionization of lithium atoms to form Li^+ ions in the gas phase:

$$Li(g) \rightarrow Li^+(g) + e^-$$

This process corresponds to the first ionization energy for lithium, which is 520 kJ/mol.

Lithium fluoride.

STEP 3

Dissociation of fluorine molecules. We need to form a mole of fluorine atoms by breaking the F—F bonds in a half mole of F_2 molecules:

$$\tfrac{1}{2}F_2(g) \rightarrow F(g)$$

The energy required to break this bond is 154 kJ/mol. In this case we are breaking the bonds in a half mole of fluorine, so the energy required for this step is (154 kJ)/2, or 77 kJ.

STEP 4

Formation of F^- ions from fluorine atoms in the gas phase:

$$F(g) + e^- \rightarrow F^-(g)$$

The energy change for this process corresponds to the electron affinity of fluorine, which is −328 kJ/mol.

STEP 5

Formation of solid lithium fluoride from the gaseous Li^+ and F^- ions:

$$Li^+(g) + F^-(g) \rightarrow LiF(s)$$

This corresponds to the lattice energy for LiF, which is −1047 kJ/mol.

Since the sum of these five processes yields the desired overall reaction, the sum of the individual energy changes gives the overall energy change:

Process	Energy Change (kJ)
$Li(s) \rightarrow Li(g)$	161
$Li(g) \rightarrow Li^+(g) + e^-$	520
$\tfrac{1}{2}F_2(g) \rightarrow F(g)$	77
$F(g) + e^- \rightarrow F^-(g)$	−328
$Li^+(g) + F^-(g) \rightarrow LiF(s)$	−1047
Overall: $Li(s) + \tfrac{1}{2}F_2(g) \rightarrow LiF(s)$	−617 kJ (per mole of LiF)

In doing this calculation, we have ignored the small difference between ΔH_{sub} and ΔE_{sub}.

This process is summarized by the energy diagram in Fig. 8.8. Note that the formation of solid lithium fluoride from its elements is highly exothermic, mainly because of the very large negative lattice energy. A great deal of energy is released when the ions combine to form the solid. In fact, note that the energy released when an electron is added to a fluorine atom to form the F^- ion (328 kJ/mol) is not enough to remove an electron from lithium (520 kJ/mol). That is, when a metallic lithium atom reacts with a nonmetallic fluorine atom to form *separated* ions,

$$Li(g) + F(g) \rightarrow Li^+(g) + F^-(g)$$

the process is endothermic and thus unfavorable. Clearly, then, the main impetus for the formation of the ionic compound rather than a covalent compound results from the strong mutual attractions among the Li^+ and F^- ions in the solid. The lattice energy is the dominant energy term.

The structure of the solid lithium fluoride is represented in Fig. 8.9. Note the alternating arrangement of the Li^+ and F^- ions. Also note that each Li^+ is surrounded by six F^- ions and each F^- ion is surrounded by six Li^+ ions. This structure can be rationalized by assuming that the ions behave as hard spheres that

(a)

(b)

Figure 8.8

The energy changes involved in the formation of solid lithium fluoride from its elements. The numbers in parentheses refer to the reaction steps discussed in the text.

Figure 8.9

The structure of lithium fluoride. (a) Represented by a ball-and-stick model. Note that each Li^+ ion is surrounded by six F^- ions, and each F^- ion is surrounded by six Li^+ ions. (b) Represented with the ions shown as spheres. The structure is determined by packing the spherical ions in a way that both maximizes the ionic attractions and minimizes the ionic repulsions.

pack together in a way that both maximizes the attractions among the oppositely charged ions and minimizes the repulsions among the identically charged ions.

All the binary ionic compounds formed by an alkali metal and a halogen have the structure shown in Fig. 8.9, except for the cesium salts. The arrangement of ions shown in Fig. 8.9 is often called the **sodium chloride structure,** after the most common substance that possesses it.

Lattice Energy Calculations

In discussing the energetics of the formation of solid lithium fluoride, we emphasized the importance of lattice energy in contributing to the stability of the ionic solid. Lattice energy can be represented by a modified form of Coulomb's law,

$$\text{Lattice energy} = k\left(\frac{Q_1 Q_2}{r}\right)$$

where k is a proportionality constant that depends on the structure of the solid and the electron configurations of the ions, Q_1 and Q_2 are the charges on the ions, and r is the shortest distance between the centers of the cations and anions. Note that the lattice energy has a negative sign when Q_1 and Q_2 have opposite signs. This result is expected, since bringing cations and anions together is an exothermic process. Also note that the process becomes more exothermic as the ionic charges increase and as the distances between the ions in the solid decrease.

The importance of the charges in ionic solids can be illustrated by comparing the energies involved in the formation of $NaF(s)$ and $MgO(s)$. These solids contain the isoelectronic ions Na^+, F^-, Mg^{2+}, and O^{2-}. The energy diagram for the formation of the two solids is given in Fig. 8.10. Note several important features:

The energy released when the gaseous Mg^{2+} and O^{2-} ions combine to form solid MgO is much greater (more than four times greater) than that released when the gaseous Na^+ and F^- ions combine to form solid NaF.

The energy required to remove two electrons from the magnesium atom (735 kJ/mol for the first and 1445 kJ/mol for the second, yielding a total of 2180 kJ/mol) is much greater than the energy required to remove one electron from a sodium atom (495 kJ/mol).

Figure 8.10

Comparison of the energy changes involved in the formation of solid sodium fluoride and solid magnesium oxide. Note the large lattice energy for magnesium oxide (where doubly charged ions are combining), compared with that for sodium fluoride (where singly charged ions are combining).

Energy (737 kJ/mol) is required to add two electrons to the oxygen atom in the gas phase. Addition of the first electron is exothermic (−141 kJ/mol), but addition of the second electron is quite endothermic (878 kJ/mol). This latter energy must be obtained indirectly, since the $O^{2-}(g)$ is not stable.

In view of the facts that twice as much energy is required to remove the second electron from magnesium as to remove the first and that addition of an electron to the gaseous O^- ion is quite endothermic, it seems puzzling that magnesium oxide contains Mg^{2+} and O^{2-} ions rather than Mg^+ and O^- ions. The answer lies in the lattice energy. Note that the lattice energy for combining gaseous Mg^{2+} and O^{2-} ions to form $MgO(s)$ is 3000 kJ/mol more negative than that for combining gaseous Na^+ and F^- ions to form $NaF(s)$. Thus the energy released in forming a solid containing Mg^{2+} and O^{2-} ions rather than Mg^+ and O^- ions more than compensates for the energies required for the processes that produce the Mg^{2+} and O^{2-} ions.

If there is so much lattice energy to be gained in going from singly charged to doubly charged ions in the case of magnesium oxide, why then does solid sodium fluoride contain Na^+ and F^- ions rather than Na^{2+} and F^{2-} ions? We can answer this question by recognizing that both Na^+ and F^- ions have the neon electron configuration. Removal of an electron from Na^+ requires an extremely large quantity of energy (4560 kJ/mol) because a $2p$ electron must be removed. Conversely, the addition of an electron to F^- would require use of the relatively high energy $3s$ orbital, which is also an unfavorable process. Thus we can say that for sodium fluoride the extra energy required to form the doubly charged ions is greater than the gain in lattice energy that would result.

This discussion of the energies involved in the formation of solid ionic compounds illustrates that a variety of factors operate to determine the composition and structure of these compounds. The most important of these factors involve the balancing of the energies required to form highly charged ions and the energy released when highly charged ions combine to form the solid.

Since the equation for lattice energy contains the product Q_1Q_2, the lattice energy for a solid with 2+ and 2− ions should be four times that for a solid with 1+ and 1− ions. That is,

$$\frac{(+2)(-2)}{(+1)(-1)} = 4$$

For MgO and NaF, the observed ratio of lattice energies (see Fig. 8.10) is:

$$\frac{-3925 \text{ kJ}}{-923 \text{ kJ}} = 4.25$$

(a)

(b)

(c)

Figure 8.11

The three possible types of bonds: (a) a covalent bond formed between identical atoms; (b) a polar covalent bond, with both ionic and covalent components; and (c) an ionic bond with no electron sharing.

8.6 Partial Ionic Character of Covalent Bonds

Purpose

• To show the relationship between electronegativity and the ionic character of a bond.

Recall that when atoms with different electronegativities react to form molecules, the electrons are not shared equally. The possible result is a polar covalent bond or, in the case of a large electronegativity difference, a complete transfer of one or more electrons to form ions. The cases are summarized in Fig. 8.11.

How well can we tell the difference between an ionic bond and a polar covalent bond? The only honest answer to this question is that there are probably no totally ionic bonds between *discrete pairs of atoms*. The evidence for this statement comes from calculations of the percent ionic character for the bonds of various binary compounds in the gas phase. These calculations are based on comparisons of the measured dipole moments for molecules of the type X—Y with the calculated dipole moments for the completely ionic case, X^+Y^-. The percent ionic character of a bond can be defined as

Percent ionic character of a bond

$$= \left(\frac{\text{measured dipole moment of X—Y}}{\text{calculated dipole moment of } X^+Y^-} \right) \times 100$$

Figure 8.12

The relationship between the ionic character of a covalent bond and the electronegativity difference of the bonded atoms.

Molten NaCl conducts an electric current, indicating the presence of mobile Na^+ and Cl^- ions.

Application of this definition to various compounds (in the gas phase) gives the results shown in Fig. 8.12, where percent ionic character is plotted versus the difference in the electronegativity values of X and Y. Note from this plot that ionic character increases with electronegativity difference, as expected. However, none of the bonds reaches 100% ionic character, even though compounds with the maximum possible electronegativity differences are considered. Thus, according to this definition, no individual bonds are completely ionic. This conclusion is in contrast to the usual classification of many of these compounds (as solids). All the compounds shown in Fig. 8.12 with more than 50% ionic character are normally considered to be ionic solids. Recall, however, the results in Fig. 8.12 are for the gas phase, where individual XY molecules exist. These results cannot necessarily be assumed to apply to the solid state, where the existence of ions is favored by the multiple ion interactions.

Another complication in identifying ionic compounds is that many substances contain polyatomic ions. For example, NH_4Cl contains NH_4^+ and Cl^- ions, and Na_2SO_4 contains Na^+ and SO_4^{2-} ions. The ammonium and sulfate ions are held together by covalent bonds. Thus calling NH_4Cl and Na_2SO_4 ionic compounds is somewhat ambiguous.

We will avoid these problems by adopting an operational definition of ionic compounds: *any compound that conducts an electric current when melted will be classified as ionic*. Also, the generic term *salt* will be used interchangeably with *ionic compound* in this book.

8.7 The Covalent Chemical Bond: A Model

Purpose

• To discuss the covalent bonding model.

Before we develop specific models for covalent chemical bonding, it will be helpful to summarize some of the concepts introduced in this chapter.

What is a chemical bond? Chemical bonds can be viewed as forces that cause a group of atoms to behave as a unit.

Why do chemical bonds occur? There is no principle of nature that states that bonds are favored or disfavored. Bonds are neither inherently "good" nor inherently "bad" as far as nature is concerned; *bonds result from the tendency of a system to seek its lowest possible energy.* From a simplistic point of view, bonds occur when collections of atoms are more stable (lower in energy) than the separate atoms. For example, approximately 1652 kJ of energy is required to break a mole of methane (CH_4) molecules into separate C and H atoms. Or, taking the opposite view, 1652 kJ of energy is released when 1 mole of methane is formed from 1 mole of gaseous C atoms and 4 moles of gaseous H atoms. Thus we can say that 1 mole of CH_4 molecules in the gas phase is 1652 kJ lower in energy than 1 mole of carbon atoms plus 4 moles of hydrogen atoms. Methane is therefore a stable molecule relative to its separated atoms.

We find it useful to interpret molecular stability in terms of a model called a **chemical bond.** To understand why this model was invented, let's continue with methane, which consists of four hydrogen atoms arranged at the corners of a tetrahedron around a carbon atom:

A tetrahedron has four equal triangular faces.

Given this structure, it is natural to envision four individual C—H interactions (we call them bonds). The energy of stabilization of CH_4 is divided equally among the four bonds to give an average C—H bond energy per mole of C—H bonds:

$$\frac{1652 \text{ kJ/mol}}{4} = 413 \text{ kJ/mol}$$

Next, consider methyl chloride, which consists of CH_3Cl molecules having the structure

Experiments have shown that approximately 1578 kJ of energy is required to break down 1 mole of gaseous CH_3Cl molecules into gaseous carbon, chlorine, and hydrogen atoms. The reverse process can be represented as

$$C(g) + Cl(g) + 3H(g) \rightarrow CH_3Cl(g) + 1578 \text{ kJ/mol}$$

A mole of gaseous methyl chloride is lower in energy by 1578 kJ than its separate gaseous atoms. Thus a mole of methyl chloride is held together by 1578 kJ of energy. Again, it is very useful to divide this energy into individual bonds. Methyl chloride can be visualized as containing one C—Cl bond and three C—H bonds. If we assume arbitrarily that a C—H interaction represents the same quantity of energy in any situation (that is, that the strength of a C—H bond is independent of its molecular environment), we can do the following bookkeeping:

$$1 \text{ mol C—Cl bonds plus 3 mol C—H bonds} = 1578 \text{ kJ}$$
$$\text{C—Cl bond energy} + 3(\text{average C—H bond energy}) = 1578 \text{ kJ}$$
$$\text{C—Cl bond energy} + 3(413 \text{ kJ/mol}) = 1578 \text{ kJ}$$
$$\text{C—Cl bond energy} = 1578 - 1239 = 339 \text{ kJ/mol}$$

These assumptions allow us to associate given quantities of energy with C—H and C—Cl bonds.

It is important to note that the bond concept is a human invention. Bonds provide a method for dividing up the energy evolved when a stable molecule is formed from its component atoms. Thus in this context a bond represents a quantity of energy obtained from the overall molecular energy of stabilization in a rather arbitrary way. This is not to say that the concept of individual bonds is a bad idea. In fact, the modern concept of the chemical bond, conceived by the American chemists G. N. Lewis and Linus Pauling, is one of the most useful ideas chemists have ever developed.

Models: An Overview

The framework of chemistry, like that of any science, consists of **models**—attempts to explain how nature operates on the microscopic level based on experiences in the macroscopic world. To understand chemistry, one must understand its models and how they are used. We will use the concept of bonding to reemphasize the important characteristics of models, including their origin, structure, and uses.

Models originate from our observations of the properties of nature. For example, the concept of bonds arose from the observations that most chemical processes involve collections of atoms and that chemical reactions involve rearrangements of the ways the atoms are grouped. Therefore, to understand reactions, we must understand the forces that bind atoms together.

In natural processes there is a tendency toward lower energy. Collections of atoms therefore occur because the aggregated state has lower energy than the separated atoms. Why? As we saw earlier in this chapter, the best explanations for the energy change involve atoms sharing electrons or atoms transferring electrons to become ions. In the case of electron sharing, we find it convenient to assume that individual bonds occur between pairs of atoms. Let's explore the validity of this assumption and see how it is useful.

In a diatomic molecule such as H_2, it is natural to assume that a bond exists between the atoms, holding them together. It is also useful to assume that individual bonds are present in polyatomic molecules such as CH_4. Therefore, instead of thinking of CH_4 as a unit with a stabilization energy of 1652 kJ per mole, we choose to think of CH_4 as containing four C—H bonds, each worth 413 kJ of energy per mole of bonds. Without this concept of individual bonds in molecules, chemistry would be hopelessly complicated. There are millions of different chemical compounds, and if each of these compounds had to be considered as an entirely new entity, the task of understanding chemical behavior would be overwhelming.

The bonding model provides a framework to systematize chemical behavior by enabling us to think of molecules as collections of common fundamental components. For example, a typical biomolecule, such as a protein, contains hundreds of atoms and might seem discouragingly complex. However, if we think of a protein

Bonding is a model proposed to explain molecular stability.

The concept of individual bonds makes it much easier to deal with complex molecules such as DNA. A small segment of a DNA molecule is shown here, using ball-and-stick models.

◄ **CHEMICAL IMPACT** ►

Testing for Toxicity by Computer

When a new compound that will come in contact with humans is synthesized, the compound's safety must be tested. Currently this is done with expensive bacterial or animal tests. However, computers are now being introduced to screen new compounds to detect those which are likely to be toxic in some way.

The fundamental idea is that the toxicity of a compound is due to some part or parts of the molecular structure. That is, certain types of molecular fragments seem to always lead to a particular kind of toxicity, such as carcinogenicity (ability to cause cancer). The new procedure involves entering known structure–toxicity relationships into the computer database. When a new compound is prepared, its structure is compared by the computer with this database. If the computer finds a fragment in the new molecule that is known to cause a toxic response, this information will alert the researcher to the possible problems. The hope is that this approach will prevent many compounds from being tested only to be rejected after much time and money have already been spent. This should make products both safer and less expensive.

as constructed of individual bonds, C—C, C—H, C—N, C—O, N—H, and so on, it helps tremendously in predicting and understanding the protein's behavior. The essential idea is that we expect a given bond to behave about the same in any molecular environment. Used in this way, the model of the chemical bond has helped chemists to systematize the reactions of the millions of existing compounds.

In addition to being very useful, the bonding model is also physically sensible. It makes sense that atoms can form stable groups by sharing electrons; shared electrons give a lower energy state because they are simultaneously attracted by two nuclei.

Also, as we will see in the next section, bond energy data support the existence of discrete bonds that are relatively independent of the molecular environment. It is very important to remember, however, that the chemical bond is only a model. Although our concept of discrete bonds in molecules agrees with many of our observations, some molecular properties require that we think of a molecule as a whole, with the electrons free to move through the entire molecule. This is called **delocalization** of the electrons, a concept that will be discussed more completely in the next chapter.

Fundamental Properties of Models

- Models are human inventions, always based on an incomplete understanding of how nature works. *A model does not equal reality.*

- Models are often wrong. This property derives from the first property. Models are based on speculation and are always oversimplifications.

- Models tend to become more complicated as they age. As flaws are discovered in our models, we "patch" them and thus add more detail.

- It is very important to understand the assumptions inherent in a particular model before you use it to interpret observations or to make predictions. Simple models usually involve very restrictive assumptions and can only be expected to yield qualitative information. Asking for a sophisticated explanation from a simple model is like expecting to get an accurate mass for a diamond using a bathroom scale.

  For a model to be used effectively, we must understand its strengths and weaknesses and ask only appropriate questions. An illustration of this point is the simple aufbau principle used to account for the electron configurations of the elements. Although this model correctly predicts the configuration for most atoms, chromium and copper, for example, do not agree with the predictions. Detailed studies show that the configurations of chromium and copper result from complex electron interactions that are not taken into account in the simple model. However, this does not mean that we should discard the simple model that is so useful for most atoms. Instead, we must apply it with caution and not expect it to be correct in every case.

- When a model is wrong, we often learn much more than when it is right. If a model makes a wrong prediction, it usually means we do not understand some fundamental characteristics of nature. We often learn by making mistakes. (Try to remember this when you get back your next chemistry test.)

8.8 Covalent Bond Energies and Chemical Reactions

Purpose

- To show how bond energies can be used to calculate heats of reaction.

In this section we will consider the energies associated with various types of bonds and see how the bonding concept is useful in dealing with the energies of chemical reactions. One important consideration is to establish the sensitivity of a particular type of bond to its molecular environment. For example, consider the stepwise decomposition of methane:

Process	Energy Required (kJ/mol)
$CH_4(g) \rightarrow CH_3(g) + H(g)$	435
$CH_3(g) \rightarrow CH_2(g) + H(g)$	453
$CH_2(g) \rightarrow CH(g) + H(g)$	425
$CH(g) \rightarrow C(g) + H(g)$	339
	Total = 1652
	Average $= \dfrac{1652}{4} = 413$

Although a C—H bond is broken in each case, the energy required varies in a nonsystematic way. This example shows that the C—H bond is somewhat sensitive to its environment. We use the *average* of these individual bond dissociation energies even though this quantity only approximates the energy associated with a C—H bond in a particular molecule. The degree of sensitivity of a bond to its environment also can be seen from experimental measurements of the energy required to break the C—H bond in the following molecules:

Molecule	Measured C—H Bond Energy (kJ/mol)
$HCBr_3$	380
$HCCl_3$	380
HCF_3	430
C_2H_6	410

Table 8.4

Average Bond Energies (kJ/mol)								
Single Bonds							Multiple Bonds	
H—H	432	N—H	391	I—I	149	C=C	614
H—F	565	N—N	160.	I—Cl	208	C≡C	839
H—Cl	427	N—F	272	I—Br	175	O=O	495
H—Br	363	N—Cl	200.			C=O	799
H—I	295	N—Br	243	S—H	347	C≡O	1072
		N—O	201	S—F	327	N=O	607
C—H	413	O—H	467	S—Cl	253	N=N	418
C—C	347	O—O	146	S—Br	218	N≡N	941
C—N	305	O—F	190.	S—S	266	C≡N	891
C—O	358	O—Cl	203			C=N	615
C—F	485	O—I	234	Si—Si	340		
C—Cl	339			Si—H	393		
C—Br	276	F—F	154	Si—C	360		
C—I	240.	F—Cl	253	Si—O	452		
C—S	259	F—Br	237				
		Cl—Cl	239				
		Cl—Br	218				
		Br—Br	193				

These data show that the C—H bond strength varies significantly with its environment, but the concept of an average C—H bond strength remains useful to chemists. The average values of bond energies for various types of bonds are listed in Table 8.4.

So far we have discussed bonds in which one pair of electrons is shared. This type of bond is called a **single bond.** As we will see in more detail later, atoms sometimes share two pairs of electrons, forming a **double bond,** or share three pairs of electrons, forming a **triple bond.** The bond energies for these **multiple bonds** are also given in Table 8.4.

A relationship also exists between the number of shared electron pairs and the bond length. As the number of shared electrons increases, the bond length shortens. This relationship is shown for selected bonds in Table 8.5.

Table 8.5

Bond Lengths for Selected Bonds			
Bond	Bond Type	Bond Length (pm)	Bond Energy (kJ/mol)
C—C	Single	154	347
C=C	Double	134	614
C≡C	Triple	120	839
C—O	Single	143	358
C=O	Double	123	799
C—N	Single	143	305
C=N	Double	138	615
C≡N	Triple	116	891

Bond Energy and Enthalpy

Bond energy values can be used to calculate approximate energies for reactions. To illustrate how this is done, we will calculate the change in energy that accompanies the following reaction:

$$H_2(g) + F_2(g) \rightarrow 2HF(g)$$

This reaction involves breaking one H—H and one F—F bond and forming two H—F bonds. For bonds to be broken, energy must be *added* to the system—an endothermic process. Consequently, the energy terms associated with bond breaking have *positive* signs. The formation of a bond *releases* energy, an exothermic process, so the energy terms associated with bond making carry a *negative* sign. We can write the enthalpy change for a reaction as follows:

ΔH = sum of the energies required to break old bonds (positive signs)
plus the sum of the energies released in the formation of new bonds (negative signs)

This leads to the expression

$$\Delta H = \underbrace{\Sigma D \text{ (bonds broken)}}_{\text{Energy required}} - \underbrace{\Sigma D \text{ (bonds formed)}}_{\text{Energy released}}$$

where Σ represents the sum of terms, and D represents the bond energy per mole of bonds. (D *always* has a positive sign.)

In the case of the formation of HF,

$$\Delta H = D_{H—H} + D_{F—F} - 2D_{H—F}$$

$$= 1 \text{ mol} \times \frac{432 \text{ kJ}}{\text{mol}} + 1 \text{ mol} \times \frac{154 \text{ kJ}}{\text{mol}} - 2 \text{ mol} \times \frac{565 \text{ kJ}}{\text{mol}}$$

$$= -544 \text{ kJ}$$

Thus when 1 mol $H_2(g)$ and 1 mol $F_2(g)$ react to form 2 mol $HF(g)$, 544 kJ of energy should be released.

This result can be compared with the calculation of ΔH for this reaction from the standard enthalpy of formation for HF (-271 kJ/mol):

$$\Delta H° = 2 \text{ mol} \times (-271 \text{ kJ/mol}) = -542 \text{ kJ}$$

Thus the use of bond energies to calculate ΔH works quite well in this case.

Sample Exercise 8.5

Using the bond energies listed in Table 8.4, calculate ΔH for the reaction of methane with chlorine and fluorine to give Freon-12 (CF_2Cl_2).

$$CH_4(g) + 2Cl_2(g) + 2F_2(g) \rightarrow CF_2Cl_2(g) + 2HF(g) + 2HCl(g)$$

Solution

The idea here is to break the bonds in the gaseous reactants to give individual atoms and then assemble these atoms into the gaseous products by forming new bonds:

$$\text{Reactants} \xrightarrow[\text{required}]{\text{Energy}} \text{atoms} \xrightarrow[\text{released}]{\text{Energy}} \text{products}$$

We then combine the energy changes to calculate ΔH:

ΔH = energy required to break bonds − energy released when bonds form

where the minus sign gives the correct sign to the energy terms for the exothermic processes.

Reactant bonds broken:

CH_4:   4 mol C—H $4 \text{ mol} \times \dfrac{413 \text{ kJ}}{\text{mol}} = 1652 \text{ kJ}$

$2Cl_2$:   2 mol Cl—Cl $2 \text{ mol} \times \dfrac{239 \text{ kJ}}{\text{mol}} = 478 \text{ kJ}$

$2F_2$:   2 mol F—F $2 \text{ mol} \times \dfrac{154 \text{ kJ}}{\text{mol}} = 308 \text{ kJ}$

 Total energy required = $\overline{2438 \text{ kJ}}$

Product bonds formed:

CF_2Cl_2:   2 mol C—F $2 \text{ mol} \times \dfrac{485 \text{ kJ}}{\text{mol}} = 970 \text{ kJ}$
 and
 2 mol C—Cl $2 \text{ mol} \times \dfrac{339 \text{ kJ}}{\text{mol}} = 678 \text{ kJ}$

HF: 2 mol H—F $2 \text{ mol} \times \dfrac{565 \text{ kJ}}{\text{mol}} = 1130 \text{ kJ}$

HCl: 2 mol H—Cl $2 \text{ mol} \times \dfrac{427 \text{ kJ}}{\text{mol}} = 854 \text{ kJ}$

 Total energy released = $\overline{3632 \text{ kJ}}$

We now can calculate ΔH:

ΔH = energy required to break bonds − energy released when bonds form

$= 2438 \text{ kJ} - 3632 \text{ kJ}$

$= -1194 \text{ kJ}$

Since the sign of the value for the enthalpy change is negative, this means that 1194 kJ of energy is released per mole of CF_2Cl_2 formed.

8.9 *The Localized Electron Bonding Model*

Purpose

• To introduce the localized electron model.

So far we have discussed the general characteristics of the chemical bonding model and have seen that properties such as bond strength and polarity can be assigned to individual bonds. In this section we introduce a specific model used to describe covalent bonds. We need a simple model that can be applied easily even to very complicated molecules and that can be used routinely by chemists to interpret and organize the wide variety of chemical phenomena. The model that serves this purpose is the **localized electron (LE) model,** which assumes that *a molecule is composed of atoms that are bound together by sharing pairs of electrons using the atomic orbitals of the bound atoms.* Electron pairs in the molecule are assumed to be localized on a particular atom or in the space between two atoms. Those pairs of electrons localized on an atom are called **lone pairs,** and those found in the space between the atoms are called **bonding pairs.**

As we will apply it, the LE model has three parts:

1. Description of the valence electron arrangement in the molecule using Lewis structures will be discussed in the next section.

2. Prediction of the geometry of the molecule using the valence shell electron pair repulsion (VSEPR) model will be discussed in Section 8.13.

3. Description of the types of atomic orbitals used by the atoms to share electrons or hold lone pairs will be discussed in Chapter 9.

8.10 Lewis Structures

Purpose

Figure 8.13
G. N. Lewis (1875–1946).

Lewis structures show only valence electrons.

• To show how to write Lewis structures.

The **Lewis structure** of a molecule shows how the valence electrons are arranged among the atoms in the molecule. These representations are named after G. N. Lewis (Fig. 8.13). The rules for writing Lewis structures are based on observations of thousands of molecules. From experiment, chemists have learned that the *most important requirement for the formation of a stable compound is that the atoms achieve noble gas electron configurations.*

We have already seen that when metals and nonmetals react to form binary ionic compounds, electrons are transferred and the resulting ions typically have noble gas electron configurations. An example is the formation of KBr, where the K^+ ion has the [Ar] electron configuration and the Br^- ion has the [Kr] electron configuration. In writing Lewis structures, the rule is that *only the valence electrons are included.* Using dots to represent electrons, the Lewis structure for KBr is

No dots are shown on the K^+ ion because it has no valence electrons. The Br^- ion is shown with eight electrons because it has a filled valence shell.

Next we will consider Lewis structures for molecules with covalent bonds, involving elements in the first and second periods. The principle of achieving a noble gas electron configuration applies to these elements as follows:

Hydrogen forms stable molecules where it shares two electrons. That is, it follows a **duet rule.** For example, when two hydrogen atoms, each with one electron, combine to form the H_2 molecule, we have

By sharing electrons, each hydrogen in H_2, in effect, has two electrons; that is, each hydrogen has a filled valence shell.

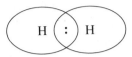

Helium does not form bonds because its valence orbital is already filled; it is a noble gas. Helium has the electron configuration $1s^2$ and can be represented by the Lewis structure

$$He :$$

The second-row nonmetals carbon through fluorine form stable molecules when they are surrounded by enough electrons to fill the valence orbitals, that is, the $2s$ and the three $2p$ orbitals. Since eight electrons are required to fill these orbitals, these elements typically obey the **octet rule;** they are surrounded by eight electrons. An example is the F_2 molecule, which has the following Lewis structure:

F atom with seven valence electrons $\qquad$ F_2 molecule $\qquad$ F atom with seven valence electrons

Note that each fluorine atom in F_2 is, in effect, surrounded by eight electrons, two of which are shared with the other atom. This is a *bonding pair* of electrons, as discussed earlier. Each fluorine atom also has three pairs of electrons not involved in bonding. These are the *lone pairs.*

Neon does not form bonds because it already has an octet of valence electrons (it is a noble gas). The Lewis structure is

$$: Ne :$$

Note that only the valence electrons of the neon atom ($2s^2 2p^6$) are represented by the Lewis structure. The $1s^2$ electrons are core electrons and are not shown.

From the preceding discussion we can formulate the following rules for writing Lewis structures of molecules containing atoms from the first two periods.

Rules for Writing Lewis Structures

- Sum the valence electrons from all the atoms. Do not worry about keeping track of which electrons come from which atoms. It is the *total* number of electrons that is important.

- Use a pair of electrons to form a bond between each pair of bound atoms.

- Arrange the remaining electrons to satisfy the duet rule for hydrogen and the octet rule for the second-row elements.

To see how these rules are applied, we will draw the Lewis structures of a few molecules. We will first consider the water molecule and follow the rules above.

Carbon, nitrogen, oxygen, and fluorine always obey the octet rule in stable molecules.

STEP 1

We sum the *valence* electrons for H_2O as shown:

$$1 + 1 + 6 = 8 \text{ valence electrons}$$
$$\text{H} \quad \text{H} \quad \text{O}$$

STEP 2

Using a pair of electrons per bond, we draw in the two O—H single bonds:

$$\text{H—O—H}$$

Note that *a line instead of a pair of dots is used to indicate each **pair** of bonding electrons*. This is the standard notation.

STEP 3

We distribute the remaining electrons to achieve a noble gas electron configuration for each atom. Since four electrons have been used in forming the two bonds, four electrons $(8 - 4)$ remain to be distributed. Hydrogen is satisfied with two electrons (duet rule), but oxygen needs eight electrons to have a noble gas configuration. Thus the remaining four electrons are added to oxygen as two lone pairs. Dots are used to represent the lone pairs:

This is the correct Lewis structure for the water molecule. Each hydrogen has two electrons and the oxygen has eight, as shown below:

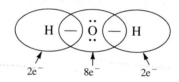

As a second example, let's write the Lewis structure for carbon dioxide. Summing the valence electrons gives

$$4 + 6 + 6 = 16$$
$$\text{C} \quad \text{O} \quad \text{O}$$

After forming a bond between the carbon and each oxygen,

$$\text{O—C—O}$$

the remaining electrons are distributed to achieve noble gas configurations on each atom. In this case we have 12 electrons $(16 - 4)$ remaining after the bonds are drawn. The distribution of these electrons is determined by a trial-and-error process. We have 6 pairs of electrons to distribute. Suppose we try 3 pairs on each oxygen to give

$$:\ddot{\text{O}}\text{—C—}\ddot{\text{O}}:$$

Is this correct? To answer this we need to check two things:

1. The total number of electrons. There are 16 valence electrons in this structure, which is the correct number.

H—O—H represents H : O : H

2. The octet rule for each atom. Each oxygen has 8 electrons, but the carbon only has 4. This cannot be the correct Lewis structure.

How can we arrange the 16 available electrons to achieve an octet for each atom? Suppose there are 2 shared pairs between the carbon and each oxygen:

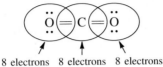

8 electrons   8 electrons   8 electrons

$\ddot{O}=C=\ddot{O}$ represents

$\ddot{O}::C::\ddot{O}$

Now each atom is surrounded by 8 electrons, and the total number of electrons is 16, as required. This is the correct Lewis structure for carbon dioxide, which has two double bonds and four lone pairs.

Finally, let's consider the Lewis structure of the CN^- (cyanide) ion. Summing the valence electrons, we have

$$CN^-$$
$$4 + 5 + 1 = 10$$

Note that the negative charge means an extra electron must be added. After drawing a single bond (C—N), we distribute the remaining electrons to achieve a noble gas configuration for each atom. Eight electrons remain to be distributed. We can try various possibilities, for example:

$$\overset{..}{\underset{..}{C}} - \overset{..}{\underset{..}{N}}$$

This structure is incorrect because C and N have only six electrons each instead of eight. The correct arrangement is

$$[:C \equiv N:]^-$$

(Satisfy yourself that both carbon and nitrogen have eight electrons.)

Sample Exercise 8.6

Give the Lewis structure for each of the following.

a. HF   **b.** N_2 **c.** NH_3 **d.** CH_4 **e.** CF_4 **f.** NO^+

Solution

In each case we apply the three rules for writing Lewis structures. Recall that lines are used to indicate shared electron pairs and that dots are used to indicate nonbonding pairs (lone pairs). We have the following tabulated results:

	Total Valence Electrons	Draw Single Bonds	Calculate Number of Electrons Remaining	Use Remaining Electrons to Achieve Noble Gas Configurations	Check Number of Electrons
a. HF	$1 + 7 = 8$	H—F	6	H—$\ddot{F}$:	H, 2 F, 8

	Total Valence Electrons	Draw Single Bonds	Calculate Number of Electrons Remaining	Use Remaining Electrons to Achieve Noble Gas Configurations	Check Number of Electrons
b. N_2	$5 + 5 = 10$	N—N	8	$: N \equiv N :$	N, 8

c. NH_3	$5 + 3(1) = 8$	H—N—H
		    |
		    H
			2	H—N̈—H
				    |
				    H
					H, 2
					N, 8

d. CH_4	$4 + 4(1) = 8$	H
		    |
		H—C—H
		    |
		    H
			0	H
				    |
				H—C—H
				    |
				    H
					H, 2
					C, 8

e. CF_4	$4 + 4(7) = 32$	F
		    |
		F—C—F
		    |
		    F
			24	: F̈ :
				    |
				: F̈—C—F̈ :
				    |
				    : F̈ :
					F, 8
					C, 8

f. NO^+	$5 + 6 - 1 = 10$	N—O	8	$[: N \equiv O :]^+$	N, 8 O, 8

When writing Lewis structures, do not worry about which electrons come from which atoms in a molecule. The best way to look at a molecule is to regard it as a new entity that uses all the available valence electrons of the atoms to achieve the lowest possible energy.* The valence electrons belong to the molecule, rather than to the individual atoms. Simply distribute all valence electrons so that the various rules are satisfied, without regard for the origin of each particular electron.

8.11 Exceptions to the Octet Rule

Purpose

• To show how to write Lewis structures for certain special cases.

The localized electron model is a simple but very successful model, and the rules we have used for Lewis structures apply to most molecules. However, with such a simple model, some exceptions are inevitable. Boron, for example, tends to form compounds in which the boron atom has fewer than eight electrons around it—it does not have a complete octet. Boron trifluoride (BF_3), a gas at normal temperatures and pressures, reacts very energetically with molecules such as water and ammonia that have available electron pairs (lone pairs). The violent reactivity of

---

*In a sense this approach corrects for the fact that the localized electron model overemphasizes that a molecule is simply a sum of its parts, that is, that the atoms retain their individual identities in the molecule.

BF_3 with electron-rich molecules arises because the boron atom is electron-deficient. Boron trifluoride has 24 valence electrons. The Lewis structure that seems most consistent with the properties of BF_3 is

Note that in this structure boron has only 6 electrons around it. The octet rule for boron can be satisfied by drawing a structure with a double bond, such as

However, since fluorine is much more electronegative than boron, this does not make sense. In fact, experiments indicate that the character of each B—F bond is closest to that of a single bond in accordance with the first Lewis structure. This structure is also consistent with the reactivity of BF_3 toward electron-rich molecules, for example, toward NH_3 to form H_3NBF_3:

In this stable compound, boron has an octet of electrons.

It is characteristic of boron to form molecules in which the boron atom is electron-deficient. On the other hand, carbon, nitrogen, oxygen, and fluorine can be counted on to obey the octet rule.

Some atoms exceed the octet rule. This behavior is observed only for those elements in Period 3 of the periodic table and beyond. To see how this arises, we will consider the Lewis structure for sulfur hexafluoride (SF_6), a well-known and very stable molecule. The sum of the valence electrons is

$$6 + 6(7) = 48 \text{ electrons}$$

Indicating the single bonds gives the structure on the left below:

We have used 12 electrons to form the S—F bonds, which leaves 36 electrons. Since fluorine always follows the octet rule, we complete the six fluorine octets to give the structure on the right above. This structure uses all 48 valence electrons for SF_6, but sulfur has 12 electrons around it; that is, sulfur *exceeds* the octet rule. How can this happen?

To answer this question, we need to consider the different types of valence orbitals characteristic of second- and third-period elements. The second-row elements have $2s$ and $2p$ valence orbitals, and the third-row elements have $3s$, $3p$, and $3d$ orbitals. The $3s$ and $3p$ orbitals fill with electrons in going from sodium to argon, but the $3d$ orbitals remain empty. For example, the valence orbital diagram for a sulfur atom is

$$
\boxed{\uparrow\downarrow}\quad \boxed{\uparrow\downarrow \;|\; \uparrow \;|\; \uparrow}\quad \boxed{\;|\;|\;|\;|\;|\;}
$$

$$
\;3s\qquad\qquad 3p\qquad\qquad\qquad 3d
$$

Third-row elements can exceed the octet rule.

The localized electron model assumes that the empty $3d$ orbitals can be used to accommodate extra electrons. Thus the sulfur atom in SF_6 can have 12 electrons around it by using the $3s$ and $3p$ orbitals to hold 8 electrons, with the extra 4 electrons placed in the formerly empty $3d$ orbitals.

Lewis Structures: Comments About the Octet Rule

- The second-row elements C, N, O, and F should always be assumed to obey the octet rule.
- The second-row elements B and Be often have fewer than eight electrons around them in their compounds. These electron-deficient compounds are very reactive.
- The second-row elements never exceed the octet rule, since their valence orbitals ($2s$ and $2p$) can accommodate only eight electrons.
- Third-row and heavier elements often satisfy the octet rule but can exceed the octet rule by using their empty valence d orbitals.
- When writing the Lewis structure for a molecule, satisfy the octet rule for the atoms first. If electrons remain after the octet rule has been satisfied, then place them on the elements having available d orbitals (elements in Period 3 or beyond).

Whether the atoms that exceed the octet rule actually place the extra electrons in their d orbitals is a matter of controversy among theoretical chemists. We will not consider this issue in this text.

Sample Exercise 8.7

Write the Lewis structure for PCl_5.

Solution

We can follow the same stepwise procedure we used above for sulfur hexafluoride.

STEP 1

Sum the valence electrons.

$$
5 \; + 5(7) = 40 \text{ electrons}
$$
$$
\uparrow \qquad \uparrow
$$
$$
\text{P} \qquad \text{Cl}
$$

STEP 2

Indicate single bonds between bound atoms.

$$
\begin{array}{c}
\;\;\;\;\;\text{Cl}\;\;\text{Cl}\\
\;\;\;\;\;|\;/\\
\text{Cl}\!-\!\text{P}\\
\;\;\;\;\;|\;\backslash\\
\;\;\;\;\;\text{Cl}\;\;\text{Cl}
\end{array}
$$

STEP 3

Distribute the remaining electrons. In this case, 30 electrons ($40 - 10$) remain. These are used to satisfy the octet rule for each chlorine atom. The final Lewis structure is

$$:Cl \quad \overset{\cdot\cdot}{Cl}:$$

(Lewis structure of PCl_5 with P central, bonded to five Cl atoms each with lone pairs)

Note that phosphorus, which is a third-row element, has exceeded the octet rule by two electrons.

· ·

In the PCl_5 and SF_6 molecules, the central atoms (P and S, respectively) must have the extra electrons. However, in molecules having more than one atom that can exceed the octet rule, it is not always clear which atom should have the extra electrons. Consider the Lewis structure for the triiodide ion (I_3^-), which has

$$3(7) + 1 = 22 \text{ valence electrons}$$
$$\uparrow \qquad \uparrow$$
$$1 \qquad 1 - \text{charge}$$

Indicating the single bonds gives I—I—I. At this point, 18 electrons (22 − 4) remain. Trial and error will convince you that one of the iodine atoms must exceed the octet rule, but *which* one?

The rule we will follow is that *when it is necessary to exceed the octet rule for one of several third-row (or higher) elements, assume that the extra electrons should be placed on the central atom.*

Thus for I_3^- the Lewis structure is

$$\left[:\overset{\cdot\cdot}{I} - \overset{\cdot\cdot}{I} - \overset{\cdot\cdot}{I}: \right]^-$$

where the central iodine exceeds the octet rule. This structure agrees with known properties of I_3^-.

Sample Exercise 8.8

Write the Lewis structure for each molecule or ion.

a. ClF_3 **b.** XeO_3 **c.** $RnCl_2$ **d.** $BeCl_2$ **e.** ICl_4^-

Solution

a. The chlorine atom (third row) accepts the extra electrons.

(Lewis structure of ClF_3 with Cl central bonded to three F atoms)

b. All atoms obey the octet rule.

(Lewis structure of XeO_3 with Xe central bonded to three O atoms)

c. Radon, a noble gas in Period 6, accepts the extra electrons.

$$:\ddot{\text{Cl}}—\dot{\text{Rn}}·—\ddot{\text{Cl}}:$$

d. Beryllium is electron-deficient.

$$:\ddot{\text{Cl}}—\text{Be}—\ddot{\text{Cl}}:$$

e. Iodine exceeds the octet rule.

$$\left[\begin{array}{c} :\ddot{\text{Cl}} \qquad \ddot{\text{Cl}}: \\ \diagdown \quad \diagup \\ \text{I} \\ \diagup \quad \diagdown \\ :\ddot{\text{Cl}} \qquad \ddot{\text{Cl}}: \end{array} \right]^{-}$$

8.12 Resonance

Purpose

- To illustrate the concept of resonance.
- To show how to write resonance structures.

Sometimes more than one valid Lewis structure (one that obeys the rules we have outlined) is possible for a given molecule. Consider the Lewis structure for the nitrate ion (NO_3^-), which has 24 valence electrons. To achieve an octet of electrons around each atom, a structure like this is required:

$$\left[\begin{array}{c} \ddot{\text{O}} \\ \| \\ \text{N} \\ \diagup \quad \diagdown \\ :\ddot{\text{O}}: \quad :\ddot{\text{O}}: \end{array} \right]^{-}$$

If this structure accurately represents the bonding in NO_3^-, there should be two types of N---O bonds observed in the molecule: one shorter bond (the double bond) and two identical longer ones (the two single bonds). However, experiments clearly show that NO_3^- exhibits only *one* type of N---O bond with a length and strength *between* those expected for a single bond and a double bond. Thus, although the structure we have shown above is a valid Lewis structure, it does *not* correctly represent the bonding in NO_3^-. This is a serious problem, and it means that the model must be modified.

Look again at the proposed Lewis structure for NO_3^-. There is no reason for choosing a particular oxygen atom to have the double bond. There are really three valid Lewis structures:

$$\left[\begin{array}{c} \ddot{\text{O}} \\ \| \\ \text{N} \\ \diagup \quad \diagdown \\ :\ddot{\text{O}} \quad \ddot{\text{O}}: \end{array} \right]^{-} \quad \left[\begin{array}{c} :\ddot{\text{O}}: \\ \| \\ \text{N} \\ \diagup \quad \diagdown \\ :\ddot{\text{O}} \quad \ddot{\text{O}}: \end{array} \right]^{-} \quad \left[\begin{array}{c} :\ddot{\text{O}}: \\ \| \\ \text{N} \\ \diagup \quad \diagdown \\ :\ddot{\text{O}} \quad \ddot{\text{O}}: \end{array} \right]^{-}$$

Is any of these structures a correct description of the bonding in NO_3^-? No, because NO_3^- does not have one double and two single bonds—it has three equivalent bonds. We can solve this problem by making the following assumption: the correct description of NO_3^- is *not given by any one* of the three Lewis structures but is given only by the *superposition of all three*.

The nitrate ion does not exist as any of the three extreme structures but exists as an average of all three. **Resonance** *occurs when more than one valid Lewis structure can be written for a particular molecule.* The resulting electron structure of the molecule is given by the average of these **resonance structures.** This situation is usually represented by double-headed arrows as follows:

Note that in all these resonance structures the arrangement of the nuclei is the same. Only the placement of the electrons differs. The arrows do not mean that the molecule "flips" from one resonance structure to another. They simply show that the *actual structure is an average of the three resonance structures.*

The concept of resonance is necessary because the localized electron model postulates that electrons are localized between a given pair of atoms. However, nature does not really operate this way. Electrons are really delocalized—they can move around the entire molecule. The valence electrons in the NO_3^- molecule distribute themselves to provide equivalent N---O bonds. Resonance is necessary to compensate for the defective assumption of the localized electron model. However, this model is so useful that we retain the concept of localized electrons and add resonance to allow the model to treat species such as NO_3^-.

Sample Exercise 8.9

Describe the electron arrangement in the nitrite anion (NO_2^-) using the localized electron model.

Solution

We will follow the usual procedure for obtaining the Lewis structure for the NO_2^- ion. In NO_2^- there are $5 + 2(6) + 1 = 18$ valence electrons. Indicating the single bonds gives the structure

$$O—N—O$$

The remaining 14 electrons ($18 - 4$) can be distributed to produce these structures:

This is a resonance situation. Two equivalent Lewis structures can be drawn. *The electronic structure of the molecule is not correctly represented by either resonance structure but by the average of the two.* There are two equivalent N---O bonds, each one intermediate between a single and a double bond.

Odd-Electron Molecules

Relatively few molecules formed from nonmetals contain odd numbers of electrons. One common example is nitric oxide (NO), which is formed when nitrogen and oxygen gases react at the high temperatures in automobile engines. Nitric oxide is emitted into the air, where it immediately reacts with oxygen to form gaseous nitrogen dioxide (NO_2), another odd-electron molecule.

Since the localized electron model is based on pairs of electrons, it does not handle odd-electron cases in a natural way. To treat odd-electron molecules, a more sophisticated model is needed.

Formal Charge

Equivalent Lewis structures contain the same numbers of single and multiple bonds. For example, the resonance structures for O_3

are equivalent Lewis structures. These are equally important in describing the bonding in O_3. Nonequivalent Lewis structures contain different numbers of single and multiple bonds.

Molecules or polyatomic ions containing atoms that can exceed the octet rule often have many nonequivalent Lewis structures, all of which obey the rules for writing Lewis structures. For example, as we will see in detail below, the sulfate ion has a Lewis structure with all single bonds and several Lewis structures that contain double bonds. How do we decide which of the many possible Lewis structures best describes the actual bonding in sulfate? One method is to estimate the charge on each atom in the various possible Lewis structures and use these charges to select the most appropriate structure(s). We will see below how this is done, but first we must decide on a method to assign atomic charges in molecules.

In Chapter 4 we discussed one system for obtaining charges, called **oxidation states.** However, in assigning oxidation states, we always count *both* the shared electrons as belonging to the more electronegative atom in a bond. This practice leads to highly exaggerated estimates of charge. In other words, although oxidation states are useful for bookkeeping electrons in redox reactions, they are not realistic estimates of the actual charges on individual atoms in a molecule, so they are not suitable for judging the appropriateness of Lewis structures. Another definition of the charge on an atom in a molecule, the formal charge, can, however, be used to evaluate Lewis structures. As we will see below, the **formal charge** of an atom in a molecule is *the difference between the number of valence electrons on the free atom and the number of valence electrons assigned to the atom in the molecule.*

Therefore, to determine the formal charge of a given atom in a molecule, we need to know two things:

1. The number of valence electrons on the free neutral atom (which has zero net charge because the number of electrons equals the number of protons).

2. The number of valence electrons "belonging" to the atom in a molecule.

We then compare these numbers. If in the molecule the atom has the same number of valence electrons as it does in the free state, the positive and negative charges just balance, and it has a formal charge of zero. If the atom has one more valence electron in a molecule than it has as a free atom, it has a formal charge of -1, and so on. Thus the formal charge on an atom in a molecule is defined as

Formal charge = (number of valence electrons on free atom)
        − (number of valence electrons assigned to the atom in the molecule)

To compute the formal charge of an atom in a molecule, we assign the valence electrons in the molecule to the various atoms, making the following assumptions:

1. Lone pair electrons belong entirely to the atom in question.

2. Shared electrons are *divided equally* between the two sharing atoms.

Thus the number of valence electrons assigned to a given atom is calculated as follows:

$$(\text{Valence electrons})_{\text{assigned}} = (\text{number of lone pair electrons})$$
$$+ \tfrac{1}{2} (\text{number of shared electrons})$$

We will illustrate the procedures for calculating formal charges by considering two of the possible Lewis structures for the sulfate ion, which as 32 valence electrons. For the Lewis structure

$$\left[\begin{array}{c} :\overset{\cdot\cdot}{O}: \\ | \\ :\overset{\cdot\cdot}{O}\!-\!\overset{\cdot\cdot}{S}\!-\!\overset{\cdot\cdot}{O}: \\ | \\ :\overset{\cdot\cdot}{O}: \end{array} \right]^{2-}$$

each oxygen atom has 6 lone pair electrons and shares 2 electrons with the sulfur atom. Thus, using the preceding assumptions, each oxygen is assigned 7 valence electrons:

$$\text{Valence electrons assigned to each oxygen} = 6\ plus\ \tfrac{1}{2}(2) = 7$$

Lone pair electrons   Shared electrons

$$\text{Formal charge on oxygen} = 6\ minus\ 7 = -1$$

Valence electrons on a free O atom

Valence electrons assigned to each O in SO_4^{2-}

The formal charge on each oxygen is -1.

For the sulfur atom there are no lone pair electrons and eight electrons are shared with the oxygen atoms. Thus, for sulfur,

$$\text{Valence electrons assigned to sulfur} = 0\ plus\ \tfrac{1}{2}(8) = 4$$

Lone pair electrons   Shared electrons

$$\text{Formal charge on sulfur} = 6\ minus\ 4 = 2$$

Valence electrons on free S atom

Valence electrons assigned to S in SO_4^{2-}

A second possible Lewis structure is

$$\left[\begin{array}{c} :\!\overset{..}{O}\!: \\ \| \\ :\!\overset{..}{O}\!-\!\overset{..}{S}\!-\!\overset{..}{O}\!: \\ \| \\ :\!\overset{..}{O}\!: \end{array}\right]^{2-}$$

In this case the formal charges are as follows:

For oxygen atoms with single bonds:

$$\text{Valence electrons assigned} = 6 + \tfrac{1}{2}(2) = 7$$
$$\text{Formal charge} = 6 - 7 = -1$$

For oxygen atoms with double bonds:

$$\text{Valence electrons assigned} = 4 + \tfrac{1}{2}(4) = 6$$

$\uparrow$
Each double
bond has 4
electrons

$$\text{Formal charge} = 6 - 6 = 0$$

For the sulfur atom:

$$\text{Valence electrons assigned} = 0 + \tfrac{1}{2}(12) = 6$$
$$\text{Formal charge} = 6 - 6 = 0$$

We will use two fundamental assumptions about formal charges to evaluate Lewis structures:

1. Atoms in molecules try to achieve formal charges as close to zero as possible.

2. Any negative formal charges are expected to reside on the most electronegative atoms.

We can use these principles to evaluate the two Lewis structures for sulfate given previously. Notice that in the structure with only single bonds each oxygen has a formal charge of -1, while the sulfur has a formal charge of $+2$. In contrast, in the structure with two double bonds and two single bonds, the sulfur and two oxygen atoms have a formal charge of O, while two oxygens have a formal charge of -1. Based on the assumptions given above, the structure with two double bonds is preferred—it has lower formal charges and the -1 formal charges are on electronegative oxygen atoms. Thus, for the sulfate ion, we might expect resonance structures such as

$$\left[\begin{array}{c} :\!\overset{..}{O}\!: \\ \| \\ :\!\overset{..}{O}\!-\!\overset{..}{S}\!-\!\overset{..}{O}\!: \\ \| \\ :\!\overset{..}{O}\!: \end{array}\right]^{2-} \longleftrightarrow \left[\begin{array}{c} :\!\overset{..}{O}\!: \\ \| \\ :\!\overset{..}{O}\!=\!\overset{..}{S}\!=\!\overset{..}{O} \\ \| \\ :\!\overset{..}{O}\!: \end{array}\right]^{2-}$$

to more closely describe the bonding than the Lewis structure with only single bonds.

Rules Governing Formal Charge

• To calculate the formal charge on an atom:

1. Take the sum of the lone pair electrons and one-half the shared electrons. This is the number of valence electrons assigned to the atom in the molecule.

   2. Subtract the number of assigned electrons from the number of valence electrons on the free, neutral atom to obtain the formal charge.

- The sum of the formal charges of all atoms in a given molecule or ion must equal the overall charge on that species.

- If nonequivalent Lewis structures exist for a species, those with formal charges closest to zero and with any negative formal charges on the most electronegative atoms are considered to best describe the bonding in the molecule or ion.

Sample Exercise 8.10

Give possible Lewis structures for XeO_3, an explosive compound of xenon. Which Lewis structure or structures are most appropriate according to the formal charges?

Solution

For XeO_3 (26 valence electrons) we can draw the following possible Lewis structures (formal charges are indicated in parentheses):

Based on the ideas of formal charge, we would predict that the Lewis structures with the lower values of formal charge would be most appropriate for describing the bonding in XeO_3.

As a final note there are a couple of cautions about formal charge to keep in mind. First, although formal charges are closer to actual atomic charges in molecules than are oxidation states, formal charges still provide only *estimates* of charge—they should not be taken as actual atomic charges. Second, the evaluation of Lewis structures using formal charge ideas can lead to erroneous predictions. Tests based on experiments must be used to make the final decisions on the correct description of bonding in a molecule or polyatomic ion.

8.13 Molecular Structure: The VSEPR Model

Purpose

- To describe how molecular geometry can be predicted from the number of electron pairs.

The structures of molecules play a very important role in determining their chemical properties. As we will see later, this is particularly important for biologic molecules; a slight change in the structure of a large biomolecule can completely destroy its usefulness to a cell or may even change the cell from a normal one to a cancerous one.

Many accurate methods now exist for determining **molecular structure,** the three-dimensional arrangement of the atoms in a molecule. These methods must be used if precise information about structure is required. However, it is often useful to be able to predict the approximate molecular structure of a molecule. In this section we consider a simple model that allows us to do this. This model, called the **valence shell electron pair repulsion (VSEPR) model,** is useful in predicting the geometries of molecules formed from nonmetals. The main postulate of this model is that *the structure around a given atom is determined principally by minimizing electron-pair repulsions.* The idea here is that the bonding and nonbonding pairs around a given atom will be positioned as far apart as possible. To see how this model works, we will first consider the molecule $BeCl_2$, which has the Lewis structure

$$: \overset{..}{Cl} - Be - \overset{..}{Cl} :$$

Note that there are two pairs of electrons around the beryllium atom. What arrangement of these electron pairs allows them to be as far apart as possible to minimize the repulsions? Clearly, the best arrangement places the pairs on opposite sides of the beryllium atom at 180 degrees from each other:

$$-Be-$$
$$180°$$

This is the maximum possible separation for two electron pairs. Once we have determined the optimal arrangement of the electron pairs around the central atom, we can specify the molecular structure of $BeCl_2$, that is, the positions of the atoms. Since each electron pair on beryllium is shared with a chlorine atom, the molecule has a **linear structure** with a 180-degree bond angle:

$$Cl-Be-Cl$$
$$180°$$

Next, let's consider BF_3, which has the Lewis structure

$$: \overset{..}{F} - \underset{\overset{|}{\underset{:\overset{..}{F}:}{}}}{B} - \overset{..}{F} :$$

Here the boron atom is surrounded by three pairs of electrons. What arrangement will minimize the repulsions? The electron pairs are farthest apart at angles of 120 degrees:

$$\underset{B}{|} 120°$$

Since each of the electron pairs is shared with a fluorine atom, the molecular structure will be

$$\underset{F \quad \diagup \overset{B}{\diagdown} \quad F}{\overset{F}{\underset{|}{}}} 120°$$

This is a planar (flat) and triangular molecule, which is commonly described as a **trigonal planar structure.**

Next, let's consider the methane molecule, which has the Lewis structure

There are four pairs of electrons around the central carbon atom. What arrangement of these electron pairs best minimizes the repulsions? First, let's try a square planar arrangement:

The carbon atom and the electron pairs are centered in the plane of the paper, and the angles between the pairs are all 90 degrees.

Is there another arrangement with angles greater than 90 degrees that would put the electron pairs even further away from each other? The answer is yes. The **tetrahedral arrangement** has angles of 109.5 degrees:

It can be shown that this is the maximum possible separation of four pairs around a given atom. This means that *whenever four pairs of electrons are present around an atom, they should always be arranged tetrahedrally.*

Now that we have the electron-pair arrangement that gives the least repulsion, we can determine the positions of the atoms and thus the molecular structure of CH_4. In methane, each of the four electron pairs is shared between the carbon atom and a hydrogen atom. Thus the hydrogen atoms are placed as in Fig. 8.14, and the molecule has a tetrahedral structure with the carbon atom at the center.

Recall that the main idea of the VSEPR model is to find the arrangement of electron pairs around the central atom that minimizes the repulsions. Then we can determine the molecular structure from knowing how the electron pairs are shared with the peripheral atoms. Use the following steps to predict the structure of a molecule using the VSEPR model.

Figure 8.14

The molecular structure of methane. The tetrahedral arrangement of electron pairs produces a tetrahedral arrangement of hydrogen atoms.

STEP 1
Draw the Lewis structure for the molecule.

STEP 2
Count the electron pairs and arrange them in the way that minimizes repulsion (that is, put the pairs as far apart as possible).

STEP 3
Determine the positions of the atoms from the *way the electron pairs are shared.*

STEP 4
Determine the name of the molecular structure from the *positions of the atoms.*

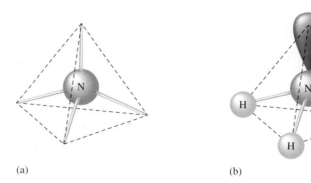

(a)

(b)

Lone pair

Figure 8.15

(a) The tetrahedral arrangement of electron pairs around the nitrogen atom in the ammonia molecule. (b) Three of the electron pairs around nitrogen are shared with hydrogen atoms as shown and one is a lone pair. Although the arrangement of *electron pairs* is tetrahedral, as in the methane molecule, the hydrogen atoms in the ammonia molecule occupy only three corners of the tetrahedron. A lone pair occupies the fourth corner.

We will predict the structure of ammonia (NH_3) using this stepwise approach.

STEP 1

Draw the Lewis structure:

STEP 2

Count the pairs of electrons and arrange them to minimize repulsions. The NH_3 molecule has four pairs of electrons: three bonding pairs and one nonbonding pair. From the discussion of the methane molecule, we know that the best arrangement of four electron pairs is a tetrahedral array, as shown in Fig. 8.15(a).

STEP 3

Determine the positions of the atoms. The three H atoms share electron pairs, as shown in Fig. 8.15(b).

STEP 4

Name the molecular structure. It is very important to recognize that the *name* of the molecular structure is always based on the *positions of the atoms*. The placement of the electron pairs determines the structure, but the name is based on the positions of the atoms. Thus it is incorrect to say that the NH_3 molecule is tetrahedral. It has a tetrahedral arrangement of electron pairs but not a tetrahedral arrangement of atoms. The molecular structure of ammonia is a **trigonal pyramid** (one side is different from the other three) rather than a tetrahedron.

(a)

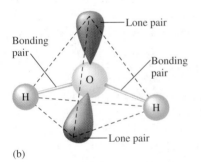

Bonding pair

Lone pair

Bonding pair

Lone pair

(b)

(c)

Figure 8.16

(a) The tetrahedral arrangement of the four electron pairs around oxygen in the water molecule. (b) Two of the electron pairs are shared between oxygen and the hydrogen atoms and two are lone pairs. (c) The V-shaped molecular structure of the water molecule.

Sample Exercise 8.11

Describe the molecular structure of the water molecule.

Solution

The Lewis structure for water is

$$H-\overset{..}{\underset{..}{O}}-H$$

There are four pairs of electrons: two bonding pairs and two nonbonding pairs. To minimize repulsions, these are best arranged in a tetrahedral array, as shown in Fig. 8.16(a). Although H_2O has a tetrahedral arrangement of electron pairs, it is not a tetrahedral molecule. The atoms in the H_2O molecule form a V shape, as shown in Fig. 8.16(b) and (c).

From Sample Exercise 8.11 we see that the H_2O molecule is V-shaped, or bent, because of the presence of the lone pairs. If no lone pairs were present, the molecule would be linear, the polar bonds would cancel, and the molecule would have no dipole moment. This would make water very different from the polar substance so familiar to us.

From the previous discussion we would predict that the H—X—H bond angle (where X is the central atom) in CH_4, NH_3, and H_2O should be the tetrahedral angle of 109.5 degrees. Experimental studies, however, show that the actual bond angles are those given in Fig. 8.17. What significance do these results have for the VSEPR model? One possible point of view is that we should be pleased to have the observed angles so close to the tetrahedral angle. The opposite view is that the deviations are significant enough to require modification of the simple model so that it can more accurately handle similar cases. We will take the latter view.

Let us examine the following data:

	CH_4	NH_3	H_2O
Number of lone pairs	0	1	2
Bond angle	109.5°	107°	104.5°

One interpretation of the trend observed here is that lone pairs require more space than bonding pairs; in other words, as the number of lone pairs increases, the bonding pairs are increasingly squeezed together.

This interpretation seems to make physical sense if we think in the following terms. A bonding pair is shared between two nuclei, and the electrons can be close to either nucleus. They are relatively confined between the two nuclei. A lone pair is localized on only one nucleus, and both electrons will be close only to that nucleus, as shown schematically in Fig. 8.18. These pictures help us understand why a lone pair may require more space near an atom than a bonding pair.

(a)

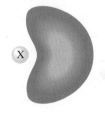

(b)

Figure 8.18

(a) In a bonding pair of electrons, the electrons are shared by two nuclei. (b) In a lone pair, both electrons must be close to a single nucleus and tend to take up more of the space around that atom.

Figure 8.17

The bond angles in the CH_4, NH_3, and H_2O molecules. Note that the bond angle between bonding pairs decreases as the number of lone pairs increases.

Methane   Ammonia   Water

109.5°   107°   104.5°

Table 8.6

Arrangements of Electron Pairs Around an Atom Yielding Minimum Repulsion

Number of Electron Pairs	Arrangement of Electron Pairs		Example
2	Linear	$:\!-\!\!-\!A\!-\!\!-\!:$	
3	Trigonal planar		
4	Tetrahedral		
5	Trigonal bipyramidal		
6	Octahedral		

As a result of these observations, we make the following addition to the original postulate of the VSEPR model: *lone pairs require more room than bonding pairs and tend to compress the angles between the bonding pairs.*

So far we have considered cases with two, three, and four electron pairs around the central atom. These are summarized in Table 8.6. For five pairs of electrons, there are several possible choices. The one that produces minimum repulsion is a **trigonal bipyramid.** Note from Table 8.6 that this arrangement has two different angles, 90 degrees and 120 degrees. As the name suggests, the structure formed by this arrangement of pairs consists of two trigonal-based pyramids that share a common base. Six pairs of electrons can best be arranged around a given atom with 90-degree angles to form an **octahedral structure,** as shown in Table 8.6.

In order to use the VSEPR model to determine the geometric structures of molecules, you should memorize the relationships between the number of electron pairs and their best arrangement.

Sample Exercise 8.12

When phosphorus reacts with excess chlorine gas, the compound phosphorus pentachloride (PCl_5) is formed. In the gaseous and liquid states, this substance consists of PCl_5 molecules, but in the solid state it consists of a 1:1 mixture of PCl_4^+ and PCl_6^- ions. Predict the geometric structures of PCl_5, PCl_4^+, and PCl_6^-.

Solution

The Lewis structure for PCl_5 is shown in the margin. Five pairs of electrons around the phosphorus atom require a trigonal bipyramidal arrangement (see Table 8.6). When the chlorine atoms are included, a trigonal bipyramidal molecule results:

Lewis structure for PCl_5:

The Lewis structure for the PCl_4^+ ion [$5 + 4(7) - 1 = 32$ valence electrons] is shown in the margin. There are four pairs of electrons surrounding the phosphorus atom in the PCl_4^+ ion, which requires a tetrahedral arrangement of the pairs, as shown in the figure in the margin. Since each pair is shared with a chlorine atom, a tetrahedral PCl_4^+ cation results.

Lewis structure for PCl_4^+:

The Lewis structure for PCl_6^- [$5 + 6(7) + 1 = 48$ valence electrons] is

Since phosphorus is surrounded by six pairs of electrons, an octahedral arrangement is required to minimize repulsions, as shown below on the left. Since each electron pair is shared with a chlorine atom, an octahedral PCl_6^- anion is predicted.

Tetrahedral PCl_4^+ cation

Crystals of xenon tetrafluoride.

Sample Exercise 8.13

Because the noble gases have filled *s* and *p* valence orbitals, they were not expected to be chemically reactive. In fact, for many years these elements were called **inert gases** because of this supposed inability to form any compounds. However, in the early 1960s several compounds of krypton, xenon, and radon were synthesized. For example, a team at the Argonne National Laboratory produced the stable colorless compound xenon tetrafluoride (XeF_4). Predict its structure and whether it has a dipole moment.

Solution

The Lewis structure for XeF_4 is

The xenon atom in this molecule is surrounded by six pairs of electrons, which means an octahedral arrangement:

The structure predicted for this molecule will depend on how the lone pairs and bonding pairs are arranged. Consider the two possibilities shown in Fig. 8.19. The bonding pairs are indicated by the presence of the fluorine atoms. Since the structure predicted differs in the two cases, we must decide which of these arrangements is preferable. The key is to look at the lone pairs. In the structure in part (a), the lone pair–lone pair angle is 90 degrees; in the structure in part (b), the lone pairs are separated by 180 degrees. Since lone pairs require more room than bonding pairs, a structure with two lone pairs at 90 degrees is unfavorable. Thus the arrangement in Fig. 8.19(b) is preferred, and the molecular structure is predicted to be square planar. Note that this molecule is *not* described as being octahedral. There is an *octahedral arrangement of electron pairs,* but the *atoms* form a **square planar** structure.

Although each Xe—F bond is polar (fluorine has a greater electronegativity than xenon), the square planar arrangement of these bonds causes the polarities to cancel.

Thus XeF_4 has no dipole moment, as shown in the margin.

We can further illustrate the use of the VSEPR model for molecules or ions with lone pairs by considering the triiodide ion (I_3^-). The Lewis structure for I_3^- is

(a)

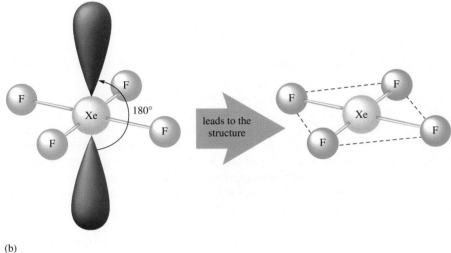

(b)

Figure 8.19

Possible electron pair arrangements for XeF_4. Since arrangement (a) has lone pairs at 90° from each other, it is less favorable than arrangement (b), where the lone pairs are at 180°.

$$\left[:\overset{..}{I} — \overset{..}{\underset{..}{I}} — \overset{..}{I}: \right]^{-}$$

The central iodine atom has five pairs around it, which requires a trigonal bipyramidal arrangement. Several possible arrangements of the lone pairs are shown in Fig. 8.20. Note that structures (a) and (b) have lone pairs at 90 degrees, whereas in (c) all lone pairs are at 120 degrees. Thus structure (c) is preferred. The resulting molecular structure for I_3^- is linear:

$$[I—I—I]^{-}$$

The VSEPR Model and Multiple Bonds

So far in our treatment of the VSEPR model we have not considered any molecules with multiple bonds. To see how these molecules are handled by this model, let's

(a)

(b)

(c)

Figure 8.20

Three possible arrangements of the electron pairs in the I_3^- ion. Arrangement (c) is preferred because there are no 90° lone pair–lone pair interactions.

consider the NO_3^- ion, which requires three resonance structures to describe its electronic structure:

$$\left[\begin{array}{c} \ddot{O} \\ \| \\ N \\ \diagup \diagdown \\ :\ddot{O} \quad :\ddot{O}: \end{array} \right]^- \longleftrightarrow \left[\begin{array}{c} :\ddot{O}: \\ | \\ N \\ \diagup \diagdown \\ \ddot{O} \quad :\ddot{O}: \end{array} \right]^- \longleftrightarrow \left[\begin{array}{c} :\ddot{O}: \\ | \\ N \\ \diagup \diagdown \\ :\ddot{O} \quad \ddot{O} \end{array} \right]^-$$

The NO_3^- ion is known to be planar with 120-degree bond angles:

This planar structure is the one expected for three pairs of electrons around a central atom, which means that *a double bond should be counted as one effective pair* in using the VSEPR model. This makes sense because the two pairs of electrons involved in the double bond are *not* independent pairs. Both the electron pairs must be in the space between the nuclei of the two atoms in order to form the double bond. In other words, the double bond acts as one center of electron density to repel the other pairs of electrons. The same holds true for triple bonds. This leads us to another general rule: *for the VSEPR model, multiple bonds count as one effective electron pair.*

The molecular structure of nitrate also shows us one more important point: *when a molecule exhibits resonance, any one of the resonance structures can be used to predict the molecular structure using the VSEPR model.* These rules are illustrated in Sample Exercise 8.14.

Sample Exercise 8.14

Predict the molecular structure of the sulfur dioxide molecule. Is this molecule expected to have a dipole moment?

Solution

First, we must determine the Lewis structure for the SO_2 molecule, which has 18 valence electrons. The expected resonance structures are

$$:\ddot{O} \diagdown_{\underset{..}{S}} \diagup \ddot{O}: \longleftrightarrow :\ddot{O} \diagdown_{\underset{..}{S}} \diagup \ddot{O}:$$

To determine the molecular structure, we must count the electron pairs around the sulfur atom. In each resonance structure the sulfur has one lone pair, one pair in a single bond, and one double bond. Counting the double bond as one pair yields three effective pairs around the sulfur. According to Table 8.6, a trigonal planar arrangement is required, which yields a V-shaped molecule:

$$O \overset{120°}{\underset{S}{\curvearrowleft}} O$$

Thus the structure of the SO_2 molecule is expected to be V-shaped, with a 120-degree bond angle. The molecule has a dipole moment directed as shown:

$$O \overset{\uparrow}{\underset{S}{\diagup \!\!\!\! \diagdown}} O$$

Since the molecule is V-shaped, the polar bonds do not cancel.

It should be noted at this point that lone pairs that are oriented at least 120 degrees from other pairs do not produce significant distortions of bond angles. For example, the angle in the SO_2 molecule is actually quite close to 120 degrees. We will follow the general principle that *a 120-degree angle provides lone pairs with enough space so that distortions do not occur. Angles less than 120 degrees are distorted when lone pairs are present.*

Molecules Containing No Single Central Atom

So far we have considered molecules consisting of one central atom surrounded by other atoms. The VSEPR model can be readily extended to more complicated molecules, such as methanol (CH_3OH). This molecule is represented by the following Lewis structure:

$$H-\overset{\overset{\displaystyle H}{|}}{\underset{\underset{\displaystyle H}{|}}{C}}-\overset{..}{\underset{..}{O}}-H$$

The molecular structure can be predicted from the arrangement of pairs around the carbon and oxygen atoms. Note that there are four pairs of electrons around the carbon, which calls for a tetrahedral arrangement, as shown in Fig. 8.21(a). The oxygen also has four pairs, which requires a tetrahedral arrangement. However, in this case the tetrahedron will be slightly distorted by the space requirements of the lone pairs [Fig. 8.21(b)]. The overall geometric arrangement for the molecule is shown in Fig. 8.21(c).

Summary of the VSEPR Model

The rules for using the VSEPR model to predict molecular structure are

- Determine the Lewis structure(s) for the molecule.
- For molecules with resonance structures, use any of the structures to predict the molecular structure.
- Sum the electron pairs around the central atom.
- In counting pairs, count each multiple bond as a single effective pair.

(a)

(b)

(c)

Figure 8.21

The molecular structure of methanol. (a) The arrangement of electron pairs and atoms around the carbon atom. (b) The arrangement of bonding and lone pairs around the oxygen atom. (c) The molecular structure.

◀ C H E M I C A L   I M P A C T ▶

Chemical Structure and Communication: Semiochemicals

In this chapter we have stressed the importance of being able to predict the three-dimensional structure of a molecule. Molecular structure is important because of its effect on chemical reactivity. This is especially true in biologic systems, where reactions must be efficient and highly specific. Among the hundreds of types of molecules in the fluids of a typical biologic system, the appropriate reactants must find and react only with each other—they must be very discriminating. This specificity depends largely on structure. The molecules are constructed so that only the appropriate partners can approach each other in a way that allows reaction.

Another area where molecular structure is central is in the use of molecules as a means of communication. Examples of chemical communication occur in humans in the conduction of nerve impulses across synapses, the control of the manufacture and storage of key chemicals in cells, and the senses of smell and taste. Plants and animals also use chemical communication. For example, ants lay down a chemical trail so that other ants can find a particular food supply. Ants also warn their fellow workers of approaching danger by emitting certain chemicals.

Molecules convey messages by fitting into appropriate receptor sites in a very specific way, which is determined by their structure. When a molecule occupies a receptor site, chemical processes are stimulated that produce the appropriate response. Sometimes receptors can be fooled, as in the use of artificial sweeteners—molecules fit the sites on the taste buds that stimulate a "sweet" response in the brain, but they are not metabolized in the same way as natural sugars. Similar deception is useful in insect control. If an area is sprayed with synthetic female sex attractant molecules, the males of that species become so confused that mating does not occur.

A **semiochemical** is a molecule that delivers a message between members of the same or different species of plant or animal. There are three groups of these chemical messengers: allomones, kairomones, and pheromones. Each is of great ecological importance.

An **allomone** is defined as a chemical that somehow gives adaptive advantage to the producer. For example, leaves of the black walnut tree contain a herbicide, juglone, that appears after the leaves fall to the ground. Juglone is not toxic to grass or certain grains, but it is effective against

plants such as apple trees that would compete for the available water and food supplies.

Antibiotics are also allomones, since the microorganisms produce them to inhibit other species from growing near them.

Many plants produce bad-tasting chemicals to protect themselves from plant-eating insects and animals. The familiar compound nicotine deters animals from eating the tobacco plant. The millipede sends an unmistakable "back off" message by squirting a predator with benzaldehyde and hydrogen cyanide.

Defense is not the only use of allomones, however. Flowers use scent as a way to attract pollinating insects. Honeybees, for instance, are guided to alfalfa flowers by a series of sweet-scented compounds.

Kairomones are chemical messengers that bring advantageous news to the receiver, and the floral scents are kairomones from the honeybees' viewpoint. Many predators are guided by kairomones emitted by their food. For example, apple skins exude a chemical that attracts the codling moth larva. In some cases kairomones help the underdog. Certain marine mollusks can pick up

- The arrangement of the pairs is determined by minimizing electron-pair repulsions. These arrangements are shown in Table 8.6.

- Lone pairs require more space than bonding pairs. Choose an arrangement that gives the lone pairs as much room as possible. Recognize that the lone pairs may produce a slight distortion of the structure at angles less than 120 degrees.

The VSEPR Model—How Well Does It Work?

The VSEPR model is very simple. There are only a few rules to remember, yet the model correctly predicts the molecular structures of most molecules formed from nonmetallic elements. Molecules of any size can be treated by applying the VSEPR model to each appropriate atom (those bonded to at least two other atoms) in the molecule. Thus we can use this model to predict the structures of molecules with

◀ C H E M I C A L   I M P A C T ▶

the "scent" of their predators, the sea stars, and make their escape.

Pheromones are chemicals that affect receptors of the same species as the donor. That is, they are specific within a species. **Releaser pheromones** cause an immediate reaction in the receptor, and **primer pheromones** cause long-term effects. Examples of releaser pheromones are the sex attractants of insects, generated in some species by the males and in others by the females. Sex pheromones also have been found in plants and mammals.

Alarm pheromones are highly volatile compounds (ones easily changed to a gas) released to warn of danger. Honeybees produce isoamyl acetate ($C_7H_{14}O_2$) in their sting glands. Because of its high volatility, this compound does not linger after the state of alert is over. Social behavior in insects is characterized by the

use of **trail pheromones,** which are used to indicate a food source. Social insects such as bees, ants, wasps, and termites use these substances. Since trail pheromones are less volatile compounds, the indicators persist for some time.

Primer pheromones, which cause long-term behavioral changes, are harder to isolate and identify. One example, however, is the "queen substance" produced by queen honeybees. All the eggs in a colony are laid by one queen bee. If she is removed from the hive or dies, the worker bees are activated by the absence of the queen substance and begin to feed royal jelly to bee larvae in order to raise a new queen. The queen substance also prevents the development of the workers' ovaries so that only the queen herself can produce eggs.

Many studies of insect pheromones are now underway in the hope that they will

A queen honeybee and her attendants.

provide a method of controlling insects that is more efficient and safer than the current chemical pesticides.

---

hundreds of atoms. It does, however, fail in a few instances. For example, phosphine (PH_3), which has a Lewis structure analogous to that of ammonia,

$$
\overset{..}{\underset{\underset{H}{|}}{H-P-H}}
\qquad
\overset{..}{\underset{\underset{H}{|}}{H-N-H}}
$$

would be predicted to have a molecular structure similar to that for NH_3, with bond angles of approximately 107 degrees. However, the bond angles of phosphine are actually 94 degrees. There are ways of explaining this structure, but more rules have to be added to the model.

This again illustrates the point that simple models are bound to have exceptions. In introductory chemistry we want to use simple models that fit the majority of cases; we are willing to accept a few failures rather than complicate the model. The amazing thing about the VSEPR model is that such a simple model predicts correctly the structures of so many molecules.

F O R   R E V I E W

Summary

Chemical bonds hold groups of atoms together. Bonding occurs when a group of atoms can lower its total energy by aggregating. Bonds can be classified into several types. In an ionic bond there is a transfer of electrons to form ions; in a covalent bond electrons are shared. Between these extremes, in a polar covalent bond electrons are shared unequally. The percent ionic character of the bond in a diatomic molecule XY can be defined as

$$\text{Percent ionic character} = \left(\frac{\text{measured dipole moment of X—Y}}{\text{calculated dipole moment of X}^+\text{Y}^-} \right) \times 100$$

Electronegativity is defined as the relative ability of an atom in a molecule to attract the electrons shared in a bond. The electronegativity difference of the atoms involved in a bond determines the polarity of that bond. The spatial arrangement of polar bonds determines the overall polarity, or dipole moment, of a molecule.

Stable molecules usually contain atoms that have filled valence orbitals. Nonmetals bonding to each other achieve noble gas configurations in their valence orbitals by covalent bonding. A nonmetal and a representative-group metal achieve the same result by transferring electrons to form ions.

Ions have significantly different sizes from their parent atoms. Cations are smaller because the parent atom has lost electrons to become an ion. Anions, because they have more electrons than the parent atom, are larger. In general, ion size increases going down a group. Isoelectronic ions (having the same number of electrons) decrease in size with increasing Z values.

Lattice energy is the change in energy that takes place when separated gaseous ions are packed together to form an ionic solid. Bond energy, the energy necessary to break a covalent bond, varies with the number of shared electron pairs. A single bond involves one electron pair; a double bond, two electron pairs; and a triple bond, three electron pairs. Bond energies can be used to calculate the enthalpy change for a reaction.

The Lewis structure of a molecule shows how the valence electrons are arranged among the atoms. The duet rule for hydrogen and the octet rule for second-row elements reflect the observation that atoms tend to fill their valence orbitals. Elements in the third row and beyond can exceed the octet rule because of the availability of empty d orbitals.

Sometimes more than one valid Lewis structure can be drawn for the same molecule, which is accounted for by the concept of resonance. The actual electronic structure is represented by the superposition of the resonance structures in such cases.

When several nonequivalent Lewis structures can be drawn for a molecule, formal charge is often used to choose the most appropriate structure(s). The VSEPR model is very useful in predicting the geometries of molecules formed from nonmetals. The principal postulate of this model is that the structure around a given atom is determined by minimizing electron-pair repulsions.

Key Terms

Section 8.1	Section 8.2	Section 8.5	Section 8.9	duet rule
bond energy	electronegativity	lattice energy	localized electron	octet rule
ionic bonding			(LE) model	
ionic compound	Section 8.3	Section 8.8	lone pair	Section 8.12
Coulomb's law	dipole moment	single bond	bonding pair	resonance
bond length		double bond		resonance structure
covalent bonding	Section 8.4	triple bond	Section 8.10	formal charge
polar covalent bond	isoelectronic ions		Lewis structure	

Section 8.13
molecular structure
valence shell electron
  pair repulsion

(VSEPR) model
linear structure
trigonal planar structure
tetrahedral structure

trigonal pyramid
trigonal bipyramid
octahedral structure
square planar structure

A blue question or exercise number indicates that the answer to that question or exercise appears at the back of this book and a solution appears in the Solutions Guide.

Questions

1. Explain the difference between the following pairs of terms.
   a. Electronegativity and electron affinity
   b. Covalent bond and polar covalent bond
   c. Polar covalent bond and ionic bond

2. Define the term *isoelectronic*. When comparing sizes of ions of elements in the same period in the periodic table, why is it advantageous to compare isoelectronic species?

3. Would you expect the electronegativity of titanium to be the same in the species Ti, Ti^{2+}, Ti^{3+}, and Ti^{4+}? Explain.

4. The second electron affinity values for both oxygen and sulfur are unfavorable (endothermic). Explain.

5. What two requirements must be satisfied for a molecule to be polar?

6. Give a rationalization for the octet rule in terms of orbitals.

Exercises

In this section similar exercises are paired.

Chemical Bonds and Electronegativity

7. Without using Fig. 8.3, predict the order of increasing electronegativity in each of the following groups of elements.
   a. C, N, O   d. Tl, S, Ge
   b. S, Se, Cl
   c. Si, Ge, Sn

8. Without using Fig. 8.3, predict the order of increasing electronegativity in each of the following groups of elements.
   a. Na, K, Rb
   b. B, O, Ga
   c. F, Cl, Br
   d. S, O, F

9. Without using Fig. 8.3, predict which bond in each of the following groups will be the most polar.
   a. C—F, Si—F, Ge—F
   b. P—Cl, S—Cl
   c. S—F, S—Cl, S—Br
   d. Ti—Cl, Si—Cl, Ge—Cl

10. Without using Fig. 8.3, predict which bond in each of the following groups will be the most polar.
    a. C—H, Si—H, Sn—H
    b. Al—Br, Ga—Br, In—Br, Tl—Br
    c. C—O or Si—O
    d. O—F or O—Cl

11. Repeat Exercises 7 and 9, this time using the values for the electronegativities of the elements given in Fig. 8.3. Are there differences in your answers?

12. Repeat Exercises 8 and 10, this time using the values of the electronegativities of the elements given in Fig. 8.3. Are there differences in your answers?

Ionic Compounds

13. For each of the following groups, place the atoms and/or ions in order of decreasing size.
    a. Cu, Cu^+, Cu^{2+}
    b. Ni^{2+}, Pd^{2+}, Pt^{2+}
    c. O^{2-}, S^{2-}, Se^{2-}
    d. La^{3+}, Eu^{3+}, Gd^{3+}, Yb^{3+}
    e. Te^{2-}, I^-, Xe, Cs^+, Ba^{2+}, La^{3+}

14. For each of the following groups, place the atoms and/or ions in order of decreasing size.
    a. Co, Co^+, Co^{2+}, Co^{3+}
    b. N, N^-, N^{2-}, N^{3-}
    c. F^-, Cl^-, Br^-
    d. S^{2-}, Cl^-, Ar, K^+, Ca^{2+}
    e. Be^{2+}, Mg^{2+}, Ca^{2+}

15. Write electron configurations for
    a. The cations Mg^{2+}, Sn^{2+}, K^+, Al^{3+}, Tl^+, and As^{3+}.
    b. The anions N^{3-}, O^{2-}, F^-, and Te^{2-}.
    c. The most stable ion formed by each of the elements Be, Rb, Ba, Se, and I.

16. Write electron configurations for
    a. The cations Sn^{4+}, Cs^+, Ga^{3+}, Tl^{3+}, and As^{5+}.
    b. The anions P^{3-}, S^{2-}, and Br^-.
    c. The most stable ion formed by each of the elements Ca, Cl, Sr, and Li.

17. Which of the following ions have noble gas electron configurations?
    a. Fe^{2+}, Fe^{3+}, Sc^{3+}, Co^{3+}
    c. Pu^{4+}, Ce^{4+}, Ti^{4+}
    b. Tl^+, Te^{2-}, Cr^{3+}
    d. Ba^{2+}, Pt^{2+}, Mn^{2+}

18. Which of the following ions have noble gas electron configurations?
    a. Cr^{2+}, Cr^{3+}, Mn^{2+}
    b. Eu^{3+}, Hf^{4+}, Zn^{2+}
    c. O^-, N^-, F^-
    d. Cs^+, Mg^+, Al^+

19. Give three ions that are isoelectronic with the krypton atom.

20. Give three ions that are isoelectronic with the argon atom.

21. Which compound in each of the following pairs of ionic substances has the most exothermic lattice energy? Justify your answers.
    a. NaCl, KCl
    b. LiF, LiCl
    c. $Mg(OH)_2$, MgO
    d. $Fe(OH)_2$, $Fe(OH)_3$
    e. NaCl, Na_2O
    f. MgO, BaS

22. Which compound in each of the following pairs of ionic substances has the most exothermic lattice energy? Justify your answers.
    a. LiF, CsF
    b. NaBr, NaI
    c. $BaCl_2$, BaO
    d. Na_2SO_4, $CaSO_4$
    e. KF, K_2O
    f. Li_2O, Na_2S

23. Use the following data to estimate ΔH_f° for sodium chloride.

$$Na(s) + \tfrac{1}{2}Cl_2(g) \rightarrow NaCl(s)$$

Lattice energy	-786 kJ/mol
Ionization energy for Na	495 kJ/mol
Electron affinity of Cl	-348 kJ/mol
Bond energy of Cl_2	239 kJ/mol
Enthalpy of sublimation for Na	108 kJ/mol

24. Use the following data to estimate ΔH_f° for barium chloride.

$$Ba(s) + Cl_2(g) \rightarrow BaCl_2(s)$$

Lattice energy	-2056 kJ/mol
First ionization energy of Ba	503 kJ/mol
Second ionization energy of Ba	965 kJ/mol
Electron affinity of Cl	-348 kJ/mol
Bond energy of Cl_2	239 kJ/mol
Enthalpy of sublimation of Ba	178 kJ/mol

25. Consider the following energy changes:

	ΔH (kJ/mol)
$Mg(g) \rightarrow Mg^+(g) + e^-$	735
$Mg^+(g) \rightarrow Mg^{2+}(g) + e^-$	1445
$O(g) + e^- \rightarrow O^-(g)$	-141
$O^-(g) + e^- \rightarrow O^{2-}(g)$	$+878$

a. Magnesium oxide exists as $Mg^{2+}O^{2-}$ and not as Mg^+O^-. Explain.
b. What simple experiment could be done to confirm that magnesium oxide does not exist as Mg^+O^-?

26. Using data from Exercise 25, calculate ΔH for the reaction

$$O(g) + 2e^- \rightarrow O^{2-}(g)$$

27. Rationalize the following lattice energy values:

Compound	Lattice Energy (kJ/mol)
CaSe	−2862
Na_2Se	−2130
CaTe	−2721
Na_2Te	−2095

28. The lattice energies of the oxides and chlorides of iron(II) and iron(III) are −2631, −3865, −5359, and −14,774 kJ/mol. Match the appropriate formula to each lattice energy. Explain.

29. Predict the empirical formulas of the ionic compounds formed from the following pairs of elements. Name each compound.
    a. Li and N
    b. Ga and O
    c. Rb and Cl
    d. Ba and S

30. Predict the empirical formulas of the ionic compounds formed from the following pairs of elements. Name each compound.
    a. Al and Cl
    b. Na and O
    c. Sr and F
    d. Ca and S

Bond Energies

31. Use bond energies (Table 8.4) to predict ΔH for the isomerization of methyl isocyanide to acetonitrile:

$$CH_3NC(g) \rightarrow CH_3CN(g)$$

32. Use bond energy values (Table 8.4) to estimate ΔH for each of the following reactions in the gas phase.
    a. $H_2 + Cl_2 \rightarrow 2HCl$
    b. $N_2 + 3H_2 \rightarrow 2NH_3$

    c. $\underset{H}{\overset{H}{\diagdown}}C{=}C\underset{H}{\overset{H}{\diagup}}$ + Br_2 → CH_2BrCH_2Br

    d. $C_2H_4 + H_2O_2 \rightarrow \overset{\text{OH}\quad\text{OH}}{CH_2{-}CH_2}$

33. Use bond energies to calculate the value of ΔH for the oxidation of methylhydrazine by dinitrogen tetroxide, and compare this value to the one you obtained in Exercise 50 of Chapter 6.

34. Compare your answers from parts a and b of Exercise 32 with ΔH values calculated for each reaction from standard enthalpies of formation in Appendix 4. Do enthalpy changes calculated from bond energies give a reasonable estimate of the actual values?

35. Calculate ΔH for the following reaction using bond energies.

$$C_2H_4(g) + O_3(g) \rightarrow CH_3CHO(g) + O_2(g)$$

Compare this result to that obtained using standard enthalpies of formation in Exercise 71 of Chapter 6.

36. Acetic acid is responsible for the sour taste of vinegar. It can be manufactured using the following reaction:

$$CH_3OH + CO \rightarrow CH_3\overset{O}{\overset{\|}{C}}{-}OH$$

Use tabulated values of bond energies (Table 8.4) to estimate ΔH for this reaction.

37. The standard enthalpies of formation for $S(g)$, $F(g)$, $SF_4(g)$, and $SF_6(g)$ are +278.8, +79.0, −775, and −1209 kJ/mol, respectively.
    a. Use these data to estimate the energy of an S—F bond.
    b. Compare your calculated values to the value given in Table 8.4. What conclusions can you draw?
    c. Why are the ΔH_f° values for $S(g)$ and $F(g)$ not equal to zero, since sulfur and fluorine are elements?

38. Use the following standard enthalpies of formation to estimate the N—H bond energy in ammonia: $N(g)$, 472.7 kJ/mol, $H(g)$, 216.0 kJ/mol, $NH_3(g)$, −46.1 kJ/mol. Compare your value to the one in Table 8.4.

Lewis Structures and Resonance

39. Write Lewis structures that obey the octet rule for each of the following.

a. HCN   c. $CHCl_3$ e. BF_4^-

b. PH_3 d. NH_4^+ f. SeF_2

40. Write Lewis structures that obey the octet rule for each of the following molecules and ions. (In each case the first atom listed is the central atom.)

a. $POCl_3$, SO_4^{2-}, XeO_4, PO_4^{3-}, ClO_4^-

b. NF_3, SO_3^{2-}, PO_3^{3-}, ClO_3^-

c. ClO_2^-, SCl_2, PCl_2^-

d. Considering your answers to parts a, b, and c, what conclusions can you draw concerning the structures of species containing the same number of atoms and the same number of valence electrons?

41. Write Lewis structures for the following. Show all resonance structures where applicable.

a. NO_2^-, HNO_2, NO_3^-, HNO_3

b. SO_4^{2-}, HSO_4^-, H_2SO_4

c. CN^-, HCN

d. OCN^-, SCN^-, N_3^-

e. C_2N_2 (atomic arrangement is NCCN)

42. Some of the important pollutants in the atmosphere are ozone, sulfur dioxide, and sulfur trioxide. Write Lewis structures for these three molecules.

43. Peroxyacetyl nitrate, or PAN, is a product of photochemical smog. Write Lewis structures, including resonance structures, for PAN. The skeletal arrangement of atoms is

44. A toxic cloud covered Bhopal, India, in December 1984 when water got into a tank of methyl isocyanate and the product escaped into the atmosphere. Methyl isocyanate is used in the production of many pesticides. Draw the Lewis structures of methyl isocyanate (CH_3NCO), including resonance forms.

45. Benzene (C_6H_6) consists of a six-membered ring of carbon atoms with one hydrogen bonded to each carbon. Write Lewis structures for benzene, including resonance structures.

46. Borazine ($B_3N_3H_6$), has often been called ''inorganic'' benzene. Write Lewis structures for borazine. Borazine contains a six-membered ring of alternating boron and nitrogen atoms.

47. Write Lewis structures for the following molecules, which have central atoms that do not obey the octet rule: PF_5, $Be(CH_3)_2$, BCl_3, $XeOF_4$ (Xe is the central atom), and XeF_6.

48. ClF_3 and BrF_3 are both used to fluorinate uranium to produce UF_6 in the processing and reprocessing of nuclear fuel. Write Lewis structures for ClF_3 and BrF_3.

49. Order the following species with respect to carbon–oxygen bond length (longest to shortest).

$$CO, \quad CO_2, \quad CO_3^{2-}, \quad CH_3OH$$

What is the order from the weakest to the strongest carbon–oxygen bond?

50. Place the species below in order of the shortest to the longest nitrogen–oxygen bond.

$$H_2NOH, \quad N_2O, \quad NO^+, \quad NO_2^-, \quad NO_3^-$$

Formal Charge

51. Use formal charge arguments to rationalize why BF_3 does not follow the octet rule.

52. Use formal charge arguments to explain why CO has a much smaller dipole moment than would be expected on the basis of electronegativity.

53. Write Lewis structures that obey the octet rule for the following species. Assign the formal charge for each central atom.

a. $POCl_3$ c. ClO_4^- e. SO_2Cl_2 g. ClO_3^-

b. SO_4^{2-} d. PO_4^{3-} f. XeO_4 h. NO_4^{3-}

54. Write Lewis structures for the species in Exercise 53 that involve minimum formal charges.

Molecular Structure and Polarity

55. Predict the molecular structure and bond angles for each molecule or ion in Exercises 39 and 41.

56. Predict the molecular structure and bond angles for each molecule or ion in Exercise 40.

57. Predict the molecular structure (including bond angles) for each of the following.
 a. BF_3 b. BH_2^-,   c. $COCl_2$

58. Predict the molecular structure (including bond angles) for each of the following.
 a. SeO_3^{2-} b. SeH_2 c. SeO_4^{2-}

59. Predict the molecular structure (including bond angles) for each of the following ions.
 a. I_3^- b. ClF_3 c. IF_4^+ d. SF_5^+

60. Predict the molecular structure (including bond angles) for each of the following.
 a. BrF_5 b. KrF_4 c. IF_6^+

61. The addition of antimony pentafluoride (SbF_5) to liquid hydrogen produces a solution called a **superacid**. Superacids are capable of acting as acids toward many compounds that we normally expect not to act as bases. For example, in the following reaction, HF acts as a base:

$$SbF_5 + 2HF \rightarrow SbF_6^- + H_2F^+$$

Write Lewis structures for and predict the molecular structures of the reactants and products in this reaction.

62. Write Lewis structures and predict the molecular structures of the following.
 a. Chromate ion
 b. Dichromate ion
 c. Thiosulfate ion ($S_2O_3^{2-}$)
 d. Peroxydisulfate ion ($S_2O_8^{2-}$)

63. Write Lewis structures and predict the molecular structures of the following.
 a. OCl_2, Br_3^-, BeH_2, BH_2^-
 b. BCl_3, NF_3, IF_3
 c. CF_4, SeF_4, XeF_4
 d. IF_5, AsF_5

 Which of these compounds have dipole moments?

64. Write Lewis structures and predict whether each of the following is polar or nonpolar.
 a. HOCN
 b. BeF_2
 c. KrF_4
 d. CF_2Cl_2
 e. H_2NNH_2 (hydrazine)
 f. H_2CO

Additional Exercises

65. Use bond energies (Table 8.4) to estimate ΔH for the following reactions.
 a. $C_3H_8(g) + 5O_2(g) \rightarrow 3CO_2(g) + 4H_2O(g)$
 b. $C_6H_{12}O_6(s) \rightarrow 2CO_2(g) + 2C_2H_5OH(l)$
 The structure of glucose ($C_6H_{12}O_6$) is

66. Three processes that have been used for the industrial manufacture of acrylonitrile, an important chemical used in the manufacture of plastics, synthetic rubber, and fibers, are shown below. Use bond energy values (Tables 8.4 and 8.5) to estimate ΔH for each of the reactions.

a.

b. $4CH_2{=}CHCH_3 + 6NO \xrightarrow[\text{Ag}]{700°C}$
$$4CH_2{=}CHCN + 6H_2O + N_2$$

The nitrogen–oxygen bond energy in nitric oxide (NO) is 630 kJ/mol.

c. $2CH_2{=}CHCH_3 + 2NH_3 + 3O_2 \xrightarrow[\text{425–510°C}]{\text{Catalyst}}$
$$2CH_2{=}CHCN + 6H_2O$$

d. Is the elevated temperature noted in parts b and c needed to provide energy to endothermic reactions?

67. The standard enthalpy of formation of $N_2H_4(g)$ is 95.4 kJ/mol. Use this and the data in Exercise 38 to estimate the N—N single bond energy. Compare this with the value in Table 8.4.

68. What is the relationship between ΔH_f° for $H(g)$ given in Exercise 38 and the H—H bond energy in Table 8.4.

69. Use bond energies (Table 8.4), values of electron affinities (Table 7.7), and the ionization energy of hydrogen (1312 kJ/mol) to estimate ΔH for each of the following reactions.
    a. $HF(g) \rightarrow H^+(g) + F^-(g)$
    b. $HCl(g) \rightarrow H^+(g) + Cl^-(g)$
    c. $HI(g) \rightarrow H^+(g) + I^-(g)$
    d. $H_2O(g) \rightarrow H^+(g) + OH^-(g)$
    [Electron affinity of $OH(g) = -180$ kJ/mol.]

70. For each of the following, write an equation that corresponds to the energy given.
    a. Lattice energy of NaCl
    b. Lattice energy of NH_4Br
    c. Lattice energy of MgS
    d. ΔH_f° of $O(g)$
    e. $O=O$ double bond energy beginning with $O_2(g)$ as a reactant

71. Some of the important properties of ionic compounds are
    i. Low electrical conductivity as solids and high conductivity in solution or when molten
    ii. Relatively high melting and boiling points
    iii. Brittleness
    iv. Solubility in polar solvents

    How does the concept of ionic bonding discussed in this chapter account for these properties?

72. Which member of the following pairs would you expect to be more energetically stable? Justify each choice.
    a. SO_4 and SO_4^{2-}
    b. NF_5 or PF_5
    c. OF_6 or SF_6
    d. BH_3 or BH_4^-
    e. MgF or MgO
    f. $CsCl$ or $CsCl_2$
    g. KBr or K_2Br

73. S_2Cl_2 and SCl_2 are important industrial chemicals used primarily in the vapor-phase vulcanization of certain rubbers. Write Lewis structures for S_2Cl_2 and SCl_2.

74. Disulfur dinitrogen (S_2N_2) exists as a ring of alternating sulfur and nitrogen atoms. S_2N_2 will polymerize to polythiazyl, which acts as a metallic conductor of electricity along the polymer chain. Write a Lewis structure for S_2N_2.

75. Aluminum chloride exists as discrete Al_2Cl_6 molecules in the gas phase. The skeletal structure is

    a. Complete the Lewis structure.
    b. Predict the bond angles around each Al atom.
    c. Is the molecule polar or nonpolar?

76. Write Lewis structures for CO_3^{2-}, HCO_3^-, and H_2CO_3. When acid is added to an aqueous solution containing carbonate or bicarbonate ions, carbon dioxide gas is formed. We generally say that carbonic acid (H_2CO_3) is unstable. Use bond energies to estimate ΔH for the reaction (in the gas phase)

$$H_2CO_3 \rightarrow CO_2 + H_2O$$

    Specify a possible cause for the instability of carbonic acid.

77. Consider the following bond lengths:

$$C-O \quad 143 \text{ pm} \qquad C=O \quad 123 \text{ pm} \qquad C\equiv O \quad 109 \text{ pm}$$

    In the CO_3^{2-} ion, all three C—O bonds have identical bond lengths of 136 pm. Why?

78. Write a Lewis structure and predict the molecular structure of each of the following.
    a. SiF_4 b. SeF_4 c. KrF_4
    Why do these three molecules have different molecular structures? Which, if any, of the molecules are polar?

79. Write a Lewis structure and predict the molecular structure of each of the following.
    a. BF_3 b. PF_3 c. BrF_3
    Why are the molecular structures different? Which, if any, of the molecules are polar?

80. Although both Br_3^- and I_3^- ions are known, the F_3^- ion has not been observed. Explain.

81. There are three possible structures of $PF_3(CH_3)_2$, where P is the central atom. Draw them and describe how measurements of dipole moments might be used to distinguish among them.

82. The molecules BF_3, CF_4, CO_2, PF_5, and SF_6 are all nonpolar, even though they all contain polar bonds. Why?

83. Two molecules exist with the formula N_2F_2. The Lewis structures are

    a. What are the N—N—F bond angles in the two molecules?
    b. What is the polarity of each molecule?

84. Refer back to Exercises 53 and 54. Would you make the same prediction for the molecular structure for each case using the Lewis structure obtained in Exercise 53 as compared with the one obtained in Exercise 54?

85. The xenon–oxygen bond energy in XeO_3 is 84 kJ/mol. Which of the Lewis structures in Sample Exercise 8.10 is most consistent with this fact?

Challenge Problems

86. Look up the energies of the bonds in CO and N_2. Although the bond in CO is stronger, CO is considerably more reactive than N_2. Give a possible explanation.

87. Use the following data to estimate ΔH for the reaction $S^-(g) + e^- \rightarrow S^{2-}(g)$. Include an estimate of uncertainty.

	ΔH_f°	Lattice Energy	I.E. of M	ΔH_{sub} of M
Li_2S	-500	-2472	520	162
Na_2S	-365	-2203	496	108
K_2S	-381	-2052	419	90
Rb_2S	-361	-1949	409	82
Cs_2S	-360	-1850	382	78

$$S(s) \rightarrow S(g) \qquad \Delta H = 277 \text{ kJ/mol}$$
$$S(g) + e^- \rightarrow S^-(g) \qquad \Delta H = -200 \text{ kJ/mol}$$

Assume that all values are known to ± 1 kJ.

88. Carbon tetrachloride and silicon tetrachloride both exist as nonpolar liquids. When $CCl_4(l)$ is added to water, distinct layers form. When $SiCl_4(l)$ is added to water, a violent reaction occurs:

$$SiCl_4(l) + 2H_2O(l) \rightarrow SiO_2(s) + 4HCl(aq)$$

Explain why $SiCl_4$ is so much more reactive toward water than CCl_4.

89. An important observation supporting the need for resonance in the localized electron model was that there are only three different structures of dichlorobenzene ($C_6H_4Cl_2$). How does this fact support the need for the concept of resonance?

90. Many times extra stability is characteristic of a molecule or ion in which resonance is possible. How could this be used to explain the acidities of the following compounds? (The acidic hydrogen is marked by an asterisk.) Part c shows resonance in the C_6H_5 ring.

a. $H-\overset{\overset{\displaystyle O}{\|}}{C}-OH^*$ b. $CH_3-\overset{\overset{\displaystyle O}{\|}}{C}-CH=\overset{\overset{\displaystyle OH^*}{|}}{C}-CH_3$ c.

91. Write a Lewis structure and predict the molecular structure and polarity for each of the following sulfur fluorides: SF_2, SF_4, SF_6, and S_2F_4 (exists as F_3S-SF). Predict the $F-S-F$ bond angles in each molecule.

92. Draw a Lewis structure for the N,N-dimethylformamide molecule. The skeletal structure is

Various types of evidence lead to the conclusion that there is some double bond character to the C—N bond. Draw one or more resonance structures that support this observation.

93. Which of the following molecules have dipole moments? For the molecules that are polar, indicate the polarity of each bond and the direction of the net dipole moment of the molecule.
   a. CH_2Cl_2, $CHCl_3$, CCl_4
   b. CO_2, N_2O
   c. PH_3, NH_3, AsH_3

94. Nitrous oxide (N_2O) has three possible Lewis structures:

Given the following bond lengths,

N—N	167 pm	N=O	115 pm
N=N	120 pm	N—O	147 pm
N≡N	110 pm		

rationalize the observations that the N—N bond length in N_2O is 112 pm and that the N—O bond length is 119 pm. Assign formal charges to the resonance structures for N_2O. Can you eliminate any of the resonance structures on the basis of formal charges? Is this consistent with observation?

95. a. Although not often used, the electronegativities of the noble gases are quite high (Ne = 4.4; Ar = 4.0; Kr = 2.9; Xe = 2.6). Explain these high values relative to those of the other elements using an alternative definition of the electronegativity

$$\text{Electronegativity} \propto (\text{I.E.} - \text{E.A.})$$

where I.E. is the ionization energy and E.A. is the electron affinity using the sign convention of this book.
   b. Elemental fluorine (F_2) reacts directly with xenon to produce three different compounds: XeF_2, XeF_4, XeF_6. Would you expect any of the other noble gases to react with fluorine?

CHAPTER 9

Covalent Bonding: Orbitals

In Chapter 8 we discussed the fundamental concepts of bonding and introduced the most widely used simple model for covalent bonding: the localized electron model. We saw the usefulness of a bonding model as a means for systematizing chemistry by allowing us to look at molecules in terms of individual bonds. We also saw that molecular structure can be predicted by minimizing electron-pair repulsions. In this chapter we will examine bonding models in more detail, particularly focusing on the role of orbitals.

9.1 Hybridization and the Localized Electron Model

Purpose

- To show how special atomic orbitals are formed in covalent bonding.

As we saw in Chapter 8, the localized electron model views a molecule as a collection of atoms bound together by sharing electrons between their atomic orbitals. The arrangement of valence electrons is represented by the Lewis structure (or structures, where resonance occurs), and the molecular geometry can be predicted from the VSEPR model. In this section we will describe the atomic orbitals used to share electrons and hence to form the bonds.

< A tetrahedron made of Steuben glass.

sp³ Hybridization

Let us reconsider the bonding in methane, which has the Lewis structure and molecular geometry shown in Fig. 9.1. In general, we assume that bonding involves only the valence orbitals. This means that the hydrogen atoms in methane use $1s$ orbitals. The valence orbitals of a carbon atom are the $2s$ and $2p$ orbitals shown in Fig. 9.2. In thinking about how carbon can use these orbitals to bond to the hydrogen atoms, we can see two related problems:

1. Using the $2p$ and $2s$ atomic orbitals will lead to two different types of C—H bonds: (a) those from the overlap of a $2p$ orbital of carbon and a $1s$ orbital of hydrogen (there will be three of these) and (b) those from the overlap of a $2s$ orbital of carbon and a $1s$ orbital of hydrogen (there will be one of these). This is a problem because methane is known to have four identical C—H bonds.

2. Since the carbon $2p$ orbitals are mutually perpendicular, we might expect the three C—H bonds formed with these orbitals to be oriented at 90-degree angles:

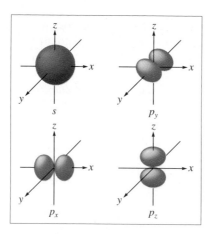

However, the methane molecule is known by experiment to be tetrahedral with bond angles of 109.5 degrees.

This analysis leads to one of two conclusions: either the simple localized electron model is wrong or carbon adopts a set of atomic orbitals other than its "native" $2s$ and $2p$ orbitals to bond to the hydrogen atoms in forming the methane molecule. The second conclusion seems more reasonable. The $2s$ and $2p$ orbitals present on an *isolated* carbon atom may not be the best set of orbitals for bonding; a new set of atomic orbitals might better serve the carbon atom in forming molecules. To account for the known structure of methane, it makes sense to assume that the carbon atom has four equivalent atomic orbitals, arranged tetrahedrally. In fact, such a set of orbitals can be obtained quite readily by combining the carbon $2s$ and $2p$ orbitals, as shown schematically in Fig. 9.3. This mixing of the native atomic orbitals to form special orbitals for bonding is called **hybridization.** The four new orbitals are called sp^3 orbitals because they are formed from one $2s$ and three $2p$ orbitals (s^1p^3).

The valence orbitals are the orbitals associated with the highest principal quantum level that contains electrons on a given atom.

Hybridization is a modification of the localized electron model to account for the observation that atoms often seem to use special atomic orbitals in forming molecules.

(a)   (b)

Figure 9.1

(a) The Lewis structure of the methane molecule. (b) The tetrahedral molecular geometry of the methane molecule.

Figure 9.2

The valence orbitals on a free carbon atom: $2s$, $2p_x$, $2p_y$, and $2p_z$.

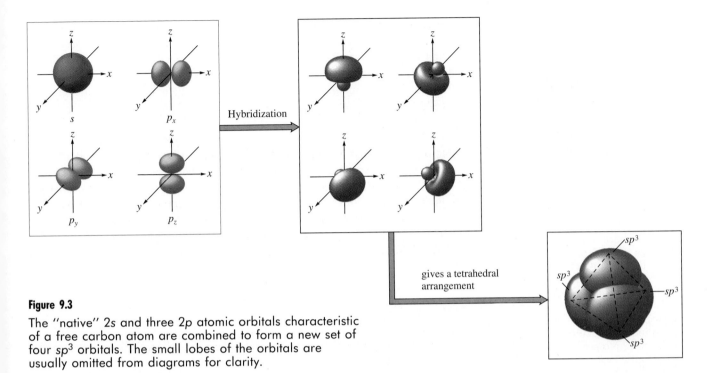

Hybridization

gives a tetrahedral
arrangement

Figure 9.3

The "native" 2s and three 2p atomic orbitals characteristic
of a free carbon atom are combined to form a new set of
four sp^3 orbitals. The small lobes of the orbitals are
usually omitted from diagrams for clarity.

We say that the carbon atom undergoes sp^3 **hybridization** or is sp^3 **hybridized.** The
four sp^3 orbitals are identical in shape, each one having a large lobe and a small lobe
(see Fig. 9.4). The four orbitals are oriented in space so that the large lobes form a
tetrahedral arrangement, as shown in Fig. 9.3.

The hybridization of the carbon 2s and 2p orbitals also can be represented by an
orbital energy-level diagram, as shown in Fig. 9.5. Note that electrons have been
omitted because we do not need to be concerned with the electron arrangements on
the individual atoms—it is the total number of electrons and the arrangement of
these electrons in the *molecule* that are important. We are assuming that carbon's
atomic orbitals are rearranged to accommodate the best electron arrangement for the
molecule as a whole. The new sp^3 atomic orbitals on carbon are used to share
electron pairs with the 1s orbitals from the four hydrogen atoms, as shown in
Fig. 9.6.

At this point let's summarize the bonding in the methane molecule. The experimentally known structure of this molecule can be explained if we assume that the
carbon atom adopts a special set of atomic orbitals. These new orbitals are obtained

sp^3 hybridization gives a tetrahedral
set of orbitals.

Figure 9.4

Cross section of an sp^3 orbital.
Generated from a program by
Robert Allendoerfer on Project
SERAPHIM disk PC2402; printed
with permission.

E

Orbitals in a
free C atom

Orbitals in C in
the CH_4 molecule

Figure 9.5

An energy-level diagram showing the formation of four sp^3 orbitals.

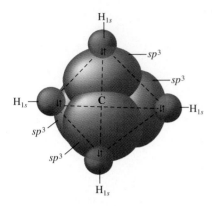

Figure 9.6

The tetrahedral set of four sp^3 orbitals of the carbon atom are used to share electron pairs with the four 1s orbitals of the hydrogen atoms to form the four equivalent C—H bonds. This accounts for the known tetrahedral structure of the CH$_4$ molecule. Note that in this figure and those that follow, the hybrid orbitals are drawn with narrowed lobes to show their orientations more clearly.

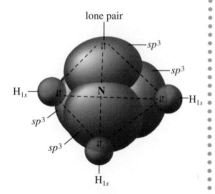

Figure 9.7

The nitrogen atom in ammonia is sp^3 hybridized.

by combining the $2s$ and the three $2p$ orbitals of the carbon atom to produce four identically shaped orbitals that are oriented toward the corners of a tetrahedron and are used to bond to the hydrogen atoms. Thus the four sp^3 orbitals on carbon in methane are postulated to account for its known structure.

Remember this principle: *whenever a set of equivalent tetrahedral atomic orbitals is required by an atom, this model assumes that the atom adopts a set of sp^3 orbitals; the atom becomes sp^3 hybridized.*

It is really not surprising that an atom in a molecule might adopt a different set of atomic orbitals (called **hybrid orbitals**) from those it has in the free state. It does not seem unreasonable that to achieve minimum energy, an atom uses one set of atomic orbitals in the free state and a different set in a molecule. This is consistent with the idea that a molecule is more than simply a sum of its parts. What the atoms in a molecule were like before the molecule was formed is not so important as how the electrons are best arranged in the molecule. Therefore, this model assumes that the individual atoms respond as needed to achieve the minimum energy for the molecule.

Sample Exercise 9.1

Describe the bonding in the ammonia molecule using the localized electron model.

Solution

A complete description of the bonding involves three steps:

1. Writing the Lewis structure
2. Determining the arrangement of electron pairs using the VSEPR model
3. Determining the hybrid atomic orbitals needed to describe the bonding in the molecule

The Lewis structure for NH$_3$ is

$$H-\overset{\cdot\cdot}{N}-H$$
$$|$$
$$H$$

The four electron pairs around the nitrogen atom require a tetrahedral arrangement to minimize repulsions. We have seen that a tetrahedral set of sp^3 hybrid orbitals is obtained by combining the $2s$ and three $2p$ orbitals. In the NH$_3$ molecule three of the sp^3 orbitals are used to form bonds to the three hydrogen atoms, and the fourth sp^3 orbital holds the lone pair, as shown in Fig. 9.7.

sp^2 Hybridization

Ethylene (C$_2$H$_4$) is an important starting material in the manufacture of plastics. The C$_2$H$_4$ molecule has 12 valence electrons and the following Lewis structure:

$$\begin{array}{ccc} H & & H \\ \diagdown & & \diagup \\ & C{=}C & \\ \diagup & & \diagdown \\ H & & H \end{array}$$

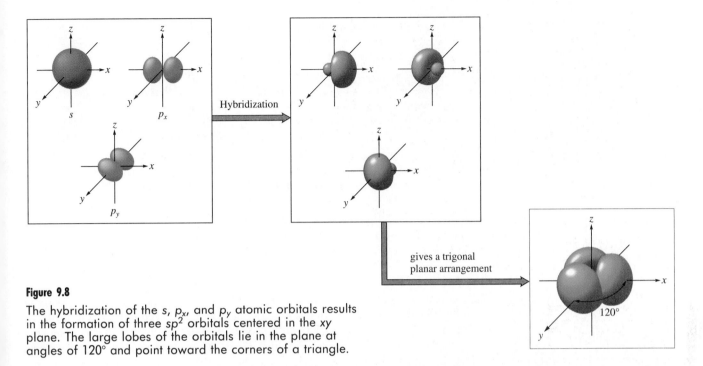

Figure 9.8

The hybridization of the s, p_x, and p_y atomic orbitals results in the formation of three sp^2 orbitals centered in the xy plane. The large lobes of the orbitals lie in the plane at angles of $120°$ and point toward the corners of a triangle.

We saw in Chapter 8 that a double bond acts as one effective pair, so in the ethylene molecule each carbon is surrounded by three effective pairs. This requires a trigonal planar arrangement with bond angles of 120 degrees. What orbitals do the carbon atoms in this molecule employ? The molecular geometry requires a set of orbitals in one plane at angles of 120 degrees. Since the $2s$ and $2p$ valence orbitals of carbon do not have the required arrangement, we need a set of hybrid orbitals.

The sp^3 orbitals we have just considered will not work because they are at angles of 109.5 degrees rather than the required 120 degrees. In ethylene the carbon atom must hybridize in a different manner. A set of three orbitals arranged at 120-degree angles in the same plane can be obtained by combining one s orbital and two p orbitals, as shown in Fig. 9.8. The orbital energy-level diagram for this arrangement is shown in Fig. 9.9. Since one $2s$ and two $2p$ orbitals are used to form these hybrid orbitals, this is called sp^2 **hybridization.** Note from Fig. 9.8 that the plane of the sp^2 hybridized orbitals is determined by which p orbitals are used. Since in this case we have arbitrarily decided to use the p_x and p_y orbitals, the hybrid orbitals are centered in the xy plane.

In forming the sp^2 orbitals, one $2p$ orbital on carbon has not been used. This remaining p orbital (p_z) is oriented perpendicular to the plane of the sp^2 orbitals, as shown in Fig. 9.10.

A double bond acts as one effective electron pair.

sp^2 hybridization gives a trigonal planar arrangement of atomic orbitals.

Note in Fig. 9.10 and the figures that follow that the orbital lobes are artificially narrowed to more clearly show their relative orientations.

$$ \underset{\text{Orbitals in an isolated}}{\underset{\text{carbon atom}}{E \quad \begin{array}{c} \text{—} \; \text{—} \; \text{—} \; 2p \\[2mm] \text{——} \; 2s \end{array}}} \xrightarrow{\text{Hybridization}} \underset{\text{Carbon orbitals in ethylene}}{\begin{array}{c} \text{——} \; 2p \\[2mm] \text{—} \; \text{—} \; \text{—} \; \text{—} \; sp^2 \end{array}} $$

Figure 9.9

An orbital energy-level diagram for sp^2 hybridization. Note that one p orbital remains unchanged.

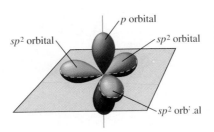

Figure 9.10

When an *s* and two *p* orbitals are mixed to form a set of three sp^2 orbitals, one *p* orbital remains unchanged and is perpendicular to the plane of the hybrid orbitals.

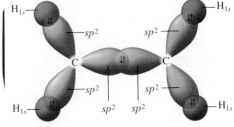

Figure 9.11

The σ bonds in ethylene. Note that for each bond the shared electron pair occupies the region directly between the atoms.

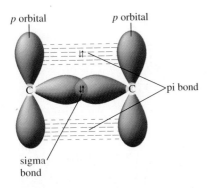

Figure 9.12

A carbon-carbon double bond consists of a σ bond and a π bond. In the σ bond the shared electrons occupy the space directly between the atoms. The π bond is formed from the unhybridized *p* orbitals on the two carbon atoms. In a π bond the shared electron pair occupies the space above and below a line joining the atoms.

Now we will see how these orbitals can be used to account for the bonds in ethylene. The three sp^2 orbitals on each carbon can be used to share electrons, as shown in Fig. 9.11. In each of these bonds, the electron pair is shared in an area centered on a line running between the atoms. This type of covalent bond is called a **sigma (σ) bond.** In the ethylene molecule, the σ bonds are formed using sp^2 orbitals on each carbon atom and the 1s orbital on each hydrogen atom.

How can we explain the double bond between the carbon atoms? In the σ bond, the electron pair occupies the space between the carbon atoms. The second bond must therefore result from sharing an electron pair in the space *above and below* the σ bond. This type of bond can be formed using the 2p orbital perpendicular to the sp^2 hybrid orbitals on each carbon atom (refer to Fig. 9.10). These parallel p orbitals can share an electron pair, which occupies the space above and below a line joining the atoms, to form a **pi (π) bond,** as shown in Fig. 9.12.

Note that σ bonds are formed from orbitals whose lobes point toward each other, but π bonds result from parallel orbitals. A *double bond always consists of one σ bond,* where the electron pair is located directly between the atoms, *and one π bond,* where the shared pair occupies the space above and below the σ bond.

We can now completely specify the orbitals that this model assumes are used to form the bonds in the ethylene molecule. As shown in Fig. 9.13, the carbon atoms use sp^2 hybrid orbitals to form the σ bonds to the hydrogen atoms and to each other and they use p orbitals to form the π bond with each other. Note that we have accounted fully for the Lewis structure of ethylene with its carbon–carbon double bond and carbon–hydrogen single bonds.

This example illustrates an important general principle of this model: *whenever an atom is surrounded by three effective pairs, a set of sp^2 hybrid orbitals is required.*

sp Hybridization

Another type of hybridization occurs in carbon dioxide, which has the following Lewis structure:

(a)

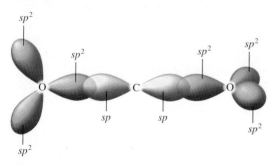

(b)

Figure 9.13

(a) The orbitals used to form the bonds in ethylene. (b) The Lewis structure for ethylene.

In the CO_2 molecule the carbon atom has two effective pairs that will be arranged at an angle of 180 degrees. We therefore need a pair of atomic orbitals oriented in opposite directions. This requires a new type of hybridization, since neither sp^3 nor sp^2 hybrid orbitals will fit this case. To obtain two hybrid orbitals arranged at 180 degrees requires **sp hybridization,** involving one s orbital and one p orbital, as shown in Fig. 9.14.

In terms of this model, *two effective pairs around an atom will always require sp hybridization of that atom.* The sp orbitals of carbon in carbon dioxide can be seen in Fig. 9.15, and the corresponding orbital energy-level diagram for their formation is given in Fig. 9.16. These sp hybrid orbitals are used to form the σ bonds between the carbon and the oxygen atoms. Note that two $2p$ orbitals remain unchanged on the sp hybridized carbon. These are used to form the π bonds with the oxygen atoms.

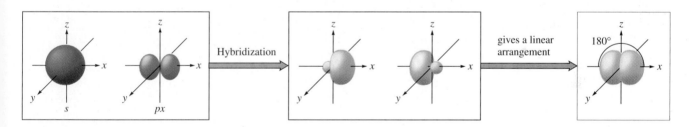

Figure 9.14

When one s orbital and one p orbital are hybridized, a set of two sp orbitals oriented at 180° results.

Figure 9.15

The hybrid orbitals in the CO_2 molecule.

Figure 9.16

The orbital energy-level diagram for the formation of sp hybrid orbitals on carbon.

Figure 9.17

The orbitals of an *sp* hybridized carbon atom.

Figure 9.18

The orbital arrangement for an sp^2 hybridized oxygen atom.

Figure 9.19

(a) The orbitals used to form the bonds in carbon dioxide. Note that the carbon-oxygen double bonds each consist of one σ bond and one π bond. (b) The Lewis structure for carbon dioxide.

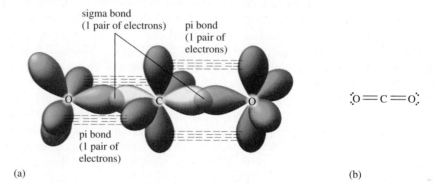

(a)   (b)

In the CO_2 molecule each oxygen atom has three effective pairs around it, requiring a trigonal planar arrangement of the pairs. Since a trigonal set of hybrid orbitals requires sp^2 hybridization, each oxygen atom is sp^2 hybridized. One *p* orbital on each oxygen is unchanged and is used for the π bond with the carbon atom.

Now we are ready to use our model to describe the bonding in carbon dioxide. The *sp* orbitals on carbon form σ bonds with the sp^2 orbitals on the two oxygen atoms (Fig. 9.15). The remaining sp^2 orbitals on the oxygen atoms hold lone pairs. The π bonds between the carbon atom and each oxygen atom are formed by the overlap of parallel 2*p* orbitals. The *sp* hybridized carbon atom has two unhybridized *p* orbitals, pictured in Fig. 9.17. Each of these *p* orbitals is used to form a π bond with an oxygen atom (see Fig. 9.18). The total bonding picture for the CO_2 molecule is shown in Fig. 9.19. Note that this picture of the bonding neatly explains the arrangement of electrons predicted by the Lewis structure.

Sample Exercise 9.2

Describe the bonding in the N_2 molecule.

Solution

The Lewis structure for the nitrogen molecule is

$$: N \equiv N :$$

where each nitrogen atom is surrounded by two effective pairs. (Remember that multiple bonds count as one effective pair.) This gives a linear arrangement (180 degrees) requiring a pair of oppositely directed orbitals. This situation requires *sp* hybridization. Each nitrogen atom in the nitrogen molecule has two *sp* hybrid orbitals and two unchanged *p* orbitals, as shown in Fig. 9.20(a). The *sp* orbitals are used to form the σ bond between the nitrogen atoms and to hold lone pairs, as shown in Fig. 9.20(b). The *p* orbitals are used to form the two π bonds [see Fig. 9.20(c)]; each pair of overlapping parallel *p* orbitals holds one electron pair. Such bonding accounts for the electron arrangement given by the Lewis structure. The triple bond consists of a σ bond (overlap of two *sp* orbitals) and two π bonds (each one from an overlap of two *p* orbitals). In addition, a lone pair occupies an *sp* orbital on each nitrogen atom.

dsp^3 Hybridization

To illustrate the treatment of a molecule in which the central atom exceeds the octet rule, consider the bonding in the phosphorus pentachloride molecule (PCl_5). The Lewis structure

shows that the phosphorus atom is surrounded by five electron pairs. Since five pairs require a trigonal bipyramidal arrangement, we need a trigonal bipyramidal set of atomic orbitals on phosphorus. Such a set of orbitals is formed by dsp^3 **hybridization** of one *d* orbital, one *s* orbital, and three *p* orbitals, as shown in Fig. 9.21.

The dsp^3 hybridized phosphorus atom in the PCl_5 molecule uses its five dsp^3 orbitals to share electrons with the five chlorine atoms. *Note that a set of five effective pairs around a given atom always requires a trigonal bipyramidal arrangement, which in turn requires dsp^3 hybridization of that atom.*

The Lewis structure for PCl_5 shows that each chlorine atom is surrounded by four electron pairs. This requires a tetrahedral arrangement, which in turn requires a set of four sp^3 orbitals on each chlorine atom.

Now we can describe the bonding in the PCl_5 molecule. The five P—Cl σ bonds are formed by sharing electrons between a dsp^3 orbital* on the phosphorus atom and

Figure 9.20

An *sp* hybridized nitrogen atom. There are two *sp* hybrid orbitals and two unhybridized *p* orbitals. (b) The sigma bond in the N_2 molecule. (c) The two π bonds in N_2 are formed when electron pairs are shared between two sets of parallel *p* orbitals.

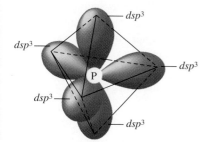

Figure 9.21

A set of dsp^3 hybrid orbitals on a phosphorus atom. Note that the set of five dsp^3 orbitals has a trigonal bipyramidal arrangement. (Each dsp^3 orbital also has a small lobe that is not shown in this diagram.)

*There is considerable controversy about whether the *d* orbitals are as heavily involved in the bonding in these molecules as this model predicts. However, this matter is beyond the scope of this text.

Figure 9.22

The orbitals used to form the bonds in the PCl_5 molecule. The phosphorus uses a set of five dsp^3 orbitals to share electron pairs with sp^3 orbitals on the five chlorine atoms. The other sp^3 orbitals on each chlorine atom hold lone pairs.

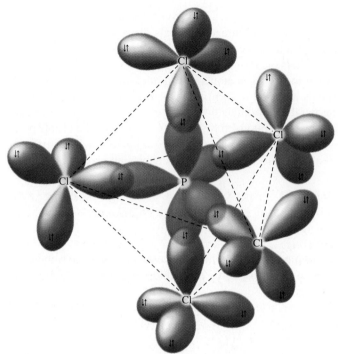

an sp^3 orbital on each chlorine.* The other sp^3 orbitals on each chlorine hold lone pairs. This is shown in Fig. 9.22.

Sample Exercise 9.3

Describe the bonding in the triiodide ion (I_3^-).

Solution

The Lewis structure for I_3^-

$$\left[:\ddot{I}\!-\!\ddot{I}\!-\!\ddot{I}: \right]^-$$

shows that the central iodine atom has five pairs of electrons (see Section 8.11). A set of five pairs requires a trigonal bipyramidal arrangement, which in turn requires a set of dsp^3 orbitals. The outer iodine atoms have four pairs of electrons, which calls for a tetrahedral arrangement and sp^3 hybridization.

Thus the central iodine is dsp^3 hybridized. Three of these hybrid orbitals hold lone pairs, and two of them overlap with sp^3 orbitals of the other two iodine atoms to form σ bonds.

---

*Although we have no way of proving conclusively that each chlorine is sp^3 hybridized, we assume that minimizing electron-pair repulsions is as important for peripheral atoms as for the central atom. Thus we will apply the VSEPR model and hybridization to both central and peripheral atoms.

d^2sp^3 Hybridization

Some molecules have six pairs of electrons around a central atom; an example is sulfur hexafluoride (SF_6), which has the Lewis structure

This requires an octahedral arrangement of pairs and in turn an octahedral set of six hybrid orbitals, or d^2sp^3 **hybridization,** in which two d orbitals, one s orbital, and three p orbitals are combined (see Fig. 9.23). Note that *six electron pairs around an atom are always arranged octahedrally and require d^2sp^3 hybridization of the atom.* Each of the d^2sp^3 orbitals on the sulfur atom is used to bond to a fluorine atom. Since there are four pairs on each fluorine atom, the fluorine atoms are assumed to be sp^3 hybridized.

d^2sp^3 hybridization gives six orbitals arranged octahedrally.

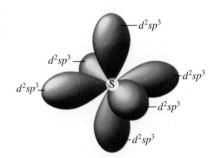

Figure 9.23

An octahedral set of d^2sp^3 orbitals on a sulfur atom. The small lobe of each hybrid orbital has been omitted for clarity.

Sample Exercise 9.4

How is the xenon atom in XeF_4 hybridized?

Solution

As seen in Sample Exercise 8.13, XeF_4 has six pairs of electrons around xenon that are arranged octahedrally to minimize repulsions. An octahedral set of six atomic orbitals is required to hold these electrons, and the xenon atom is d^2sp^3 hybridized.

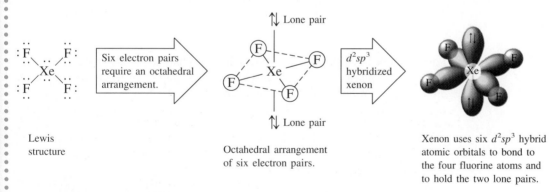

Lewis structure

Octahedral arrangement of six electron pairs.

Xenon uses six d^2sp^3 hybrid atomic orbitals to bond to the four fluorine atoms and to hold the two lone pairs.

The Localized Electron Model: A Summary

The description of a molecule using the localized electron model involves three distinct steps:

• Draw the Lewis structure(s).

- Determine the arrangement of electron pairs using the VSEPR model.
- Specify the hybrid orbitals needed to accommodate the electron pairs.

It is important to do the steps in this order. For a model to be successful, it must follow nature's priorities. In the case of bonding, it seems clear that the tendency for a molecule to minimize its energy is more important than the maintenance of the characteristics of atoms as they exist in the free state. The atoms adjust to meet the "needs" of the molecule. When considering the bonding in a particular molecule, therefore, we always start with the molecule rather than the component atoms. In the molecule the electrons will be arranged to give each atom a noble gas configuration, where possible, and to minimize electron-pair repulsions. We then assume that the atoms adjust their orbitals by hybridization to allow the molecule to adopt the structure that gives the minimum energy.

In applying the localized electron model, we must remember not to overemphasize the characteristics of the separate atoms. It is not where the valence electrons originate that is important; it is where they are needed in the molecule to achieve stability. In the same vein, it is not the orbitals in the isolated atom that matter, but what orbitals the molecule requires for minimum energy.

The requirements for the various types of hybridization are summarized in Fig. 9.24.

Sample Exercise 9.5

For each of the following molecules or ions, predict the hybridization of each atom, and describe the molecular structure.

a. CO   **b.** BF_4^- **c.** XeF_2

Solution

a. The CO molecule has 10 valence electrons, and its Lewis structure is

$$: C \equiv O :$$

Each atom has two effective pairs, which means that both are sp hybridized. The triple bond consists of a σ bond produced by overlap of an sp orbital from each atom and two π bonds produced by overlap of $2p$ orbitals from each atom. The lone pairs are in sp orbitals. Since the CO molecule has only two atoms, it must be linear.

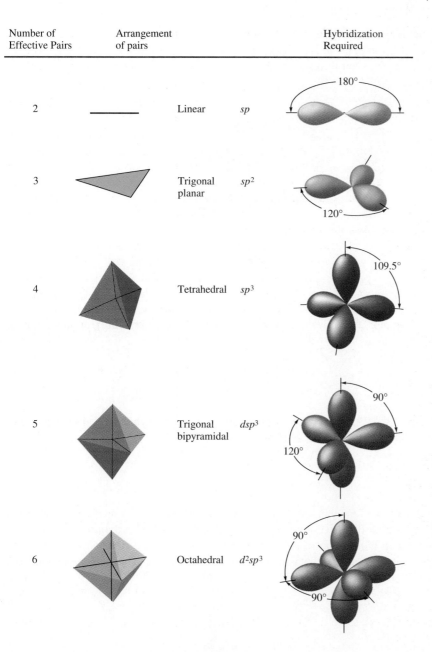

Number of Effective Pairs	Arrangement of pairs		Hybridization Required	
2	———	Linear	sp	
3		Trigonal planar	sp^2	
4		Tetrahedral	sp^3	
5		Trigonal bipyramidal	dsp^3	
6		Octahedral	d^2sp^3	

Figure 9.24

The relationship of the number of effective pairs, their spatial arrangement, and the hybrid orbital set required.

b. The BF_4^- ion has 32 valence electrons. The Lewis structure shows four pairs of electrons around the boron atom, which means a tetrahedral arrangement:

$$\left[\begin{array}{c} :\!\ddot{F}\!: \\ :\!\ddot{F}\!-\!B\!-\!\ddot{F}\!: \\ :\!\ddot{F}\!: \end{array} \right]^- \xrightarrow[\text{around B}]{\text{4 electron pairs}}$$

This requires sp^3 hybridization of the boron atom. Each fluorine atom also has four electron pairs and can be assumed to be sp^3 hybridized (only one sp^3 orbital is shown for each fluorine atom). The BF_4^- ion's molecular structure is tetrahedral.

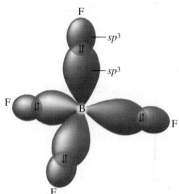

c. The XeF_2 molecule has 22 valence electrons. The Lewis structure shows five electron pairs on the xenon atom, which requires a trigonal bipyramidal arrangement:

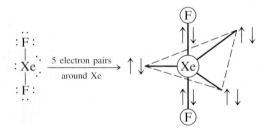

Note that the lone pairs are placed in the plane where they are 120 degrees apart. To accommodate five pairs at the vertices of a trigonal bipyramid requires that the xenon atom adopt a set of five dsp^3 orbitals. Each fluorine atom has four electron pairs and can be assumed to be sp^3 hybridized. The XeF_2 molecule has a linear arrangement of atoms.

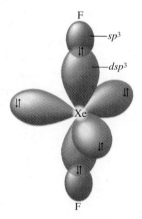

9.2 *The Molecular Orbital Model*

Purpose

- To show how molecular orbitals are formed in a molecule.
- To define bond order and demonstrate how to calculate it.

We have seen that the localized electron model is of great value in interpreting the structure and bonding of molecules. However, there are some problems with this model. For example, it incorrectly assumes that electrons are localized, and so the concept of resonance must be added. Also, the model does not deal effectively with molecules containing unpaired electrons. And finally, the model gives no direct information about bond energies.

Another model often used to describe bonding is the **molecular orbital model.** To introduce the assumptions, methods, and results of this model, we will consider the simplest of all molecules, H_2, which consists of two protons and two electrons. A very stable molecule, H_2 is lower in energy than the separated hydrogen atoms by 432 kJ/mol.

Molecular orbital theory parallels the atomic theory discussed in Chapter 7.

Since the hydrogen molecule consists of protons and electrons, the same components found in separated hydrogen atoms, it seems reasonable to use a theory similar to the atomic theory discussed in Chapter 7, which assumes that the electrons in an atom exist in orbitals of a given energy. Can we apply this same type of model to the hydrogen molecule? Yes, in fact, describing the H_2 molecule in terms of quantum mechanics is quite straightforward.

However, even though it is formulated rather easily, this problem cannot be solved exactly. The difficulty is the same as that in dealing with polyelectronic atoms—the electron correlation problem. Since we do not know the details of the electron movements, we cannot deal with the electron–electron interactions in a specific way. We need to make approximations that allow solution of the problem but do not destroy the model's physical integrity. The success of these approximations can only be measured by comparing predictions based on theory with experimental observations. In this case we will see that the simplified model works very well.

Just as atomic orbitals are solutions to the quantum mechanical treatment of atoms, **molecular orbitals (MOs)** are solutions to the molecular problem. Molecular orbitals have many of the same characteristics as atomic orbitals. Two of the most important are that they can hold two electrons with opposite spins and that the square of the molecular orbital wave function indicates electron probability.

We will now describe the bonding in the hydrogen molecule using this model. The first step is to obtain the hydrogen molecule's orbitals, a process that is greatly simplified if we assume that the molecular orbitals can be constructed from the hydrogen $1s$ atomic orbitals.

When the quantum mechanical equations for the hydrogen molecule are solved, two molecular orbitals result, which can be represented as

$$MO_1 = 1s_A + 1s_B$$
$$MO_2 = 1s_A - 1s_B$$

where $1s_A$ and $1s_B$ represent the $1s$ orbitals from the two separated hydrogen atoms. This process is shown schematically in Fig. 9.25.

Figure 9.25

The combination of hydrogen $1s$ atomic orbitals to form molecular orbitals.

The orbital properties of most interest are size, shape (described by the electron probability distribution), and energy. These properties for the hydrogen molecular orbitals are represented in Fig. 9.26. From Fig. 9.26 we can note several important points:

1. The electron probability of both molecular orbitals is centered along the line passing through the two nuclei. For MO_1 the greatest electron probability is *between* the nuclei, and for MO_2 it is on *either side* of the nuclei. This type of electron distribution is described as *sigma* (σ), as in the localized electron model. Accordingly, we refer to MO_1 and MO_2 as **sigma (σ) molecular orbitals.**

2. In the molecule only the molecular orbitals are available for occupation by electrons. The $1s$ atomic orbitals of the hydrogen atoms no longer exist, because the H_2 molecule—a new entity—has its own set of new orbitals.

3. MO_1 is lower in energy than the $1s$ orbitals of free hydrogen atoms, while MO_2 is higher in energy than the $1s$ orbitals. This fact has very important implications for the stability of the H_2 molecule, since if the two electrons (one from each hydrogen atom) occupy the lower-energy MO_1, they will have lower energy than they do in the two separate hydrogen atoms. This situation favors molecule formation, because nature tends to seek the lowest energy state. That is, the driving force for molecule formation is that the molecular orbital available to the two electrons has lower energy than the atomic orbitals these electrons occupy in the separated atoms. This situation is favorable to bonding, or *probonding*.

   On the other hand, if the two electrons were forced to occupy the higher-energy MO_2, they would be definitely *antibonding*. In this case, these electrons would have lower energy in the separated atoms than in the molecule, and the separated state would be favored. Of course, since the lower-energy MO_1 *is* available, the two electrons occupy that MO and the molecule is stable.

   We have seen that the molecular orbitals of the hydrogen molecule fall into two classes: bonding and antibonding. A **bonding molecular orbital** is *lower in energy than the atomic orbitals of which it is composed.* Electrons in this type of orbital will favor the molecule; that is, they will favor bonding. An **antibonding molecular orbital** is *higher in energy than the atomic orbitals of which it is composed.* Electrons in this type of orbital will favor the separated atoms (they are antibonding). Figure 9.27 illustrates these ideas.

4. Figure 9.26 shows that for the bonding molecular orbital in the H_2 molecule the electrons have the greatest probability of being between the nuclei. This is exactly what we would expect, since the electrons can lower their energies by being simultaneously attracted by both nuclei. On the other hand, the electron distribution for the antibonding molecular orbital is such that the electrons are mainly outside the space between the nuclei. This type of distribution is not expected to provide any bonding force. In fact, it causes the electrons to be higher in energy than in the separated atoms. Thus the molecular orbital model produces electron distributions and energies that agree with our basic ideas of bonding. This fact reassures us that the model is physically reasonable.

5. The labels on molecular orbitals indicate their symmetry (shape), the parent atomic orbitals, and whether they are bonding or antibonding. Antibonding character is indicated by an asterisk. For the H_2 molecule, both MOs have σ

Bonding will result if the molecule has lower energy than the separated atoms.

Energy diagram

(a)

Electron probability distribution

(b)

Figure 9.26

(a) The molecular orbital energy-level diagram for the H_2 molecule. (b) The shapes of the molecular orbitals are obtained by squaring the wave functions for MO_1 and MO_2.

symmetry and both are constructed from hydrogen $1s$ atomic orbitals. The molecular orbitals for H_2 are therefore labeled as follows:

$$MO_1 = \sigma_{1s}$$

$$MO_2 = \sigma_{1s}^*$$

6. Molecular electron configurations can be written in much the same way as atomic configurations. Since the H_2 molecule has two electrons in the σ_{1s} molecular orbital, the electron configuration is σ_{1s}^2.

7. Each molecular orbital can hold two electrons, but the spins must be opposite.

8. Orbitals are conserved. The number of molecular orbitals will always be the same as the number of atomic orbitals used to construct them.

Many of the above points are summarized in Fig. 9.28.

Now suppose we could form the H_2^- ion from a hydride ion (H^-) and a hydrogen atom. Would this species be stable? Since the H^- ion has the configuration $1s^2$ and the H atom has a $1s^1$ configuration, we will use $1s$ atomic orbitals to construct the MO diagram for the H_2^- ion, as shown in Fig. 9.29. The electron configuration for H_2^- is $\sigma_{1s}^2(\sigma_{1s}^*)^1$.

The key idea is that the H_2^- ion will be stable if it has a lower energy than its separated parts. From Fig. 9.29 we see that in going from the separated H^- ion and H atom to the H_2^- ion, the model predicts that two electrons are lowered in energy and one electron is raised in energy. In other words, two electrons are bonding and one electron is antibonding. Since more electrons favor bonding, H_2^- is predicted to be a stable entity—a bond has formed. But how would we expect the bond strengths in the molecules of H_2 and H_2^- to compare?

In the formation of the H_2 molecule, two electrons are lowered in energy and no electrons are raised in energy compared with the parent atoms. When H_2^- is formed, two electrons are lowered in energy and one is raised, producing *a net lowering of the energy of only one electron*. Thus the model predicts that H_2 is *twice as stable* as H_2^- with respect to their separated components. In other words, the bond in the H_2 molecule is predicted to be about twice as strong as the bond in the H_2^- ion.

Bond Order

To indicate bond strength, we use the concept of bond order. **Bond order** is *the difference between the number of bonding electrons and the number of antibonding electrons divided by two.*

$$\text{Bond order} = \frac{\text{number of bonding electrons} - \text{number of antibonding electrons}}{2}$$

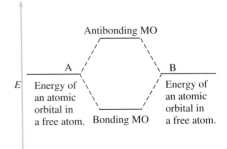

Figure 9.27

Bonding and antibonding molecular orbitals (MOs).

Although the model predicts that H_2^- should be stable, this ion has never been observed, again emphasizing the perils of simple models.

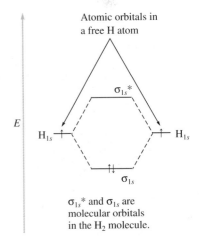

Figure 9.28

A molecular orbital energy-level diagram for the H_2 molecule.

Figure 9.29

The molecular orbital energy-level diagram for the H_2^- ion.

We divide by 2 because, from the localized electron model, we are used to thinking of bonds in terms of *pairs* of electrons.

Since the H_2 molecule has two bonding electrons and no antibonding electrons, the bond order is

$$\text{Bond order} = \frac{2 - 0}{2} = 1$$

The $H_2{}^-$ ion has two bonding electrons and one antibonding electron; the bond order is

$$\text{Bond order} = \frac{2 - 1}{2} = \frac{1}{2}.$$

Bond order is an indication of bond strength because it reflects the difference between the number of bonding electrons and the number of antibonding electrons. *Larger bond order means greater bond strength.*

We will now apply the molecular orbital model to the helium molecule (He_2). Does this model predict that this molecule will be stable? Since the He atom has a $1s^2$ configuration, $1s$ orbitals are used to construct the molecular orbitals, and the molecule will have four electrons. From the diagram shown in Fig. 9.30, it is apparent that two electrons are raised in energy and two are lowered in energy. Thus the bond order is zero:

$$\frac{2 - 2}{2} = 0$$

This implies that the He_2 molecule is *not* stable with respect to the two free He atoms, which agrees with the observation that helium gas consists of individual He atoms.

Figure 9.30

The molecular orbital energy-level diagram for the He_2 molecule.

9.3 Bonding in Homonuclear Diatomic Molecules

Purpose

- To discuss the bonding in certain molecules of the general formula X_2.
- To relate paramagnetism to the filling of molecular orbitals.
- To correlate bond order, bond energy, and bond length.

In this section we consider **homonuclear diatomic molecules** (those composed of two identical atoms) of elements in Period 2 of the periodic table. Since the lithium atom has a $1s^2 2s^1$ electron configuration, it would seem that we should use the Li $1s$ and $2s$ orbitals to form the molecular orbitals of the Li_2 molecule. However, the $1s$ orbitals on the lithium atoms are much smaller than the $2s$ orbitals and therefore do not overlap in space to any appreciable extent (see Fig. 9.31). Thus the two electrons in each $1s$ orbital can be assumed to be localized and not to participate in the bonding. *In order to participate in molecular orbitals, atomic orbitals must overlap in space.* This means that only the valence orbitals of the atoms contribute significantly to the molecular orbitals of a particular molecule.

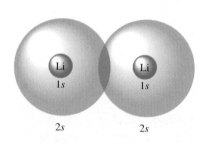

Figure 9.31

The relative sizes of the lithium $1s$ and $2s$ atomic orbitals.

The following text appears at the top.

MO shapes

Figure 9.32
The molecular orbital energy-level diagram for the Li_2 molecule.

The molecular orbital diagram of the Li_2 molecule and the shapes of its bonding and antibonding MOs are shown in Fig. 9.32. The electron configuration for Li_2 (valence electrons only) is σ_{2s}^2 and the bond order is:

$$\frac{2 - 0}{2} = 1$$

Thus Li_2 is a stable molecule (has lower energy than two separated lithium atoms). However, this does not mean that Li_2 is the most stable form of elemental lithium. In fact, at normal temperature and pressure, lithium exists as a solid containing many lithium atoms bound to each other.

For the beryllium molecule (Be_2) the bonding and antibonding orbitals both contain two electrons. In this case the bond order is $(2 - 2)/2 = 0$, and since Be_2 is not more stable than two separated Be atoms, no molecule forms. However, beryllium metal contains many beryllium atoms bonded to each other and is stable for reasons we will discuss in Chapter 10.

Since the boron atom has a $1s^2 2s^2 2p^1$ configuration, we describe the B_2 molecule by considering how p atomic orbitals combine to form molecular orbitals. Recall that p orbitals have two lobes and that they occur in sets of three mutually perpendicular orbitals [see Fig. 9.33(a)]. When two B atoms approach each other, two

Beryllium metal.

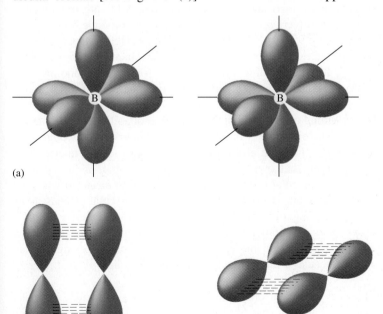

Figure 9.33
(a) The three mutually perpendicular $2p$ orbitals on two adjacent boron atoms. Two pairs of parallel p orbitals can overlap as shown in (b) and (c), and the third pair can overlap head-on as shown in (d).

(a)

(b)   (c)   (d)

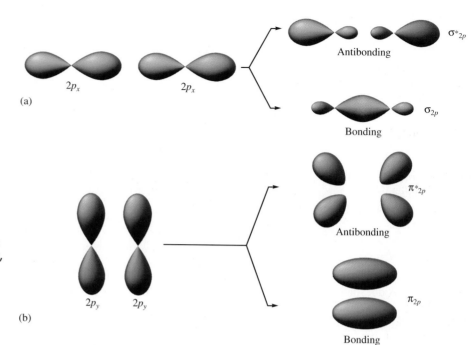

Figure 9.34

(a) The two p orbitals on the boron atom that overlap head-on produce two σ molecular orbitals, one bonding and one antibonding. (b) Two p orbitals that lie parallel overlap to produce two π molecular orbitals, one bonding and one antibonding.

Figure 9.35

The *expected* molecular orbital energy-level diagram resulting from the combination of the 2p orbitals on two boron atoms.

pairs of p orbitals can overlap in a parallel fashion [Fig. 9.33(b) and (c)] and one pair can overlap head-on [Fig. 9.33(d)].

First, let's consider the molecular orbitals from the head-on overlap, as shown in Fig. 9.34(a). Note that the electrons in the bonding MO are, as expected, concentrated between the nuclei, and the electrons in the antibonding MO are concentrated outside the area between the two nuclei. Also both these MOs are σ molecular orbitals. The p orbitals that overlap in a parallel fashion also produce bonding and antibonding orbitals [Figure 9.34(b)]. Since the electron probability lies above and below the line between the nuclei, both the orbitals are π molecular orbitals. They are designated as π_{2p} for the bonding MO and π_{2p}^* for the antibonding MO.

Let's try to make an educated guess about the relative energies of the σ and π molecular orbitals formed from the $2p$ atomic orbitals. Would we expect the electrons to prefer the σ bonding orbital (where the electron probability is concentrated in the area between the nuclei) or the π bonding orbital? The σ orbital would seem to have the lower energy, since the electrons are closest to the two nuclei. This agrees with the observation that σ interactions are stronger than π interactions.

Figure 9.35 gives the molecular orbital energy-level diagram *expected* when the two sets of $2p$ orbitals on the boron atoms combine to form molecular orbitals. Note that there are two π bonding orbitals at the same energy (degenerate orbitals) formed from the two pairs of parallel p orbitals, and there are two degenerate π antibonding orbitals. The energy of the π_{2p} orbitals is expected to be higher than that of the σ_{2p} orbital because σ interactions are generally stronger than π interactions.

To construct the total molecular orbital diagram for the B_2 molecule, we make the assumption that the $2s$ and $2p$ orbitals combine separately (in other words, there is no $2s$–$2p$ mixing). The resulting diagram is shown in Fig. 9.36. Note that B_2 has six *valence* electrons. (Remember the $1s$ orbitals and electrons are assumed not to participate in the bonding.) This diagram predicts the bond order:

$$\frac{4-2}{2} = 1$$

Therefore, B_2 should be a stable molecule.

Paramagnetism

At this point we need to discuss an additional molecular property—magnetism. Most materials have no magnetism until they are placed in a magnetic field. However, in the presence of such a field, magnetism of two types can be induced. **Paramagnetism** causes the substance to be attracted into the inducing magnetic field. **Diamagnetism** causes the substance to be repelled from the inducing magnetic field. Figure 9.37 illustrates how paramagnetism is measured. The sample is weighed with the electromagnet turned off and then weighed again with the electromagnet turned on. An increase in weight when the field is turned on indicates the sample is paramagnetic. Studies have shown that *paramagnetism is associated with unpaired electrons and diamagnetism is associated with paired electrons*. Any substance that has both paired and unpaired electrons will exhibit a net paramagnetism, since the effect of paramagnetism is much stronger than that of diamagnetism.

The molecular orbital energy-level diagram represented in Fig. 9.36 predicts that the B_2 molecule will be diamagnetic, since the MOs contain only paired electrons. However, experiments show that B_2 is actually paramagnetic with two unpaired electrons. Why does the model yield the wrong prediction? This is yet another illustration of how models are developed and used. In general, we try to use the simplest possible model that accounts for all the important observations. In this case, although the simplest model successfully describes the diatomic molecules up to B_2, it certainly is suspect if it cannot describe the B_2 molecule correctly. This means we must either discard the model or find a way to modify it.

Let's reconsider one assumption that we made. In our treatment of B_2, we have assumed that the s and p orbitals combine separately to form molecular orbitals. Calculations show that when the s and p orbitals are allowed to mix in the same molecular orbital, a different energy-level diagram results for B_2 (see Fig. 9.38). Note that even though the s and p contributions to the MOs are no longer separate, we retain the simple orbital designations. The energies of π_{2p} and σ_{2p} orbitals are reversed by p–s mixing, and the σ_{2s} and the $\sigma_{2s}*$ orbitals are no longer equally spaced relative to the energy of the free $2s$ orbital.

When the six valence electrons of the B_2 molecule are placed in the modified energy-level diagram, each of the last two electrons goes into one of the degenerate π_{2p} orbitals. This produces a paramagnetic molecule in agreement with experimental results. Thus, when the model is extended to allow p–s mixing in molecular orbitals, it predicts the correct magnetism. Note that the bond order is $(4-2)/2 = 1$, as before.

The remaining homonuclear diatomic molecules of the Period 2 elements can be described using the same molecular orbitals as for B_2 (see Fig. 9.38) and inserting the correct number of electrons. These are summarized in Fig. 9.39, together with experimentally obtained bond strengths and lengths. Several significant points arise from these results:

1. There are definite correlations between bond order, bond energy, and bond length. As the bond order predicted by the molecular orbital model increases,

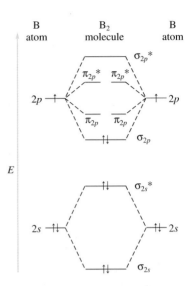

Figure 9.36

The *expected* molecular orbital energy-level diagram for the B_2 molecule.

Figure 9.37

Diagram of the kind of apparatus used to measure the paramagnetism of a sample. A paramagnetic sample will appear heavier when the electromagnet is turned on because the sample is attracted into the inducing magnetic field.

Figure 9.38

The *correct* molecular orbital energy-level diagram for the B_2 molecule. When *p-s* mixing is allowed, the energies of the σ_{2p} and π_{2p} orbitals are reversed. The two electrons from the B $2p$ orbitals now occupy separate, degenerate π_{2p} molecular orbitals and thus have parallel spins. Therefore, this diagram explains the observed paramagnetism of B_2.

Bond energy increases with increasing bond order; bond length decreases with increasing bond order.

Figure 9.39

The molecular orbital energy-level diagrams, bond orders, bond energies, and bond lengths for the diatomic molecules B_2 through F_2. There is evidence that for O_2 and F_2 the σ_{2p} orbital is lower in energy than the π_{2p} orbitals. However, since this does not affect the predicted magnetism or bond order for these molecules, we will use the same order of MOs for all the diatomic molecules of the Period 2 elements.

the bond energy increases and the bond length decreases. This is a clear indication that the bond order predicted by the model accurately reflects bond strength, and it strongly supports the reasonableness of the MO model.

2. Comparison of the bond energies of the B_2 and F_2 molecules indicates that bond order cannot automatically be associated with a particular bond energy. Although both molecules have a bond order of 1, the bond in B_2 appears to be about twice as strong as the bond in F_2. As we will see in our later discussion of the halogens, F_2 has an unusually weak single bond due to larger than usual electron–electron repulsions (there are 14 valence electrons on the small F_2 molecule).

3. Note the very large bond energy associated with the N_2 molecule, which the molecular orbital model predicts will have a bond order of 3, a triple bond. The very strong bond in N_2 is the principal reason that many nitrogen-containing compounds are used as high explosives. The reactions involving these explosives give the very stable N_2 molecule as a product, thus releasing large quantities of energy.

4. The O_2 molecule is known to be paramagnetic. This can be very convincingly demonstrated by pouring liquid oxygen between the poles of a strong magnet, as shown in Fig. 9.40. The oxygen remains there until it evaporates. Significantly, the molecular orbital model correctly predicts oxygen's paramagnetism, while the localized electron model predicts a diamagnetic molecule.

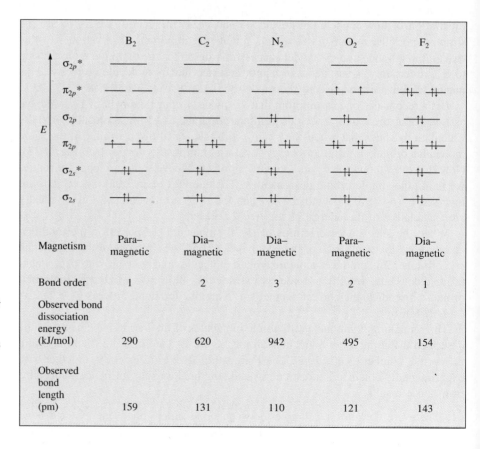

	B_2	C_2	N_2	O_2	F_2
Magnetism	Para–magnetic	Dia–magnetic	Dia–magnetic	Para–magnetic	Dia–magnetic
Bond order	1	2	3	2	1
Observed bond dissociation energy (kJ/mol)	290	620	942	495	154
Observed bond length (pm)	159	131	110	121	143

Sample Exercise 9.6

For the species O_2, O_2^+, and O_2^-, give the electron configuration and the bond order for each. Which has the strongest bond?

Solution

The O_2 molecule has 12 valence electrons (6 + 6); O_2^+ has 11 valence electrons (6 + 6 − 1); and O_2^- has 13 valence electrons (6 + 6 + 1). We will assume that the ions can be treated using the same molecular orbital diagram as for the neutral diatomic molecule:

The electron configuration for each species can then be taken from the diagram:

$$O_2: \quad (\sigma_{2s})^2(\sigma_{2s}{}^*)^2(\pi_{2p})^4(\sigma_{2p})^2(\pi_{2p}{}^*)^2$$
$$O_2{}^+: \quad (\sigma_{2s})^2(\sigma_{2s}{}^*)^2(\pi_{2p})^4(\sigma_{2p})^2(\pi_{2p}{}^*)^1$$
$$O_2{}^-: \quad (\sigma_{2s})^2(\sigma_{2s}{}^*)^2(\pi_{2p})^4(\sigma_{2p})^2(\pi_{2p}{}^*)^3$$

The bond orders are

$$\text{For } O_2: \quad \frac{8-4}{2} = 2$$

$$\text{For } O_2{}^+: \quad \frac{8-3}{2} = 2.5$$

$$\text{For } O_2{}^-: \quad \frac{8-5}{2} = 1.5$$

Thus O_2^+ is expected to have the strongest bond of the three species.

Figure 9.40

When liquid oxygen is poured into the space between the poles of a strong magnet, it remains there until it boils away. This attraction of liquid oxygen for the magnetic field demonstrates the paramagnetism of the O_2 molecule.

Sample Exercise 9.7

Use the molecular orbital model to predict the bond order and magnetism of each of the following molecules.

a. Ne_2 **b.** P_2

Solution

a. The valence orbitals for Ne are $2s$ and $2p$. Thus we can use the molecular orbitals we have already constructed for the diatomic molecules of the Period 2 elements. The Ne_2 molecule has 16 valence electrons (8 from each atom). Placing these electrons in the appropriate molecular orbitals produces the following diagram:

$$
E \left\uparrow
\begin{array}{ll}
\sigma_{2p}^* & \text{\uparrow\downarrow} \\
\pi_{2p}^* & \text{\uparrow\downarrow} \quad \text{\uparrow\downarrow} \\
\sigma_{2p} & \text{\uparrow\downarrow} \\
\pi_{2p} & \text{\uparrow\downarrow} \quad \text{\uparrow\downarrow} \\
\sigma_{2s}^* & \text{\uparrow\downarrow} \\
\sigma_{2s} & \text{\uparrow\downarrow}
\end{array}
\right.
$$

The bond order is $(8 - 8)/2 = 0$, and Ne_2 does not exist.

b. The P_2 molecule contains phosphorus atoms from the third row of the periodic table. We will assume that the diatomic molecules of the Period 3 elements can be treated in a way very similar to that which we have used so far. The only change will be that the molecular orbitals will be formed from $3s$ and $3p$ atomic orbitals. The P_2 molecule has 10 valence electrons (5 from each phosphorus atom). The resulting molecular orbital diagram is

$$
E \left\uparrow
\begin{array}{ll}
\sigma_{3p}^* & \text{------} \\
\pi_{3p}^* & \text{---} \quad \text{---} \\
\sigma_{3p} & \text{\uparrow\downarrow} \\
\pi_{3p} & \text{\uparrow\downarrow} \quad \text{\uparrow\downarrow} \\
\sigma_{3s}^* & \text{\uparrow\downarrow} \\
\sigma_{3s} & \text{\uparrow\downarrow}
\end{array}
\right.
$$

The molecule has a bond order of 3 and is expected to be diamagnetic.

9.4 Bonding in Heteronuclear Diatomic Molecules

Purpose

- To use the molecular orbital model to treat bonding between two different atoms.

In this section we will deal with selected examples of **heteronuclear** (different atoms) **diatomic molecules.** A special case involves molecules containing atoms adjacent to each other in the periodic table. Since the atoms involved in such a molecule are so similar, we can use the molecular orbital diagram for homonuclear molecules. For example, we can predict the bond order and magnetism of nitric oxide (NO) by placing its 11 valence electrons (5 from nitrogen and 6 from oxygen) in the molecular orbital energy-level diagram shown in Fig. 9.41. The molecule should be paramagnetic and has a bond order of

$$
\frac{8 - 3}{2} = 2.5
$$

$$
E \left\uparrow
\begin{array}{ll}
\sigma_{2p}^* & \text{------} \\
\pi_{2p}^* & \text{\uparrow} \quad \text{---} \\
\sigma_{2p} & \text{\uparrow\downarrow} \\
\pi_{2p} & \text{\uparrow\downarrow} \quad \text{\uparrow\downarrow} \\
\sigma_{2s}^* & \text{\uparrow\downarrow} \\
\sigma_{2s} & \text{\uparrow\downarrow}
\end{array}
\right.
$$

Figure 9.41

The molecular orbital energy-level diagram for the NO molecule. The bond order is 2.5.

Experimentally, nitric oxide is indeed found to be paramagnetic. Notice that this odd electron molecule is described very naturally by the MO model. In contrast, the localized electron model, in the simple form used in this text, cannot be used readily to treat such molecules.

Sample Exercise 9.8

Use the molecular orbital model to predict the magnetism and bond order of the NO^+ and CN^- ions.

Solution

The NO^+ ion has 10 valence electrons $(5 + 6 - 1)$. The CN^- ion also has 10 valence electrons $(4 + 5 + 1)$. Both ions are therefore diamagnetic and have a bond order derived from the equation

$$\frac{8 - 2}{2} = 3$$

The molecular orbital diagram for these two ions is the same (see Fig. 9.42).

Figure 9.42

The molecular orbital energy-level diagram for both the NO^+ and CN^- ions.

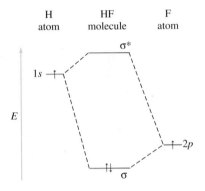

Figure 9.43

A partial molecular orbital energy-level diagram for the HF molecule.

When the two atoms of a diatomic molecule are very different, the energy-level diagram for homonuclear molecules can no longer be used. A new diagram must be devised for each molecule. We will illustrate this case by considering the hydrogen fluoride (HF) molecule. The electron configurations of the hydrogen and fluorine atoms are $1s^1$ and $1s^2 2s^2 2p^5$, respectively. To keep things as simple as possible, we will assume that fluorine uses only one of its $2p$ orbitals to bond to hydrogen. Thus the molecular orbitals for HF will be composed of fluorine $2p$ and hydrogen $1s$ orbitals. Figure 9.43 gives the partial molecular orbital energy-level diagram for HF, focusing only on the orbitals involved in the bonding. We are assuming that fluorine's other valence electrons remain localized on the fluorine. The $2p$ orbital of fluorine is shown at a lower energy than the $1s$ orbital of hydrogen on the diagram because fluorine binds its valence electrons more tightly. Thus the $2p$ electron on a free fluorine atom is at lower energy than the $1s$ electron on a free hydrogen atom. The diagram predicts that the HF molecule should be stable because both electrons are lowered in energy relative to their energy in the free hydrogen and fluorine atoms, and this is the driving force for bond formation.

Because the fluorine $2p$ orbital is lower in energy than the hydrogen $1s$ orbital, the electrons prefer to be closer to the fluorine atom. That is, the σ molecular orbital containing the bonding electron pair shows greater electron probability close to the fluorine (see Fig. 9.44). The electron pair is not shared equally. This causes the fluorine atom to have a slight excess of negative charge and leaves the hydrogen atom partially positive. This is *exactly* the bond polarity observed for HF. Thus the molecular orbital model accounts in a straightforward way for the different electronegativities of hydrogen and fluorine and the resulting unequal charge distribution.

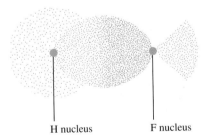

Figure 9.44

The electron probability distribution in the bonding molecular orbital of the HF molecule. Note the greater electron density close to the fluorine atom.

9.5 *Combining the Localized Electron and Molecular Orbital Models*

Purpose

- To show how the need for resonance is eliminated if the localized electron and molecular orbital models are combined.

One of the main difficulties with the localized electron model is its assumption that electrons are localized. This problem is most apparent with molecules for which several valid Lewis structures can be drawn. It is clear that none of these structures taken alone adequately describes the electronic structure of the molecule. The concept of resonance was invented to solve this problem. However, even with resonance included, the localized electron model does not describe molecules and ions such as O_3 and NO_3^- in a very satisfying way.

It would seem that the ideal bonding model would be one with the simplicity of the localized electron model but with the delocalization characteristic of the molecular orbital model. We can achieve this by combining the two models to describe molecules that require resonance. Note that for species such as O_3 and NO_3^- the double bond changes position in the resonance structures (see Fig. 9.45). Since a double bond involves one σ and one π bond, there is a σ bond between all bound atoms in each resonance structure. It is really the π bond that has different locations in the various resonance structures.

We can conclude that the σ bonds in a molecule can be described as being localized with no apparent problems. It is the π bonding that must be treated as being delocalized. Thus, for molecules that require resonance, we will use the localized electron model to describe the σ bonding and the molecular orbital model to describe the π bonding. This allows us to keep the bonding model as simple as possible and yet give a more physically accurate description of such molecules.

We will illustrate the general method by considering the bonding in benzene, an important industrial chemical that must be handled carefully because it is a known carcinogen. The benzene molecule (C_6H_6) consists of a planar hexagon of carbon atoms with one hydrogen atom bound to each carbon atom, as shown in Fig. 9.46(a). In the molecule all six C—C bonds are known to be equivalent. To explain this fact, the localized electron model must invoke resonance [see Fig. 9.46(b)].

A better description of the bonding in benzene results when we use a combination of the models, as described above. In this description it is assumed that the σ bonds of carbon involve sp^2 orbitals, as shown in Fig. 9.47. These σ bonds are all centered in the plane of the molecule.

In molecules that require resonance, it is the π bonding that is most clearly delocalized.

Figure 9.45

The resonance structures for O_3 and NO_3^-. Note that it is the double bond that occupies various positions in the resonance structures.

(a)

(b)

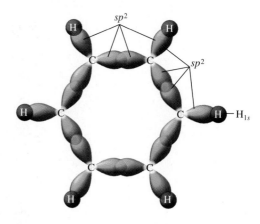

Figure 9.46

(a) The benzene molecule consists of a ring of six carbon atoms with one hydrogen atom bound to each carbon; all atoms are in the same plane. All of the C—C bonds are known to be equivalent. (b) Two of the resonance structures for the benzene molecule. The localized electron model must invoke resonance to account for the six equal C—C bonds.

Figure 9.47

The σ bonding system in the benzene molecule.

Since each carbon atom is sp^2 hybridized, a p orbital perpendicular to the plane of the ring remains on each carbon atom. These six p orbitals can be used to form π molecular orbitals, as shown in Fig. 9.48(a). The electrons in the resulting π molecular orbitals are delocalized above and below the plane of the ring, as shown in Fig. 9.48(b). This gives six equivalent C—C bonds, as required by the known structure of the benzene molecule. The benzene structure is often written as

to indicate the **delocalized π bonding** in the molecule.

Very similar treatments can be applied to other planar molecules for which resonance is required by the localized electron model. For example, the NO_3^- ion can be described using the π molecular orbital system shown in Fig. 9.49. In this molecule each atom is assumed to be sp^2 hybridized, which leaves one p orbital on eachch atom perpendicular to the plane of the ion. These p orbitals can combine to form the π molecular orbital system.

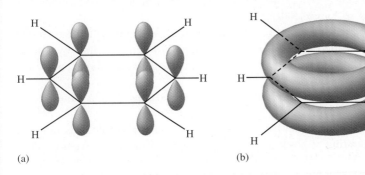

(a)

(b)

Figure 9.48

(a) The π molecular orbital system in benzene is formed by combining the six p orbitals from the six sp^2 hybridized carbon atoms. (b) The electrons in the resulting π molecular orbitals are delocalized over the entire ring of carbon atoms, giving six equivalent bonds. A composite of these orbitals is represented here.

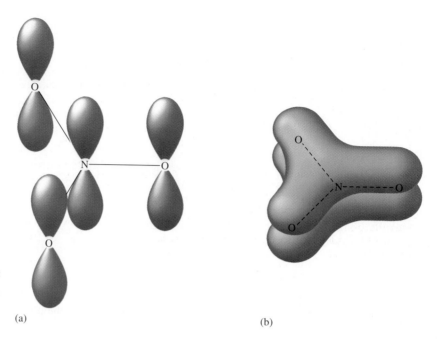

Figure 9.49

(a) The p orbitals used to form the π bonding system in the NO_3^- ion. (b) A representation of the delocalization of the electrons in the π molecular orbital system of the NO_3^- ion.

(a)

(b)

FOR REVIEW

Summary

In this chapter we have emphasized the role of orbitals in the covalent bonding in molecules. The two most useful models are the localized electron model and the molecular orbital model.

In the localized electron model, a molecule is pictured as a group of atoms sharing electron pairs using atomic orbitals. Because the requirements of the molecule are different from those of separated atoms, the original atomic orbitals are combined to form new hybrid orbitals, which are used by the atoms in the molecule. The specific set of hybrid orbitals needed is determined by the arrangement of electron pairs that gives the minimum repulsion. For example, an atom surrounded by four electron pairs requires a tetrahedral arrangement and a set of sp^3 hybrid orbitals; a trigonal planar arrangement requires sp^2 hybridization, and a linear arrangement requires sp hybridization.

When an electron pair is shared in the area centered on a line joining the atoms, the covalent bond is called a σ bond. A π bond occurs when p orbitals overlap in a parallel fashion. The shared electron pair then occupies the space above and below the line joining the bonded atoms.

Multiple bonds involve σ and π bonds. A double bond consists of a σ bond and a π bond; a triple bond involves a σ bond and two π bonds.

In the molecular orbital model for covalent bonding, the molecule is assumed to be a new entity consisting of positively charged nuclei and electrons. We use calculations similar to those used for atoms to determine the allowed orbitals in the molecule. The molecular orbitals are constructed from the valence orbitals of the atoms involved in forming the molecule.

Molecular orbitals are classified in two ways:

1. MOs are classified according to their energy. A bonding MO is an orbital that is lower in energy than the original atomic orbitals. In going from the free atoms to the molecule, electrons occupying bonding MOs are lowered in energy. This favors formation of a stable molecule (bonds are formed). An antibonding MO is an orbital that is higher in energy than the original atomic orbitals. In going from the free atoms to the molecule, electrons in antibonding MOs are raised in energy. These electrons oppose bonding.

2. MOs are classified according to their shape (symmetry). Sigma (σ) molecular orbitals have their electron probability centered about a line passing through the two nuclei. Pi (π) molecular orbitals have their electron probability concentrated above and below the line passing through the nuclei.

Bond order is an index of bond strength:

$$\text{Bond order} = \frac{\text{number of bonding electrons} - \text{number of antibonding electrons}}{2}$$

The greater the difference between the number of electrons that are lowered in energy (bonding electrons) and the number of electrons that are raised in energy (antibonding electrons) when the molecule forms, the greater will be the stability of the molecule (the stronger the bonding).

The main strengths of the molecular orbital model are that it correctly predicts the relative bond strength and magnetism of simple diatomic molecules (the correct prediction of the paramagnetism of the oxygen molecule is an important example), it accounts for bond polarity, and it correctly portrays electrons as being delocalized in polyatomic molecules. The main disadvantage of the molecular orbital model is that it is difficult to apply qualitatively to polyatomic molecules.

The concept of resonance is required for certain molecules because the localized electron model incorrectly assumes that electrons are located between a given pair of atoms in a molecule. A more physically accurate description of these molecules can be given by combining the localized electron and molecular orbital models. The σ bonds in these molecules can be regarded as localized, while the π bonding is best described as delocalized.

Key Terms

Section 9.1
hybridization
sp^3 hybridization
hybrid orbitals
sp^2 hybridization
sigma (σ) bond
pi (π) bond
sp hybridization
dsp^3 hybridization
d^2sp^3 hybridization

Section 9.2
molecular orbital model
molecular orbital (MO)
sigma (σ) molecular orbital
bonding molecular orbital
antibonding molecular orbital
bond order

Section 9.3
pi (π) molecular orbital

paramagnetism
diamagnetism

Section 9.4
heteronuclear diatomic molecule

Section 9.5
delocalized π bonding

A blue question or exercise number indicates that the answer to that question or exercise appears at the back of this book and a solution appears in the Solutions Guide.

Questions

1. What are the relationships among bond order, bond energy, and bond length? Which of these quantities can be measured?

2. What is misleading about the following statement: "The methane molecule (CH_4) is a tetrahedral molecule because the carbon atom is sp^3 hybridized"? What is a more correct statement about the relationship between the molecular structure and the hybridization in methane?

3. What type of experiment can be done to determine if a material is paramagnetic?

4. Describe the differences between bonding and antibonding molecular orbitals in terms of electron distribution and energy.

Exercises

In this section similar exercises are paired.

The Localized Electron Model and Hybrid Orbitals

5. For each of the following molecules, write the Lewis structure(s), predict the molecular structure (including bond angles), give the expected hybrid orbitals on the central atom, and predict the overall polarity.
   a. CF_4
   b. NF_3
   c. OF_2
   d. BF_3
   e. BeH_2
   f. TeF_4
   g. AsF_5
   h. KrF_2
   i. KrF_4
   j. SeF_6
   k. $XeOF_4$
   l. $XeOF_2$
   m. XeO_4

6. For each of the following molecules or ions that contain sulfur, write the Lewis structure(s), predict the molecular structure (including bond angles), and give the expected hybrid orbitals for sulfur.
   a. SO_2
   b. SO_3

   c. $S_2O_3{}^{2-}$

$$\begin{bmatrix} & O & \\ & \| & \\ S - S - O \\ & \| & \\ & O & \end{bmatrix}^{2-}$$

   d. $S_2O_8{}^{2-}$

$$\begin{bmatrix} & O & & O & \\ & \| & & \| & \\ O - S - O - O - S - O \\ & \| & & \| & \\ & O & & O & \end{bmatrix}^{2-}$$

   e. $SO_3{}^{2-}$
   f. $SO_4{}^{2-}$
   g. SF_2
   h. SF_4
   i. SF_6
   j. F_3S-SF
   k. $SF_5{}^+$

7. Why must all six atoms in C_2H_4 be in the same plane?

8. The allene molecule has the following Lewis structure:

$$\underset{H}{\overset{H}{\diagdown}} C = C = C \underset{H}{\overset{H}{\diagup}}$$

Are all four hydrogen atoms in the same plane? If not, what is their spatial relationship? Explain.

9. Biacetyl and acetoin are added to magarine to make it taste more like butter.

Biacetyl   Acetoin

Complete the Lewis structures, predict values for all C—C—O bond angles, and give the hybridization of the carbon atoms in these two compounds. Are the four carbons and two oxygens in biacetyl in the same plane? How many σ bonds and how many π bonds are there in biacetyl and acetoin?

11. One of the first drugs to be approved for use in treatment of acquired immune deficiency syndrome (AIDS) is azidothymidine (AZT). Complete the Lewis structure of AZT.

a. How many carbon atoms are sp^3 hybridized?
b. How many carbon atoms are sp^2 hybridized?
c. What atom is sp hybridized?
d. How many σ bonds are in the molecule?
e. How many π bonds are in the molecule?
f. Which ring(s) is/are planar?
g. What is the N—N—N bond angle in the azide (—N_3) group?
h. What is the H—O—C bond angle in the side group attached to the five-membered ring?
i. What is the hybridization of the oxygen atom in the —CH_2OH group?

10. Many important compounds in the chemical industry are derivatives of ethylene (C_2H_4). Two of them are methyl methacrylate and acrylonitrile.

Methyl methacrylate   Acrylonitrile

Complete the Lewis structures, showing all lone pairs. Give approximate values for bond angles a through f. Give the hybridization of all carbon atoms. In methyl methacrylate, how many of the atoms in the molecule lie in the same plane? How many σ bonds and how many π bonds are there in methyl methacrylate and acrylonitrile?

12. Cyanamide (H_2NCN), an important industrial chemical, is produced by the following steps:

$$CaC_2 + N_2 \longrightarrow CaNCN + C$$

$$CaNCN \xrightarrow{\text{Acid}} \underset{\text{Cyanamide}}{H_2NCN}$$

Calcium cyanamide (CaNCN) is used as a direct-application fertilizer, weed killer, and cotton defoliant. It is also used to make cyanamide, dicyandiamide, and melamine plastics:

$$H_2NCN \xrightarrow{\text{Acid}} \underset{\text{Dicyandiamide}}{NCNC(NH_2)_2}$$

$$NCNC(NH_2) \xrightarrow[\text{NH}_3]{\text{Heat}}$$

Melamine
(π bonds
not shown)

a. Write Lewis structures for NCN^{2-}, H_2NCN, dicyandiamide, and melamine, including resonance structures where appropriate.
b. Give the hybridization of the C and N atoms in each species.
c. How many σ bonds and how many π bonds are in each species?
d. Is the ring in melamine planar?
e. There are three different C—N distances in dicyandiamide, $NCNC(NH_2)$, and the molecule is nonlinear. Of all the resonance structures you drew for this molecule, predict which should be the most important.

13. The red color of tomatoes is due to the presence of the compound lycopene.

Note: The right half of lycopene is just the reverse of the left half (shown).

a. How many carbon atoms are sp^3 hybridized? sp^2 hybridized? sp hybridized?

b. How many σ and π bonds are there between carbon atoms in the entire molecule?

14. The hot taste of chili peppers results from the presence of capsaicin. Humans are very sensitive to this substance and can detect 10 parts per million of capsaicin in food. The structure of capsaicin is

a. What is the hybridization of the nitrogen atom?

b. How many carbon atoms are sp, sp^2, and sp^3 hybridized?

c. What are the values of the bond angles marked a through e?

d. How many π bonds are in the molecule?

e. Are all the carbon atoms in capsaicin in the same plane?

The Molecular Orbital Model

15. Which of the following are predicted by the molecular orbital model to be stable diatomic species?

a. H_2^+, H_2, H_2^-, H_2^{2-}

b. He_2^{2+}, He_2^+, He_2

16. Which of the following are predicted by the molecular orbital model to be stable diatomic species?

a. N_2^{2-}, O_2^{2-}, F_2^{2-}

b. Be_2, B_2, Li_2

17. Using the molecular orbital model, write electron configurations for the following diatomic species and calculate the bond orders. Which ones are paramagnetic?

a. H_2 d. CN^+ g. N_2
b. B_2 e. CN h. N_2^+
c. F_2 f. CN^- i. N_2^-

18. Using the molecular orbital model to describe the bonding in O_2^+, O_2, O_2^-, and O_2^{2-}, predict the bond orders and the relative bond lengths for these four species. How many unpaired electrons are present in each one?

19. Show how two $2p$ atomic orbitals can combine to form a σ or a π molecular orbital.

20. Show how a hydrogen $1s$ atomic orbital and a fluoride $2p$ atomic orbital overlap to form bonding and antibonding molecular orbitals in the hydrogen fluoride molecule. Are these molecular orbitals σ or π molecular orbitals?

21. Place the species CN^+, CN, and CN^- in order of increasing bond length and increasing bond energy. Use your results from Exercise 17.

22. Place the species N_2, N_2^+, and N_2^- in order of increasing bond length and increasing bond energy. Use your results from Exercise 17.

23. Acetylene (C_2H_2) can be produced from the reaction of calcium carbide (CaC_2) with water. Use both the localized electron and molecular orbital models to describe the bonding in the acetylide anion (C_2^{2-}). What neutral heteronuclear diatomic molecule is isoelectronic with the acetylide anion?

24. Construct a molecular orbital energy level diagram for the P_2 molecule.

Additional Exercises

25. A variety of chlorine oxide fluorides and related cations and anions are known. They tend to be powerful oxidizing and fluorinating agents. $FClO_3$ is the most stable of this group of compounds and has been studied as an oxidizing component of rocket propellents. Draw the Lewis structures, predict the molecular structures, and describe the bonding (in terms of hybrid orbitals) for the following:

a. $FClO$ d. F_3ClO
b. $FClO_2$ e. F_3ClO_2
c. $FClO_3$

26. $FClO_2$ and F_3ClO can both gain a fluoride ion to form stable anions. F_3ClO and F_3ClO_2 will both lose a fluoride ion to form stable cations. Draw the Lewis structures and describe the hybrid orbitals used by chlorine in these ions.

27. Antimony pentafluoride exists in the liquid phase not as discrete SbF_5 molecules but as a polymer (a large aggregate of small molecules). Describe the molecular structure and the hybrid orbitals in discrete SbF_5 molecules. What hybrid orbitals does antimony employ in the polymer?

Experimental observations indicate that the fluorine atoms are in three distinct types of chemical environments in liquid antimony pentafluoride. Indicate the different types of fluorine atoms in the polymer.

28. Indigo is the dye used in coloring blue jeans. The term *navy blue* is derived from the use of indigo to dye British naval uniforms in the eighteenth century. The structure of the indigo molecule is

a. What other resonance structures are possible?
b. How many σ bonds and π bonds exist in the molecule?
c. Are the two sets of rings coplanar or at an angle to each other?
d. What hybrid orbitals are used by the carbon atoms in the indigo molecule?

29. Using bond energies from Table 8.4, estimate the barrier to rotation about a carbon–carbon double bond. To do this, consider what must happen to go from

to

in terms of making and breaking chemical bonds; that is, what must happen in terms of the π bond?

30. Describe the bonding in the O_3 molecule and the NO_2^- ion using the localized electron model. How would the molecular orbital model describe the π bonding in these two species?

31. Phosphorus forms many compounds with "cage" structures. Some are shown below. Complete the Lewis structures, including all unshared electron pairs. What is the hybridization of phosphorus in each of the molecules? Predict approximate values of the O—P—O and P—O—P bond angles.

a. P_4 b. P_4O_6

c. P_4O_{10}

32. Cholesterol ($C_{27}H_{46}O$) has the following structure:

In such shorthand structures, each point where lines meet represents a carbon atom and most H atoms are not shown. Draw the complete structure showing all carbon and hydrogen atoms. (There will be four bonds to each carbon atom.) Indicate which carbon atoms use sp^2 or sp^3 hybrid orbitals. Are all carbon atoms in the same plane, as implied by the structure?

33. Complete the Lewis structures of the following molecules. Predict the molecular structure, polarity, bond angles, and hybrid orbitals used by the atoms marked by asterisks for each molecule.
    a. $COCl_2$

    O
    ‖
    C*
    ╱ ╲
    Cl   Cl

    b. N_2F_2

    F—N*—N*—F

    c. N_2O_3

    O—*N—*N
              ╲
               O
              O

    d. COS

    O—C*—S

    e. ICl_3

    Cl—I*—Cl
        |
        Cl

34. Which of the species in Exercise 33 exhibit resonance? Draw all resonance structures for each, including formal charges for all structures.

35. Complete the following resonance structures for $OPCl_3$:

    O   O
    ‖   ‖
    Cl—P—Cl ⟷ Cl—P—Cl
        | |
        Cl   Cl
       (A)   (B)

    a. Would you predict the same molecular structure from each resonance structure?
    b. What is the hybridization of P in each structure?
    c. What orbitals can the P atom use to form the π bond in structure B?
    d. Which resonance structure would be favored on the basis of formal charges?

36. The N_2O molecule is linear and polar.
    a. On the basis of this experimental evidence, which arrangement, NNO or NON, is correct? Explain your answer.

b. On the basis of your answer in (a) above, write the Lewis structure of N_2O (including resonance forms). Give the formal charge on each atom and the hybridization of the central atom.
c. How would the multiple bonding in : N≡N—O̤ : be described in terms of orbitals?

37. Describe the bonding in NO^+, NO^-, and NO using both the localized electron and molecular orbital models. From the molecular orbital model, predict the order of bond energies and bond lengths for the nitrogen–oxygen bond in the three species.

38. Does the molecular orbital model or the localized electron model account better for the bonding in nitric oxide (NO)? Explain.

39. Describe the bonding in the first excited state of N_2 (the one closest in energy to the ground state) using the molecular orbital model. What differences do you expect in the properties of the molecule in the ground state as compared to the first excited state? (An excited state of a molecule corresponds to an electron arrangement other than that giving the lowest possible energy.)

40. Describe the bonding in the Be_2 molecule using the localized electron model. How does this compare with the description of the bonding in Be_2 using the molecular orbital model?

41. A Lewis structure obeying the octet rule can be drawn for O_2 as follows:

    O̤=O̤

    Use the molecular orbital energy-level diagram for O_2 to show that the above Lewis structure corresponds to an excited state.

Challenge Problems

42. Two structures can be drawn for cyanuric acid:

    a. Are these two resonance structures of the same molecule? Explain.
    b. Give the hybridization of the carbon and nitrogen atoms in each structure.
    c. Use bond energies (Table 8.4) to predict which form is more stable; that is, which contains the strongest bonds?

43. Consider the following structure for vitamin C (ascorbic acid):

$$CH_2OH$$

HO—CH O

H—C   C=O

C=C

HO   OH

Indicate which carbon atoms use sp, sp^2, or sp^3 hybrid orbitals. Are all five atoms in the ring in the same plane? Explain. Ascorbic acid is a weak acid. The two hydrogens marked with asterisks are the acidic hydrogens. Draw resonance structures for the $C_6H_6O_6^{2-}$ anion.

44. The molecules N_2 and CO are isoelectronic, but their properties are quite different. Although as a first approximation we often use the same molecular orbital diagram for both, suggest how the molecular orbitals in N_2 and CO might be different.

45. As compared with CO and O_2, CS and S_2 are very unstable molecules. Give an explanation based on the relative abilities of the sulfur and oxygen atoms to form π bonds.

46. Use Figs. 9.43 and 9.44 to answer the following questions:
a. Would the bonding molecular orbital in HF place greater electron density near the H or the F atom? Why?
b. Would the bonding molecular orbital have greater fluorine $2p$ character, greater hydrogen $1s$ character, or an equal contribution from both? Why?
c. Answer the previous two questions for the antibonding molecular orbital in HF.

47. Use orbital energy diagrams such as that shown for B_2 in Fig. 9.38 to answer the following questions:
a. The first ionization energy of N_2 (1501 kJ/mol) is greater than the first ionization energy of atomic nitrogen (1402 kJ/mol). Explain.
b. Would you expect F_2 to have a lower or higher first ionization energy than atomic fluorine? Why?

48. The diatomic molecule OH exists in the gas phase. The bond length and bond energy have been measured to be 97.06 pm and 424.7 kJ/mol, respectively. Assume that the OH mole-

cule is analogous to the HF molecule discussed in the chapter and that molecular orbitals result from the overlap of a p_z orbital from oxygen with the $1s$ orbital of hydrogen.
a. Draw pictures of the sigma bonding and antibonding molecular orbitals in OH.
b. Which of the two molecular orbitals will have the greater hydrogen $1s$ character?
c. Can the $2p_x$ orbital of oxygen form molecular orbitals with the $1s$ orbital of hydrogen? Explain.
d. Knowing that only the $2p$ orbitals of oxygen will interact significantly with the $1s$ orbital of hydrogen, complete the molecular orbital energy-level diagram for OH. Place the correct number of electrons in the energy levels.
e. Estimate the bond order for OH.
f. Predict whether the bond order of OH^+ will be greater than, less than, or the same as that of OH. Explain.

49. A flask containing gaseous N_2 is irradiated with 25-nm light. Using the following information, indicate what species can form in this flask during irradiation.

$$N_2(g) \rightarrow 2N(g) \qquad \Delta H° = 941 \text{ kJ/mol}$$
$$N_2(g) \rightarrow N_2^+(g) + e^- \qquad \Delta H° = 1501 \text{ kJ/mol}$$
$$N(g) \rightarrow N^+(g) + e^- \qquad \Delta H° = 1402 \text{ kJ/mol}$$

What range of wavelengths will produce atomic nitrogen in the flask but will not produce any ions?

CHAPTER 10

Liquids and Solids

You have only to think about water to appreciate how different the three states of matter are. Flying, swimming, and ice skating are all done in contact with water in its various forms. Clearly, the arrangements of the water molecules must be significantly different in its gas, liquid, and solid forms.

In Chapter 5 we saw that a gas can be pictured as a substance whose component particles are far apart, are in rapid random motion, and exert relatively small forces on each other. The kinetic molecular model was constructed to account for the ideal behavior that most gases approach at high temperatures and low pressures.

Solids are obviously very different from gases. A gas has low density and high compressibility and completely fills its container. Solids have much greater densities, are compressible only to a very slight extent, and are rigid—a solid maintains its shape irrespective of its container. These properties indicate that the components of a solid are close together and exert large attractive forces on each other.

The properties of liquids lie somewhere between those of solids and gases, but not midway between, as can be seen from some of the properties of the three states of water. For example, compare the enthalpy change for the melting of ice at 0°C (the heat of fusion) with that for vaporizing liquid water at 100°C (the heat of vaporization):

$$H_2O(s) \rightarrow H_2O(l) \qquad \Delta H°_{fus} = 6.02 \text{ kJ/mol}$$
$$H_2O(l) \rightarrow H_2O(g) \qquad \Delta H°_{vap} = 40.7 \text{ kJ/mol}$$

These values show a much greater change in structure in going from the liquid to the gaseous state than in going from the solid to the liquid state. This suggests that there are extensive attractive forces among the molecules in liquid water, similar to but not so strong as those in the solid state.

A micrograph of a liquid crystal array. Liquid crystal behavior is exhibited by molecules that behave as rigid rods that line up preferentially to form a phase with properties between those of the traditional liquid and solid.

439

Gas   Liquid   Solid

Figure 10.1

Schematic representations of the three states of matter.

Table 10.1	
Densities of the Three States of Water	
State	Density (g/cm³)
Solid (0°C, 1 atm)	0.9168
Liquid (25°C, 1 atm)	0.9971
Gas (400°C, 1 atm)	3.26×10^{-4}

The relative similarity of the liquid and solid states also can be seen in the densities of the three states of water. As shown in Table 10.1, the densities for liquid and solid water are quite close.* Compressibilities also can be used to explore the relationship among water's states. At 25°C, the density of liquid water changes from 0.99707 g/cm³ at a pressure of 1 atm to 1.046 g/cm³ at 1065 atm. Given the large change in pressure, this is a very small variation in the density. Ice also shows little variation in density with increased pressure. On the other hand, at 400°C, the density of gaseous water changes from 3.26×10^{-4} g/cm³ at 1 atm pressure to 0.157 g/cm³ at 242 atm—a huge variation.

The conclusion is clear. The liquid and solid states show many similarities and are strikingly different from the gaseous state, as shown schematically in Fig. 10.1. We must bear this in mind as we develop models for the structures of solids and liquids.

We will proceed in our study of liquids and solids by first considering the properties and structures of liquids and solids. Then we will consider the changes in state that occur between solid and liquid, liquid and gas, and solid and gas.

10.1 Intermolecular Forces

Purpose

- To define dipole–dipole forces, hydrogen bonding forces, and London dispersion forces.
- To describe the effects these forces have on the properties of liquids and solids.

In Chapters 8 and 9 we saw that atoms can form stable units called molecules by sharing electrons. This is called **intramolecular** (within the molecule) **bonding.** In this chapter we consider the properties of the **condensed states** of matter (liquids and solids) and the forces that cause the aggregation of the components of a substance to form a liquid or a solid. These forces may involve covalent or ionic bonding, or they may involve weaker interactions usually called **intermolecular forces** (because they occur between, rather than within, molecules).

Intermolecular forces were introduced in Chapter 5 to explain nonideal gas behavior.

---

*Although the densities of solid and liquid water are quite similar, as is typical for substances, water is quite unusual in that the density of its solid state is slightly less than that of its liquid state. For most substances, the density of the solid state is slightly greater than that of the liquid state.

It is important to recognize that when a substance such as water changes from solid to liquid to gas, *the molecules remain intact*. The changes in states are due to changes in the forces *among* the molecules rather than in those *within* the molecules. In ice, as we will see later in this chapter, the molecules are virtually locked in place, although they can vibrate about their positions. If energy is added, the motions of the molecules increase, and they eventually achieve the greater movement and disorder characteristic of liquid water. The ice has melted. As more energy is added, the gaseous state is eventually reached, with the individual molecules far apart and interacting relatively little. However, the gas still consists of water molecules. It would take much more energy to overcome the covalent bonds and decompose the water molecules into their component atoms. This can be seen by comparing the energy needed to vaporize 1 mole of liquid water (40.7 kJ) with that needed to break the O—H bonds in 1 mole of water molecules (934 kJ).

> Remember that temperature is a measure of the random motions of the particles in a substance.

Dipole–Dipole Forces

As we saw in Section 8.3, molecules with polar bonds often behave in an electric field as if they had a center of positive charge and a center of negative charge. That is, they exhibit a dipole moment. Molecules with dipole moments can attract each other electrostatically by lining up so that the positive and negative ends are close to each other, as shown in Fig. 10.2(a). This is called a **dipole–dipole attraction.** In a condensed state such as a liquid, where many molecules are in close proximity, the dipoles find the best compromise between attraction and repulsion. That is, the molecules orient themselves to maximize the $\oplus$---$\ominus$ interactions and to minimize $\oplus$---$\oplus$ and $\ominus$---$\ominus$ interactions, as represented in Fig. 10.2(b).

> Dipole–dipole forces are forces that act between polar molecules.

Dipole–dipole forces are typically only about 1% as strong as covalent or ionic bonds, and they rapidly become weaker as the distance between the dipoles increases. At low pressures in the gas phase, where the molecules are far apart, these forces are relatively unimportant.

Particularly strong dipole–dipole forces, however, are seen among molecules in which hydrogen is bound to a highly electronegative atom, such as nitrogen, oxygen, or fluorine. Two factors account for the strengths of these interactions: the great polarity of the bond and the close approach of the dipoles, allowed by the very small size of the hydrogen atom. Because dipole–dipole attractions of this type are so unusually strong, they are given a special name—**hydrogen bonding.** Figure 10.3 (on page 442) shows hydrogen bonding among water molecules.

Hydrogen bonding has a very important effect on physical properties. For example, the boiling points for the covalent hydrides of the elements in Groups 4A, 5A, 6A, and 7A are given in Fig. 10.4 (on page 442). Note that the nonpolar tetrahedral hydrides of Group 4A show a steady increase in boiling point with molar mass (that is, in going down the group), whereas, for the other groups, the lightest member has an unexpectedly high boiling point. Why? The answer lies in the especially large hydrogen bonding interactions that exist among the smallest molecules with the most polar X—H bonds. These unusually strong hydrogen bonding forces are due primarily to two factors. One factor is the relatively large electronegativity values of the lightest elements in each group, which leads to especially polar X—H bonds. The second factor is the small size of the first element of each group, which allows for the close approach of the dipoles, further strengthening the intermolecular forces. Because the interactions among the molecules containing the lightest elements in Groups 5A and 6A are so strong, an unusually large quantity of energy

(a)

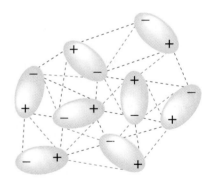

Attraction ----------
Repulsion ----------

(b)

Figure 10.2

(a) The electrostatic interaction of two polar molecules. (b) The interaction of many dipoles in a condensed state.

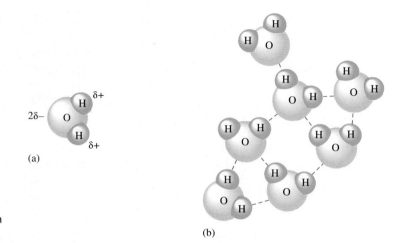

Figure 10.3

(a) The polar water molecule.
(b) Hydrogen bonding among water molecules. Note that the small size of the hydrogen atom allows for close interactions.

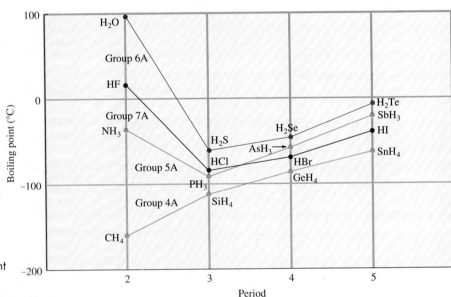

Figure 10.4

The boiling points of the covalent hydrides of the elements in Groups 4A, 5A, 6A, and 7A.

must be supplied to overcome these interactions and separate the molecules to produce the gaseous state. These molecules will remain together in the liquid state even at high temperatures; hence the very high boiling points.

Boiling point will be defined precisely in Section 10.8.

London Dispersion Forces

Even molecules without dipole moments must exert forces on each other. We know this because all substances—even the noble gases—exist in the liquid and solid states under certain conditions. The relatively weak forces that exist among noble gas atoms and nonpolar molecules are called **London dispersion forces.** To understand the origin of these forces, let's consider a pair of noble gas atoms. Although we usually assume that the electrons of an atom are uniformly distributed about the nucleus, this is apparently not true at every instant. As the electrons move about the nucleus, a momentary nonsymmetrical electron distribution can develop that produces a temporary dipolar arrangement of charge. The formation of this temporary

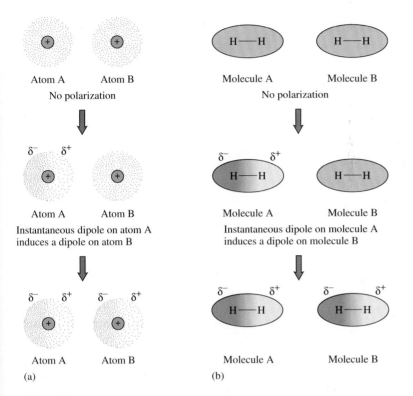

Figure 10.5

(a) An instantaneous polarization can occur on atom A, creating an instantaneous dipole. This dipole creates an induced dipole on neighboring atom B. (b) Nonpolar molecules such as H_2 also can develop instantaneous and induced dipoles.

Table 10.2	
The Freezing Points of the Group 8A Elements	
Element	Freezing Point (°C)
Helium*	−269.7
Neon	−248.6
Argon	−189.4
Krypton	−157.3
Xenon	−111.9

*Helium is the only element that will not freeze by lowering its temperature at 1 atm. Pressure must be applied to freeze helium.

dipole can, in turn, affect the electron distribution of a neighboring atom. That is, this *instantaneous dipole* that occurs accidentally in a given atom can then *induce* a similar dipole in a neighboring atom, as represented in Fig. 10.5(a). This phenomenon leads to an interatomic attraction that is relatively weak and short-lived, but which can be very significant for large atoms (see below). For these interactions to become strong enough to produce a solid, the motions of the atoms must be greatly slowed down. This explains, for instance, why the noble gas elements have such low freezing points (see Table 10.2).

Note from Table 10.2 that the freezing point rises going down the group. The principal cause for this trend is that as the atomic number increases, the number of electrons increases, and there is an increased chance of the occurrence of momentary dipole interactions. We describe this phenomenon using the term **polarizability,** which indicates the ease with which the electron "cloud" of an atom can be distorted to give a dipolar charge distribution. Thus we say that large atoms with many electrons exhibit a higher polarizability than small atoms. This means that the importance of London dispersion forces increases greatly as the size of the atom increases.

These same ideas also apply to nonpolar molecules such as H_2, CH_4, CCl_4, and CO_2 [see Fig. 10.5(b)]. Since none of these molecules has a permanent dipole moment, their principal means of attracting each other is through London dispersion forces.

The dispersion forces in molecules with large atoms are quite significant and are often actually more important than dipole–dipole forces.

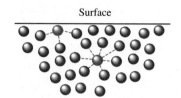

Surface

Figure 10.6

A molecule in the interior of a liquid is attracted by the molecules surrounding it, whereas a molecule at the surface of a liquid is attracted only by molecules below it and on each side.

For a given volume, a sphere has a smaller surface area than any other shape.

Surface tension: the resistance of a liquid to an increase in its surface area.

The composition of glass is discussed in Section 10.5.

Viscosity: a measure of a liquid's resistance to flow.

10.2 The Liquid State

Purpose

• To describe some properties of liquids: surface tension, capillary action, and viscosity.

Liquids and liquid solutions are vital to our lives. Of course, water is the most important liquid. Besides being essential to life, water provides a medium for food preparation, for transportation, for cooling in many types of machines and industrial processes, for recreation, for cleaning, and for a myriad of other uses.

Liquids exhibit many characteristics that help us understand their natures. We have already mentioned their low compressibility, lack of rigidity, and high density compared with gases. Many of the properties of liquids give us direct information about the forces that exist among the particles. For example, when a liquid is poured onto a solid surface, it tends to bead as droplets, a phenomenon that depends on the intermolecular forces. Although molecules in the interior of the liquid are completely surrounded by other molecules, those at the liquid surface are subject to attractions only from the side and from below (Fig. 10.6). The effect of this uneven pull on the surface molecules tends to draw them into the body of the liquid and causes a droplet of liquid to assume the shape that has the minimum surface area—a sphere.

To increase a liquid's surface area, molecules must move from the interior of the liquid to the surface. This requires energy, since some intermolecular forces must be overcome. The resistance of a liquid to an increase in its surface area is called the **surface tension** of the liquid. As we would expect, liquids with relatively large intermolecular forces, such as those with polar molecules, tend to have relatively high surface tensions.

Polar liquids typically exhibit **capillary action,** the spontaneous rising of a liquid in a narrow tube. Two different types of forces are responsible for this property: **cohesive forces,** the intermolecular forces among the molecules of the liquid; and **adhesive forces,** the forces between the liquid molecules and their container. We have already seen how cohesive forces operate among polar molecules. Adhesive forces occur when a container is made of a substance that has polar bonds. For example, glass contains many oxygen atoms with partial negative charges that are attractive to the positive end of a polar molecule such as water. This ability of water to "wet" glass makes it creep up the walls of the tube where the water surface touches the glass. This, however, tends to increase the surface area of the water, which is opposed by the cohesive forces that try to minimize the surface. Thus, because water has both strong cohesive (intermolecular) forces and strong adhesive forces to glass, it "pulls itself" up a glass capillary tube (a tube with a small diameter) to a height where the weight of the column of water just balances the water's tendency to be attracted to the glass surface. The concave shape of the meniscus (see Fig. 10.7) shows that water's adhesive forces toward the glass are stronger than its cohesive forces. A nonpolar liquid such as mercury (see Fig. 10.7) shows a convex meniscus. This behavior is characteristic of a liquid in which the cohesive forces are stronger than the adhesive forces toward glass.

Another property of liquids strongly dependent on intermolecular forces is **viscosity,** a measure of a liquid's resistance to flow. As might be expected, liquids with large intermolecular forces tend to be highly viscous. For example, glycerol,

Figure 10.7
Nonpolar liquid mercury forms a convex meniscus in a glass tube, whereas polar water forms a concave meniscus.

Beads of water on a waxed car finish.

whose structure is

$$
\begin{array}{c}
\text{H} \\
| \\
\text{H—C—O—H} \\
\text{H—C—O—H} \\
\text{H—C—O—H} \\
| \\
\text{H}
\end{array}
$$

has an unusually high viscosity due mainly to a high capacity to form hydrogen bonds.

Molecular complexity also leads to higher viscosity because very large molecules can become entangled with each other. For example, nonviscous gasoline contains hydrocarbon molecules of the type $CH_3—(CH_2)_n—CH_3$, where n varies from about 3 to 8. However, grease, which is very viscous, contains much larger hydrocarbon molecules in which n varies from 20 to 25.

Bonding Models for Liquids

In many respects, the development of a structural (bonding) model for liquids presents greater challenges than developing such a model for the other two states of matter. In the gaseous state the particles are so far apart and are moving so rapidly that intermolecular forces are negligible under most circumstances. This means that we can use a relatively simple model for gases. In the solid state, although the intermolecular forces are large, the molecular motions are minimal, and fairly simple models are again possible. The liquid state, however, has both strong intermolecular forces *and* significant molecular motions. Such a situation precludes the use of really simple models for liquids. Recent advances in spectroscopy, the study of the manner in which substances interact with electromagnetic radiation, make it possible to follow the very rapid changes that occur in liquids. As a result, our models of liquids are becoming more accurate. As a starting point, a typical liquid might best be viewed as containing a large number of regions where the arrangements of the components are similar to those found in the solid, but with more disorder, and a smaller number of regions where holes are present. The situation is highly dynamic, with rapid fluctuations occurring in both types of regions.

10.3 *An Introduction to Structures and Types of Solids*

Purpose

- To contrast crystalline and amorphous solids.
- To introduce X-ray diffraction as a means for structure determination.

There are many ways to classify solids, but the broadest categories are **crystalline solids,** those with a highly regular arrangement of their components, and **amorphous solids,** those with considerable disorder in their structures.

The regular arrangement of the components of a crystalline solid at the microscopic level produces the beautiful, characteristic shapes of crystals, such as those shown in Fig. 10.8. The positions of the components in a crystalline solid are usually represented by a **lattice,** a three-dimensional system of points designating the centers of the components (atoms, ions, or molecules) that make up the substance. The *smallest repeating unit* of the lattice is called the **unit cell.** Thus a particular lattice can be generated by repeating the unit cell in all three dimensions to form the extended structure. Three common unit cells and their lattices are shown in Fig. 10.9. Note from Fig. 10.9 that the extended structure in each case can be viewed as a series of repeating unit cells that share common faces in the interior of the solid.

Although we will concentrate on crystalline solids in this book, there are many important noncrystalline (amorphous) materials. An example is common glass,

Figure 10.8

Two crystalline solids: pyrite *(left)*, amethyst *(right).*

Unit cell	Lattice	Example

(a) Simple cubic — Polonium metal

(b) Body-centered cubic — Uranium metal

(c) Face-centered cubic — Gold metal

Figure 10.9

Three cubic unit cells and the corresponding lattices.

which is best pictured as a solution in which the components are ''frozen in place'' before they can achieve an ordered arrangement. Although glass is a solid (it has a rigid shape), a great deal of disorder exists in its structure.

X-ray Analysis of Solids

The structures of crystalline solids are most commonly determined by **X-ray diffraction.** Diffraction occurs when beams of light are scattered from a regular array

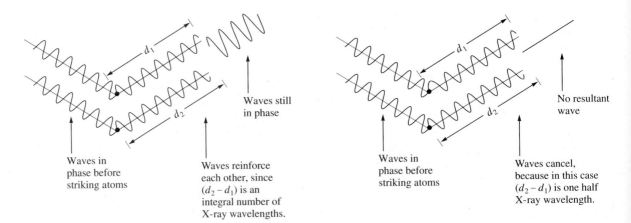

Figure 10.10

X rays that are scattered from two different atoms may either (a) reinforce or (b) cancel each other, depending on whether they are in phase or out of phase.

of points in which the spacings between the components are comparable with the wavelength of the light. Diffraction is due to constructive interference when the waves of parallel beams are in phase and to destructive interference when the waves are out of phase.

When X rays of a single wavelength are directed at a crystal, a diffraction pattern is obtained, as we saw in Fig. 7.5. The light and dark areas on the photographic plate occur because the waves scattered from various atoms may reinforce or cancel each other (see Fig. 10.10). The key to whether the waves reinforce or cancel is the difference in distance traveled by the waves after they strike the atoms. The waves are in phase before they are reflected, so if the difference in distance traveled after reflection is an *integral number of wavelengths*, the waves will still be in phase.

Since the distance traveled after reflection depends on the distance between the atoms, the diffraction pattern can be used to determine the interatomic spacings. The exact relationship can be worked out using the diagram in Fig. 10.11, which shows two in-phase waves being reflected by atoms in two different layers in a crystal. The extra distance traveled by the lower wave is the sum of the distances xy and yz, and the waves will be in phase after reflection if

$$xy + yz = n\lambda \tag{10.1}$$

where n is an integer and λ is the wavelength of the X rays. Using trigonometry (see Fig. 10.11), we can show that

$$xy + yz = 2d \sin \theta \tag{10.2}$$

Figure 10.11

Reflection of X rays of wavelength λ from a pair of atoms in two different layers of a crystal. The lower wave travels an extra distance equal to the sum of xy and yz. If this distance is an integral number of wavelengths ($n = 1, 2, 3, \ldots$), the waves will reinforce each other when they exit the crystal.

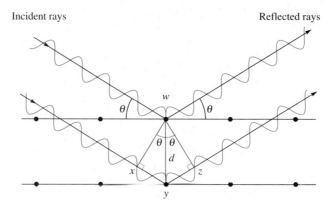

where d is the distance between the atoms and θ is the angle of incidence and reflection. Combining Equation (10.1) and Equation (10.2) gives

$$n\lambda = 2d \sin \theta \qquad (10.3)$$

Equation (10.3) is called the **Bragg equation** after William Henry Bragg (1862–1942) and his son William Lawrence Bragg (1890–1972), who shared the Nobel prize in physics in 1915 for their pioneering work in X-ray crystallography.

A diffractometer is a computer-controlled instrument used for carrying out the X-ray analysis of crystals. It rotates the crystal with respect to the X-ray beam and collects the data produced by the scattering of the X rays from the various planes of atoms in the crystal. The results are then analyzed by computer. The techniques for crystal structure analysis have reached a level of sophistication that allows the determination of very complex structures, such as those important in biologic systems. Using X-ray diffraction, we can gather data on bond lengths and angles and in so doing can test the predictions of our models of molecular geometry.

Sample Exercise 10.1

X rays of wavelength 1.54 Å were used to analyze an aluminum crystal. A reflection was produced at $\theta = 19.3$ degrees. Assuming $n = 1$, calculate the distance d between the planes of atoms producing this reflection.

Solution

To determine the distance between the planes, we use Equation (10.3) with $n = 1$, $\lambda = 1.54$ Å, and $\theta = 19.3$ degrees. Since $2d \sin \theta = n\lambda$,

$$d = \frac{n\lambda}{2 \sin \theta} = \frac{(1)(1.54 \text{ Å})}{(2)(0.3305)} = 2.33 \text{ Å} = 233 \text{ pm}$$

Types of Crystalline Solids

There are many different types of crystalline solids. For example, although both sugar and salt dissolve readily in water, the properties of the resulting solutions are quite different. The salt solution readily conducts an electric current, whereas the sugar solution does not. This behavior arises from the nature of the components in these two solids. Common salt (NaCl) is an ionic solid; it contains Na^+ and Cl^- ions. When solid sodium chloride dissolves in the polar water, sodium and chloride ions are distributed throughout the resulting solution and are free to conduct electric current. Table sugar (sucrose), on the other hand, is composed of neutral molecules that are dispersed throughout the water when the solid dissolves. No ions are present, and the resulting solution does not conduct electricity. These examples illustrate two important types of solids: **ionic solids,** represented by sodium chloride, and **molecular solids,** represented by sucrose. Ionic solids have ions at the points of the lattice that describes the structure of the solid. A molecular solid, on the other hand, has discrete covalently bonded molecules at each of its lattice points. Ice is a molecular solid that has an H_2O molecule at each lattice point (see Fig. 10.12).

(a) Diamond

= C

(b) Sodium chloride

= Cl
= Na

(c) Ice

= H_2O

Figure 10.12

Examples of three types of crystalline solids. Only part of the structure is shown in each case. (a) An atomic solid. (b) An ionic solid. (c) A molecular solid. The dashed lines show the hydrogen bonding interactions among the polar water molecules.

Buckminsterfullerene, C_{60}, is a particular member of the fullerene family.

The internal forces in a solid determine the properties of the solid.

A third type of solid is represented by elements such as carbon (which exists in the forms graphite, diamond, and the fullerenes), boron, silicon, and all metals. These substances all have atoms at the points of the lattice that describes the structure of the solid. Therefore, we call solids of this type **atomic solids.** Examples of these three types of solids are shown in Fig. 10.12.

To summarize, we find it convenient to classify solids according to what type of component occupies the lattice points. This leads to the classifications *atomic solids* (atoms at the lattice points), *molecular solids* (discrete, relatively small molecules at the lattice points), and *ionic solids* (ions at the lattice points). In addition, atomic solids are placed into the following subgroups based on the bonding that exists among the atoms in the solid: *metallic solids, network solids,* and *Group VIIIA solids.* In metallic solids, a special type of delocalized nondirectional covalent bonding occurs. In network solids, the atoms bond to each other with strong directional covalent bonds that lead to giant molecules, or networks, of atoms. In the Group VIIIA solids, the noble gas elements are attracted to each other with weak London dispersion forces. The classification of solids is summarized in Table 10.3.

The markedly different bonding present in the various atomic solids leads to dramatically different properties for the resulting solids. For example, although argon, copper, and diamond all are atomic solids, they have strikingly different properties. Argon (a Group VIIIA solid) has a very low melting point ($-189°C$), whereas diamond (a network solid) and copper (a metallic solid) melt at high temperatures (about 3500 and 1083°C, respectively). Copper is an excellent conductor of electricity, whereas argon and diamond are both insulators. Copper can easily be changed in shape; it is both malleable (can be formed into thin sheets) and ductile (can be pulled into a wire). Diamond on the other hand, is the hardest natural

Table 10.3

	Atomic Solids			Molecular Solids	Ionic Solids
	Metallic	**Network**	**Group VIIIA**		
Components that occupy the lattice points:	Metal atoms	Nonmetal atoms	Group VIIIA atoms	Discrete molecules	Ions
Bonding:	Delocalized covalent	Directional covalent (leading to giant molecules)	London dispersion forces	Dipole–dipole and/or London dispersion forces	Ionic

Classification of Solids

substance known. We will explore the structure and bonding of atomic solids in the next two sections.

10.4 Structure and Bonding in Metals

Purpose

- To discuss the concept of closest packing of metal atoms.
- To describe two models for bonding in metals.
- To define and classify alloys.

Metals are characterized by high thermal and electrical conductivity, malleability, and ductility. As we will see, these properties can be traced to the nondirectional covalent bonding found in metallic crystals.

A metallic crystal can be pictured as containing spherical atoms packed together and bonded to each other equally in all directions. We can model such a structure by packing uniform, hard spheres in a manner that most efficiently uses the available space. Such an arrangement is called **closest packing.** The spheres are packed in layers, as shown in Fig. 10.13(a) (on page 452), in which each sphere is surrounded by six others. In the second layer the spheres do not lie directly over those in the first layer. Instead, each one occupies an indentation (or dimple) formed by three spheres in the first layer [see Fig. 10.13(b)]. In the third layer the spheres can occupy the dimples of the second layer in two possible ways: they can occupy positions so that each sphere in the third layer lies directly over a sphere in the first layer (the *aba* arrangement), or they can occupy positions so that no sphere in the third layer lies over one in the first layer (the *abc* arrangement).

The *aba* arrangement has the *hexagonal* unit cell shown in Fig. 10.14 (on page 452), and the resulting structure is called the **hexagonal closest packed (hcp) structure.** The *abc* arrangement has a *face-centered cubic* unit cell, as shown in Fig. 10.15 (on page 453), and the resulting structure is called the **cubic closest packed (ccp) structure.** Note that in the hcp structure the spheres in every other layer occupy the same vertical position (*ababab* ···), whereas in the ccp structure the spheres in every fourth layer occupy the same vertical position (*abcabca* ···). A characteristic of both structures is that each sphere has 12 equivalent nearest neigh-

The closest packing model for metallic crystals assumes that metal atoms are uniform, hard spheres.

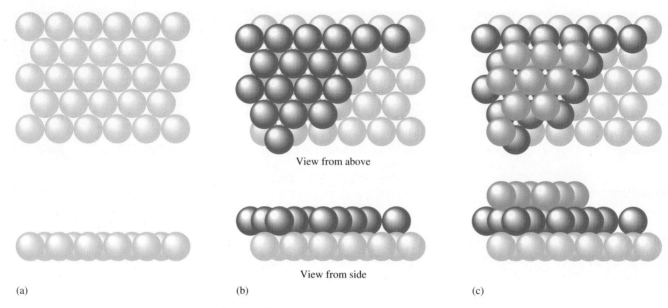

(a)

(b)

View from above

View from side

(c)

Figure 10.13

The closest packing arrangement of uniform spheres. (a) A typical layer where each sphere is surrounded by six others. (b) The second layer is like the first, but it is displaced so that each sphere in the second layer occupies a dimple in the first layer. (c) The spheres in the third layer can occupy dimples in the second layer so that the spheres in the third layer lie directly over those in the first layer (aba) as shown here, or they can occupy dimples in the second layer so that no spheres in the third layer lie above any in the first layer (abc).

Figure 10.14

When spheres are closest packed so that the spheres in the third layer are directly over those in the first layer (aba), the unit cell is the hexagonal prism illustrated here in red.

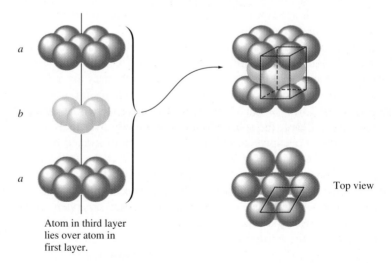

a

b

a

Atom in third layer lies over atom in first layer.

Top view

bors: 6 in the same layer, 3 in the layer above, and 3 in the layer below (that form the dimples). This is illustrated for the hcp structure in Fig. 10.16.

Knowing the *net* number of spheres (atoms) in a particular unit cell is important for many applications involving solids. To illustrate how to find the net number of spheres in a unit cell, we will consider a face-centered cubic unit cell (Fig. 10.17). Note that this unit cell is defined by the *centers* of the spheres on the cube's corners.

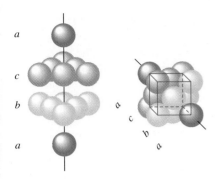

Figure 10.15

When spheres are packed in the *abc* arrangement, the unit cell is face-centered cubic. To make the cubic arrangement easier to see, the vertical axis has been tilted as shown.

hcp

Figure 10.16

The indicated sphere has 12 nearest neighbors.

(a)

(b)

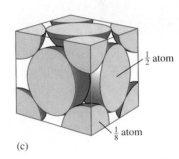

$\frac{1}{2}$ atom

$\frac{1}{8}$ atom

(c)

Figure 10.17

The net number of spheres in a face-centered cubic unit cell. (a) Note that the sphere on a corner of the colored cell is shared with 7 other unit cells (a total of 8). Thus $\frac{1}{8}$ of such a sphere lies within a given unit cell. Since there are 8 corners in a cube, there are 8 of these $\frac{1}{8}$ pieces, or 1 net sphere. (b) The sphere on the center of each face is shared by 2 unit cells, and thus each unit cell has $\frac{1}{2}$ of each of these types of spheres. There are 6 of these $\frac{1}{2}$ spheres to give 3 net spheres. (c) Thus the face-centered cubic unit cell contains 4 net spheres (all of the pieces can be assembled to give 4 spheres).

Thus 8 cubes share a given sphere, so $\frac{1}{8}$ of this sphere lies inside each unit cell. Since a cube has 8 corners, there are $8 \times \frac{1}{8}$ pieces, or enough to put together 1 whole sphere. The spheres at the center of each face are shared by 2 unit cells, so $\frac{1}{2}$ of each lies inside a particular unit cell. Since the cube has 6 faces, we have $6 \times \frac{1}{2}$ pieces, or enough to construct 3 whole spheres. Thus the net number of spheres in a face-centered cubic unit cell is

$$\left(8 \times \frac{1}{8}\right) + \left(6 \times \frac{1}{2}\right) = 4$$

Sample Exercise 10.2

Silver crystallizes in a cubic closest packed structure. The radius of a silver atom is 1.44 Å (1 Å = 10^{-8} cm). Calculate the density of solid silver.

Solution

Density is mass per unit volume. Thus we need to know how many silver atoms occupy a given volume in the crystal. The structure is cubic closest packed, which means the unit cell is face-centered cubic, as shown in the accompanying figure.

Crystalline silver contains cubic closest packed silver atoms.

We must find the volume of this unit cell for silver and the net number of atoms it contains. Note that in this structure the atoms touch along the diagonals for each face and not along the edges of the cube. Thus the length of the diagonal is $r + 2r + r$, or $4r$. We use this fact to find the length of the edge of the cube by the Pythagorean theorem:

$$d^2 + d^2 = (4r)^2$$
$$2d^2 = 16r^2$$
$$d^2 = 8r^2$$
$$d = \sqrt{8r^2} = r\sqrt{8}$$

Since $r = 1.44$ Å for a silver atom,

$$d = (1.44 \text{ Å})(\sqrt{8}) = 4.07 \text{ Å}$$

The volume of the unit cell is d^3, which is $(4.07 \text{ Å})^3$, or 67.4 Å^3. We convert this to cubic centimeters as follows:

$$67.4 \text{ Å}^3 \times \left(\frac{1.00 \times 10^{-8} \text{ cm}}{\text{Å}}\right)^3 = 6.74 \times 10^{-23} \text{ cm}^3$$

Since we know that the net number of atoms in the face-centered cubic unit cell is 4, we have 4 silver atoms contained in a volume of $6.74 \times 10^{-23} \text{ cm}^3$. The density is therefore

$$\text{Density} = \frac{\text{mass}}{\text{volume}} = \frac{(4 \text{ atoms})(107.9 \text{ g/mol})(1 \text{ mol}/6.022 \times 10^{23} \text{ atoms})}{6.74 \times 10^{-23} \text{ cm}^3}$$
$$= 10.6 \text{ g/cm}^3$$

Examples of metals that form cubic closest packed solids are aluminum, iron, copper, cobalt, and nickel. Magnesium and zinc are hexagonal closest packed. Calcium and certain other metals can crystallize in either of these structures. Some metals, however, assume structures that are not closest packed. For example, the alkali metals have structures characterized by a **body-centered cubic (bcc) unit cell** (see Fig. 10.9), where the spheres touch along the body diagonal of the cube. In this structure, each sphere has 8 nearest neighbors (count the number of atoms around the atom at the center of the unit cell), as compared with 12 in the closest packed structures. Why a particular metal adopts the structure it does is not well understood.

Bonding Models for Metals

Any successful bonding model for metals must account for the typical physical properties of metals: malleability, ductility, and the efficient and uniform conduction of heat and electricity in all directions. Although the shapes of most pure metals can be changed relatively easily, most metals are durable and have high melting points. These facts indicate that the bonding in most metals is both *strong* and *nondirectional*. That is, although it is difficult to separate metal atoms, it is relatively easy to move them, provided the atoms stay in contact with each other.

The simplest picture that explains these observations is the **electron sea model,** which envisions a regular array of metal cations in a ''sea'' of valence electrons (see

Fig. 10.18). The mobile electrons can conduct heat and electricity, and the metal ions can be easily moved around as the metal is hammered into a sheet or pulled into a wire.

A related model that gives a more detailed view of the electron energies and motions is the **band model,** or **molecular orbital (MO) model,** for metals. In this model, the electrons are assumed to travel around the metal crystal in molecular orbitals formed from the valence atomic orbitals of the metal atoms (Fig. 10.19).

Recall that in the MO model for the gaseous Li_2 molecule (Section 9.3), two widely spaced molecular orbital energy levels (bonding and antibonding) result when two identical atomic orbitals interact. However, when many metal atoms interact, as in a metal crystal, the large number of resulting molecular orbitals become more closely spaced and finally form a virtual continuum of levels, called **bands,** as shown in Fig. 10.19.

As an illustration, picture a magnesium metal crystal, which has an hcp structure. Since each magnesium atom has one $3s$ and three $3p$ valence atomic orbitals, a crystal with n magnesium atoms has available $n(3s)$ and $3n(3p)$ orbitals to form the molecular orbitals, as illustrated in Fig. 10.20 (on page 457). Note that the core electrons are localized, as shown by their presence in the energy ''well'' around each magnesium atom. However, the valence electrons occupy closely spaced molecular orbitals, which are only partially filled.

The existence of empty molecular orbitals close in energy to filled molecular orbitals explains the thermal and electrical conductivity of metal crystals. Metals conduct electricity and heat very efficiently because of the availability of highly mobile electrons. For example when an electric potential is placed across a strip of metal, for current to flow, electrons must be free to move. In the band model for metals, mobile electrons are furnished when electrons in filled molecular orbitals are excited into empty ones. These conduction electrons are free to travel throughout the metal crystal as dictated by the potential imposed on the metal. The molecular orbitals occupied by these conducting electrons are called **conduction bands.** These mobile electrons also account for the efficiency of the conduction of heat through metals. When one end of a metal rod is heated, the mobile electrons can rapidly transmit the thermal energy to the other end.

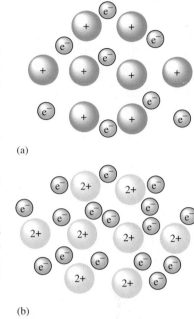

(a)

(b)

Figure 10.18

The electron sea model for metals postulates a regular array of cations in a "sea" of valence electrons. (a) Representation of an alkali metal (Group 1A) with one valence electron. (b) Representation of an alkaline earth metal (Group 2A) with two valence electrons.

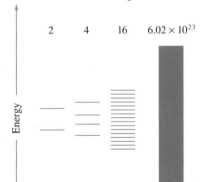

Number of interacting atomic orbitals

2   4   16 6.02×10^{23}

Energy

Figure 10.19

The molecular orbital energy levels produced when various numbers of atomic orbitals interact. Note that for two atomic orbitals two rather widely spaced energy levels result. (Recall the description of H_2 in Section 9.2.) As more atomic orbitals are available to form molecular orbitals, the resulting energy levels are more closely spaced, finally producing a band of very closely spaced orbitals.

◀ **C H E M I C A L   I M P A C T** ▶

Superconductivity

Although metals such as copper and aluminum are good conductors of electricity, up to 20% of the total energy is wasted in the transmission of a current by resistance heating of the wires. However, this loss of energy may be avoidable. Certain kinds of materials undergo a remarkable transition as they are cooled; their electrical resistance changes virtually to zero. These substances, called **superconductors,** conduct electricity with no wasted heat energy.

There is, of course, a catch. In the past, superconductivity has been observed only at very low temperatures and is thus very expensive to maintain. In 1911 mercury was observed to exhibit superconductivity, but only at ≈4 K, the boiling point of liquid helium. In the next 75 years several niobium alloys showed superconductivity at temperatures as high as 23 K. However, in 1986 researchers realized that certain metallic oxides are superconductors at temperatures well above 23 K. The graph shows how rapidly our knowledge of superconductors is increasing.

The current class of high-temperature superconductors is called **perovskites,** a well-known class of compounds that contain copper, an alkaline earth metal, a lanthanide metal, and oxygen. In the unit cell (see accompanying figure) for the compounds with formula $YBa_2Cu_3O_x$, in which x has an average value of 6.527, the small open circles indicate the expected oxygen positions, but some of these positions are vacant in the known materials—thus the variable oxygen content.

In addition to exhibiting superconductivity at temperatures above the boiling point of liquid nitrogen (77 K), these ceramic materials can sustain very high currents, an important characteristic necessary for any large-scale application. More recent results have shown that materials containing thallium and calcium ions in place of the lanthanide ions superconduct at 125 K.

What does all this mean for the future? Superconducting materials could easily cause a revolution similar to that brought about by solid-state electronics. For example, one can envision electrical power transmitted with virtually no loss of energy. Also, new generations of superconducting electromagnets could lead to the operation of particle accelerators at unprecedented energies and the development of superfast, magnetically levitated trains.

After a great surge of progress in the late 1980s, the pace slowed greatly in the early 1990s, as theory tried to catch up with the results from experiments. We need to develop an understanding of why these ceramic materials are superconducting so that we can design better materials that superconduct at even higher temperatures. And there are many practical problems. For example, metal conductors can be bent easily into coils to allow construction of electromagnets, but anyone who has ever dropped a plate knows how brittle ceramic materials are. However, there seems to be little doubt that ingenious solutions will be found to the problems. The answers are already beginning to appear.

○ = O or vacancy
⬤ = Cu

A magnet is levitated over a superconducting ceramic immersed in liquid nitrogen.

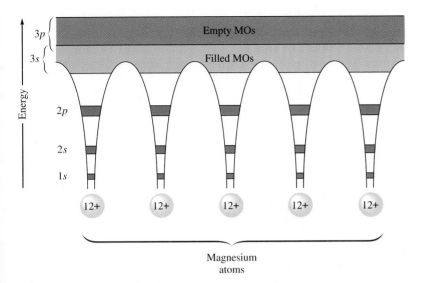

Figure 10.20

A representation of the energy levels (bands) in a magnesium crystal. The electrons in the 1s, 2s, and 2p orbitals are close to the nuclei and thus are localized on each magnesium atom as shown. However, the 3s and 3p valence orbitals overlap and mix to form molecular orbitals. Electrons in these energy levels can travel throughout the crystal.

Metal Alloys

Because of the nature of the structure and bonding of metals, other elements can be introduced into a metallic crystal relatively easily to produce substances called alloys. An **alloy** is best defined as *a substance that contains a mixture of elements and has metallic properties.* Alloys can be conveniently classified into two types.

In a **substitutional alloy** some of the host metal atoms are *replaced* by other metal atoms of similar size. For example, in brass, approximately one-third of the atoms in the host copper metal have been replaced by zinc atoms, as shown in Fig. 10.21(a). Sterling silver (93% silver and 7% copper), pewter (85% tin, 7% copper, 6% bismuth, and 2% antimony), and plumber's solder (67% lead and 33% tin) are other examples of substitutional alloys.

An **interstitial alloy** is formed when some of the interstices (holes) in the closest packed metal structure are occupied by small atoms, as shown in Fig. 10.21(b). Steel, the best known interstitial alloy, contains carbon atoms in the holes of an iron crystal. The presence of the interstitial atoms changes the properties of the host metal. Pure iron is relatively soft, ductile, and malleable due to the absence of directional bonding. The spherical metal atoms can be rather easily moved with respect to each other. However, when carbon, which forms strong directional bonds, is introduced into an iron crystal, the presence of the directional carbon–iron bonds makes the resulting alloy harder, stronger, and less ductile than pure iron. The amount of carbon directly affects the properties of steel. *Mild steels,* containing less than 0.2% carbon, are ductile and malleable and are used for nails, cables, and chains. *Medium steels,* containing 0.2 to 0.6% carbon, are harder than mild steels and are used in rails and structural steel beams. *High-carbon steels,* containing 0.6 to 1.5% carbon, are tough and hard and are used for springs, tools, and cutlery.

Many types of steel also contain elements in addition to iron and carbon. Such steels are often called *alloy steels,* and they can be viewed as being mixed interstitial (carbon) and substitutional (other metals) alloys. Bicycle frames, for example, are constructed from a wide variety of alloy steels. The compositions of the two brands of steel tubing most commonly used in expensive racing bicycles are given in Table 10.4.

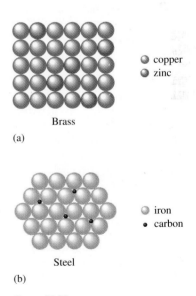

copper
zinc

Brass

(a)

iron
carbon

Steel

(b)

Figure 10.21

Two types of alloys.

Table 10.4					
The Composition of the Two Brands of Steel Tubing Commonly Used to Make Lightweight Racing Bicycles					
Brand of Tubing	% C	% Si	% Mn	% Mo	% Cr
Reynolds	0.25	0.25	1.3	0.20	—
Columbus	0.25	0.30	0.65	0.20	1.0

10.5 Carbon and Silicon: Network Atomic Solids

Purpose

- To show how the bonding in elemental carbon and silicon accounts for the widely different properties of their compounds.
- To explain how a semiconductor works.

Many atomic solids contain strong directional covalent bonds to form a solid that might best be viewed as a "giant molecule." We call these substances **network solids.** In contrast to metals, these materials are typically brittle and do not efficiently conduct heat or electricity. To illustrate network solids, in this section we will discuss two very important elements, carbon and silicon, and some of their compounds.

The two most common forms of carbon, diamond and graphite, are typical network solids. In diamond, the hardest naturally occurring substance, each carbon atom is surrounded by a tetrahedral arrangement of other carbon atoms to form a huge molecule [see Fig. 10.22(a)]. This structure is stabilized by covalent bonds, which, in terms of the localized electron model, are formed by the overlap of sp^3 hybridized carbon atomic orbitals.

It is also useful to consider the bonding among the carbon atoms in diamond in terms of the molecular orbital model. Energy-level diagrams for diamond and a typical metal are given in Fig. 10.23. Recall that the conductivity of metals can be explained by postulating that electrons are excited from filled levels into the very

(a)   Diamond

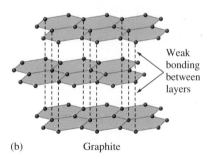

Weak bonding between layers

(b)   Graphite

Figure 10.22

The structures of diamond and graphite. In each case only a small part of the entire structure is shown.

Figure 10.23

Partial representation of the molecular orbital energies in (a) diamond and (b) a typical metal.

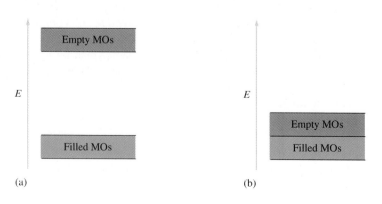

near empty levels, or conduction bands. However, note that in the energy-level diagram for diamond there is *a large gap between the filled and the empty levels*. This means that electrons cannot be transferred easily to the empty conduction bands. As a result, diamond is not expected to be a good electrical conductor. In fact, this prediction of the model agrees exactly with the observed behavior of diamond, which is known to be an electrical insulator—it does not conduct an electric current.

Graphite is very different from diamond. While diamond is hard, basically colorless, and an insulator, graphite is slippery, black, and a conductor. These differences, of course, arise from the differences in bonding in the two types of solids. In contrast to the tetrahedral arrangement of carbon atoms in diamond, the structure of graphite is based on layers of carbon atoms arranged in fused six-membered rings, as shown in Fig. 10.22(b). Each carbon atom in a particular layer of graphite is surrounded by three other carbon atoms in a trigonal planar arrangement with 120-degree bond angles. The localized electron model predicts sp^2 hybridization in this case. The three sp^2 orbitals on each carbon are used to form σ bonds with three other carbon atoms. One $2p$ orbital remains unhybridized on each carbon and is perpendicular to the plane of carbon atoms, as shown in Fig. 10.24. These orbitals combine to form a group of closely spaced π molecular orbitals that are important in two ways. First, they contribute significantly to the stability of the graphite layers because of the π bond formation. Second, the π molecular orbitals with their delocalized electrons account for the electrical conductivity of graphite. These closely spaced orbitals are exactly analogous to the conduction bands found in metal crystals.

Graphite is often used as a lubricant in locks (where oil is undesirable because it collects dirt). The slipperiness that is characteristic of graphite can be explained by noting that graphite has very strong bonding *within* the layers of carbon atoms but little bonding *between* the layers (the valence electrons are all used to form σ and π bonds among carbons within the layers). This arrangement allows the layers to slide past one another quite readily. Graphite's layered structure is quite obvious when

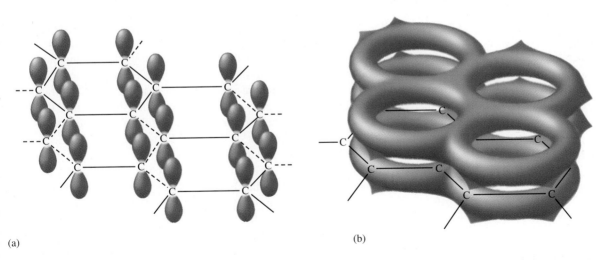

(a)

(b)

Figure 10.24

The *p* orbitals (a) perpendicular to the plane of the carbon ring system in graphite can combine to form (b) an extensive π-bonding network.

Figure 10.25

A high-resolution image of crystalline graphite (×2,500,000) taken by an electron microscope.

The bonding in the CO_2 molecule was described in Section 9.1.

Figure 10.26

The structure of quartz (empirical formula SiO_2). Quartz contains chains of SiO_4 tetrahedra that share oxygen atoms.

viewed with a high-magnification electron microscope (Fig. 10.25). This is in contrast to diamond which has uniform bonding in all directions in the crystal.

Because of their extreme hardness, diamonds are used extensively in industrial cutting implements. Thus it is desirable to convert cheaper graphite to diamond. As we might expect from the higher density of diamond (3.5 g/cm^3) compared with that of graphite (2.2 g/cm^3), this transformation can be accomplished by applying very high pressures to graphite. The application of 150,000 atm of pressure at 2800°C converts graphite virtually completely to diamond. The high temperature is required to break the strong bonds in graphite so the rearrangement can occur.

Silicon is an important constituent of the compounds that make up the earth's crust. In fact, silicon is to geology as carbon is to biology. Just as carbon compounds are the basis for most biologically significant systems, silicon compounds are fundamental to most of the rocks, sands, and soils found in the earth's crust. However, although carbon and silicon are next to each other in Group 4A of the periodic table, the carbon-based compounds of biology and the silicon-based compounds of geology have markedly different structures. Carbon compounds typically contain long strings of carbon–carbon bonds, whereas the most stable silicon compounds involve chains with silicon–oxygen bonds.

The fundamental silicon–oxygen compound is **silica**, which has the empirical formula SiO_2. Knowing the properties of the similar compound carbon dioxide, one might expect silica to be a gas that contains discrete SiO_2 molecules. In fact, nothing could be further from the truth—quartz and some types of sand are typical of the materials composed of silica. What accounts for this difference? The answer lies in the bonding.

Recall that the Lewis structure for CO_2 is

$$\overset{..}{\underset{..}{O}}=C=\overset{..}{\underset{..}{O}}$$

and that each C=O bond can be viewed as a combination of a σ bond involving a carbon sp hybrid orbital and a π bond involving a carbon $2p$ orbital. On the contrary, silicon cannot use its valence $3p$ orbitals to form strong π bonds with oxygen, mainly because of the larger size of the silicon atom and its orbitals, which results in less effective overlap with the smaller oxygen orbitals. Therefore, instead of forming π bonds, the silicon atom satisfies the octet rule by forming single bonds with four oxygen atoms, as shown in the representation of the structure of quartz in Fig. 10.26. Note that each silicon atom is at the center of a tetrahedral arrangement of oxygen atoms, which are shared with other silicon atoms. Although the empirical formula for quartz is SiO_2, the structure is based on a *network* of SiO_4 tetrahedra with shared oxygen atoms rather than discrete SiO_2 molecules. It is obvious that the differing abilities of carbon and silicon to form π bonds with oxygen have profound effects on the structures and properties of CO_2 and SiO_2.

Compounds closely related to silica and found in most rocks, soils, and clays are the **silicates**. Like silica, the silicates are based on interconnected SiO_4 tetrahedra. However, in contrast to silica, where the O/Si ratio is 2:1, silicates have O/Si ratios greater than 2:1 and contain silicon–oxygen *anions*. This means that to form the neutral solid silicates, cations are needed to balance the excess negative charge. In other words, silicates are salts containing metal cations and polyatomic silicon–oxygen anions. Examples of important silicate anions are shown in Fig. 10.27.

When silica is heated above its melting point (about 1600°C) and cooled rapidly, an amorphous solid called a **glass** results (see Fig. 10.28). Note that a glass contains a good deal of disorder, in contrast to the crystalline nature of quartz. Glass more

SiO_4^{4-}

$Si_2O_7^{6-}$

$Si_3O_9^{6-}$

$(Si_4O_{11})_n^{6n-}$

○ Silicon
○ Oxygen

Figure 10.27

Examples of silicate anions, all of which are based on SiO_4^{4-} tetrahedra.

(a)

(b)

Figure 10.28

Two-dimensional representations of (a) a quartz crystal and (b) a quartz glass.

closely resembles a very viscous solution than it does a crystalline solid. Common glass results when substances such as Na_2CO_3 are added to the silica melt, which is then cooled. The properties of glass can be varied greatly by varying the additives. For example, addition of B_2O_3 produces a glass (called *borosilicate glass*) that expands and contracts little under large temperature changes. Thus it is useful for labware and cooking utensils. The most common brand name for this glass is Pyrex. The addition of K_2O produces an especially hard glass that can be ground to the precise shapes needed for eyeglass and contact lenses. The compositions of several types of glass are shown in Table 10.5.

Ceramics

Ceramics are typically made from clays (which contain silicates) and hardened by firing at high temperatures. Ceramics are nonmetallic materials that are strong, brittle, and resistant to heat and attack by chemicals.

Like glass, ceramics are based on silicates, but with that the resemblance ends. Glass can be melted and remelted as often as desired, but once a ceramic has been hardened, it is resistant to extremely high temperatures. This behavior results from

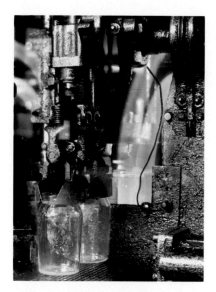

The manufacture of Ball jars for use in canning fruits and vegetables.

Early Bronze Age (~3000 B.C.) teapot from the Middle East.

Table 10.5

Compositions of Some Common Types of Glass

Type of Glass	Percentages of Various Components						
	SiO_2	CaO	Na_2O	B_2O_3	Al_2O_3	K_2O	MgO
Window (soda-lime glass)	72	11	13	—	0.3	3.8	—
Cookware (aluminosilicate glass)	55	15	—	—	20	—	10
Heat-resistant (borosilicate glass)	76	3	5	13	2	0.5	—
Optical	69	12	6	0.3	—	12	—

the very different structures of glasses and ceramics. A glass is a *homogeneous,* noncrystalline "frozen solution," and a ceramic is *heterogeneous.* A ceramic contains two phases: minute crystals of silicates that are suspended in a glassy cement.

To understand how ceramics harden, it is necessary to know something about the structure of clays. Clays are formed by the weathering action of water and carbon dioxide on the mineral feldspar, which is a mixture of silicates with empirical formulas such as $K_2O \cdot Al_2O_3 \cdot 6SiO_2$ and $Na_2O \cdot Al_2O_3 \cdot 6SiO_2$. Feldspar is really an **aluminosilicate** in which aluminum as well as silicon atoms are part of the oxygen-bridged polyanion. The weathering of feldspar produces kaolinite, consisting of tiny thin platelets with the empirical formula $Al_2Si_2O_5(OH)_4$. When dry, the platelets cling together; when water is present, they can slide over one another, giving clay its plasticity. As clay dries, the platelets begin to interlock again. When the remaining water is driven off during firing, the silicates and cations form a glass that binds the tiny crystals of kaolinite.

Ceramics have a very long history. Rocks, which are natural ceramic materials, served as the earliest tools. Later, clay vessels dried in the sun or baked in fires served as containers for food and water. These early vessels were no doubt crude and quite porous. With the discovery of glazing, which probably occurred about 3000 B.C. in Egypt, pottery became more serviceable as well as more beautiful. Prized porcelain is essentially the same material as crude earthenware, but specially selected clays and glazings are used for porcelain and the clay object is fired at a very high temperature.

Although ceramics have been known since antiquity, they are not obsolete materials. On the contrary, ceramics constitute one of the most important classes of "high-tech" materials. Because of their stability at high temperatures and resistance to corrosion, ceramics seem an obvious choice for constructing jet and automobile engines in which the greatest fuel efficiencies are possible at very high temperatures. But ceramics are brittle—they break rather than bend—and this limits their usefulness. However, more flexible ceramics can be obtained by adding small amounts of organic polymers. Taking their cue from natural "organoceramics" such as teeth and shells of sea creatures that contain small amounts of organic polymers, materials scientists have found that incorporating tiny amounts of long organic molecules into ceramics as they form produces materials that are much less subject to fracture. These materials should be useful for lighter, more durable engine parts, as well as for flexible superconducting wire and microelectronic devices. In addition, these organoceramics hold great promise for prosthetic devices such as artificial bones.

Semiconductors

Elemental silicon has the same structure as diamond, as might be expected from its position in the periodic table (in Group 4A directly under carbon). Recall that in diamond there is a large energy gap between the filled and empty molecular orbitals (see Fig. 10.23). This gap prevents excitation of electrons to the empty molecular orbitals (conduction bands) and makes diamond an insulator. In silicon the situation is similar, but the energy gap is smaller. A few electrons can cross the gap at 25°C, making silicon a **semiconducting element,** or **semiconductor.** In addition, at higher temperatures, where more energy is available to excite electrons into the conduction bands, the conductivity of silicon increases. This is typical behavior for a semiconducting element and is in contrast to that of metals, whose conductivity decreases with increasing temperature.

The small conductivity of silicon can be enhanced at normal temperatures if the silicon crystal is **doped** with certain other elements. For example, when a small fraction of silicon atoms is replaced by arsenic atoms, each having *one more* valence electron than silicon, extra electrons become available for conduction, as shown in Fig. 10.29(a). This produces an **n-type semiconductor,** a substance whose conductivity is increased by doping it with atoms having more valence electrons than the atoms in the host crystal. These extra electrons lie close in energy to the conduction bands and can be easily excited into these levels, where they can conduct an electric current [see Fig. 10.30(a)].

We also can enhance the conductivity of silicon by doping the crystal with an element such as boron, which has only three valence electrons, *one less* than silicon. Because boron has one less electron than is required to form the bonds with the surrounding silicon atoms, an electron vacancy, or *hole,* is created, as shown in Fig. 10.29(b). As an electron fills this hole, it leaves a new hole, and this process can be repeated. Thus the hole advances through the crystal in a direction opposite to movement of the electrons jumping to fill the hole. Another way of thinking about this phenomenon is that in pure silicon each atom has four valence electrons and the low-energy molecular orbitals are exactly filled. Replacing silicon atoms with boron atoms leaves vacancies in these molecular orbitals, as shown in Fig. 10.30(b). This

n-type semiconductor

(a)

p-type semiconductor

(b)

Figure 10.29

(a) A silicon crystal doped with arsenic, which has one more valence electron than silicon. (b) A silicon crystal doped with boron, which has one less electron than silicon.

(a)

(b)

Figure 10.30

Energy-level diagrams for (a) an n-type semiconductor and (b) a p-type semiconductor.

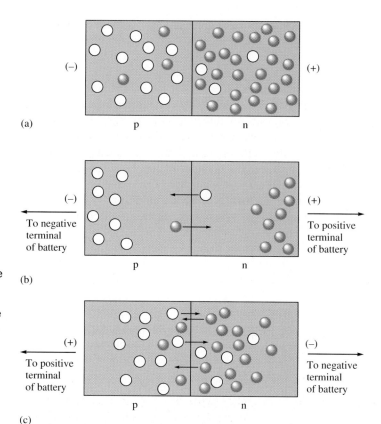

(a)

(b)

(c)

Figure 10.31

The p–n junction involves the contact of a p-type and an n-type semiconductor. (a) The charge carriers of the p-type region are holes (○). In the n-type region the charge carriers are electrons (●). (b) No current flows (reverse bias). (c) Current readily flows (forward bias). Note that each electron that crosses the boundary leaves a hole behind. Thus the electrons and the holes move in opposite directions.

Electrons must be in singly occupied molecular orbitals to conduct a current.

means that there is only one electron in some of the molecular orbitals, and these unpaired electrons can function as conducting electrons. Thus the substance becomes a better conductor. When semiconductors are doped with atoms having fewer valence electrons than the atoms of the host crystal, they are called **p-type semiconductors,** so named because the positive holes can be viewed as the charge carriers.

Most important applications of semiconductors involve connection of a p-type and an n-type to form a **p–n junction.** Figure 10.31(a) shows a typical junction; the dark circles represent excess electrons in the n-type semiconductor, and the white circles represent holes (electron vacancies) in the p-type semiconductor. At the junction, a small number of electrons migrate from the n-type region into the p-type region, where there are vacancies in the low-energy molecular orbitals. The effect of these migrations is to place a negative charge on the p-type region (since it now has a surplus of electrons) and a positive charge on the n-type region (since it has lost electrons, leaving holes in its low-energy molecular orbitals). This charge buildup, called the **contact potential,** or **junction potential,** prevents further migration of electrons.

Now suppose an external electric potential is applied by connecting the negative terminal of a battery to the p-type region and the positive terminal to the n-type region. The situation represented in Fig. 10.31(b) results. Electrons are drawn toward the positive terminal, and the resulting holes move toward the negative terminal—exactly opposite to the natural flow of electrons at the p–n junction. The junction resists the imposed current flow in this direction and is said to be under **reverse bias.** No current flows through the system.

On the other hand, if the battery is connected so that the negative terminal is connected to the n-type region and the positive terminal is connected to the p-type region [Fig. 10.31(c)], the movement of electrons (and holes) is in the favored direction. The junction has low resistance, and a current flows easily. The junction is said to be under **forward bias.**

A p–n junction makes an excellent **rectifier,** a device that produces a pulsating direct current (flows in one direction) from alternating current (flows in both directions alternately). When placed in a circuit where the potential is constantly reversing, a p–n junction transmits current only under forward bias, thus converting the alternating current to direct current. Radios, computers, and other electric devices formerly used bulky, unreliable vacuum tubes as rectifiers. The p–n junction has revolutionized electronics; modern solid-state components contain p–n junctions in printed circuits.

Printed circuits are discussed in a Chemical Impact feature in this chapter.

10.6 Molecular Solids

Purpose

• To describe the bonding in molecular solids.

So far we have considered solids in which atoms occupy the lattice positions. In some of these substances (network solids), the solid can be considered to be one giant molecule. In addition, there are many types of solids that contain discrete molecular units at each lattice position. A common example is ice, where the lattice positions are occupied by water molecules [see Fig. 10.12(c)]. Other examples are dry ice (solid carbon dioxide), some forms of sulfur that contain S_8 molecules [Fig. 10.32(a)], and certain forms of phosphorus that contain P_4 molecules [Fig. 10.32(b)]. These substances are characterized by strong covalent bonding *within* the

A "steaming" piece of dry ice.

Figure 10.32

(*Left*) Sulfur crystals (yellow) contain S_8 molecules. (*Right*) White phosphorus (containing P_4 molecules) is so reactive with the oxygen in air that it must be stored under water.

◀ **C H E M I C A L   I M P A C T** ▶

Gallium Arsenide Lasers

Lasers are an essential part of modern life, providing the most efficient way to carry telephone communications by cable, the best quality music using compact disc players, and the most accurate method for reading grocery prices. The laser (the word *lase* is an acronym for "light amplification by stimulated emission") is a device for producing an intense, coherent beam of light that results when excited electrons release photons as they change to a lower energy state. Excited electrons can return to a lower energy level by spontaneous, random emission of light. However, there is another mechanism in which the emission process is actually stimulated by a passing photon that has the same energy as the emitted photon. This is the phenomenon on which the laser is based. We will have more to say about this presently.

Gallium arsenide is a prominent member of the so-called 3–5 class of semiconductors, those containing elements from Groups 3A and 5A of the periodic table. An n-type semiconductor results when the arsenic-to-gallium ratio is greater than 1. A p-type semiconductor results when gallium is in excess. By carefully controlling the conditions under which a Ga–As semiconductor is made, one can design p–n junctions into the material. At each p–n junction electrons from the n-type region are available to "fall into" holes in the p-type region, producing photons (see the accompanying figure). As the emitted photons travel through the solid, they *stimulate* the emission of additional photons. A mirror at the edge of the solid reflects these photons back through the substance, where they stimulate even more emission events. All these stimulated emissions produce photons with their waves in phase. Thus this process leads to a large number of coherent (in-phase) photons, which proceed out the other end of the solid where a "half-mirror" is placed. This mirror reflects some of the

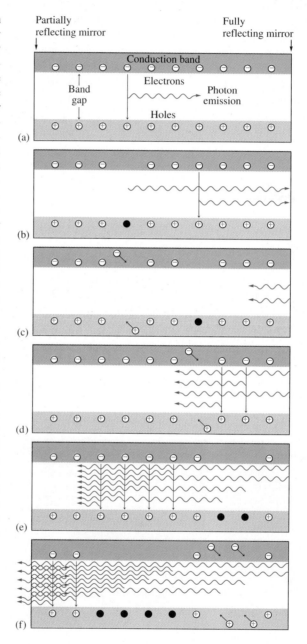

photons and allows the rest to leave as an intense, coherent "laser beam" of light. A current driven through the substance by an applied potential difference provides a continuous supply of electrons (and removes electrons to make new holes) so that the process occurs continuously while the power is on.

Table 10.6

Comparison of Atomic Separations Within Molecules (Covalent Bonds) and Between Molecules (Intermolecular Interactions)		
Solid	Distance Between Atoms in Molecule*	Closest Distance Between Molecules in the Solid
P_4	220 pm	380 pm
S_8	206 pm	370 pm
Cl_2	199 pm	360 pm

*The shorter distances within the molecules indicate stronger bonding.

molecules but relatively weak forces *between* the molecules. For example, it takes only 6 kJ of energy to melt 1 mole of solid water (ice) because only intermolecular (H_2O—H_2O) interactions must be overcome. However, 470 kJ of energy is required to break 1 mole of covalent O—H bonds. The differences between the covalent bonds within the molecules and the forces between the molecules are apparent from the comparison of the interatomic and intermolecular distances in solids shown in Table 10.6.

The forces that exist among the molecules in a molecular solid depend on the nature of the molecules. Many molecules such as CO_2, I_2, P_4, and S_8 have no dipole moment, and the intermolecular forces are London dispersion forces. Because these forces are often relatively small, we might expect all these substances to be gaseous at 25°C, as is the case for carbon dioxide. However, as the size of the molecules increases, the London forces become quite large, causing many of these substances to be solids at 25°C.

When molecules do have dipole moments, their intermolecular forces are significantly greater, especially when hydrogen bonding is possible. Water molecules are particularly well suited to interact with each other because each molecule has two polar O—H bonds and two lone pairs on the oxygen atom. This can lead to the association of four hydrogen atoms with each oxygen: two by covalent bonds and two by dipole forces:

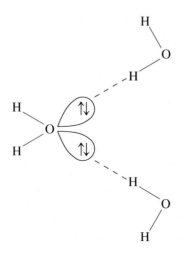

Note the two relatively short covalent oxygen–hydrogen bonds and the two longer oxygen–hydrogen dipole interactions that can be seen in the ice structure in Fig. 10.12(c).

10.7 Ionic Solids

Purpose

- To model the structures of ionic solids using the packing of spheres.

(a)

(b)

(c)

Figure 10.33

The holes that exist among closest packed uniform spheres. (a) The trigonal hole formed by three spheres in a given plane. (b) The tetrahedral hole formed when a sphere occupies a dimple formed by three spheres in an adjacent layer. (c) The octahedral hole formed by six spheres in two adjacent layers.

Closest packed structures contain twice as many tetrahedral holes as packed spheres. Closest packed structures contain the same number of octahedral holes as packed spheres.

Ionic solids are stable, high-melting substances held together by the strong electrostatic forces that exist between oppositely charged ions. The principles governing the structures of ionic solids were introduced in Section 8.5. In this section we will review and extend these principles.

The structures of most binary ionic solids, such as sodium chloride, can be explained by the closest packing of spheres. Typically, the larger ions, usually the anions, are packed in one of the closest packing arrangements (hcp or ccp), and the smaller cations fit into holes among the close packed anions. The packing is done in a way that maximizes the electrostatic attractions among oppositely charged ions and minimizes the repulsions among ions with like charges.

There are three types of holes in closest packed structures:

1. Trigonal holes are formed by three spheres in the same layer [Fig. 10.33(a)].

2. Tetrahedral holes are formed when a sphere sits in the dimple of three spheres in an adjacent layer [Fig. 10.33(b)].

3. Octahedral holes are formed between two sets of three spheres in adjoining layers of the closest packed structures [Fig. 10.33(c)].

For spheres of a given diameter, the holes increase in size in the order

$$\text{trigonal} < \text{tetrahedral} < \text{octahedral}$$

In fact, trigonal holes are so small that they are never occupied in binary ionic compounds. Whether the tetrahedral or octahedral holes in a given binary ionic solid are occupied depends mainly on the *relative* sizes of the anion and cation. For example, in zinc sulfide the S^{2-} ions (ionic radius = 180 pm) are arranged in a cubic closest packed structure with the smaller Zn^{2+} ions (ionic radius = 70 pm) in the tetrahedral holes. The locations of the tetrahedral holes in the face-centered cubic unit cell of the ccp structure are shown in Fig. 10.34(a). Note from this figure that there are eight tetrahedral holes in the unit cell. Also recall from the discussion in Section 10.4 that there are four net spheres in the face-centered cubic unit cell. Thus there are *twice as many tetrahedral holes as packed anions* in the closest packed structure. Zinc sulfide must have the same number of S^{2-} ions and Zn^{2+} ions to achieve electrical neutrality. Thus in the zinc sulfide structure only *half* the tetrahedral holes contain Zn^{2+} ions, as shown in Fig. 10.34(c).

The structure of sodium chloride can be described in terms of a cubic closest packed array of Cl^- ions with Na^+ ions in all the octahedral holes. The locations of the octahedral holes in the face-centered cubic unit cell are shown in Fig. 10.35(a). The easiest octahedral hole to find in this structure is the one at the center of the cube. Note that this hole is surrounded by six spheres, as is required to form an octahedron. The remaining octahedral holes are shared with other unit cells and are

(a)

(b)

ZnS

(c)

Figure 10.34

(a) The location (x) of a tetrahedral hole in the face-centered cubic unit cell. (b) One of the tetrahedral holes. (c) The unit cell for ZnS where the S^{2-} ions (yellow) are closest packed with the Zn^{2+} ions (red) in alternating tetrahedral holes.

more difficult to visualize. However, it can be shown that the number of octahedral holes in the ccp structure is the *same* as the number of packed anions. Figure 10.35(b) shows the structure for sodium chloride that results from Na^+ ions filling all the octahedral holes in a ccp array of Cl^- ions.

A great variety of ionic solids exists. Our purpose in this section is not to give an exhaustive treatment of ionic solids, but to emphasize the fundamental principles governing their structures. As we have seen, the most useful model for explaining the structures of these solids regards the ions as hard spheres that are packed to maximize attractions and minimize repulsions.

Sample Exercise 10.3

Determine the net number of Na^+ and Cl^- ions in the sodium chloride unit cell.

Solution

Note from Fig. 10.35(b) that the Cl^- ions are cubic closest packed and thus form a face-centered cubic unit cell. There is a Cl^- ion on each corner and one at the center of each face of the cube. Thus the net number of Cl^- ions present in a unit cell is

$$8(\tfrac{1}{8}) + 6(\tfrac{1}{2}) = 4$$

The Na^+ ions occupy the octahedral holes located in the center of the cube and midway along each edge. The Na^+ ion in the center of the cube is contained entirely in the unit cell, whereas those on the edges are shared by four unit cells (four cubes share a common edge). Since the number of edges in a cube is 12, the net number of Na^+ ions present is

$$1(1) + 12(\tfrac{1}{4}) = 4$$

We have shown that the net number of ions in a unit cell is 4 Na^+ ions and 4 Cl^- ions, which agrees with the 1:1 stoichiometry of sodium chloride.

(a)

(b)

Figure 10.35

(a) The locations (x) of the octahedral holes in the face-centered cubic unit cell. (b) Representation of the unit cell for solid NaCl. The Cl^- ions (blue spheres) have a ccp arrangement with Na^+ ions (yellow spheres) in all the octahedral holes.

Table 10.7

Types and Properties of Solids

Type of solid:	Atomic			Molecular	Ionic
	Network	**Metallic**	**Group VIIIA**		
Structural unit:	Atom	Atom	Atom	Molecule	Ion
Type of bonding:	Directional covalent bonds	Nondirectional covalent bonds involving electrons that are delocalized throughout the crystal	London dispersion forces	Polar molecules: dipole–dipole interactions Nonpolar molecules: London dispersion forces	Ionic
Typical properties:	Hard	Wide range of hardness	Very low melting	Soft	Hard
	High melting point	Wide range of melting points		Low melting point	High melting point
	Insulator	Conductor		Insulator	Insulator
Examples:	Diamond	Silver Iron Brass	Argon(s)	Ice (solid H_2O) Dry ice (solid CO_2)	Sodium chloride Calcium fluoride

In this chapter we have considered various types of solids. Table 10.7 summarizes these types of solids and some of their properties.

Sample Exercise 10.4

Using Table 10.7, classify each of the following substances according to the type of solid it forms.

a. Gold   **b.** Carbon dioxide   **c.** Lithium fluoride   **d.** Krypton

Solution

a. Solid gold is an atomic solid with metallic properties.
b. Solid carbon dioxide contains nonpolar carbon dioxide molecules and is a molecular solid.
c. Solid lithium fluoride contains Li^+ and F^- ions and is a binary ionic solid.
d. Solid krypton contains krypton atoms that can interact only through London dispersion forces. It is an atomic solid but has properties characteristic of a molecular solid with nonpolar molecules.

10.8 Vapor Pressure and Changes of State

Purpose

• To define the vapor pressure of a liquid.
• To discuss the features of heating curves.

Now that we have considered the general properties of the three states of matter, we can explore the processes by which matter changes state. One very familiar example of a change in state occurs when a liquid evaporates from an open container. This is clear evidence that the molecules of a liquid can escape the liquid's surface and form a gas, a process called **vaporization, or evaporation.** Vaporization is endothermic because energy is required to overcome the relatively strong intermolecular forces in the liquid. The energy required to vaporize 1 mole of a liquid at a pressure of 1 atm is called the **heat of vaporization,** or the **enthalpy of vaporization,** and is usually symbolized as ΔH_{vap}.

The endothermic nature of vaporization has great practical significance; in fact, one of the most important roles that water plays in our world is to act as a coolant. Because of the strong hydrogen bonding among its molecules in the liquid state, water has an unusually large heat of vaporization (40.7 kJ/mol). A significant portion of the sun's energy that reaches earth is spent evaporating water from the oceans, lakes, and rivers rather than warming the earth. The vaporization of water is also crucial to the body's temperature-control system through evaporation of perspiration.

> Vapor is the usual term for the gas phase of a substance that exists as a solid or liquid at 25°C and 1 atm.

Vapor Pressure

When a liquid is placed in a closed container, the amount of liquid at first decreases but eventually becomes constant. The decrease occurs because there is an initial net transfer of molecules from the liquid to the vapor phase (Fig. 10.36). However, as the number of vapor molecules increases, so does the rate of return of these molecules to the liquid. The process by which vapor molecules reform a liquid is called **condensation.** Eventually, enough vapor molecules are present above the liquid so that the rate of condensation equals the rate of evaporation (see Fig. 10.37 on page 472). *At this point no further net change occurs in the amount of liquid or vapor because the two opposite processes exactly balance each other;* the system is at **equilibrium.** Note that this system is highly *dynamic* on the molecular level—molecules are constantly escaping from and entering the liquid at a high rate. However, there is no *net* change because the two opposite processes just *balance* each other.

> A system at equilibrium is dynamic on the molecular level but shows no macroscopic changes.

The pressure of the vapor present at equilibrium is called the **equilibrium vapor pressure,** or more commonly, the **vapor pressure** of the liquid. A simple barometer can measure the vapor pressure of a liquid, as shown below in Fig. 10.38(a) (on page 472). The liquid is injected at the bottom of the tube of mercury and floats to the surface because the mercury is so dense. A portion of the liquid evaporates at the top of the column, producing a vapor whose pressure pushes some mercury out of the tube. When the system reaches equilibrium, the vapor pressure can be determined from the change in the height of the mercury column since

$$P_{\text{atmosphere}} = P_{\text{vapor}} + P_{\text{Hg column}}$$

Thus

$$P_{\text{vapor}} = P_{\text{atmosphere}} - P_{\text{Hg column}}$$

Figure 10.36

Behavior of a liquid in a closed container. (a) Initially, net evaporation occurs as molecules are transferred from the liquid to the vapor phase, so the amount of liquid decreases. (b) As the number of vapor molecules increases, the rate of return to the liquid (condensation) increases, until finally the rate of condensation equals the rate of evaporation. The system is at equilibrium, and no further changes occur in the amounts of vapor or liquid.

(a)   (b)

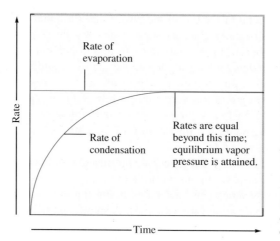

Figure 10.37

The rates of condensation and evaporation over time for a liquid sealed in a closed container. The rate of evaporation remains constant and the rate of condensation increases as the number of molecules in the vapor phase increases, until the two rates become equal. At this point, the equilibrium vapor pressure is attained.

Figure 10.38

(a) The vapor pressure of a liquid can be measured easily using a simple barometer of the type shown here. (b) The three liquids water, ethanol (C_2H_5OH), and diethyl ether [(C_2H_5)$_2$O] have quite different vapor pressures. Ether is by far the most volatile of the three. Note that in each case a little liquid remains (floating on the mercury).

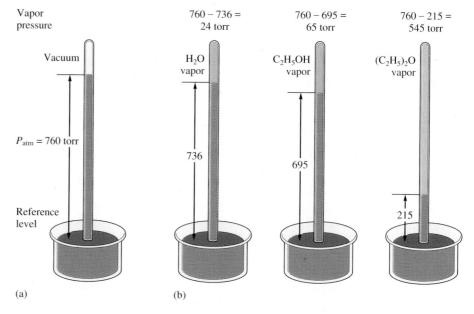

The vapor pressures of liquids vary widely [see Fig. 10.38(b)]. Liquids with high vapor pressures are said to be *volatile*—they evaporate rapidly from an open dish. The vapor pressure of a liquid is principally determined by the size of the *intermolecular forces* in the liquid. Liquids in which the intermolecular forces are large have relatively low vapor pressures because the molecules need high energies to escape to the vapor phase. For example, although water has a much lower molar mass than diethyl ether, the strong hydrogen-bonding forces that exist among water molecules in the liquid cause water's vapor pressure to be much lower than that of diethyl ether [see Fig. 10.38(b)]. In general, substances with large molar masses have relatively low vapor pressures, mainly because of the large dispersion forces. The more electrons a substance has, the more polarizable it is, and the greater are the dispersion forces.

Measurements of the vapor pressure for a given liquid at several temperatures show that *vapor pressure increases significantly with temperature*. Figure 10.39

(a) Kinetic energy   (b) Kinetic energy

Figure 10.39

The number of molecules in a liquid with a given energy versus kinetic energy at two temperatures. Part (a) shows a lower temperature than that in part (b). Note that the proportion of molecules with enough energy to escape the liquid to the vapor phase (indicated by shaded areas) increases dramatically with temperature. This causes vapor pressure to increase markedly with temperature.

illustrates the distribution of molecular kinetic energy present in a liquid at two different temperatures. To overcome the intermolecular forces in a liquid, a molecule must have sufficient kinetic energy. As the temperature of the liquid is increased, the fraction of molecules having the minimum energy needed to overcome these forces and escape to the vapor phase increases markedly. Thus the vapor pressure of a liquid increases dramatically with temperature. Values for water at several temperatures are given in Table 10.8.

The quantitative nature of the temperature dependence of vapor pressure can be represented graphically. Plots of vapor pressure versus temperature for water, ethanol, and diethyl ether are shown in Fig. 10.40(a). Note the nonlinear increase in

(a)

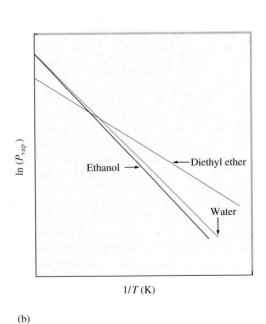

(b)

Figure 10.40

(a) The vapor pressures of water, ethanol, and diethyl ether as a function of temperature. (b) Plots of $\ln(P^{vap})$ versus $1/T$ (Kelvin temperature) for water, ethanol, and diethyl ether.

vapor pressure for all the liquids as the temperature is increased. We find that a straight line can be obtained by plotting $\ln(P^{vap})$ versus $1/T$, where T is the Kelvin temperature, as shown in Fig. 10.40(b). We can represent this behavior by the equation

$$\ln(P^{vap}) = -\frac{\Delta H_{vap}}{R}\left(\frac{1}{T}\right) + C \tag{10.4}$$

where ΔH_{vap} is the enthalpy of vaporization, R is the universal gas constant, and C is a constant characteristic of a given liquid. The symbol ln means that the natural logarithm of the vapor pressure is taken.

Natural logarithms are reviewed in Appendix 1.2.

Equation (10.4) is the equation for a straight line of the form $y = mx + b$, where

$$y = \ln(P^{vap})$$

$$x = \frac{1}{T}$$

$$m = \text{slope} = -\frac{\Delta H_{vap}}{R}$$

$$b = \text{intercept} = C$$

Table 10.8

The Vapor Pressure of Water as a Function of Temperature

$T(°C)$	P (torr)
0.0	4.579
10.0	9.209
20.0	17.535
25.0	23.756
30.0	31.824
40.0	55.324
60.0	149.4
70.0	233.7
90.0	525.8

Sample Exercise 10.5

Using the plots in Fig. 10.40(b), determine whether water or diethyl ether has the larger enthalpy of vaporization.

Solution

When $\ln(P^{vap})$ is plotted versus $1/T$, the slope of the resulting straight line is

$$-\frac{\Delta H_{vap}}{R}$$

Note from Fig. 10.40(b) that the slopes of the lines for water and diethyl ether are both negative, as expected, and that the line for ether has the smaller slope. Thus ether has the smaller value of ΔH_{vap}. This makes sense because the hydrogen bonding in water causes it to have a relatively large enthalpy of vaporization.

Equation (10.4) is important for several reasons. For example, we can determine the heat of vaporization for a liquid by measuring P^{vap} at several temperatures and then evaluating the slope of a plot of $\ln(P^{vap})$ versus $1/T$. On the other hand, if we know the values of ΔH_{vap} and P^{vap} at one temperature, we can use Equation (10.4) to calculate P^{vap} at another temperature. This can be done by recognizing that the constant C does not depend on temperature. Thus at two temperatures T_1 and T_2 we can solve Equation (10.4) for C and then write the equality

$$\ln(P_{T_1}^{vap}) + \frac{\Delta H_{vap}}{RT_1} = C = \ln(P_{T_2}^{vap}) + \frac{\Delta H_{vap}}{RT_2}$$

This can be rearranged to

$$\ln(P_{T_1}^{\text{vap}}) - \ln(P_{T_2}^{\text{vap}}) = \frac{\Delta H_{\text{vap}}}{R}\left(\frac{1}{T_2} - \frac{1}{T_1}\right)$$

or

$$\ln\left(\frac{P_{T_1}^{\text{vap}}}{P_{T_2}^{\text{vap}}}\right) = \frac{\Delta H_{\text{vap}}}{R}\left(\frac{1}{T_2} - \frac{1}{T_1}\right) \qquad (10.5)$$

Equation 10.5 is called the **Clausius–Clapeyron equation.**

Sample Exercise 10.6

The vapor pressure of water at 25°C is 23.8 torr, and the heat of vaporization of water is 43.9 kJ/mol. Calculate the vapor pressure of water at 50.°C.

Solution

We will use Equation (10.5):

$$\ln\left(\frac{P_{T_1}^{\text{vap}}}{P_{T_2}^{\text{vap}}}\right) = \frac{\Delta H_{\text{vap}}}{R}\left(\frac{1}{T_2} - \frac{1}{T_1}\right)$$

For water we have

$$P_{T_1}^{\text{vap}} = 23.8 \text{ torr}$$
$$T_1 = 25 + 273 = 298 \text{ K}$$
$$T_2 = 50. + 273 = 323 \text{ K}$$
$$\Delta H_{\text{vap}} = 43.9 \text{ kJ/mol} = 43,900 \text{ J/mol}$$
$$R = 8.3145 \text{ J/K mol}$$

In solving this problem, we ignore the fact that ΔH_{vap} is slightly temperature dependent.

Thus

$$\ln\left(\frac{23.8 \text{ torr}}{P_{T_2}^{\text{vap}} \text{ (torr)}}\right) = \frac{43,900 \text{ J/mol}}{8.3145 \text{ J/K mol}}\left(\frac{1}{323 \text{ K}} - \frac{1}{298 \text{ K}}\right)$$

$$\ln\left(\frac{23.8}{P_{T_2}^{\text{vap}}}\right) = -1.37$$

Taking the antilog (see Appendix 1.2) of both sides gives

$$\frac{23.8}{P_{T_2}^{\text{vap}}} = 0.254$$

$$P_{T_2}^{\text{vap}} = 93.7 \text{ torr}$$

Figure 10.41
Sublimation of iodine.

Like liquids, solids have vapor pressures. Figure 10.41 shows iodine vapor in equilibrium with solid iodine in a closed flask. Under normal conditions iodine **sublimes;** that is, it goes directly from the solid to the gaseous state without passing through the liquid state. **Sublimation** also occurs with dry ice (solid carbon dioxide).

Sublimation: a process in which a substance goes directly from the solid to the gaseous state.

Changes of State

What happens when a solid is heated? Typically, it will melt to form a liquid. If the heating continues, the liquid will at some point boil and form the vapor phase. This

Figure 10.42

The heating curve for a given quantity of water where energy is added at a constant rate. The plateau at the boiling point is longer than the plateau at the melting point because it takes almost seven times more energy (and thus seven times the heating time) to vaporize liquid water than to melt ice. The slopes of the other lines are different because the different states of water have different molar heat capacities (the energy required to raise the temperature of 1 mole of a substance by 1°C).

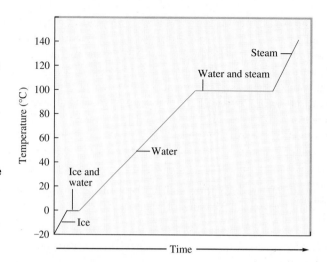

Phase changes of carbon dioxide are discussed in Section 10.9.

Ionic solids such as NaCl and NaF have very high melting points and enthalpies of fusion because of the strong ionic forces in these solids. At the other extreme is $O_2(s)$, a molecular solid containing nonpolar molecules with weak intermolecular forces.

The melting and boiling points will be defined more precisely later in this section.

process can be represented by a **heating curve:** a plot of temperature versus time for a process where energy is added at a constant rate.

The heating curve for water is given in Fig. 10.42. As energy flows into the ice, the random vibrations of the water molecules increase as the temperature rises. Eventually, the molecules become so energetic that they break loose from their lattice positions, and the change from solid to liquid occurs. This is indicated by a plateau at 0°C on the heating curve. At this temperature, called the **melting point,** all the added energy is used to disrupt the ice structure by breaking the hydrogen bonds, thus increasing the potential energy of the water molecules. The enthalpy change that occurs at the melting point when a solid melts is called the **heat of fusion,** or more accurately, the **enthalpy of fusion, ΔH_{fus}.** The melting points and enthalpies of fusion for several representative solids are listed in Table 10.9.

The temperature remains constant until the solid has completely changed to liquid; then it begins to increase again. At 100°C the liquid water reaches its **boiling point,** and the temperature then remains constant as the added energy is used to vaporize the liquid. When the liquid is completely changed to vapor, the temperature again begins to rise. Note that changes of state are physical changes; although

Table 10.9		
Melting Points and Enthalpies of Fusion for Several Representative Solids		
Compound	Melting Point (°C)	Enthalpy of Fusion (kJ/mol)
O_2	−218	0.45
HCl	−114	1.99
HI	−51	2.87
CCl_4	−23	2.51
$CHCl_3$	−64	9.20
H_2O	0	6.02
NaF	992	29.3
NaCl	801	30.2

intermolecular forces have been overcome, no chemical bonds have been broken. If the water vapor were heated to much higher temperatures, the water molecules would break down into the individual atoms. This would be a chemical change, since covalent bonds are broken. We no longer have water after this occurs.

The melting and boiling points for a substance are determined by the vapor pressures of the solid and liquid states. Figure 10.43 shows the vapor pressures of solid and liquid water as functions of temperature near 0°C. Note that below 0°C the vapor pressure of ice is less than the vapor pressure of liquid water. Also note that the vapor pressure of ice has a larger temperature dependence than that of the liquid. That is, the vapor pressure of ice increases more rapidly for a given rise in temperature than does the vapor pressure of water. Thus, as the temperature of the solid is increased, a point is eventually reached where the *liquid and solid have identical vapor pressures*. This is the melting point.

These concepts can be demonstrated experimentally using the apparatus illustrated in Fig. 10.44, where ice occupies one compartment and liquid water the other. Consider the following cases.

Case 1. A temperature at which the vapor pressure of the solid is greater than that of the liquid. At this temperature the solid requires a higher pressure than the liquid does to be in equilibrium with the vapor. Thus, as vapor is released from the solid to try to achieve equilibrium, the liquid will absorb vapor in an attempt to reduce the vapor pressure to its equilibrium value. The net effect is a conversion from solid to liquid through the vapor phase. In fact, no solid can exist under these conditions. The amount of solid will steadily decrease and the volume of liquid will increase. Finally, there will be only liquid in the right compartment, which will come to equilibrium with the water vapor, and no further changes will occur in the system. This temperature must be *above the melting point* of ice, since only the liquid state can exist.

Case 2. A temperature at which the vapor pressure of the solid is less than that of the liquid. This is the opposite of the situation in Case 1. In this case, the liquid requires a higher pressure than the solid does to be in equilibrium with the vapor, so the liquid will gradually disappear, and the amount of ice will increase.

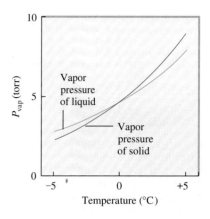

Figure 10.43

The vapor pressures of solid and liquid water as a function of temperature. The data for liquid water below 0°C are obtained from supercooled water. The data for solid water above 0°C are estimated by extrapolation of vapor pressure from below 0°C.

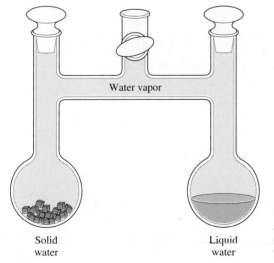

Solid water   Liquid water

Figure 10.44

An apparatus that allows solid and liquid water to interact only through the vapor state.

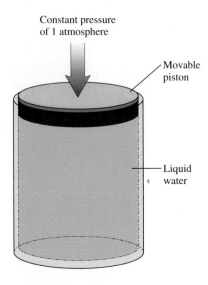

Constant pressure of 1 atmosphere

Movable piston

Liquid water

Figure 10.45

Water in a closed system with a pressure of 1 atm exerted on the piston. No bubbles can form within the liquid as long as the vapor pressure is less than 1 atm.

Finally, only the solid will remain, which will achieve equilibrium with the vapor. This temperature must be *below the melting point* of ice, since only the solid state can exist.

Case 3. A temperature at which the vapor pressures of the solid and liquid are identical. In this case, the solid and liquid states have the same vapor pressure, so they can coexist in the apparatus at equilibrium simultaneously with the vapor. This temperature represents the *melting point* where both the solid and liquid states can exist.

We can now describe the melting point of a substance more precisely. The **normal melting point** is defined as *the temperature at which the solid and liquid states have the same vapor pressure under conditions where the total pressure is 1 atmosphere.*

Boiling occurs when the vapor pressure of a liquid becomes equal to the pressure of its environment. The **normal boiling point** of a liquid is *the temperature at which the vapor pressure of the liquid is exactly 1 atmosphere.* This concept is illustrated in Fig. 10.45. At temperatures where the vapor pressure of the liquid is less than 1 atmosphere, no bubbles of vapor can form because the pressure on the surface of the liquid is greater than the pressure in any spaces in the liquid where the bubbles are trying to form. Only when the liquid reaches a temperature at which the pressure of vapor in the spaces in the liquid is 1 atmosphere can bubbles form and boiling occur.

However, changes of state do not always occur exactly at the boiling point or melting point. For example, water can be readily **supercooled;** that is, it can be cooled below 0°C at 1 atm pressure and remain in the liquid state. Supercooling occurs because, as it is cooled, the water may not achieve the degree of organization necessary to form ice at 0°C, and thus it continues to exist as the liquid. At some point the correct ordering occurs and ice rapidly forms, releasing energy in the exothermic process and bringing the temperature back up to the melting point, where the remainder of the water freezes (see Fig. 10.46).

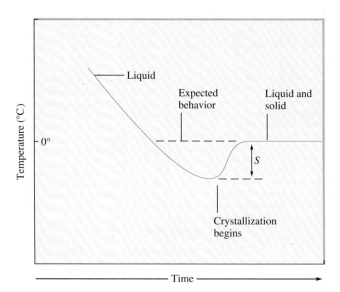

Figure 10.46

The supercooling of water. The extent of supercooling is given by *S*.

A liquid also can be **superheated,** or raised to temperatures above its boiling point, especially if it is heated rapidly. Superheating can occur because bubble formation in the interior of the liquid requires that many high-energy molecules gather in the same vicinity, and this may not happen at the boiling point, especially if the liquid is heated rapidly. If the liquid becomes superheated, the vapor pressure in the liquid is greater than the atmospheric pressure. Once a bubble does form, since its internal pressure is greater than that of the atmosphere, it can burst before rising to the surface, blowing the surrounding liquid out of the container. This is called *bumping* and has ruined many experiments. It can be avoided by adding boiling chips to the flask containing the liquid. Boiling chips are bits of porous ceramic material containing trapped air that escapes on heating, forming tiny bubbles that act as "starters" for vapor bubble formation. This allows a smooth onset of boiling as the boiling point is reached.

10.9 *Phase Diagrams*

Purpose

• To discuss the features of phase diagrams.

A **phase diagram** is a convenient way of representing the phases of a substance as a function of temperature and pressure. For example, the phase diagram for water (Fig. 10.47) shows which state exists at a given temperature and pressure. It is important to recognize that a phase diagram describes conditions and events in a *closed* system of the type represented in Fig. 10.45, where no material can escape into the surroundings and no air is present.

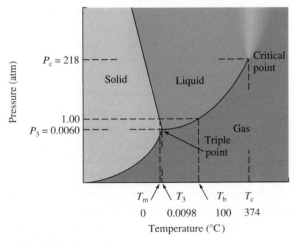

Figure 10.47

The phase diagram for water. T_m represents the normal melting point; T_3 and P_3 denote the triple point; T_b represents the normal boiling point; T_c represents the critical temperature; P_c represents the critical pressure. The negative slope of the solid/liquid line reflects the fact that the density of ice is less than that of liquid water.

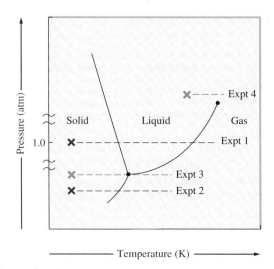

Figure 10.48

Diagrams of various heating experiments on samples of water in a closed system.

To show how to interpret the phase diagram for water, we will consider heating experiments at several pressures, shown by the dashed lines in Fig. 10.48.

Experiment 1. Pressure is 1 atm. This experiment begins with the cylinder shown in Fig. 10.45 completely filled with ice at a temperature of −20°C and the piston exerting a pressure of 1 atm directly on the ice (there is no air space). Since at temperatures below 0°C the vapor pressure of ice is less than 1 atm—which is the constant external pressure on the piston—no vapor is present in the cylinder. As the cylinder is heated, ice is the only component until the temperature reaches 0°C, where the ice changes to liquid water as energy is added. This is the normal melting point of water. When the solid has completely changed to liquid, the temperature again rises. At this point, the cylinder contains only liquid water. *No vapor is present* because the vapor pressure of liquid water under these conditions is less than 1 atm, the constant external pressure on the piston. Heating continues until the temperature of the liquid water reaches 100°C. At this point, the vapor pressure of liquid water is 1 atm, and boiling occurs, with the liquid changing to vapor. This is the normal boiling point of water. After the liquid has been completely converted to steam, the temperature again rises as the heating continues. The cylinder now contains only water vapor.

Experiment 2. Pressure is 2.0 torr. Again we start with ice as the only component in the cylinder at −20°C. The pressure exerted by the piston in this case is only 2.0 torr. As heating proceeds, the temperature rises to −10°C, where the ice changes directly to vapor, a process known as *sublimation*. Sublimation occurs when the vapor pressure of ice is equal to the external pressure, which in this case is only 2.0 torr. No liquid water appears under these conditions because the vapor pressure of liquid water is always greater than 2.0 torr, and thus it cannot exist at this pressure. If liquid water were placed in a cylinder under such a low pressure, it would vaporize immediately at temperatures above −10°C or freeze at temperatures below −10°C.

Experiment 3. Pressure is 4.588 torr. Again we start with ice as the only component in the cylinder at −20°C. In this case the pressure exerted on the ice by the piston is 4.588 torr. As the cylinder is heated, no new phase appears until the temperature reaches 0.0098°C. At this point, called the **triple point,** solid and liquid water have identical vapor pressures of 4.588 torr. Thus *at 0.0098°C* *and 4.588 torr all three states of water are present*. In fact, *only* under these conditions can all three states of water coexist.

Experiment 4. Pressure is 225 atm. In this experiment we start with liquid water in the cylinder at 300°C; the pressure exerted by the piston on the water is 225 atm. Liquid water can be present at this temperature because of the high external pressure. As the temperature increases, something happens that we did not see in the first three experiments: the liquid gradually changes into a vapor but goes through an intermediate "fluid" region, which is neither true liquid nor vapor. This is quite unlike the behavior at lower temperatures and pressures, say at 100°C and 1 atm, where the temperature remains constant while a definite phase change from liquid to vapor occurs. This unusual behavior occurs because the conditions are beyond the critical point for water. The **critical temperature** can be defined as the temperature above which the vapor cannot be liquefied no matter what pressure is applied. The **critical pressure** is the pressure required to produce liquefaction *at* the critical temperature. Together, the critical temperature and the critical pressure define the **critical point.** For water the critical point is 374°C and 218 atm. Note that the liquid/vapor line on the phase diagram for water ends at the critical point. Beyond this point the transition from one state to another involves the intermediate "fluid" region just described.

Applications of the Phase Diagram for Water

There are several additional interesting features of the phase diagram for water. Note that the solid/liquid boundary line has a negative slope. This means that the melting point of water *decreases* as the external pressure *increases*. This behavior, which is opposite to that observed for most substances, occurs because the density of ice is *less* than that of liquid water at the melting point. The maximum density of water occurs at 4°C; when liquid water freezes, its volume increases.

We can account for the effect of pressure on the melting point of water using the following reasoning. At the melting point, liquid and solid water coexist—they are in dynamic equilibrium, since the rate at which ice is melting is just balanced by the rate at which the water is freezing. What happens if we apply pressure to this system? When subjected to increased pressure, matter reduces its volume. This behavior is most dramatic for gases but also occurs for condensed states. Since a given mass of ice at 0°C has a larger volume than the same mass of liquid water, the system can reduce its volume in response to the increased pressure by changing to liquid. Thus at 0°C and an external pressure greater than 1 atm, water is liquid. In other words, the freezing point of water is less than 0°C when the pressure is greater than 1 atm.

Fig. 10.49 (on page 482) illustrates the effect of pressure on ice. At the point *X* on the phase diagram, ice is subjected to increased pressure at constant temperature. Note that as the pressure is increased, the solid/liquid line is crossed, indicating that the ice melts. This phenomenon seems to be important in ice skating. The narrow blade of the skate exerts a large pressure, since the skater's weight is supported by the small area of the blade. Also, the frictional heating due to the moving skate contributes to the melting of the ice.* After the blade passes, the liquid refreezes as normal pressure and temperature return. Without this lubrication effect due to the

*The physics of ice skating is quite complex, and there is disagreement about whether the pressure or the frictional heating of the ice skate is most important. See "Letter to the Editor," by R. Silberman, *J. Chem. Ed.* **65** (1988): 186.

Kristi Yamaguchi, who won the gold medal in figure skating for the United States in the 1992 Winter Olympic Games.

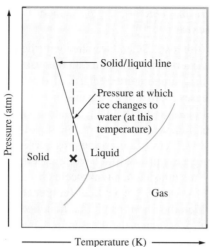

Figure 10.49

The phase diagram for water. At point x on the phase diagram, water is a solid. However, as the external pressure is increased while the temperature remains constant (indicated by the vertical dotted line), the solid/liquid line is crossed and the ice melts.

Water boils at 89°C in Leadville, Colorado.

thawing ice, ice skating would not be the smooth, graceful activity that many people enjoy.

Ice's lower density has other implications. When water freezes in a pipe or an engine block, it will expand and break the container. This is why water pipes are insulated in cold climates and antifreeze is used in water-cooled engines. The lower density of ice also means that ice formed on rivers and lakes will float, providing a layer of insulation that helps prevent bodies of water from freezing solid in the winter. Aquatic life can therefore continue to live through periods of freezing temperatures.

A liquid boils at the temperature where the vapor pressure of the liquid equals the external pressure. Thus the boiling point of a substance, like the melting point, depends on the external pressure. This is why water boils at different temperatures at different elevations (see Table 10.10), and any cooking carried out in boiling water will be affected by this variation. For example, it takes longer to hard-boil an egg in Leadville, Colorado (elevation: 10,150 ft), than in San Diego, California (sea level), since water boils at a lower temperature in Leadville.

Table 10.10

Boiling Point of Water at Various Locations

Location	Feet Above Sea Level	P_{atm} (torr)	Boiling Point (°C)
Top of Mt. Everest, Tibet	29,028	240	70
Top of Mt. McKinley, Alaska	20,320	340	79
Top of Mt. Whitney, Calif.	14,494	430	85
Leadville, Colo.	10,150	510	89
Top of Mt. Washington, N.H.	6,293	590	93
Boulder, Colo.	5,430	610	94
Madison, Wis.	900	730	99
New York City, N.Y.	10	760	100
Death Valley, Calif.	−282	770	100.3

◀ **CHEMICAL IMPACT** ▶

Making Diamonds at Low Pressures: Fooling Mother Nature

In 1955 Robert H. Wentorf, Jr., accomplished something that borders on alchemy—he turned peanut butter into diamonds. He and his coworkers at the General Electric Research and Development Center also changed roofing pitch, wood, coal, and many other carbon-containing materials into diamonds, using a process involving temperatures of $\approx 2000°C$ and pressures of $\approx 10^5$ atm. Although the first diamonds made by this process looked like black sand because of the impurities present, the process has now been developed to a point such that beautiful, clear, gem-quality diamonds can be produced. General Electric now has the capacity to produce 150 million carats (30,000 kg) of diamonds annually (virtually all of which is "diamond grit" used for industrial purposes such as abrasive coatings on cutting tools). The production of large, gem-quality diamonds by this process is still too expensive to compete with the natural sources of these stones. However, this may change as methods are developed for making diamonds at low pressures.

The high temperatures and pressures used in the GE process for making diamonds make sense if one looks at the accompanying phase diagram for carbon. Note that graphite—not diamond—is the most stable form of carbon under ordinary conditions of temperature and pressure. However, diamond becomes more stable than graphite at very high pressures (as one would expect from the greater density of diamond). The high temperature used in the GE process is necessary to disrupt the bonds in graphite so that diamond (the most stable form of carbon at the high pressures used in the process) can form. Once the diamond is produced, the elemental carbon is "trapped" in this form at normal conditions (25°C, 1 atm) because

the reaction back to the graphite form is so slow. That is, even though graphite is more stable than diamond at 25°C and 1 atm, diamond can exist almost indefinitely because the conversion to graphite is a *very slow* reaction. As a result, diamonds formed at the high pressures found deep in the earth's crust can be brought to the earth's surface by natural geologic processes and continue to exist for millions of years.*

We have seen that diamond formed in the laboratory at high pressures is "trapped" in this form, but this process is very expensive. Can diamond be formed at low pressures? The phase diagram for carbon says no. However, researchers have found that under the right conditions diamonds can be "grown" at low pressures. The process used is called **chemical vapor deposition (CVD).** CVD uses an energy source to release carbon atoms from a compound such as methane into a steady flow of hydrogen gas (some of which is dissociated to produce hydrogen atoms). The carbon atoms then deposit as a diamond film on a surface maintained at a temperature between 600 and 900°C. Why does diamond form on this surface rather than the favored graphite? Nobody is sure, but it has been suggested that at these relatively high temperatures the diamond structure grows faster than the

*In Morocco a 50-km-long slab called Beni Bousera contains chunks of graphite that were probably once diamonds formed in the deposit when it was buried 150 km underground. As this slab slowly rose to the surface over millions of years, the very slow reaction changing diamond to graphite had time to occur. On the other hand, in the diamond-rich kimberlite deposits in South Africa, which rise to the surface much faster, the diamonds have not had sufficient time to revert to graphite.

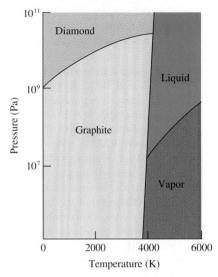

The phase diagram for carbon.

graphite structure and so diamond is favored under these conditions. It also has been suggested that the hydrogen atoms present react much faster with graphite fragments than with diamond fragments, effectively removing any graphite from the growing film. Once it forms, of course, diamond is trapped. The major advantage of CVD is that there is no need for the extraordinarily high pressures used in the traditional process for synthesizing diamonds.

The first products with diamond films are already on the market. Audiophiles can buy tweeters that have diaphragms coated with a thin diamond film that limits sound distortion. Watches with diamond-coated crystals are planned, as are diamond-coated windows in infrared scanning devices used in analytical instruments and missile guidance systems. These applications represent only the beginning for diamond-coated products.

◀ **CHEMICAL IMPACT** ▶

Transistors and Printed Circuits

Transistors have had an immense impact on the technology of electronic devices for which signal amplification is needed, such as communications equipment and computers. Before the invention of the transistor at Bell Laboratories in 1947, amplification was provided exclusively by vacuum tubes, which were both bulky and unreliable. The first electronic digital computer, ENIAC, built at the University of Pennsylvania, had 19,000 vacuum tubes and consumed 150,000 watts of electricity. Because of the discovery and development of the transistor and the printed circuit, a hand-held calculator run by a small battery has the same computing power as ENIAC.

A *junction transistor* is made by joining n-type and p-type semiconductors so as to form an n–p–n or a p–n–p junction. The former type is shown in Fig. 10.50. In this diagram the input signal (to be amplified) occurs in circuit 1, which has a small resistance and a forward-biased n–p junction (junction 1). As the voltage of the input signal to this circuit varies, the current in the circuit varies, which means there is a change in the number of elec-

trons crossing the n–p junction. Circuit 2 has a relatively large resistance and is under reverse bias. The key to operation of the transistor is that current only flows in circuit 2 when electrons crossing junction 1 also cross junction 2 and travel to the positive terminal. Since the current in circuit 1 determines the number of electrons crossing junction 1, the number of electrons available to cross junction 2 is also directly proportional to the current in circuit 1. The current in circuit 2 therefore varies depending on the current in circuit 1.

The voltage *V*, current *I*, and resistance *R* in a circuit are related by the equation

$$V = IR$$

Since circuit 2 has a large resistance, a given current in circuit 2 produces a larger voltage than the same current in circuit 1, which has a small resistance. Thus a signal of variable voltage in circuit 1, such as might be produced by a human voice on a telephone, is reproduced in circuit 2, but with much greater voltage changes. That is, the input signal has been *amplified* by

the junction transistor. This device, which has replaced the large vacuum tube, is a tiny component of a printed circuit on a silicon chip.

Silicon chips are really "planar" transistors constructed from thin layers of n-type and p-type regions connected by conductors. A chip less than 1 cm wide can contain hundreds of printed circuits and be used in computers, radios, and televisions.

A printed circuit has many n–p–n junction transistors. Fig. 10.51 illustrates the formation of one transistor area. The chip begins as a thin wafer of silicon that has been doped with an n-type impurity. A protective layer of silicon dioxide is then produced on the wafer by exposing it in a furnace to an oxidizing atmosphere. The next step is to produce a p-type semiconductor. To do this, the surface of the oxide is covered by a light-sensitive wax, as shown in Fig. 10.51(a). A template that only allows light to shine through in selected areas is then placed on top [Fig. 10.51(b)], and light is shown on the chip. The wax that has been exposed to light undergoes a chemical change that causes

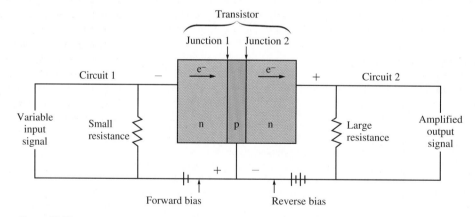

Figure 10.50

A schematic of two circuits connected by a transistor. The signal in circuit 1 is amplified in circuit 2.

◀ **CHEMICAL IMPACT** ▶

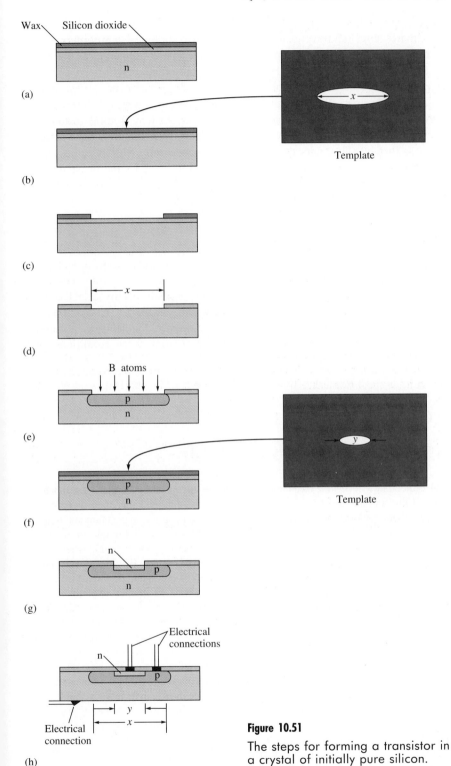

its solubility to be different from the un-exposed wax. The exposed wax is dissolved using selective solvents [Fig. 10.51(c)], and the exposed area is treated with an etching solution to dissolve the oxide coating [Fig. 10.51(d)]. When the remaining wax is dissolved, the silicon wafer has its oxide coating intact except at the one spot (of diameter x), as shown in Fig. 10.51(d).

Exposing the wafer to a p-type impurity such as boron at about 1000°C causes a p-type semiconductor area to be formed in the exposed spot as the boron atoms diffuse into the silicon crystal [Fig. 10.51(e)]. Next, to form a small n-type area in the center of the p-type region, the wafer is again placed in the oxidizing furnace to be recoated over its entire surface with oxide. Then a new wax covering is applied, which is illuminated through a template with a transparent area indicated by y [Fig. 10.51(f)]. The wax and oxide are then removed from the illuminated area, and the wafer is exposed to an n-type impurity to form a small n-type region as shown in Fig. 10.51(g). Next, conductors are layered onto the chip giving the finished transistor [Fig. 10.51(h)], which has two circuits connected through an n–p–n junction (see Fig. 10.50). This transistor then becomes a part of a large circuit layered onto the chip and interconnected by conductors.

The method given here for producing a printed circuit does not represent the latest technology in this field. The manufacture of printed circuits is a highly competitive business, and changes in methodology occur almost daily.

Figure 10.51

The steps for forming a transistor in a crystal of initially pure silicon.

Ice fishing in Michigan.

As we mentioned earlier, the phase diagram for water describes a closed system. Therefore, we must be very cautious in using the phase diagram to explain the behavior of water in a natural setting, such as on the earth's surface. For example, in dry climates (low humidity), snow and ice seem to sublime—a minimum amount of slush is produced. Wet clothes put on an outside line at temperatures below 0°C freeze and then dry while frozen. However, the phase diagram (Fig. 10.47) shows that ice should *not* be able to sublime at normal atmospheric pressures. What is happening in these cases? Ice in the natural environment is not in a closed system. The pressure is provided by the atmosphere rather than by a solid piston. This means that the vapor produced over the ice can escape from the immediate region as soon as it is formed. The vapor does not come to equilibrium with the solid, and the ice slowly disappears. Sublimation, which seems forbidden by the phase diagram, does in fact occur under these conditions, although it is not the sublimation under equilibrium conditions described by the phase diagram.

The Phase Diagram for Carbon Dioxide

The phase diagram for carbon dioxide (Fig. 10.52) differs from that for water. The solid/liquid line has a positive slope, since solid carbon dioxide is more dense than liquid carbon dioxide. The triple point for carbon dioxide occurs at 5.1 atm and −56.6°C, and the critical point occurs at 72.8 atm and 31°C. At a pressure of 1 atm, solid carbon dioxide sublimes at −78°C, a property that leads to its common name, **dry ice.** No liquid phase occurs under normal atmospheric conditions, making dry ice a convenient refrigerant.

◀ **C H E M I C A L   I M P A C T** ▶

Diamonds—A Computer's Best Friend?

Diamond, a form of elemental carbon, has remarkable properties. It is the hardest known natural substance, it has an incredibly high melting point of 3500°C, it forms beautiful gems, and it is an electrical insulator but has an extraordinary ability to conduct heat, having four times the thermal conductivity of silver and copper. This last combination of properties makes diamond an attractive candidate for use in solid-state electronic devices. As microelectronic chips get smaller and the circuits become packed more densely, heat-buildup problems are becoming severe. Diamond is such an efficient conductor of heat that diamonds are already used as "heat sinks" on some circuit boards, and if diamond could be doped to make it a semiconductor, it would allow much greater miniaturiza-tion. Silicon now forms the basis for most microchips, and since silicon and carbon are neighbors in Group IV, one might predict that carbon would behave similarly. However, the extraordinary stability of the diamond structure makes it difficult to insert "foreign" atoms. Some natural diamonds do contain boron (for example, the famous blue Hope Diamond). Also, diamond films containing Group III atoms have been laid down by vapor deposition (a process where solids are grown at low pressures from atoms in the gas phase). These films behave as p-type semiconductors, but diamond has resisted the incorporation of Group V atoms to make n-type semiconductors. However, in the summer of 1990, a Japanese group claimed to have formed a 10-μm n-type film of diamond containing phosphorus on a silicon base. Further, the Japanese scientists reported that they had made a functioning p-n-p type diamond transistor. Another breakthrough in diamond technology occurred recently when scientists at General Electric developed a method of producing diamonds of almost pure carbon-12 (rather than the natural mixture of 99% ^{12}C and 1% ^{13}C). These new diamonds have 50% higher thermal conductivity than natural diamonds, and GE estimates a potential market up to $100 million per year for these diamonds. At this point the use of diamonds in electronic devices is in its infancy, but there is little doubt that this technology will become increasingly important in the next few years.

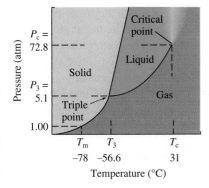

Figure 10.52

The phase diagram for carbon dioxide. The liquid state does not exist at a pressure of 1 atm. The solid/liquid line has a positive slope, since the density of solid carbon dioxide is greater than that of liquid carbon dioxide.

Carbon dioxide is often used in fire extinguishers, where it exists as a liquid at 25°C under high pressures. Liquid carbon dioxide released from the extinguisher into the environment at 1 atm immediately changes to a vapor. Being heavier than air, this vapor smothers the fire by keeping oxygen away from the flame. The liquid/vapor transition is highly endothermic, so cooling also results, which helps to put out the fire. The "fog" produced by a carbon dioxide extinguisher is not solid carbon dioxide but rather moisture frozen from the air.

FOR REVIEW

Summary

Liquids and solids are the two condensed states of matter; their formation is caused by intermolecular forces among the molecules, atoms, or ions. Dipole–dipole forces are attractions between molecules that have dipole moments. These forces are particularly strong for molecules containing hydrogen bonded to a highly electronegative element such as nitrogen, oxygen, or fluorine. In these cases the resulting dipole forces are called hydrogen bonds and account for the unusually high boiling points of the hydrides of the first elements in Groups 5A, 6A, and 7A. London dispersion forces caused by instantaneous dipoles are important in substances composed of nonpolar molecules. Liquids exhibit various properties—surface tension, capillary action, and viscosity—that depend on the strengths of the intermolecular forces.

The two broadest categories of solids are crystalline and amorphous solids. Crystalline solids have a regular arrangement, or lattice, of component particles, the smallest repeating unit of which is the unit cell. Crystalline solids can be classified according to what type of components occupy the lattice points: atoms (atomic solids), ions (ionic solids), or molecules (molecular solids). The arrangement of particles in a crystalline solid can be determined by X-ray diffraction techniques, and the interatomic distances in the crystal can be related to the wavelength and angle of reflection of the X rays by the Bragg equation.

The structure of metals is modeled by assuming atoms to be uniform spheres and packing them as compactly as possible. There are two closest packing arrangements: hexagonal and cubic.

The bonding in metallic crystals can be described in terms of the electron sea model (valence electrons are assumed to move freely about the metal cations) or in terms of the band model (electrons are assumed to travel through the metal crystal in molecular orbitals formed from the valence atomic orbitals of the metal atoms). In the band model the large number of available atomic orbitals form closely spaced energy levels. Electricity can be readily conducted by electrons in conduction bands, which are molecular orbitals containing only a single electron.

Metals form alloys, which can be classified as substitutional or interstitial.

Carbon is a typical network solid containing strong directional covalent bonds. Diamond and graphite are two allotropes of carbon, with very different physical properties determined by their different bonding.

Silicon should be very similar in properties to carbon since carbon and silicon are next to each other in Group 4A, but in fact their compounds are markedly dissimilar. Silica, the fundamental silicon–oxygen compound, does not contain discrete SiO_2 molecules but rather a network of interconnected SiO_4 tetrahedra. Silicates, salts containing polyatomic anions of silicon and oxygen, are components of rocks, soil, clays, glass, and ceramics.

Semiconductors are formed when pure silicon is doped with other elements. An n-type semiconductor contains atoms with more valence electrons than the silicon atom, and a p-type semiconductor has atoms with fewer valence electrons than silicon. The modern electronics industry is based on devices with p–n junctions.

Molecular solids have small molecules at the lattice points and are held together by relatively weak intermolecular forces. Ice is an example. Ionic solids, on the other hand, are held together by strong electrostatic attractions. The crystal structure of ionic solids can often be described by fitting the smaller ions (usually cations) into holes in the closest packed structures formed by the larger ions (usually anions).

The phase change between liquid and vapor is called vaporization, or evaporation, and the energy required to change 1 mole of liquid to its vapor is the heat of vaporization (ΔH_{vap}). Condensation is the reverse process by which vapor molecules return to the liquid state. When the rates of evaporation and condensation exactly balance in a closed container, the system is at equilibrium, and the resulting pressure of the vapor is called the vapor pressure.

The volatility of liquids depends on intermolecular forces. Liquids with strong intermolecular forces tend to have low vapor pressures. The normal melting point of a solid is defined as the temperature at which the solid and its liquid have identical vapor pressures. The normal boiling point of a liquid occurs at a temperature where the vapor pressure of the liquid is 1 atmosphere.

A phase diagram for a substance shows which state exists at a given temperature and pressure. The triple point on a phase diagram represents the temperature and pressure where all three states coexist. The critical point is defined by the critical temperature and critical pressure. Critical temperature is that temperature above which the vapor cannot be liquefied no matter what pressure is applied. The critical pressure is the pressure required to produce liquefaction at the critical temperature.

Key Terms

Section 10.1

condensed states
intermolecular forces
dipole–dipole attraction
hydrogen bonding
London dispersion forces

Section 10.2

surface tension
capillary action
viscosity

Section 10.3

crystalline solid

amorphous solid
lattice
unit cell
X-ray diffraction
ionic solid
molecular solid

atomic solid

Section 10.4

closest packing
hexagonal closest packed
  (hcp) structure

cubic closest packed
  (ccp) structure
band model
alloy
substitutional alloy
interstitial alloy

Section 10.5

network solid
silica
silicate
glass
ceramic
semiconductor
n-type semiconductor
p-type semiconductor
p–n junction

Section 10.8

vaporization
heat of vaporization
enthalpy of vaporization (ΔH_{vap})
vapor pressure
condensation
equilibrium
sublimation
heating curve
enthalpy of fusion (ΔH_{fus})

normal melting point
normal boiling point
supercooled
superheated

Section 10.9

phase diagram
triple point
critical temperature
critical pressure
critical point

A blue question or exercise number indicates that the answer to that question or exercise appears at the back of this book and a solution appears in the Solutions Guide.

Questions

1. Describe the relationship between the polarity of individual molecules and the nature and strength of intermolecular forces.

2. List the major types of intermolecular forces in order of increasing strength. Is there some overlap? That is, can the strongest London dispersion forces be greater than some dipole–dipole forces? Give examples of such instances.

3. Describe the relationship between molecular size and the strength of London dispersion forces.

4. Is it possible for the dispersion forces in a particular substance to be stronger than the hydrogen bonding forces in another substance? Explain your answer.

5. How do the following physical properties depend on the strength of intermolecular forces?
   a. Surface tension
   b. Viscosity
   c. Melting point
   d. Boiling point
   e. Vapor pressure

6. Does the nature of intermolecular forces change when a substance goes from a solid to a liquid, or from a liquid to a gas? What causes a substance to undergo a phase change?

7. How do typical dipole–dipole forces differ from hydrogen bonds? In what ways are they similar?

8. Distinguish between the following pairs.
   a. Polarizability and polarity
   b. London dispersion forces and dipole–dipole forces
   c. Intermolecular forces and intramolecular forces

9. In what ways are liquids similar to solids? In what ways are liquids similar to gases?

10. Define critical temperature and critical pressure. In terms of the kinetic molecular theory, why is it impossible for a substance to exist as a liquid above its critical temperature?

11. What is the relationship between critical temperature and intermolecular forces?

12. Use the kinetic molecular theory to explain why a liquid gets cooler as it evaporates from an insulated container.

13. Distinguish between the items in the following pairs.
    a. Crystalline solid and amorphous solid
    b. Ionic solid and molecular solid
    c. Molecular solid and network solid
    d. Metallic solid and network solid

14. Will a crystalline solid or an amorphous solid give a simpler X-ray diffraction pattern? Why?

15. Is it possible to generalize that amorphous solids always have weaker or stronger interparticle forces than crystalline solids? Explain.

16. Use the band model to describe differences among insulators, conductors, and semiconductors.

17. Use the band model to explain why each of the following increases the conductivity of a semiconductor.
    a. Increasing the temperature
    b. Irradiating with light
    c. Adding an impurity

18. How do conductors and semiconductors differ as to the effect of temperature on electrical conductivity?

19. Define each of the following.
    a. Condensation
    b. Evaporation
    c. Sublimation
    d. Supercooled liquid

20. Describe what is meant by a dynamic equilibrium in terms of the vapor pressure of a volatile liquid.

21. How does each of the following affect the rate of evaporation of a liquid in an open dish?
    a. Intermolecular forces

b. Temperature
c. Surface area

22. When wet laundry is hung on a clothesline on a cold winter day, it will freeze but eventually dry. Explain.

23. Why is a burn from steam typically much more severe than a burn from boiling water?

24. Why is the enthalpy of vaporization for water much greater than its enthalpy of fusion? What does this say about changes in intermolecular forces in going from solid to liquid to vapor?

Exercises

In this section similar exercises are paired.

Intermolecular Forces and Physical Properties

25. Identify the most important types of interparticle forces present in the solids of each of the following substances.
   a. $BaSO_4$ e. Cs
   b. H_2S f. Hg
   c. Xe   g. P_4
   d. C_2H_6 h. H_2O

26. Identify the most important types of interparticle forces present in the solids of each of the following substances.
   a. NH_4Cl
   b. Steel
   c. Teflon, $CF_3(CF_2CF_2)_nCF_3$
   d. Polyethylene, $CH_3(CH_2CH_2)_nCH_3$
   e. $CHCl_3$
   f. Ge
   g. NO
   h. BF_3

27. Predict which substance in each of the following pairs would have the greater interparticle forces.
   a. CO_2 or OCS
   b. PF_3 or PF_5
   c. SF_2 or SF_6
   d. SO_3 or SO_2

28. For which molecule in each of the following pairs would you expect greater interparticle forces?
   a. $CH_3CH_2CH_2NH_2$ or $H_2NCH_2CH_2NH_2$
   b. $B(OH)_3$ or BH_3
   c. CH_3OH or H_2CO
   d. HF or HI

29. Rationalize the difference in boiling points for each of the following pairs of substances:

   a. n-Pentane $CH_3CH_2CH_2CH_2CH_3$ 36.2°C

   $$Neopentane \quad H_3C-\overset{\overset{\displaystyle CH_3}{|}}{\underset{\underset{\displaystyle CH_3}{|}}{C}}-CH_3 \quad 9.5°C$$

   b. Dimethyl ether CH_3OCH_3 −25°C
      Ethanol CH_3CH_2OH 79°C
   c. HF   20°C
      HCl   −85°C
   d. $TiCl_4$ 136°C
      LiCl   1360°C
   e. HCl   −85°C
      LiCl   1360°C
   f. LiCl   1360°C
      CsCl   1290°C

30. Rationalize the following differences in physical properties in terms of intermolecular forces. Compare the first three substances with each other, compare the last three with each other, and then compare all six. Can you account for any anomalies?

	bp (°C)	mp (°C)	ΔH_{vap} (kJ/mol)
Benzene, C_6H_6	80	6	33.9
Naphthalene, $C_{10}H_8$	218	80	51.5
Carbon tetrachloride	76	−23	31.8
Acetone, CH_3COCH_3	56	−95	31.8
Acetic acid, CH_3CO_2H	118	17	39.7
Benzoic acid, $C_6H_5CO_2H$	249	122	68.2

31. Consider the following enthalpy changes:

$$F^- + HF \rightarrow FHF^- \qquad \Delta H = -155 \text{ kJ/mol}$$

$$(CH_3)_2C{=}O + HF \rightarrow (CH_3)_2C{=}O\text{---}HF$$
$$\Delta H = -46 \text{ kJ/mol}$$

$$H_2O(g) + HOH(g) \rightarrow H_2O\text{---}HOH \text{ (in ice)}$$
$$\Delta H = -21 \text{ kJ/mol}$$

How do the strengths of hydrogen bonds vary with the electronegativity of the element to which hydrogen is bonded? Where in the above series would you expect hydrogen bonds of the following type to fall?

32. The strongest known hydrogen bond is found in potassium bifluoride (KHF_2). Potassium bifluoride is produced by reacting KF and HF in water. What structure would you predict for the bifluoride ion (FHF^-)? Why?

33. In each of the following groups of substances, pick the one that has the given property. Justify each answer.
   a. Highest boiling point: Hg, NaCl, or N_2
   b. Smallest surface tension: H_2O, CH_3CN, or CH_3OH
   c. Lowest freezing point: H_2, CH_4, or CO
   d. Smallest vapor pressure at 25°C: SiO_2, CO_2, or H_2O
   e. Greatest viscosity: $CH_3CH_2CH_2CH_3$, CH_3CH_2OH, or $HOCH_2CH_2OH$
   f. Strongest hydrogen bonding: NH_3, PH_3, or SbH_3
   g. Greatest heat of vaporization: HF, HCl, HBr, or HI
   h. Smallest enthalpy of fusion: H_2O, CO_2, MgO, or Li_2O

34. In each of the following groups of substances, pick the one that has the given property. Justify your answer.
   a. Lowest boiling point: CH_3CH_3 or $CH_3CH_2CH_2CH_3$
   b. Highest freezing point: H_2O, NaCl, or CH_4
   c. Highest vapor pressure at 25°C: Hg, Ti, H_2O, or gasoline
   d. Lowest melting point: N_2, CO, KCl, or CO_2
   e. Strongest hydrogen bonds: H_2O, $(CH_3)_2NH$, or HF
   f. Smallest heat of vaporization: CH_4, CH_3CH_3, or $CH_3CH_2CH_3$
   g. Largest enthalpy of fusion: H_2O, CO_2, MgO, or Li_2O
   h. Lowest vapor pressure at 25°C: $CH_3CH_2CH_3$, $CH_3\overset{\text{O}}{\overset{\|}{C}}CH_3$, or $CH_3CH_2CH_2OH$

Properties of Liquids

35. The shape of the meniscus of water in a glass tube is different from that of mercury in a glass tube. Why?

H₂O in glass   Hg in glass

What would be the shape of the meniscus of water in a polyethylene tube? [Polyethylene can be represented as $CH_3(CH_2)_nCH_3$, where n is a large number on the order of 1000.]

36. Will water rise to a greater height by capillary action in a glass tube or in a polyethylene tube of the same diameter?

37. Hydrogen peroxide (H_2O_2) is a syrupy liquid with a relatively low vapor pressure and a normal boiling point of 152.2°C. Rationalize the differences of these physical properties from those of water.

38. Carbon diselenide (CSe_2) is a liquid at room temperature. The normal boiling point is 125°C, and the melting point is −45.5°C. Carbon disulfide (CS_2) is also a liquid at room temperature with normal boiling and melting points of 46.5°C and −111.6°C, respectively. How do the strengths of the interparticle forces vary from CO_2 to CS_2 to CSe_2? Explain.

Structures and Properties of Solids

39. What type of solid will each of the following substances form?

a. CO_2 g. KBr
b. SiO_2 h. H_2O
c. Si i. NaOH
d. CH_4 j. U
e. Ru k. $CaCO_3$
f. I_2 l. PH_3

40. What type of solid will each of the following substances form?

a. C g. NH_4Cl
b. CO h. BaS
c. P_4 i. Li_2O
d. S_8 j. Xe
e. Mo k. H_2S
f. Pt l. $NaHSO_4$

41. When a metal was exposed to X rays, it emitted X rays of a different wavelength. The emitted X rays were diffracted by a LiF crystal ($d = 201$ pm), and first-order diffraction ($n = 1$ in the Bragg equation) was detected at an angle of 34.68°. Calculate the wavelength of the X ray emitted by the metal.

42. The value of $2d$ for mica, a silicate mineral, is 19.93 Å (1 Å $= 10^{-10}$ m). What would be the angle for first-order diffraction ($n = 1$ in the Bragg equation) of X rays from a molybdenum X-ray source ($\lambda = 0.712$ Å)?

43. A metallic solid with atoms in a face-centered cubic unit cell with an edge length of 392 pm has a density of 21.45 g/cm^3. Calculate the atomic mass and the atomic radius of the metal. What element might this metal be?

44. Iridium (Ir) has a face-centered cubic unit cell with an edge length of 383.3 pm. The density of iridium is 22.61 g/cm^3. Use these data to calculate a value for Avogadro's number.

45. Titanium metal has a body-centered cubic unit cell. The density of titanium is 4.50 g/cm^3. Calculate the edge length of the unit cell and a value for the atomic radius of titanium. (*Hint:* In a body-centered arrangement of spheres, the spheres touch across the body diagonal.)

46. Tungsten metal, which has the highest melting point of all the elements except for carbon, exists in a body-centered cubic structure. The atomic radius of tungsten is 139 pm. Calculate the density of solid tungsten.

47. Nickel has a face-centered cubic unit cell. The density of nickel is 6.84 g/cm^3. Calculate a value for the atomic radius of nickel.

48. The ionic radius of gold is 144 pm, and the density is 19.32 g/cm^3. Does elemental gold have a face-centered cubic structure or a body-centered cubic structure?

49. Superalloys have been made of nickel and aluminum. (See *Scientific American*, October 1986, p. 159). The alloy owes its strength to the formation of an ordered phase, called the gamma-prime phase, in which Al atoms are at the corners of a cubic unit cell and Ni atoms are at the face centers. What is the composition (relative numbers of atoms) for this phase of the nickel–aluminum superalloy?

50. The unit cell for nickel arsenide is shown below. What is the formula of this compound?

Ni
As

51. Perovskite is a mineral containing calcium, titanium, and oxygen. Two different representations of the unit cell are shown below. Show that both these representations give the same formula and the same number of oxygen atoms around each titanium atom.

52. Materials, containing the elements Y, Ba, Cu, and O, that are superconductors (electrical resistance equals zero) at temperatures above that of liquid nitrogen were recently discovered. The structures of these materials are based on the perovskite structure. Were they to have the ideal perovskite structure, the superconductor would have the structure shown in part (a) of the accompanying figure.

    a. What is the formula of this ideal perovskite material?

    b. How is this structure related to the perovskite structure shown in Exercise 51?

    These materials, however, do not act as superconductors unless they are deficient in oxygen. The structure of the actual superconducting phase appears to be that shown in part (b) of the figure.

    c. What is the formula of this material?

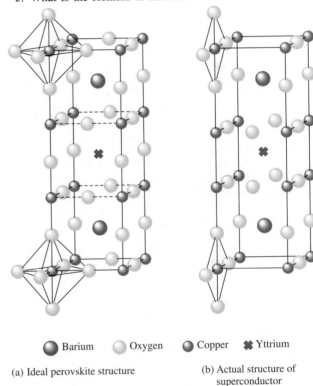

(a) Ideal perovskite structure   (b) Actual structure of superconductor

53. Selenium is a semiconductor used in photocopying machines. What type of semiconductor would be formed if a small amount of indium impurity is added to pure selenium?

54. The Group 3/Group 5 semiconductors are composed of equal amounts of atoms from Group 3A and Group 5A, for example, InP and GaAs. These types of semiconductors are used in light-emitting diodes and solid-state lasers. What would you add to make a p-type semiconductor from pure GaAs? How would you dope pure GaAs to make an n-type semiconductor?

55. The band gap in aluminum phosphide (ATP) is 2.5 electron-volts (1 eV = 1.6×10^{-19} J). What wavelength of light is emitted by an ATP diode?

56. An aluminum antimonide solid-state laser emits light with a wavelength of 730 nm. Calculate the band gap in joules.

57. The structures of some common crystalline substances are shown below. Show that the net composition of each unit cell corresponds to the correct formula of each substance.

○ = Cl   ○ = Na

○ = Cl   ● = Cs

○ = S   ● = Zn

○ = O   ● = Ti

58. The unit cell for a pure xenon fluoride compound is shown below.
   a. What is the formula of the compound?
   b. The unit cell of XeF_2 has a height of 702 pm, and the edge of the square base is 432 pm. Calculate the density of XeF_2.

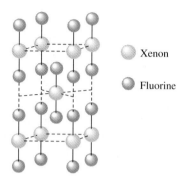

○ Xenon

○ Fluorine

Phase Changes and Phase Diagrams

59. The temperature inside a pressure cooker is 115°C. Use Equation (10.5) to calculate the vapor pressure of water inside the pressure cooker. What would be the temperature inside the pressure cooker if the vapor pressure of water was 3.5 atm?

60. What pressure would have to be applied to steam at 350°C to condense the steam to liquid water?

61. How much energy does it take to convert 0.50 kg ice at −20°C to steam at 250°C? Specific heat capacities: ice, 2.1 J/g · °C; liquid, 4.2 J/g · °C; steam, 1.8 J/g · °C. $\Delta H_{vap} = 40.7$ kJ/mol, $\Delta H_{fus} = 6.0$ kJ/mol.

62. What is the final temperature when 0.850 kJ of energy is added to 10.0 g ice at 0°C?

63. The enthalpy of vaporization of acetone is 32.0 kJ/mol. The normal boiling point of acetone is 56.5°C. What is the vapor pressure of acetone at 25.0°C?

64. At an elevation of 5300 ft the atmospheric pressure is about 630. torr. What would be the boiling point of acetone ($\Delta H_{vap} = 32.0$ kJ/mol) at this elevation? What would be the vapor pressure at 25°C at this elevation?

65. Plot the following data and determine ΔH_{vap} for magnesium and lithium. In which metal is the bonding stronger?

Vapor Pressure (mm Hg)	Temperature (°C)	
	Li	Mg
1.	750.	620.
10.	890.	740.
100.	1080.	900.
400.	1240.	1040.
760.	1310.	1110.

66. From the following data for liquid nitric acid, determine its heat of vaporization and normal boiling point.

Temperature (°C)	Vapor Pressure (mm Hg)
0	14.4
10	26.6
20	47.9
30	81.3
40	133
50	208
80	670

67. Describe how a phase diagram can be constructed from the heating curve for a substance.

68. A substance has the following properties:

		Specific Heat Capacities	
ΔH_{vap}	20 kJ/mol	$C(s)$	3.0 J/g · °C
ΔH_{fus}	5 kJ/mol	$C(l)$	2.5 J/g · °C
bp	75°C	$C(g)$	1.0 J/g · °C
mp	−15°C		

Sketch a heating curve for the substance starting at −50°C.

69. Consider the phase diagram given below. What phases are present at points A through H? Identify the triple point, normal boiling point, normal freezing point, and critical point.

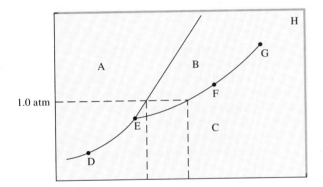

70. Use the accompanying phase diagram for sulfur to answer the following questions.
    a. How many triple points are in the phase diagram?
    b. What phases are in equilibrium at each of the triple points?
    c. What phase is stable at room temperature and 1.0 atm pressure?
    d. Can monoclinic sulfur exist in equilibrium with sulfur vapor?

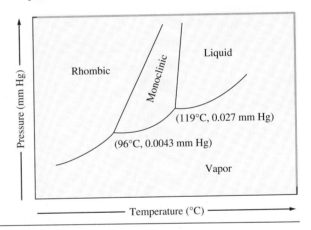

Additional Exercises

71. Rationalize the following boiling points.

72. Many organic acids, such as acetic acid (CH_3CO_2H), whose structure is shown in Exercise 71, exist in the gas phase as hydrogen-bonded dimers (two molecule units). Draw a reasonable structure for such dimers.

73. X rays from a copper X-ray tube ($\lambda = 1.54$ Å) were diffracted at an angle of 14.22 degrees by a crystal of silicon. Assuming first-order diffraction ($n = 1$ in the Bragg equation), what is the interplanar spacing in silicon?

74. Cobalt exists in two crystalline forms. Below 417°C cobalt is in the α-form, which has a hexagonal closest packed structure and a density of 8.90 g/cm³. Above 417°C cobalt is in the β-form, a cubic closest packed arrangement. The atomic radius of cobalt is 125 pm. Is there a change in the density of cobalt in going from the α-form to the β-form?

75. How could you tell experimentally if TiO_2 is an ionic solid or a network solid? What would you predict on the basis of electronegativity differences?

76. Titanium(IV) chloride is a liquid that boils at 136°C. What might explain why $TiCl_4$ exists as discrete covalent molecules rather than as an ionic substance?

77. The heats of vaporization of the hydrogen halides are

HF	7.5 kJ/mol
HCl	16.1 kJ/mol
HBr	17.6 kJ/mol
HI	19.7 kJ/mol

The boiling points for the hydrogen halides follow the same trend as those of the hydrides of the elements in Group 5 and Group 6. Can you account for any discrepancies between these data and your predictions in part g of Exercise 33? *Hint:* Think about the effects of aggregates in the vapor phase.

78. Consider the following values for lattice energies (Section 8.5) and interionic distances (center to center) for some of the alkali metal halides:

	Lattice Energy (kJ/mol)	Interionic Distance (Å)
LiF	−1034	2.01
LiCl	−840	2.57
LiBr	−781	2.75
LiI	−718	3.02
NaF	−914	2.31
NaCl	−770	2.81
NaBr	−728	2.98
NaI	−680	3.23
KCl	−701	3.14
RbCl	−682	3.28
CsCl	−629	3.56
CsF	−744	3.00

Plot the lattice energies of these compounds as a function of interionic distance and as a function of the reciprocal of the interionic distance. Which plot is most nearly linear? Why? Are there any discrepancies in the linear plot? Account for them.

79. In solid KCl the smallest distance between the centers of a potassium ion and a chloride ion is 314 pm. Calculate the length of the edge of the unit cell and the density of KCl, assuming it has the same structure as sodium chloride.

80. The enthalpy of vaporization of mercury is 59.1 kJ/mol. The normal boiling point of mercury is 357°C. What is the vapor pressure of mercury at 25°C?

81. In regions with dry climates, evaporative coolers are used to cool air. A typical electric air conditioner is rated at 1.00×10^4 Btu/h (1 Btu, or British thermal unit = amount of energy to raise the temperature of 1 lb of water by 1°F). How much water must be evaporated each hour to dissipate as much heat as a typical electric air conditioner?

82. Calculate the enthalpy of vaporization and the normal boiling point of methanol using the following data:

Temperature (°C)	Vapor Pressure (mm Hg)
−6.0°C	20.0
5.0°C	40.0
12.1°C	60.0
21.2°C	100.0
49.9°C	400.0

83. Use the accompanying phase diagram for carbon to answer the following questions.
    a. How many triple points are in the phase diagram?
    b. What phases can coexist at each triple point?
    c. What happens if graphite is subjected to very high pressures at room temperature?
    d. If we assume that the density increases with an increase in pressure, which is more dense, graphite or diamond?

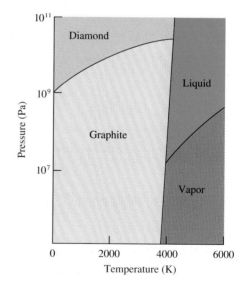

Challenge Problems

84. Using the heats of fusion and vaporization for water, calculate the change in enthalpy for the sublimation of water:

$$H_2O(s) \rightarrow H_2O(g)$$

Using the ΔH value given in Exercise 31 and the number of hydrogen bonds formed with each water molecule, estimate what portion of the intermolecular forces in ice can be accounted for by hydrogen bonding.

85. Oil of wintergreen, or methyl salicylate, has the following structure:

mp = $-8°C$

Methyl-4-hydroxybenzoate is another molecule with exactly the same molecular formula; it has the following structure:

mp = $127°C$

Account for the large difference in the melting points of the two substances.

86. Some of the physical properties of H_2O and D_2O are as follows:

	H_2O	D_2O
Density at 20°C (g/mL)	0.997	1.108
Boiling point (°C)	100.00	101.41
Melting point (°C)	0.00	3.79
ΔH_{vap} (kJ/mol)	40.7	41.61
ΔH_{fus} (kJ/mol)	6.02	6.3

Account for the differences. (*Note:* D is a symbol often used for ^2H, the deuterium isotope of hydrogen.)

87. Consider the following melting point data:

Compound:	NaCl	MgCl$_2$	AlCl$_3$	SiCl$_4$	PCl$_3$	SCl$_2$	Cl$_2$
mp (°C):	801	708	190	-70	-91	-78	-101
Compound:	NaF	MgF$_2$	AlF$_3$	SiF$_4$	PF$_5$	SF$_6$	F$_2$
mp (°C):	997	1396	1040	-90	-94	-56	-220

Account for the trends in melting points in terms of interparticle forces.

88. Boron nitride (BN) exists in two forms. The first is a slippery solid formed from the reaction of BCl_3 with NH_3, followed by heating in an ammonia atmosphere at 750°C. Subjecting the first form of BN to a pressure of 85,000 atm at 1800°C produces a second form that is the second hardest substance known. Both forms of BN remain solids to 3000°C. Suggest structures for the two forms of BN.

89. A crystal of hafnium (Hf) was exposed to X rays from a Mo X-ray tube ($\lambda = 71.2$ pm). First-order diffraction ($n = 1$ in the Bragg equation) was observed at an angle of 5.564 degrees. The density of hafnium is 13.28 g/cm^3. Assuming that the distance calculated from the Bragg equation gives the edge length of the cubic unit cell, does hafnium exist in a body-centered or a face-centered cubic arrangement? Calculate the atomic radius of hafnium.

90. What fraction of the total volume of a cubic closest packed structure is occupied by atoms?

91. Use the diagram of the unit cell for the hexagonal closest packed structure in Fig. 10.14 to calculate the net number of atoms in the unit cell.

92. The compounds K_2O, CuI, and ZrI_4 all can be described as cubic closest packed anions with the cations in tetrahedral holes. What fraction of the tetrahedral holes is occupied for each case?

93. Spinel is a mineral that contains 37.9% aluminum, 17.1% magnesium, and 45.0% oxygen, by mass, and has a density of 3.57 g/cm^3. The edge of the cubic unit cell measures 809 pm. How many of each type of atom are present in the unit cell?

94. You are given a small bar of an unknown metal X. You find the density of the metal to be 10.5 g/cm^3. An X-ray diffraction experiment measures the edge of the face-centered cubic unit cell as 4.09 Å (1 Å = 10^{-10} m). Identify X.

95. You are asked to help set up a historical display in the park by stacking some cannonballs next to a Revolutionary War cannon. You are told to stack them by starting with a triangle in which each side is composed of four touching cannonballs. You are to continue stacking them until you have a single ball on the top centered over the middle of the triangular base.
   a. How many cannonballs do you need?
   b. What type of closest packing is displayed by the cannonballs?
   c. The four corners of the pyramid of cannonballs form the corners of what type of regular geometric solid?

96. Some water is placed in a sealed glass container connected to a vacuum pump (a device used to pump gases from a container), and the pump is turned on. The water appears to boil and then freezes. Explain these changes using the phase diagram for water. What would happen to the ice if the vacuum pump was left on indefinitely?

97. A 0.250-g chunk of sodium metal is cautiously dropped into a mixture of 50.0 g water and 50.0 g ice at 0°C. The reaction is

$$2Na(s) + 2H_2O(l) \rightarrow 2NaOH(aq) + H_2(g) \quad \Delta H = -368 \text{ kJ}$$

Will the ice melt? Assuming that the final mixture has a specific heat capacity of 4.18 J/g · °C, calculate the final temperature.

CHAPTER 11

Properties of Solutions

Most of the substances we encounter in daily life are mixtures: wood, milk, gasoline, champagne, seawater, shampoo, steel, and air are common examples. When the components of a mixture are uniformly intermingled—that is, when a mixture is homogeneous—it is called a **solution.** Solutions can be gases, liquids, or solids, as shown in Table 11.1. However, we will be concerned in this chapter with the properties of liquid solutions, particularly those containing water. As we saw in Chapter 4, many essential chemical reactions occur in aqueous solutions because water is capable of dissolving so many substances.

Table 11.1

Various Types of Solutions

Example	State of Solution	State of Solute	State of Solvent
Air, natural gas	Gas	Gas	Gas
Vodka in water, antifreeze	Liquid	Liquid	Liquid
Brass, steel	Solid	Solid	Solid
Carbonated water (soda)	Liquid	Gas	Liquid
Seawater, sugar solution	Liquid	Solid	Liquid
Hydrogen in platinum	Solid	Gas	Solid

< A flame burns in a homogeneous, supercritical mixture of 70% water and 30% methane at 450°C and 1000 bar. Oxygen is injected from below at a rate of several cubic milliliters per second; the flame height is about 3 mm.

11.1 Solution Composition

Purpose

• To define various ways of describing solution composition.

A solute is the substance being dissolved. The solvent is the dissolving medium.

Because a mixture, unlike a chemical compound, has a variable composition, the relative amounts of substances in a solution must be specified. The qualitative terms *dilute* (relatively little solute present) and *concentrated* (relatively large amount of solute) are often used to describe solution content, but we need to define solution composition more precisely in order to perform calculations. For example, in dealing with the stoichiometry of solution reactions in Chapter 4, we found it useful to describe solution composition in terms of **molarity**, or the number of moles of solute per liter of solution (symbolized by M).

$$\text{Molarity} = \frac{\text{moles of solute}}{\text{liters of solution}}$$

Other ways of describing solution composition are also useful. **Mass percent** (sometimes called **weight percent**) is the percent by mass of the solute in the solution:

$$\text{Mass percent} = \left(\frac{\text{mass of solute}}{\text{mass of solution}}\right) \times 100$$

When liquids are mixed, the liquid present in the largest amount is called the solvent.

Another way of describing solution composition is the **mole fraction** (symbolized by the Greek lowercase letter chi, χ), the ratio of the number of moles of a given component to the total number of moles of solution. For a two-component solution, where n_A and n_B represent the number of moles of the two components,

$$\text{Mole fraction of component A} = \chi_A = \frac{n_A}{n_A + n_B}$$

In very dilute aqueous solutions, the magnitude of the molality and the molarity are almost the same.

Still another way of describing solution composition is **molality** (symbolized by m), the number of moles of solute per *kilogram of solvent:*

$$\text{Molality} = \frac{\text{moles of solute}}{\text{kilograms of solvent}}$$

Sample Exercise 11.1

A solution is prepared by mixing 1.00 g ethanol (C_2H_5OH) with 100.0 g water to give a final volume of 101 mL. Calculate the molarity, mass percent, mole fraction, and molality of ethanol in this solution.

Solution

Since molarity depends on the volume of the solution, it changes slightly with temperature. Molality is independent of temperature because it depends only on mass.

Molarity: The moles of ethanol can be obtained from its molar mass (46.07 g/mol):

$$1.00 \text{ g } C_2H_5OH \times \frac{1 \text{ mol } C_2H_5OH}{46.07 \text{ g } C_2H_5OH} = 2.17 \times 10^{-2} \text{ mol } C_2H_5OH$$

$$\text{Volume} = 101 \text{ mL} \times \frac{1 \text{ L}}{1000 \text{ mL}} = 0.101 \text{ L}$$

$$\text{Molarity of } C_2H_5OH = \frac{\text{moles of } C_2H_5OH}{\text{liters of solution}} = \frac{2.17 \times 10^{-2} \text{ mol}}{0.101 \text{ L}}$$

$$= 0.215 \ M$$

Mass percent:

$$\text{Mass percent } C_2H_5OH = \left(\frac{\text{mass of } C_2H_5OH}{\text{mass of solution}}\right) \times 100$$

$$= \left(\frac{1.00 \text{ g } C_2H_5OH}{100.0 \text{ g } H_2O + 1.00 \text{ g } C_2H_5OH}\right) \times 100$$

$$= 0.990\% \ C_2H_5OH$$

Mole fraction:

$$\text{Mole fraction of } C_2H_5OH = \frac{n_{C_2H_5OH}}{n_{C_2H_5OH} + n_{H_2O}}$$

$$n_{H_2O} = 100.0 \text{ g } H_2O \times \frac{1 \text{ mol } H_2O}{18.0 \text{ g } H_2O} = 5.56 \text{ mol}$$

$$\chi_{C_2H_5OH} = \frac{2.17 \times 10^{-2} \text{ mol}}{2.17 \times 10^{-2} \text{ mol} + 5.56 \text{ mol}}$$

$$= \frac{2.17 \times 10^{-2}}{5.58} = 0.00389$$

Molality:

$$\text{Molality of } C_2H_5OH = \frac{\text{moles of } C_2H_5OH}{\text{kilograms of } H_2O} = \frac{2.17 \times 10^{-2} \text{ mol}}{100.0 \text{ g} \times \dfrac{1 \text{ kg}}{1000 \text{ g}}}$$

$$= \frac{2.17 \times 10^{-2} \text{ mol}}{0.1000 \text{ kg}}$$

$$= 0.217 \ m$$

Another concentration measure sometimes encountered is **normality** (symbolized by N). Normality is defined as the number of *equivalents* per liter of solution, where the definition of an equivalent depends on the reaction taking place in the solution. *For an acid–base reaction,* the equivalent is the mass of acid or base that can furnish or accept exactly 1 mole of protons (H^+ ions). In Table 11.2 (on page 503) note, for example, that the equivalent mass of sulfuric acid is the molar mass divided by 2, since each mole of H_2SO_4 can furnish 2 moles of protons. The equivalent mass of calcium hydroxide is also half the molar mass, since each mole of $Ca(OH)_2$ contains 2 moles of OH^- ions that can react with 2 moles of protons. Note that the equivalent is defined so that 1 equivalent of acid will react with exactly 1 equivalent of base.

For oxidation–reduction reactions, the equivalent is defined as the quantity of oxidizing or reducing agent that can accept or furnish 1 mole of electrons. Thus 1 equivalent of reducing agent will react with exactly 1 equivalent of oxidizing agent. The equivalent mass of an oxidizing or reducing agent can be calculated from the

The definition of an equivalent depends on the reaction taking place in the solution.

The quantity we call equivalent mass here traditionally has been called equivalent weight.

Oxidation–reduction half-reactions were discussed in Section 4.10.

◀ CHEMICAL IMPACT ▶

An Energy Solution

In today's society we face many serious problems related to energy: turmoil in the Middle East, the greenhouse effect, and polluted city air. Clearly, the search for readily available, economical, and clean energy sources is of crucial importance. The solution may be in our backyards—literally.

When the sun shines on a swimming pool, the water is warmed by the solar energy. Because water is colorless (does not absorb visible light), the visible light from the sun passes through the water and strikes the bottom of the pool, where some of the light is absorbed and transformed to heat energy. This energy causes the water near the pool bottom to become warmer than the water above it. This warmer water, which has a lower density than the cooler water above it, then tends to rise toward the surface. This sets up convection currents, which circulate the warmer water to the surface, where it is cooled (mainly by evaporation). The convection currents keep the temperature of the water in the pool relatively uniform throughout.

How can this convective cooling process be stopped, thus allowing a pool of water to be an effective heat sink? The answer lies in adding common salt, NaCl. When sufficient salt is added to a pool of water 10 to 15 ft deep, a salinity gradient is established. That is, the salt concentration is not uniform in the pool. In fact, three distinct layers can be identified. The top layer, called the **convective layer,** has a salt concentration of about 2% by mass and is only about half a meter thick. The

bottom layer has a very high salt concentration (about 27% by mass) and serves as the **heat-storage layer.** The middle layer, the so-called **nonconvective layer** is about 1.5 m thick. Being intermediate in density between the top and bottom layers, the nonconvective layer is trapped between these layers and acts as an insulator.

Because the bottom layer of the solution in the pool is so much more dense than the other layers, it can get very hot without setting up significant convection currents. With a black, light-absorbing coating on the pool bottom, the water in the deepest layer of the pool can easily reach temperatures in the range of 90 to 100°C. In fact, a temperature as high as 107°C has been reported. (The boiling point of this very concentrated solution is much higher than 100°C.) Energy from the pool can be extracted by pumping the hot brine from the storage layer through a

The solar pond in En Bokek, Israel, near the Dead Sea.

heat exchanger to heat water or some other fluid.

A solar pond can be used to generate electricity by employing special turbines that use a working fluid other than water. Typical steam turbines cannot be used, because the solar pond cannot produce temperatures high enough to generate steam efficiently. However, lower-boiling liquids can be used.

Solar ponds are now in use. A 52-acre pond at En Bokek near the Dead Sea produces 2.5 MW of electricity at peak power and could produce as much as 5 MW if more heat exchangers and turbines were installed in the powerhouse. This is a useful amount of electricity, but 200 such ponds would be required to provide the electricity produced by a typical conventional power plant. In the United States such installations probably would be most feasible in the Southwest, with its abundant land and sunshine. However, the concept may be more widely applicable. A study financed by the U.S. Department of Energy indicates that a 27,000-acre solar pond producing 600 MW of electricity would be competitive with conventional power plants in all states except Alaska.

Solar ponds are relatively inexpensive to build, easy to maintain, and nonpolluting if the pond bottom is sealed to prevent any leakage of the salt water. It has been estimated that by 2010 as much as 7% of the energy requirements of the United States could be supplied by solar ponds with a combined surface area about four times that of the Great Salt Lake.

number of electrons in its half-reaction. For example, MnO_4^- reacting in acidic solution absorbs five electrons to produce Mn^{2+}:

$$MnO_4^- + 5e^- + 8H^+ \rightarrow Mn^{2+} + 4H_2O$$

Since the MnO_4^- ion present in 1 mole of $KMnO_4$ consumes 5 moles of electrons, the equivalent mass is the molar mass divided by 5:

$$\text{Equivalent mass of } KMnO_4 = \frac{\text{molar mass}}{5} = \frac{158 \text{ g}}{5} = 31.6 \text{ g}$$

Table 11.2			
The Molar Mass, Equivalent Mass, and Relationship of Molarity and Normality for Several Acids and Bases			
Acid or Base	Molar Mass	Equivalent Mass	Relationship of Molarity and Normality
HCl	36.5	36.5	$1\ M = 1\ N$
H_2SO_4	98	$\dfrac{98}{2} = 49$	$1\ M = 2\ N$
H_3PO_4	98	$\dfrac{98}{3} = 32.6$	$1\ M = 3\ N$
NaOH	40	40	$1\ M = 1\ N$
$Ca(OH)_2$	74	$\dfrac{74}{2} = 37$	$1\ M = 2\ N$

Sample Exercise 11.2

The electrolyte in automobile lead storage batteries is a 3.75 M sulfuric acid solution that has a density of 1.230 g/mL. Calculate the mass percent, molality, mole fraction, and normality of the sulfuric acid.

Solution

The density of the solution in grams per liter is

$$1.230\ \frac{g}{mL} \times \frac{1000\ mL}{1\ L} = 1.230 \times 10^3\ g/L$$

Thus 1 liter of this solution contains 1230. g of the mixture of sulfuric acid and water. Since the solution is 3.75 M, we know that 3.75 mol H_2SO_4 is present per liter of solution. The number of grams of H_2SO_4 present is

$$3.75\ mol \times \frac{98.1\ g\ H_2SO_4}{1\ mol} = 368\ g\ H_2SO_4$$

The amount of water present in 1 liter of solution is obtained from the difference

$$1230.\ g\ solution - 368\ g\ H_2SO_4 = 862\ g\ H_2O$$

$$862\ g\ H_2O \times \frac{1\ mol\ H_2O}{18.0\ g\ H_2O} = 47.9\ mol\ H_2O$$

Since we now know the masses of the solute and solvent, we can calculate the mass percent.

$$\text{Mass percent } H_2SO_4 = \frac{\text{mass of } H_2SO_4}{\text{mass of solution}} \times 100 = \frac{368\ g}{1230.\ g} \times 100$$
$$= 29.9\%\ H_2SO_4$$

From the moles of solute and the mass of solvent we can calculate the molality.

A modern 12-volt lead storage battery of the type used in automobiles.

$$\text{Molality of } H_2SO_4 = \frac{\text{moles } H_2SO_4}{\text{kilograms of } H_2O}$$

$$= \frac{3.75 \text{ mol } H_2SO_4}{862 \text{ g } H_2O \times \dfrac{1 \text{ kg } H_2O}{1000 \text{ g } H_2O}} = 4.35 \text{ } m$$

The mole fraction of solute can be obtained from moles of solute and solvent.

$$\text{Mole fraction of } H_2SO_4 = \frac{\text{moles of } H_2SO_4}{\text{moles of } H_2SO_4 + \text{moles of } H_2O}$$

$$= \frac{3.75}{3.75 + 47.9} = 0.0726$$

Since each sulfuric acid molecule can furnish two protons, 1 mol H_2SO_4 represents 2 equivalents. Thus a solution with 3.75 mol H_2SO_4 per liter contains $2 \times 3.75 = 7.50$ equivalents per liter, and the normality is 7.50 N.

A brown pelican's egg in Everglades National Park, Florida. The presence of DDT in many birds causes their eggs' shells to become too thin.

Polar solvents dissolve polar solutes; nonpolar solvents dissolve nonpolar solutes.

11.2 The Energies of Solution Formation

Purpose

- To define the heat of solution and discuss its various energy components.

Dissolving solutes in liquids is very common. We dissolve salt in the water used to cook vegetables, sugar in iced tea, stains in cleaning fluid, gaseous carbon dioxide in water to make soda water, ethanol in gasoline to make gasohol, and so on.

Solubility is important in other ways. For example, because the pesticide DDT is fat-soluble, it is retained and concentrated in animal tissues, where it causes detrimental effects. This is why DDT, even though it is effective for killing mosquitos, has been banned in the United States. Also, the solubility of various vitamins is important in determining correct dosages. The insolubility of barium sulfate means it can be used safely to improve X rays of the gastrointestinal tract, even though Ba^{2+} ions are quite toxic.

What factors affect solubility? The cardinal rule of solubility is *like dissolves like*. We find that we must use a polar solvent to dissolve a polar or ionic solute and a nonpolar solvent to dissolve a nonpolar solute. Now we will try to understand why this behavior occurs. To simplify the discussion, we will assume that the formation of a liquid solution takes place in three distinct steps:

STEP 1

Breaking up the solute into individual components (expanding the solute).

STEP 2

Overcoming intermolecular forces in the solvent to make room for the solute (expanding the solvent).

STEP 3

Allowing the solute and solvent to interact to form the solution.

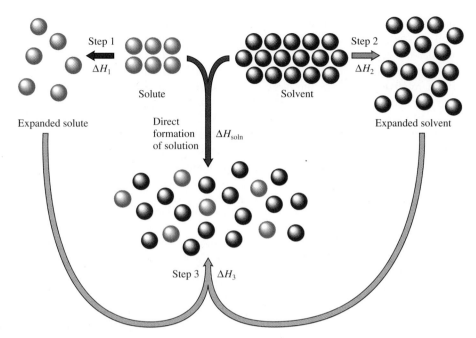

Figure 11.1

The formation of a liquid solution can be divided into three steps: (1) expanding the solute, (2) expanding the solvent, and (3) combining the expanded solute and solvent to form the solution.

These steps are illustrated in Fig. 11.1. Steps 1 and 2 require energy, since forces must be overcome to expand the solute and solvent. Step 3 usually releases energy. In other words, Steps 1 and 2 are endothermic, and Step 3 is often exothermic. The enthalpy change associated with the formation of the solution, called the **enthalpy (heat) of solution** (ΔH_{soln}), is the sum of the ΔH values for the steps:

$$\Delta H_{soln} = \Delta H_1 + \Delta H_2 + \Delta H_3$$

The enthalpy of solution is the sum of the energies used in expanding both solvent and solute and the energy of solvent–solute interaction.

where ΔH_{soln} may have a positive sign (energy absorbed) or a negative sign (energy released), as shown in Fig. 11.2.

To illustrate the importance of the various energy terms in the equation for ΔH_{soln}, we will consider two specific cases. First, we know that oil is not soluble in water. When oil tankers leak, the petroleum forms an oil slick that floats on the

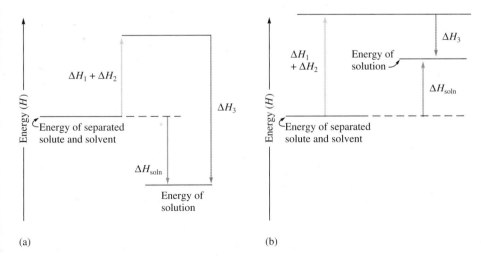

Figure 11.2

The heat of solution (a) ΔH_{soln} has a negative sign (the process is exothermic) if Step 3 releases more energy than that required by Steps 1 and 2. (b) ΔH_{soln} has a positive sign (the process is endothermic) if Steps 1 and 2 require more energy than is released in Step 3. (If the energy changes for Steps 1 and 2 equal that for Step 3, then ΔH_{soln} is zero.)

Gasoline floating on water. Because gasoline is nonpolar, it is immiscible with water.

water and is eventually carried onto the beaches. We can explain the immiscibility of oil and water by considering the energy terms involved. Oil is a mixture of nonpolar molecules that interact through London dispersion forces, which depend on molecule size. We expect ΔH_1 to be small for a typical nonpolar solute, but it will be relatively large for the large oil molecules. The term ΔH_3 will be small, since interactions between the nonpolar solute molecules and the polar water molecules will be negligible. However, ΔH_2 will be large and positive because it takes considerable energy to overcome the hydrogen bonding forces among the water molecules to expand the solvent. Thus ΔH_{soln} will be large and positive because of the ΔH_1 and ΔH_2 terms. Since a large amount of energy would have to be expended to form an oil–water solution, this process does not occur to any appreciable extent. These same arguments hold true for any nonpolar solute and polar solvent—the combination of a nonpolar solute and a highly polar solvent is not expected to produce a solution.

As a second case, let's consider the solubility of an ionic solute, such as sodium chloride, in water. Here the term ΔH_1 is large and positive because the strong ionic forces in the crystal must be overcome, and ΔH_2 is large and positive because hydrogen bonds must be broken in the water. Finally, ΔH_3 is large and negative because of the strong interactions between the ions and the water molecules. In fact, the exothermic and endothermic terms essentially cancel, as shown from the known values:

$$NaCl(s) \rightarrow Na^+(g) + Cl^-(g) \qquad\qquad \Delta H_1 = 786 \text{ kJ/mol}$$
$$H_2O(l) + Na^+(g) + Cl^-(g) \rightarrow Na^+(aq) + Cl^-(aq) \qquad \Delta H_{\text{hyd}} = \Delta H_2 + \Delta H_3$$
$$= -783 \text{ kJ/mol}$$

Here the **enthalpy (heat) of hydration** (ΔH_{hyd}) combines the terms ΔH_2 (for expanding the solvent) and ΔH_3 (for solvent–solute interactions). The heat of hydration represents the enthalpy change associated with the dispersal of a gaseous solute in water. Thus the heat of solution for dissolving sodium chloride is the sum of ΔH_1 and ΔH_{hyd}:

$$\Delta H_{\text{soln}} = 786 \text{ kJ/mol} - 783 \text{ kJ/mol} = 3 \text{ kJ/mol}$$

Note that ΔH_{soln} is small but positive; the dissolving process requires a small amount of energy. Then why is NaCl so soluble in water? The answer lies in nature's tendency toward disorder. That is, processes naturally run in the direction that leads to greater disorder. For example, imagine equal numbers of orange and yellow spheres separated by a partition, as shown in Fig. 11.3(a). If we remove the partition and shake the container, the spheres will mix [Fig. 11.3(b)], and no amount of shaking will cause them to return to the state of separated orange and yellow. Why? The mixed, or disordered, state is simply much more likely to occur (more probable) than the original separate, or ordered, state because there are many more ways of placing the spheres to give a mixed state than a separated state. This is a general principle. *One factor that favors a process is an increase in disorder.*

But energy considerations are also important. *Processes that require large amounts of energy tend not to occur.* Since dissolving 1 mole of solid NaCl requires only a small amount of energy, the solution forms, presumably because of the large increase in disorder occurring when the solute and solvent mix.

The various possible cases for solution formation are summarized in Table 11.3. Note that in two cases, polar–polar and nonpolar–nonpolar, the heat of solution is

(a)   (b)

Figure 11.3

(a) Orange and yellow spheres separated by a partition in a closed container. (b) The spheres after the partition is removed and the container has been shaken for some time.

expected to be small. In these cases, the solution forms because of the increase in disorder. In the other cases (polar–nonpolar and nonpolar–polar), the heat of solution is expected to be large and positive, and the large quantity of energy required acts to prevent the solution from forming. Although this discussion has greatly oversimplified the complex driving forces for solubility, these ideas are a useful starting point for understanding the observation that *like dissolves like*.

Sample Exercise 11.3

Decide whether liquid hexane (C_6H_{14}) or liquid methanol (CH_3OH) is the more appropriate solvent for the substances grease ($C_{20}H_{42}$) and potassium iodide (KI).

Solution

Hexane is a nonpolar solvent because it contains nonpolar C—H bonds. Thus hexane will work best for the nonpolar solute grease. Methanol has an O—H group that makes it significantly polar. Thus it will serve as the better solvent for the ionic solid KI.

Table 11.3

The Energy Terms for Various Types of Solutes and Solvents

	ΔH_1	ΔH_2	ΔH_3	ΔH_{soln}	Outcome
Polar solvent, polar solute	Large	Large	Large, negative	Small	Solution forms
Polar solvent, nonpolar solute	Small	Large	Small	Large, positive	No solution forms
Nonpolar solvent, nonpolar solute	Small	Small	Small	Small	Solution forms
Nonpolar solvent, polar solute	Large	Small	Small	Large, positive	No solution forms

---

◀ **CHEMICAL IMPACT** ▶

Miracle Solvents

When a substance is heated beyond its critical temperature (T_c) and then placed under extremely high pressure, it forms a **supercritical fluid.** Although these fluids resemble liquids, they technically are not liquids. A liquid cannot exist above the critical temperature for a substance. For example, if a gaseous substance is maintained above T_c and pressure is gradually applied, there is no distinct point where the gas changes to a liquid, as would occur below T_c, but the supercritical fluid gradually forms as the pressure is increased.

In recent experiments at the Agriculture Department's Northern Regional Research Center in Peoria, Illinois, scientists have found that supercritical carbon dioxide behaves as a very useful nonpolar solvent for removing fat from meat. At temperatures above 31°C (T_c for CO_2) and several hundred atmospheres of pressure, the carbon dioxide fluid can dissolve virtually all the fat from samples of meat. Even more important, the fluid also will dissolve any pesticide or drug residues that may be present in the meat. When the carbon dioxide fluid is returned to normal pressures, it immediately vaporizes, and the fat, drug, and pesticide molecules come "raining" out to allow easy analysis of the types and amounts of contaminants present in the meat. Therefore, this method provides an efficient way to test meat for trace pesticide and drug residues.

Like supercritical carbon dioxide, supercritical water is also a very interesting substance that has strikingly different properties from those of liquid water. For example, recent experiments have shown

(*left*) A multistage supercritical fluid extraction apparatus. The scientist draws off extracted material into a receiver flask. (*above*) Chicken fat obtained by using supercritical carbon dioxide as the extracting agent.

that supercritical (superfluid) water can behave simultaneously as both a polar and a nonpolar solvent. While the reasons for this unusual behavior remain unclear, the practical value of this behavior is very clear: it makes superfluid water a very useful reaction medium for a wide variety of substances. One extremely important application of this idea involves the environmentally sound destruction of industrial wastes. Most hazardous organic (nonpolar) substances can be dissolved in supercritical water and oxidized by dissolved O_2 in a matter of minutes. The products of these reactions are water, carbon dioxide, and possibly simple acids (which result when halogen-containing compounds are reacted). Therefore, the aqueous mixture that results from the reaction often can be disposed of with little

further treatment. In contrast to the incinerators used to destroy organic waste products, a supercritical water reactor is a closed system (has no emissions).

Supercritical water has strange and wonderful properties, one of the most astonishing being that a flame can burn within the supercritical fluid during the reaction of O_2 with an organic substance (see the photograph on p. 498). These properties promise to make supercritical water a miracle medium for chemical reactions.

Suggested Reading

R. W. Shaw, T. B. Brill, A. A. Clifford, C. A. Eckert, and E. U. Franck, "Supercritical Water," *Chem. Eng. News*, Dec. 23, 1991: 26.

11.3 Factors Affecting Solubility

Purpose

- To show how molecular structure, pressure, and temperature affect solubility.

Structure Effects

In the last section we saw that solubility is favored if the solute and solvent have similar polarities. Since it is the molecular structure that determines polarity, there should be a definite connection between structure and solubility. Vitamins provide an excellent example of the relationship of molecular structure, polarity, and solubility.

Recently, there has been considerable publicity about the pros and cons of consuming large quantities of vitamins. For example, large doses of vitamin C have been advocated to combat various illnesses, including the common cold. Vitamin E has been extolled as a youth-preserving elixir and a protector against the carcinogenic (cancer-causing) effects of certain chemicals. However, there are possible detrimental effects from taking large amounts of some vitamins, depending on their solubilities.

Vitamins can be divided into two classes: *fat-soluble* (vitamins A, D, E, and K) and *water-soluble* (vitamins B and C). The reason for the differing solubility characteristics can be seen by comparing the structures of vitamins A and C (Fig. 11.4). Vitamin A, composed mostly of carbon and hydrogen atoms that have similar electronegativities, is virtually nonpolar. This causes it to be soluble in nonpolar materials such as body fat, which is also largely composed of carbon and hydrogen, but not soluble in polar solvents such as water. On the other hand, vitamin C has many polar O—H and C—O bonds, making the molecule polar and thus water-soluble. We often describe nonpolar materials such as vitamin A as **hydrophobic** (water-fearing) and polar substances such as vitamin C as **hydrophilic** (water-loving).

Because of their solubility characteristics, the fat-soluble vitamins can build up in the fatty tissues of the body. This has both positive and negative effects. Since these vitamins can be stored, the body can tolerate for a time a diet deficient in vitamins A, D, E, or K. Conversely, if excessive amounts of these vitamins are consumed, their buildup can lead to the illness *hypervitaminosis*.

In contrast, the water-soluble vitamins are excreted by the body and must be consumed regularly. This fact was first recognized when the British navy discov-

Figure 11.4

The molecular structures of (*left*) vitamin A (nonpolar, fat-soluble) and (*right*) vitamin C (polar, water-soluble). The circles indicate polar bonds. Note that vitamin C contains far more polar bonds than vitamin A.

Carbonation in a bottle of soda.

ered that scurvy, a disease often suffered by sailors, could be prevented if the sailors regularly ate fresh limes (which are a good source of vitamin C) when aboard ship (hence the name "limey" for the British sailor).

Pressure Effects

While pressure has little effect on the solubilities of solids or liquids, it does significantly increase the solubility of a gas. Carbonated beverages, for example, are always bottled at high pressures of carbon dioxide to ensure a high concentration of carbon dioxide in the liquid. The fizzing that occurs when you open a can of soda results from the escape of gaseous carbon dioxide because under these conditions the pressure of CO_2 above the solution is much lower than that used in the bottling process.

The increase in gas solubility with pressure can be understood from Fig. 11.5. Figure 11.5(a) shows a gas in equilibrium with a solution; that is, the gas molecules are entering and leaving the solution at the same rate. If the pressure is suddenly increased [Fig. 11.5(b)], the number of gas molecules per unit volume increases, and the gas enters the solution at a higher rate than it leaves. As the concentration of dissolved gas increases, the rate of the escape of the gas also increases until a new equilibrium is reached [Fig. 11.5(c)], where the solution contains more dissolved gas than before.

The relationship between gas pressure and the concentration of dissolved gas is given by **Henry's law:**

$$P = kC$$

where P represents the partial pressure of the gaseous solute above the solution, C represents the concentration of the dissolved gas, and k is a constant characteristic of a particular solution. In words, Henry's law states that *the amount of a gas dissolved in a solution is directly proportional to the pressure of the gas above the solution.*

William Henry (1774–1836), a close friend of John Dalton, formulated his law in 1801.

Figure 11.5

(a) A gaseous solute in equilibrium with a solution. (b) The piston is pushed in, which increases the pressure of the gas and the number of gas molecules per unit volume. This causes an increase in the rate at which the gas enters the solution, so the concentration of dissolved gas increases. (c) The greater gas concentration in the solution causes an increase in the rate of escape. A new equilibrium is reached.

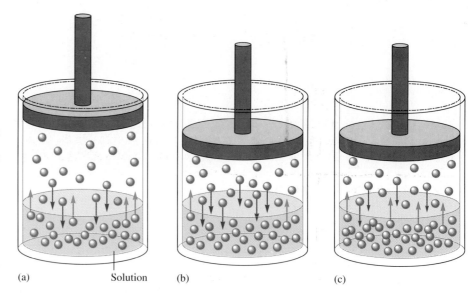

(a)   Solution   (b)   (c)

◀ **CHEMICAL IMPACT** ▶

The Lake Nyos Tragedy

On August 21, 1986, a cloud of gas suddenly boiled from Lake Nyos in Cameroon, killing nearly 2000 people. Although at first it was speculated that the gas was hydrogen sulfide, it now seems clear it was carbon dioxide. What would cause Lake Nyos to emit this huge, suffocating cloud of CO_2? Although the answer may never be known for certain, many scientists believe that the lake suddenly "turned over," bringing to the surface water that contained huge quantities of dissolved carbon dioxide. Lake Nyos is a deep lake that is thermally stratified: layers of warm, less dense water near the surface float on the colder, denser water layers nearer the lake's bottom. Under normal conditions the lake stays this way: there is little mixing among the different layers. Scientists believe that over hundreds or thousands of years, carbon dioxide gas had seeped into the cold water at the lake's bottom and dissolved in great amounts because of the large pressure of

Lake Nyos in Cameroon.

CO_2 present (in accordance with Henry's law). For some reason on August 21, 1986, the lake apparently suffered an overturn, possibly due to wind or to unusual cooling of the lake's surface by monsoon clouds. This caused water that was

greatly supersaturated with CO_2 to reach the surface and release tremendous quantities of gaseous CO_2 that suffocated humans and animals before they know what hit them—a tragic, monumental illustration of Henry's law.

Henry's law is obeyed most accurately for dilute solutions of gases that do not dissociate in or react with the solvent. For example, Henry's law is obeyed by oxygen gas in water, but it does *not* correctly represent the behavior of gaseous hydrogen chloride in water because of the dissociation reaction

> Henry's law holds only when there is no chemical reaction between the solute and solvent.

$$HCl(g) \xrightarrow{\text{H}_2\text{O}} H^+(aq) + Cl^-(aq)$$

Sample Exercise 11.4

A certain soft drink is bottled so that a bottle at 25°C contains CO_2 gas at a pressure of 5.0 atm over the liquid. Assuming that the partial pressure of CO_2 in the atmosphere is 4.0×10^{-4} atm, calculate the equilibrium concentrations of CO_2 in the soda both before and after the bottle is opened. The Henry's law constant for CO_2 in aqueous solution is $32 \text{ L} \cdot \text{atm/mol}$ at 25°C.

Solution

We can write Henry's law for CO_2 as

$$P_{CO_2} = k_{CO_2} C_{CO_2}$$

where $k_{CO_2} = 32$ L · atm/mol. In the *unopened* bottle, $P_{CO_2} = 5.0$ atm and

$$C_{CO_2} = \frac{P_{CO_2}}{k_{CO_2}} = \frac{5.0 \text{ atm}}{32 \text{ L} \cdot \text{atm/mol}} = 0.16 \text{ mol/L}$$

In the *opened* bottle, the CO_2 in the soda eventually reaches equilibrium with the atmospheric CO_2, so $P_{CO_2} = 4.0 \times 10^{-4}$ atm and

$$C_{CO_2} = \frac{P_{CO_2}}{k_{CO_2}} = \frac{4.0 \times 10^{-4} \text{ atm}}{32 \text{ L} \cdot \text{atm/mol}} = 1.2 \times 10^{-5} \text{ mol/L}$$

Note the large change in concentration of CO_2. This is why soda goes "flat" after being open for a while.

Temperature Effects (for Aqueous Solutions)

ΔH°_{soln} refers to the formation of a 1.0 *M* ideal solution and is not necessarily relevant to the process of dissolving a solid in a saturated solution. Thus ΔH°_{soln} is of limited use in predicting the variation of solubility with temperature.

Everyday experiences of dissolving substances such as sugar may lead you to think that solubility always increases with temperature. This is not the case. The dissolving of a solid occurs *more rapidly* at higher temperatures, but the amount of solid that can be dissolved may increase or decrease with increasing temperature. The effect of temperature on the solubility in water of several solids is shown in Fig. 11.6. Note that although the solubility of most solids in water increases with temperature, the solubilities of some substances (such as sodium sulfate and cerium sulfate) decrease with increasing temperature.

Predicting the temperature dependence of solubility is very difficult. For example, although there is some correlation between the sign of ΔH°_{soln} and the variation of solubility with temperature, important exceptions exist.* The only sure way to determine the temperature dependence of a solid's solubility is by experiment.

Figure 11.6

The solubilities of several solids as a function of temperature. Note that while most substances become more soluble in water with increasing temperature, sodium sulfate and cerium sulfate become less soluble.

*For more information see R. S. Treptow, "Le Châtelier's Principle Applied to the Temperature Dependence of Solubility," *J. Chem. Ed.* **61** (1984): 499.

◀ **CHEMICAL IMPACT** ▶

Recyclable Heat

The current rise in athletic activities has led to many injuries and has necessitated new products to treat those injuries. Of the many instant hot and cold packs available (also see Chemical Impact: Heat Packs in Chapter 6), one of the most interesting types produces heat by the exothermic precipitation of a solid from a solution. The heat pack looks like a tiny air mattress with two compartments. The larger compartment contains a viscous supersaturated solution of sodium thiosulfate ($Na_2S_2O_3$) dissolved in water,

and the smaller one contains crystals of solid sodium thiosulfate.

Because sodium thiosulfate crystals do not readily precipitate from aqueous solution, water can be greatly supersaturated with the solid. That is, much more solid $Na_2S_2O_3$ can be dissolved in water than should be possible at a given temperature. However, as soon as the supersaturated solution is exposed to a seed crystal of $Na_2S_2O_3$, to provide a pattern for crystal growth, the solid forms, releasing a considerable quantity of energy as heat over

several hours. The pack is activated by squeezing out a seed crystal so that it comes into contact with the solution. The resulting formation of the solid gives a pleasantly warm temperature of 48°C (118°F).

This heat pack can be recycled by simply placing it in boiling water to redissolve the sodium thiosulfate. As the pack cools, the solid remains dissolved—it again becomes supersaturated. The pack can be reused until the supply of seed crystals runs out.

The behavior of gases dissolving in water appears less complex. The solubility of a gas in water typically decreases with increasing temperature,* as is shown for several cases in Fig. 11.7. This temperature effect has important environmental implications because of the widespread use of water from lakes and rivers for industrial cooling. After being used, the water is returned to its natural source at a higher than ambient temperature (**thermal pollution** has occurred). Because it is warmer, this water contains less than the normal concentration of oxygen and is also less dense; it tends to ''float'' on the colder water below, thus blocking normal oxygen absorption. This effect can be especially important in deep lakes. The warm upper layer can seriously decrease the amount of oxygen available to aquatic life in the deeper layers of the lake.

The decreasing solubility of gases with increased temperature is also responsible for the formation of *boiler scale.* As we will see in more detail in Chapter 14, the bicarbonate ion is formed when carbon dioxide is dissolved in water containing the carbonate ion:

$$CO_3{}^{2-}(aq) + CO_2(aq) + H_2O(l) \rightarrow 2HCO_3{}^-(aq)$$

When the water also contains Ca^{2+} ions, this reaction is especially important—calcium bicarbonate is soluble in water, but calcium carbonate is insoluble. When the water is heated, the carbon dioxide is driven off. In order for the system to replace the lost carbon dioxide, the reverse reaction occurs:

$$2HCO_3{}^-(aq) \rightarrow H_2O(l) + CO_2(aq) + CO_3{}^{2-}(aq)$$

This reaction, however, also increases the concentration of carbonate ions, causing solid calcium carbonate to form. This solid is the boiler scale that coats the walls of containers such as industrial boilers and tea kettles. Boiler scale reduces the efficiency of heat transfer and can lead to blockage of pipes (see Fig. 11.8 on page 514).

Figure 11.7

The solubilities of several gases in water as a function of temperature at a constant pressure of 1 atm of gas above the solution.

---

*The opposite behavior is observed for most nonaqueous solvents.

Figure 11.8

A pipe with accumulated mineral deposits. The lengthwise section (*left*) shows the formation of scale. The cross section (*right*) clearly indicates the reduction in pipe capacity.

11.4 The Vapor Pressures of Solutions

Purpose

- To show how a solution's vapor pressure is affected by the concentration of solute and the interactions of solute and solvent.

Liquid solutions have physical properties significantly different from those of the pure solvent, a fact that has great practical importance. For example, we add antifreeze to the water in a car's cooling system to prevent freezing in winter and boiling in summer. We also melt ice on sidewalks and streets by spreading salt. These preventatives work because of the solute's effect on the solvent's properties.

A nonvolatile solute has no tendency to escape from solution into the vapor phase.

To explore how a nonvolatile solute affects a solvent, we will consider the experiment represented in Fig. 11.9, in which a sealed container encloses a beaker containing an aqueous sugar solution and a beaker containing pure water. Gradually, the volume of the sugar solution increases and the volume of the pure water decreases. Why? We can explain this observation if the vapor pressure of the pure solvent is greater than that of the solution. Under these conditions, the pressure of vapor necessary to achieve equilibrium with the pure solvent is greater than that required to reach equilibrium with the aqueous sugar solution. Thus, as the pure

Figure 11.9

An aqueous solution and pure water in a closed environment. (a) Initial stage. (b) After a period of time, the water is transferred to the solution.

solvent emits vapor to attempt to reach equilibrium, the aqueous sugar solution absorbs vapor to try to lower the vapor pressure toward its equilibrium value. This process results in a net transfer of water from the pure water through the vapor phase to the sugar solution. The system can only reach an equilibrium vapor pressure when all the water is transferred to the solution. This experiment is just one of many observations indicating that the presence of a *nonvolatile solute lowers the vapor pressure of a solvent*.

We can account for this behavior in terms of the simple model shown in Fig. 11.10. The dissolved nonvolatile solute decreases the number of solvent molecules per unit volume. Thus it lowers the number of solvent molecules at the surface, and it should proportionately lower the escaping tendency of the solvent molecules. For example, in a solution consisting of half nonvolatile solute molecules and half solvent molecules, we might expect the observed vapor pressure to be half that of the pure solvent, since only half as many molecules can escape. In fact, this is what is observed.

Detailed studies of the vapor pressures of solutions containing nonvolatile solutes were carried out by François M. Raoult (1830–1901). His results are described by the equation known as **Raoult's law:**

$$P_{soln} = \chi_{solvent}P^0_{solvent}$$

where P_{soln} is the observed vapor pressure of the solution, $\chi_{solvent}$ is the mole fraction of solvent, and $P^0_{solvent}$ is the vapor pressure of the pure solvent. Note that for a solution of half solute and half solvent molecules, $\chi_{solvent}$ is 0.5, so the vapor pressure of the solution is half that of the pure solvent. On the other hand, for a solution in which three-fourths of the solution molecules are solvent, $\chi_{solvent} = \frac{3}{4} = 0.75$, and $P_{soln} = 0.75P^0_{solvent}$. The idea is that the nonvolatile solute simply dilutes the solvent.

Raoult's law is a linear equation of the form $y = mx + b$, where $y = P_{soln}$, $x = \chi_{solvent}$, $m = P^0_{solvent}$, and $b = 0$. Thus a plot of P_{soln} versus $\chi_{solvent}$ gives a straight line with a slope equal to $P^0_{solvent}$, as is shown in Fig. 11.11.

The presence of a nonvolatile solute reduces the tendency of solvent molecules to escape.

Pure solvent   Solution with a nonvolatile solute

Figure 11.10

The presence of a nonvolatile solute inhibits the escape of solvent molecules from the liquid and so lowers the vapor pressure of the solvent.

Raoult's law states that the vapor pressure of a solution is directly proportional to the mole fraction of solvent present.

Sample Exercise 11.5

Calculate the expected vapor pressure at 25°C for a solution prepared by dissolving 158.0 g of common table sugar (sucrose, molar mass = 342.3 g/mol) in 643.5 cm³ of water. At 25°C the density of water is 0.9971 g/cm³ and the vapor pressure is 23.76 torr.

Solution

We will use Raoult's law in the form

$$P_{soln} = \chi_{H_2O}P^0_{H_2O}$$

To calculate the mole fraction of water in the solution, we must first determine the number of moles of sucrose:

$$\text{Moles of sucrose} = 158.0 \text{ g sucrose} \times \frac{1 \text{ mol sucrose}}{342.3 \text{ g sucrose}}$$

$$= 0.4616 \text{ mol sucrose}$$

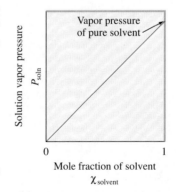

Figure 11.11

For a solution that obeys Raoult's law, a plot of P_{soln} versus $\chi_{solvent}$ gives a straight line.

To determine the moles of water present, we first convert volume to mass using the density:

$$643.5 \text{ cm}^3 \text{ H}_2\text{O} \times \frac{0.9971 \text{ g H}_2\text{O}}{\text{cm}^3 \text{ H}_2\text{O}} = 641.6 \text{ g H}_2\text{O}$$

The number of moles of water is therefore

$$641.6 \text{ g H}_2\text{O} \times \frac{1 \text{ mol H}_2\text{O}}{18.01 \text{ g H}_2\text{O}} = 35.63 \text{ mol H}_2\text{O}$$

The mole fraction of water in the solution is

$$\chi_{\text{H}_2\text{O}} = \frac{\text{mol H}_2\text{O}}{\text{mol H}_2\text{O} + \text{mol sucrose}} = \frac{35.63 \text{ mol}}{35.63 \text{ mol} + 0.4616 \text{ mol}}$$

$$= \frac{35.63 \text{ mol}}{36.09 \text{ mol}} = 0.9873$$

Then $\qquad P_{\text{soln}} = \chi_{\text{H}_2\text{O}} P_{\text{H}_2\text{O}}^0 = (0.9873)(23.76 \text{ torr}) = 23.46 \text{ torr}$

Thus the vapor pressure of water has been lowered from 23.76 torr in the pure state to 23.46 torr in the solution. The vapor pressure has been lowered by 0.30 torr.

The phenomenon of the lowering of the vapor pressure gives us a convenient way to ''count'' molecules and thus provides a means for experimentally determining molar masses. Suppose a certain mass of a compound is dissolved in a solvent and the vapor pressure of the resulting solution is measured. Using Raoult's law, we can determine the number of moles of solute present. Since the mass of this number of moles is known, we can calculate the molar mass as shown in Sample Exercise 11.6.

Sample Exercise 11.6

A solution was prepared by adding 20.0 g urea to 125 g water at 25°C, a temperature at which pure water has a vapor pressure of 23.76 torr. The observed vapor pressure of the solution was found to be 22.67 torr. Calculate the molar mass of urea.

Solution

Raoult's law can be rearranged to give

$$\chi_{\text{H}_2\text{O}} = \frac{P_{\text{soln}}}{P_{\text{H}_2\text{O}}^0}$$

This form allows us to determine the mole fraction of water in the solution:

$$\chi_{\text{H}_2\text{O}} = \frac{22.67 \text{ torr}}{23.76 \text{ torr}} = 0.9541$$

However, we are interested in the urea. To find its molar mass, we must find the number of moles represented by 20.0 g. We can calculate the number of moles of urea from the definition of $\chi_{\text{H}_2\text{O}}$:

Photomicrograph of urea crystals.

$$\chi_{H_2O} = \frac{\text{mol } H_2O}{\text{mol } H_2O + \text{mol urea}} = \frac{n_{H_2O}}{n_{H_2O} + n_{\text{urea}}}$$

From the mass of water used to prepare the solution, we have

$$n_{H_2O} = 125 \text{ g } H_2O \times \frac{1 \text{ mol } H_2O}{18.0 \text{ g } H_2O} = 6.94 \text{ mol } H_2O$$

Since $\chi_{H_2O} = 0.9541$, we deduce the following:

$$\chi_{H_2O} = 0.9541 = \frac{n_{H_2O}}{n_{H_2O} + n_{\text{urea}}} = \frac{6.94}{6.94 + n_{\text{urea}}}$$

or

$$0.9541 \,(6.94 + n_{\text{urea}}) = 6.94$$

Solving for the number of moles of urea gives

$$n_{\text{urea}} = \frac{6.94 - 6.62}{0.9541} = 0.335 \text{ mol}$$

Since 20.0 g urea was originally dissolved, 0.335 mol urea weighs 20.0 g. Thus

$$\frac{20.0 \text{ g}}{0.335 \text{ mol}} = 59.7 \text{ g/mol}$$

The value for the molar mass of urea determined in this experiment is thus 59.7. Urea has the formula $(NH_2)_2CO$ and a molar mass of 60.0 g/mol, so the result obtained in this experiment agrees well with the known molar mass.

We can also use vapor pressure measurements to characterize solutions. For example, 1 mole of sodium chloride dissolved in water lowers the vapor pressure approximately twice as much as expected because the solid has two ions per formula unit, which separate when it dissolves. Thus vapor pressure measurements can give valuable information about the nature of the solute after it dissolves.

The lowering of vapor pressure depends on the number of solute particles present in the solution.

Sample Exercise 11.7

Predict the vapor pressure of a solution prepared by mixing 35.0 g solid Na_2SO_4 (molar mass = 142 g/mol) with 175 g water at 25°C. The vapor pressure of pure water at 25°C is 23.76 torr.

Solution

First, we need to know the mole fraction of H_2O.

$$n_{H_2O} = 175 \text{ g } H_2O \times \frac{1 \text{ mol } H_2O}{18.0 \text{ g } H_2O} = 9.72 \text{ mol } H_2O$$

$$n_{Na_2SO_4} = 35.0 \text{ g } Na_2SO_4 \times \frac{1 \text{ mol } Na_2SO_4}{142 \text{ g } Na_2SO_4} = 0.246 \text{ mol } Na_2SO_4$$

It is essential to recognize that when 1 mol solid Na_2SO_4 dissolves, it produces 2 mol Na^+ ions and 1 mol SO_4^{2-} ions. Thus the number of solute particles present in this solution is three times the number of moles of solute dissolved:

$$n_{\text{solute}} = 3(0.246) = 0.738 \text{ mol}$$

$$\chi_{\text{H}_2\text{O}} = \frac{n_{\text{H}_2\text{O}}}{n_{\text{solute}} + n_{\text{H}_2\text{O}}} = \frac{9.72 \text{ mol}}{0.738 \text{ mol} + 9.72 \text{ mol}} = \frac{9.72 \text{ mol}}{10.458} = 0.929$$

Now we can use Raoult's law to preduct the vapor pressure:

$$P_{\text{soln}} = \chi_{\text{H}_2\text{O}} P_{\text{H}_2\text{O}}^0 = (0.929)(23.76 \text{ torr}) = 22.1 \text{ torr}$$

Nonideal Solutions

So far we have assumed that the solute is nonvolatile and so does not contribute to the vapor pressure over the solution. However, for liquid–liquid solutions where both components are volatile, a modified form of Raoult's law applies:

$$P_{\text{TOTAL}} = P_A + P_B = \chi_A P_A^0 + \chi_B P_B^0$$

where P_{TOTAL} represents the total vapor pressure of a solution containing A and B, χ_A and χ_B are the mole fractions of A and B, P_A^0 and P_B^0 are the vapor pressures of pure A and pure B, and P_A and P_B are the partial pressures resulting from molecules of A and of B in the vapor above the solution.

A liquid–liquid solution that obeys Raoult's law is called an **ideal solution.** Raoult's law is to solutions what the ideal gas law is to gases. As with gases, ideal behavior for solutions is never perfectly achieved but is sometimes closely approached. Nearly ideal behavior is often observed when the solute–solute, solvent–solvent, and solute–solvent interactions are very similar. That is, in solutions where the solute and solvent are very much alike, the solute simply acts to dilute the solvent. However, if the solvent has a special affinity for the solute, such as if hydrogen bonding occurs, the tendency of the solvent molecules to escape will be lowered more than expected. The observed vapor pressure will be *lower* than the value predicted by Raoult's law; there will be a *negative deviation from Raoult's law.*

When a solute and solvent release large quantities of energy in the formation of a solution, that is, when ΔH_{soln} is large and negative, we can assume that strong interactions exist between the solute and solvent. In this case we expect a negative deviation from Raoult's law, because both components will have a lower escaping tendency in the solution than in the pure liquids. This behavior is illustrated by an acetone–water solution, where the molecules can hydrogen bond effectively:

In contrast, if two liquids mix endothermically, this indicates that the solute–solvent interactions are weaker than the interactions among the molecules in the pure liquids. More energy is required to expand the liquids than is released when the liquids are mixed. In this case the molecules in the solution have a higher tendency to escape than expected, and *positive* deviations from Raoult's law are observed (see Fig. 11.12). An example of this case is provided by a solution of ethanol and hexane, whose Lewis structures are as follows:

Strong solute–solvent interaction gives a vapor pressure lower than that predicted by Raoult's law.

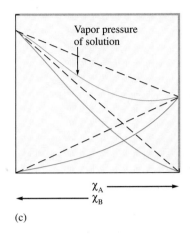

(a)

(b)

(c)

Figure 11.12

Vapor pressure for a solution of two volatile liquids. (a) The behavior predicted for an ideal liquid–liquid solution by Raoult's law. (b) A solution for which P_{TOTAL} is larger than the value calculated from Raoult's law. This solution shows a positive deviation from Raoult's law. (c) A solution for which P_{TOTAL} is smaller than the value calculated from Raoult's law. This solution shows a negative deviation from Raoult's law.

Ethanol   Hexane

The polar ethanol and the nonpolar hexane molecules are not able to interact effectively. Thus the enthalpy of solution is positive, as is the deviation from Raoult's law.

Finally, for a solution of very similar liquids, such as benzene and toluene,

CH$_3$

Benzene   Toluene

the enthalpy of solution is very close to zero, and thus the solution closely obeys Raoult's law (ideal behavior).

A summary of the behavior of various types of solutions is given in Table 11.4.

Sample Exercise 11.8

A solution is prepared by mixing 5.81 g acetone (C_3H_6O, molar mass = 58.1 g/mol) and 11.9 g chloroform ($HCCl_3$, molar mass = 119.4 g/mol). At 35°C this solution has a total vapor pressure of 260 torr. Is this an ideal solution? The vapor pressures of pure acetone and pure chloroform at 35°C are 345 and 293 torr, respectively.

Solution

To decide whether or not this solution behaves ideally, we first calculate the expected vapor pressure using Raoult's law:

$$P_{\text{TOTAL}} = \chi_A P_A^0 + \chi_C P_C^0$$

where A stands for acetone and C stands for chloroform. The calculated value can then be compared to the observed vapor pressure.

First, we must calculate the number of moles of acetone and chloroform:

$$5.81 \text{ g acetone} \times \frac{1 \text{ mol acetone}}{58.1 \text{ g acetone}} = 0.100 \text{ mol acetone}$$

$$11.9 \text{ g chloroform} \times \frac{1 \text{ mol chloroform}}{119 \text{ g chloroform}} = 0.100 \text{ mol chloroform}$$

Since the solution contains equal numbers of moles of acetone and chloroform, that is,

$$\chi_A = 0.500 \quad \text{and} \quad \chi_C = 0.500$$

the expected vapor pressure is

$$P_{\text{TOTAL}} = (0.500)(345 \text{ torr}) + (0.500)(293 \text{ torr}) = 319 \text{ torr}$$

Comparing this value with the observed pressure of 260 torr shows that the solution does not behave ideally. The observed value is lower than that expected. This negative deviation from Raoult's law can be explained in terms of the following hydrogen bonding interaction:

which lowers the tendency of these molecules to escape from the solution.

Table 11.4

Summary of the Behavior of Various Types of Solutions

Interactive Forces between Solute (A) and Solvent (B) Particles	ΔH_{soln}	ΔT for Solution Formation	Deviation from Raoult's Law	Example
A ↔ A, B ↔ B ≡ A ↔ B	Zero	Zero	None (ideal solution)	Benzene–toluene
A ↔ A, B ↔ B < A↔B	Negative (exothermic)	Positive	Negative	Acetone–water
A ↔ A, B ↔ B > A ↔ B	Positive (endothermic)	Negative	Positive	Ethanol–hexane

11.5 Boiling-Point Elevation and Freezing-Point Depression

Purpose

- To explain the effect of a solute on the boiling and freezing points of a solvent.

In the preceding section we saw how a solute affects the vapor pressure of a liquid solvent. Because changes of state depend on vapor pressure, the presence of a solute also affects the freezing point and boiling point of a solvent. Freezing-point depression, boiling-point elevation, and osmotic pressure (discussed in Section 11.6) are called **colligative properties.** As we will see, they are grouped together because they depend only on the number, and not on the identity, of the solute particles in an ideal solution. Because of their direct relationship to the number of solute particles, the colligative properties are very useful for characterizing the nature of a solute after it is dissolved in a solvent and for determining molar masses of substances.

The relationships between vapor pressure and changes of state were discussed in Section 10.8.

Boiling-Point Elevation

The normal boiling point of a liquid occurs at the temperature where the vapor pressure is equal to 1 atmosphere. We have seen that a nonvolatile solute lowers the vapor pressure of the solvent. Therefore, such a solution must be heated to a higher temperature than the boiling point of the pure solvent to reach a vapor pressure of 1 atmosphere. This means that *a nonvolatile solute elevates the boiling point of the solvent.* Figure 11.13 shows the phase diagram for an aqueous solution containing a nonvolatile solute. Note that the liquid/vapor line is shifted to higher temperatures than those for pure water.

Normal boiling point was defined in Section 10.8.

As you might expect, the magnitude of the boiling-point elevation depends on the concentration of the solute. The change in boiling point can be represented by the equation

$$\Delta T = K_b m_{solute}$$

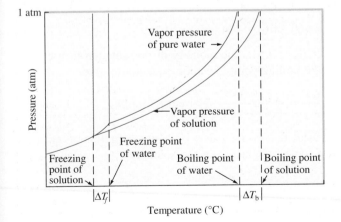

Temperature (°C)

Figure 11.13

Phase diagrams for pure water (red lines) and for an aqueous solution containing a nonvolatile solute (blue lines). Note that the boiling point of the solution is higher than that of pure water. Conversely, the freezing point of the solution is lower than that of pure water. The effect of a nonvolatile solute is to extend the liquid range of a solvent.

Table 11.5				
Molal Boiling-Point Elevation Constants (K_b) and Freezing-Point Depression Constants (K_f) for Several Solvents				
Solvent	Boiling Point (°C)	K_b (°C · kg/mol)	Freezing Point (°C)	K_f (°C · kg/mol)
Water (H_2O)	100.0	0.51	0	1.86
Carbon tetrachloride (CCl_4)	76.5	5.03	−22.99	30.
Chloroform ($CHCl_3$)	61.2	3.63	−63.5	4.70
Benzene (C_6H_6)	80.1	2.53	5.5	5.12
Carbon disulfide (CS_2)	46.2	2.34	−111.5	3.83
Ethyl ether ($C_4H_{10}O$)	34.5	2.02	−116.2	1.79
Camphor ($C_{10}H_{16}O$)	208.0	5.95	179.8	40.

where ΔT is the boiling-point elevation, or the difference between the boiling point of the solution and that of the pure solvent, K_b is a constant that is characteristic of the solvent and is called the **molal boiling-point elevation constant,** and m_{solute} is the *molality* of the solute in the solution.

Values of K_b for some common solvents are given in Table 11.5. The molar mass of a solute can be determined from the observed boiling-point elevation, as shown in Sample Exercise 11.9.

Sample Exercise 11.9

A solution was prepared by dissolving 18.00 g glucose in 150.0 g water. The resulting solution was found to have a boiling point of 100.34°C. Calculate the molar mass of glucose. Glucose is a molecular solid that is present as individual molecules in solution.

Solution

We make use of the equation

$$\Delta T = K_b m_{solute}$$

where
$$\Delta T = 100.34°C - 100.00°C = 0.34°C$$

From Table 11.5, for water $K_b = 0.51$. The molality of this solution then can be calculated by rearranging the boiling-point elevation equation to give

$$m_{solute} = \frac{\Delta T}{K_b} = \frac{0.34°C}{0.51°C \cdot kg/mol} = 0.67 \text{ mol/kg}$$

The solution was prepared using 0.1500 kg water. Using the definition of molality, we can find the number of moles of glucose in the solution.

$$m_{solute} = 0.67 \text{ mol/kg} = \frac{\text{mol solute}}{\text{kg solvent}} = \frac{n_{glucose}}{0.1500 \text{ kg}}$$

$$n_{glucose} = (0.670 \text{ mol/kg})(0.1500 \text{ kg}) = 0.10 \text{ mol}$$

Thus 0.10 mol glucose has a mass of 18.00 g, and 1.0 mol glucose has a mass of 180 g (10×18.00 g). The molar mass of glucose is 180 g/mol.

Freezing-Point Depression

When a solute is dissolved in a solvent, the freezing point of the solution is lower than that of the pure solvent. Why? Recall that the vapor pressures of ice and liquid water are the same at 0°C. Suppose a solute is dissolved in water. The resulting solution will not freeze at 0°C because *the water in the solution has a lower vapor pressure than that of pure ice.* No ice will form under these conditions. However, the vapor pressure of ice decreases more rapidly than that of liquid water as the temperature decreases. Therefore, as the solution is cooled, the vapor pressure of the ice and that of the liquid water in the solution will eventually become equal. The temperature at which this occurs is the new freezing point of the solution and is below 0°C. The freezing point has been *depressed.*

We can account for this behavior in terms of the simple model shown in Fig. 11.14. The presence of the solute lowers the rate at which molecules in the liquid return to the solid state. Thus, for an aqueous solution, only the liquid state is found at 0°C. As the solution is cooled, the rate at which water molecules leave the solid ice decreases until this rate and the rate of formation of ice become equal and equilibrium is reached. This is the freezing point of the water in the solution.

Because a solute lowers the freezing point of water, compounds such as sodium chloride and calcium chloride are often spread on streets and sidewalks to prevent ice from forming in freezing weather. Of course, if the outside temperature is lower than the freezing point of the resulting salt solution, ice forms anyway. So this procedure is not effective at extremely cold temperatures.

The solid/liquid line for an aqueous solution is shown on the phase diagram for water in Fig. 11.13. Since the presence of a solute elevates the boiling point and depresses the freezing point of the solvent, adding a solute has the effect of extending the liquid range.

The equation for freezing-point depression is analogous to that for boiling-point elevation:

$$\Delta T = K_f m_{solute}$$

where ΔT is the freezing-point depression, or the difference between the freezing point of the pure solvent and that of the solution, and K_f is a constant that is characteristic of a particular solvent and is called the **molal freezing-point depression constant.** Values of K_f for common solvents are listed in Table 11.5.

Like the boiling-point elevation, the observed freezing-point depression can be used to determine molar masses and to characterize solutions.

Melting point and freezing point both refer to the temperature where the solid and liquid coexist.

(a)   (b)

Figure 11.14

(a) Ice in equilibrium with liquid water. (b) Ice in equilibrium with liquid water containing a dissolved solute (shown in color).

Crystals of rock salt causing ice to melt.

Sample Exercise 11.10

What mass of ethylene glycol ($C_2H_6O_2$, molar mass = 62.1 g/mol), the main component of antifreeze, must be added to 10.0 L water to produce a solution for use in a car's radiator that freezes at $-10.0°F$ ($-23.3°C$)? Assume the density of water is exactly 1 g/mL.

The addition of antifreeze lowers the freezing point of water in a car's radiator, in this case a 1928 Lincoln.

Solution

The freezing point must be lowered from 0°C to −23.3°C. To determine the molality of ethylene glycol needed to accomplish this, we can use the equation

$$\Delta T = K_f m_{solute}$$

where $\Delta T = 23.3°C$ and $K_f = 1.86$ (from Table 11.5). Solving for the molality gives

$$m_{solute} = \frac{\Delta T}{K_f} = \frac{23.3°C}{1.86°C \cdot kg/mol} = 12.5 \text{ mol/kg}$$

This means that 12.5 mol ethylene glycol must be added per kilogram of water. We have 10.0 L, or 10.0 kg, of water. Therefore, the total number of moles of ethylene glycol needed is

$$\frac{12.5 \text{ mol}}{kg} \times 10.0 \text{ kg} = 1.25 \times 10^2 \text{ mol}$$

The mass of ethylene glycol needed is

$$1.25 \times 10^2 \text{ mol} \times \frac{62.1 \text{ g}}{mol} = 7.76 \times 10^3 \text{ g (or 7.76 kg)}$$

Sample Exercise 11.11

A chemist is trying to identify a human hormone, which controls metabolism, by determining its molar mass. A sample weighing 0.546 g was dissolved in 15.0 g benzene, and the freezing-point depression was determined to be 0.240°C. Calculate the molar mass of the hormone.

Solution

From Table 11.5, K_f for benzene is 5.12°C · kg/mol, so the molality of the hormone is

$$m_{hormone} = \frac{\Delta T}{K_f} = \frac{0.240°C}{5.12°C \cdot kg/mol} = 4.69 \times 10^{-2} \text{ mol/kg}$$

The moles of hormone can be obtained from the definition of molality:

$$4.69 \times 10^{-2} \text{ mol/kg} = m_{solute} = \frac{\text{mol hormone}}{0.0150 \text{ kg benzene}}$$

or

$$\text{mol hormone} = \left(4.69 \times 10^{-2} \frac{\text{mol}}{\text{kg}}\right)(0.0150 \text{ kg}) = 7.04 \times 10^{-4} \text{ mol}$$

Since 0.546 g hormone was dissolved, 7.04×10^{-4} mol hormone has a mass of 0.546 g, and

$$\frac{0.546 \text{ g}}{7.04 \times 10^{-4} \text{ mol}} = \frac{x \text{ g}}{1.00 \text{ mol}}$$

$$x = 776 \text{ g/mol}$$

Thus the molar mass of the hormone is 776 g/mol.

11.6 Osmotic Pressure

Purpose

- To explain osmosis and describe its applications.

Osmotic pressure, another of the colligative properties, can be understood from Fig. 11.15. A solution and pure solvent are separated by a **semipermeable membrane,** which allows *solvent but not solute* molecules to pass through. As time passes, the volume of the solution increases and that of the solvent decreases. This flow of solvent into the solution through the semipermeable membrane is called **osmosis.** Eventually the liquid levels stop changing, indicating that the system has reached equilibrium. Because the liquid levels are different at this point, there is a greater hydrostatic pressure on the solution than on the pure solvent. This excess pressure is called the **osmotic pressure.**

We can take another view of this phenomenon, as illustrated in Fig. 11.16. Osmosis can be prevented by applying a pressure to the solution. *The minimum pressure that stops the osmosis is equal to the osmotic pressure of the solution.* A simple model to explain osmotic pressure can be constructed as shown in Fig. 11.17 (on page 526). The membrane allows only solvent molecules to pass through. However, the initial rates of solvent transfer to and from the solution are not the same. The solute particles interfere with the passage of solvent, so the rate of transfer is slower from the solution to the solvent than in the reverse direction. Thus there is a net transfer of solvent molecules into the solution, which causes the solution volume to increase. As the solution level rises in the tube, the resulting pressure exerts an extra "push" on the solvent molecules in the solution, forcing

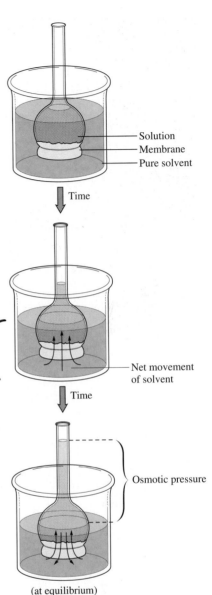

Solution
Membrane
Pure solvent

Time

Net movement of solvent

Time

Osmotic pressure

(at equilibrium)

Figure 11.15

A tube with a bulb on the end that is covered by a semi-permeable membrane. The solution is inside the tube and is bathed in the pure solvent. There is a net transfer of solvent molecules into the solution until the hydrostatic pressure equalizes the solvent flow in both directions. The solvent level shows little change because the narrow stem of the bulb has a very small volume.

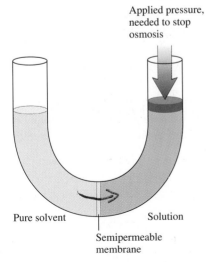

Applied pressure, needed to stop osmosis

Pure solvent

Solution

Semipermeable membrane

Figure 11.16

The normal flow of solvent into the solution (osmosis) can be prevented by applying an external pressure to the solution. The minimum pressure required to stop the osmosis is equal to the osmotic pressure of the solution.

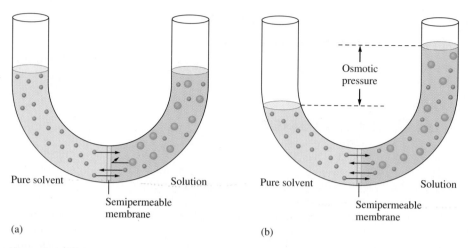

Figure 11.17
(a) A pure solvent and its solution (containing a nonvolatile solute) are separated by a semipermeable membrane through which solvent molecules (blue) can pass but solute molecules (green) cannot. The rate of solvent transfer is greater from solvent to solution than from solution to solvent. (b) The system at equilibrium, where the rate of solvent transfer is the same in both directions.

them back through the membrane. Eventually, enough pressure develops so that the solvent transfer becomes equal in both directions. At this point, equilibrium is achieved and the levels stop changing.

Osmotic pressure can be used to characterize solutions and determine molar masses, as can the other colligative properties, but osmotic pressure is particularly useful because a small concentration of solute produces a relatively large osmotic pressure.

Experiments show that the dependence of the osmotic pressure on solution concentration is represented by the equation

$$\pi = MRT$$

where π is the osmotic pressure in atmospheres, M is the molarity of the solute, R is the gas law constant, and T is the Kelvin temperature.

A molar mass determination using osmotic pressure is illustrated in Sample Exercise 11.12.

Sample Exercise 11.12

To determine the molar mass of a certain protein, 1.00×10^{-3} g of it was dissolved in enough water to make 1.00 mL of solution. The osmotic pressure of this solution was found to be 1.12 torr at 25.0°C. Calculate the molar mass of the protein.

Solution

We use the equation

$$\pi = MRT$$

In this case we have

$$\pi = 1.12 \text{ torr} \times \frac{1 \text{ atm}}{760 \text{ torr}} = 1.47 \times 10^{-3} \text{ atm}$$

$$R = 0.08206 \text{ L} \cdot \text{atm/K} \cdot \text{mol}$$
$$T = 25.0 + 273 = 298 \text{ K}$$

Note that the osmotic pressure must be converted to atmospheres because of the units of R.

Solving for M gives

$$M = \frac{1.47 \times 10^{-3} \text{ atm}}{(0.08206 \text{ L} \cdot \text{atm/K} \cdot \text{mol})(298 \text{ K})} = 6.01 \times 10^{-5} \text{ mol/L}$$

Since 1.00×10^{-3} g protein was dissolved in 1 mL solution, the mass of protein per liter of solution is 1.00 g. The solution's concentration is 6.01×10^{-5} mol/L. This concentration is produced from 1.00×10^{-3} g protein per milliliter, or 1.00 g/L. Thus 6.01×10^{-5} mol protein has a mass of 1.00 g and

$$\frac{1.00 \text{ g}}{6.01 \times 10^{-5} \text{ mol}} = \frac{x \text{ g}}{1.00 \text{ mol}}$$
$$x = 1.66 \times 10^4$$

The molar mass of the protein is 1.66×10^4 g/mol. This molar mass may seem very large, but it is relatively small for a protein.

Measurements of osmotic pressure generally give much more accurate molar mass values than those from freezing-point or boiling-point changes.

In osmosis, a semipermeable membrane prevents transfer of *all* solute particles. A similar phenomenon, called **dialysis**, occurs at the walls of most plant and animal cells. However, in this case the membrane allows transfer of both solvent molecules and *small* solute molecules and ions. One of the most important applications of dialysis is the use of artificial kidney machines to purify the blood. The blood is passed through a cellophane tube, which acts as the semipermeable membrane. The tube is immersed in a dialyzing solution (see Fig. 11.18 on page 528). This "washing" solution contains the same concentrations of ions and small molecules as blood but has none of the waste products normally removed by the kidneys. The resulting dialysis (movement of waste molecules into the washing solution) cleanses the blood.

Solutions that have identical osmotic pressures are said to be **isotonic solutions.** Fluids administered intravenously must be isotonic with body fluids. For example, if cells are bathed in a hypertonic solution, which is a solution having an osmotic pressure higher than that of the cell fluids, the cells will shrivel because of a net transfer of water out of the cells. This phenomenon is called **crenation.** The opposite phenomenon, called **lysis,** occurs when cells are bathed in a hypotonic solution, a solution with an osmotic pressure lower than that of the cell fluids. In this case, the cells rupture because of the flow of water into the cells.

The brine used in pickling causes the cucumbers to shrivel.

We can use the phenomenon of crenation to our advantage. Food can be preserved by treating its surface with a solute that gives a solution that is hypertonic to bacteria cells. Bacteria on the food then tend to shrivel and die. This is why salt can be used to protect meat and sugar can be used to protect fruit.

Sample Exercise 11.13

What concentration of sodium chloride in water is needed to produce an aqueous solution isotonic with blood ($\pi = 7.70$ atm at 25°C)?

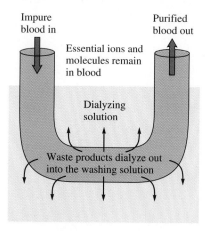

Figure 11.18

Representation of the functioning of an artificial kidney.

We can calculate the molarity of the solute from the equation

$$\pi = MRT \quad \text{or} \quad M = \frac{\pi}{RT}$$

$$M = \frac{7.70 \text{ atm}}{(0.08206 \text{ L} \cdot \text{atm/K} \cdot \text{mol})(298 \text{ K})} = 0.315 \text{ mol/L}$$

This represents the total molarity of solute particles. But NaCl gives two ions per formula unit. Therefore, the concentration of NaCl needed is 0.315/2, or 0.158 M. That is,

$$\underset{0.1575\,M}{\text{NaCl}} \quad \rightarrow \quad \underset{0.1575\,M}{\text{Na}^+} \quad + \quad \underset{0.1575\,M}{\text{Cl}^-}$$
$$\underbrace{\qquad\qquad\qquad}_{0.315\,M}$$

Reverse Osmosis

If a solution in contact with pure solvent across a semipermeable membrane is subjected to an external pressure larger than its osmotic pressure, **reverse osmosis** occurs. The pressure will cause a net flow of solvent from the solution to the solvent, as shown in Fig. 11.19. In reverse osmosis, the semipermeable membrane acts as a "molecular filter" to remove solute particles. This fact is potentially applicable to the desalination (removal of dissolved salts) of seawater, which is highly hypertonic to body fluids and thus is not drinkable.

As the population of the sun belt areas of the United States increases, more demand will be placed on the limited supplies of fresh water there. One obvious source of fresh water is from the desalination of seawater. Various schemes have been suggested, including solar evaporation, reverse osmosis, and even a plan for

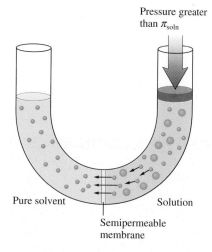

Pressure greater than π_{soln}

Pure solvent

Solution

Semipermeable membrane

Figure 11.19

Reverse osmosis. A pressure greater than the osmotic pressure of the solution is applied, which causes a net flow of solvent molecules (blue) from the solution to the pure solvent. The solute molecules (green) remain behind.

Figure 11.20

Machinery in the desalination plant for Catalina Island, California.

5. Brine is pumped into ocean.

1. Salt water pumped from underground wells.

2. Salt water is forced through 20-micron and 5-micron filters at a pressure of 800 pounds per square inch.

3. Fresh water is forced through additional filters.

4. Fresh water is pumped into water supply.

Figure 11.21

Residents of Santa Catalina Island off the coast of southern California are benefitting from a new desalination plant that can supply 132,000 gallons a day, or one-third of the island's daily needs.

towing icebergs from Antarctica (remember that pure water freezes out of an aqueous solution). The problem, of course, is that all the available processes are expensive. However, as water shortages increase, desalination is becoming necessary. For example, the first full-time public desalination plant has just started operations on Catalina Island, just off the coast of California (see Fig. 11.20). This plant, which can produce 132,000 gallons of drinkable water from the Pacific Ocean every day, operates by reverse osmosis. Powerful pumps, developing over 800 lb/in^2 of pressure, are employed to force seawater through synthetic semipermeable membranes.

Catalina Island's plant seems to be just the beginning (Fig. 11.21). The city of Santa Barbara opened a $40 million desalination plant in 1992 that can produce 8 million gallons of drinkable water a day, and other plants are in the planning stages.

A small-scale, manually operated reverse osmosis desalinator has been developed by the U.S. Navy to provide fresh water on life rafts. Potable water can be supplied by this desalinator at the rate of 1.25 gallons of water per hour—enough to keep 25 people alive. This compact desalinator weighs only 10 pounds and will replace the bulky cases of fresh water now stored in Navy life rafts.

An iceberg floating in Baffin Bay, in the Arctic. Pure water freezes out of an aqueous solution.

11.7 Colligative Properties of Electrolyte Solutions

Purpose

- To show how the colligative properties of electrolyte solutions can be used to characterize the solute.

As we have seen previously, the colligative properties of solutions depend on the total concentration of solute particles. For example, a 0.10 *m* glucose solution shows a freezing-point depression of 0.186°C:

$$\Delta T = K_f m = (1.86°C \cdot kg/mol)(0.10 \text{ mol/kg}) = 0.186°C$$

On the other hand, a 0.10 *m* sodium chloride solution should show a freezing-point depression of 0.37°C, since the solution is 0.10 *m* Na$^+$ ions and 0.10 *m* Cl$^-$ ions. Therefore, the solution contains a total of 0.20 *m* solute particles, and $\Delta T = (1.86°C \cdot kg/mol)(0.20 \text{ mol/kg}) = 0.37°C$. The relationship between the moles of solute dissolved and the moles of particles in solution is usually expressed using the **van't Hoff factor** *i*:

Dutch chemist J. H. van't Hoff (1852–1911) received the first Nobel prize in chemistry in 1901.

$$i = \frac{\text{moles of particles in solution}}{\text{moles of solute dissolved}}$$

The *expected* value for *i* can be calculated for a salt by noting the number of ions per formula unit. For example, for NaCl, *i* is 2; for K$_2$SO$_4$, *i* is 3; and for Fe$_3$(PO$_4$)$_2$, *i* is 5. These calculated values assume that when a salt dissolves, it completely dissociates into its component ions, which then move around independently. This assumption is not always true. For example, the freezing-point depression observed for 0.10 *m* NaCl is 1.87 times that for 0.10 *m* glucose rather than twice as great. That is, for a 0.10 *m* NaCl solution the observed value for *i* is 1.87 rather than 2. Why? The best explanation is that **ion pairing** occurs in solution (see Fig. 11.22). At a given instant a small percentage of the sodium and chloride ions are paired and thus count as a single particle. In general, ion pairing is most important in concentrated solutions. As the solution becomes more dilute, the ions are farther apart and less ion pairing occurs. For example, in a 0.0010 *m* NaCl solution, the observed value of *i* is 1.97, which is very close to the expected value.

Figure 11.22

In an aqueous solution a few ions aggregate, forming ion pairs that behave as a unit.

Ion pairing occurs to some extent in all electrolyte solutions. Table 11.6 shows expected and observed values of *i* for a given concentration of various electrolytes. Note that the deviation of *i* from the expected value tends to be greatest where the ions have multiple charges. This is expected because ion pairing ought to be most important for highly charged ions.

The colligative properties of electrolyte solutions are described by including the van't Hoff factor in the appropriate equation. For example, for changes in freezing and boiling points, the modified equation is

$$\Delta T = imK$$

where *K* represents the freezing-point depression or boiling-point elevation constant for the solvent.

For the osmotic pressure of electrolyte solutions, the equation is

$$\pi = iMRT$$

Table 11.6		
Expected and Observed Values of the van't Hoff Factor for 0.05 *m* Solutions of Several Electrolytes		
Electrolyte	*i* (expected)	*i* (observed)
NaCl	2.0	1.9
$MgCl_2$	3.0	2.7
$MgSO_4$	2.0	1.3
$FeCl_3$	4.0	3.4
HCl	2.0	1.9
Glucose*	1.0	1.0
*A nonelectrolyte shown for comparison.		

Sample Exercise 11.14

The observed osmotic pressure for a 0.10 *M* solution of $Fe(NH_4)_2(SO_4)_2$ at 25°C is 10.8 atm. Compare the expected and experimental values for *i*.

Solution

The ionic solid $Fe(NH_4)_2(SO_4)_2$ dissociates in water to produce 5 ions:

$$Fe(NH_4)_2(SO_4)_2 \xrightarrow{\text{H}_2\text{O}} Fe^{2+} + 2NH_4^+ + 2SO_4^{2-}$$

Thus the expected value for *i* is 5. We can obtain the experimental value for *i* by using the equation for osmotic pressure:

$$\pi = iMRT \quad \text{or} \quad i = \frac{\pi}{MRT}$$

where $\pi = 10.8$ atm, $M = 0.10$ mol/L, $R = 0.08206$ L · atm/K · mol, and $T = 25 + 273 = 298$ K. Substituting these values into the equation gives

$$i = \frac{\pi}{MRT} = \frac{10.8 \text{ atm}}{(0.10 \text{ mol/L})(0.08206 \text{ L} \cdot \text{atm/K} \cdot \text{mol})(298 \text{ K})} = 4.42$$

The experimental value for *i* is less than the expected value, presumably because of ion pairing.

11.8 Colloids

Purpose

• To define a colloid and explain how it is stabilized.

Mud can be suspended in water by vigorous stirring. When the stirring stops, most of the particles rapidly settle out, but even after several days some of the smallest particles remain suspended. Although undetected in normal lighting, their

◀ **C H E M I C A L   I M P A C T** ▶

Organisms and Ice Formation

The ice-cold waters of the polar oceans are teeming with fish that seem immune to freezing. One might think that these fish have some kind of antifreeze in their blood. However, studies show that they are protected from freezing in a very different way from the way antifreeze protects our cars. As we have seen in this chapter, solutes such as sugar, salt, and ethylene glycol lower the temperature at which the solid and liquid phases of water can coexist. However, the fish could not tolerate high concentrations of solutes in their blood because of the osmotic pressure effects. Instead, they are protected by proteins in their blood. These proteins allow the water in the bloodstream to be supercooled—exist below 0°C—without forming ice. They apparently coat the surface of each tiny ice crystal, as soon as it begins to form, preventing it from growing to a size that would cause biologic damage.

Although it might at first seem surprising, this research on polar fish has at-tracted the attention of ice cream manu-facturers. Premium quality ice cream is smooth; it does not have large ice crystals in it. The makers of ice cream would like to incorporate these polar fish proteins, or molecules that behave similarly, into ice cream to prevent the growth of ice crystals during storage.

Fruit and vegetable growers have a similar interest: they also want to prevent ice formation that damages their crops during an unusual cold wave. However, this is a very different kind of problem than keeping polar fish from freezing. Many types of fruits and vegetables are colonized by bacteria that manufacture a protein that *encourages* freezing by acting as a nucleating agent to start an ice crys-tal. Chemists have identified the offend-ing protein in the bacteria and the gene that is responsible for making it. They have learned to modify the genetic mate-rial of these bacteria in a way that re-moves their ability to make the protein that encourages ice crystal formation. If

An Antarctic fish, *Chaerophalus aceratus*.

testing shows that these modified bacteria have no harmful effects on the crop or the environment, the original bacteria strain will be replaced with the new form so that ice crystals will not form so readily when a cold snap occurs.

presence can be demonstrated by shining a beam of intense light through the suspen-sion. The beam is visible from the side because the light is scattered by the sus-pended particles (Fig. 11.23). In a true solution, on the other hand, the beam is invisible from the side because the individual ions and molecules dispersed in the solution are too small to scatter visible light.

Figure 11.23
The Tyndall effect.

Table 11.7			
Types of Colloids			
Examples	Dispersing Medium	Dispersed Substance	Colloid Type
Fog, aerosol sprays	Gas	Liquid	Aerosol
Smoke, airborne bacteria	Gas	Solid	Aerosol
Whipped cream, soap suds	Liquid	Gas	Foam
Milk, mayonnaise	Liquid	Liquid	Emulsion
Paint, clays, gelatin	Liquid	Solid	Sol
Marshmallow, polystyrene foam	Solid	Gas	Solid foam
Butter, cheese	Solid	Liquid	Solid emulsion
Ruby glass	Solid	Solid	Solid sol

The scattering of light by particles is called the **Tyndall effect** and is often used to distinguish between a suspension and a true solution.

A suspension of tiny particles in some medium is called a **colloidal dispersion,** or a **colloid.** The suspended particles are single large molecules or aggregates of molecules or ions ranging in size from 1 to 1000 nm. Colloids are classified according to the states of the dispersed phase and the dispersing medium. Table 11.7 summarizes various types of colloids.

What stabilizes a colloid? Why do the particles remain suspended rather than forming larger aggregates and precipitating out? The answer is complicated, but the main factor seems to be *electrostatic repulsion.* A colloid, like all other macroscopic substances, is electrically neutral. However, when a colloid is placed in an electric field, the dispersed particles all migrate to the same electrode and thus must all have the same charge. How is this possible? The center of a colloidal particle (a tiny ionic crystal, a group of molecules, or a single large molecule) attracts from the medium a layer of ions, all of the same charge. This group of ions, in turn, attracts another layer of oppositely charged ions, as shown in Fig. 11.24. Because the colloidal particles all have an outer layer of ions with the same charge, they repel each other and do not easily aggregate to form particles that are large enough to precipitate.

The destruction of a colloid, called **coagulation,** usually can be accomplished either by heating or by adding an electrolyte. Heating increases the velocities of the colloidal particles, causing them to collide with enough energy that the ion barriers are penetrated and the particles can aggregate. Because this is repeated many times, the particle grows to a point where it settles out. Adding an electrolyte neutralizes the adsorbed ion layers. This is why clay suspended in rivers is deposited where the river reaches the ocean, forming the deltas characteristic of large rivers like the Mississippi. The high salt content of the seawater causes the colloidal clay particles to coagulate.

The removal of soot from smoke is another example of the coagulation of a colloid. When smoke is passed through an electrostatic precipitator (Fig. 11.25), the suspended solids are removed. The use of precipitators has produced an immense improvement in the air quality of heavily industrialized cities.

Figure 11.24

A representation of two colloidal particles. In each the center particle is surrounded by a layer of positive ions, with negative ions in the outer layer. Thus, although the particles are electrically neutral, they still repel each other because of their outer negative layer of ions.

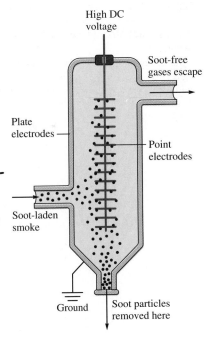

Figure 11.25

The Cottrell precipitator installed in a smokestack. The charged plates attract the colloidal particles because of their ion layers and thus remove them from the smoke.

FOR REVIEW

Summary

Solution composition can be described in terms of molarity (the moles per liter of solution), mass percent (the ratio of grams of solute to grams of solution multiplied by 100), mole fraction (the moles of a given component per total number of moles of all components of the solution), or molality (the moles of solute per kilogram of solvent).

Normality is defined as the number of equivalents per liter of solution. The definition of an equivalent depends on the reaction taking place in the solution. For an acid–base reaction, the equivalent is the mass of acid (or base) that can furnish (or accept) exactly 1 mole of protons. For an oxidation–reduction reaction, the equivalent is the quantity of reducing (or oxidizing) agent that can furnish (or accept) 1 mole of electrons.

The enthalpy of solution ΔH_{soln} is the enthalpy change accompanying solution formation. It can be broken down into terms expressing energies associated with overcoming interactions between solute particles and interactions between solvent particles (endothermic processes) and a term expressing energies associated with the formation of interactions between solute and solvent particles (an exothermic process).

Various factors affect solubility. Molecular structure determines the polarity of a molecule. Polar molecules tend to be soluble in polar solvents, and nonpolar molecules tend to be soluble in nonpolar solvents. Pressure has little effect on the solubilities of liquids or solids, but increased pressure increases the solubility of gases. Henry's law, which applies to gases that do not react chemically with the solvent, states that the concentration of a gaseous solute in a solvent is directly proportional to the partial pressure of the same gas above the solution. An increase in temperature decreases the solubility of a gas in water, but the effect of temperature on the solubility of a solid in water varies with the identity of the solid.

The vapor pressure of a solution containing a nonvolatile solute is always less than the vapor pressure of the pure solvent, because the presence of the solute decreases the number of solvent molecules per unit volume and thus proportionately lowers the escaping tendency of the solvent molecules. Raoult's law states that the vapor pressure of a solution is directly proportional to the mole fraction of the solvent. Raoult's law holds for an ideal solution. However, if a solute has a special affinity for the solvent, nonideal behavior is seen in the form of a negative deviation from Raoult's law (a lower vapor pressure than is predicted).

The colligative properties of solutions, which depend on the number of solute particles present, include boiling-point elevation, freezing-point depression, and osmotic pressure. Because a nonvolatile solute lowers the freezing point and raises the boiling point, it extends the liquid range of the solvent.

Osmosis occurs when a pure solvent and its solution are separated by a semipermeable membrane that prevents the passage of solute molecules. Under these circumstances, solvent molecules flow from the solvent into the solution. Osmotic pressure, the exact pressure that must be applied to a solution to prevent osmosis, is directly related to the molarity of the solution. Reverse osmosis occurs when an external pressure larger than the solution's osmotic pressure is applied. The effect is to cause a net flow of solvent from the solution into the pure solvent.

To describe the colligative properties of electrolyte solutions, the number of ions must be taken into account by use of the van't Hoff factor i. Because of ion pairing, the experimental value for i is often significantly less than the expected value.

A colloid is a suspension of tiny particles in solution. Colloids are stabilized because of the electrostatic repulsions between the ion layers surrounding the individual particles. A colloid can be coagulated by heating or by adding an electrolyte.

Key Terms

Section 11.1
molarity
mass percent
mole fraction
molality
normality

Section 11.2
enthalpy (heat) of solution
enthalpy (heat) of hydration

Section 11.3
Henry's law
thermal pollution

Section 11.4
Raoult's law
ideal solution

Section 11.5
colligative properties
molal boiling-point elevation constant
molal freezing-point depression constant

Section 11.6
semipermeable membrane
osmosis
osmotic pressure
dialysis

isotonic solution
reverse osmosis
desalination

Section 11.7
van't Hoff factor
ion pairing

Section 11.8
Tyndall effect
colloid
coagulation

A blue question or exercise number indicates that the answer to that question or exercise appears at the back of this book and a solution appears in the Solutions Guide.

Solution Review

If you have trouble with these exercises, review Sections 4.1 to 4.3 in Chapter 4.

1. A solution is prepared by dissolving 125 g sucrose ($C_{12}H_{22}O_{11}$) in enough water to produce 1.00 L solution. What is the molarity of this solution?

2. What mass of sodium oxalate ($Na_2C_2O_4$) is needed to prepare 0.250 L of a 0.100 M solution?

3. A solution is prepared by diluting 25.00 mL of a 0.308 M solution of $NiCl_2$ to a final volume of 0.500 L. What is the concentration of nickel chloride in this solution? What are the concentrations of nickel ions and chloride ions in this solution?

4. A 158.5-mg sample of pure Cu metal is dissolved in a small amount of concentrated nitric acid giving Cu^{2+} ions in solution. It is then diluted to a final volume of 1.00 L. What is the molar concentration of Cu^{2+} ions in the final solution?

5. An aqueous solution contains 2.8 mg Cd^{2+} ions per milliliter of solution. What is the concentration of Cd^{2+} ions in mol/L?

6. A solution contains 1.06×10^{-3} M $Ca(NO_3)_2$.
   a. What are the molar concentrations of calcium cations and nitrate anions in this solution?

   b. What is the mass (in grams) of the Ca^{2+} ions in 1 mL of this solution?
   c. How many nitrate ions are there in 1.0×10^{-6} L (1 μL) of this solution?

7. What volume of 0.25 M HCl solution must be diluted to prepare 1.00 L of 0.040 M HCl?

8. Write equations showing the ions present after the following strong electrolytes are dissolved in water.
   a. HNO_3 d. $SrBr_2$ g. NH_4NO_3
   b. Na_2SO_4 e. $KClO_4$ h. $CuSO_4$
   c. $AlCl_3$ f. NH_4Br i. $NaOH$

Questions

9. Is molarity or molality dependent on temperature? Explain your answer. Why is molality, and not molarity, used in the equations describing freezing-point depression and boiling-point elevation?

10. What specific feature of chemical substances do we refer to when we say that "like dissolves like"?

11. Define the terms *hydrophobic* and *hydrophilic*.

12. Rationalize the temperature dependence of the solubility of a gas in water in terms of the kinetic molecular theory.

13. In terms of intermolecular forces, what factors give rise to positive and negative deviations from Raoult's law?

14. If a solution shows positive deviations from Raoult's law, would you expect it to have a higher or lower boiling point than if it were ideal? Why?

15. When pure methanol is mixed with water, the resulting solution feels warm. Would you expect this solution to be ideal? Explain.

16. Why is the observed freezing-point depression for electrolyte solutions sometimes less than the calculated value? Is the discrepancy greater for concentrated or dilute solutions?

17. Before refrigeration was common, many foods were preserved by salting them heavily, and many fruits were preserved by mixing them with a large amount of sugar (fruit preserves). How do salt and sugar act as preservatives?

18. Distinguish between a strong electrolyte and a weak electrolyte. How can colligative properties be used to distinguish between strong and weak electrolytes?

Exercises

In this section similar exercises are paired.

Concentration of Solutions

19. A commonly purchased disinfectant is a 3.0% (by mass) solution of hydrogen peroxide (H_2O_2) in water. Assuming that the density of the solution is 1.0 g/cm^3, calculate the molarity, molality, and mole fraction of H_2O_2.

20. A solution is made by dissolving 25 g NaCl in enough water to make 1.0 L solution. Assume that the density of the solution is 1.0 g/cm^3. Calculate the mass percent, molarity, molality, and mole fraction of NaCl.

21. Common commerical acids and bases are aqueous solutions with the following properties:

	Density (g/cm^3)	Mass Percent of Solute
Hydrochloric acid	1.19	38
Nitric acid	1.42	70.
Sulfuric acid	1.84	95
Acetic acid	1.05	99
Ammonia	0.90	28

Calculate the molarity, molality, and mole fraction of each of the above reagents.

22. The most concentrated aqueous solution of NaOH that can be prepared is approximately 50% NaOH by mass. Calculate the mole fraction and molality of NaOH in this solution.

23. A solution is prepared by mixing 50.0 mL toluene ($C_6H_5CH_3$, $d = 0.867$ g/cm^3) with 125 mL benzene (C_6H_6, $d = 0.874$ g/cm^3). Assuming that the volumes add upon mixing, calculate the mass percent, mole fraction, molality, and molarity of the toluene.

24. Calculate the molarity and mole fraction of acetone in a 1.0 m solution of acetone (CH_3COCH_3) in ethanol (C_2H_5OH). (Density of acetone = 0.788 g/cm^3; density of ethanol = 0.789 g/cm^3.) Assume that the volumes of acetone and ethanol add.

25. A 1.37 M solution of citric acid ($H_3C_6H_5O_7$) in water has a density of 1.10 g/cm^3. Calculate the mass percent, molality, and mole fraction of the citric acid.

26. A solution is prepared by dissolving 50.0 g cesium chloride (CsCl) in 50.0 g water. The density of the solution is 1.58 g/cm^3. Calculate the mass percent, molarity, molality, and mole fraction of the cesium chloride.

27. A bottle of wine contains 12.5% ethanol by volume. The density of ethanol (C_2H_5OH) is 0.79 g/cm^3. Calculate the concentration of ethanol in wine in terms of mass percent and molality.

28. In a solution of acetone and ethanol, the mole fraction of acetone is 0.40. What is the concentration of acetone as a mass percent?

Energetics of Solutions and Solubility

29. What factors cause one solute to be more strongly hydrated than another? For each of the following pairs, predict which substance would be more soluble in water.
a. CH_3CH_2OH or $CH_3CH_2CH_3$
b. $CHCl_3$ or CCl_4
c. CH_3CO_2H or $CH_3(CH_2)_{14}CO_2H$
d. Na_2S or CuS
e. $AlCl_3$ or Al_2O_3
f. CO_2 or SiO_2

30. For each of the following pairs, predict which substance would be more soluble in water.
a. NH_3 or PH_3
b. CH_3CN or CH_3CH_3
c. CH_3C-OH or $CH_3-C-OCH_3$
     $\quad\quad\overset{\|}{O}\quad\quad\quad\quad\quad\overset{\|}{O}$
d. $MgCl_2$ or MgO
e. HCl or $AgCl$
f. NH_3 or CO_2

31. The lattice energy* of KCl is -715 kJ/mol, and the enthalpy of hydration is -684 kJ/mol. Calculate the enthalpy of solution per mole of solid KCl. Describe the process to which this enthalpy change applies.

32. a. Use the following data to calculate the enthalpy of hydration for cesium iodide and cesium hydroxide.

	Lattice Energy*	ΔH_{soln}
$CsI(s)$	-604 kJ/mol	33 kJ/mol
$CsOH(s)$	-724 kJ/mol	-72 kJ/mol

*Lattice energy was defined in Chapter 8 as the energy change for the process $M^+(g) + X^-(g) \rightarrow MX(s)$.

b. Based on your answers to part a, which ion, OH^- or I^-, is more strongly hydrated?

33. Which ion in each of the following pairs would you expect to be more strongly hydrated? Why?
a. Na^+ or Mg^{2+}
b. Mg^{2+} or Be^{2+}
c. Fe^{2+} or Fe^{3+}

34. Which ion in each of the following pairs would you expect to be more strongly hydrated? Why?
a. Li^+ or Cs^+
b. F^- or Br^-
c. Cl^- or ClO_4^-

35. Which solvent, water or carbon tetrachloride, would you choose to dissolve each of the following?
a. $Cu(NO_3)_2$
b. CS_2
c. CH_3C-OH
     $\quad\quad\overset{\|}{O}$
d. $CH_3(CH_2)_{16}CH_2OH$
e. HCl
f. C_6H_6

36. Which solvent, water or hexane (C_6H_{14}), would you choose to dissolve each of the following?
a. $NaCl$
b. HF
c. octane (C_8H_{18})
d. $(NH_4)_2SO_4$

37. Rationalize the trend in water solubility for the following simple alcohols:

Alcohol	Solubility (g/100 g H_2O at 20°C)
Methanol, CH_3OH	Soluble in all proportions
Ethanol, CH_3CH_2OH	Soluble in all proportions
Propanol, $CH_3CH_2CH_2OH$	Soluble in all proportions
Butanol, $CH_3(CH_2)_2CH_2OH$	8.14
Pentanol, $CH_3(CH_2)_3CH_2OH$	2.64
Hexanol, $CH_3(CH_2)_4CH_2OH$	0.59
Heptanol, $CH_3(CH_2)_5CH_2OH$	0.09

38. A typical detergent is sodium dodecylsulfate, or SDS, $CH_3(CH_2)_{10}CH_2SO_4^- Na^+$. In aqueous solution, small aggregates of detergent anions called *micelles* form. Propose a structure for the micelles.

39. Is Henry's law valid for the solubility of CO_2 in a basic solution? *Hint:* $CO_2 + OH^- \rightarrow HCO_3^-$.

40. Calculate the solubility of O_2 in water at a partial pressure of O_2 of 120 torr at 25°C. The Henry's law constant for O_2 is 7.8×10^2 atm · L/mol for Henry's law in the form $P = kC$ when C is the gas concentration (mol/L).

Vapor Pressures of Solutions

41. A solution is prepared by mixing 50.0 g glucose with 600.0 g water. What is the vapor pressure of this solution at 25°C? (At 25°C the vapor pressure of pure water is 23.8 torr.)

42. The normal boiling point of methanol is 64.7°C. A solution containing a nonvolatile solute dissolved in methanol has a vapor pressure of 710.0 torr at 64.7°C. What is the mole fraction of methanol in this solution?

43. A solution is made by dissolving 25.8 g urea (CH_4N_2O), a nonelectrolyte, in 275 g water. Calculate the vapor pressures of this solution at 25°C and 45°C. (The vapor pressure of pure water is 23.8 torr at 25°C and 71.9 torr at 45°C.)

44. A solution of urea (CH_4N_2O) in water has a vapor pressure of 19.6 torr at 25°C. What is the mole fraction of urea in this solution? What would be the vapor pressure of this solution at 45°C? (See Exercise 43 for relevant data.)

45. Pentane (C_5H_{12}) and hexane (C_6H_{14}) form an ideal solution. At 25°C the vapor pressures of pentane and hexane are 511 and 150. torr, respectively. A solution is prepared by mixing 25 mL pentane (density, 0.63 g/mL) with 45 mL hexane (density, 0.66 g/mL).
a. What is the vapor pressure of the resulting solution?
b. What is the composition by mole fraction of pentane in the vapor that is in equilibrium with this solution?

46. What is the composition of a pentane–hexane solution that has a vapor pressure of 350 torr at 25°C? What is the composition of the vapor in equilibrium with this solution? (See Exercise 45 for the vapor pressures of pure hexane and pentane.)

47. The vapor in equilibrium with a pentane–hexane solution at 25°C has a mole fraction of pentane equal to 0.15 at 25°C. What is the mole fraction of pentane in the solution? (See Exercise 45 for the vapor pressures of the pure liquids.)

48. What is the composition of a solution containing pentane and hexane for which the vapor pressures of pentane and hexane are equal? What is the composition of the vapor in equilibrium with this solution? (See Exercise 45.)

49. Which of the following will have the lowest total vapor pressure at 25°C?
a. Pure water
b. A solution of glucose in water with $\chi_{glucose} = 0.01$
c. A solution of sodium chloride in water with $\chi_{NaCl} = 0.01$
d. A solution of methanol in water with $\chi_{CH_3OH} = 0.2$ [Consider the vapor pressure of both methanol (143 torr at 25°C) and water.]

50. Which of the choices in Exercise 49 has the highest vapor pressure?

Colligative Properties

51. A solution is prepared by dissolving 4.9 g sucrose ($C_{12}H_{22}O_{11}$) in 175 g water. Calculate the boiling point, freezing point, and osmotic pressure of this solution at 25°C. Sucrose is a nonelectrolyte. Assume that the molality and molarity of this solution are equal.

52. Propylene glycol is produced commercially by the reaction of propylene oxide with water at high temperature:

$$CH_3-CH-CH_2 + H_2O \rightarrow CH_3CH-CH_2$$

Calculate the freezing point and boiling point of a solution of 200.0 g propylene glycol in 400.0 g water.

53. a. Calculate the freezing-point depression and osmotic pressure at 25°C of an aqueous solution containing 1.0 g/L of a protein (molar mass = 9.0×10^4 g/mol) if the density of the solution is 1.0 g/cm^3.

b. Considering your answer to part a, which colligative property, freezing-point depression or osmotic pressure, would be better used to determine the molar masses of large molecules. Explain.

54. A 20.0-mg sample of a protein is dissolved in water to make 25.0 mL of solution. The osmotic pressure of the solution is 0.56 torr at 25°C. What is the molar mass of the protein?

55. Reserpine is a natural product isolated from the roots of the shrub *Rauwolfia serpentina*. It was first synthesized in 1956 by Nobel prize winner R. B. Woodward. It is used as a tranquilizer and sedative. When 1.00 g reserpine is dissolved in 25.0 g camphor, the freezing-point depression is 2.63°C (K_f for camphor is 40.°C · kg/mol). Calculate the molality of the solution and the molar mass of reserpine.

56. If the fluid inside a tree is approximately 0.1 *M* more concentrated in solute than the groundwater that bathes the roots, how high will a column of fluid rise in the tree? Assume the density of the fluid is 1.0 g/cm^3. (The density of mercury is 13.6 g/cm^3.)

Properties of Electrolyte Solutions

57. Seawater is approximately 0.5 *M* NaCl. What is the minimum pressure that must be applied at 25°C to purify seawater by reverse osmosis?

58. Consider the following:

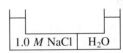

What would happen to the level of liquid in the two arms if the semipermeable membrane were permeable to

a. H$_2$O only?

b. H$_2$O, Na$^+$, and Cl$^-$?

59. Place the following solutions in order by the size of the freezing-point depression.

a. 1.0 *m* glucose in water

b. 1.0 *m* NaCl in water

c. 1.0 *m* HOCl in water (HOCl is a weak acid)

d. 1.0 *m* MgCl$_2$ in water

60. From the following:

pure water

solution of sucrose ($\chi = 0.01$) in water

solution of NaCl ($\chi = 0.01$) in water

solution of CaCl$_2$ ($\chi = 0.01$) in water

choose the one with the

a. Highest freezing point

b. Lowest freezing point

c. Highest boiling point

d. Lowest boiling point

e. Highest osmotic pressure

61. Calculate the freezing point of a 0.5 *m* solution of Ca(NO$_3$)$_2$ in water. (Assume that $i = 3.0$.) Would you expect the measured freezing point of 0.5 *m* Ca(NO$_3$)$_2$ to be higher or lower than the value you calculated? Explain.

62. A 1.00-g sample of each of the following compounds is dissolved separately in 25.0 g water. The freezing-point depression for solution is as follows:

Compound	ΔT
Co(NH$_2$CH$_2$CH$_2$NH$_2$)$_2$Cl$_3$	0.52°C
Co(NH$_2$CH$_2$CH$_2$NH$_2$)$_3$Cl$_3$	0.87°C

What is the experimental value of *i* for each of the compounds?

63. Use the following data for three solutions of $CaCl_2$ to calculate the apparent value of the van't Hoff factor.

Molality	Freezing-Point Depression
0.091	0.440
0.279	1.330
0.475	2.345

64. The freezing-point depression of a 0.091 m solution of CsCl is 0.302°C. The freezing-point depression of a 0.091 m solution of $CaCl_2$ is 0.440°C. In which solution does ion association appear to be greater? Explain.

Additional Exercises

65. The solubility of benzoic acid,

is 0.34 g/100 mL in water at 25°C and is 10.0 g/100 mL in benzene (C_6H_6) at 25°C. Rationalize this solubility behavior.

66. Would benzoic acid be more or less soluble in a basic aqueous solution than it is in water? Explain.

67. An aqueous antifreeze solution is 40.0% ethylene glycol ($C_2H_6O_2$) by mass. The density of the solution is 1.05 g/cm^3. Calculate the molality, molarity, and mole fraction of the ethylene glycol.

68. In lab you need to prepare 100 mL of each of the following solutions. Explain how you would proceed using the given information.
    a. 2.0 m KCl in water (density unknown to you)
    b. 15% NaOH by mass in water (density unknown to you)
    c. 25% NaOH by mass in CH_3OH ($d = 0.79$ g/cm^3)
    d. 30.% C_2H_5OH by volume in water

69. Although $Al(OH)_3$ is insoluble in water, NaOH is very soluble. Explain in terms of lattice energies.

70. In flushing and cleaning columns used in liquid chromatography to remove adsorbed contaminants, a series of solvents is used. Hexane, chloroform, methanol, and water are passed through the column in that order. Rationalize the order in terms of intermolecular forces and the mutual solubility (miscibility) of the solvents.

71. For each case choose the pair of substances you would expect to give the most nearly ideal solution. Explain your choices.
    a. CF_3CF_3 and $CF_3CF_2CF_3$ or H_2O and CH_3CCH_3 (with O double-bonded to the middle C)
    b. $CH_3(CH_2)_5CH_3$ and $CH_3(CH_2)_4CH_3$ or CHF_3 and CH_3-O-CH_3
    c. H_3PO_4 and H_2O or CCl_4 and CF_4

72. A solution is made by mixing 50.0 g acetone and 50.0 g methanol. What is the vapor pressure of this solution at 25°C?

What is the composition of the vapor expressed as a mole fraction? Assume ideal solution and gas behavior. (At 25°C the vapor pressures of pure acetone and pure methanol are 271 and 143 torr, respectively.) Is it reasonable to assume that this is an ideal solution? Explain.

73. A solution is prepared by mixing 1.0 mol methanol (CH_3OH) and 1.0 mol propanol ($CH_3CH_2CH_2OH$). What is the composition of the vapor (in terms of mole fractions) at 40°C? At 40°C the vapor pressures of pure methanol and pure propanol are 303 and 44.6 torr, respectively.

74. Cellophane is a form of cellulose that has undergone the viscose process. The structure of the cellophane polymer is

What structural features allow cellophane to act as a semipermeable membrane for water? (*Hint:* What types of intermolecular forces are possible between cellophane and water?)

75. Anthraquinone contains only carbon, hydrogen, and oxygen. When 4.80 mg anthraquinone is burned, 14.22 mg CO_2 and 1.66 mg H_2O are produced. The freezing point of camphor is lowered by 22.3°C when 1.32 g anthraquinone is dissolved in 11.4 g camphor. Calculate the empirical and molecular formulas of anthraquinone.

76. Calculate the freezing point of each of the following solutions. (For parts a and d, assume that the solute is undissociated. For parts b and c, assume complete dissociation.)
    a. 5.0 g glucose ($C_6H_{12}O_6$) in 25 g H_2O
    b. 5.0 g NaCl in 25 g H_2O
    c. 2.0 g $Al(NO_3)_3$ in 15 g H_2O
    d. 1.0 g benzaldehyde (C_6H_5CHO) in 10.0 g benzene

77. Calculate the freezing point and boiling point of an antifreeze solution that is 40.0% by mass of ethylene glycol ($HOCH_2CH_2OH$) in water.

78. How would you prepare 1.0 L of an aqueous solution of sucrose ($C_{12}H_{22}O_{11}$) that would have an osmotic pressure of 15 atm at a temperature of 25°C?

79. What mass of urea ($NH_2)_2CO$, (a nonelectrolyte), must be dissolved in 150.0 g water to give a solution with a freezing point of −3.00°C?

80. A 0.15-g sample of a purified protein is dissolved in water to give 2.0 mL of solution. The osmotic pressure is found to be 18.6 torr at 25°C. Calculate the protein's molar mass.

81. An unknown compound contains only carbon, hydrogen, and oxygen. Combustion analysis of the compound gives mass percents of 31.57% C and 5.30% H. The molar mass is determined by measuring the freezing-point depression of an aqueous solution. A freezing point of −5.20°C is recorded for a solution made by dissolving 10.56 g of the compound in 25.0 mL water. Determine the empirical formula, molar mass, and molecular formula of the compound. Assume that the compound is a nonelectrolyte.

Challenge Problems

82. Specifications for lactated Ringer's solution, which is used for intravenous (IV) injections, are as follows for each 100 mL of solution:

285–315 mg Na^+

14.1–17.3 mg K^+

4.9–6.0 mg Ca^{2+}

368–408 mg Cl^-

231–261 mg lactate, $C_3H_5O_3^-$

a. Specify the amounts of NaCl, KCl, $CaCl_2 \cdot 2H_2O$, and $NaC_3H_5O_3$ needed to prepare 100 mL lactated Ringer's solution.

b. What is the range of the osmotic pressure of the solution at 37°C, given the above specifications?

83. A 1.60-g sample of a mixture of naphthalene ($C_{10}H_8$) and anthracene ($C_{14}H_{10}$) is dissolved in 20.0 g benzene (C_6H_6). The freezing point of the solution is 2.8°C. What is the composition as mass percent of the sample mixture? The freezing point of benzene is 5.5°C, and K_f is 5.12°C · kg/mol.

84. A solid consists of a mixture of $NaNO_3$ and $Mg(NO_3)_2$. When 6.5 g of the solid is dissolved in 50.0 g water, the freezing point is lowered by 5.4°C. What is the composition, by mass, of the solid?

85. A forensic chemist is given a white solid that is suspected of being pure cocaine ($C_{17}H_{21}NO_4$, molar mass = 303.35 g/mol). She dissolves 1.22 ± 0.01 g of the solid in 15.60 ± 0.01 g benzene. The freezing point is lowered by 1.32 ± 0.04°C.

a. What is the molar mass of the substance? Assuming that the percent uncertainty in the calculated molar mass is the same as the percent uncertainty in the temperature change, calculate the uncertainty in the molar mass.

b. Could the chemist unequivocally state that the substance is cocaine? For example, is the uncertainty small enough to distinguish cocaine from codeine ($C_{18}H_{21}NO_3$, molar mass = 299.36 g/mol)?

c. Assuming that the absolute uncertainties in the measurements of temperature and mass remain unchanged, how could the chemist improve the precision of her results?

86. How would you prepare at least 2.0 L of an aqueous solution of $CaCl_2$ that would have a freezing point of −10.0°C?

a. Assuming $i = 3$

b. Taking into account the data for Exercise 63

Marathon Problem*

87. Using only the periodic table, a calculator, and the information below, identify the strong electrolyte whose general formula is

$$M_x(A)_y \cdot zH_2O$$

Ignore the effect of interionic attractions in the solution.

1. A^{n-} is a common oxyanion. When 30.0 mg of the anhydrous sodium salt containing this oxyanion (Na_nA, where $n = 1$, 2, or 3) is reduced in a reaction that involves the gain of 2 moles of electrons per mole of oxyanion, 15.26 mL of 0.02313 M reducing agent is required to react completely with the Na_nA present.[†]

2. The cation is derived from a silvery white metal that is relatively expensive. The metal itself crystallizes in a body-centered cubic unit cell and has an atomic radius of 198.4 pm. The solid, pure metal has a density of 5.243 g/cm³. The oxidation number of M in the strong electrolyte in question is +3.

3. When 33.4 mg of the compound is present (dissolved) in 10.0 mL of aqueous solution at 25°C, the solution has an osmotic pressure of 558 torr.

---

*This Marathon Problem was developed by James H. Burness of Penn State University, York Campus.

[†]Assume one mole of A^{n-} reacts with one mole of reducing agent.

CHAPTER 12

Chemical Kinetics

The applications of chemistry focus largely on chemical reactions, and the commercial use of a reaction requires knowledge of several of its characteristics, including its stoichiometry, energetics, and rate. A reaction is defined by its reactants and products, whose identity must be learned by experiment. Once the reactants and products are known, the equation for the reaction can be written and balanced, and stoichiometric calculations can be carried out. Another very important characteristic of a reaction is its spontaneity. Spontaneity refers to the *inherent tendency* for the process to occur; however, it implies nothing about speed. *Spontaneous does not mean fast.* There are many spontaneous reactions that are so slow that no apparent reaction occurs over a period of weeks or years at normal temperatures. For example, there is a strong inherent tendency for gaseous hydrogen and oxygen to combine, that is,

$$2H_2(g) + O_2(g) \rightarrow 2H_2O(l)$$

but in fact the two gases can coexist indefinitely at 25°C. Similarly, the gaseous reactions

$$H_2(g) + Cl_2(g) \rightarrow 2HCl(g)$$
$$N_2(g) + 3H_2(g) \rightarrow 2NH_3(g)$$

are both highly likely to occur from a thermodynamic standpoint, but we observe no reactions under normal conditions. In addition, the process of changing diamond to graphite is spontaneous but is so slow that it is not detectable.

To be useful, reactions must occur at a reasonable rate. To produce the 20 million tons of ammonia needed each year for fertilizer, we cannot simply mix nitrogen and hydrogen gases at 25°C and wait for them to react. It

---

< A computer simulation of a porous aluminophosphate sheet, a potential solid state catalyst. The atoms are indicated by colors: aluminum (yellow), phosphorus (purple), oxygen (red), carbon (green), and nitrogen (blue).

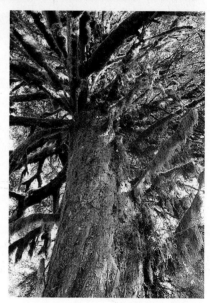

The metabolism of food to provide energy for human activities, the growth of trees, and the combustion of fuel in a race car all result from chemical reactions.

is not enough to understand the stoichiometry and thermodynamics of a reaction; we must also understand the factors that govern the rate of the reaction. The area of chemistry that concerns reaction rates is called **chemical kinetics.**

One of the main goals of chemical kinetics is to understand the steps by which a reaction takes place. This series of steps is called the **reaction mechanism.** Understanding the mechanism allows us to find ways to facilitate the reaction. For example, the Haber process for the production of ammonia requires high temperatures to achieve commercially feasible reaction rates. However, even higher temperatures (and more cost) would be required without the use of iron oxide, which speeds up the reaction.

In this chapter we will consider the main ideas of chemical kinetics. We will explore rate laws, reaction mechanisms, and simple models for chemical reactions.

12.1 Reaction Rates

Purpose

- To define reaction rate and to show how rates can be measured from experimental data.

To introduce the concept of the rate of a reaction, we will consider the decomposition of nitrogen dioxide, a gas that causes air pollution. Nitrogen dioxide decomposes to nitric oxide and oxygen as follows:

$$2NO_2(g) \rightarrow 2NO(g) + O_2(g)$$

Suppose in a particular experiment we start with a flask of nitrogen dioxide at 300°C and measure the concentrations of nitrogen dioxide, nitric oxide, and oxygen as the nitrogen dioxide decomposes. The results of this experiment are summarized in Table 12.1, and the data are plotted in Fig. 12.1 (on p. 546).

Note from these results that the concentration of the reactant (NO_2) decreases with time and the concentrations of the products (NO and O_2) increase with time. Chemical kinetics deals with the speed at which these changes occur. The speed, or **rate,** of a process is defined as the change in a given quantity over a specific period of time. For chemical reactions, the quantity that changes is the amount or concentration of a reactant or product. So the **reaction rate** of a chemical reaction is defined as the *change in concentration of a reactant or product per unit time:*

$$\text{Rate} = \frac{\text{concentration of A at time } t_2 - \text{concentration of A at time } t_1}{t_2 - t_1}$$

$$= \frac{\Delta[A]}{\Delta t}$$

where A is the reactant or product being considered and the square brackets indicate concentration in mol/L. As usual, the symbol Δ indicates a *change* in a given quantity. Note that a change can be positive (increase) or negative (decrease), thus leading to a positive or negative reaction rate by this definition. However, for

The kinetics of air pollution is discussed in Section 12.8.

[A] means concentration of A in mol/L.

Table 12.1			
Concentrations of Reactant and Products as a Function of Time for the Reaction $2NO_2(g) \rightarrow 2NO(g) + O_2(g)$ (at 300°C)			
	Concentration (mol/L)		
Time (±1 s)	NO_2	NO	O_2
0	0.0100	0	0
50	0.0079	0.0021	0.0011
100	0.0065	0.0035	0.0018
150	0.0055	0.0045	0.0023
200	0.0048	0.0052	0.0026
250	0.0043	0.0057	0.0029
300	0.0038	0.0062	0.0031
350	0.0034	0.0066	0.0033
400	0.0031	0.0069	0.0035

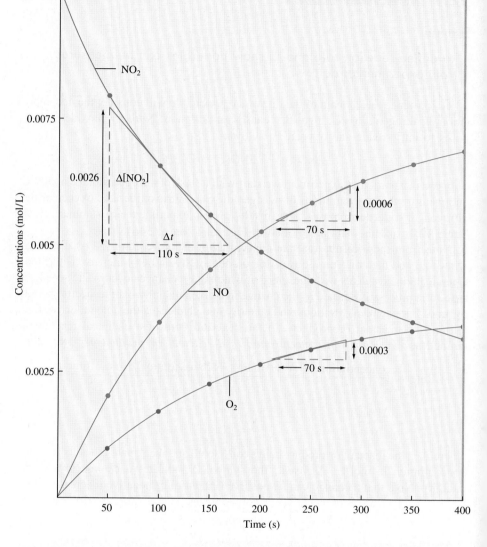

Figure 12.1

Starting with a flask of nitrogen dioxide at 300°C, the concentrations of nitrogen dioxide, nitric oxide, and oxygen are plotted versus time.

convenience, we will always define the rate as a positive quantity, as we will see below.

Now let us calculate the average rate at which the concentration of NO_2 changes over the first 50 seconds of the reaction using the data given in Table 12.1.

$$\frac{\text{Change in } [NO_2]}{\text{Time elapsed}} = \frac{\Delta[NO_2]}{\Delta t}$$

$$= \frac{[NO_2]_{t=50} - [NO_2]_{t=0}}{50 \text{ s} - 0 \text{ s}}$$

$$= \frac{0.0079 \text{ mol/L} - 0.0100 \text{ mol/L}}{50 \text{ s}}$$

$$= -4.2 \times 10^{-5} \text{ mol/L} \cdot \text{s}$$

Note that since the concentration of NO_2 decreases with time, $\Delta[NO_2]$ is a negative quantity. Because it is customary to work with *positive* reaction rates, we define the rate of this particular reaction as

$$\text{Rate} = -\frac{\Delta[NO_2]}{\Delta t}$$

Since the concentrations of reactants always decrease with time, any rate expression involving a reactant will include a negative sign. The average rate of this reaction from 0 to 50 seconds is then

$$\begin{aligned}\text{Rate} &= -\frac{\Delta[NO_2]}{\Delta t} \\ &= -(-4.2 \times 10^{-5} \text{ mol/L} \cdot \text{s}) \\ &= 4.2 \times 10^{-5} \text{ mol/L} \cdot \text{s}\end{aligned}$$

The average rates for this reaction during several other time intervals are given in Table 12.2. Note that the rate is not constant, but decreases with time. The rates given in Table 12.2 are **average rates** over 50-second time intervals. The value of the rate at a particular time (the **instantaneous rate**) can be obtained by computing the slope of a line tangent to the curve at that point. Figure 12.1 shows a tangent drawn at $t = 100$ seconds. The *slope* of this line gives the rate at $t = 100$ seconds as follows:

Appendix 1.3 reviews slopes of straight lines.

$$\begin{aligned}\text{Slope of the tangent line} &= \frac{\text{change in } y}{\text{change in } x} \\ &= \frac{\Delta[NO_2]}{\Delta t}\end{aligned}$$

But

$$\text{Rate} = -\frac{\Delta[NO_2]}{\Delta t}$$

Therefore,

$$\begin{aligned}\text{Rate} &= -(\text{slope of the tangent line}) \\ &= -\left(\frac{-0.0026 \text{ mol/L}}{110 \text{ s}}\right) \\ &= 2.4 \times 10^{-5} \text{ mol/L} \cdot \text{s}\end{aligned}$$

So far we have discussed the rate of this reaction only in terms of the reactant. The rate also can be defined in terms of the products. However, in doing so we must take into account the coefficients in the balanced equation for the reaction, because the stoichiometry determines the relative rates of consumption of reactants and generation of products. For example, in the reaction we are considering,

$$2NO_2(g) \rightarrow 2NO(g) + O_2(g)$$

both the reactant NO_2 and the product NO have a coefficient of 2, so NO is produced at the same rate as NO_2 is consumed. We can verify this from Fig. 12.1. Note that the curve for NO is the same shape as the curve for NO_2, except that it is inverted, or flipped over. This means that, at any point in time, the slope of the tangent to the curve for NO will be the negative of the slope to the curve for NO_2. (Verify this at the point $t = 100$ seconds on both curves.) In the balanced equation,

Table 12.2
Average Rate (in mol/L · s) of Decomposition of Nitrogen Dioxide as a Function of Time*

$-\dfrac{\Delta[NO_2]}{\Delta t}$	Time Period (s)
4.2×10^{-5}	$0 \rightarrow 50$
2.8×10^{-5}	$50 \rightarrow 100$
2.0×10^{-5}	$100 \rightarrow 150$
1.4×10^{-5}	$150 \rightarrow 200$
1.0×10^{-5}	$200 \rightarrow 250$

*Note that the *rate* decreases with time.

the product O_2 has a coefficient of 1, which means it is produced half as fast as NO, since NO has a coefficient of 2. That is, the rate of NO production is twice the rate of O_2 production.

We can also verify this fact from Fig. 12.1. For example, at $t = 250$ seconds,

$$\text{Slope of the tangent to the NO curve} = \frac{6.0 \times 10^{-4} \text{ mol/L}}{70 \text{ s}}$$
$$= 8.6 \times 10^{-6} \text{ mol/L} \cdot \text{s}$$

$$\text{Slope of the tangent to the } O_2 \text{ curve} = \frac{3.0 \times 10^{-4} \text{ mol/L}}{70 \text{ s}}$$
$$= 4.3 \times 10^{-6} \text{ mol/L} \cdot \text{s}$$

The slope at $t = 250$ seconds on the NO curve is twice the slope of that point on the O_2 curve, showing that the rate of production of NO is twice that of O_2.

The rate information can be summarized as follows:

Rate of consumption of NO_2	=	rate of production of NO	=	2(rate of production of O_2)
$-\dfrac{\Delta[NO_2]}{\Delta t}$	=	$\dfrac{\Delta[NO]}{\Delta t}$	=	$2\left(\dfrac{\Delta[O_2]}{\Delta t}\right)$

We have seen that the rate of a reaction is not constant, but that it changes with time. This is because the concentrations change with time (Fig. 12.1).

Because the reaction rate changes with time, and because the rate is different (by factors that depend on the coefficients in the balanced equation) depending on which reactant or product is being studied, we must be very specific when we describe a rate for a chemical reaction.

12.2 Rate Laws: An Introduction

Purpose

• To describe the two types of rate laws.

Chemical reactions are *reversible*. In our discussion of the decomposition of nitrogen dioxide, we have so far considered only the *forward reaction*, as shown here:

$$2NO_2(g) \rightarrow 2NO(g) + O_2(g)$$

However, the *reverse reaction* also can occur. As NO and O_2 accumulate, they can react to re-form NO_2:

$$O_2(g) + 2NO(g) \rightarrow 2NO_2(g)$$

When gaseous NO_2 is placed in an otherwise empty container, initially the dominant reaction is

$$2NO_2(g) \rightarrow 2NO(g) + O_2(g)$$

and the change in the concentration of NO_2 ($\Delta[NO_2]$) depends only on the forward reaction. However, after a period of time, enough products accumulate so that the reverse reaction becomes important. Now $\Delta[NO_2]$ depends on the *difference in the rates of the forward and reverse reactions*. This complication can be avoided if we study the rate of a reaction under conditions where the reverse reaction makes only a negligible contribution. Typically, this means that we must study a reaction at a point soon after the reactants are mixed, before the products have had time to build up to significant levels.

If we choose conditions where the reverse reaction can be neglected, the *reaction rate will depend only on the concentrations of the reactants*. For the decomposition of nitrogen dioxide, we can write

$$\text{Rate} = k[NO_2]^n \tag{12.1}$$

Such an expression, which shows how the rate depends on the concentrations of reactants, is called a **rate law.** The proportionality constant k, called the **rate constant,** and n, called the **order** of the reactant, must both be determined by experiment. The order of a reactant can be an integer (including zero) or a fraction. For the relatively simple reactions we will consider in this book, the orders will often be positive integers.

Note two important points about Equation (12.1):

1. The concentrations of the products do not appear in the rate law because the reaction rate is being studied under conditions where the reverse reaction does not contribute to the overall rate.

2. The value of the exponent n must be determined by experiment; it cannot be written from the balanced equation.

Before we go further we must define exactly what we mean by the term *rate* in Equation (12.1). In Section 12.1 we saw that reaction rate means a change in concentration per unit time. However, which reactant or product concentration do we choose in defining the rate? For example, for the decomposition of NO_2 to produce O_2 and NO considered in Section 12.1, we could define the rate in terms of any of these three species. However, since O_2 is produced only half as fast as NO, we must be careful to specify which species we are talking about in a given case. For instance, we might choose to define the reaction rate in terms of the consumption of NO_2:

$$\text{Rate} = -\frac{\Delta[NO_2]}{\Delta t} = k[NO_2]^n$$

On the other hand, we could define the rate in terms of the production of O_2:

$$\text{Rate}' = \frac{\Delta[O_2]}{\Delta t} = k'[NO_2]^n$$

Note that because $2NO_2$ molecules are consumed for every O_2 molecule produced,

$$\text{Rate} = 2 \times \text{Rate}'$$

or

$$k[NO_2]^n = 2k'[NO_2]^n$$

and

$$k = 2 \times k'$$

Thus the value of the rate constant depends on how the rate is defined.

When forward and reverse reaction rates are equal, there will be no changes in the concentrations of reactants or products. This is called **chemical equilibrium** and is discussed fully in Chapter 13.

In this text we will always be careful to define exactly what is meant by the rate for a given reaction so that there will be no confusion about which specific rate constant is being used.

Types of Rate Laws

Notice that the rate law we have used to this point expresses rate as a function of concentration. For example, for the decomposition of NO_2 we have defined

$$\text{Rate} = -\frac{\Delta[NO_2]}{\Delta t} = k[NO_2]^n$$

which tells us (once we have determined the value of n) exactly how the rate depends on the concentration of the reactant, NO_2. A rate law that expresses how the *rate depends on concentration* is technically called the **differential rate law,** but it is often simply called the **rate law.** Thus when we use the term *the rate law* in this text, we mean the expression that gives the rate as a function of concentration.

A second kind of rate law, the **integrated rate law,** also will be important in our study of kinetics. The integrated rate law expresses how the *concentrations depend on time*. Although we will not consider the details here, a given differential rate law is always related to a certain type of integrated rate law, and vice versa. That is, if we determine the differential rate law for a given reaction, we automatically know the form of the integrated rate law for the reaction. This means that once we determine experimentally either type of rate law for a reaction, we also know the other one.

Which rate law we choose to determine by experiment often depends on what types of data are easiest to collect. If we can conveniently measure how the rate changes as the concentrations are changed, we can readily determine the differential (rate/concentration) rate law. On the other hand, if it is more convenient to measure the concentration as a function of time, we can determine the form of the integrated (concentration/time) rate law. We will discuss how rate laws are actually determined in the next several sections.

Why are we interested in determining the rate law for a reaction? How does it help us? It helps us because we can work backward from the rate law to infer the steps by which the reaction occurs. Most chemical reactions do not take place in a single step but result from a series of sequential steps. To understand a chemical reaction, we must learn what these steps are. For example, a chemist who is designing an insecticide may study the reactions involved in the process of insect growth to see what type of molecule might interrupt this series of reactions. Or an industrial chemist may be trying to make a reaction occur faster or using less expensive conditions. To accomplish this, he or she must know which step is slowest, because it is that step that must be speeded up. Thus a chemist is usually not interested in a rate law for its own sake but because of what it tells about the steps by which a reaction occurs. We will develop a process for finding the reaction steps in this chapter.

Rate Laws: A Summary

- There are two types of rate laws.

  1. The differential rate law (often called simply the rate law) shows how the rate of a reaction depends on concentrations.

The name differential rate law comes from a mathematical term. We will regard it simply as a label. The terms differential rate law and rate law will be used interchangeably in this text.

2. The integrated rate law shows how the concentrations of species in the reaction depend on time.

- Because we typically consider reactions only under conditions where the reverse reaction is unimportant, our rate laws will involve only concentrations of reactants.

- Because the differential and integrated rate laws for a given reaction are related in a well-defined way, the experimental determination of *either* of the rate laws is sufficient.

- Experimental convenience usually dictates which type of rate law is determined experimentally.

- Knowing the rate law for a reaction is important mainly because we can usually infer the individual steps involved in the reaction from the specific form of the rate law.

12.3 Determining the Form of the Rate Law

Purpose

- To learn methods for determining the rate law for a reaction.

The first step in understanding how a given chemical reaction occurs is to determine the *form* of the rate law. That is, we need to determine experimentally the power to which each reactant concentration must be raised in the rate law. In this section we will explore ways to obtain the differential rate law for a reaction. First, we will consider the decomposition of dinitrogen pentoxide in carbon tetrachloride solution:

$$2N_2O_5(soln) \rightarrow 4NO_2(soln) + O_2(g)$$

Data for this reaction at 45°C are listed in Table 12.3 and plotted in Fig. 12.2 (on p. 552). In this reaction the oxygen gas escapes from the solution and thus does not

Table 12.3	
Concentration/Time Data for the Reaction **$2N_2O_5(soln) \rightarrow 4NO_2(soln) + O_2(g)$ (at 45°C)**	
[N_2O_5] (mol/L)	Time (s)
1.00	0
0.88	200
0.78	400
0.69	600
0.61	800
0.54	1000
0.48	1200
0.43	1400
0.38	1600
0.34	1800
0.30	2000

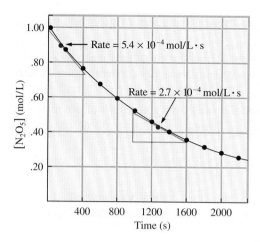

Figure 12.2

A plot of the concentration of N_2O_5 as a function of time for the reaction $2N_2O_5(soln) \rightarrow 4NO_2(soln) + O_2(g)$ (at 45°C). Note that the reaction rate at $[N_2O_5] = 0.90\ M$ is twice that at $[N_2O_5] = 0.45\ M$.

react with the nitrogen dioxide, so we do not have to be concerned about the effects of the reverse reaction at any time over the life of the reaction. That is, the reverse reaction is negligible at all times over the course of this reaction.

Evaluation of the reaction rates at concentrations of N_2O_5 of 0.90 M and 0.45 M, by taking the slopes of the tangents to the curve at these points (see Fig. 12.2), yields the following data:

$[N_2O_5]$	Rate (mol/L · s)
0.90 M	5.4×10^{-4}
0.45 M	2.7×10^{-4}

Note that when $[N_2O_5]$ is halved, the rate is also halved. This means that the rate of this reaction depends on the concentration of N_2O_5 to the *first power*. In other words, the (differential) rate law for this reaction is

$$\text{Rate} = -\frac{\Delta[N_2O_5]}{\Delta t} = k[N_2O_5]^1 = k[N_2O_5]$$

First order: rate = $k[A]$. Doubling the concentration of A doubles the reaction rate.

Thus the reaction is *first order* in N_2O_5. Note that for this reaction the order is *not* the same as the coefficient of N_2O_5 in the balanced equation for the reaction. This reemphasizes the fact that the order of a particular reactant must be obtained by *observing* how the reaction rate depends on the concentration of that reactant.

We have seen that by determining the instantaneous rate at two different reactant concentrations, the rate law for the decomposition of N_2O_5 is shown to have the form

$$\text{Rate} = -\frac{\Delta[A]}{\Delta t} = k[A]$$

where A represents N_2O_5.

Method of Initial Rates

The value of the initial rate is determined for each experiment at the same value of t as close to $t = 0$ as possible.

One common method for experimentally determining the form of the rate law for a reaction is the **method of initial rates**. The **initial rate** of a reaction is the instantaneous rate determined just after the reaction begins (just after $t = 0$). The idea is to determine the instantaneous rate before the initial concentrations of reactants have changed significantly. Several experiments are carried out using different initial concentrations, and the initial rate is determined for each run. The results are then compared to see how the initial rate depends on the initial concentrations. This allows the form of the rate law to be determined. We will illustrate the method of initial rates using the following equation:

$$NH_4^+(aq) + NO_2^-(aq) \rightarrow N_2(g) + 2H_2O(l)$$

Table 12.4 gives initial rates obtained from three experiments involving different initial concentrations of reactants. The general form of the rate law for this reaction is

$$\text{Rate} = -\frac{\Delta[NH_4^+]}{\Delta t} = k[NH_4^+]^n[NO_2^-]^m$$

We can determine the values of n and m by observing how the initial rate depends on the initial concentrations of NH_4^+ and NO_2^-. In Experiments 1 and 2, where the initial concentration of NH_4^+ remains the same but the initial concentration of NO_2^- doubles, the observed initial rate also doubles. Since

$$\text{Rate} = k[NH_4^+]^n[NO_2^-]^m$$

we have for Experiment 1

$$\text{Rate} = 1.35 \times 10^{-7} \text{ mol/L} \cdot \text{s} = k(0.100 \text{ mol/L})^n(0.0050 \text{ mol/L})^m$$

and for Experiment 2

$$\text{Rate} = 2.70 \times 10^{-7} \text{ mol/L} \cdot \text{s} = k(0.100 \text{ mol/L})^n(0.010 \text{ mol/L})^m$$

The ratio of these rates is

$$\frac{\text{Rate 2}}{\text{Rate 1}} = \underbrace{\frac{2.70 \times 10^{-7} \text{ mol/L} \cdot \text{s}}{1.35 \times 10^{-7} \text{ mol/L} \cdot \text{s}}}_{2.00} = \frac{\cancel{k(0.100 \text{ mol/L})^n}(0.010 \text{ mol/L})^m}{\cancel{k(0.100 \text{ mol/L})^n}(0.0050 \text{ mol/L})^m}$$

$$= \frac{(0.010 \text{ mol/L})^m}{(0.0050 \text{ mol/L})^m} = (2.0)^m$$

Thus

$$\frac{\text{Rate 2}}{\text{Rate 1}} = 2.00 = (2.0)^m$$

Rates 1, 2, and 3 were determined at the same value of t (very close to $t = 0$).

which means the value of m is 1. The rate law for this reaction is first order in the reactant NO_2^-.

Table 12.4			
Initial Rates from Three Experiments for the Reaction $NH_4^+(aq) + NO_2^-(aq) \rightarrow N_2(g) + 2H_2O(l)$			
Experiment	Initial Concentration of NH_4^+	Initial Concentration of NO_2^-	Initial Rate (mol/L · s)
1	0.100 M	0.0050 M	1.35×10^{-7}
2	0.100 M	0.010 M	2.70×10^{-7}
3	0.200 M	0.010 M	5.40×10^{-7}

A similar analysis of the results for Experiments 2 and 3 yields the ratio

$$\frac{\text{Rate 3}}{\text{Rate 2}} = \frac{5.40 \times 10^{-7} \text{ mol/L} \cdot \text{s}}{2.70 \times 10^{-7} \text{ mol/L} \cdot \text{s}} = \frac{(0.200 \text{ mol/L})^n}{(0.100 \text{ mol/L})^n}$$

$$= 2.00 = \left(\frac{0.200}{0.100}\right)^n = (2.00)^n$$

The value of n is also 1.

We have shown that the values of n and m are both 1 and the rate law is

$$\text{Rate} = k[\text{NH}_4^+][\text{NO}_2^-]$$

This rate law is first order in both NO_2^- and NH_4^+. Note that it is merely a coincidence that n and m have the same values as the coefficients of NH_4^+ and NO_2^- in the balanced equation for the reaction.

Overall reaction order is the sum of the orders for the various reactants.

The **overall reaction order** is the sum of n and m. For this reaction, $n + m = 2$. The reaction is second order overall.

The value of the rate constant k can now be calculated using the results of *any* of the three experiments shown in Table 12.4. From the data for Experiment 1, we know that

$$\text{Rate} = k[\text{NH}_4^+][\text{NO}_2^-]$$

$$1.35 \times 10^{-7} \text{ mol/L} \cdot \text{s} = k(0.100 \text{ mol/L})(0.0050 \text{ mol/L})$$

Then

$$k = \frac{1.35 \times 10^{-7} \text{ mol/L} \cdot \text{s}}{(0.100 \text{ mol/L})(0.0050 \text{ mol/L})} = 2.7 \times 10^{-4} \text{ L/mol} \cdot \text{s}$$

Sample Exercise 12.1

The reaction between bromate ions and bromide ions in acidic aqueous solution is given by the equation

$$\text{BrO}_3^-(aq) + 5\text{Br}^-(aq) + 6\text{H}^+(aq) \rightarrow 3\text{Br}_2(l) + 3\text{H}_2\text{O}(l)$$

Table 12.5 gives the results from four experiments. Using these data, determine the orders for all three reactants, the overall reaction order, and the value of the rate constant.

Table 12.5

The Results from Four Experiments to Study the Reaction
$\text{BrO}_3^-(aq) + 5\text{Br}^-(aq) + 6\text{H}^+(aq) \rightarrow 3\text{Br}_2(l) + 3\text{H}_2\text{O}(l)$

Experiment	Initial Concentration of BrO_3^- (mol/L)	Initial Concentration of Br^- (mol/L)	Initial Concentration of H^+ (mol/L)	Measured Initial Rate (mol/L · s)
1	0.10	0.10	0.10	8.0×10^{-4}
2	0.20	0.10	0.10	1.6×10^{-3}
3	0.20	0.20	0.10	3.2×10^{-3}
4	0.10	0.10	0.20	3.2×10^{-3}

Solution

The general form of the rate law for this reaction is

$$\text{Rate} = k[BrO_3^-]^n[Br^-]^m[H^+]^p$$

We can determine the values of n, m, and p by comparing the rates from the various experiments. To determine the value of n, we use the results from Experiments 1 and 2, in which only $[BrO_3^-]$ changes:

$$\frac{\text{Rate 2}}{\text{Rate 1}} = \frac{1.60 \times 10^{-3} \text{ mol/L} \cdot \text{s}}{8.00 \times 10^{-4} \text{ mol/L} \cdot \text{s}} = \frac{k(0.20 \text{ mol/L})^n(0.10 \text{ mol/L})^m(0.10 \text{ mol/L})^p}{k(0.10 \text{ mol/L})^n(0.10 \text{ mol/L})^m(0.10 \text{ mol/L})^p}$$

$$2.0 = \left(\frac{0.20 \text{ mol/L}}{0.10 \text{ mol/L}}\right)^n = (2.0)^n$$

Thus n is equal to 1.

To determine the value of m, we use the results from Experiments 2 and 3, in which only $[Br^-]$ changes:

$$\frac{\text{Rate 3}}{\text{Rate 2}} = \frac{3.20 \times 10^{-3} \text{ mol/L} \cdot \text{s}}{1.60 \times 10^{-3} \text{ mol/L} \cdot \text{s}} = \frac{k(0.20 \text{ mol/L})^n(0.20 \text{ mol/L})^m(0.10 \text{ mol/L})^p}{k(0.20 \text{ mol/L})^n(0.10 \text{ mol/L})^m(0.10 \text{ mol/L})^p}$$

$$2.0 = \left(\frac{0.20 \text{ mol/L}}{0.10 \text{ mol/L}}\right)^m = (2.0)^m$$

Thus m is equal to 1.

To determine the value of p, we use the results from Experiments 1 and 4, in which $[BrO_3^-]$ and $[Br^-]$ are constant but $[H^+]$ differs:

$$\frac{\text{Rate 4}}{\text{Rate 1}} = \frac{3.20 \times 10^{-3} \text{ mol/L} \cdot \text{s}}{8.00 \times 10^{-4} \text{ mol/L} \cdot \text{s}} = \frac{k(0.10 \text{ mol/L})^n(0.10 \text{ mol/L})^m(0.20 \text{ mol/L})^p}{k(0.10 \text{ mol/L})^n(0.10 \text{ mol/L})^m(0.10 \text{ mol/L})^p}$$

$$4.0 = \left(\frac{0.20 \text{ mol/L}}{0.10 \text{ mol/L}}\right)^p$$

$$4.0 = (2.0)^p = (2.0)^2$$

Thus p is equal to 2.

The rate of this reaction is first order in BrO_3^- and Br^- and second order in H^+. The overall reaction order is $n + m + p = 4$.

The rate law can now be written

$$\text{Rate} = k[BrO_3^-][Br^-][H^+]^2$$

The value of the rate constant k can be calculated from the results of any of the four experiments. For Experiment 1, the initial rate is 8.0×10^{-4} mol/L $\cdot$ s and $[BrO_3^-] = 0.100 \ M$, $[Br^-] = 0.10 \ M$, and $[H^+] = 0.10 \ M$. Using these values in the rate law gives

$$8.0 \times 10^{-4} \text{ mol/L} \cdot \text{s} = k(0.10 \text{ mol/L})(0.10 \text{ mol/L})(0.10 \text{ mol/L})^2$$

$$8.0 \times 10^{-4} \text{ mol/L} \cdot \text{s} = k(1.0 \times 10^{-4} \text{ mol}^4/\text{L}^4)$$

$$k = \frac{8.0 \times 10^{-4} \text{ mol/L} \cdot \text{s}}{1.0 \times 10^{-4} \text{ mol}^4/\text{L}^4} = 8.0 \text{ L}^3/\text{mol}^3 \cdot \text{s}$$

CHECK: Verify that the same value of k can be obtained from the results of the other experiments.

12.4 *The Integrated Rate Law*

Purpose

• To develop rate laws relating concentration to reaction time and to show how they can be used to determine reaction order.

The rate laws we have considered so far express the rate as a function of the reactant concentrations. It is also useful to be able to express the reactant concentrations as a function of time, given the (differential) rate law for the reaction. In this section we show how this is done.

We will proceed by first looking at reactions involving a single reactant:

$$aA \rightarrow products$$

all of which have a rate law of the form

$$Rate = -\frac{\Delta[A]}{\Delta t} = k[A]^n$$

We will develop the integrated rate laws individually for the cases $n = 1$ (first order), $n = 2$ (second order), and $n = 0$ (zero order).

First-Order Rate Laws

For the reaction

$$2N_2O_5(soln) \rightarrow 4NO_2(soln) + O_2(g)$$

we have found that the rate law is

$$Rate = -\frac{\Delta[N_2O_5]}{\Delta t} = k[N_2O_5]$$

Since the rate of this reaction depends on the concentration of N_2O_5 to the first power, it is a **first-order reaction.** This means that if the concentration of N_2O_5 in a flask were suddenly doubled, the rate of production of NO_2 and O_2 would also double. This rate law can be put into a different form using a calculus operation known as integration, which yields the expression

$$\ln[N_2O_5] = -kt + \ln[N_2O_5]_0$$

Appendix 1.2 contains a review of logarithms.

where ln indicates the natural logarithm, t is the time, $[N_2O_5]$ is the concentration of N_2O_5 at time t, and $[N_2O_5]_0$ is the initial concentration of N_2O_5 (at $t = 0$, the start of the experiment). Note that such an equation, called the **integrated rate law,** expresses the *concentration of the reactant as a function of time*.

For a chemical reaction of the form

$$aA \rightarrow products$$

where the kinetics are first order in [A], the rate law is

$$Rate = -\frac{\Delta[A]}{\Delta t} = k[A]$$

and the **integrated first-order rate law** is

$$\ln[A] = -kt + \ln[A]_0 \qquad (12.2)$$

There are several important things to note about Equation (12.2):

1. The equation shows how the concentration of A depends on time. If the initial concentration of A and the rate constant k are known, the concentration of A at any time can be calculated.

An integrated rate law relates concentration to reaction time.

2. Equation (12.2) is of the form $y = mx + b$, where a plot of y versus x is a straight line with slope m and intercept b. In Equation (12.2),

$$y = \ln[A] \qquad x = t \qquad m = -k \qquad b = \ln[A]_0$$

Thus, for a first-order reaction, plotting the natural logarithm of concentration versus time always gives a straight line. This fact is often used to test whether a reaction is first order or not. For the reaction

For a first-order reaction, a plot of $\ln[A]$ versus t is always a straight line.

$$aA \rightarrow products$$

the *reaction is first order in A if a plot of ln[A] versus t is a straight line.* Conversely, if this plot is not a straight line, the reaction is not first order in A.

3. This integrated rate law for a first-order reaction also can be expressed in terms of a *ratio* of [A] and [A]₀ as follows:

$$\ln\left(\frac{[A]_0}{[A]}\right) = kt$$

Sample Exercise 12.2

The decomposition of N_2O_5 in the gas phase was studied at constant temperature.

$$2N_2O_5(g) \rightarrow 4NO_2(g) + O_2(g)$$

The following results were collected:

[N₂O₅] (mol/L)	Time (s)
0.1000	0
0.0707	50
0.0500	100
0.0250	200
0.0125	300
0.00625	400

Using these data, verify that the rate law is first order in $[N_2O_5]$, and calculate the value of the rate constant, where the rate $= -\Delta[N_2O_5]/\Delta t$.

Solution

We can verify that the rate law is first order in $[N_2O_5]$ by constructing a plot of $\ln[N_2O_5]$ versus time. The values of $\ln[N_2O_5]$ at various times are given below, and the plot of $\ln[N_2O_5]$ versus time is shown in Fig. 12.3.

Figure 12.3

A plot of $\ln[N_2O_5]$ versus time.

$\ln[N_2O_5]$	Time (s)
-2.303	0
-2.649	50
-2.996	100
-3.689	200
-4.382	300
-5.075	400

The fact that the plot is a straight line confirms that the reaction is first order in N_2O_5, since it follows the equation $\ln[N_2O_5] = -kt + \ln[N_2O_5]_0$.

Since the reaction is first order, the slope of the line equals $-k$, where

$$\text{Slope} = \frac{\text{change in } y}{\text{change in } x} = \frac{\Delta y}{\Delta x} = \frac{\Delta(\ln[N_2O_5])}{\Delta t}$$

Since the first and last points are exactly on the line, we will use these points to calculate the slope:

$$\text{Slope} = \frac{-5.075 - (-2.303)}{400 \text{ s} - 0 \text{ s}} = \frac{-2.772}{400 \text{ s}} = -6.93 \times 10^{-3} \text{ s}^{-1}$$

$$k = -(\text{slope}) = 6.93 \times 10^{-3} \text{ s}^{-1}$$

Sample Exercise 12.3

Using the data given in Sample Exercise 12.2, calculate $[N_2O_5]$ at 150. s after the start of the reaction.

Solution

We know from Sample Exercise 12.2 that $[N_2O_5] = 0.0500$ mol/L at 100 s and $[N_2O_5] = 0.0250$ mol/L at 200 s. Since 150 s is halfway between 100 and 200 s, it is tempting to assume that we can simply use an arithmetic average to obtain $[N_2O_5]$ at that time. This is incorrect because it is $\ln[N_2O_5]$, not $[N_2O_5]$, that is directly proportional to t. To calculate $[N_2O_5]$ after 150 s, we use Equation (12.2):

$$\ln[N_2O_5] = -kt + \ln[N_2O_5]_0$$

where $t = 150.$ s, $k = 6.93 \times 10^{-3}$ s^{-1} (as determined in Sample Exercise 12.2), and $[N_2O_5]_0 = 0.1000$ mol/L.

$$\ln([N_2O_5])_{t=150} = -(6.93 \times 10^{-3} \text{ s}^{-1})(150. \text{ s}) + \ln(0.100)$$

$$= -1.040 - 2.303 = -3.343$$

$$[N_2O_5]_{t=150} = \text{antilog}(-3.343) = 0.0353 \text{ mol/L}$$

The antilog operation means to exponentiate (see Appendix 1.2).

Note that this value of $[N_2O_5]$ is *not* halfway between 0.0500 and 0.0250 mol/L.

Half-Life of a First-Order Reaction

The time required for a reactant to reach half its original concentration is called the **half-life of a reaction** and is designated by the symbol $t_{1/2}$. For example, we can calculate the half-life of the decomposition reaction discussed in Sample Exercise 12.2. The data plotted in Fig. 12.4 show that the half-life for this reaction is 100 seconds. We can see this by considering the following numbers:

$[N_2O_5]$(mol/L)	t (s)		
0.100	0	$\Delta t = 100$ s;	$\dfrac{[N_2O_5]_{t=100}}{[N_2O_5]_{t=0}} = \dfrac{0.050}{0.100} = \dfrac{1}{2}$
0.0500	100		
0.0250	200	$\Delta t = 100$ s;	$\dfrac{[N_2O_5]_{t=200}}{[N_2O_5]_{t=100}} = \dfrac{0.025}{0.050} = \dfrac{1}{2}$
0.0125	300	$\Delta t = 100$ s;	$\dfrac{[N_2O_5]_{t=300}}{[N_2O_5]_{t=200}} = \dfrac{0.0125}{0.0250} = \dfrac{1}{2}$

Note that it *always* takes 100 seconds for $[N_2O_5]$ to be halved in this reaction.

A general formula for the half-life of a first-order reaction can be derived from the integrated rate law for the general reaction

$$aA \rightarrow \text{products}$$

If the reaction is first order in [A],

$$\ln\left(\frac{[A]_0}{[A]}\right) = kt$$

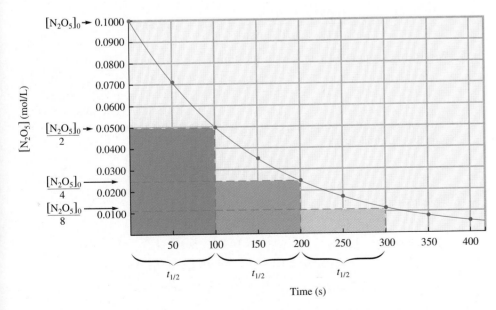

Figure 12.4

A plot of $[N_2O_5]$ versus time for the decomposition reaction of N_2O_5.

By definition, when $t = t_{1/2}$,

$$[A] = \frac{[A]_0}{2}$$

Then, for $t = t_{1/2}$, the integrated rate law becomes

$$\ln\left(\frac{[A]_0}{[A]_0/2}\right) = kt_{1/2}$$

or

$$\ln(2) = kt_{1/2}$$

Substituting the value of $\ln(2)$ and solving for $t_{1/2}$ gives

$$t_{1/2} = \frac{0.693}{k} \tag{12.3}$$

For a first-order reaction, $t_{1/2}$ is independent of the initial concentration.

This is the *general equation for the half-life of a first-order reaction.* Equation (12.3) can be used to calculate $t_{1/2}$ if k is known or k if $t_{1/2}$ is known. Note that for a first-order reaction, *the half-life does not depend on concentration.*

Sample Exercise 12.4

A certain first-order reaction has a half-life of 20.0 minutes.

a. Calculate the rate constant for this reaction.
b. How much time is required for this reaction to be 75% complete?

Solution

a. Solving Equation (12.3) for k gives

$$k = \frac{0.693}{t_{1/2}} = \frac{0.693}{20.0 \text{ min}} = 3.47 \times 10^{-2} \text{ min}^{-1}$$

b. We use the integrated rate law in the form

$$\ln\left(\frac{[A]_0}{[A]}\right) = kt$$

If the reaction is 75% complete, 75% of the reactant has been consumed, leaving 25% in the original form:

$$\frac{[A]}{[A]_0} \times 100 = 25$$

This means that

$$\frac{[A]}{[A]_0} = 0.25 \quad \text{or} \quad \frac{[A]_0}{[A]} = \frac{1}{0.25} = 4.0$$

Then

$$\ln\left(\frac{[A]_0}{[A]}\right) = \ln(4.0) = kt = \left(\frac{3.47 \times 10^{-2}}{\text{min}}\right)t$$

and

$$t = \frac{\ln(4.0)}{\dfrac{3.47 \times 10^{-2}}{\text{min}}} = 40. \text{ min}$$

Thus it takes 40. minutes for this particular reaction to reach 75% completion.

Let's consider another way of solving this problem using the definition of half-life. After one half-life the reaction has gone 50% to completion. If the initial concentration were 1.0 mol/L, after one half-life the concentration would be 0.50 mol/L. One more half-life would produce a concentration of 0.25 mol/L. Comparing 0.25 mol/L with the original 1.0 mol/L shows that 25% of the reactant is left after two half-lives. This is a general result. (What percentage of reactant remains after three half-lives?) Two half-lives for this reaction is 2(20.0 min), or 40.0 min, which agrees with the above answer.

Second-Order Rate Laws

For a general reaction involving a single reactant, that is,

$$aA \rightarrow products$$

that is second order in A, the rate law is

$$Rate = -\frac{\Delta[A]}{\Delta t} = k[A]^2 \qquad (12.4)$$

Second order: rate = $k[A]^2$. Doubling the concentration of A quadruples the reaction rate; tripling the concentration of A increases the rate by nine times.

The **integrated second-order rate law** has the form

$$\frac{1}{[A]} = kt + \frac{1}{[A]_0} \qquad (12.5)$$

Note the following characteristics of Equation (12.5):

1. A plot of $1/[A]$ versus t will produce a straight line with a slope equal to k.
2. Equation (12.5) shows how [A] depends on time and can be used to calculate [A] at any time t, provided k and $[A]_0$ are known.

For second-order reactions, a plot of $1/[A]$ versus t will be linear.

When one half-life of the second-order reaction has elapsed ($t = t_{1/2}$), by definition,

$$[A] = \frac{[A]_0}{2}$$

Equation (12.5) then becomes

$$\frac{1}{\dfrac{[A]_0}{2}} = kt_{1/2} + \frac{1}{[A]_0}$$

$$\frac{2}{[A]_0} - \frac{1}{[A]_0} = kt_{1/2}$$

$$\frac{1}{[A]_0} = kt_{1/2}$$

Solving for $t_{1/2}$ gives *the expression for the half-life of a second-order reaction:*

$$t_{1/2} = \frac{1}{k[A]_0} \qquad (12.6)$$

When two identical molecules combine, the resulting molecule is called a **dimer.**

Sample Exercise 12.5

Butadiene reacts to form its dimer according to the equation

$$2C_4H_6(g) \rightarrow C_8H_{12}(g)$$

The following data were collected for this reaction at a given temperature:

$[C_4H_6]$ (mol/L)	Time (± 1 s)
0.01000	0
0.00625	1000
0.00476	1800
0.00370	2800
0.00313	3600
0.00270	4400
0.00241	5200
0.00208	6200

a. Is this reaction first order or second order?

b. What is the value of the rate constant for the reaction?

c. What is the half-life for the reaction under the conditions of this experiment?

Solution

a. To decide whether the rate law for this reaction is first order or second order, we must see whether the plot of $\ln[C_4H_6]$ versus time is a straight line (first order) or the plot of $1/[C_4H_6]$ versus time is a straight line (second order). The data necessary to make these plots are as follows:

t (s)	$\dfrac{1}{[C_4H_6]}$	$\ln[C_4H_6]$
0	100	-4.605
1000	160	-5.075
1800	210	-5.348
2800	270	-5.599
3600	320	-5.767
4400	370	-5.915
5200	415	-6.028
6200	481	-6.175

The resulting plots are shown in Fig. 12.5. Since the $\ln[C_4H_6]$ versus t plot [Fig. 12.5(a)] is not a straight line, the reaction is *not* first order. The reaction is, however, second order, as shown by the linearity of the $1/[C_4H_6]$ versus t plot [Fig. 12.5(b)]. Thus we can now write the rate law for this second-order reaction:

$$\text{Rate} = -\frac{\Delta[C_4H_6]}{\Delta t} = k[C_4H_6]^2$$

b. For a second-order reaction, a plot of $1/[C_4H_6]$ versus t produces a straight line of slope k. In terms of the standard equation for a straight line, $y = mx + b$, we have $y = 1/[C_4H_6]$ and $x = t$. Thus the slope of the line can be expressed as follows:

$$\text{Slope} = \frac{\Delta y}{\Delta x} = \frac{\Delta\left(\dfrac{1}{[C_4H_6]}\right)}{\Delta t}$$

Using the points at $t = 0$ and $t = 6200$, we can find the rate constant for the reaction:

$$k = \text{slope} = \frac{(481 - 100)\ \text{L/mol}}{(6200 - 0)\ \text{s}} = \frac{381}{6200}\ \text{L/mol} \cdot \text{s} = 6.14 \times 10^{-2}\ \text{L/mol} \cdot \text{s}$$

c. The expression for the half-life of a second-order reaction is

$$t_{1/2} = \frac{1}{k[A]_0}$$

In this case $k = 6.14 \times 10^{-2}$ L/mol · s (from part b) and $[A]_0 = [C_4H_6]_0 = 0.01000\ M$ (the concentration at $t = 0$). Thus

$$t_{1/2} = \frac{1}{(6.14 \times 10^{-2}\ \text{L/mol} \cdot \text{s})(1.000 \times 10^{-2}\ \text{mol/L})} = 1.63 \times 10^3\ \text{s}$$

The initial concentration of C_4H_6 is halved in 1630 s.

(a)

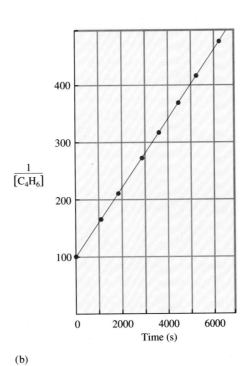

(b)

Figure 12.5

(a) A plot of $\ln[C_4H_6]$ versus t. (b) A plot of $1/[C_4H_6]$ versus t.

For a second-order reaction, $t_{1/2}$ is dependent on $[A]_0$. For a first-order reaction, $t_{1/2}$ is independent of $[A]_0$.

It is important to recognize the difference between the half-life for a first-order reaction and the half-life for a second-order reaction. For a second-order reaction, $t_{1/2}$ depends on both k and $[A]_0$; for a first-order reaction, $t_{1/2}$ depends only on k. For a first-order reaction, a constant time is required to reduce the concentration of the reactant by half, and then by half again, and so on, as the reaction proceeds. From Sample Exercise 12.5 we can see that this is *not* true for a second-order reaction. For that second-order reaction, we found that the first half-life (the time required to go from $[C_4H_6] = 0.010$ M to $[C_4H_6] = 0.0050$ M) is 1630 seconds. We can estimate the second half-life from the concentration data as a function of time. Note that to reach 0.0024 M C_4H_6 (approximately 0.0050/2) requires 5200 seconds of reaction time. Thus to get from 0.0050 M C_4H_6 to 0.0024 M C_4H_6 takes 3570 seconds (5200 − 1630). The second half-life is much longer than the first. This pattern is characteristic of second-order reactions. In fact, *for a second-order reaction, each successive half-life is double the preceding one* (provided the effects of the reverse reaction can be ignored, as we are assuming here). Prove this to yourself by examining the equation $t_{1/2} = 1/(k[A]_0)$.

For each successive half-life, $[A]_0$ is halved. Since $t_{1/2} = 1/k[A]_0$, $t_{1/2}$ doubles.

Zero-Order Rate Laws

Most reactions involving a single reactant show either first-order or second-order kinetics. However, sometimes such a reaction can be a **zero-order reaction.** The rate law for a zero-order reaction is

$$\text{Rate} = k[A]^0 = k(1) = k$$

A zero-order reaction has a constant rate.

For a zero-order reaction, the rate is constant. It does not change with concentration as it does for first-order or second-order reactions.

The **integrated rate law for a zero-order reaction** is

$$[A] = -kt + [A]_0 \qquad (12.7)$$

In this case a plot of $[A]$ versus t gives a straight line of slope $-k$, as shown in Fig. 12.6.

The expression for the half-life of a zero-order reaction can be obtained from the integrated rate law. By definition, $[A] = [A]_0/2$ when $t = t_{1/2}$, so

$$\frac{[A]_0}{2} = -kt_{1/2} + [A]_0$$

or

$$kt_{1/2} = \frac{[A]_0}{2}$$

Solving for $t_{1/2}$ gives

$$t_{1/2} = \frac{[A]_0}{2k} \qquad (12.8)$$

Figure 12.6

A plot of $[A]$ versus t for a zero-order reaction.

Zero-order reactions are most often encountered when a substance such as a metal surface or an enzyme is required for the reaction to occur. For example, the decomposition reaction

$$2N_2O(g) \rightarrow 2N_2(g) + O_2(g)$$

occurs on a hot platinum surface. When the platinum surface is completely covered with N_2O molecules, an increase in the concentration of N_2O has no effect on the

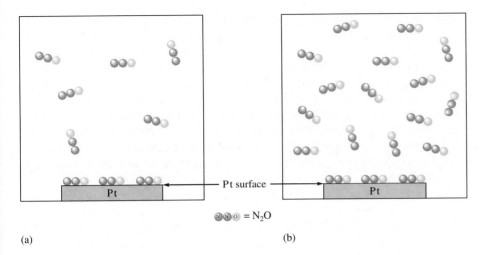

(a)   (b)

Figure 12.7

The decomposition reaction $2N_2O(g) \rightarrow 2N_2(g) + O_2(g)$ takes place on a platinum surface. Although $[N_2O]$ is twice as great in (b) as in (a), the rate of decomposition of N_2O is the same in both cases because the platinum surface can only accommodate a certain number of molecules. As a result, this reaction is zero order.

rate, since only those N_2O molecules on the surface can react. Under these conditions, *the rate is a constant* because it is controlled by what happens on the platinum surface rather than by the total concentration of N_2O, as illustrated in Fig. 12.7. This reaction also can occur at high temperatures with no platinum surface present, but under these conditions, it is not zero order.

Integrated Rate Laws for Reactions with More than One Reactant

So far we have considered the integrated rate laws for simple reactions with only one reactant. Special techniques are required to deal with more complicated reactions. Let's consider the reaction

$$BrO_3^-(aq) + 5Br^-(aq) + 6H^+(aq) \rightarrow 3Br_2(l) + 3H_2O(l)$$

From experimental evidence we know that the rate law is

$$\text{Rate} = -\frac{\Delta[BrO_3^-]}{\Delta t} = k[BrO_3^-][Br^-][H^+]^2$$

Suppose we run this reaction under conditions where $[BrO_3^-]_0 = 1.0 \times 10^{-3}\ M$, $[Br^-]_0 = 1.0\ M$, and $[H^+]_0 = 1.0\ M$. As the reaction proceeds, $[BrO_3^-]$ decreases significantly, but because the Br^- ion and H^+ ion concentrations are so large initially, relatively little of these two reactants is consumed. Thus $[Br^-]$ and $[H^+]$ remain *approximately constant*. In other words, under the conditions where the Br^- ion and H^+ ion concentrations are much larger than the BrO_3^- ion concentration, we can assume that throughout the reaction

$$[Br^-] = [Br^-]_0 \quad \text{and} \quad [H^+] = [H^+]_0$$

This means that the rate law can be written

$$\text{Rate} = k[Br^-]_0[H^+]_0^2[BrO_3^-] = k'[BrO_3^-]$$

where, since $[Br^-]_0$ and $[H^+]_0$ are constant,

$$k' = k[Br^-]_0[H^+]_0^2$$

The rate law

$$\text{Rate} = k'[BrO_3^-]$$

is first order. However, since this law was obtained by simplifying a more complicated one, it is called a **pseudo-first-order rate law.** Under the conditions of this experiment, a plot of $\ln[BrO_3^-]$ versus t will give a straight line where the slope is equal to $-k'$. Since $[Br^-]_0$ and $[H^+]_0$ are known, the value of k can be calculated from the equation

$$k' = k[Br^-]_0[H^+]_0^2$$

which can be rearranged to give

$$k = \frac{k'}{[Br^-]_0[H^+]_0^2}$$

Note that the kinetics of complicated reactions can be studied by observing the behavior of one reactant at a time. If the concentration of one reactant is much smaller than the concentrations of the others, then the amounts of those reactants present in large concentrations will not change significantly and can be regarded as constant. The change in concentration with time of the reactant present in a relatively small amount can then be used to determine the order of the reaction in that component. This technique allows us to determine rate laws for complex reactions.

12.5 Rate Laws: A Summary

Purpose

- To summarize the two types of rate laws and the methods by which they can be determined.

In the last several sections we have developed the following important points:

1. To simplify the rate laws for reactions, we have always assumed that the rate is being studied under conditions where only the forward reaction is important. This produces rate laws that only contain reactant concentrations.

2. There are two types of rate laws.
   a. The differential rate law (often called *the rate law*) shows how the rate depends on the concentrations. The forms of the rate laws for zero-order, first-order, and second-order kinetics of reactions with single reactants are shown in Table 12.6.
   b. The integrated rate law shows how concentration depends on time. The integrated rate laws corresponding to zero-order, first-order, and second-order kinetics of one-reactant reactions are given in Table 12.6.

3. Whether we determine the differential rate law or the integrated rate law depends on the type of data that can be collected conveniently and accurately. Once we have experimentally determined either type of rate law, we can write the other for a given reaction.

4. The most common method for experimentally determining the differential rate law is the method of initial rates. In this method several experiments are run at different initial concentrations and the instantaneous rates are determined for each at the same value of t (as close to $t = 0$ as possible). The point is to evaluate the rate before the concentrations change significantly from the initial values. From a comparison of the initial rates and the initial concentrations the dependence of the rate on the concentrations of various reactants can be obtained—that is, the order in each reactant can be determined.

5. To experimentally determine the integrated rate law for a reaction, concentrations are measured at various values of t as the reaction proceeds. Then the job is to see which integrated rate law correctly fits the data. Typically this is done, visually, by ascertaining which type of plot gives a straight line. A summary for one-reactant reactions is given in Table 12.6. Once the correct straight-line plot is found, the correct integrated rate law can be chosen and the value of k obtained from the slope. Also, the (differential) rate law for the reaction can then be written.

6. The integrated rate law for a reaction that involves several reactants can be treated by choosing conditions such that the concentration of only one reactant varies in a given experiment. This is done by having the concentration of one reactant small compared with the concentrations of all the others, causing a rate law such as

$$\text{Rate} = k[A]^n[B]^m[C]^p$$

to reduce to

$$\text{Rate} = k'[A]^n$$

where $k' = k[B]_0^m[C]_0^p$ and $[B]_0 \gg [A]_0$ and $[C]_0 \gg [A]_0$. The value of n is obtained by determining whether a plot of $[A]$ versus t is linear ($n = 0$), a plot

Table 12.6			
Summary of the Kinetics for Reactions of the Type $aA \rightarrow$ Products That Are Zero, First, or Second Order in $[A]$			
		Order	
	Zero	First	Second
Rate law	$\text{Rate} = k$	$\text{Rate} = k[A]$	$\text{Rate} = k[A]^2$
Integrated rate law	$[A] = -kt + [A]_0$	$\ln[A] = -kt + \ln[A]_0$	$\dfrac{1}{[A]} = kt + \dfrac{1}{[A]_0}$
Plot needed to give a straight line	$[A]$ versus t	$\ln[A]$ versus t	$\dfrac{1}{[A]}$ versus t
Relationship of rate constant to the slope of straight line	$\text{Slope} = -k$	$\text{Slope} = -k$	$\text{Slope} = k$
Half-life	$t_{1/2} = \dfrac{[A]_0}{2k}$	$t_{1/2} = \dfrac{0.693}{k}$	$t_{1/2} = \dfrac{1}{k[A]_0}$

of $\ln[A]$ versus t is linear ($n = 1$), or a plot of $1/[A]$ versus t is linear ($n = 2$). The value of k' is determined from the slope of the appropriate plot. The values of m, p, and k can be found by determining the value of k' at several different concentrations of B and C.

12.6 Reaction Mechanisms

Purpose

- To explore the relationship between the reaction pathway and the rate law.

Most chemical reactions occur by a *series of steps* called the **reaction mechanism.** To understand a reaction, we must know its mechanism, and one of the main purposes for studying kinetics is to learn as much as possible about the steps involved in a reaction. In this section we explore some of the fundamental characteristics of reaction mechanisms.

Consider the reaction between nitrogen dioxide and carbon monoxide:

$$NO_2(g) + CO(g) \rightarrow NO(g) + CO_2(g)$$

The rate law for this reaction is known from experiment to be

$$\text{Rate} = k[NO_2]^2$$

A balanced equation does not tell us *how* the reactants become products.

As we will see below, this reaction is more complicated than it appears from the balanced equation. This is quite typical; the balanced equation for a reaction tells us the reactants, the products, and the stoichiometry but gives no direct information about the reaction mechanism.

For the reaction between nitrogen dioxide and carbon monoxide, the mechanism is thought to involve the following steps:

$$NO_2(g) + NO_2(g) \xrightarrow{k_1} NO_3(g) + NO(g)$$

$$NO_3(g) + CO(g) \xrightarrow{k_2} NO_2(g) + CO_2(g)$$

An intermediate is formed in one step and used up in a subsequent step and so is never seen as a product.

where k_1 and k_2 are the rate constants of the individual reactions. In this mechanism, gaseous NO_3 is an **intermediate,** a species that is neither a reactant nor a product but that is formed and consumed during the reaction sequence.

Each of these two reactions is called an **elementary step,** *a reaction whose rate law can be written from its molecularity.* **Molecularity** is defined as the number of species that must collide to produce the reaction indicated by that step. A reaction involving one molecule is called a **unimolecular step.** Reactions involving the collision of two and three species are termed **bimolecular** and **termolecular,** respectively. Termolecular steps are quite rare, because the probability of three molecules colliding simultaneously is very small. Examples of these three types of elementary steps and the corresponding rate laws are shown in Table 12.7. Note from Table 12.7 that the rate law for an elementary step follows *directly* from the molecularity of that step. For example, for a bimolecular step the rate law is always second order, either of the form $k[A]^2$ for a step with a single reactant or of the form $k[A][B]$ for a step involving two reactants.

The prefix *uni-* means one, *bi-* means two, and *ter-* means three.

A unimolecular elementary step is always first order, a bimolecular step is always second order, and so on.

Table 12.7		
Examples of Elementary Steps		
Elementary Step	Molecularity	Rate Law
A → products	*Uni*molecular	Rate = $k[A]$
A + A → products	*Bi*molecular	Rate = $k[A]^2$
(2A → products)		
A + B → products	*Bi*molecular	Rate = $k[A][B]$
A + A + B → products	*Ter*molecular	Rate = $k[A]^2[B]$
(2A + B → products)		
A + B + C → products	*Ter*molecular	Rate = $k[A][B][C]$

We can now define a reaction mechanism more precisely. It is a *series of elementary steps that must satisfy two requirements:*

1. The sum of the elementary steps must give the overall balanced equation for the reaction.

2. The mechanism must agree with the experimentally determined rate law.

To see how these requirements are applied, we will consider the mechanism given above for the reaction of nitrogen dioxide and carbon monoxide. First, note that the sum of the two steps gives the overall balanced equation:

$$NO_2(g) + NO_2(g) \longrightarrow NO_3(g) + NO(g)$$
$$NO_3(g) + CO(g) \longrightarrow NO_2(g) + CO_2(g)$$
$$\overline{\cancel{NO_2}(g) + NO_2(g) + \cancel{NO_3}(g) + CO(g) \longrightarrow \cancel{NO_3}(g) + NO(g) + \cancel{NO_2}(g) + CO_2(g)}$$

Overall reaction: $NO_2(g) + CO(g) \longrightarrow NO(g) + CO_2(g)$

The first requirement for a correct mechanism is met. To see whether the mechanism meets the second requirement, we need to introduce a new idea: the **rate-determining step.** Multistep reactions often have one step that is much slower than all the others. Reactants can become products only as fast as they can get through this slowest step. That is, the overall reaction can be no faster than the slowest, or rate-determining, step in the sequence. An analogy for this situation is the pouring of water rapidly into a container through a funnel. The water collects in the container at a rate that is essentially determined by the size of the funnel opening and not by the rate of pouring.

A reaction is only as fast as its slowest step.

Which is the rate-determining step in the reaction of nitrogen dioxide and carbon monoxide? Let's *assume* that the first step is rate-determining and the second step is relatively fast:

$$NO_2(g) + NO_2(g) \longrightarrow NO_3(g) + NO(g) \quad \text{Slow (rate-determining)}$$
$$NO_3(g) + CO(g) \longrightarrow NO_2(g) + CO_2(g) \quad \text{Fast}$$

What we have really assumed here is that the formation of NO_3 occurs much more slowly than its reaction with CO. The rate of CO_2 production is then controlled by the rate of formation of NO_3 in the first step. Since this is an elementary step, we can write the rate law from the molecularity. The bimolecular first step has the rate law

$$\text{Rate of formation of } NO_3 = \frac{\Delta[NO_3]}{\Delta t} = k_1[NO_2]^2$$

Since the overall reaction rate can be no faster than the slowest step,

$$\text{Overall rate} = k_1[NO_2]^2$$

Note that this rate law agrees with the experimentally determined rate law given earlier. The mechanism we assumed above satisfies the two requirements stated earlier and *may* be the correct mechanism for the reaction.

How does a chemist deduce the mechanism for a given reaction? The rate law is always determined first. Then, using chemical intuition and following the two rules given above, the chemist constructs possible mechanisms and tries, with further experiments, to eliminate those that are least likely. *A mechanism can never be proved absolutely.* We can only say that a mechanism that satisfies the two requirements is *possibly* correct. Deducing mechanisms for chemical reactions can be difficult and requires skill and experience. We will only touch on this process in this text.

Sample Exercise 12.6

The balanced equation for the reaction of the gases nitrogen dioxide and fluorine is

$$2NO_2(g) + F_2(g) \rightarrow 2NO_2F(g)$$

The experimentally determined rate law is

$$\text{Rate} = k[NO_2][F_2]$$

A suggested mechanism for this reaction is

$$NO_2 + F_2 \xrightarrow{k_1} NO_2F + F \quad \text{Slow}$$

$$F + NO_2 \xrightarrow{k_2} NO_2F \quad\quad \text{Fast}$$

Is this an acceptable mechanism? That is, does it satisfy the two requirements?

Solution

The first requirement for an acceptable mechanism is that the sum of the steps should give the balanced equation:

$$NO_2 + F_2 \rightarrow NO_2F + F$$
$$\underline{F + NO_2 \rightarrow NO_2F}$$
$$2NO_2 + F_2 + \cancel{F} \rightarrow 2NO_2F + \cancel{F}$$

Overall reaction: $\quad 2NO_2 + F_2 \rightarrow 2NO_2F$

The first requirement is met.

The second requirement is that the mechanism must agree with the experimentally determined rate law. Since the proposed mechanism states that the first step is rate-determining, the overall reaction rate must be that of the first step. The first step is bimolecular, so the rate law is

$$\text{Rate} = k_1[NO_2][F_2]$$

This has the same form as the experimentally determined rate law. The proposed mechanism is acceptable because it satisfies both requirements. (Note that we have not proved that it is *the correct* mechanism.)

12.7 A Model for Chemical Kinetics

Purpose

- To discuss the temperature dependence of reaction rates.
- To describe the collision model.
- To define and show how to calculate activation energy.

How do chemical reactions occur? We already have given some indications. For example, we have seen that the rates of chemical reactions depend on the concentrations of the reacting species. The initial rate for the reaction

$$aA + bB \rightarrow \text{products}$$

can be described by the rate law

$$\text{Rate} = k[A]^n[B]^m$$

where the order of each reactant depends on the detailed reaction mechanism. This explains why reaction rates depend on concentration. But what about some of the other factors affecting reaction rates? For example, how does temperature affect the speed of a reaction?

We can answer this question qualitatively from our experience. We have refrigerators because food spoilage is retarded at low temperatures. The combustion of wood occurs at a measurable rate only at high temperatures. An egg cooks in boiling water much faster at sea level than in Leadville, Colorado (elevation 10,000 ft), where the boiling point of water is approximately 90°C. These observations and others lead us to conclude that *chemical reactions speed up when the temperature is increased*. Experiments have shown that virtually all rate constants show an exponential increase with absolute temperature, as represented in Fig. 12.8.

In this section we discuss a model used to account for the observed characteristics of reaction rates. This model, called the **collision model,** is built around the central idea that *molecules must collide to react*. We have already seen how this assumption explains the concentration dependence of reaction rates. Now we need to consider whether this model can account for the observed temperature dependence of reaction rates.

The kinetic molecular theory of gases predicts that an increase in temperature raises molecular velocities and so increases the frequency of collisions between molecules. This idea agrees with the observation that reaction rates are greater at higher temperatures. Thus there is qualitative agreement between the collision model and experimental observations. However, it is found that the rate of reaction is much smaller than the calculated collision frequency in a collection of gas particles. This must mean that *only a small fraction of the collisions produces a reaction*. Why?

This question was first addressed in the 1880s by Svante Arrhenius. He proposed the existence of a *threshold energy*, called the **activation energy,** that must be overcome to produce a chemical reaction. Such a proposal makes sense, as we can see by considering the decomposition of BrNO in the gas phase:

$$2BrNO(g) \rightarrow 2NO(g) + Br_2(g)$$

In this reaction two Br—N bonds must be broken and one Br—Br bond must be formed. Breaking a Br—N bond requires considerable energy (243 kJ/mol), which

Figure 12.8

A plot showing the exponential dependence of the rate constant on absolute temperature. The exact temperature dependence of k is different for each reaction. This plot represents the behavior of a rate constant that doubles for every increase in temperature of 10 K.

Figure 12.9

The change in potential energy as a function of reaction progress for the reaction $2BrNO \rightarrow 2NO + Br_2$. The activation energy E_a represents the energy needed to disrupt the BrNO molecules so that they can form products. The quantity ΔE represents the net change in energy in going from reactant to products.

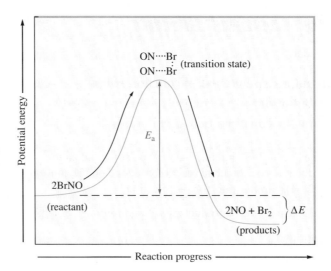

The higher the activation energy, the slower is the reaction at a given temperature.

Food and other supplies on Ross Island left by the 1910 Scott expedition to the South Pole. The low temperatures that prevail in this region greatly slow the reactions that cause spoilage and corrosion.

must come from somewhere. The collision model postulates that the energy comes from the kinetic energies possessed by the reacting molecules before the collision. This kinetic energy is changed into potential energy as the molecules are distorted during a collision to break bonds and rearrange the atoms into the product molecules.

We can envision the reaction progress as shown in Fig. 12.9. The arrangement of atoms found at the top of the potential energy "hill," or barrier, is called the **activated complex,** or **transition state.** The conversion of BrNO to NO and Br_2 is exothermic, as indicated by the fact that the products have lower potential energy than the reactant. However, ΔE has no effect on the rate of the reaction. Rather the rate depends on the size of the activation energy E_a.

The main point here is that a certain minimum energy is required for two BrNO molecules to "get over the hill" so that products can form. This energy is furnished by the energy of the collision. A collision between two BrNO molecules with small kinetic energies will not have enough energy to get over the barrier. At a given temperature only a certain fraction of the collisions possesses enough energy to be effective (to result in product formation).

We can be more precise by recalling from Chapter 5 that a distribution of velocities exists in a sample of gas molecules. Therefore, a distribution of collision energies also exists, as shown in Fig. 12.10 for two different temperatures. Fig. 12.10 also shows the activation energy for the reaction in question. Only collisions with energy greater than the activation energy are able to react (get over the barrier). At the lower temperature, T_1, the fraction of effective collisions is quite small. However, as the temperature is increased to T_2, the fraction of collisions with the required activation energy increases dramatically. When the temperature is doubled, the fraction of effective collisions much more than doubles. In fact, the fraction of effective collisions increases *exponentially* with temperature. This is encouraging for our theory; remember that rates of reactions are observed to increase exponentially with temperature. Arrhenius postulated that the number of collisions having an energy greater than or equal to the activation energy is given by the expression:

Number of collisions with the activation energy

$$= \text{(total number of collisions)}e^{-E_a/RT}$$

where E_a is the activation energy, R is the universal gas constant, and T is the Kelvin temperature. The factor $e^{-E_a/RT}$ represents the fraction of collisions with energy E_a or greater at temperature T.

We have seen that not all molecular collisions are effective in producing chemical reactions because a minimum energy is required for the reaction to occur. There is, however, another complication. Experiments show that the *observed reaction rate is considerably smaller than the rate of collisions with enough energy to surmount the barrier*. This means that many collisions, even though they have the required energy, still do not produce a reaction. Why not?

The answer lies in the **molecular orientations** during collisions. We can illustrate this using the reaction between two BrNO molecules, as shown in Fig. 12.11. Some collision orientations can lead to reaction, and others cannot. Therefore, we must include a correction factor to allow for collisions with nonproductive molecular orientations.

To summarize, two requirements must be satisfied for reactants to collide successfully (to rearrange to form products):

1. The collision must involve enough energy to produce the reaction; that is, the collision energy must equal or exceed the activation energy.

2. The relative orientation of the reactants must allow formation of any new bonds necessary to produce products.

Taking these factors into account, we can represent the rate constant as

$$k = zpe^{-E_a/RT}$$

where z is the collision frequency, p is called the **steric factor** (always less than 1) and reflects the fraction of collisions with effective orientations, and $e^{-E_a/RT}$ represents the fraction of collisions with sufficient energy to produce a reaction. This expression is most often written in form

$$k = Ae^{-E_a/RT} \tag{12.9}$$

which is called the **Arrhenius equation.** In this equation, A replaces zp and is called the **frequency factor** for the reaction.

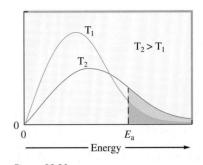

Figure 12.10

Plot showing the number of collisions with a particular energy at T_1 and T_2, where $T_2 > T_1$.

A snowy tree cricket. The frequency of a cricket's chirps depends on the temperature of the cricket.

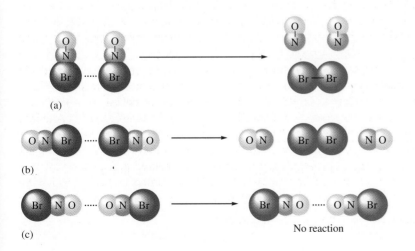

No reaction

Figure 12.11

Several possible orientations for a collision between two BrNO molecules. Orientations (a) and (b) can lead to a reaction, but orientation (c) cannot.

Taking the natural logarithm of each side of the Arrhenius equation gives

$$\ln(k) = -\frac{E_a}{R}\left(\frac{1}{T}\right) + \ln(A) \qquad (12.10)$$

Equation (12.10) is a linear equation of the type $y = mx + b$, where $y = \ln(k)$, $m = -E_a/R = \text{slope}$, $x = 1/T$, and $b = \ln(A) = \text{intercept}$. Thus, for a reaction where the rate constant obeys the Arrhenius equation, a plot of $\ln(k)$ versus $1/T$ gives a straight line. The slope and intercept can be used to determine, respectively, the values of E_a and A characteristic of that reaction. The fact that most rate constants obey the Arrhenius equation to a good approximation indicates that the collision model for chemical reactions is physically reasonable.

Sample Exercise 12.7

The reaction

$$2N_2O_5(g) \rightarrow 4NO_2(g) + O_2(g)$$

was studied at several temperatures, and the following values of k were obtained:

k (s^{-1})	T (°C)
2.0×10^{-5}	20
7.3×10^{-5}	30
2.7×10^{-4}	40
9.1×10^{-4}	50
2.9×10^{-3}	60

Calculate the value of E_a for this reaction.

Solution

To obtain the value of E_a, we need to construct a plot of $\ln(k)$ versus $1/T$. First we must calculate values of $\ln(k)$ and $1/T$, as shown below:

T (°C)	T (K)	$1/T$ (K)	k (s^{-1})	$\ln(k)$
20	293	3.41×10^{-3}	2.0×10^{-5}	-10.82
30	303	3.30×10^{-3}	7.3×10^{-5}	-9.53
40	313	3.19×10^{-3}	2.7×10^{-4}	-8.22
50	323	3.10×10^{-3}	9.1×10^{-4}	-7.00
60	333	3.00×10^{-3}	2.9×10^{-3}	-5.84

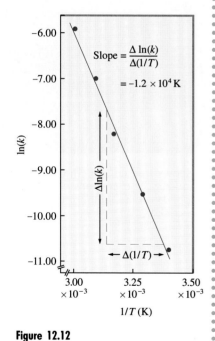

The plot of $\ln(k)$ versus $1/T$ is shown in Fig. 12.12, where the slope

$$\frac{\Delta\ln(k)}{\Delta\left(\dfrac{1}{T}\right)}$$

Figure 12.12

Plot of $\ln(k)$ versus $1/T$ for the reaction $2N_2O_5(g) \rightarrow 4NO_2(g) + O_2(g)$. The value of the activation energy for this reaction can be obtained from the slope of the line, which equals $-E_a/R$.

is found to be -1.2×10^4 K. The value of E_a can be determined by solving the following equation:

$$\text{Slope} = -\frac{E_a}{R}$$

$$E_a = -R(\text{slope}) = -(8.3145 \text{ J/K} \cdot \text{mol})(-1.2 \times 10^4 \text{ K})$$
$$= 1.0 \times 10^5 \text{ J/mol}$$

Thus the value of the activation energy for this reaction is 1.0×10^5 J/mol.

The most common procedure for finding E_a for a reaction involves measuring the rate constant k at several temperatures and then plotting $\ln(k)$ versus $1/T$, as shown in Sample Exercise 12.7. However, E_a also can be calculated from the values of k at only two temperatures by using a formula that can be derived as follows from Equation (12.10).

At temperature T_1, where the rate constant is k_1,

$$\ln(k_1) = -\frac{E_a}{RT_1} + \ln(A)$$

At temperature T_2, where the rate constant is k_2,

$$\ln(k_2) = -\frac{E_a}{RT_2} + \ln(A)$$

Subtracting the first equation from the second gives

$$\ln(k_2) - \ln(k_1) = \left(-\frac{E_a}{RT_2} + \ln(A)\right) - \left(-\frac{E_a}{RT_1} + \ln(A)\right)$$

$$= -\frac{E_a}{RT_2} + \frac{E_a}{RT_1}$$

And
$$\ln\left(\frac{k_2}{k_1}\right) = \frac{E_a}{R}\left(\frac{1}{T_1} - \frac{1}{T_2}\right) \tag{12.11}$$

Therefore, the values of k_1 and k_2 measured at temperatures T_1 and T_2 can be used to calculate E_a, as shown in Sample Exercise 12.8.

Sample Exercise 12.8

The gas-phase reaction between methane and diatomic sulfur is given by the equation

$$CH_4(g) + 2S_2(g) \rightarrow CS_2(g) + 2H_2S(g)$$

At 550°C the rate constant for this reaction is 1.1 L/mol · s, and at 625°C the rate constant is 6.4 L/mol · s. Using these values, calculate E_a for this reaction.

Solution

The relevant data are shown in the table on the following page.

k (L/mol · s)	T (°C)	T (K)
$1.1 = k_1$	550	$823 = T_1$
$6.4 = k_2$	625	$898 = T_2$

Substituting these values into Equation (12.11) gives

$$\ln\left(\frac{6.4}{1.1}\right) = \frac{E_a}{8.3145 \text{ J/K} \cdot \text{mol}}\left(\frac{1}{823 \text{ K}} - \frac{1}{898 \text{ K}}\right)$$

Solving for E_a gives

$$E_a = \frac{(8.3145 \text{ J/K} \cdot \text{mol})\ln\left(\frac{6.4}{1.1}\right)}{\left(\frac{1}{823 \text{ K}} - \frac{1}{898 \text{ K}}\right)}$$

$$= 1.4 \times 10^5 \text{ J/mol}$$

12.8 Catalysis

Purpose

- To explain how a catalyst speeds up a reaction.
- To discuss heterogeneous and homogeneous catalysis.

We have seen that the rate of a reaction increases dramatically with temperature. If a particular reaction does not occur fast enough at normal temperatures, we can speed it up by raising the temperature. However, sometimes this is not feasible. For example, living cells can survive only in a rather narrow temperature range, and the human body is designed to operate at an almost constant temperature of 98.6°F. But many of the complicated biochemical reactions keeping us alive would be much too slow at this temperature without intervention. We exist only because the body contains many substances called **enzymes,** which increase the rates of these reactions. In fact, almost every biologically important reaction is assisted by a specific enzyme.

Although it is possible to use higher temperatures to speed up commercially important reactions, such as the Haber process for synthesizing ammonia, this is very expensive. In a chemical plant an increase in temperature means significantly increased costs for energy. The use of an appropriate catalyst allows a reaction to proceed rapidly at a relatively low temperature and can therefore hold down production costs.

A **catalyst** is *a substance that speeds up a reaction without being consumed itself.* Just as virtually all vital biologic reactions are assisted by enzymes (biologic catalysts), almost all industrial processes also involve the use of catalysts. For example, the production of sulfuric acid uses vanadium(V) oxide, and the Haber process uses a mixture of iron and iron oxide.

How does a catalyst work? Remember that for each reaction a certain energy barrier must be surmounted. How can we make a reaction occur faster without raising the temperature to increase the molecular energies? The solution is to provide a new pathway for the reaction, one with a *lower activation energy*. This is what a catalyst does, as is shown in Fig. 12.13. Because the catalyst allows the reaction to occur with a lower activation energy, a much larger fraction of collisions is effective at a given temperature, and the reaction rate is increased. This effect is illustrated in Fig. 12.14. Note from this diagram that although a catalyst lowers the activation energy E_a for a reaction, it does not affect the energy difference ΔE between products and reactants.

Catalysts are classified as homogeneous or heterogeneous. A **homogeneous catalyst** is one that is *present in the same phase as the reacting molecules*. A **heterogeneous catalyst** exists *in a different phase*, usually as a solid.

Heterogeneous Catalysis

Heterogeneous catalysis most often involves gaseous reactants being adsorbed on the surface of a solid catalyst. **Adsorption** refers to the collection of one substance on the surface of another substance; *absorption* refers to the penetration of one substance into another. Water is *absorbed* by a sponge.

An important example of heterogeneous catalysis occurs in the hydrogenation of unsaturated hydrocarbons, compounds composed mainly of carbon and hydrogen with some carbon–carbon double bonds. Hydrogenation is an important industrial process used to change unsaturated fats, occurring as oils, to saturated fats (solid shortenings such as Crisco) in which the C=C bonds have been converted to C—C bonds through addition of hydrogen.

A simple example of hydrogenation involves ethylene:

$$
\underset{\text{Ethylene}}{\overset{\displaystyle \text{H}\!\!\diagdown\hspace{2pt}\diagup\!\!\text{H}}{\underset{\text{H}\diagup\hspace{6pt}\diagdown\text{H}}{\text{C}=\text{C}}}}\ (g) + \text{H}_2(g) \rightarrow \underset{\text{Ethane}}{\overset{\text{H H}}{\underset{\text{H H}}{\text{H}-\text{C}-\text{C}-\text{H}}}}\ (g)
$$

This reaction is quite slow at normal temperatures, mainly because the strong bond in the hydrogen molecule results in a large activation energy for the reaction. However, the reaction rate can be greatly increased by using a solid catalyst of platinum, palladium, or nickel. The hydrogen and ethylene adsorb on the catalyst surface, where the reaction occurs. The main function of the catalyst apparently is to allow formation of metal–hydrogen interactions that weaken the H—H bonds and facilitate the reaction. The mechanism is illustrated in Fig. 12.15 (on p. 578).

Typically, heterogeneous catalysis involves four steps:

1. Adsorption and activation of the reactants
2. Migration of the adsorbed reactants on the surface
3. Reaction of the adsorbed substances
4. Escape, or *desorption*, of the products

Heterogeneous catalysis also occurs in the oxidation of gaseous sulfur dioxide to gaseous sulfur trioxide. This process is especially interesting because it illustrates both positive and negative consequences of chemical catalysis.

The negative side is the formation of damaging air pollutants. Recall that sulfur dioxide, a toxic gas with a choking odor, is formed whenever sulfur-containing fuels are burned. However, it is sulfur trioxide that causes most of the environmen-

Figure 12.13

Energy plots for a catalyzed and an uncatalyzed pathway for a given reaction.

Figure 12.14

Effect of a catalyst on the number of reaction-producing collisions. Because a catalyst provides a reaction pathway with a lower activation energy, a much greater fraction of the collisions is effective for the catalyzed pathway (b) than for the uncatalyzed pathway (a) (at a given temperature). This allows reactants to become products at a much higher rate, even though there is no temperature increase.

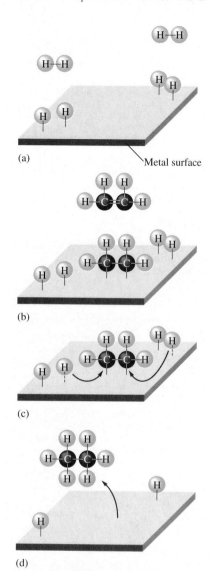

(a)

(b)

(c)

(d)

Figure 12.15

Heterogeneous catalysis of the hydrogenation of ethylene. (a) Hydrogen is adsorbed onto the metal surface, forming metal–hydrogen bonds and breaking the H—H bonds. (b) The π bond in ethylene is broken and metal–carbon bonds are formed during adsorption. (c) The adsorbed molecules and atoms migrate toward each other on the metal surface, forming new C—H bonds. (d) The C atoms in ethane (C_2H_6) have completely saturated bonding capacities and so cannot bind strongly to the metal surfaces. The C_2H_6 molecule thus escapes.

tal damage, mainly through the production of acid rain. When sulfur trioxide combines with a droplet of water, sulfuric acid is formed:

$$H_2O(l) + SO_3(g) \rightarrow H_2SO_4(aq)$$

This sulfuric acid can cause considerable damage to vegetation, buildings and statues, and fish populations.

Sulfur dioxide is *not* rapidly oxidized to sulfur trioxide in clean, dry air. Why, then, is there a problem? The answer is catalysis. Dust particles and water droplets catalyze the reaction between SO_2 and O_2 in the air.

On the positive side, the heterogeneous catalysis of the oxidation of SO_2 is used to advantage in the manufacture of sulfuric acid, where the reaction of O_2 and SO_2 to form SO_3 is catalyzed by a solid mixture of platinum and vanadium(V) oxide.

Heterogeneous catalysis is also utilized in the catalytic converters in automobile exhaust systems. The exhaust gases, containing compounds such as nitric oxide, carbon monoxide, and unburned hydrocarbons, are passed through a converter containing beads of solid catalyst (see Fig. 12.16). The catalyst promotes the conversion of carbon monoxide to carbon dioxide, hydrocarbons to carbon dioxide and water, and nitric oxide to nitrogen gas to lessen the environmental impact of the exhaust gases. However, this beneficial catalysis can, unfortunately, be accompanied by the unwanted catalysis of the oxidation of SO_2 to SO_3, which reacts with the moisture present to form sulfuric acid.

Because of the complex nature of the reactions that take place in the converter, a mixture of catalysts is used. The most effective catalytic materials are transition metal oxides and noble metals such as palladium and platinum.

One consequence of the widespread use of catalytic converters has been the need to remove lead from gasoline. Tetraethyl lead was used for more than 50 years as a very effective "octane booster" owing to its antiknocking characteristics. However, lead quickly destroys much of a converter's catalytic efficiency. This poisoning effect, along with the serious adverse health effects of lead, has necessitated the removal of lead from gasoline. This has caused a search for other antiknock additives and the redesign of engines to run on lower-octane gasoline.

Figure 12.16

The exhaust gases from an automobile engine are passed through a catalytic converter to minimize environmental damage.

Homogeneous Catalysis

A homogeneous catalyst exists in the same phase as the reacting molecules. There are many examples in both the gas and liquid phases. One such example is the unusual catalytic behavior of nitric oxide toward ozone. In the troposphere, that part of the atmosphere closest to earth, nitric oxide catalyzes ozone production. However, in the upper atmosphere it catalyzes the decomposition of ozone. Both of these effects are unfortunate environmentally.

In the lower atmosphere, NO is produced in any high-temperature combustion process where N_2 is present. The reaction

$$N_2(g) + O_2(g) \rightarrow 2NO(g)$$

is very slow at normal temperatures because of the very strong $N{\equiv}N$ and $O{=}O$ bonds. However, at elevated temperatures, such as those found in the internal combustion engines of automobiles, significant quantities of NO form. Some of this NO is converted back to N_2 in the catalytic converter, but significant amounts escape into the atmosphere to react with oxygen:

$$2NO(g) + O_2(g) \rightarrow 2NO_2(g)$$

In the atmosphere, NO_2 can absorb light and decompose as follows:

$$NO_2(g) \xrightarrow{\text{Light}} NO(g) + O(g)$$

The oxygen atom is very reactive and can combine with oxygen molecules to form ozone:

$$O_2(g) + O(g) \rightarrow O_3(g)$$

Ozone is a powerful oxidizing agent that can react with other air pollutants to form substances irritating to the eyes and lungs, and is itself very toxic.

In this series of reactions, nitric oxide is acting as a true catalyst because it assists the production of ozone without being consumed itself. This can be seen by summing the reactions:

$$
\begin{aligned}
NO(g) + \tfrac{1}{2}O_2(g) &\longrightarrow NO_2(g) \\
NO_2(g) &\xrightarrow{\text{Light}} NO(g) + O(g) \\
\underline{O_2(g) + O(g) } &\underline{\longrightarrow O_3(g)} \\
\tfrac{3}{2}O_2(g) &\longrightarrow O_3(g)
\end{aligned}
$$

In the upper atmosphere, the presence of nitric oxide has the opposite effect—the depletion of ozone. The series of reactions involved is

$$
\begin{aligned}
NO(g) + O_3(g) &\longrightarrow NO_2(g) + O_2(g) \\
\underline{O(g) + NO_2(g)} &\underline{\longrightarrow NO(g) + O_2(g)} \\
O(g) + O_3(g) &\longrightarrow 2O_2(g)
\end{aligned}
$$

Nitric oxide is again catalytic, but here its effect is to change O_3 to O_2. This is a potential problem because O_3, which absorbs ultraviolet light, is necessary to protect us from the harmful effects of this high-energy radiation. That is, we want O_3 in the upper atmosphere to block ultraviolet radiation from the sun but not in the lower atmosphere, where we would have to breathe it and its oxidation products.

Although O_2 is represented here as the oxidizing agent for NO, the actual oxidizing agent is probably some type of peroxide compound produced by reaction of oxygen with pollutants. The direct reaction of NO and O_2 is very slow.

Enzymes: Nature's Catalysts

The most impressive examples of homogeneous catalysis occur in nature, where the complex reactions necessary for plant and animal life are made possible by enzymes. Enzymes are large molecules specifically tailored to facilitate a given type of reaction. Usually enzymes are proteins, an important class of biomolecules constructed from α-amino acids that have the general structure

where R represents any one of 20 different substituents. These amino acid molecules can be "hooked together" to form a polymer (a word meaning "many parts") called a **protein.** The general structure of a protein can be represented as follows:

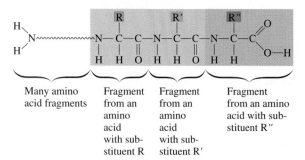

Many amino acid fragments

Fragment from an amino acid with substituent R

Fragment from an amino acid with substituent R′

Fragment from an amino acid with substituent R″

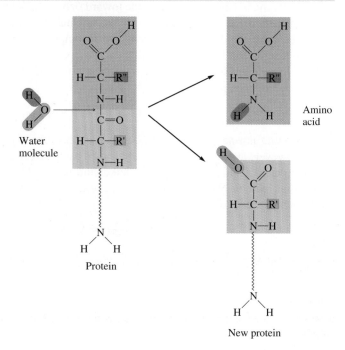

Water molecule

Protein

Amino acid

New protein

Figure 12.17

The removal of the end amino acid from a protein by reaction with a molecule of water. The products are an amino acid and a new, smaller protein.

Since specific proteins are needed by the human body, the proteins in food must be broken into their constituent amino acids, which are then used to construct new proteins in the body's cells. The reaction in which a protein is broken down one amino acid at a time is shown in Fig. 12.17. Note that in this reaction a water molecule reacts with a protein molecule to produce an amino acid and a new protein containing one less amino acid. Without the enzymes found in human cells, this reaction would be much too slow to be useful. One of these enzymes is *carboxy-*

peptidase-A, a zinc-containing protein (Fig. 12.18).

Carboxypeptidase-A captures the protein to be acted on (called the **substrate**) in a special groove and positions the substrate so that the end is in the **active site,** where the catalysis occurs (Fig. 12.19). Note that the Zn^{2+} ion bonds to the oxygen of the C=O (carbonyl) group. This polarizes the electron density in the carbonyl group, allowing the neighboring C—N bond to be broken much more easily. When the reaction is completed, the remaining portion of the substrate protein

and the newly formed amino acid are released by the enzyme.

The process just described for carboxypeptidase-A is characteristic of the behavior of other enzymes. Enzyme catalysis can be represented by the series of reactions shown below:

$$E + S \rightarrow E \cdot S$$
$$E \cdot S \rightarrow E + P$$

where E represents the enzyme, S represents the substrate, $E \cdot S$ represents the enzyme–substrate complex, and P repre-

◀ **CHEMICAL IMPACT** ▶

Figure 12.18

The structure of the enzyme carboxypeptidase-A, which contains 307 amino acids.

Figure 12.19

Protein–substrate interaction. The substrate is shown in black and red, with the red representing the terminal amino acid. Blue indicates sidechains from the enzyme that help bind the substrate.

sents the products. The enzyme and substrate form a complex, where the reaction occurs. The enzyme then releases the product and is ready to repeat the process. The most amazing thing about enzymes is their efficiency. Because an enzyme plays its catalytic role over and over and very rapidly, only a tiny amount of enzyme is required. This makes the isolation of enzymes for study quite difficult.

A false-color map indicating the atmospheric ozone concentrations over the last several years. The ozone "hole" is shown in pink.

The ozone layer is also threatened by *Freons,** a group of stable, noncorrosive compounds used as refrigerants and as propellants in aerosol cans. The most commonly used substance of this type is Freon-12 (CCl_2F_2). The chemical inertness of Freons makes them valuable but also creates a problem, since they remain in the environment a long time. Eventually, they migrate into the upper atmosphere to be decomposed by high-energy light. Among the decomposition products are chlorine atoms:

$$CCl_2F_2(g) \xrightarrow{\text{Light}} CClF_2(g) + Cl(g)$$

These chlorine atoms can catalyze the decomposition of ozone:

$$Cl(g) + O_3(g) \longrightarrow ClO(g) + O_2(g)$$
$$\underline{O(g) + ClO(g) \longrightarrow Cl(g) + O_2(g)}$$
$$O(g) + O_3(g) \longrightarrow 2O_2(g)$$

The problem of Freons has been brought into strong focus by the recent discovery of a mysterious "hole" in the ozone layer in the stratosphere over Antarctica. Studies performed there to find the reason for the hole have found unusually high levels of chlorine monoxide (ClO). This strongly implicates the Freons in the atmosphere as being at least partially responsible for the ozone destruction in the area.

Because they pose environmental problems, Freons have been banned by the U.S. government for use in aerosol cans, but they are still widely used in air conditioners and refrigerators. However, the chemical industry is actively seeking adequate substitutes for these applications also.

*For more information, see S. Elliott and F. S. Rowland, "Chlorofluorocarbons and Stratospheric Ozone," *J. Chem. Ed.* **64** (1987): 387.

Summary

Even though a chemical reaction may have a strong tendency to occur thermodynamically, it is not necessarily fast. Chemical kinetics is the study of the factors that control the rates of chemical reactions. The reaction rate is defined as the change in concentration of a reactant or product per unit of time. Kinetic measurements are usually made under conditions where the reverse reaction is insignificant. Then only the forward reaction is important in determining the rate.

There are two kinds of rate laws: the differential rate law (or just rate law) and the integrated rate law. The rate law for a reaction of the type

$$aA \rightarrow products$$

describes the dependence of the rate on the concentration of A:

$$Rate = -\frac{\Delta[A]}{\Delta t} = k[A]^n$$

where k is called the rate constant and n is the order of the reaction in A. The rate is defined as the negative of $\Delta[A]/\Delta t$ because [A] is decreasing (as the reactants are used up in the reaction). The value for n (the order) cannot be determined from the balanced equation for the reaction, but must be found experimentally. For a first-order reaction n is 1 and the rate = $k[A]$. For a second-order reaction n is 2 and the rate = $k[A]^2$. For a zero-order reaction n is 0 and the rate = k.

A common experimental method for determining the rate is the method of initial rates in which several runs are carried out with different initial concentrations, and the rate is measured for each at a value of t close to $t = 0$.

An integrated rate law expresses reactant concentrations as a function of time. The integrated rate law for a first-order reaction is

$$\ln[A] = -kt + \ln[A]_0$$

where $[A]_0$ is the initial concentration of A. Thus we can calculate [A] at any time, given $[A]_0$ and k. For a reaction that shows first-order kinetics, a plot of $\ln[A]$ versus time is a straight line.

The half-life ($t_{1/2}$) of a reaction is the time required for a reactant to reach half of its original concentration. For first-order reactions the half-life is independent of concentration:

$$t_{1/2} = \frac{0.693}{k}$$

The integrated rate law for a second-order reaction is

$$\frac{1}{[A]} = kt + \frac{1}{[A]_0}$$

Consequently, if a plot of $1/[A]$ versus time for a given reaction is a straight line, then the rate must be second order in A. For second-order kinetics, the half-life is dependent on both k and $[A]_0$:

$$t_{1/2} = \frac{1}{k[A]_0}$$

The integrated rate law for a zero-order reaction is

$$[A] = -kt + [A]_0$$

and the half-life is

$$t_{1/2} = \frac{[A]_0}{2k}$$

For a reaction with several reactants, the overall reaction order is the sum of the individual orders. We can determine the orders for this type of reaction by making the concentration of a particular reactant small in comparison to those of the other reactants.

A reaction mechanism is a series of elementary steps by which a given reaction occurs. The rate law for each step can be written from its molecularity, that is, the number of species that must collide to produce the reaction indicated by that step. A unimolecular step is always first order, and a bimolecular step is always second order.

For a mechanism to be acceptable, the sum of the elementary steps must give the overall balanced equation for the reaction, and the mechanism must give a rate law that agrees with the experimentally determined rate law. Multistep reactions often have one step that is much slower than the others. This is called the rate-determining step, since the overall rate of the reaction is limited by the rate of this step.

Chemical kinetics can be described by the collision model, which assumes that molecules must collide to react. In terms of this model, a certain threshold energy called the activation energy E_a must be overcome for a collision to produce a chemical reaction. E_a is the energy needed to rearrange the bonds in the molecules to form products. Both the rate of a reaction and the effect of temperature on the rate depend on the size of E_a.

Molecular orientation during a collision is also important, since not every collision will have the molecules aligned in an effective way. The factors affecting k can be described by the Arrhenius equation

$$k = Ae^{-E_a/RT}$$

where A is a factor reflecting collision frequency and molecular orientation and $e^{-E_a/RT}$ represents the fraction of collisions with sufficient energy to produce a reaction. The value of E_a can be determined by measuring values of k at two or more temperatures.

A catalyst is a substance that speeds up a reaction without being consumed. A catalyst operates by providing a lower energy pathway for the reaction in question. Enzymes are biologic catalysts. A homogeneous catalyst is present in the same phase as the reacting molecules, and a heterogeneous catalyst exists in a different phase.

Key Terms

chemical kinetics

Section 12.1
reaction rate
instantaneous rate

Section 12.2
rate law

rate constant
order
(differential) rate law
integrated rate law

Section 12.3
method of initial rates

initial rate
overall reaction order

Section 12.4
first-order reaction
integrated first-order rate law
half-life of a reaction

integrated second-order rate law
zero-order reaction
integrated zero-order rate law
pseudo-first-order rate law

Section 12.6
reaction mechanism
intermediate
elementary step
molecularity
unimolecular step

bimolecular step
termolecular step
rate-determining step

Section 12.7
collision model
activation energy
activated complex (transition state)
molecular orientations
steric factor
Arrhenius equation

frequency factor

Section 12.8
enzyme
catalyst
homogeneous catalyst
heterogeneous catalyst
adsorption

A blue question or exercise number indicates that the answer to that question or exercise appears at the back of this book and a solution appears in the Solutions Guide.

Questions

1. Distinguish among the initial rate, average rate, and instantaneous rate of a chemical reaction.

2. Define each of the following.
   a. Elementary step
   b. Reaction mechanism
   c. Rate-determining step

3. Why is the rate of a reaction affected by each of the following?
   a. Frequency of collisions
   b. Kinetic energy of collisions
   c. Orientation of collisions

4. Define what is meant by unimolecular and bimolecular steps.

5. Why are termolecular steps infrequently seen in chemical reactions?

6. Define each of the following.
   a. Homogeneous catalyst
   b. Heterogeneous catalyst

7. Why does a catalyst increase the rate of a chemical reaction?

8. Should the concentration of a homogeneous catalyst appear in the rate law?

9. Would a given reaction have the same rate law for both a catalyzed and an uncatalyzed pathway? Explain.

10. Hydrogen reacts explosively with oxygen. However, a mixture of H_2 and O_2 can exist indefinitely at room temperature. Explain why H_2 and O_2 do not react under these conditions.

Exercises*

In this section similar exercises are paired.

Reaction Rates

11. Thiosulfate ion is oxidized by iodine according to the following reaction:

$$2S_2O_3^{2-}(aq) + I_2(aq) \rightarrow S_4O_6^{2-}(aq) + 2I^-(aq)$$

If, in a certain experiment, 0.0080 mol $S_2O_3^{2-}$ is consumed in 1.0 L of solution each second, what is the rate of consumption of I_2? At what rates are $S_4O_6^{2-}$ and I^- produced in this solution?

12. In the Haber process for the production of ammonia,

$$N_2(g) + 3H_2(g) \rightarrow 2NH_3(g)$$

what is the relationship between the rate of production of ammonia and the rate of consumption of hydrogen?

*In the Exercises the term *rate law* always refers to the differential rate law.

13. What are the units for each of the following if the concentrations are expressed in moles per liter?
    a. Rate of a chemical reaction
    b. Rate constant for a zero-order rate law
    c. Rate constant for a first-order rate law
    d. Rate constant for a second-order rate law
    e. Rate constant for a third-order rate law

14. Concentrations of trace substances in the atmosphere are often expressed in molecules per cubic centimeter. What are the units for the quantities in Exercise 13 if the concentrations are expressed in these units?

15. The hydroxyl radical (OH) is an important oxidizing agent in the atmosphere. At 298 K, the rate constant for the reaction of OH with benzene is 1.24×10^{-12} cm^3/molecule · s. Calculate the value of the rate constant in L/mol · s.

16. A rate constant for a gas-phase reaction has the value of 4.4×10^{-6} L/mol · s. What is the value of the rate constant in cm^3/molecule · s?

Rate Laws from Experimental Data: Initial Rates Method

17. The reaction

$$2NO(g) + Cl_2(g) \rightarrow 2NOCl(g)$$

was studied at $-10°C$. The following results were obtained where

$$\text{Rate} = -\frac{\Delta[Cl_2]}{\Delta t}$$

$[NO]_0$ (mol/L)	$[Cl_2]_0$ (mol/L)	Initial Rate (mol/L · min)
0.10	0.10	0.18
0.10	0.20	0.35
0.20	0.20	1.45

a. What is the rate law?
b. What is the value of the rate constant?

18. The reaction

$$2I^-(aq) + S_2O_8^{2-}(aq) \rightarrow I_2(aq) + 2SO_4^{2-}(aq)$$

was studied at 25°C. The following results were obtained where

$$\text{Rate} = -\frac{\Delta[S_2O_8^{2-}]}{\Delta t}$$

$[I^-]_0$ (mol/L)	$[S_2O_8^{2-}]_0$ (mol/L)	Initial Rate (mol/L · s)
0.080	0.040	12.50×10^{-6}
0.040	0.040	6.250×10^{-6}
0.080	0.020	5.560×10^{-6}
0.032	0.040	4.350×10^{-6}
0.060	0.030	6.410×10^{-6}

a. Determine the rate law.
b. Calculate a value for the rate constant for each experiment and an average value for the rate constant.

19. The reaction

$$I^-(aq) + OCl^-(aq) \rightarrow IO^-(aq) + Cl^-(aq)$$

was studied and the following data were obtained:

$[I^-]_0$ (mol/L)	$[OCl^-]_0$ (mol/L)	Initial Rate (mol/L · s)
0.12	0.18	7.91×10^{-2}
0.060	0.18	3.95×10^{-2}
0.030	0.090	9.88×10^{-3}
0.24	0.090	7.91×10^{-2}

a. What is the rate law?
b. Calculate the rate constant.

20. The decomposition of nitrosyl chloride was studied:

$$2NOCl(g) \rightleftharpoons 2NO(g) + Cl_2(g)$$

The following data were obtained where

$$\text{Rate} = -\frac{\Delta[NOCl]}{\Delta t}$$

$[NOCl]_0$ (molecules/cm^3)	Initial Rate (molecules/cm^3 · s)
3.0×10^{16}	5.98×10^4
2.0×10^{16}	2.66×10^4
1.0×10^{16}	6.64×10^3
4.0×10^{16}	1.06×10^5

a. What is the rate law?
b. Calculate the rate constant.
c. Calculate the rate constant for the concentrations given in moles per liter.

21. The following data were obtained for the reaction

$$2ClO_2(aq) + 2OH^-(aq)$$
$$\rightarrow ClO_3^-(aq) + ClO_2^-(aq) + H_2O(l)$$

where

$$\text{Rate} = -\frac{\Delta[ClO_2]}{\Delta t}$$

[ClO$_2$] (mol/L)	[OH$^-$] (mol/L)	Initial Rate (mol/L · s)
0.0500	0.100	5.75×10^{-2}
0.100	0.100	2.30×10^{-1}
0.100	0.050	1.15×10^{-1}

Determine the rate law and the value of the rate constant.

22. The following data were obtained for the gas-phase decomposition of dinitrogen pentoxide,

$$2N_2O_5(g) \rightarrow 4NO_2(g) + O_2(g)$$

[N$_2$O$_5$]$_0$ mol/L	Initial Rate (mol/L · s)
0.075	8.90×10^{-4}
0.190	2.26×10^{-3}
0.275	3.26×10^{-3}
0.410	4.85×10^{-3}

Defining the rate as $-\dfrac{\Delta[N_2O_5]}{\Delta t}$, write the rate law and calculate the value of the rate constant.

Integrated Rate Laws from Experimental Data

23. The dimerization of butadiene

$$2C_4H_6(g) \rightarrow C_8H_{12}(g)$$

was studied at 500 K, and the following data were obtained:

Time (s)	[C$_4$H$_6$] (mol/L)
195	1.6×10^{-2}
604	1.5×10^{-2}
1246	1.3×10^{-2}
2180	1.1×10^{-2}
6210	0.68×10^{-2}

Assuming that

$$\text{Rate} = -\frac{\Delta[C_4H_6]}{\Delta t}$$

determine the form of the rate law, the integrated rate law, and the rate constant for this reaction. (These are actual experimental data, so they may not give a perfectly straight line.)

24. Determine the form of the integrated rate law and the rate law for the decomposition of benzenediazonium chloride:

$$C_6H_5N_2Cl(aq) \rightarrow C_6H_5Cl(l) + N_2(g)$$

from the following data, which were collected at 50°C and 1 atm (the total solution volume was 40.0 mL).

Time (s)	N$_2$ Evolved (mL)
6	19.3
9	26.0
14	36.0
22	45.0
30	50.4
∞	58.3

25. The decomposition of hydrogen peroxide was studied, and the following data were obtained at a particular temperature:

Time (s)	$[H_2O_2]$ (mol/L)
0	1.0
120 ± 1	0.91
300 ± 1	0.78
600 ± 1	0.59
1200 ± 1	0.37
1800 ± 1	0.22
2400 ± 1	0.13
3000 ± 1	0.082
3600 ± 1	0.050

Assuming that

$$\text{Rate} = -\frac{\Delta[H_2O_2]}{\Delta t}$$

determine the integrated rate law and the value of the rate constant. Also write the rate law.

26. The rate of the reaction

$$NO_2(g) + CO(g) \rightarrow NO(g) + CO_2(g)$$

depends only on the concentration of nitrogen dioxide below 225°C. At a temperature below 225°C the following data were collected:

Time (s)	$[NO_2]$ (mol/L)
0	0.500
1.20×10^3	0.444
3.00×10^3	0.381
4.50×10^3	0.340
9.00×10^3	0.250
1.80×10^4	0.174

Determine the integrated rate law and the value of the rate constant at this temperature. Also write the rate law.

Half-Life

27. Radioactive decay is a process that follows a first-order rate law: Rate = kN, where N is the number of nuclei and the rate is the nuclear disintegrations per unit time. The half-life for the decay of ^{239}Pu is 24,360 years. The half-life for the decay of ^{241}Pu is 13 years.
    a. Calculate the rate constants for the decay of ^{239}Pu and ^{241}Pu.
    b. Which species decays more rapidly?
    c. If one starts with 5.0 g of pure ^{241}Pu, how many disintegrations per second occur initially? What mass of ^{241}Pu is left after 1.0 year, 10. years, 100. years?

28. Radioactive copper-64 decays by first-order kinetics with a half-life of 12.8 days.
    a. What is the value of k in s^{-1}?
    b. A sample contains 28.0 mg ^{64}Cu. How many decays will be produced in the first second?
    c. A chemist obtains a fresh sample of ^{64}Cu and measures its radioactivity. She then determines that to do the experiment she has in mind, the radioactivity cannot go below 3% of the initial measured value. How long does she have to do the experiment?

29. A certain radioactive decay process (first-order) is 45.0% complete in 65 s. What are the rate constant and the half-life for this process?

30. The radioactive isotope ^{32}P decays by first-order kinetics and has a half-life of 14.3 days. How long does it take for 95.0% of a sample of ^{32}P to decay?

31. It took 143 s for 50.0% of a particular substance to decompose. If the initial concentration was 0.060 M and the decomposition reaction follows second-order kinetics, what is the value of the rate constant?

32. A certain substance, initially at 0.10 M in solution, decomposes by second-order kinetics. If the rate constant for this process is 4.0×10^{-1} L/mol · min, how much time is required for the concentration to reach 0.050 M?

33. A first-order reaction is 38.5% complete in 480 s.
    a. Calculate the rate constant.
    b. What is the value of the half-life?
    c. How long will it take for the reaction to go to 25%, 75%, and 95% completion?

34. A certain first-order reaction is 50.% complete in 3.5 hours. What period of time is required for the reaction to be 88% complete?

Reaction Mechanisms

35. Write the rate laws for the following elementary reactions.
a. $CH_3NC(g) \rightarrow CH_3CN(g)$
b. $O_3(g) + NO(g) \rightarrow O_2(g) + NO_2(g)$

36. Write the rate laws for the following elementary reactions.
a. $O_3(g) \rightarrow O_2(g) + O(g)$
b. $O_3(g) + O(g) \rightarrow 2O_2(g)$

37. The mechanism for the decomposition of hydrogen peroxide is

$$H_2O_2 \rightarrow 2OH$$
$$H_2O_2 + OH \rightarrow H_2O + HO_2$$
$$HO_2 + OH \rightarrow H_2O + O_2$$

Using your results from Exercise 25, specify which step is the rate-determining step.

38. The mechanism for the reaction of nitrogen dioxide with carbon monoxide to form nitric oxide and carbon dioxide is thought to be

$NO_2 + NO_2 \rightarrow NO_3 + NO$	Slow
$NO_3 + CO \rightarrow NO_2 + CO_2$	Fast

Write the rate law expected for this mechanism.

Temperature Dependence of Rate Constants and the Collision Model

39. At 25°C the first-order rate constant for a reaction is 2.0×10^3 s^{-1}. The activation energy is 15.0 kJ/mol. What is the value of the rate constant at 75°C?

40. A first-order reaction has rate constants of 4.6×10^{-2} s^{-1} and 8.1×10^{-2} s^{-1} at 0°C and 20°C, respectively. What is the value of the activation energy?

41. For the reaction

$$H_2(g) + I_2(g) \rightarrow 2HI(g)$$

where the rate law is

$$-\frac{\Delta[H_2]}{\Delta t} = k[H_2][I_2]$$

the rate constants are 2.45×10^{-4} L/mol · s and 0.950 L/mol · s at 302°C and 508°C, respectively.
a. Calculate the values of E_a and A for this reaction.
b. Calculate the value of k at 375°C.

42. Chemists commonly use a rule of thumb that an increase of 10 K in temperature doubles the rate of a reaction. What must the activation energy be for this statement to be true for a temperature increase from 25°C to 35°C?

43. Experimental values for the temperature dependence of the rate constant for the gas-phase reaction

$$NO + O_3 \rightarrow NO_2 + O_2$$

are as follows:

T (K)	k (L/mol · s)
195	1.08×10^9
230	2.95×10^9
260	5.42×10^9
298	12.0×10^9
369	35.5×10^9

Make the appropriate graph using these data, and determine the activation energy for this reaction.

44. The rate constant for the gas-phase decomposition of N_2O_5, that is,

$$N_2O_5 \rightarrow 2NO_2 + \tfrac{1}{2}O_2$$

has the following temperature dependence:

T (K)	k (s^{-1})
338	4.9×10^{-3}
318	5.0×10^{-4}
298	3.5×10^{-5}

Make the appropriate graph using these data, and determine the activation energy for this reaction.

45. For each of the following reaction profiles, indicate
    a. The positions of reactants and products.
    b. The activation energy.
    c. ΔE for the reaction.
    d. Which point on the second plot represents the energy of the intermediate?

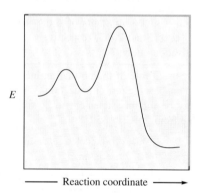

46. Draw a rough sketch of the energy profile for each of the following cases:
    a. $\Delta E = +10$ kJ/mol, $E_a = 25$ kJ/mol
    b. $\Delta E = -10$ kJ/mol, $E_a = 50$ kJ/mol
    c. $\Delta E = -50$ kJ/mol, $E_a = 50$ kJ/mol
    Which of the reactions will have the greatest rate at 298 K? Assume that the frequency factor A is the same for all three reactions.

47. The activation energy for the reaction

$$H_2(g) + I_2(g) \rightarrow 2HI(g)$$

is 167 kJ/mol, and ΔE for the reaction is $+28$ kJ/mol. What is the activation energy for the decomposition of HI?

48. For a certain process, the activation energy is greater for the forward reaction than for the reverse reaction. Is this reaction endothermic or exothermic?

49. One mechanism for the destruction of ozone in the upper atmosphere is

$$O_3(g) + NO(g) \rightarrow NO_2(g) + O_2(g) \quad \text{Slow}$$
$$\underline{NO_2(g) + O(g) \rightarrow NO(g) + O_2(g) \quad \text{Fast}}$$
Overall reaction: $O_3(g) + O(g) \rightarrow 2O_2(g)$

a. Which species is a catalyst?
b. Which species is an intermediate?
c. E_a for the uncatalyzed reaction

$$O_3(g) + O(g) \rightarrow 2O_2$$

is 14.0 kJ. E_a for the same reaction when catalyzed is 11.9 kJ. What is the ratio of the rate constant for the catalyzed reaction to that for the uncatalyzed reaction at 25°C? Assume that the frequency factor A is the same for each reaction.

50. One of the concerns about the use of Freons is that they will migrate to the upper atmosphere, where chlorine atoms can be generated by the following reaction:

$$CCl_2F_2 \xrightarrow{h\nu} CF_2Cl + Cl$$
$$\text{Freon-12}$$

Chlorine atoms can act as a catalyst for the destruction of ozone. The activation energy for the reaction

$$Cl + O_3 \rightarrow ClO + O_2$$

is 2.1 kJ/mol. Which is the more effective catalyst for the destruction of ozone, Cl or NO? (See Exercise 49.)

51. Assuming that the mechanism for the hydrogenation of C_2H_4 given in Section 12.8 is correct, would you predict that the product of the reaction of C_2H_4 with D_2 would be CH_2D—CH_2D or CHD_2—CH_3?

52. How could the reaction of C_2H_4 with D_2 be used to confirm the mechanism for the hydrogenation of C_2H_4 given in Section 12.8 (see Exercise 51).

Additional Exercises

53. The rate law for the reaction

$$Cl_2(g) + CHCl_3(g) \rightarrow HCl(g) + CCl_4(g)$$

is $\text{Rate} = k[Cl_2]^{1/2}[CHCl_3]$

What are the units for k?

54. The decomposition of hydrogen iodide on finely divided gold at 150°C is zero order with respect to HI. The rate defined below is constant at 1.20×10^{-4} mol/L · s.

$$2HI(g) \xrightarrow{\text{Au}} H_2(g) + I_2(g)$$

$$\text{Rate} = -\frac{\Delta[HI]}{\Delta t} = k = 1.20 \times 10^{-4} \text{ mol/L} \cdot \text{s}$$

a. If an experiment has an initial HI concentration of 0.250 mol/L, what is the concentration of HI after 25 minutes?

b. How long will it take for all of the HI to decompose?

c. Give the rates of formation for H_2 and I_2.

55. The reaction

$$H_2SeO_3(aq) + 6I^-(aq) + 4H^+(aq) \rightarrow$$
$$Se(s) + 2I_3^-(aq) + 3H_2O(l)$$

was studied at 0°C, and the following data were obtained:

$[H_2SeO_3]_0$	$[H^+]_0$	$[I^-]_0$	Initial Rate (mol/L · s)
1.0×10^{-4}	2.0×10^{-2}	2.0×10^{-2}	1.66×10^{-7}
2.0×10^{-4}	2.0×10^{-2}	2.0×10^{-2}	3.33×10^{-7}
3.0×10^{-4}	2.0×10^{-2}	2.0×10^{-2}	4.99×10^{-7}
1.0×10^{-4}	4.0×10^{-2}	2.0×10^{-2}	6.66×10^{-7}
1.0×10^{-4}	1.0×10^{-2}	2.0×10^{-2}	0.42×10^{-7}
1.0×10^{-4}	2.0×10^{-2}	4.0×10^{-2}	13.2×10^{-7}
1.0×10^{-4}	1.0×10^{-2}	4.0×10^{-2}	3.36×10^{-7}

These relationships hold only if there is an insignificant amount of I_3^- present. What is the rate law and the value of the rate constant? $\left(\text{Assume that rate} = -\dfrac{\Delta[H_2SeO_3]}{\Delta t}.\right)$

56. The rate of the reaction

$$O(g) + NO_2(g) \rightarrow NO(g) + O_2(g)$$

was studied. This reaction is one step of the nitric oxide–catalyzed destruction of ozone in the upper atmosphere.

a. In the first set of experiments, NO_2 was in large excess, at a concentration of 1.0×10^{13} molecules/cm³.

Time (s)	[O] (atoms/cm³)
0	5.0×10^9
1.0×10^{-2}	1.9×10^9
2.0×10^{-2}	6.8×10^8
3.0×10^{-2}	2.5×10^8

What is the order of the reaction with respect to oxygen atoms?

b. The reaction is known to be first order with respect to NO_2. What are the overall rate law and the value of the rate constant?

57. Sulfuryl chloride (SO_2Cl_2) decomposes to sulfur dioxide (SO_2) and chlorine (Cl_2) by a first-order reaction in the gas phase. The following data were obtained when a sample containing 5.00×10^{-2} mol sulfuryl chloride was heated to $600 \text{ K} \pm 1 \text{ K}$ in a 5.00×10^{-1} L container.

Time (hours)	0.00	1.00	2.00	4.00	8.00	16.00
Pressure (atm)	4.93	5.60	6.34	7.33	8.56	9.52

Defining the rate as $-\dfrac{\Delta[SO_2Cl_2]}{\Delta t}$,

a. Determine the value of the rate constant for the decomposition of sulfuryl chloride at 600 K.

b. What is the half-life of the reaction?

c. What would be the pressure in the vessel after 0.500 h and after 12.0 h?

d. What fraction of the sulfuryl chloride remains after 20.0 h?

58. The decomposition of many substances on the surface of a heterogeneous catalyst shows the following behavior:

Concentration of reactant

How do you account for the rate law changing from first order to zero order in the concentration of reactant?

59. The decomposition of NH_3 to N_2 and H_2 was studied on two surfaces:

Surface	E_a (kJ/mol)
W	163
Os	197

Without a catalyst the activation energy is 335 kJ/mol.
a. Which surface is the better heterogeneous catalyst for the decomposition of NH_3? Why?
b. How many times faster is the reaction at 298 K on the W surface compared with the reaction with no catalyst present?
c. The decomposition reaction on the two surfaces obeys a rate law of the form

$$\text{Rate} = k\frac{[NH_3]}{[H_2]}$$

How can you explain the inverse dependence of the rate on the H_2 concentration?

60. For enzyme-catalyzed reactions the elementary steps are

$$E + S \longrightarrow E \cdot S$$
$$E \cdot S \longrightarrow E + P$$

and a graph of the rate as a function of [S], the concentration of the substrate, has the following general appearance:

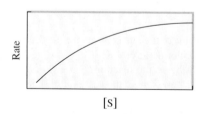

Note that at high substrate concentrations the rate no longer changes with [S]. Suggest a reason for this.

Challenge Problems

61. A study was made of the effect of the hydroxide concentration on the rate of the reaction

$$I^-(aq) + OCl^-(aq) \rightarrow IO^-(aq) + Cl^-(aq)$$

The following data were obtained:

$[I^-]_0$ (mol/L)	$[OCl^-]_0$ (mol/L)	$[OH^-]_0$ (mol/L)	Initial Rate (mol/L · s)
0.0013	0.012	0.10	9.4×10^{-3}
0.0026	0.012	0.10	18.7×10^{-3}
0.0013	0.006	0.10	4.7×10^{-3}
0.0013	0.018	0.10	14.0×10^{-3}
0.0013	0.012	0.05	18.7×10^{-3}
0.0013	0.012	0.20	4.7×10^{-3}
0.0013	0.018	0.20	7.0×10^{-3}

Determine the rate law and the value of the rate constant for this reaction.

62. The thermal degradation of silk was studied by Kuruppillai, Hersh, and Tucker ("Historic Textile and Paper Materials, *ACS Advances in Chemistry Series,* No. 212, 1986) by measuring the tensile strength of silk fibers at various times of exposure to elevated temperature. The loss of tensile strength follows first-order kinetics

$$\frac{\Delta s}{\Delta t} = -ks$$

where s is the strength of the fiber retained after heating and k is the first-order rate constant. The effects of adding a deacidifying agent and an antioxidant to the silk were studied and the following data were obtained:

Heating Time (Days)	Strength Retained (%)		
	Untreated	Deacidifying Agent	Antioxidant
0.00	100.0	100.1	114.6
1.00	67.9	60.8	65.2
2.00	38.9	26.8	28.1
3.00	16.1	—	11.3
6.00	6.8	—	—

a. Determine the first-order rate constants for the thermal degradation of silk for each of the three experiments.
b. Does either of the two additives appear to retard the degradation of silk?
c. Calculate the half-life for the thermal degradation of silk for each of the three experiments.

63. The reaction

$$NO(g) + O_3(g) \rightarrow NO_2(g) + O_2(g)$$

was studied by performing two experiments. In the first experiment the rate of disappearance of NO was followed in the presence of a large excess of O_3. The results were as follows

([O_3] remains effectively constant at 1.0×10^{14} molecules/cm^3):

Time (ms)	[NO] (molecules/cm^3)
0	6.0×10^8
100 ± 1	5.0×10^8
500 ± 1	2.4×10^8
700 ± 1	1.7×10^8
1000 ± 1	9.9×10^7

In the second experiment [NO] was held constant at 2.0×10^{14} molecules/cm^3. The data for the disappearance of O_3 are as follows:

Time (ms)	[O_3] (molecules/cm^3)
0	1.0×10^{10}
50 ± 1	8.4×10^9
100 ± 1	7.0×10^9
200 ± 1	4.9×10^9
300 ± 1	3.4×10^9

a. What is the order with respect to each reactant?
b. What is the overall rate law?
c. What is the value of the rate constant from each set of experiments?

$$\text{Rate} = k'[\text{NO}]^x \qquad \text{Rate} = k''[\text{O}_3]^y$$

d. What is the value of the rate constant for the overall rate law?

$$\text{Rate} = k[\text{NO}]^x[\text{O}_3]^y$$

CHAPTER 13

Chemical Equilibrium

In doing stoichiometry calculations we assumed that reactions proceed to completion, that is, until one of the reactants runs out. Many reactions *do* proceed essentially to completion. For such reactions it can be assumed that the reactants are quantitatively converted to products and that the amount of limiting reactant that remains is negligible. On the other hand, there are many chemical reactions that stop far short of completion. An example is the dimerization of nitrogen dioxide:

$$NO_2(g) + NO_2(g) \rightarrow N_2O_4(g)$$

The reactant NO_2 is a dark brown gas, and the product N_2O_4 is a colorless gas. When NO_2 is placed in an evacuated, sealed glass vessel at 25°C, the initial dark brown color decreases in intensity as it is converted to colorless N_2O_4. However, even over a long period of time, the contents of the reaction vessel do not become colorless. Instead, the intensity of the brown color eventually becomes constant, which means that the concentration of NO_2 is no longer changing. This observation is a clear indication that the reaction has stopped short of completion. In fact, the system has reached **chemical equilibrium**, *the state where the concentrations of all reactants and products remain constant with time.*

Any chemical reactions carried out in a closed vessel will reach equilibrium. For some reactions the equilibrium position so favors the products that the reaction appears to have gone to completion. We say that the equilib-

< The effect of temperature on the endothermic, aqueous equilibrium:

$$Co(H_2O)_6^{2+} + 4Cl^- \rightleftharpoons CoCl_4^{2-} + 6H_2O$$
$$\text{pink} \qquad\qquad\qquad \text{blue}$$

The violet solution in the center is at 25°C and contains significant quantities of both pink $Co(H_2O)_6^{2+}$ and blue $CoCl_4^{2-}$. When the solution is cooled, it turns pink because the equilibrium is shifted to the left. Heating the solution favors the blue $CoCl_4^{2-}$ ions.

595

rium position for such reactions lies *far to the right*, (in the direction of the products. For example, when gaseous hydrogen and oxygen are mixed in stoichiometric quantities and react to form water vapor, the reaction proceeds essentially to completion. The amounts of the reactants that remain when the system reaches equilibrium are so tiny as to be negligible. By contrast, some reactions occur only to a slight extent. For example, when solid CaO is placed in a closed vessel at 25°C, the decomposition to solid Ca and gaseous O_2 is virtually undetectable. In cases like this, the equilibrium position is said to lie *far to the left*, in the direction of the reactants).

In this chapter we will discuss how and why a chemical system comes to equilibrium and the characteristics of equilibrium. In particular, we will discuss how to calculate the concentrations of the reactants and products present for a given system at equilibrium.

13.1 The Equilibrium Condition

Purpose

• To discuss how equilibrium is established.

Since no changes occur in the concentrations of reactants or products in a reaction system at equilibrium, it may appear that everything has stopped. However, this is not the case. On the molecular level, there is frantic activity. Equilibrium is not static, but is a highly *dynamic situation*. The concept of chemical equilibrium is analogous to the flow of cars across a bridge connecting two island cities. Suppose the traffic flow on the bridge is the same in both directions. It is obvious that there is motion, since one can see the cars traveling back and forth across the bridge, but the number of cars in each city is not changing because equal numbers of cars are entering and leaving. The result is no *net* change in the car population.

To see how this concept applies to chemical reactions, consider the reaction between steam and carbon monoxide in a closed vessel at a high temperature where the reaction takes place rapidly:

$$H_2O(g) + CO(g) \rightleftharpoons H_2(g) + CO_2(g)$$

Assume that the same number of moles of gaseous CO and gaseous H_2O are placed in a closed vessel and allowed to react. The plots of the concentrations of reactants and products versus time are shown in Fig. 13.1. Note that since CO and H_2O were originally present in equal molar quantities, and since they react in a 1:1 ratio, the concentrations of the two gases are always equal. Also, since H_2 and CO_2 are formed in equal amounts, they are always present in the same concentrations.

Equilibrium is a dynamic situation.

Figure 13.1

The changes in concentrations with time for the reaction $H_2O(g) + CO(g) \rightleftharpoons H_2(g) + CO_2(g)$ when equimolar quantities of $H_2O(g)$ and $CO(g)$ are mixed.

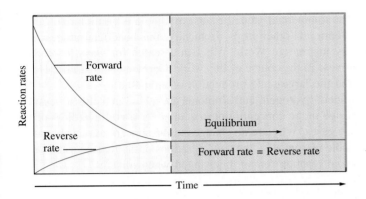

Figure 13.2

The changes with time in the rates of forward and reverse reactions for $H_2O(g) + CO(g) \rightleftharpoons H_2(g) + CO_2(g)$ when equimolar quantities of $H_2O(g)$ and $CO(g)$ are mixed. The rates do not change in the same way with time because the forward reaction has a much larger rate constant than the reverse reaction.

Figure 13.1 is a profile of the progress of the reaction. When CO and H_2O are mixed, they immediately begin to react to form H_2 and CO_2. This leads to a decrease in the concentrations of the reactants, but the concentrations of the products, which were initially at zero, are increasing. Beyond a certain time, indicated by the dashed line in Fig. 13.1, the concentrations of reactants and products no longer change—equilibrium has been reached. Unless the system is somehow disturbed, no further changes in concentrations will occur. Note that although the equilibrium position lies far to the right, the concentrations of reactants never go to zero; the reactants will always be present in small but constant concentrations.

Why does equilibrium occur? We have seen in Chapter 12 that molecules react by colliding with one another, and the more collisions, the faster is the reaction. This is why reaction rates depend on concentrations. In this case the concentrations of H_2O and CO are lowered by the forward reaction:

$$H_2O + CO \rightarrow H_2 + CO_2$$

As the concentrations of the reactants decrease, the forward reaction slows down (Fig. 13.2). As in the bridge traffic analogy, there is also a reverse direction:

$$H_2O + CO \leftarrow H_2 + CO_2$$

Initially in this experiment no H_2 and CO_2 were present, and this reverse reaction could not occur. However, as the forward reaction proceeds, the concentrations of H_2 and CO_2 build up and the rate of the reverse reaction increases (Fig. 13.2) as the forward reaction slows down. Eventually, the concentrations reach levels where the rate of the forward reaction equals the rate of the reverse reaction. The system has reached equilibrium.

The equilibrium position of a reaction—left, right, or somewhere in between— is determined by many factors: the initial concentrations, the relative energies of the reactants and products, and the relative degree of "organization" of the reactants and products. Energy and organization come into play because nature tries to achieve minimum energy and maximum disorder, as we will show in detail in Chapter 16. For now, we will simply view the equilibrium phenomenon in terms of the rates of opposing reactions.

A double arrow ($\rightleftharpoons$) is used to show that a reaction can occur in either direction.

The relationship between equilibrium and thermodynamics is explored in Section 16.8.

The Characteristics of Chemical Equilibrium

To explore the important characteristics of chemical equilibrium, we will consider the synthesis of ammonia from elemental nitrogen and hydrogen:

$$N_2(g) + 3H_2(g) \rightleftharpoons 2NH_3(g)$$

The United States produces about 20 million tons of ammonia annually.

Molecules with strong bonds have large activation energies and tend to react slowly at 25°C.

Figure 13.3

A concentration profile for the reaction $N_2(g) + 3H_2(g) \rightleftharpoons 2NH_3(g)$ when only $N_2(g)$ and $H_2(g)$ are mixed initially.

This process is of great commercial value because ammonia is an important fertilizer for the growth of corn and other crops. Ironically, this beneficial process was discovered in Germany just before World War I in a search for ways to produce nitrogen-based explosives. In the course of this work, German chemist Fritz Haber (1868–1934) pioneered the large-scale production of ammonia.

When gaseous nitrogen, hydrogen, and ammonia are mixed in a closed vessel at 25°C, no apparent change in the concentrations occurs over time, regardless of the original amounts of the gases. Why are no changes in the concentrations observed?

There are two possible reasons why the concentrations of the reactants and products of a given chemical reaction remain unchanged when mixed:

1. The system is at chemical equilibrium.

2. The forward and reverse reactions are so slow that the system moves toward equilibrium at a rate that cannot be detected.

The second reason applies to the nitrogen, hydrogen, and ammonia mixture at 25°C. As we saw in Chapters 8 and 9, the N_2 molecule has a very strong triple bond (941 kJ/mol) and thus is very unreactive. The H_2 molecule also has an unusually strong single bond (432 kJ/mol). Therefore, mixtures of N_2, H_2 and NH_3 at 25°C can exist with no apparent change over long periods of time, unless a catalyst is introduced to speed up the forward and reverse reactions. Under appropriate conditions, the system does reach equilibrium, as shown in Fig. 13.3. Note that because of the reaction stoichiometry, H_2 disappears three times as fast as N_2 does and NH_3 forms twice as fast as N_2 disappears.

13.2 The Equilibrium Constant

Purpose

• To introduce the law of mass action and to show how to calculate values for the equilibrium constant.

Science is fundamentally empirical—it is based on experiment. The development of the equilibrium concept is typical. From their observations of many chemical reactions, two Norwegian chemists, Cato Maximilian Guldberg (1836–1902) and Peter Waage (1833–1900), proposed in 1864 the **law of mass action** as a general description of the equilibrium condition. Guldberg and Waage postulated that for a reaction of the type

The law of mass action is based on experimental observation.

$$jA + kB \rightleftharpoons lC + mD$$

where A, B, C, and D represent chemical species and j, k, l, and m are their coefficients in the balanced equation, the law of mass action is represented by the following **equilibrium expression:**

$$K = \frac{[C]^l[D]^m}{[A]^j[B]^k}$$

The square brackets indicate the concentrations of the chemical species *at equilibrium*, and K is a constant called the **equilibrium constant.**

Sample Exercise 13.1

Write the equilibrium expression for the following reaction:

$$4NH_3(g) + 7O_2(g) \rightleftharpoons 4NO_2(g) + 6H_2O(g)$$

Solution

Applying the law of mass action gives

Coefficient of NO$_2$

Coefficient of H$_2$O

$$K = \frac{[NO_2]^4[H_2O]^6}{[NH_3]^4[O_2]^7}$$

Coefficient of O$_2$

Coefficient of NH$_3$

The square brackets indicate concentration in units of mol/L.

The value of the equilibrium constant at a given temperature can be calculated if we know the equilibrium concentrations of the reaction components, as illustrated in Sample Exercise 13.2.

Sample Exercise 13.2

The following equilibrium concentrations were observed for the Haber process at 127°C:

$$[NH_3] = 3.1 \times 10^{-2} \text{ mol/L}$$
$$[N_2] = 8.5 \times 10^{-1} \text{ mol/L}$$
$$[H_2] = 3.1 \times 10^{-3} \text{ mol/L}$$

a. Calculate the value of K at 127°C for this reaction.
b. Calculate the value of the equilibrium constant at 127°C for the reaction

$$2NH_3(g) \rightleftharpoons N_2(g) + 3H_2(g)$$

c. Calculate the value of the equilibrium constant at 127°C for the reaction given by the equation

$$\tfrac{1}{2}N_2(g) + \tfrac{3}{2}H_2(g) \rightleftharpoons NH_3(g)$$

Solution

a. The balanced equation for the Haber process is

$$N_2(g) + 3H_2(g) \rightleftharpoons 2NH_3(g)$$

Thus

$$K = \frac{[NH_3]^2}{[N_2][H_2]^3} = \frac{(3.1 \times 10^{-2} \text{ mol/L})^2}{(8.5 \times 10^{-1} \text{ mol/L})(3.1 \times 10^{-3} \text{ mol/L})^3}$$
$$= 3.8 \times 10^4 \text{ L}^2/\text{mol}^2$$

b. This reaction is written in the reverse order from the equation given in part a. This leads to the equilibrium expression

$$K' = \frac{[N_2][H_2]^3}{[NH_3]^2}$$

which is the reciprocal of the expression used in part a. Therefore,

$$K' = \frac{[N_2][H_2]^3}{[NH_3]^2} = \frac{1}{K} = \frac{1}{3.8 \times 10^4 \text{ L}^2/\text{mol}^2} = 2.6 \times 10^{-5} \text{ mol}^2/\text{L}^2$$

c. We use the law of mass action:

$$K'' = \frac{[NH_3]}{[N_2]^{1/2}[H_2]^{3/2}}$$

If we compare this expression to that obtained in part a, we see that since

$$\frac{[NH_3]}{[N_2]^{1/2}[H_2]^{3/2}} = \left(\frac{[NH_3]^2}{[N_2][H_2]^3} \right)^{1/2}$$

$$K'' = K^{1/2}$$

Thus $K'' = K^{1/2} = (3.8 \times 10^4 \text{ L}^2/\text{mol}^2)^{1/2} = 1.9 \times 10^2 \text{ L/mol}$

We can draw some important conclusions from the results of Sample Exercise 13.2. For a reaction of the form

$$jA + kB \rightleftharpoons lC + mD$$

the equilibrium expression is

$$K = \frac{[C]^l[D]^m}{[A]^j[B]^k}$$

If this reaction is reversed, then the new equilibrium expression is

$$K' = \frac{[A]^j[B]^k}{[C]^l[D]^m} = \frac{1}{K}$$

If the original reaction is multiplied by some factor n to give

$$njA + nkB \rightleftharpoons nlC + nmD$$

the equilibrium expression becomes

$$K'' = \frac{[C]^{nl}[D]^{nm}}{[A]^{nj}[B]^{nk}} = K^n$$

We Can Summarize These Conclusions About the Equilibrium Expression as Follows:

- The equilibrium expression for a reaction is the reciprocal of that for the reaction written in reverse.

- When the balanced equation for a reaction is multiplied by a factor n, the equilibrium expression for the new reaction is the original expression raised to the nth power. Thus $K_{\text{new}} = (K_{\text{original}})^n$.

- The units for K are determined by the powers of the various concentration terms. The units for K therefore depend on the reaction being considered.

The units of equilibrium constants are discussed at the end of Section 13.3.

The law of mass action is widely applicable. It correctly describes the equilibrium behavior of an amazing variety of chemical systems in solution and in the gas phase. Although, as we will see later, corrections must be applied in certain cases, such as for concentrated aqueous solutions and for gases at high pressures, the law of mass action provides a remarkably accurate description of all types of chemical equilibria.

The law of mass action applies to solution and gaseous equilibria.

Consider again the ammonia synthesis reaction. The equilibrium constant K always has the same value at a given temperature. At 500°C the value of K is 6.0×10^{-2} L²/mol². Whenever N_2, H_2, and NH_3 are mixed together at this temperature, the system will always come to an equilibrium position such that

$$\frac{[NH_3]^2}{[N_2][H_2]^3} = 6.0 \times 10^{-2} \text{ L}^2/\text{mol}^2$$

This expression has the same value at 500°C, *regardless of the amounts of the gases that are mixed together initially.*

Although the special ratio of products to reactants defined by the equilibrium expression is constant for a given reaction system at a given temperature, the *equilibrium concentrations will not always be the same.* Table 13.1 gives three sets of data for the synthesis of ammonia, showing that even though the individual sets of equilibrium concentrations are quite different for the different situations, the *equilibrium constant, which depends on the ratio of the concentrations, remains the same* (within experimental error). Note that subscript zeros indicate initial concentrations.

Each *set of equilibrium concentrations* is called an **equilibrium position.** It is essential to distinguish between the equilibrium constant and the equilibrium positions for a given reaction system. There is only *one* equilibrium constant for a particular system at a particular temperature, but there are an *infinite* number of equilibrium positions. The specific equilibrium position adopted by a system depends on the initial concentrations, but the equilibrium constant does not.

A cross section showing how anhydrous ammonia is injected into the soil to act as a fertilizer.

For a reaction at a given temperature, there are many equilibrium positions but only one value for K.

Table 13.1

Results of Three Experiments for the Reaction $N_2(g) + 3H_2(g) \rightleftharpoons 2NH_3(g)$

Experiment	Initial Concentrations	Equilibrium Concentrations	$K = \dfrac{[NH_3]^2}{[N_2][H_2]^3}$
I	$[N_2]_0 = 1.000\ M$ $[H_2]_0 = 1.000\ M$ $[NH_3]_0 = 0$	$[N_2] = 0.921\ M$ $[H_2] = 0.763\ M$ $[NH_3] = 0.157\ M$	$K = 6.02 \times 10^{-2}$ L²/mol²
II	$[N_2]_0 = 0$ $[H_2]_0 = 0$ $[NH_3]_0 = 1.000\ M$	$[N_2] = 0.399\ M$ $[H_2] = 1.197\ M$ $[NH_3] = 0.203\ M$	$K = 6.02 \times 10^{-2}$ L²/mol²
III	$[N_2]_0 = 2.00\ M$ $[H_2]_0 = 1.00\ M$ $[NH_3]_0 = 3.00\ M$	$[N_2] = 2.59\ M$ $[H_2] = 2.77\ M$ $[NH_3] = 1.82\ M$	$K = 6.02 \times 10^{-2}$ L²/mol²

Sample Exercise 13.3

The following results were collected for two experiments involving the reaction at 600°C between gaseous sulfur dioxide and oxygen to form gaseous sulfur trioxide:

Experiment 1		Experiment 2	
Initial	Equilibrium	Initial	Equilibrium
$[SO_2]_0 = 2.00\ M$	$[SO_2] = 1.50\ M$	$[SO_2]_0 = 0.500\ M$	$[SO_2] = 0.590\ M$
$[O_2]_0 = 1.50\ M$	$[O_2] = 1.25\ M$	$[O_2]_0 = 0$	$[O_2] = 0.0450\ M$
$[SO_3]_0 = 3.00\ M$	$[SO_3] = 3.50\ M$	$[SO_3]_0 = 0.350\ M$	$[SO_3] = 0.260\ M$

Show that the equilibrium constant is the same in both cases.

Solution

The balanced equation for the reaction is

$$2SO_2(g) + O_2(g) \rightleftharpoons 2SO_3(g)$$

From the law of mass action

$$K = \frac{[SO_3]^2}{[SO_2]^2[O_2]}$$

For Experiment 1,

$$K_1 = \frac{(3.50\ \text{mol/L})^2}{(1.50\ \text{mol/L})^2(1.25\ \text{mol/L})} = 4.36\ \text{L/mol}$$

For Experiment 2,

$$K_2 = \frac{(0.260\ \text{mol/L})^2}{(0.590\ \text{mol/L})^2(0.0450\ \text{mol/L})} = 4.32\ \text{L/mol}$$

The value of K is constant, within experimental error.

13.3 Equilibrium Expressions Involving Pressures

Purpose

• To show how K and K_p are related.

So far we have been describing equilibria involving gases in terms of concentrations. Equilibria involving gases also can be described in terms of pressures. The relationship between the pressure and the concentration of a gas can be seen from the ideal gas equation:

The ideal gas equation is discussed in Section 5.3.

$$PV = nRT \quad \text{or} \quad P = \left(\frac{n}{V}\right)RT = CRT$$

where C equals n/V, or the number of moles n of gas per unit volume V. Thus C represents the *molar concentration of the gas.*

For the ammonia synthesis reaction, the equilibrium expression can be written in terms of concentrations, that is,

$$K = \frac{[NH_3]^2}{[N_2][H_2]^3} = \frac{C_{NH_3}{}^2}{(C_{N_2})(C_{H_2}{}^3)} = K_c$$

or in terms of the *equilibrium partial pressures of the gases*, that is,

$$K_p = \frac{P_{NH_3}{}^2}{(P_{N_2})(P_{H_2}{}^3)}$$

Both of the symbols K and K_c are commonly used for an equilibrium constant in terms of concentrations. We will always use K in this book. The symbol K_p represents an equilibrium constant in terms of partial pressures.

K involves concentrations; K_p involves pressures. In some books the symbol K_c is used instead of K.

Sample Exercise 13.4

The reaction for the formation of nitrosyl chloride

$$2NO(g) + Cl_2(g) \rightleftharpoons 2NOCl(g)$$

was studied at 25°C. The pressures at equilibrium were found to be

$$P_{NOCl} = 1.2 \text{ atm}$$
$$P_{NO} = 5.0 \times 10^{-2} \text{ atm}$$
$$P_{Cl_2} = 3.0 \times 10^{-1} \text{ atm}$$

Calculate the value of K_p for this reaction at 25°C.

Solution

For this reaction,

$$K_p = \frac{P_{NOCl}{}^2}{(P_{NO}{}^2)(P_{Cl_2})} = \frac{(1.2 \text{ atm})^2}{(5.0 \times 10^{-2} \text{ atm})^2(3.0 \times 10^{-1} \text{ atm})}$$
$$= 1.9 \times 10^3 \text{ atm}^{-1}$$

The relationship between K and K_p for a particular reaction follows from the fact that for an ideal gas, $C = P/RT$. For example, for the ammonia synthesis reaction,

$$K = \frac{[NH_3]^2}{[N_2][H_2]^3} = \frac{C_{NH_3}{}^2}{(C_{N_2})(C_{H_2}{}^3)}$$

$$= \frac{\left(\dfrac{P_{NH_3}}{RT}\right)^2}{\left(\dfrac{P_{N_2}}{RT}\right)\left(\dfrac{P_{H_2}}{RT}\right)^3} = \frac{P_{NH_3}{}^2}{(P_{N_2})(P_{H_2}{}^3)} \times \frac{\left(\dfrac{1}{RT}\right)^2}{\left(\dfrac{1}{RT}\right)^4}$$

$$= \frac{P_{NH_3}{}^2}{(P_{N_2})(P_{H_2}{}^3)}(RT)^2$$

$$= K_p(RT)^2$$

$P = CRT$

or

$C = \dfrac{P}{RT}$

However, for the synthesis of hydrogen fluoride from its elements,

$$H_2(g) + F_2(g) \rightleftharpoons 2HF(g)$$

the relationship between K and K_p is given by

$$K = \frac{[HF]^2}{[H_2][F_2]} = \frac{C_{HF}^2}{(C_{H_2})(C_{F_2})}$$

$$= \frac{\left(\dfrac{P_{HF}}{RT}\right)^2}{\left(\dfrac{P_{H_2}}{RT}\right)\left(\dfrac{P_{F_2}}{RT}\right)} = \frac{P_{HF}^2}{(P_{H_2})(P_{F_2})}$$

$$= K_p$$

Thus, for this reaction, K is equal to K_p. This equality occurs because the sum of the coefficients on either side of the balanced equation is identical, so the terms in RT cancel out. In the equilibrium expression for the ammonia synthesis reaction, the sum of the powers in the numerator is different from that in the denominator, and K does not equal K_p.

For the general reaction

$$jA + kB \rightleftharpoons lC + mD$$

the relationship between K and K_p is

$$K_p = K(RT)^{\Delta n}$$

where Δn is the sum of the coefficients of the *gaseous* products minus the sum of the coefficients of the *gaseous* reactants. This equation is quite easy to derive from the definitions of K and K_p and the relationship between pressure and concentration. For the preceding general reaction,

$$K_p = \frac{(P_C^l)(P_D^m)}{(P_A^j)(P_B^k)} = \frac{(C_C \times RT)^l(C_D \times RT)^m}{(C_A \times RT)^j(C_B \times RT)^k}$$

$$= \frac{(C_C^l)(C_D^m)}{(C_A^j)(C_B^k)} \times \frac{(RT)^{l+m}}{(RT)^{j+k}} = K(RT)^{(l+m)-(j+k)}$$

$$= K(RT)^{\Delta n}$$

Δn always involves products minus reactants.

where $\Delta n = (l + m) - (j + k)$, the difference in the sums of the coefficients for the gaseous products and reactants.

Sample Exercise 13.5

Using the value of K_p obtained in Sample Exercise 13.4, calculate the value of K at 25°C for the reaction

$$2NO(g) + Cl_2(g) \rightleftharpoons 2NOCl(g)$$

Solution

From the value of K_p, we can calculate K using

$$K_p = K(RT)^{\Delta n}$$

where $T = 25 + 273 = 298$ K and

$$\Delta n = 2 - (2 + 1) = -1$$

Sum of
product
coefficients

Sum of
reactant
coefficients

Thus

$$K_p = K(RT)^{-1} = \frac{K}{RT}$$

$$K = K_p(RT)$$

$$= \left(\frac{1.9 \times 10^3}{\text{atm}}\right)\left(0.08206 \frac{\text{L} \cdot \text{atm}}{\text{K} \cdot \text{mol}}\right)(298 \text{ K})$$

$$= 4.6 \times 10^4 \text{ L/mol}$$

We have seen that the units of the equilibrium constant depend on the specific reaction. For example, for the reaction

$$H_2(g) + F_2(g) \rightleftharpoons 2HF(g)$$

the units for K and K_p can be found as follows:

$$K = \frac{C_{HF}^2}{(C_{H_2})(C_{F_2})} = \frac{(\text{mol/L})^2}{(\text{mol/L})(\text{mol/L})} \Rightarrow \text{no units}$$

$$K_p = \frac{P_{HF}^2}{(P_{H_2})(P_{F_2})} = \frac{(\text{atm})^2}{(\text{atm})(\text{atm})} \Rightarrow \text{no units}$$

For this reaction, neither K nor K_p has units, and K is equal to K_p. The identical powers in the numerator and denominator cause the units to cancel. For equilibrium expressions in which the sum of the powers in the numerator and denominator are not the same, the equilibrium constants will have units and K will not equal K_p. You should note, however, that the units are often omitted when equilibrium constants are listed in tables.

The equilibrium constants used in this chapter involve *observed* concentrations and pressures. These K values have units (unless the units cancel because the sums of the powers in the numerator and denominator are the same). However, when corrections are made for nonideal behavior, the resulting equilibrium constants (called **thermodynamic equilibrium constants**) are unitless. Thus it is quite common to see K values given without units. (*See* F. G. Helfferich, Letter to the Editor, *J. Chem. Ed.* **64** (1987): 1069.)

13.4 Heterogeneous Equilibria

Purpose

• To show how condensed phases are treated in constructing the equilibrium expression.

So far we have discussed equilibria only for systems in the gas phase, where all reactants and products are gases. These are **homogeneous equilibria.** However, many equilibria involve more than one phase and are called **heterogeneous equilibria.** For example, the thermal decomposition of calcium carbonate in the commer-

Lime is among the top five chemicals manufactured in the United States in terms of the amount produced.

cial preparation of lime occurs by a reaction involving both solid and gas phases:

$$CaCO_3(s) \rightleftharpoons CaO(s) + CO_2(g)$$

$$\uparrow$$
$$\text{Lime}$$

Straightforward application of the law of mass action leads to the equilibrium expression

$$K' = \frac{[CO_2][CaO]}{[CaCO_3]}$$

The concentrations of pure liquids and solids are constant.

However, experimental results show that the *position of a heterogeneous equilibrium does not depend on the amounts of pure solids or liquids present*. The fundamental reason for this behavior is that the concentrations of pure solids and liquids cannot change. Thus the equilibrium expression for the decomposition of solid calcium carbonate might be represented as

$$K' = \frac{[CO_2]C_1}{C_2}$$

where C_1 and C_2 are constants representing the concentrations of the solids CaO and $CaCO_3$, respectively. This expression can be rearranged to give

$$\frac{C_2 K'}{C_1} = K = [CO_2]$$

We can generalize from this result as follows. If pure solids or pure liquids are involved in a chemical reaction, their concentrations *are not included in the equilibrium expression* for the reaction. This simplification occurs *only* with pure solids or liquids, not with solutions or gases, since in these last two cases the concentrations can vary.

For example, in the decomposition of liquid water to gaseous hydrogen and oxygen,

$$2H_2O(l) \rightleftharpoons 2H_2(g) + O_2(g)$$

where

$$K = [H_2]^2[O_2] \quad \text{and} \quad K_p = (P_{H_2}{}^2)(P_{O_2})$$

water is not included in either equilibrium expression because it is a pure liquid. However, if the reaction were carried out under conditions where the water is a gas rather than a liquid, that is,

$$2H_2O(g) \rightleftharpoons 2H_2(g) + O_2(g)$$

then

$$K = \frac{[H_2]^2[O_2]}{[H_2O]^2} \quad \text{and} \quad K_p = \frac{(P_{H_2}{}^2)(P_{O_2})}{P_{H_2O}{}^2}$$

because the concentration or pressure of water vapor can change.

Sample Exercise 13.6

Write the expressions for K and K_p for the following processes:

a. The decomposition of solid phosphorus pentachloride to liquid phosphorus trichloride and chlorine gas.

b. Deep blue solid copper(II) sulfate pentahydrate is heated to drive off water vapor to form white solid copper(II) sulfate.

Hydrated copper(II) sulfate on the left. Water applied to anhydrous copper(II) sulfate, on the right, forms the hydrated compound.

Solution

a. The reaction is

$$PCl_5(s) \rightleftharpoons PCl_3(l) + Cl_2(g)$$

The equilibrium expressions are

$$K = [Cl_2] \quad \text{and} \quad K_p = P_{Cl_2}$$

In this case neither the pure solid PCl_5 nor the pure liquid PCl_3 is included in the equilibrium expressions.

b. The reaction is

$$CuSO_4 \cdot 5H_2O(s) \rightleftharpoons CuSO_4(s) + 5H_2O(g)$$

The equilibrium expressions are

$$K = [H_2O]^5 \quad \text{and} \quad K_p = P_{H_2O}{}^5$$

The solids are not included.

13.5 *Applications of the Equilibrium Constant*

Purpose

- To show how the equilibrium constant is used to predict the direction a system will move to reach equilibrium.
- To demonstrate the calculation of equilibrium concentrations given initial concentrations.

[handwritten notes in margin: "Products" "K > 1 = right" "K < 1 = left" "reactants"]

Knowing the equilibrium constant for a reaction allows us to predict several important features of the reaction: the tendency of the reaction to occur (but not the speed of the reaction), whether or not a given set of concentrations represents an equilibrium condition, and the equilibrium position that will be achieved from a given set of initial concentrations.

The Extent of a Reaction

(a)

(b)

Figure 13.4

(a) A physical analogy illustrating the difference between thermodynamic and kinetic stabilities. The boulder is thermodynamically more stable (lower potential energy) in position B than in position A but cannot get over the hump H.
(b) The reactants H_2 and O_2 have a strong tendency to form H_2O. That is, H_2O has lower energy than H_2 and O_2. However, the large activation energy E_a prevents the reaction at 25°C. In other words, the magnitude of K for the reaction depends on ΔE, but the reaction rate depends on E_a.

The inherent tendency for a reaction to occur is indicated by the magnitude of the equilibrium constant. A value of K much larger than 1 means that at equilibrium the reaction system will consist of mostly products—the equilibrium lies to the right. Another way of saying this is that reactions with very large equilibrium constants go essentially to completion. On the other hand, a very small value of K means that the system at equilibrium will consist of mostly reactants—the equilibrium position is far to the left. The given reaction does not occur to any significant extent.

It is important to understand that *the size of K and the time required to reach equilibrium are not directly related.* The time required to achieve equilibrium depends on the reaction rate, which is determined by the size of the activation energy. The size of K is determined by thermodynamic factors such as the difference in energy between products and reactants. This difference is represented in Fig. 13.4 and will be discussed in detail in Chapter 16.

Reaction Quotient

When reactants and products of a given chemical reaction are mixed, it is useful to know whether the mixture is at equilibrium or, if not, the direction in which the system will shift to reach equilibrium. If the concentration of one of the reactants or products is zero, the system will shift in the direction that produces the missing component. However, if all the initial concentrations are nonzero, it is more difficult to determine the direction of the move toward equilibrium. To determine the shift in such cases, we use the **reaction quotient Q.** The reaction quotient is obtained by applying the law of mass action using *initial concentrations* instead of equilibrium concentrations. For example, for the synthesis of ammonia

$$N_2(g) + 3H_2(g) \rightleftharpoons 2NH_3(g)$$

the expression for the reaction quotient is

$$Q = \frac{[NH_3]_0^2}{[N_2]_0[H_2]_0^3}$$

where the subscript zeros indicate initial concentrations.

To determine in which direction a system will shift to reach equilibrium, we compare the values of Q and K. There are three possible cases:

1. Q *is equal to* K. The system is at equilibrium; no shift will occur.
2. Q *is greater than* K. In this case, the ratio of initial concentrations of products to initial concentrations of reactants is too large. To reach equilibrium, a net change of products to reactants must occur. The system *shifts to the left,* consuming products and forming reactants, until equilibrium is achieved.
3. Q *is less than* K. In this case, the ratio of initial concentrations of products to initial concentrations of reactants is too small. The *system must shift to the right,* consuming reactants and forming products, to attain equilibrium.

Sample Exercise 13.7

For the synthesis of ammonia at 500°C, the equilibrium constant is 6.0×10^{-2} L^2/mol^2. Predict the direction in which the system will shift to reach equilibrium in each of the following cases:

a. $[NH_3]_0 = 1.0 \times 10^{-3}\ M$; $[N_2]_0 = 1.0 \times 10^{-5}\ M$; $[H_2]_0 = 2.0 \times 10^{-3}\ M$
b. $[NH_3]_0 = 2.00 \times 10^{-4}\ M$; $[N_2]_0 = 1.50 \times 10^{-5}\ M$; $[H_2]_0 = 3.54 \times 10^{-1}\ M$
c. $[NH_3]_0 = 1.0 \times 10^{-4}\ M$; $[N_2]_0 = 5.0\ M$; $[H_2]_0 = 1.0 \times 10^{-2}\ M$

Solution

a. First we calculate the value of Q:

$$Q = \frac{[NH_3]_0^2}{[N_2]_0[H_2]_0^3} = \frac{(1.0 \times 10^{-3}\ mol/L)^2}{(1.0 \times 10^{-5}\ mol/L)(2.0 \times 10^{-3}\ mol/L)^3}$$
$$= 1.3 \times 10^7\ L^2/mol^2$$

Since $K = 6.0 \times 10^{-2}\ L^2/mol^2$, Q is much greater than K. To attain equilibrium, the concentrations of the products must be decreased and the concentrations of the reactants increased. The system will shift to the left:

$$N_2 + 3H_2 \leftarrow 2NH_3$$

b. We calculate the value of Q:

$$Q = \frac{[NH_3]_0^2}{[N_2]_0[H_2]_0^3} = \frac{(2.00 \times 10^{-4}\ mol/L)^2}{(1.50 \times 10^{-5}\ mol/L)(3.54 \times 10^{-1}\ mol/L)^3}$$
$$= 6.01 \times 10^{-2}\ L^2/mol^2$$

In this case $Q = K$, so the system is at equilibrium. No shift will occur.

c. The value of Q is

$$Q = \frac{[NH_3]_0^2}{[N_2]_0[H_2]_0^3} = \frac{(1.0 \times 10^{-4}\ mol/L)^2}{(5.0\ mol/L)(1.0 \times 10^{-2}\ mol/L)^3}$$
$$= 2.0 \times 10^{-3}\ L^2/mol^2$$

Here Q is less than K, so the system will shift to the right to attain equilibrium by increasing the concentration of the product and decreasing the reactant concentrations:

$$N_2 + 3H_2 \rightarrow 2NH_3$$

Calculating Equilibrium Pressures and Concentrations

A typical equilibrium problem involves finding the equilibrium concentrations (or pressures) of reactants and products, given the value of the equilibrium constant and the initial concentrations (or pressures). However, since such problems sometimes become complicated mathematically, we will develop useful strategies for solving them by considering cases for which we know one or more of the equilibrium concentrations (or pressures).

Sample Exercise 13.8

Dinitrogen tetroxide in its liquid state was used as one of the fuels on the lunar lander for the NASA Apollo missions. In the gas phase it decomposes to gaseous nitrogen dioxide:

$$N_2O_4(g) \rightleftharpoons 2NO_2(g)$$

Consider an experiment in which gaseous N_2O_4 was placed in a flask and allowed to reach equilibrium at a temperature where $K_p = 0.133$ atm. At equilibrium, the pressure of N_2O_4 was found to be 2.71 atm. Calculate the equilibrium pressure of $NO_2(g)$.

Solution

We know that the equilibrium pressures of the gases NO_2 and N_2O_4 must satisfy the relationship

$$K_p = \frac{P_{NO_2}^2}{P_{N_2O_4}} = 0.133 \text{ atm}$$

Since we know $P_{N_2O_4}$, we can simply solve for P_{NO_2}:

$$P_{NO_2}^2 = K_p(P_{N_2O_4}) = (0.133 \text{ atm})(2.71 \text{ atm}) = 0.360 \text{ atm}^2$$

Therefore, $\qquad\qquad P_{NO_2} = \sqrt{0.360 \text{ atm}^2} = 0.600 \text{ atm}$

Sample Exercise 13.9

At a certain temperature a 1.00-L flask initially contained 0.298 mol $PCl_3(g)$ and 8.70×10^{-3} mol $PCl_5(g)$. After the system had reached equilibrium, 2.00×10^{-3} mol $Cl_2(g)$ was found in the flask. Gaseous PCl_5 decomposes according to the reaction

$$PCl_5(g) \rightleftharpoons PCl_3(g) + Cl_2(g)$$

Calculate the equilibrium concentrations of all species and the value of K.

Solution

The equilibrium expression for this reaction is

$$K = \frac{[Cl_2][PCl_3]}{[PCl_5]}$$

To find the value of K, we must calculate the equilibrium concentrations of all species and then substitute these quantities into the equilibrium expression. The best method for finding the equilibrium concentrations is to begin with the initial concentrations, which we will define as the concentrations before any shift toward equilibrium has occurred. We will then modify these initial concentrations appropriately to find the equilibrium concentrations.

The initial concentrations are

$$[Cl_2]_0 = 0$$

$$[PCl_3]_0 = \frac{0.298 \text{ mol}}{1.00 \text{ L}} = 0.298 \ M$$

$$[PCl_5]_0 = \frac{8.70 \times 10^{-3} \text{ mol}}{1.00 \text{ L}} = 8.70 \times 10^{-3} \ M$$

Next, we find the change required to reach equilibrium. Since no Cl_2 was initially present but $2.00 \times 10^{-3} \ M \ Cl_2$ is present at equilibrium, 2.00×10^{-3} mol PCl_5 must have decomposed to form 2.00×10^{-3} mol Cl_2 and 2.00×10^{-3} mol PCl_3. In other words, to reach equilibrium, the reaction shifted to the right:

$$PCl_5(g) \quad \rightarrow \quad PCl_3(g) \quad + \quad Cl_2(g)$$
$$2.00 \times 10^{-3} \text{ mol} \rightarrow 2.00 \times 10^{-3} \text{ mol} + 2.00 \times 10^{-3} \text{ mol}$$

Net amount of PCl_5 decomposed

Net amounts of products formed

Now we apply this change to the initial concentrations to obtain the equilibrium concentrations:

$$[Cl_2] = 0 + \frac{2.00 \times 10^{-3} \text{ mol}}{1.00 \text{ L}} = 2.00 \times 10^{-3} \ M$$

$[Cl_2]_0$

$$[PCl_3] = 0.298 \ M + \frac{2.00 \times 10^{-3} \text{ mol}}{1.00 \text{ L}} = 0.300 \ M$$

$[PCl_3]_0$

$$[PCl_5] = 8.70 \times 10^{-3} \ M - \frac{2.00 \times 10^{-3} \text{ mol}}{1.00 \text{ L}} = 6.70 \times 10^{-3} \ M$$

$[PCl_5]_0$

These equilibrium concentrations can now be used to find K:

$$K = \frac{[Cl_2][PCl_3]}{[PCl_5]} = \frac{(2.00 \times 10^{-3} \text{ mol/L})(0.300 \text{ mol/L})}{6.70 \times 10^{-3} \text{ mol/L}}$$

$$= 8.96 \times 10^{-2} \text{ mol/L}$$

Sometimes we are not given any of the equilibrium concentrations (or pressures), only the initial values. Then we must use the stoichiometry of the reaction to express concentrations (or pressures) at equilibrium in terms of the initial values. This is illustrated in Sample Exercise 13.10.

Sample Exercise 13.10

Carbon monoxide reacts with steam to produce carbon dioxide and hydrogen. At 700 K the equilibrium constant is 5.10. Calculate the equilibrium concentrations of all species if 1.000 mol of each component is mixed in a 1.000-L flask.

Solution

The balanced equation for the reaction is

$$CO(g) + H_2O(g) \rightleftharpoons CO_2(g) + H_2(g)$$

and

$$K = \frac{[CO_2][H_2]}{[CO][H_2O]} = 5.10$$

Next, we calculate the initial concentrations:

$$[CO]_0 = [H_2O]_0 = [CO_2]_0 = [H_2]_0 = \frac{1.000 \text{ mol}}{1.000 \text{ L}} = 1.000 \, M$$

Is the system at equilibrium, and if not, which way will it shift to reach the equilibrium position? These questions can be answered by calculating Q:

$$Q = \frac{[CO_2]_0[H_2]_0}{[CO]_0[H_2O]_0} = \frac{(1.000 \text{ mol/L})(1.000 \text{ mol/L})}{(1.000 \text{ mol/L})(1.000 \text{ mol/L})} = 1.000$$

Since Q is less than K, the system is not initially at equilibrium but must shift to the right.

What are the equilibrium concentrations? As before, we start with the initial concentrations and modify them to obtain the equilibrium concentrations. We must ask this question: how much will the system shift to the right to attain the equilibrium condition? In Sample Exercise 13.9 the change needed for the system to reach equilibrium was given. However, in this case we do not have this information.

Since the required change in concentrations is unknown at this point, we will define it in terms of x. Let's assume that x mol/L CO must react for the system to reach equilibrium. This means that the initial concentration of CO will decrease by x mol/L:

$$[CO] = [CO]_0 - x$$

       ↑   ↑   ↑

Equilibrium   Initial   Change

Since each CO molecule reacts with one H_2O molecule, the concentration of water vapor also must decrease by x mol/L:

$$[H_2O] = [H_2O]_0 - x$$

As the reactant concentrations decrease, the product concentrations increase. Since all the coefficients are 1 in the balanced reaction, 1 mol CO reacting with 1 mol H_2O will produce 1 mol CO_2 and 1 mol H_2. Or in the present case, to reach equilibrium, x mol/L CO will react with x mol/L H_2O to give an additional x mol/L CO_2 and x mol/L H_2:

$$xCO + xH_2O \rightarrow xCO_2 + xH_2$$

Thus the initial concentrations of CO_2 and H_2 will increase by x mol/L:

$$[CO_2] = [CO_2]_0 + x$$
$$[H_2] = [H_2]_0 + x$$

Now we have all the equilibrium concentrations defined in terms of the initial concentrations and the change x:

Initial Concentration (mol/L)	Change (mol/L)	Equilibrium Concentration (mol/L)
$[CO]_0 = 1.000$	$-x$	$1.000 - x$
$[H_2O]_0 = 1.000$	$-x$	$1.000 - x$
$[CO_2]_0 = 1.000$	$+x$	$1.000 + x$
$[H_2]_0 = 1.000$	$+x$	$1.000 + x$

Note that the sign of x is determined by the direction of the shift. In this example, the system shifts to the right, so the product concentrations increase and the reactant concentrations decrease. Also note that because the coefficients in the balanced equation are all 1, the magnitude of the change is the same for all species.

Now since we know that the equilibrium concentrations must satisfy the equilibrium expression, we can find the value of x by substituting these concentrations into the expression

$$K = 5.10 = \frac{[CO_2][H_2]}{[CO][H_2O]} = \frac{(1.000 + x)(1.000 + x)}{(1.000 - x)(1.000 - x)} = \frac{(1.000 + x)^2}{(1.000 - x)^2}$$

Since the right side of the equation is a perfect square, the solution of the problem can be simplified by taking the square root of both sides:

$$\sqrt{5.10} = 2.26 = \frac{1.000 + x}{1.000 - x}$$

Multiplying and collecting terms gives

$$x = 0.387 \text{ mol/L}$$

Thus the system shifts to the right, consuming 0.387 mol/L CO and 0.387 mol/L H_2O and forming 0.387 mol/L CO_2 and 0.387 mol/L H_2.

Now the equilibrium concentrations can be calculated:

$$[CO] = [H_2O] = 1.000 - x = 1.000 - 0.387 = 0.613 \text{ } M$$
$$[CO_2] = [H_2] = 1.000 + x = 1.000 + 0.387 = 1.387 \text{ } M$$

CHECK: These values can be checked by substituting them back into the equilibrium expression to make sure they give the correct value for K:

$$K = \frac{[CO_2][H_2]}{[CO][H_2O]} = \frac{(1.387)^2}{(0.613)^2} = 5.12$$

This result is the same as the given value of K (5.10) within round-off error, so the answer must be correct.

Sample Exercise 13.11

Assume that the reaction for the formation of gaseous hydrogen fluoride from hydrogen and fluorine has an equilibrium constant of 1.15×10^2 at a certain temperature. In a particular experiment, 3.000 mol of each component was added to a 1.500-L flask. Calculate the equilibrium concentrations of all species.

Solution

The balanced equation for the reaction is

$$H_2(g) + F_2(g) \rightleftharpoons 2HF(g)$$

The equilibrium expression is

$$K = 1.15 \times 10^2 = \frac{[HF]^2}{[H_2][F_2]}$$

We first calculate the initial concentrations:

$$[HF]_0 = [H_2]_0 = [F_2]_0 = \frac{3.000 \text{ mol}}{1.500 \text{ L}} = 2.000 \ M$$

Then we find the value of Q:

$$Q = \frac{[HF]_0^2}{[H_2]_0[F_2]_0} = \frac{(2.000)^2}{(2.000)(2.000)} = 1.000$$

Since Q is much less than K, the system must shift to the right to reach equilibrium.

What change in the concentrations is necessary? Since this is presently unknown, we will define the change needed in terms of x. Let x equal the number of moles per liter of H_2 consumed to reach equilibrium. The stoichiometry of the reaction shows that x mol/L F_2 also will be consumed and $2x$ mol/L HF will be formed:

$$H_2(g) \quad + \quad F_2(g) \quad \rightarrow \quad 2HF(g)$$
$$x \text{ mol/L} + x \text{ mol/L} \rightarrow 2x \text{ mol/L}$$

Now the equilibrium concentrations can be expressed in terms of x:

Initial Concentration (mol/L)	Change (mol/L)	Equilibrium Concentration (mol/L)
$[H_2]_0 = 2.000$	$-x$	$[H_2] = 2.000 - x$
$[F_2]_0 = 2.000$	$-x$	$[F_2] = 2.000 - x$
$[HF]_0 = 2.000$	$+2x$	$[HF] = 2.000 + 2x$

To solve for x, we substitute the equilibrium concentrations into the equilibrium expression:

$$K = 1.15 \times 10^2 = \frac{[HF]^2}{[H_2][F_2]} = \frac{(2.000 + 2x)^2}{(2.000 - x)^2}$$

The right side of this equation is a perfect square, so taking the square root of both sides gives

$$\sqrt{1.15 \times 10^2} = \frac{2.000 + 2x}{2.000 - x}$$

which yields $x = 1.528$. The equilibrium concentrations can now be calculated:

$$[H_2] = [F_2] = 2.000 \ M - x = 0.472 \ M$$
$$[HF] = 2.000 \ M + 2x = 5.056 \ M$$

CHECK: Checking these values by substituting them into the equilibrium expression gives

$$\frac{[HF]^2}{[H_2][F_2]} = \frac{(5.056)^2}{(0.472)^2} = 1.15 \times 10^2$$

which agrees with the given value of K.

13.6 Solving Equilibrium Problems

Purpose

- To generalize the procedure for doing equilibrium calculations.

We have already considered most of the strategies needed to solve equilibrium problems. The typical procedure for analyzing a chemical equilibrium problem can be summarized:

Procedure for Solving Equilibrium Problems

- Write the balanced equation for the reaction.
- Write the equilibrium expression using the law of mass action.
- List the initial concentrations.
- Calculate Q, and determine the direction of the shift to equilibrium.
- Define the change needed to reach equilibrium, and define the equilibrium concentrations by applying the change to the initial concentrations.
- Substitute the equilibrium concentrations into the equilibrium expression, and solve for the unknown.
- Check your calculated equilibrium concentrations by making sure they give the correct value of K.

So far we have been careful to choose systems in which we can solve for the unknown by taking the square root of both sides of the equation. However, this type of system is not really very common, and we must now consider a more typical problem. Suppose for a synthesis of hydrogen fluoride from hydrogen and fluorine, 3.000 mol H_2 and 6.000 mol F_2 are mixed in a 3.000-L flask. Assume that the equilibrium constant for the synthesis reaction at this temperature is 1.15×10^2. We calculate the equilibrium concentration of each component as follows:

STEP 1

We begin, as usual, by writing the balanced equation for the reaction:

$$H_2(g) + F_2(g) \rightleftharpoons 2HF(g)$$

STEP 2

The equilibrium expression is

$$K = 1.15 \times 10^2 = \frac{[HF]^2}{[H_2][F_2]}$$

STEP 3

The initial concentrations are

$$[H_2]_0 = \frac{3.000 \text{ mol}}{3.000 \text{ L}} = 1.000 \ M$$

$$[F_2]_0 = \frac{6.000 \text{ mol}}{3.000 \text{ L}} = 2.000 \ M$$

$$[HF]_0 = 0$$

STEP 4

There is no need to calculate Q, since no HF is initially present, and we know that the system must shift to the right to reach equilibrium.

STEP 5

If we let x represent the number of moles per liter of H_2 consumed to reach equilibrium, we can represent the equilibrium concentrations as follows:

Initial Concentration (mol/L)	Change (mol/L)	Equilibrium Concentration (mol/L)
$[H_2]_0 = 1.000$	$-x$	$[H_2] = 1.000 - x$
$[F_2]_0 = 2.000$	$-x$	$[F_2] = 2.000 - x$
$[HF]_0 = 0$	$+2x$	$[HF] = 0 + 2x$

STEP 6

Substituting the equilibrium concentrations into the equilibrium expression gives

$$K = 1.15 \times 10^2 = \frac{[HF]^2}{[H_2][F_2]} = \frac{(2x)^2}{(1.000 - x)(2.000 - x)}$$

Since the right side of this equation is not a perfect square, we cannot take the square root of both sides, but must use some other procedure.

First, do the indicated multiplication:

$$(1.000 - x)(2.000 - x)(1.15 \times 10^2) = (2x)^2$$

or $(1.15 \times 10^2)x^2 - 3.000(1.15 \times 10^2)x + 2.000(1.15 \times 10^2) = 4x^2$

and collect terms

$$(1.11 \times 10^2)x^2 - (3.45 \times 10^2)x + 2.30 \times 10^2 = 0$$

This is a quadratic equation of the general form

$$ax^2 + bx + c = 0$$

Use of the quadratic formula is explained in Appendix 1.4.

where the roots can be obtained from the quadratic formula:

$$x = \frac{-b \pm \sqrt{b^2 - 4ac}}{2a}$$

In this example, $a = 1.11 \times 10^2$, $b = -3.45 \times 10^2$, and $c = 2.30 \times 10^2$. Substituting these values into the quadratic formula gives two values for x:

$$x = 2.14 \text{ mol/L} \quad \text{and} \quad x = 0.968 \text{ mol/L}$$

Both these results cannot be valid (since a *given* set of initial concentrations leads to only *one* equilibrium position). How can we choose between them? Since the expression for the equilibrium concentration of H_2 is

$$[H_2] = 1.000 \ M - x$$

the value of x cannot be 2.14 mol/L (because subtracting 2.14 M from 1.000 M gives a negative concentration of H_2, which is physically impossible). Thus the correct value for x is 0.968 mol/L, and the equilibrium concentrations are as follows:

$$[H_2] = 1.000 \ M - 0.968 \ M = 3.2 \times 10^{-2} \ M$$
$$[F_2] = 2.000 \ M - 0.968 \ M = 1.032 \ M$$
$$[HF] = 2(0.968 \ M) = 1.936 \ M$$

STEP 7

We can check these concentrations by substituting them into the equilibrium expression:

$$\frac{[HF]^2}{[H_2][F_2]} = \frac{(1.936)^2}{(3.2 \times 10^{-2})(1.032)} = 1.13 \times 10^2$$

This value is in close agreement with the given value for K (1.15×10^2), so the calculated equilibrium concentrations are correct.

This procedure is further illustrated for a problem involving pressures in Sample Exercise 13.12.

Sample Exercise 13.12

Assume that gaseous hydrogen iodide is synthesized from hydrogen gas and iodine vapor at a temperature where the equilibrium constant is 1.00×10^2. Suppose HI at 5.000×10^{-1} atm, H_2 at 1.000×10^{-2} atm, and I_2 at 5.000×10^{-3} atm are mixed in a 5.000-L flask. Calculate the equilibrium pressures of all species.

Solution

The balanced equation for this process is

$$H_2(g) + I_2(g) \rightleftharpoons 2HI(g)$$

and the equilibrium expression in terms of pressure is

$$K_p = \frac{P_{HI}^2}{(P_{H_2})(P_{I_2})} = 1.00 \times 10^2$$

The given initial pressures are

$$P_{HI}^0 = 5.000 \times 10^{-1} \text{ atm}$$
$$P_{H_2}^0 = 1.000 \times 10^{-2} \text{ atm}$$
$$P_{I_2}^0 = 5.000 \times 10^{-3} \text{ atm}$$

The value of Q for this system is

$$Q = \frac{(P_{HI}^0)^2}{(P_{H_2}^0)(P_{I_2}^0)} = \frac{(5.000 \times 10^{-1} \text{ atm})^2}{(1.000 \times 10^{-2} \text{ atm})(5.000 \times 10^{-3} \text{ atm})} = 5.000 \times 10^3$$

Since Q is greater than K, the system will shift to the left to reach equilibrium.

So far we have used moles or concentrations in stoichiometric calculations. However, it is equally valid to use pressures for a gas-phase system at constant temperature and volume because in this case pressure is directly proportional to the number of moles:

$$P = n\left(\frac{RT}{V}\right) \quad \longleftarrow \text{Constant if constant } T \text{ and } V$$

Thus we can represent the change needed to achieve equilibrium in terms of pressures.

Let x be the change in pressure (in atm) of H_2 as the system shifts left toward equilibrium. This leads to the following equilibrium pressures:

Initial Pressure (atm)	Change (atm)	Equilibrium Pressure (atm)
$P_{HI}^0 = 5.000 \times 10^{-1}$	$-2x$	$P_{HI} = 5.000 \times 10^{-1} - 2x$
$P_{H_2}^0 = 1.000 \times 10^{-2}$	$+x$	$P_{H_2} = 1.000 \times 10^{-2} + x$
$P_{I_2}^0 = 5.000 \times 10^{-3}$	$+x$	$P_{I_2} = 5.000 \times 10^{-3} + x$

Substitution into the equilibrium expression gives

$$K_p = \frac{(P_{HI})^2}{(P_{H_2})(P_{I_2})} = \frac{(5.000 \times 10^{-1} - 2x)^2}{(1.000 \times 10^{-2} + x)(5.000 \times 10^{-3} + x)}$$

Multiplying and collecting terms yields the quadratic equation where $a = 9.60 \times 10^1$, $b = 3.5$, and $c = -2.45 \times 10^{-1}$:

$$(9.60 \times 10^1)x^2 + 3.5x - (2.45 \times 10^{-1}) = 0$$

From the quadratic formula, the correct value for x is $x = 3.55 \times 10^{-2}$ atm. The equilibrium pressures can now be calculated from the expressions involving x:

$$P_{HI} = 5.000 \times 10^{-1} \text{ atm} - 2(3.55 \times 10^{-2}) \text{ atm} = 4.29 \times 10^{-1} \text{ atm}$$
$$P_{H_2} = 1.000 \times 10^{-2} \text{ atm} + 3.55 \times 10^{-2} \text{ atm} = 4.55 \times 10^{-2} \text{ atm}$$
$$P_{I_2} = 5.000 \times 10^{-3} \text{ atm} + 3.55 \times 10^{-2} \text{ atm} = 4.05 \times 10^{-2} \text{ atm}$$

CHECK:

$$\frac{P_{HI}^2}{P_{H_2} \cdot P_{I_2}} = \frac{(4.29 \times 10^{-1})^2}{(4.55 \times 10^{-2})(4.05 \times 10^{-2})} = 99.9$$

This agrees with the given value of K (1.00×10^2), so the calculated equilibrium concentrations are correct.

Treating Systems That Have Small Equilibrium Constants

We have seen that fairly complicated calculations are often necessary to solve equilibrium problems. However, under certain conditions, simplifications are possible that greatly reduce the mathematical difficulties. For example, gaseous NOCl decomposes to form the gases NO and Cl_2. At 35°C the equilibrium constant is 1.6×10^{-5} mol/L. In an experiment in which 1.0 mol NOCl is placed in a 2.0-L flask, what are the equilibrium concentrations?

The balanced equation is

$$2NOCl(g) \rightleftharpoons 2NO(g) + Cl_2(g)$$

and

$$K = \frac{[NO]^2[Cl_2]}{[NOCl]^2} = 1.6 \times 10^{-5} \text{ mol/L}$$

The initial concentrations are

$$[NOCl]_0 = \frac{1.0 \text{ mol}}{2.0 \text{ L}} = 0.50 \ M \qquad [NO]_0 = 0 \qquad [Cl_2]_0 = 0$$

Since there are no products initially, the system will move to the right to reach equilibrium. We will define x as the change in concentration of Cl_2 needed to reach equilibrium. The changes in the concentrations of NOCl and NO can then be obtained from the balanced equation:

$$2NOCl(g) \rightarrow 2NO(g) + Cl_2(g)$$
$$2x \quad \rightarrow \quad 2x \quad + \quad x$$

The concentrations can be summarized as follows:

Initial Concentration (mol/L)	Change (mol/L)	Equilibrium Concentration (mol/L)
$[NOCl]_0 = 0.50$	$-2x$	$[NOCl] = 0.50 - 2x$
$[NO]_0 = 0$	$+2x$	$[NO] = 0 + 2x = 2x$
$[Cl_2]_0 = 0$	$+x$	$[Cl_2] = 0 + x = x$

The equilibrium concentrations must satisfy the equilibrium expression:

$$K = 1.6 \times 10^{-5} = \frac{[NO]^2[Cl_2]}{[NOCl]^2} = \frac{(2x)^2(x)}{(0.50 - 2x)^2}$$

Multiplying and collecting terms will give an equation with terms containing x^3, x^2, and x, which requires complicated methods to solve directly. However, we can avoid this situation by recognizing that since K is so small (1.6×10^{-5} mol/L), the system will not proceed far to the right to reach equilibrium. That is, x *represents a relatively small number*. The consequence of this fact is that the term $(0.50 - 2x)$ can be approximated by 0.50. That is, when x is small,

$$0.50 - 2x \approx 0.50$$

Making this approximation allows us to simplify the equilibrium expression:

Approximations can simplify complicated math, but their validity should be carefully checked.

$$1.6 \times 10^{-5} = \frac{(2x)^2(x)}{(0.50 - 2x)^2} \approx \frac{(2x)^2(x)}{(0.50)^2} = \frac{4x^3}{(0.50)^2}$$

Solving for x^3 gives

$$x^3 = \frac{(1.6 \times 10^{-5})(0.50)^2}{4} = 1.0 \times 10^{-6}$$

and $x = 1.0 \times 10^{-2}$ (mol/L).

How valid is this approximation? If $x = 1.0 \times 10^{-2}$, then

$$0.50 - 2x = 0.50 - 2(1.0 \times 10^{-2}) = 0.48$$

The difference between 0.50 and 0.48 is 0.02, or 4% of the initial concentration of NOCl, a relatively small discrepancy that will have little effect on the outcome. That is, since $2x$ is very small compared to 0.50, the value of x obtained in the approximate solution should be very close to the exact value. We use this approximate value of x to calculate the equilibrium concentrations:

$$[NOCl] = 0.50 - 2x \approx 0.50 \ M$$
$$[NO] = 2x = 2(1.0 \times 10^{-2} \ M) = 2.0 \times 10^{-2} \ M$$
$$[Cl_2] = x = 1.0 \times 10^{-2} \ M$$

CHECK:

$$\frac{[NO]^2[Cl_2]}{[NOCl]^2} = \frac{(2.0 \times 10^{-2})^2(1.0 \times 10^{-2})}{(0.50)^2} = 1.6 \times 10^{-5}$$

Since the given value of K is 1.6×10^{-5}, these calculated concentrations are correct.

This problem was much easier to solve than it appeared at first because the *small value of K and the resulting small shift to the right to reach equilibrium allowed simplification.* A similar problem is handled in Sample Exercise 13.13.

Sample Exercise 13.13

Gaseous phosphorus pentachloride decomposes to gaseous phosphorus trichloride and chlorine at a temperature where $K = 1.00 \times 10^{-3}$ mol/L. Suppose 2.00 mol of phosphorus pentachloride in a 2.00-L vessel is allowed to come to equilibrium. Calculate the equilibrium concentrations of all species.

Solution

The balanced equation and equilibrium expression are

$$PCl_5(g) \rightleftharpoons PCl_3(g) + Cl_2(g)$$
$$K = 1.00 \times 10^{-3} = \frac{[PCl_3][Cl_2]}{[PCl_5]}$$

The concentrations are

Initial Concentration (mol/L)	Change (mol/L)	Equilibrium Concentration (mol/L)
$[PCl_5]_0 = 2.000 \ \text{mol}/2.00 \ \text{L} = 1.00$	$-x$	$[PCl_5] = 1.00 - x$
$[PCl_3]_0 = 0$	$+x$	$[PCl_3] = 0 + x$
$[Cl_2]_0 = 0$	$+x$	$[Cl_2] = 0 + x$

Substitution in the equilibrium expression gives

$$K = 1.00 \times 10^{-3} = \frac{[PCl_3][Cl_2]}{[PCl_5]} = \frac{(x)(x)}{1.00 - x} \approx \frac{x^2}{1.00}$$

Note that since K is small, we can assume, at least temporarily, that the change in concentration of PCl_5 is negligible. The approximate value of x is then obtained as follows:

$$x^2 \approx (1.00)(1.00 \times 10^{-3})$$
$$x \approx 3.16 \times 10^{-2}$$

Now we must check the validity of this approximation. Since $x = 3.16 \times 10^{-2}$,

$$1.00 - x = 1.00 - 0.03 = 0.97$$

Thus $1.00 - x \approx 1.00$ is a good approximation. This is a relatively small difference that will have little effect on the calculated value of x. The equilibrium concentrations therefore are

$$[PCl_5] = 1.00 - x = 0.97\ M \approx 1.00\ M$$
$$[Cl_2] = [PCl_3] = x = 3.16 \times 10^{-2}\ M$$

CHECK:

$$\frac{[Cl_2][PCl_3]}{[PCl_5]} = \frac{(3.16 \times 10^{-2})(3.16 \times 10^{-2})}{1.00} = 1.00 \times 10^{-3}$$

This agrees with the given value of K.

13.7 Le Châtelier's Principle

Purpose

- To show how to predict the changes that occur when a system at equilibrium is disturbed.

It is important to understand the factors that control the *position* of a chemical equilibrium. For example, when a chemical is manufactured, the chemists and chemical engineers in charge of production want to choose conditions that favor the desired product as much as possible. That is, they want the equilibrium to lie far to the right. When Fritz Haber was developing the process for the synthesis of ammonia, he did extensive studies on how temperature and pressure affect the equilibrium concentration of ammonia. Some of his results are given in Table 13.2. Note that the equilibrium amount of NH_3 increases with an increase in pressure but decreases as the temperature is increased. Thus the amount of NH_3 present at equilibrium is favored by conditions of low temperature and high pressure.

However, this is not the whole story. Carrying out the process at low temperatures is not feasible, because then the reaction is too slow. Even though the equilibrium tends to shift to the right as the temperature is lowered, the attainment of equilibrium would be much too slow at low temperatures to be practical. This emphasizes once again that we must study both the thermodynamics and the kinetics of a reaction before we really understand the factors that control it.

We can qualitatively predict the effects of changes in concentration, pressure, and temperature on a system at equilibrium by using **Le Châtelier's principle,** which states that *if a change is imposed on a system at equilibrium, the position of*

Table 13.2			
The Percent by Mass of NH₃ at Equilibrium in a Mixture of N₂, H₂, and NH₃ as a Function of Temperature and Total Pressure*			
	Total Pressure		
Temperature (°C)	300 atm	400 atm	500 atm
400	48% NH_3	55% NH_3	61% NH_3
500	26% NH_3	32% NH_3	38% NH_3
600	13% NH_3	17% NH_3	21% NH_3
*Each experiment was begun with a 3:1 mixture of H_2 and N_2.			

the equilibrium will shift in a direction that tends to reduce that change. Although this rule sometimes oversimplifies the situation, it works remarkably well.

The Effect of a Change in Concentration

To see how we can predict the effect of change in concentration on a system at equilibrium, we will consider the ammonia synthesis reaction. Suppose there is an equilibrium position described by these concentrations:

$$[N_2] = 0.399 \ M \qquad [H_2] = 1.197 \ M \qquad [NH_3] = 0.202 \ M$$

What will happen if 1.000 mol/L N_2 is suddenly injected into the system? We can answer this question by calculating the value of Q. The concentrations before the system adjusts are

$$[N_2]_0 = 0.399 \ M + 1.000 \ M = 1.399 \ M$$

$$\uparrow$$
Added N_2

$$[H_2]_0 = 1.197 \ M$$
$$[NH_3]_0 = 0.202 \ M$$

Blue anhydrous cobalt(II) chloride and pink hydrated cobalt(II) chloride. Since the reaction $CoCl_2(s) + 6H_2O(g) \rightarrow CoCl_2 \cdot 6H_2O(s)$ is shifted to the right by water vapor, $CoCl_2$ is often used in novelty devices to detect humidity.

Note we are labeling these as "initial concentrations" because the system is no longer at equilibrium. Then

$$Q = \frac{[NH_3]_0^2}{[N_2]_0[H_2]_0^3} = \frac{(0.202)^2}{(1.399)(1.197)^3} = 1.70 \times 10^{-2}$$

Since we are not given the value of K, we must calculate it from the first set of equilibrium concentrations:

$$K = \frac{[NH_3]^2}{[N_2][H_2]^3} = \frac{(0.202)^2}{(0.399)(1.197)^3} = 5.96 \times 10^{-2}$$

As we might have expected, Q is less than K because the concentration of N_2 was increased.

The system will shift to the right to come to the new equilibrium position. Rather than do the calculations, we simply summarize the results:

Equilibrium Position I		Equilibrium Position II
$[N_2] = 0.399\ M$	1,000 mol/L	$[N_2] = 1.348\ M$
$[H_2] = 1.197\ M$	of N_2 added $\Longrightarrow$	$[H_2] = 1.044\ M$
$[NH_3] = 0.202\ M$		$[NH_3] = 0.304\ M$

Note from these data that the equilibrium position does in fact shift to the right: the concentration of H_2 decreases, the concentration of NH_3 increases, and, of course, since nitrogen is added, the concentration of N_2 shows an increase relative to the amount present at the original equilibrium position. (However, notice that the nitrogen showed a decrease relative to the amount present immediately after addition of the 1.000 mol N_2.)

We can predict this shift qualitatively by using Le Châtelier's principle. Since the change imposed is the addition of nitrogen, Le Châtelier's principle predicts that the system will shift in a direction that consumes nitrogen. This reduces the effect of the addition. Thus Le Châtelier's principle correctly predicts that adding nitrogen will cause the equilibrium to shift to the right (see Fig. 13.5).

If ammonia had been added instead of nitrogen, the system would have shifted to the left to consume ammonia. So another way of stating Le Châtelier's principle is to say that _if a reactant or product is added to a system at equilibrium, the system will shift away from the added component. If a reactant or product is removed, the system will shift toward the removed component._

(top) At a higher temperature, brown $NO_2(g)$ is favored. _(bottom)_ As the temperature decreases, a shift in equilibrium from brown $NO_2(g)$ to colorless $N_2O_4(g)$ occurs.

The system shifts in the direction that compensates for the imposed change.

Sample Exercise 13.14

Arsenic can be extracted from its ores by first reacting the ore with oxygen (called **roasting**) to form solid As_4O_6, which is then reduced using carbon:

$$As_4O_6(s) + 6C(s) \rightleftharpoons As_4(g) + 6CO(g)$$

Predict the direction of the shift of the equilibrium position in response to each of the following changes in conditions:

a. Addition of carbon monoxide

b. Addition or removal of carbon or tetraarsenic hexoxide (As_4O_6)

c. Removal of gaseous arsenic (As_4)

Figure 13.5

(a) The initial equilibrium mixture of N_2, H_2, and NH_3. (b) Addition of N_2. (c) The new equilibrium position for the system containing more N_2 (due to addition of N_2), less H_2, and more NH_3 than in (a).

Solution

a. Le Châtelier's principle predicts that the shift will be away from the substance whose concentration is increased. The equilibrium position will shift to the left when carbon monoxide is added.

b. Since the amount of a pure solid has no effect on the equilibrium position, changing the amount of carbon or tetraarsenic hexoxide will have no effect.

c. If gaseous arsenic is removed, the equilibrium position will shift to the right to form more products. In industrial processes, the desired product is often continuously removed from the reaction system to increase the yield.

The Effect of a Change in Pressure

Basically, there are three ways to change the pressure of a reaction system involving gaseous components:

1. Add or remove a gaseous reactant or product.

2. Add an inert gas (one not involved in the reaction).

3. Change the volume of the container.

We have already considered the addition or removal of a reactant or product. When an inert gas is added, there is no effect on the equilibrium position. *The addition of an inert gas increases the total pressure but has no effect on the concentrations or partial pressures of the reactants or products.* Thus the system remains at the original equilibrium position.

When the volume of the container is changed, the concentrations (and thus the partial pressures) of both reactants and products are changed. We could calculate Q and predict the direction of the shift. However, for systems involving gaseous components, there is an easier way: we focus on the volume. The central idea is that (*left*) Brown $NO_2(g)$ and colorless $N_2O_4(g)$ in equilibrium in a syringe. (*middle*) The volume is suddenly decreased, giving a greater concentration of both N_2O_4 and NO_2 (indicated by the darker brown color). (*right*) A few seconds after the sudden volume decrease, the color is much lighter brown as the equilibrium shifts from brown $NO_2(g)$ to colorless $N_2O_4(g)$ as predicted by Le Châtelier's principle, since in the equilibrium

$$2NO_2(g) \rightleftharpoons N_2O_4(g)$$

the product side has the smaller number of molecules.

when the volume of the container holding a gaseous system is reduced, the system responds by reducing its own volume. This is done by decreasing the total number of gaseous molecules in the system.

To see that this is true, we can rearrange the ideal gas law to give

$$V = \left(\frac{RT}{P}\right) n$$

or at constant T and P

$$V \propto n$$

That is, at constant temperature and pressure, the volume of a gas is directly proportional to the number of moles of gas present.

Suppose we have a mixture of the gases nitrogen, hydrogen, and ammonia at equilibrium (Fig. 13.6). If we suddenly reduce the volume, what will happen to the equilibrium position? The reaction system can reduce its volume by reducing the number of molecules present. This means that the reaction

$$N_2(g) + 3H_2(g) \rightleftharpoons 2NH_3(g)$$

will shift to the right, since in this direction four molecules (one of nitrogen and three of hydrogen) react to produce two molecules (of ammonia), thus *reducing the total number of gaseous molecules present.* The new equilibrium position will be further to the right than the original one. That is, the equilibrium position will shift toward the side of the reaction involving the smaller number of gaseous molecules in the balanced equation.

The opposite is also true. When the container volume is increased, the system will shift so as to increase its volume. An increase in volume in the ammonia synthesis system will produce a shift to the left to increase the total number of gaseous molecules present.

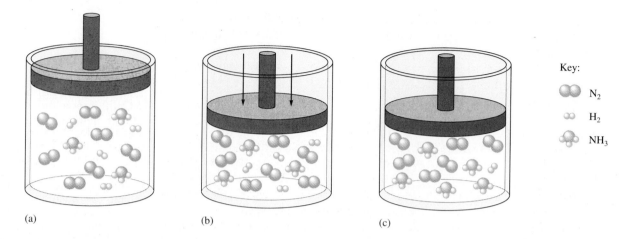

(a)   (b)   (c)

Key:

N_2

H_2

NH_3

Figure 13.6

(a) A mixture of $NH_3(g)$, $N_2(g)$, and $H_2(g)$ at equilibrium. (b) The volume is suddenly decreased. (c) The new equilibrium position for the system containing more NH_3 and less N_2 and H_2. The reaction $N_2(g) + 3H_2(g) \rightleftharpoons 2NH_3(g)$ shifts to the right (toward the side with fewer molecules) when the container volume is decreased.

Sample Exercise 13.15

Predict the shift in equilibrium position that will occur for each of the following processes when the volume is reduced.

a. The preparation of liquid phosphorus trichloride by the reaction

$$P_4(s) + 6Cl_2(g) \rightleftharpoons 4PCl_3(l)$$

b. The preparation of gaseous phosphorus pentachloride according to the equation

$$PCl_3(g) + Cl_2(g) \rightleftharpoons PCl_5(g)$$

c. The reaction of phosphorus trichloride with ammonia:

$$PCl_3(g) + 3NH_3(g) \rightleftharpoons P(NH_2)_3(g) + 3HCl(g)$$

Solution

a. Since P_4 and PCl_3 are a pure solid and a pure liquid, respectively, we need to consider only the effect of the change in volume on Cl_2. The volume is decreased, so the position of the equilibrium will shift to the right, since the reactant side contains six gaseous molecules and the product side has none.

b. Decreasing the volume will shift the given reaction to the right, since the product side contains only one gaseous molecule while the reactant side has two.

c. Both sides of the balanced reaction equation have four gaseous molecules. A change in volume will have no effect on the equilibrium position. There is no shift in this case.

The Effect of a Change in Temperature

It is important to realize that although the changes we have just discussed may alter the equilibrium *position*, they do not alter the equilibrium *constant*. For example, the addition of a reactant shifts the equilibrium position to the right but has no effect on the value of the equilibrium constant; the new equilibrium concentrations satisfy the original equilibrium constant.

The effect of temperature on equilibrium is different, however, because _the value of K changes with temperature._ We can use Le Châtelier's principle to predict the direction of the change.

The synthesis of ammonia from nitrogen and hydrogen is exothermic. We can represent this by treating energy as a product:

$$N_2(g) + 3H_2(g) \rightleftharpoons 2NH_3(g) + 92 \text{ kJ}$$

If energy is added to this system at equilibrium by heating it, Le Châtelier's principle predicts that the shift will be in the direction that consumes energy, that is, to the left. Note that this shift decreases the concentration of NH_3 and increases the concentrations of N_2 and H_2, thus _decreasing the value of K._ The experimentally observed change in K with temperature for this reaction is indicated in Table 13.3. The value of K decreases with increased temperature, as predicted.

On the other hand, for an endothermic reaction, such as the decomposition of calcium carbonate,

$$556 \text{ kJ} + CaCO_3(s) \rightleftharpoons CaO(s) + CO_2(g)$$

an increase in temperature will cause the equilibrium to shift to the right and the value of K to increase.

In summary, to use Le Châtelier's principle to describe the effect of a temperature change on a system at equilibrium, treat energy as a reactant (in an endothermic process) or as a product (in an exothermic process), and predict the direction of the shift in the same way as when an actual reactant or product is added or removed. Although Le Châtelier's principle cannot predict the size of the change in K, it does correctly predict the direction of the change.

Of course, energy is not a chemical product of this reaction, but thinking of it in this way makes it easy to apply Le Châtelier's principle.

Table 13.3

Observed Value of *K* for the Ammonia Synthesis Reaction as a Function of Temperature*

Temperature (K)	K (L^2/mol^2)
500	90
600	3
700	0.3
800	0.04

*For this exothermic reaction, the value of K decreases as the temperature increases, as predicted by Le Châtelier's principle.

Sample Exercise 13.16

For each of the following reactions, predict how the value of K changes as the temperature is increased.

a. $N_2(g) + O_2(g) \rightleftharpoons 2NO(g)$ $\Delta H° = 181 \text{ kJ}$
b. $2SO_2(g) + O_2(g) \rightleftharpoons 2SO_3(g)$ $\Delta H° = -198 \text{ kJ}$

Solution

a. This is an endothermic reaction, as indicated by the positive value for $\Delta H°$. Energy can be viewed as a reactant, and K increases (the equilibrium shifts to the right) as the temperature is increased.

b. This is an exothermic reaction (energy can be regarded as a product). As the temperature is increased, the value of K decreases (the equilibrium shifts to the left).

We have seen how Le Châtelier's principle can be used to predict the effect of several types of changes on a system at equilibrium. To summarize these ideas, Table 13.4 shows how various changes affect the equilibrium position of the endothermic reaction

$$N_2O_4(g) \rightleftharpoons 2NO_2(g)   \Delta H° = 58 \text{ kJ}$$

Table 13.4

Shifts in the Equilibrium Position for the Reaction 58 kJ + $N_2O_4(g) \rightleftharpoons 2NO_2(g)$

Change	Shift
Addition of $N_2O_4(g)$	Right
Addition of $NO_2(g)$	Left
Removal of $N_2O_4(g)$	Left
Removal of $NO_2(g)$	Right
Addition of $He(g)$	None
Decrease container volume	Left
Increase container volume	Right
Increase temperature	Right
Decrease temperature	Left

FOR REVIEW

Summary

For stoichiometry calculations, we assume that reactions run to completion. However, when a chemical reaction is carried out in a closed vessel, the system achieves chemical equilibrium, the state where the concentrations of both reactants and products remain constant over time. Although a particular equilibrium concentration may be small, it is never zero. Equilibrium is a highly dynamic state; reactants are converted continually to products, and vice versa, as molecules collide with each other. At equilibrium the rates of the forward and reverse reactions are equal.

The law of mass action is a general description of the equilibrium condition. It states that for a reaction of the type

$$jA + kB \rightleftharpoons lC + mD$$

the equilibrium expression is given by

$$K = \frac{[C]^l[D]^m}{[A]^j[B]^k}$$

where K is the equilibrium constant.

For each reaction system at a given temperature, there is only one value for the equilibrium constant but an infinite number of possible equilibrium positions. An equilibrium position is defined by a particular set of concentrations (equilibrium concentrations) that satisfies the equilibrium expression. The specific equilibrium position attained by a system depends on the initial concentrations. An equilibrium position never depends on the amount of a pure liquid or a pure solid, and therefore, these substances are not included in the equilibrium expression.

For a gas-phase reaction, equilibrium positions also can be described in terms of partial pressures. K_p, the equilibrium constant in terms of pressures, is related to K as follows:

$$K_p = K(RT)^{\Delta n}$$

where Δn is the sum of the coefficients of the gaseous products minus the sum of the coefficients of the gaseous reactants.

Homogeneous equilibria involve reactions where all reactants and products are in the same phase. However, many systems involve different phases and their equilibria are described as heterogeneous.

The value of K allows us to predict the inherent tendency of a reaction to occur. A small value of K means that the equilibrium position lies far to the left, and therefore, the reaction will not occur to any great extent. A large value of K means that the reaction will go essentially to completion—the equilibrium position lies far to the right. However, the value of K gives no information concerning how rapidly equilibrium will be achieved.

The reaction quotient Q applies the law of mass action to initial rather than equilibrium concentrations. We compare Q to K to determine in which direction a chemical system will shift to reach equilibrium. If Q is equal to K, the system is already at equilibrium; if Q is less than K, the system will shift to the right to reach equilibrium; if Q is greater than K the system will shift to the left to reach equilibrium.

To find the concentrations that characterize a given equilibrium position, it is usually best to start with the given initial concentrations (or pressures), define the change needed to reach equilibrium, and apply this change to the initial concentrations (or pressures) to define the equilibrium concentrations (or pressures).

Le Châtelier's principle allows us to predict qualitatively the effects of changes in concentration, pressure, and temperature on a system at equilibrium. This principle states that if a change is imposed, the equilibrium position will shift in a direction that tends to compensate for the imposed change.

Key Terms

chemical equilibrium

Section 13.2
law of mass action
equilibrium expression
equilibrium constant

equilibrium position

Section 13.4
homogeneous equilibria
heterogeneous equilibria

Section 13.5
reaction quotient Q

Section 13.7
Le Châtelier's principle

A blue question or exercise number indicates that the answer to that question or exercise appears at the back of this book and a solution appears in the Solutions Guide.

Questions

1. Characterize a system at chemical equilibrium with respect to each of the following:
   a. The rates of the forward and reverse reactions
   b. The overall composition of the reaction mixture

2. Is the following statement true or false? "Reactions with large equilibrium constants are very fast." Explain.

3. Distinguish between the terms *equilibrium constant* and *equilibrium position*.

4. Distinguish between the terms *equilibrium constant* and *reaction quotient*.

5. Changing the pressure in a reaction vessel by changing the volume may shift the position of a gas-phase equilibrium, whereas changing the pressure by adding an inert gas will not. Why?

6. How will the equilibrium position of a gas-phase reaction be affected by changing the volume of the reaction vessel? Are there reactions that will not have their equilibria shifted by a change in volume? Explain.

Exercises

In this section similar exercises are paired.

Characteristics of Chemical Equilibrium

7. Consider the following reaction:

$$H_2O(g) + CO(g) \rightleftharpoons H_2(g) + CO_2(g)$$

Amounts of H_2O, CO, H_2, and CO_2 are put into a flask so that the composition corresponds to an equilibrium position. If the CO placed in the flask is labeled with radioactive ^{14}C, will ^{14}C be found only in CO molecules for an indefinite period of time? Explain.

8. Consider the same reaction as in Exercise 7. In one experiment 1.0 mol $H_2O(g)$ and 1.0 mol CO(g) are put into a flask and heated to 350°C. In a second experiment 1.0 mol $H_2(g)$ and 1.0 mol $CO_2(g)$ are put into another flask with the same volume as the first. This mixture is also heated to 350°C. After equilibrium is reached, will there be any difference in the composition of the mixtures in the two flasks?

The Equilibrium Constant

9. Write the equilibrium expression (for K) for each of the following gas-phase reactions, which occur in the atmosphere:
   a. $NO(g) + O_3(g) \rightleftharpoons NO_2(g) + O_2(g)$
   b. $O_3(g) \rightleftharpoons O_2(g) + O(g)$
   c. $Cl(g) + O_3(g) \rightleftharpoons ClO(g) + O_2(g)$
   d. $2O_3(g) \rightleftharpoons 3O_2(g)$

10. Write the equilibrium expression (for K_p) for each reaction in Exercise 9. For which of the reactions in Exercise 9 is K_p equal to K?

11. At 127°C, $K = 2.6 \times 10^{-5}$ mol²/L² for the reaction

$$2NH_3(g) \rightleftharpoons N_2(g) + 3H_2(g)$$

Calculate K_p at this temperature.

12. At 1100 K, $K_p = 0.25$ atm⁻¹ for the reaction

$$2SO_2(g) + O_2(g) \rightleftharpoons 2SO_3(g)$$

What is the value of K at this temperature?

13. Write expressions for K for the following reactions.
   a. $P_4(s) + 5O_2(g) \rightleftharpoons P_4O_{10}(s)$
   b. $NH_4NO_3(s) \rightleftharpoons N_2O(g) + 2H_2O(g)$
   c. $CO_2(g) + NaOH(s) \rightleftharpoons NaHCO_3(s)$
   d. $S_8(s) + 8O_2(g) \rightleftharpoons 8SO_2(g)$

14. Write expressions for K_p for the following reactions.
   a. $2Fe(s) + \frac{3}{2}O_2(g) \rightleftharpoons Fe_2O_3(s)$
   b. $CO_2(g) + MgO(s) \rightleftharpoons MgCO_3(s)$
   c. $C(s) + H_2O(g) \rightleftharpoons CO(g) + H_2(g)$
   d. $4KO_2(s) + 2H_2O(g) \rightleftharpoons 4KOH(s) + 3O_2(g)$

15. At a given temperature, $K = 278$ for the reaction

$$2SO_2(g) + O_2(g) \rightleftharpoons 2SO_3(g)$$

Calculate values of K for the following reactions at this temperature.
   a. $SO_2(g) + \frac{1}{2}O_2(g) \rightleftharpoons SO_3(g)$
   b. $2SO_3(g) \rightleftharpoons 2SO_2(g) + O_2(g)$
   c. $SO_3(g) \rightleftharpoons SO_2(g) + \frac{1}{2}O_2(g)$
   d. $4SO_2(g) + 2O_2(g) \rightleftharpoons 4SO_3(g)$

16. For the reaction

$$H_2(g) + Br_2(g) \rightleftharpoons 2HBr(g)$$

$K_p = 3.5 \times 10^4$ at 1495 K. What is the value of K_p for the following reactions at 1495 K?
   a. $HBr(g) \rightleftharpoons \frac{1}{2}H_2(g) + \frac{1}{2}Br_2(g)$
   b. $2HBr(g) \rightleftharpoons H_2(g) + Br_2(g)$
   c. $\frac{1}{2}H_2(g) + \frac{1}{2}Br_2(g) \rightleftharpoons HBr(g)$

17. At 427°C, a 1.0-L flask contains 20.0 mol H_2, 18.0 mol CO_2, 12.0 mol H_2O, and 5.9 mol CO at equilibrium. Calculate K for the reaction

$$CO_2(g) + H_2(g) \rightleftharpoons CO(g) + H_2O(g)$$

18. At a particular temperature, a 3.0-L flask contains 3.5 mol HI, 4.1 mol H_2, and 0.3 mol I_2 in equilibrium. Calculate K at this temperature for the reaction

$$H_2(g) + I_2(g) \rightleftharpoons 2HI(g)$$

19. An equilibrium mixture contains 0.60 g solid carbon and the gases carbon dioxide and carbon monoxide at partial pressures of 2.9 atm and 2.6 atm, respectively. Calculate K_p for the reaction

$$C(s) + CO_2(g) \rightleftharpoons 2CO(g)$$

20. A sample of solid ammonium chloride was placed in an evacuated container and then heated so that it decomposed to ammonia gas and hydrogen chloride gas. After heating, the total pressure in the container was found to be 4.4 atm. Calculate K_p at this temperature for the decomposition reaction

$$NH_4Cl(s) \rightleftharpoons NH_3(g) + HCl(g)$$

21. A sample of gaseous PCl_5 was introduced into an evacuated flask so that the pressure of pure PCl_5 would be 0.50 atm at 523 K. However, PCl_5 decomposes to gaseous PCl_3 and Cl_2, and the actual pressure in the flask was found to be 0.84 atm. Calculate K_p for the decomposition reaction

$$PCl_5(g) \rightleftharpoons PCl_3(g) + Cl_2(g)$$

at 523 K. Calculate K at this temperature.

22. A flask was filled with 2.0 mol gaseous SO_2 and 2.0 mol gaseous NO_2 and heated. After equilibrium was reached, it was found that 1.3 mol gaseous NO was present. Assume that the reaction

$$SO_2(g) + NO_2(g) \rightleftharpoons SO_3(g) + NO(g)$$

occurs under these conditions. Calculate the value of the equilibrium constant for this reaction.

Equilibrium Calculations

23. The equilibrium constant is 0.0900 at 25°C for the reaction

$$H_2O(g) + Cl_2O(g) \rightleftharpoons 2HOCl(g)$$

For which of the following sets of conditions is the system at equilibrium? For those which are not at equilibrium, in which direction will the system shift?
a. $P_{H_2O} = 200.$ torr, $P_{Cl_2O} = 49.8$ torr, $P_{HOCl} = 21.0$ torr
b. $P_{H_2O} = 296$ torr, $P_{Cl_2O} = 15.0$ torr, $P_{HOCl} = 20.0$ torr
c. A 2.0-L flask contains 0.084 mol HOCl, 0.080 mol Cl_2O, and 0.98 mol H_2O.
d. A 3.0-L flask contains 0.25 mol HOCl, 0.0010 mol Cl_2O, and 0.56 mol H_2O.

24. At a particular temperature, $K_p = 0.133$ atm for the reaction

$$N_2O_4(g) \rightleftharpoons 2NO_2(g)$$

Which of the following conditions correspond to equilibrium positions?
a. $P_{NO_2} = 0.144$ atm, $P_{N_2O_4} = 0.156$ atm
b. $P_{NO_2} = 0.175$ atm, $P_{N_2O_4} = 0.102$ atm
c. $P_{NO_2} = 0.056$ atm, $P_{N_2O_4} = 0.048$ atm
d. $P_{NO_2} = 0.064$ atm, $P_{N_2O_4} = 0.0308$ atm

25. At 900°C, $K_p = 1.04$ atm for the reaction

$$CaCO_3(s) \rightleftharpoons CaO(s) + CO_2(g)$$

At a low temperature, dry ice (solid CO_2), calcium oxide, and calcium carbonate are introduced into a 50.0-L reaction chamber. The temperature is raised to 900°C. For the following mixtures, will the initial amount of calcium oxide increase, decrease, or remain the same as the system moves toward equilibrium?
a. 655 g $CaCO_3$, 95.0 g CaO, 58.4 g CO_2
b. 780 g $CaCO_3$, 1.00 g CaO, 23.76 g CO_2
c. 0.14 g $CaCO_3$, 5000 g CaO, 23.76 g CO_2
d. 715 g $CaCO_3$, 813 g CaO, 4.82 g CO_2

26. Ethyl acetate is synthesized in a nonreacting solvent (not water) according to the following reaction:

$$CH_3CO_2H + C_2H_5OH \rightleftharpoons CH_3CO_2C_2H_5 + H_2O$$

Acetic acid   Ethanol   Ethyl acetate

$$K = 2.2$$

For the following mixtures (a–d), will the concentration of H_2O increase, decrease, or remain the same as equilibrium is established?
a. $[CH_3CO_2C_2H_5] = 0.22\ M$, $[H_2O] = 0.10\ M$, $[CH_3CO_2H] = 0.010\ M$, $[C_2H_5OH] = 0.010\ M$
b. $[CH_3CO_2C_2H_5] = 0.22\ M$, $[H_2O] = 0.0020\ M$, $[CH_3CO_2H] = 0.0020\ M$, $[C_2H_5OH] = 0.10\ M$
c. $[CH_3CO_2C_2H_5] = 0.88\ M$, $[H_2O] = 0.12\ M$, $[CH_3CO_2H] = 0.044\ M$, $[C_2H_5OH] = 6.0\ M$
d. $[CH_3CO_2C_2H_5] = 4.4\ M$, $[H_2O] = 4.4\ M$, $[CH_3CO_2H] = 0.88\ M$, $[C_2H_5OH] = 10.0\ M$
e. What must the concentration of water be for a mixture with $[CH_3CO_2C_2H_5] = 2.0\ M$, $[CH_3CO_2H] = 0.10\ M$, $[C_2H_5OH] = 5.0\ M$ to be at equilibrium?
f. Why is water included in the equilibrium expression for this reaction?

27. At 2200°C, $K = 0.050$ for the reaction

$$N_2(g) + O_2(g) \rightleftharpoons 2NO(g)$$

What is the partial pressure of NO in equilibrium with N_2 and O_2 that were placed in a flask at initial pressures of 0.80 and 0.20 atm, respectively?

28. At 35°C, $K = 1.6 \times 10^{-5}$ mol/L for the reaction

$$2NOCl(g) \rightleftharpoons 2NO(g) + Cl_2(g)$$

Calculate the concentrations of all species at equilibrium for each of the following original mixtures.
a. 2.0 mol pure NOCl in a 2.0-L flask
b. 2.0 mol NO and 1.0 mol Cl_2 in a 1.0-L flask
c. 1.0 mol NOCl and 1.0 mol NO in a 1.0-L flask
d. 3.0 mol NO and 1.0 mol Cl_2 in a 1.0-L flask
e. 2.0 mol NOCl, 2.0 mol NO, and 1.0 mol Cl_2 in a 1.0-L flask
f. 1.0 mol/L concentration of all three gases

29. At 1100 K, $K_p = 0.25$ atm^{-1} for the reaction

$$2SO_2(g) + O_2(g) \rightleftharpoons 2SO_3(g)$$

Calculate the equilibrium partial pressures of SO_2, O_2, and SO_3 produced from an initial mixture in which $P_{SO_2} = P_{O_2} = 0.50$ atm and $P_{SO_3} = 0$.

30. At a particular temperature, assume that $K = 1.0 \times 10^2$ for the reaction

$$H_2(g) + F_2(g) \rightleftharpoons 2HF(g)$$

a. In an experiment, 2.0 mol H_2 and 2.0 mol F_2 are introduced into a 1.0-L flask. Calculate the concentrations of all species when equilibrium is reached.
b. To the equilibrium mixture in part a, an additional 0.50 mol H_2 is added. Calculate the new equilibrium concentrations of H_2, F_2, and HF.

31. For the reaction

$$N_2O_4(g) \rightleftharpoons 2NO_2(g)$$

$K_p = 0.25$ atm at a certain temperature. What are the equilibrium partial pressures of NO_2 and N_2O_4 for each of the following initial conditions?
a. Pure NO_2 at a pressure of 0.050 atm
b. Pure N_2O_4 at a pressure of 0.040 atm
c. A mixture with $P_{N_2O_4} = P_{NO_2} = 1.0$ atm

32. At 90°C, the equilibrium constant is 6.8×10^{-2} for the reaction

$$H_2(g) + S(s) \rightleftharpoons H_2S(g)$$

If 0.15 mol hydrogen and 1.0 mol sulfur are heated to 90.0°C in a 1.0-L container, what will be the partial pressure of H_2S at equilibrium?

Le Châtelier's Principle

33. An important reaction in the commercial production of hydrogen is

$$CO(g) + H_2O(g) \rightleftharpoons H_2(g) + CO_2(g)$$

How will this system at equilibrium shift in each of the four following cases?
a. Gaseous carbon dioxide is removed.
b. Water vapor is added.
c. The pressure is increased by adding helium gas.
d. The temperature is increased. (Use values of $\Delta H_f°$ in Appendix 4 to calculate $\Delta H°$.)

34. What will happen to the number of moles of SO_3 in equilibrium with SO_2 and O_2 in the reaction

$$2SO_3(g) \rightleftharpoons 2SO_2(g) + O_2(g) \qquad \Delta H° = 197 \text{ kJ}$$

in each of the following cases?
a. Oxygen gas is added.
b. The pressure in increased by decreasing the volume.
c. The pressure is increased by adding argon gas.
d. The temperature is decreased.
e. A catalyst is added. (See Exercise 39.)
f. Gaseous sulfur dioxide is removed.

35. In which direction will the position of the equilibrium

$$H_2(g) + I_2(g) \rightleftharpoons 2HI(g)$$

be shifted for each of the following changes.
a. $H_2(g)$ is added.
b. $I_2(g)$ is removed.
c. $HI(g)$ is removed.
d. Some $Ar(g)$ is added.
e. The volume of the container is doubled.
f. The temperature is increased. (For HI, $\Delta H_f^\circ = 25.9$ kJ/mol.)

36. Hydrogen for use in ammonia production is produced by the reaction

$$CH_4(g) + H_2O(g) \underset{750^\circ C}{\overset{\text{Ni catalyst}}{\rightleftharpoons}} CO(g) + 3H_2(g)$$

What will happen to a reaction mixture at equilibrium if
a. $H_2O(g)$ is removed.
b. The temperature is increased. (Use Appendix 4 to calculate ΔH°.)
c. An inert gas is added.
d. $CO(g)$ is removed.
e. The Ni catalyst is removed.

37. The fragrances of many naturally occurring substances are due to the presence of organic compounds called esters. For example, the ester ethyl butyrate smells like pineapple. Ethyl butyrate can be made by the following reaction:

$$\underset{\text{Butyric acid}}{CH_3CH_2CH_2\overset{\overset{\displaystyle O}{\|}}{C}\!-\!OH} + \underset{\text{Ethanol}}{CH_3CH_2OH} \rightleftharpoons$$

$$\underset{\text{Ethyl butyrate}}{CH_3CH_2CH_2\overset{\overset{\displaystyle O}{\|}}{C}\!-\!OCH_2CH_3} + H_2O$$

Butyric acid has an objectionable odor. If you were to choose a solvent for preparing ethyl butyrate, which of the following would be the best choice: water, 95% ethanol (5% water), 100% ethanol, or acetonitrile (CH_3CN, a nonreactive solvent)?

38. Novelty devices for predicting rain contain cobalt(II) chloride and are based on the following equilibrium:

$$\underset{\text{Purple}}{CoCl_2(s)} + 6H_2O(g) \rightleftharpoons \underset{\text{Pink}}{CoCl_2 \cdot 6H_2O(s)}$$

What color will such an indicator be if rain is imminent?

Kinetics and Equilibrium

39. A catalyst cannot affect the position of an equilibrium, since it lowers the activation energy for both the forward and reverse reactions by the same amount and thus changes their rates by the same factor. Why was the discovery of an appropriate catalyst vital for the use of the Haber process for ammonia production? Why is it impossible for a catalyst to catalyze only the forward reaction of a system?

40. Which of the following will be affected by the addition of a catalyst?
a. The value of the equilibrium constant.
b. The value of k_f, the forward rate constant.
c. The value of k_r, the reverse rate constant.
d. The value of the forward rate.
e. The value of the reverse rate.
f. The value of the ratio k_f/k_r.

41. The rate law for the forward reaction of the system

$$BrO_3^-(aq) + 3SO_3^{2-}(aq) \rightleftharpoons Br^-(aq) + 3SO_4^{2-}(aq)$$

in acidic solution is

$$\text{Rate} = k_1[BrO_3^-][SO_3^{2-}][H^+]$$

Write a possible rate law for the reverse reaction. *Hint:* Think of the form of the equilibrium constant expression and the fact that at equilibrium $\text{rate}_f = \text{rate}_r$.

42. The rate law for the forward reaction of the system

$$CO(g) + Cl_2(g) \rightleftharpoons COCl_2(g)$$

is

$$\text{Rate} = k_1[CO][Cl_2]^{3/2}$$

Write a possible rate law for the reverse reaction. (See hint in Exercise 41.)

Additional Exercises

43. Write the expression for K_p for the reaction

$$2O_3(g) \rightleftharpoons 3O_2(g)$$

What is the relationship between K_p for each of the following reactions and K_p for the one above?
a. $O_3(g) \rightleftharpoons \frac{3}{2}O_2(g)$ b. $3O_2(g) \rightleftharpoons 2O_3(g)$

44. In atmospheric chemistry the concentrations of trace substances are usually expressed in units of molecules/cm³. Below are data for some gas-phase reactions at 300 K (from the NASA publication "Chemical Kinetics and Photochemical Data for Use in Atmospheric Modeling, Evaluation Number 5"). K^* indicates the use of molecules/cm³ for concentration. Calculate K and K_p for each reaction.
a. $HO_2(g) + NO_2(g) \rightleftharpoons HO_2NO_2(g)$
$$K^* = 1.26 \times 10^{-11}$$
b. $CH_3O_2(g) + NO_2(g) \rightleftharpoons CH_3O_2NO_2(g)$
$$K^* = 2.09 \times 10^{-12}$$

45. Given the following equilibrium constants at 427°C:

$$Na_2O(s) \rightleftharpoons 2Na(l) + \tfrac{1}{2}O_2(g) \quad K_1 = 2 \times 10^{-25}$$
$$NaO(g) \rightleftharpoons Na(l) + \tfrac{1}{2}O_2(g) \quad K_2 = 2 \times 10^{-5}$$
$$Na_2O_2(s) \rightleftharpoons 2Na(l) + O_2(g) \quad K_3 = 5 \times 10^{-29}$$
$$NaO_2(s) \rightleftharpoons Na(l) + O_2(g) \quad K_4 = 3 \times 10^{-14}$$

determine the values for the equilibrium constants for the following.
a. $Na_2O(s) + \tfrac{1}{2}O_2(g) \rightleftharpoons Na_2O_2(s)$
b. $NaO(g) + Na_2O(s) \rightleftharpoons Na_2O_2(s) + Na(l)$
c. $2NaO(g) \rightleftharpoons Na_2O_2(s)$

Hint: When reaction equations are added, the equilibrium expressions are multiplied.

46. Calculate a value for the equilibrium constant for the reaction

$$O_2(g) + O(g) \rightleftharpoons O_3(g)$$

given

$$NO_2(g) \overset{h\nu}{\rightleftharpoons} NO(g) + O(g)$$
$$K = 6.8 \times 10^{-49}$$

$$O_3(g) + NO(g) \rightleftharpoons NO_2(g) + O_2(g)$$
$$K = 5.8 \times 10^{-34}$$

(See hint in Exercise 45.)

47. At a certain temperature, $K = 1.1 \times 10^3$ L/mol for the reaction

$$Fe^{3+}(aq) + SCN^-(aq) \rightleftharpoons FeSCN^{2+}(aq)$$

Calculate the concentrations of Fe^{3+}, SCN^-, and $FeSCN^{2+}$ if 0.10 mol $Fe(NO_3)_3$ is added to 1.0 L of 2.0 M KSCN.

48. At a certain temperature, the equilibrium constant for the gas-phase reaction between carbon monoxide and oxygen to pro-

duce carbon dioxide is 5.0×10^3 L/mol. Calculate the concentrations of all species at equilibrium if 2.0 mol each of CO and O_2 are placed in a 5.0-L vessel and allowed to come to equilibrium.

49. A system at equilibrium is described by the equation

$$\text{Energy} + SO_2Cl_2(g) \rightleftharpoons SO_2(g) + Cl_2(g)$$

Why does the temperature of the system increase when SO_2 is added to the system at equilibrium?

50. Use bond energies (Table 8.4) to estimate ΔH for the reaction to prepare methanol from hydrogen and carbon monoxide:

$$CO(g) + 2H_2(g) \rightleftharpoons CH_3OH(g)$$

If you wanted to use this reaction for producing methanol commercially, would high or low temperatures favor a maximum yield?

51. At 25°C, $K = 0.090$ for the reaction

$$H_2O(g) + Cl_2O(g) \rightleftharpoons 2HOCl(g)$$

Calculate the concentrations of all species at equilibrium for each of the following cases.
a. 1.0 g H_2O and 2.0 g Cl_2O are mixed in a 1.0-L flask.
b. 1.0 mol pure HOCl is placed in a 2.0-L flask.

52. Consider the following diagram for the *uncatalyzed* reaction

$$N_2 + O_2 \rightleftharpoons 2NO$$

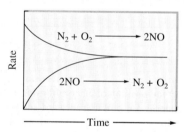

What will a similar diagram for the catalyzed reaction look like?

Challenge Problems

53. Nitric oxide and bromine, at initial partial pressures of 98.4 and 41.3 torr, respectively, were allowed to react at 300. K. At equilibrium, the total pressure was 110.5 torr. The reaction is

$$2NO(g) + Br_2(g) \rightleftharpoons 2NOBr(g)$$

a. Calculate the value of K_p.

b. What would be the partial pressures of all species if NO and Br_2, both at an initial partial pressure of 0.30 atm, were allowed to come to equilibrium at this temperature?

54. Ammonia is produced by the Haber process, in which nitrogen and hydrogen are reacted directly using an iron mesh impregnated with oxides as a catalyst. For the reaction

$$N_2(g) + 3H_2(g) \rightleftharpoons 2NH_3(g)$$

equilibrium constants as a function of temperature are

300°C, 4.34×10^{-3} atm^{-2}
500°C, 1.45×10^{-5} atm^{-2}
600°C, 2.25×10^{-6} atm^{-2}

a. Is the reaction exothermic or endothermic?
b. Typical conditions used for producing ammonia are temperatures of 400 to 500°C and total pressures of 200 to 600 atm. Why are these conditions chosen?

55. At 25°C, $K_p \approx 1 \times 10^{-31}$ for the reaction

$$N_2(g) + O_2(g) \rightleftharpoons 2NO(g)$$

a. Calculate the concentration of NO, in molecules/cm^3, that can exist in equilibrium in air at 25°C. In air, $P_{N_2} = 0.8$ atm and $P_{O_2} = 0.2$ atm.
b. Typical concentrations of NO in relatively pristine environments range from 10^8 to 10^{10} molecules/cm^3. Why is there a discrepancy between these values and your answer to part a?

56. Iodine is sparingly soluble in pure water. However, it dissolves in solutions containing excess iodide ion:

$$I^-(aq) + I_2(aq) \rightleftharpoons I_3^-(aq) \qquad K = 710 \text{ L/mol}$$

What is the ratio of $[I_3^-]$ to $[I_2]$ if 0.10 mol I_2 is added to 1.0 L of KI solution having each of the following concentrations?
a. $[I^-] = 0.20\ M$ b. $[I^-] = 1.5\ M$ c. $[I^-] = 5.0\ M$

57. The equilibrium constant K_p for the reaction

$$CCl_4(g) \rightleftharpoons C(s) + 2Cl_2(g)$$

at 700°C is 0.76 atm. Determine the initial pressure of carbon tetrachloride that will produce a total equilibrium pressure of 1.2 atm at 700°C.

58. At a certain temperature, $K_p = 6.5 \times 10^{-3}$ atm^{-2} for the ammonia synthesis reaction. Assume that a reaction vessel with a movable piston initially contains 3.0 mol $H_2(g)$ and 1.0 mol $N_2(g)$. Make a plot to show how the partial pressure of $NH_3(g)$ present at equilibrium varies for the total pressures 1.0 atm, 10.0 atm, 100. atm, and 1000. atm (assuming that K_p remains constant). [*Note:* Assume that these total pressures represent the initial total pressure of $H_2(g)$ plus $N_2(g)$, where $P_{NH_3} = 0$.]

Marathon Problem*

59. Consider the reaction

$$A(g) + B(g) \rightleftharpoons C(g)$$

for which $K = 1.30 \times 10^2$. Assume that 0.406 mol C(g) is placed in the cylinder represented below. The temperature is 300.0 K, and the barometric pressure on the piston (which is assumed to be massless and frictionless) is constant at 1.00 atm. The original volume (before the 0.406 mol C(g) begins to decompose) is 10.00 L. What is the volume in the cylinder at equilibrium?

P = 1.00 atm

Original volume = 10.00 L

T = 300.0 K

0.406 mole of pure C(g) (initially)

*This Marathon Problem was developed by James H. Burness of Penn State University, York Campus.

CHAPTER 14

Acids and Bases

I n this chapter we reencounter two very important classes of compounds, acids and bases. We will explore their interactions and apply the fundamentals of chemical equilibria discussed in Chapter 13 to systems involving proton-transfer reactions.

Acid–base chemistry is important in a wide variety of everyday applications. There are complex systems in our bodies that carefully control the acidity of our blood, since even small deviations may lead to serious illness and death. The same sensitivity exists in other life forms. If you have ever had tropical fish or goldfish, you know how important it is to monitor and control the acidity of the water in the aquarium.

Acids and bases are also important in industry. For example, the vast quantity of sulfuric acid manufactured in the United States each year is needed to produce fertilizers, polymers, steel, and many other materials (see the Chemical Impact in Chapter 3).

The influence of acids on living things has assumed special importance in the United States, Canada, and Europe in recent years as a result of the phenomenon of acid rain (see the Chemical Impact in Chapter 5). This problem is complex and has diplomatic and economic overtones that make it all the more difficult to solve.

< Healthy goldfish living in an aquarium in which the pH is carefully controlled.

14.1 The Nature of Acids and Bases

Purpose

• To discuss two models of acids and bases and to relate equilibrium concepts to acid dissociation.

Don't taste chemicals!

Acids were first recognized as a class of substances that taste sour. Vinegar tastes sour because it is a dilute solution of acetic acid; citric acid is responsible for the sour taste of a lemon. Bases, sometimes called **alkalis,** are characterized by their bitter taste and slippery feel. Commercial preparations for unclogging drains are highly basic.

Acids and bases were first discussed in Section 4.2.

The first person to recognize the essential nature of acids and bases was Svante Arrhenius. Based on his experiments with electrolytes, Arrhenius postulated that *acids produce hydrogen ions in aqueous solution, while bases produce hydroxide ions.* At the time, the **Arrhenius concept** of acids and bases was a major step forward in quantifying acid–base chemistry, but this concept is limited because it applies only to aqueous solutions and allows for only one kind of base—the hydroxide ion. A more general definition of acids and bases was suggested by the Danish chemist Johannes Brønsted (1879–1947) and the English chemist Thomas Lowry (1874–1936). In terms of the **Brønsted–Lowry model,** *an acid is a proton (H^+) donor, and a base is a proton acceptor.* For example, when gaseous HCl dissolves in water, each HCl molecule donates a proton to a water molecule, and so qualifies as a Brønsted–Lowry acid. The molecule that accepts the proton in this case, water, is a Brønsted–Lowry base.

To understand how water can act as a base, we need to remember that the oxygen of the water molecule has two unshared electron pairs, either of which can form a covalent bond with an H^+ ion. When gaseous HCl dissolves, the following reaction occurs:

$$H-\overset{..}{\underset{H}{O}}: \; + \; H-\overset{..}{\underset{..}{Cl}}: \; \longrightarrow \; \left[H-\overset{..}{\underset{H}{O}}-H\right]^+ + \left[:\overset{..}{\underset{..}{Cl}}:\right]^-$$

Common household substances that contain acids and bases. Vinegar is a dilute solution of acetic acid. Drain cleaners contain strong bases such as sodium hydroxide.

Note that the proton is transferred from the HCl molecule to the water molecule to form H_3O^+, which is called the **hydronium ion.**

The general reaction that occurs when an acid is dissolved in water can best be represented as

$$HA(aq) + H_2O(l) \rightleftharpoons H_3O^+(aq) + A^-(aq) \qquad (14.1)$$

Acid · · · · Base · · · · Conjugate · · · Conjugate
· · · · · · · · · · · · · · · · acid · · · · · · · base

Recall that (aq) means the substance is hydrated.

This representation emphasizes the significant role of the polar water molecule in pulling the proton from the acid. Note that the **conjugate base** is everything that remains of the acid molecule after a proton is lost. The **conjugate acid** is formed when the proton is transferred to the base. A **conjugate acid–base pair** consists of two substances related to each other by the donating and accepting of a single proton. In Equation (14.1) there are two conjugate acid–base pairs: HA and A^- and H_2O and H_3O^+.

It is important to note that Equation (14.1) really represents *a competition for the proton between the two bases H_2O and A^-*. If H_2O is a much stronger base than A^-, that is, if H_2O has a much greater affinity for H^+ than does A^-, the equilibrium position will be far to the right; most of the acid dissolved will be in the ionized form. Conversely, if A^- is a much stronger base than H_2O, the equilibrium position will lie far to the left. In this case most of the acid dissolved will be present at equilibrium as HA.

The equilibrium expression for the reaction given in Equation (14.1) is

$$K_a = \frac{[H_3O^+][A^-]}{[HA]} = \frac{[H^+][A^-]}{[HA]} \qquad (14.2)$$

where K_a is called the **acid dissociation constant.** Both $H_3O^+(aq)$ and $H^+(aq)$ are commonly used to represent the hydrated proton. In this book we will often use simply H^+, but you should remember that it is hydrated in aqueous solutions.

In Chapter 13 we saw that the concentration of a pure solid or a pure liquid is always omitted from the equilibrium expression. In a dilute solution we can assume that the concentration of liquid water remains essentially constant when an acid is dissolved. Thus the term $[H_2O]$ is not included in Equation (14.2), and the equilibrium expression for K_a has the same form as that for the simple dissociation

$$HA(aq) \rightleftharpoons H^+(aq) + A^-(aq)$$

In this chapter we will always represent an acid as simply dissociating. This does not mean we are using the Arrhenius model for acids. Since water does not affect the equilibrium position, it is simply easier to leave it out of the acid dissociation reaction.

You should not forget, however, that water plays an important role in causing the acid to dissociate.

Note that K_a is the equilibrium constant for the reaction in which a proton is removed from HA to form the conjugate base A^-. We use K_a to represent *only* this type of reaction. Knowing this, you can write the K_a expression for any acid, even one that is totally unfamiliar to you. As you do Sample Exercise 14.1, focus on the definition of the reaction corresponding to K_a.

Sample Exercise 14.1

Write the simple dissociation reaction (omitting water) for each of the following acids.

a. Hydrochloric acid (HCl)

b. Acetic acid ($HC_2H_3O_2$)

c. The ammonium ion (NH_4^+)

d. The anilinium ion ($C_6H_5NH_3^+$)

e. The hydrated aluminum(III) ion $[Al(H_2O)_6]^{3+}$

Solution

a. $HCl(aq) \rightleftharpoons H^+(aq) + Cl^-(aq)$

b. $HC_2H_3O_2(aq) \rightleftharpoons H^+(aq) + C_2H_3O_2^-(aq)$

c. $NH_4^+(aq) \rightleftharpoons H^+(aq) + NH_3(aq)$

d. $C_6H_5NH_3^+(aq) \rightleftharpoons H^+(aq) + C_6H_5NH_2(aq)$

e. Although this formula looks complicated, writing the reaction is simple if you concentrate on the meaning of K_a. Removing a proton, which can only come from one of the water molecules, leaves one OH^- and five H_2O molecules attached to the Al^{3+} ion. So the reaction is

$$Al(H_2O)_6^{3+}(aq) \rightleftharpoons H^+(aq) + Al(H_2O)_5OH^{2+}(aq)$$

The Brønsted–Lowry model is not limited to aqueous solutions; it can be extended to reactions in the gas phase. For example, we discussed the reaction between gaseous hydrogen chloride and ammonia when we studied diffusion (Section 5.7):

$$NH_3(g) + HCl(g) \rightleftharpoons NH_4Cl(s)$$

In this reaction, a proton is donated by the hydrogen chloride to the ammonia, as shown by these Lewis structures:

Note that this is not considered an acid–base reaction according to the Arrhenius concept.

14.2 Acid Strength

Purpose

- To relate acid strength to the position of the dissociation equilibrium.
- To discuss the autoionization of water.

The strength of an acid is defined by the equilibrium position of its dissociation reaction:

$$HA(aq) + H_2O(l) \rightleftharpoons H_3O^+(aq) + A^-(aq)$$

A **strong acid** is one for which *this equilibrium lies far to the right*. This means that almost all the original HA is dissociated at equilibrium [see Fig. 14.1(a)]. There is an important connection between the strength of an acid and that of its conjugate base. *A strong acid yields a weak conjugate base*—one that has a low affinity for a proton. A strong acid also can be described as an acid whose conjugate base is a

(a)

(b)

Figure 14.1

Graphic representation of the behavior of acids of different strengths in aqueous solution. (a) A strong acid. (b) A weak acid.

Figure 14.2

The relationship of acid strength and conjugate base strength for the dissociation reaction

$$HA(aq) + H_2O(l) \rightleftharpoons H_3O^+(aq) + A^-(aq)$$
$$\text{Acid} \qquad\qquad\qquad\qquad \text{Conjugate base}$$

much weaker base than water (see Fig. 14.2). In this case the water molecules win the competition for the H^+ ions.

Conversely, a **weak acid** is one for which the equilibrium lies far to the left. Most of the acid originally placed in the solution is still present as HA at equilibrium. That is, a weak acid dissociates only to a very small extent in aqueous solution [see Fig. 14.1(b)]. In contrast to a strong acid, a weak acid has a conjugate base that is a much stronger base than water. In this case a water molecule is not very successful in pulling an H^+ ion from the conjugate base. *A weak acid yields a relatively strong conjugate base.*

The various ways of describing the strength of an acid are summarized in Table 14.1.

The common strong acids are sulfuric acid [$H_2SO_4(aq)$], hydrochloric acid [$HCl(aq)$], nitric acid [$HNO_3(aq)$], and perchloric acid [$HClO_4(aq)$]. Sulfuric acid is actually a **diprotic acid,** an acid having two acidic protons. The acid H_2SO_4 is a strong acid, virtually 100% dissociated in water:

$$H_2SO_4(aq) \rightarrow H^+(aq) + HSO_4^-(aq)$$

A strong acid has a weak conjugate base.

Perchloric acid can explode if handled improperly.

Table 14.1

Various Ways to Describe Acid Strength

Property	Strong Acid	Weak Acid
K_a value	K_a is large	K_a is small
Position of the dissociation equilibrium	Far to the right	Far to the left
Equilibrium concentration of H^+ compared with original concentration of HA	$[H^+] \approx [HA]_0$	$[H^+] \ll [HA]_0$
Strength of conjugate base compared with that of water	A^- much weaker base than H_2O	A^- much stronger base than H_2O

$\ll$ means much less than.
$\gg$ means much greater than.

O
‖
H—O—S—O—H
‖
O
Sulfuric acid

O
‖
O—N—O—H
Nitric acid

O
‖
O—Cl—O—H
‖
O
Perchloric acid

Appendix 5.1 contains a table of K_a values.

H
|
O
|
H—O—P—O—H
‖
O
Phosphoric acid

O—N—O—H
Nitrous acid

Cl—O
\
H
Hypochlorous acid

H   O
\ ‖
H—C—C
/   \
H   O—H
Acetic   ↖ Acidic H
acid

O   O—H
\ /
C
|
⬡
Benzoic
acid

but the HSO_4^- ion is a weak acid:

$$HSO_4^-(aq) \rightleftharpoons H^+(aq) + SO_4^{2-}(aq)$$

Most acids are **oxyacids,** in which the acidic proton is attached to an oxygen atom. The strong acids mentioned above, except hydrochloric acid, are typical examples. Many common weak acids, such as phosphoric acid (H_3PO_4), nitrous acid (HNO_2), and hypochlorous acid (HOCl), are also oxyacids. **Organic acids,** those with a carbon–atom backbone, commonly contain the **carboxyl group:**

O
‖
—C
\
O—H

Acids of this type are usually weak. Examples are acetic acid (CH_3COOH), often written $HC_2H_3O_2$, and benzoic acid (C_6H_5COOH). Note that the remainder of the hydrogens in these molecules are not acidic—do not form H^+ in water.

There are some important acids in which the acidic proton is attached to an atom other than oxygen. The most significant of these are the hydrohalic acids HX, where X represents a halogen atom.

Table 14.2 contains a list of common **monoprotic acids** (those having *one* acidic proton) and their K_a values. Note that the strong acids are not listed. When a strong acid molecule such as HCl, for example, is placed in water, the position of the dissociation equilibrium

$$HCl(aq) + H_2O(l) \rightleftharpoons H^+(aq) + Cl^-(aq)$$

lies so far to the right that [HCl] cannot be measured accurately. This prevents an accurate calculation of K_a:

$$K_a = \frac{[H^+][Cl^-]}{[HCl]}$$

↖ Very small and highly uncertain

Table 14.2		

Values of K_a for Some Common Monoprotic Acids		
Formula	Name	Value of K_a*
HSO_4^-	Hydrogen sulfate ion	1.2×10^{-2}
$HClO_2$	Chlorous acid	1.2×10^{-2}
$HC_2H_2ClO_2$	Monochloracetic acid	1.35×10^{-3}
HF	Hydrofluoric acid	7.2×10^{-4}
HNO_2	Nitrous acid	4.0×10^{-4}
$HC_2H_3O_2$	Acetic acid	1.8×10^{-5}
$[Al(H_2O)_6]^{3+}$	Hydrated aluminum(III) ion	1.4×10^{-5}
HOCl	Hypochlorous acid	3.5×10^{-8}
HCN	Hydrocyanic acid	6.2×10^{-10}
NH_4^+	Ammonium ion	5.6×10^{-10}
HOC_6H_5	Phenol	1.6×10^{-10}

Increasing acid strength →

*The units of K_a are mol/L, but are customarily omitted.

Sample Exercise 14.2

Using Table 14.2, arrange the following species according to their strength as bases: H_2O, F^-, Cl^-, NO_2^-, and CN^-.

Solution

Remember that water is a stronger base than the conjugate base of a strong acid but a weaker base than the conjugate base of a weak acid. This leads to the following order:

$$Cl^- < H_2O < \text{conjugate bases of weak acids}$$

Weakest bases ⟶ Strongest bases

We can order the remaining conjugate bases by recognizing that the strength of an acid is *inversely related* to the strength of its conjugate base. Since from Table 14.2 we have

$$K_a \text{ for HF} > K_a \text{ for HNO}_2 > K_a \text{ for HCN}$$

the base strengths increase as follows:

$$F^- < NO_2^- < CN^-$$

The combined order of increasing base strength is

$$Cl^- < H_2O < F^- < NO_2^- < CN^-$$

Water as an Acid and a Base

A substance is said to be **amphoteric** if it can behave either as an acid or as a base. Water is the most common **amphoteric substance.** We can see this clearly in the **autoionization** of water, which involves the transfer of a proton from one water molecule to another to produce a hydroxide ion and a hydronium ion:

$$H_2O + H_2O \rightleftharpoons H_3O^+ + OH^-$$
acid(1)   base(1)   acid(2)   base(2)

In this reaction, one water molecule acts as an acid by furnishing a proton, and the other acts as a base by accepting the proton.

Autoionization can occur in other liquids besides water. For example, in liquid ammonia the autoionization reaction is

The autoionization reaction for water

$$2H_2O(l) \rightleftharpoons H_3O^+(aq) + OH^-(aq)$$

leads to the equilibrium expression

$$K_w = [H_3O^+][OH^-] = [H^+][OH^-]$$

where K_w, called the **ion-product constant** (or the **dissociation constant**), always refers to the autoionization of water.

Experiment shows that at 25°C

$$[H^+] = [OH^-] = 1.0 \times 10^{-7} \, M$$

which means that at 25°C

$$K_w = [H^+][OH^-] = (1.0 \times 10^{-7} \, \text{mol/L})(1.0 \times 10^{-7} \, \text{mol/L})$$
$$= 1.0 \times 10^{-14} \, \text{mol}^2/\text{L}^2$$

$K_w = [H^+][OH^-]$
$= 1.0 \times 10^{-14}$

The units are customarily omitted.

It is important to recognize the meaning of K_w. In any aqueous solution at 25°C, *no matter what it contains*, the product of $[H^+]$ and $[OH^-]$ must always equal 1.0×10^{-14}. There are three possible situations:

1. A neutral solution, where $[H^+] = [OH^-]$.
2. An acidic solution, where $[H^+] > [OH^-]$.
3. A basic solution, where $[OH^-] > [H^+]$.

In each case, however, at 25°C

$$K_w = [H^+][OH^-] = 1.0 \times 10^{-14}$$

Sample Exercise 14.3

Calculate $[H^+]$ or $[OH^-]$ as required for each of the following solutions at 25°C, and state whether the solution is neutral, acidic, or basic.

a. $1.0 \times 10^{-5} \, M \, OH^-$
b. $1.0 \times 10^{-7} \, M \, OH^-$
c. $10.0 \, M \, H^+$

Solution

a. $K_w = [H^+][OH^-] = 1.0 \times 10^{-14}$. Since $[OH^-]$ is $1.0 \times 10^{-5} \, M$, solving for $[H^+]$ gives

$$[H^+] = \frac{1.0 \times 10^{-14}}{[OH^-]} = \frac{1.0 \times 10^{-14}}{1.0 \times 10^{-5}} = 1.0 \times 10^{-9} \, M$$

Since $[OH^-] > [H^+]$, the solution is basic.

b. As in part a, solving for $[H^+]$ gives

$$[H^+] = \frac{1.0 \times 10^{-14}}{[OH^-]} = \frac{1.0 \times 10^{-14}}{1.0 \times 10^{-7}} = 1.0 \times 10^{-7} \, M$$

Since $[H^+] = [OH^-]$, the solution is neutral.

c. Solving for $[OH^-]$ gives

$$[OH^-] = \frac{1.0 \times 10^{-14}}{[H^+]} = \frac{1.0 \times 10^{-14}}{10.0} = 1.0 \times 10^{-15} \, M$$

Since $[H^+] > [OH^-]$, the solution is acidic.

Since K_w is an equilibrium constant, it varies with temperature. The effect of temperature is considered in Sample Exercise 14.4.

Sample Exercise 14.4

At 60°C, the value of K_w is 1×10^{-13}.

a. Using Le Châtelier's principle, predict whether the reaction

$$2H_2O(l) \rightleftharpoons H_3O^+(aq) + OH^-(aq)$$

is exothermic or endothermic.

b. Calculate $[H^+]$ and $[OH^-]$ in a neutral solution at 60°C.

Solution

a. K_w *increases* from 1×10^{-14} at 25°C to 1×10^{-13} at 60°C. Le Châtelier's principle states that if a system at equilibrium is heated, it will adjust to consume energy. Since the value of K_w increases with temperature, we must think of energy as a reactant, and so the process must be endothermic.

b. At 60°C,

$$[H^+][OH^-] = 1 \times 10^{-13}$$

For a neutral solution,

$$[H^+] = [OH^-] = \sqrt{1 \times 10^{-13}} = 3 \times 10^{-7} \ M$$

14.3 The pH Scale

Purpose

• To define pH, pOH, and pK and to introduce general methods for solving acid–base problems.

Because $[H^+]$ in an aqueous solution is typically quite small, the **pH scale** provides a convenient way to represent solution acidity. The pH is a log scale based on 10, where

$$pH = -\log[H^+]$$

The pH scale is a compact way to represent solution acidity

Appendix 1.2 has a review of logs.

Thus for a solution where

$$[H^+] = 1.0 \times 10^{-7} \ M$$
$$pH = -(-7.00) = 7.00$$

For $\Delta[H^+] = 10$, $\Delta pH = 1$.

At this point we need to discuss significant figures for logarithms. The rule is that *the number of decimal places in the log is equal to the number of significant figures in the original number*. Thus

2 significant figures

$$[H^+] = 1.0 \times 10^{-9} \ M$$
$$pH = 9.00$$

2 decimal places

Similar log scales are used for representing other quantities; for example,

$$pOH = -\log[OH^-]$$

$$pK = -\log K$$

The pH decreases as [H⁺] increases, and vice versa.

Since pH is a log scale based on 10, *the pH changes by 1 for every power of 10 change in [H⁺]*. For example, a solution of pH 3 has an H^+ concentration 10 times that of a solution of pH 4 and 100 times that of a solution of pH 5. Also note that because pH is defined as $-\log[H^+]$, *the pH decreases as [H⁺] increases*. The pH scale and the pH values for several common substances are shown in Fig. 14.3.

The pH of a solution is usually measured using a pH meter, an electronic device with a probe that can be inserted into a solution of unknown pH. The probe contains an acidic aqueous solution enclosed by a special glass membrane that allows migration of H^+ ions. If the unknown solution has a different pH from the solution in the probe, an electric potential results, which is registered on the meter (see Fig. 14.4).

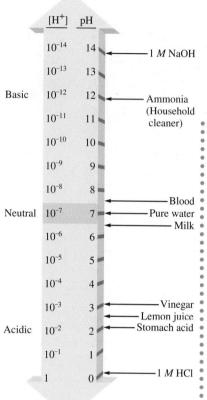

Figure 14.3

The pH scale and pH values of some common substances.

Sample Exercise 14.5

Calculate pH and pOH for each of the following solutions at 25°C.

a. 1.0×10^{-3} *M* OH^- **b.** 1.0 *M* H^+

Solution

a.

$$[H^+] = \frac{K_w}{[OH^-]} = \frac{1.0 \times 10^{-14}}{1.0 \times 10^{-3}} = 1.0 \times 10^{-11} \, M$$

$$pH = -\log[H^+] = -\log(1.0 \times 10^{-11}) = 11.00$$

$$pOH = -\log[OH^-] - -\log(1.0 \times 10^{-3}) = 3.00$$

b.

$$[OH^-] = \frac{K_w}{[H^+]} = \frac{1.0 \times 10^{-14}}{1.0} = 1.0 \times 10^{-14} \, M$$

$$pH = -\log[H^+] = -\log(1.0) = 0.00$$

$$pOH = -\log[OH^-] = -\log(1.0 \times 10^{-14}) = 14.00$$

It is useful to consider the log form of the expression

$$K_w = [H^+][OH^-]$$

That is,

$$\log K_w = \log[H^+] + \log[OH^-]$$

or

$$-\log K_w = -\log[H^+] - \log[OH^-]$$

Thus

$$pK_w = pH + pOH \qquad (14.3)$$

Since $K_w = 1.0 \times 10^{-14}$,

$$pK_w = -\log(1.0 \times 10^{-14}) = 14.00$$

Thus, for *any* aqueous solution at 25°C, pH and pOH add up to 14.00:

$$pH + pOH = 14.00 \qquad (14.4)$$

Sample Exercise 14.6

The pH of a sample of human blood was measured to be 7.41 at 25°C. Calculate pOH, $[H^+]$, and $[OH^-]$ for the sample.

The pH meter is discussed more fully in Section 17.4.

Solution

Since pH + pOH = 14.00,

$$pOH = 14.00 - pH = 14.00 - 7.41 = 6.59$$

To find $[H^+]$ we must go back to the definition of pH:

$$pH = -\log[H^+]$$

Thus $7.41 = -\log[H^+]$ or $\log[H^+] = -7.41$

We need to know the *antilog* of -7.41. As shown in Appendix 1.2, taking the antilog is the same as exponentiation; that is,

$$\text{antilog}(n) = 10^n$$

There are different methods for carrying out the antilog operation on various calculators. The most common are the $\boxed{Y^X}$ key and the two-key $\boxed{INV}\boxed{LOG}$ sequence. Consult the user's manual for your calculator to find out how to do the antilog operation.

Since $pH = -\log[H^+]$,

$$-pH = \log[H^+]$$

and $[H^+]$ can be calculated by taking the antilog of $-pH$:

$$[H^+] = \text{antilog}(-pH)$$

In the present case,

$$[H^+] = \text{antilog}(-pH) = \text{antilog}(-7.41) = 10^{-7.41} = 3.9 \times 10^{-8}$$

Similarly, $[OH^-] = \text{antilog}(-pOH)$, and

$$[OH^-] = \text{antilog}(-6.59) = 10^{-6.59} = 2.6 \times 10^{-7} \, M$$

Figure 14.4
A typical pH meter.

Now that we have considered all the fundamental definitions relevant to acid–base solutions, we can proceed to a quantitative description of the equilibria present in these solutions. The main reason that acid–base problems sometimes seem difficult is that a typical aqueous solution contains many components, so the problems tend to be complicated. However, you can deal with these problems successfully if you use the following general strategies:

- *Think chemistry*. Focus on the solution components and their reactions. It will almost always be possible to choose one reaction that is the most important.

- *Be systematic*. Acid–base problems require a step-by-step approach.

- *Be flexible*. Although all acid–base problems are similar in many ways, important differences do occur. Treat each problem as a separate entity. Do not try to force a given problem into matching any you have solved before. Look for both the similarities and the differences.

- *Be patient.* The complete solution to a complicated problem cannot be seen immediately in all its detail. Pick the problem apart into its workable steps.

- *Be confident.* Look within the problem for the solution, and let the problem guide you. Assume that you can think it out. Do not rely on memorizing solutions to problems. In fact, memorizing solutions is usually detrimental because you tend to try to force a new problem to be the same as one you have seen before. *Understand and think; don't just memorize.*

14.4 Calculating the pH of Strong Acid Solutions

Purpose

- To demonstrate the systematic treatment of solutions of strong acids.

Common Strong Acids
$HCl(aq)$
$HNO_3(aq)$
$H_2SO_4(aq)$
$HClO_4(aq)$

When we deal with acid–base equilibria, *we must focus on the solution components and their chemistry.* For example, what species are present in a 1.0 M solution of HCl? Since hydrochloric acid is a strong acid, we assume that it is completely dissociated. Thus, although the label on the bottle says 1.0 M HCl, the solution contains virtually no HCl molecules. Typically, container labels indicate the substance(s) used to make up the solution but do not necessarily describe the solution components after dissolution. Thus a 1.0 M HCl solution contains H^+ and Cl^- ions rather than HCl molecules.

The next step in dealing with aqueous solutions is to determine which components are significant and which can be ignored. We need to focus on the **major species,** those solution components present in relatively large amounts. In 1.0 M HCl, for example, the major species are H^+, Cl^-, and H_2O. Since this is a very acidic solution, OH^- is present only in tiny amounts and is classed as a minor species. In attacking acid–base problems, the importance of *writing the major species in the solution* as the first step cannot be overemphasized. *This single step is the key to solving these problems successfully.*

Always write the major species present in the solution.

To illustrate the main ideas involved, let us calculate the pH of 1.0 M HCl. We first list the major species: H^+, Cl^-, and H_2O. Since we want to calculate the pH, we will focus on those major species which can furnish H^+. Obviously, we must consider H^+ from the dissociation of HCl. However, H_2O also furnishes H^+ by autoionization, which is often represented by the simple dissociation reaction

$$H_2O(l) \rightleftharpoons H^+(aq) + OH^-(aq)$$

The H^+ from the strong acid drives the equilibrium $H_2O \rightleftharpoons H^+ + OH^-$ to the left.

However, is autoionization an important source of H^+ ions? In pure water at 25°C, $[H^+]$ is 10^{-7} M. In 1.0 M HCl solution, the water will produce even less than 10^{-7} M H^+, since by Le Châtelier's principle the H^+ from the dissociated HCl will drive the position of the water equilibrium to the left. Thus the amount of H^+ contributed by water is negligible compared with the 1.0 M H^+ from the dissociation of HCl. Therefore, we can say that $[H^+]$ in the solution is 1.0 M. The pH is then

$$pH = -\log[H^+] = -\log(1.0) = 0$$

Sample Exercise 14.7

a. Calculate the pH of 0.10 M HNO_3.
b. Calculate the pH of 1.0×10^{-10} M HCl.

Solution

a. Since HNO_3 is a strong acid, the major species in solution are

$$H^+, \quad NO_3^-, \quad \text{and} \quad H_2O$$

The concentration of HNO_3 is virtually zero, since the acid completely dissociates in water. Also, $[OH^-]$ will be very small because the H^+ ions from the acid will drive the equilibrium

$$H_2O(l) \rightleftharpoons H^+(aq) + OH^-(aq)$$

to the left. That is, this is an acidic solution where $[H^+] \gg [OH^-]$, so $[OH^-] \ll 10^{-7}$ M. The sources of H^+ are

1. H^+ from HNO_3 (0.10 M)
2. H^+ from H_2O

The number of H^+ ions contributed by the autoionization of water will be very small compared with the 0.10 M contributed by the HNO_3 and can be neglected. Since the dissolved HNO_3 is the only important source of H^+ ions in this solution,

$$[H^+] = 0.10 \ M \quad \text{and} \quad pH = -\log(0.10) = 1.00$$

b. Normally, in an aqueous solution of HCl the major species are H^+, Cl^-, and H_2O. However, in this case the amount of HCl in solution is so small that it has no effect; the only major species is H_2O. Thus the pH will be that of pure water, or pH = 7.00.

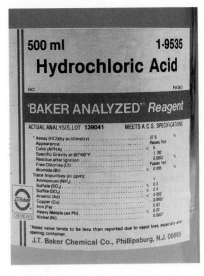

The label on a bottle of concentrated hydrochloric acid.

In pure water, only 10^{-7} M H^+ is produced.

14.5 Calculating the pH of Weak Acid Solutions

Purpose

- To demonstrate the systematic treatment of solutions of weak acids.
- To show how to calculate percent dissociation.

Since a weak acid dissolved in water can be viewed as a prototype of almost any equilibrium occurring in aqueous solution, we will proceed carefully and systematically. Although some of the procedures we develop here may seem unnecessary, they will become essential as the problems become more complicated. We will develop the necessary strategies by calculating the pH of a 1.00 M solution of HF ($K_a = 7.2 \times 10^{-4}$).

The first step, as always, is to *write the major species in the solution*. From its small K_a value, we know that hydrofluoric acid is a weak acid and will be dissociated only to a slight extent. Thus, when we write the major species, the hydrofluoric acid will be represented in its dominant form, as HF. The major species in solution are HF and H_2O.

First, always write the major species present in the solution.

The next step (since this is a pH problem) is to decide which of the major species can furnish H^+ ions. Actually, both major species can do so:

$$HF(aq) \rightleftharpoons H^+(aq) + F^-(aq) \qquad K_a = 7.2 \times 10^{-4}$$
$$H_2O(l) \rightleftharpoons H^+(aq) + OH^-(aq) \qquad K_w = 1.0 \times 10^{-14}$$

In aqueous solutions, however, typically one source of H^+ can be singled out as dominant. By comparing K_a for HF to K_w for H_2O, we see that hydrofluoric acid, although weak, is still a much stronger acid than water. Thus we will assume that hydrofluoric acid will be the dominant source of H^+. We will ignore the tiny contribution by water.

Therefore, it is the dissociation of HF that will determine the equilibrium concentration of H^+ and hence the pH:

$$HF(aq) \rightleftharpoons H^+(aq) + F^-(aq)$$

The equilibrium expression is

$$K_a = 7.2 \times 10^{-4} = \frac{[H^+][F^-]}{[HF]}$$

To solve the equilibrium problem, we follow the procedures developed in Chapter 13 for gas-phase equilibria. First, we list the initial concentrations, the *concentrations before the reaction of interest has proceeded to equilibrium*. Before any HF dissociates, the concentrations of the species in the equilibrium are

$$[HF]_0 = 1.00 \ M \qquad [F^-]_0 = 0 \qquad [H^+]_0 = 10^{-7} \ M \approx 0$$

(Note that the zero value for $[H^+]_0$ is an approximation, since we are neglecting the H^+ ions from the autoionization of water.)

The next step is to determine the change required to reach equilibrium. Since some HF will dissociate to come to equilibrium (but that amount is presently unknown), we let x be the change in the concentration of HF that is required to achieve equilibrium. That is, we assume that x mol/L HF will dissociate to produce x mol/L H^+ and x mol/L F^- as the system adjusts to its equilibrium position. Now the equilibrium concentrations can be defined in terms of x:

$$[HF] = [HF]_0 - x = 1.00 - x$$
$$[F^-] = [F^-]_0 + x = 0 + x = x$$
$$[H^+] = [H^+]_0 + x \approx 0 + x = x$$

Substituting these equilibrium concentrations into the equilibrium expression gives

$$K_a = 7.2 \times 10^{-4} = \frac{[H^+][F^-]}{[HF]} = \frac{(x)(x)}{1.00 - x}$$

This expression produces a quadratic equation that can be solved using the quadratic formula, as for the gas-phase systems in Chapter 13. However, since K_a for HF is so small, HF will dissociate only slightly, and x is expected to be small. This will allow us to simplify the calculation. If x is very small compared to 1.00, the term in the denominator can be approximated as follows:

$$1.00 - x \approx 1.00$$

The equilibrium expression then becomes

$$7.2 \times 10^{-4} = \frac{(x)(x)}{1.00 - x} \approx \frac{(x)(x)}{1.00}$$

which yields

$$x^2 \approx (7.2 \times 10^{-4})(1.00) = 7.2 \times 10^{-4}$$
$$x \approx \sqrt{7.2 \times 10^{-4}} = 2.7 \times 10^{-2}$$

How valid is the approximation that [HF] = 1.00 *M*? Because this question will arise often in connection with acid–base equilibrium calculations, we will consider it carefully. *The validity of the approximation depends on how much accuracy we demand for the calculated value of [H$^+$].* Typically, the K_a values for acids are known to an accuracy of only about ±5%. It is reasonable therefore to apply this figure when determining the validity of the approximation

The validity of an approximation should always be checked.

$$[HA]_0 - x \approx [HA]_0$$

We will use the following test. First, we calculate the value of x by making the approximation

$$K_a = \frac{x^2}{[HA]_0 - x} \approx \frac{x^2}{[HA]_0}$$

where

$$x^2 \approx K_a[HA]_0 \quad \text{and} \quad x \approx \sqrt{K_a[HA]_0}$$

We then compare the sizes of x and $[HA]_0$. If the expression

$$\frac{x}{[HA]_0} \times 100$$

is less than or equal to 5%, the value of x is small enough that the approximation

$$[HA]_0 - x \approx [HA]_0$$

will be considered valid.

In our example,

$$x = 2.7 \times 10^{-2} \text{ mol/L}$$
$$[HA]_0 = [HF]_0 = 1.00 \text{ mol/L}$$

and

$$\frac{x}{[HA]_0} \times 100 = \frac{2.7 \times 10^{-2}}{1.00} \times 100 = 2.7\%$$

The approximation we made is considered valid, and the value of x calculated using that approximation is acceptable. Thus

$$x = [H^+] = 2.7 \times 10^{-2} \text{ } M \quad \text{and} \quad pH = -\log(2.7 \times 10^{-2}) = 1.57$$

This problem illustrates all the important steps for solving a typical equilibrium problem involving a weak acid. These steps are summarized as follows:

Solving Weak Acid Equilibrium Problems

- List the major species in the solution.
- Choose the species that can produce H$^+$, and write balanced equations for the reactions producing H$^+$.

The K_a values for various weak acids are given in Table 14.2 and in Appendix 5.1.

- Using the values of the equilibrium constants for the reactions you have written, decide which equilibrium will dominate in producing H^+.
- Write the equilibrium expression for the dominant equilibrium.
- List the initial concentrations of the species participating in the dominant equilibrium.
- Define the change needed to achieve equilibrium; that is, define x.
- Write the equilibrium concentrations in terms of x.
- Substitute the equilibrium concentrations into the equilibrium expression.
- Solve for x the "easy" way; that is, by assuming that $[HA]_0 - x \approx [HA]_0$.
- Use the 5% rule to verify whether the approximation is valid.
- Calculate $[H^+]$ and pH.

We use this systematic approach in Sample Exercise 14.8.

Sample Exercise 14.8

The hypochlorite ion (OCl^-) is a strong oxidizing agent often found in household bleaches and disinfectants. It is also the active ingredient that forms when swimming pool water is treated with chlorine. In addition to its oxidizing abilities, the hypochlorite ion has a relatively high affinity for protons (it is a much stronger base than Cl^-, for example) and forms the weakly acidic hypochlorous acid (HOCl, $K_a = 3.5 \times 10^{-8}$). Calculate the pH of a 0.100 M aqueous solution of hypochlorous acid.

Solution

STEP 1

We list the major species. Since HOCl is a weak acid and remains mostly undissociated, the major species in a 0.100 M HOCl solution are

$$HOCl \quad and \quad H_2O$$

STEP 2

Both species can produce H^+:

$$HOCl(aq) \rightleftharpoons H^+(aq) + OCl^-(aq) \qquad K_a = 3.5 \times 10^{-8}$$
$$H_2O(l) \rightleftharpoons H^+(aq) + OH^-(aq) \qquad K_w = 1.0 \times 10^{-14}$$

STEP 3

Since HOCl is a significantly stronger acid than H_2O, it will dominate in the production of H^+.

STEP 4

We therefore use the following equilibrium expression:

$$K_a = 3.5 \times 10^{-8} = \frac{[H^+][OCl^-]}{[HOCl]}$$

STEP 5

The initial concentrations appropriate for this equilibrium are

$$[HOCl]_0 = 0.100 \ M$$
$$[OCl^-]_0 = 0$$
$$[H^+]_0 \approx 0 \quad \text{(We neglect the contribution from } H_2O.)$$

STEP 6

Since the system will reach equilibrium by the dissociation of HOCl, let x be the amount of HOCl (in mol/L) that dissociates in reaching equilibrium.

STEP 7

The equilibrium concentrations in terms of x are

$$[HOCl] = [HOCl]_0 - x = 0.100 - x$$
$$[OCl^-] = [OCl^-]_0 + x = 0 + x = x$$
$$[H^+] = [H^+]_0 + x \approx 0 + x = x$$

STEP 8

Substituting these concentrations into the equilibrium expression gives

$$K_a = 3.5 \times 10^{-8} = \frac{(x)(x)}{0.100 - x}$$

STEP 9

Since K_a is so small, we can expect a small value for x. Thus we make the approximation $[HA]_0 - x \approx [HA]_0$, or $0.100 - x \approx 0.100$, which leads to the expression

$$K_a = 3.5 \times 10^{-8} = \frac{x^2}{0.100 - x} \approx \frac{x^2}{0.100}$$

Solving for x gives

$$x = 5.9 \times 10^{-5}$$

STEP 10

The approximation $0.100 - x \approx 0.100$ must be validated. To do this, we compare x to $[HOCl]_0$:

$$\frac{x}{[HA]_0} \times 100 = \frac{x}{[HOCl]_0} \times 100 = \frac{5.9 \times 10^{-5}}{0.100} \times 100 = 0.059\%$$

Since this value is much less than 5%, the approximation is considered valid.

STEP 11

We calculate $[H^+]$ and pH:

$$[H^+] = x = 5.9 \times 10^{-5} \ M \quad \text{and} \quad pH = 4.23$$

The pH of a Mixture of Weak Acids

Sometimes a solution contains two weak acids of very different strengths. This case is considered in Sample Exercise 14.9. Note that the steps are again followed (though not labeled).

The same systematic approach applies to all solution equilibria.

Sample Exercise 14.9

Calculate the pH of a solution that contains 1.00 M HCN ($K_a = 6.2 \times 10^{-10}$) and 5.00 M HNO$_2$ ($K_a = 4.0 \times 10^{-4}$). Also calculate the concentration of cyanide ion (CN$^-$) in this solution at equilibrium.

Solution

Since HCN and HNO$_2$ are both weak acids and are largely undissociated, the major species in the solution are:

$$\text{HCN,} \quad \text{HNO}_2, \quad \text{and} \quad \text{H}_2\text{O}$$

All three of these components produce H$^+$:

$$\text{HCN}(aq) \rightleftharpoons \text{H}^+(aq) + \text{CN}^-(aq) \qquad K_a = 6.2 \times 10^{-10}$$
$$\text{HNO}_2(aq) \rightleftharpoons \text{H}^+(aq) + \text{NO}_2^-(aq) \qquad K_a = 4.0 \times 10^{-4}$$
$$\text{H}_2\text{O}(l) \rightleftharpoons \text{H}^+(aq) + \text{OH}^-(aq) \qquad K_w = 1.0 \times 10^{-14}$$

A mixture of three acids might lead to a very complicated problem. However, the situation is greatly simplified by the fact that even though HNO$_2$ is a weak acid, it is much stronger than the other two acids present (as revealed by the K values). Thus HNO$_2$ can be assumed to be the dominant producer of H$^+$, and we will focus on the equilibrium expression

$$K_a = 4.0 \times 10^{-4} = \frac{[\text{H}^+][\text{NO}_2^-]}{[\text{HNO}_2]}$$

The initial concentrations, the definition of x, and the equilibrium concentrations are as follows:

Initial Concentration (mol/L)		Equilibrium Concentration (mol/L)
$[\text{HNO}_2]_0 = 5.00$ $[\text{NO}_2^-]_0 = 0$ $[\text{H}^+]_0 \approx 0$	$\xrightarrow{\substack{x \text{ mol/L HNO}_2 \\ \text{dissociates}}}$	$[\text{HNO}_2] = 5.00 - x$ $[\text{NO}_2^-] = x$ $[\text{H}^+] = x$

Substituting the equilibrium concentrations in the equilibrium expression and making the approximation that $5.00 - x = 5.00$ gives

$$K_a = 4.0 \times 10^{-4} = \frac{(x)(x)}{5.00 - x} \approx \frac{x^2}{5.00}$$

We solve for x:

$$x = 4.5 \times 10^{-2}$$

Using the 5% rule, we show that the approximation is valid:

$$\frac{x}{[\text{HNO}_2]_0} \times 100 = \frac{4.5 \times 10^{-2}}{5.00} \times 100 = 0.90\%$$

Therefore,

$$[\text{H}^+] = x = 4.5 \times 10^{-2} \, M \quad \text{and} \quad \text{pH} = 1.35$$

We also want to calculate the equilibrium concentration of cyanide ion in this solution. The CN^- ions in this solution come from the dissociation of HCN:

$$HCN(aq) \rightleftharpoons H^+(aq) + CN^-(aq)$$

Although the position of this equilibrium lies far to the left and does not contribute *significantly* to $[H^+]$, HCN is the *only source* of CN^-. Thus we must consider the extent of the dissociation of HCN to calculate $[CN^-]$. The equilibrium expression for the preceding reaction is

$$K_a = 6.2 \times 10^{-10} = \frac{[H^+][CN^-]}{[HCN]}$$

We know $[H^+]$ for this solution from the results for the first part of the problem. It is important to understand that *there is only one kind of H^+ in this solution*. It does not matter from which acid the H^+ ions originate. The equilibrium $[H^+]$ we need to insert into the HCN equilibrium expression is 4.5×10^{-2} M, even though the H^+ was contributed almost entirely from the dissociation of HNO_2. What is [HCN] at equilibrium? We know $[HCN]_0 = 1.00$ M, and since K_a for HCN is so small, a negligible amount of HCN will dissociate. Thus

$$[HCN] = [HCN]_0 - \text{amount of HCN dissociated} \approx [HCN]_0 = 1.00 \ M$$

Since $[H^+]$ and [HCN] are known, we can find $[CN^-]$ from the equilibrium expression:

$$K_a = 6.2 \times 10^{-10} = \frac{[H^+][CN^-]}{[HCN]} = \frac{(4.5 \times 10^{-2})[CN^-]}{1.00}$$

$$[CN^-] = \frac{(6.2 \times 10^{-10})(1.00)}{4.5 \times 10^{-2}} = 1.4 \times 10^{-8} \ M$$

Note the significance of this result. Since $[CN^-] = 1.4 \times 10^{-8}$ M and HCN is the only source of CN^-, this means that only 1.4×10^{-8} mol/L of HCN has dissociated. This is a very small amount compared with the initial concentration of HCN, which is exactly what we would expect from its very small K_a value, and [HCN] = 1.00 M as assumed.

Percent Dissociation

It is often useful to specify the amount of weak acid that has dissociated in achieving equilibrium in an aqueous solution. The **percent dissociation** is defined as follows:

Percent dissociation is also known as **percent ionization.**

$$\text{Percent dissociation} = \frac{\text{amount dissociated (mol/L)}}{\text{initial concentration (mol/L)}} \times 100 \quad (14.5)$$

For example, we found earlier that in a 1.00 M solution of HF, $[H^+] = 2.7 \times 10^{-2}$ M. To reach equilibrium, 2.7×10^{-2} mol/L of the original 1.00 M HF dissociates, so

$$\text{Percent dissociation} = \frac{2.7 \times 10^{-2} \text{ mol/L}}{1.00 \text{ mol/L}} \times 100 = 2.7\%$$

For a given weak acid, the percent dissociation increases as the acid becomes more dilute. For example, the percent dissociation of acetic acid ($HC_2H_3O_2$, $K_a =$

◀ **CHEMICAL IMPACT** ▶

Household Chemistry

Common household bleach is an aqueous solution containing approximately 5% sodium hypochlorite, a potent oxidizing agent that can react with and decolorize chemicals that cause stains. Bleaching solutions are manufactured by dissolving chlorine gas in a sodium hydroxide solution to give the reaction

$$Cl_2(g) + 2OH^-(aq) \rightleftharpoons$$
$$OCl^-(aq) + Cl^-(aq) + H_2O(l)$$

As long as the pH of this solution is maintained above 8, the OCl^- ion is the predominant chlorine-containing species. However, if the solution is made acidic (the $[OH^-]$ lowered), elemental chlorine (Cl_2) is favored, and since Cl_2 is much less soluble in water than is sodium hypochlorite, Cl_2 gas is suddenly evolved from the solution. This is why labels on bottles of bleach carry warnings about mixing the bleach with other cleaning solutions. For example, toilet bowl cleaners usually contain acids such as H_3PO_4 or HSO_4^- and

have pH values around 2. Mixing toilet bowl cleaner with bleach can lead to a very dangerous evolution of chlorine gas.

On the other hand, if bleach is mixed with a cleaning agent containing ammonia, the chlorine and ammonia react to produce chloramines, such as NH_2Cl, $NHCl_2$, and NCl_3. These compounds produce acrid fumes that can cause respiratory distress.

1.8×10^{-5}) is significantly greater in a 0.10 M solution than in a 1.0 M solution, as is demonstrated in Sample Exercise 14.10.

Sample Exercise 14.10

Calculate the percent dissociation of acetic acid $(K_a = 1.8 \times 10^{-5})$ in each of the following solutions.

a. 1.00 M $HC_2H_3O_2$
b. 0.100 M $HC_2H_3O_2$

Solution

a. Since acetic acid is a weak acid, the major species in this solution are $HC_2H_3O_2$ and H_2O. Both species are weak acids, but acetic acid is a much stronger acid than water. Thus the dominant equilibrium will be

$$HC_2H_3O_2(aq) \rightleftharpoons H^+(aq) + C_2H_3O_2^-(aq)$$

and the equilibrium expression is

$$K_a = 1.8 \times 10^{-5} = \frac{[H^+][C_2H_3O_2^-]}{[HC_2H_3O_2]}$$

The initial concentrations, definition of x, and equilibrium concentrations are as follows:

Initial Concentration (mol/L)		Equilibrium Concentration (mol/L)
$[HC_2H_3O_2]_0 = 1.00\ M$ $[C_2H_3O_2^-]_0 = 0$ $[H^+]_0 \approx 0$	$\xrightarrow[\text{dissociates}]{x \text{ mol/L } HC_2H_3O_2}$	$[HC_2H_3O_2] = 1.00 - x$ $[C_2H_3O_2^-] = x$ $[H^+] = x$

Inserting the equilibrium concentrations into the equilibrium expression and making the usual approximation that x is small compared with $[HA]_0$ gives

$$K_a = 1.8 \times 10^{-5} = \frac{[H^+][C_2H_3O_2^-]}{[HC_2H_3O_2]} = \frac{(x)(x)}{1.00 - x} \approx \frac{x^2}{1.00}$$

Thus $\qquad x^2 \approx 1.8 \times 10^{-5}$ and $x \approx 4.2 \times 10^{-3}$

The approximation $1.00 - x \approx 1.00$ is valid by the 5% rule (check this yourself), so

$$[H^+] = x = 4.2 \times 10^{-3}\ M$$

The percent dissociation is

$$\frac{[H^+]}{[HC_2H_3O_2]_0} \times 100 = \frac{4.2 \times 10^{-3}}{1.00} \times 100 = 0.42\%$$

b. This is a similar problem, except that in this case $[HC_2H_3O_2]_0 = 0.100\ M$. Analysis of the problem leads to the expression

$$K_a = 1.8 \times 10^{-5} = \frac{[H^+][C_2H_3O_2^-]}{[HC_2H_3O_2]} = \frac{(x)(x)}{0.100 - x} \approx \frac{x^2}{0.100}$$

Thus $\qquad x = [H^+] = 1.3 \times 10^{-3}\ M$

and $\qquad$ percent dissociation $= \dfrac{1.3 \times 10^{-3}}{0.10} \times 100 = 1.3\%$

The results in Sample Exercise 14.10 show two important facts. The concentration of H^+ ion at equilibrium is smaller in the 0.10 M acetic acid solution than in the 1.0 M acetic acid solution, as we would expect. However, the percent dissociation is significantly greater in the 0.10 M solution than in the 1.0 M solution. This is a general result. *For solutions of any weak acid HA, [H$^+$] decreases as [HA]$_0$ decreases, but the percent dissociation increases as [HA]$_0$ decreases.* This phenomenon can be explained as follows.

The more dilute the weak acid solution, the greater is the percent dissociation.

Consider the weak acid HA with the initial concentration $[HA]_0$, where at equilibrium

$$[HA] = [HA]_0 - x \approx [HA]_0$$

$$[H^+] = [A^-] = x$$

Thus $\qquad K_a = \dfrac{[H^+][A^-]}{[HA]} \approx \dfrac{(x)(x)}{[HA]_0}$

Now suppose enough water is added suddenly to dilute the solution by a factor of 10. The new concentrations before any adjustment occurs are

$$[A^-]_{new} = [H^+]_{new} = \frac{x}{10}$$

$$[HA]_{new} = \frac{[HA]_0}{10}$$

More concentrated   More dilute

Acid concentration

Percent dissociation

H⁺ concentration

Figure 14.5

The effect of dilution on the percent dissociation and [H⁺] of a weak acid solution.

and Q, the reaction quotient, is

$$Q = \frac{\left(\dfrac{x}{10}\right)\left(\dfrac{x}{10}\right)}{\dfrac{[HA]_0}{10}} = \frac{1(x)(x)}{10[HA]_0} = \frac{1}{10}K_a$$

Since Q is less than K_a, the system must adjust to the right to reach the new equilibrium position. Thus the percent dissociation increases when the acid is diluted. This behavior is summarized in Fig. 14.5. In Sample Exercise 14.11 we see how the percent dissociation can be used to calculate the K_a value for a weak acid.

Sample Exercise 14.11

Lactic acid ($HC_3H_5O_3$) is a waste product that accumulates in muscle tissue during exertion, leading to pain and a feeling of fatigue. In a 0.100 M aqueous solution, lactic acid is 3.7% dissociated. Calculate the value of K_a for this acid.

Solution

From the small value for the percent dissociation, it is clear that $HC_3H_5O_3$ is a weak acid. Thus the major species in the solution are the undissociated acid and water:

$$HC_3H_5O_3 \quad \text{and} \quad H_2O$$

However, even though $HC_3H_5O_3$ is a weak acid, it is a much stronger acid than water and will be the dominant source of H^+ in the solution. The dissociation reaction is

$$HC_3H_5O_3(aq) \rightleftharpoons H^+(aq) + C_3H_5O_3{}^-(aq)$$

and the equilibrium expression is

$$K_a = \frac{[H^+][C_3H_5O_3{}^-]}{[HC_3H_5O_3]}$$

The initial and equilibrium concentrations are as follows:

Initial Concentration		Equilibrium Concentration
$[HC_3H_5O_3]_0 = 0.10\ M$		$[HC_3H_5O_3] = 0.10 - x$
$[C_3H_5O_3{}^-]_0 = 0$	$\xrightarrow[\substack{HC_3H_5O_3 \\ \text{dissociates}}]{x\ \text{mol/L}}$	$[C_3H_5O_3{}^-] = x$
$[H^+]_0 \approx 0$		$[H^+] = x$

The change needed to reach equilibrium can be obtained from the percent dissociation and Equation (14.5). For this acid,

$$\text{percent dissociation} = 3.7\% = \frac{x}{[HC_3H_5O_3]_0} \times 100 = \frac{x}{0.10} \times 100$$

and

$$x = \frac{3.7}{100}(0.10) = 3.7 \times 10^{-3}\ \text{mol/L}$$

Strenuous exercise causes a buildup of lactic acid in muscle tissues.

Now we can calculate the equilibrium concentrations:

$[HC_3H_5O_3] = 0.10 - x = 0.10\ M$ (to the correct number of significant figures)

$[C_3H_5O_3^-] = [H^+] = x = 3.7 \times 10^{-3}\ M$

These concentrations can now be used to calculate the value of K_a for lactic acid:

$$K_a = \frac{[H^+][C_3H_5O_3^-]}{[HC_3H_5O_3]} = \frac{(3.7 \times 10^{-3})(3.7 \times 10^{-3})}{0.10} = 1.4 \times 10^{-4}$$

14.6 Bases

Purpose

- To introduce equilibria involving strong and weak bases.
- To show how to calculate pH for basic solutions.

According to the Arrhenius concept, a base is a substance that produces OH^- ions in aqueous solution. According to the Brønsted–Lowry model, a base is a proton acceptor. The bases sodium hydroxide (NaOH) and potassium hydroxide (KOH) fulfill both criteria. They contain OH^- ions in the solid lattice and, behaving as strong electrolytes, dissociate completely when dissolved in aqueous solution:

In a basic solution at 25°C, pH > 7.

$$NaOH(s) \rightarrow Na^+(aq) + OH^-(aq)$$

leaving virtually no undissociated NaOH. Thus a 1.0 M NaOH solution really contains 1.0 M Na^+ and 1.0 M OH^-. Because of their complete dissociation, NaOH and KOH are called **strong bases** in the same sense as we defined strong acids.

All the hydroxides of the Group 1A elements (LiOH, NaOH, KOH, RbOH, and CsOH) are strong bases, but only NaOH and KOH are common laboratory reagents, because the lithium, rubidium, and cesium compounds are expensive. The alkaline earth (Group 2A) hydroxides—$Ca(OH)_2$, $Ba(OH)_2$, and $Sr(OH)_2$—are also strong bases. For these compounds, two moles of hydroxide ion are produced for every mole of metal hydroxide dissolved in aqueous solution.

The alkaline earth hydroxides are not very soluble and are used only when the solubility factor is not important. In fact, the low solubility of these bases can sometimes be an advantage. For example, many antacids are suspensions of metal hydroxides, such as aluminum hydroxide and magnesium hydroxide. The low solubility of these compounds prevents a large hydroxide ion concentration that would harm the tissues of the mouth, esophagus, and stomach. Yet these suspensions furnish plenty of hydroxide ion to react with the stomach acid, since the salts dissolve as this reaction proceeds.

Calcium hydroxide, $Ca(OH)_2$, often called **slaked lime,** is widely used in industry because it is inexpensive and plentiful. For example, slaked lime is used in scrubbing stack gases to remove sulfur dioxide from the exhaust of power plants and factories. In the scrubbing process a suspension of slaked lime is sprayed into the stack gases to react with sulfur dioxide gas according to the following steps:

Calcium carbonate is also used in scrubbing, as discussed in Section 5.9.

$$SO_2(g) + H_2O(l) \rightleftharpoons H_2SO_3(aq)$$

$$Ca(OH)_2(aq) + H_2SO_3(aq) \rightleftharpoons CaSO_3(s) + 2H_2O(l)$$

Slaked lime is also widely used in water treatment plants for softening hard water, which involves the removal of ions, such as Ca^{2+} and Mg^{2+}, that hamper the action of detergents. The softening method most often employed in water treatment plants is the **lime–soda process,** in which *lime* (CaO) and *soda ash* (Na_2CO_3) are added to the water. As we will see in more detail later in this chapter, the CO_3^{2-} ion reacts with water to produce the HCO_3^- ion. When the lime is added to the water, it forms slaked lime, that is,

$$CaO(s) + H_2O(l) \rightarrow Ca(OH)_2(aq)$$

which then reacts with the HCO_3^- ion from the added soda ash and a Ca^{2+} ion in the hard water to produce calcium carbonate:

$$Ca(OH)_2(aq) + \underset{\substack{\nearrow \\ \text{From hard water}}}{Ca^{2+}(aq)} + 2HCO_3^-(aq) \rightarrow 2CaCO_3(s) + 2H_2O(l)$$

Thus, for every mole of $Ca(OH)_2$ consumed, 1 mole of Ca^{2+} is removed from the hard water, thereby softening it. Some hard water naturally contains bicarbonate ions. In this case, no soda ash is needed—simply adding the lime produces the softening.

Calculating the pH of a strong base solution is relatively simple, as illustrated in Sample Exercise 14.12.

Sample Exercise 14.12

Calculate the pH of a 5.0×10^{-2} M NaOH solution.

Solution

The major species in this solution are

$$\underset{\text{From NaOH}}{\underline{Na^+, \quad OH^-,}} \quad \text{and} \quad H_2O$$

Although autoionization of water also produces OH^- ions, the pH will be dominated by the OH^- ions from the dissolved NaOH. Thus, in the solution,

$$[OH^-] = 5.0 \times 10^{-2} \, M$$

and the concentration of H^+ can be calculated from K_w:

$$[H^+] = \frac{K_w}{[OH^-]} = \frac{1.0 \times 10^{-14}}{5.0 \times 10^{-2}} = 2.0 \times 10^{-13} \, M$$

$$pH = 12.70$$

Note that this is a basic solution for which

$$[OH^-] > [H^+] \quad \text{and} \quad pH > 7$$

The added OH^- from the salt has shifted the water autoionization equilibrium

$$H_2O(l) \rightleftharpoons H^+(aq) + OH^-(aq)$$

to the left, significantly lowering $[H^+]$ compared with that in pure water.

Many types of proton acceptors (bases) do not contain the hydroxide ion. However, when dissolved in water, these substances increase the concentration of hydroxide ion because of their reaction with water. For example, ammonia reacts with water as follows:

A base does not have to contain hydroxide ion.

$$NH_3(aq) + H_2O(l) \rightleftharpoons NH_4^+(aq) + OH^-(aq)$$

The ammonia molecule accepts a proton and thus functions as a base. Water is the acid in this reaction. Note that even though the base ammonia contains no hydroxide ion, it still increases the concentration of hydroxide ion to yield a basic solution.

Bases such as ammonia typically have at least one unshared pair of electrons that is capable of forming a bond with a proton. The reaction of an ammonia molecule with a water molecule can be represented as follows:

There are many bases like ammonia that produce hydroxide ion by reaction with water. In most of these bases, the lone pair is located on a nitrogen atom. Some examples are

Methylamine   Dimethylamine   Trimethylamine   Ethylamine   Pyridine

Note that the first four bases can be thought of as substituted ammonia molecules with hydrogen atoms replaced by methyl (CH_3) or ethyl (C_2H_5) groups. The pyridine molecule is like benzene

except that a nitrogen atom replaces one of the carbon atoms in the ring. The general reaction between a base B and water is given by

$$B(aq) + H_2O(l) \rightleftharpoons BH^+(aq) + OH^-(aq) \qquad (14.6)$$
Base   Acid   Conjugate   Conjugate
acid   base

The equilibrium constant for this general reaction is

$$K_b = \frac{[BH^+][OH^-]}{[B]}$$

Appendix 5.3 contains a table of K_b values.

where K_b *always refers to the reaction of a base with water to form the conjugate acid and the hydroxide ion.*

Bases of the type represented by B in Equation (14.6) compete with OH^-, a very strong base, for the H^+ ion. Thus their K_b values tend to be small (for example, for ammonia, $K_b = 1.8 \times 10^{-5}$), and they are called **weak bases.** The values of K_b for some common weak bases are listed in Table 14.3.

◀ **CHEMICAL IMPACT** ▶

Amines

We have seen that many bases have nitrogen atoms with one lone pair and can be viewed as substituted ammonia molecules, with the general formula $R_xNH_{(3-x)}$. Compounds of this type are called **amines**. Amines are widely distributed in animals and plants, and complex amines often serve as messengers or regulators. For example, in the human nervous system, there are two amine stimulants, *norepinephrine* and *adrenaline*.

HO
HO
$\overset{OH}{\overset{|}{CHCH_2NH_2}}$

Norepinephrine

O—H H H
H—C—C—N—CH₃
CH₃

Ephedrine

Ephedrine, widely used as a decongestant, was a known drug in China over 2000 years ago. Indians in Mexico and the Southwest have used the hallucinogen *mescaline,* extracted from the peyote cactus, for centuries.

HO
HO
$\overset{OH}{\overset{|}{CHCH_2NHCH_3}}$

Adrenaline

Peyote cactus growing on a rock.

CH₂CH₂NH₂

O
CH₃   CH₃
O
CH₃

Mescaline

Many other drugs, such as codeine and quinine, are amines, but they are usually not used in their pure amine forms. Instead, they are treated with an acid to become acid salts. An example of an acid salt is ammonium chloride, obtained by the reaction.

$$NH_3 + HCl \rightarrow NH_4Cl$$

Amines also can be protonated in this way. The resulting acid salt, written as AHCl (where A represents the amine), contains AH^+ and Cl^-. In general, the acid salts are more stable and more soluble in water than the parent amines. For instance, the parent amine of the well-known local anaesthetic *novocaine* is insoluble in water, whereas the acid salt is much more soluble.

O H H H CH₂CH₃
C—O—C—C—N⁺
H H Cl⁻ CH₂CH₃

Novocaine hydrochloride

N
H   H

Refer to the steps for solving weak acid equilibrium problems. Use the same systematic approach for weak base equilibrium problems.

Table 14.3			
Values of K_b for Some Common Weak Bases			
Name	Formula	Conjugate Acid	K_b
Ammonia	NH_3	NH_4^+	1.8×10^{-5}
Methylamine	CH_3NH_2	$CH_3NH_3^+$	4.38×10^{-4}
Ethylamine	$C_2H_5NH_2$	$C_2H_5NH_3^+$	5.6×10^{-4}
Aniline	$C_6H_5NH_2$	$C_6H_5NH_3^+$	3.8×10^{-10}
Pyridine	C_5H_5N	$C_5H_5NH^+$	1.7×10^{-9}

Typically, pH calculations for solutions of weak bases are very similar to those for weak acids, as illustrated by Sample Exercises 14.13 and 14.14.

Sample Exercises 14.13

Calculate the pH for a 15.0 M solution of NH_3 ($K_b = 1.8 \times 10^{-5}$).

Solution

Since ammonia is a weak base, as can be seen from its small K_b value, most of the dissolved NH_3 will remain as NH_3. Thus the major species in solution are

$$NH_3 \quad \text{and} \quad H_2O$$

Both these substances can produce OH^- according to the reactions

$$NH_3(aq) + H_2O(l) \rightleftharpoons NH_4^+(aq) + OH^-(aq) \qquad K_b = 1.8 \times 10^{-5}$$
$$H_2O(l) \rightleftharpoons H^+(aq) + OH^-(aq) \qquad K_w = 1.0 \times 10^{-14}$$

However, the contribution from water can be neglected, since $K_b \gg K_w$. The equilibrium for NH_3 will dominate, and the equilibrium expression to be used is

$$K_b = 1.8 \times 10^{-5} = \frac{[NH_4^+][OH^-]}{[NH_3]}$$

The appropriate concentrations are

Initial Concentration (mol/L)		Equilibrium Concentration (mol/L)
$[NH_3]_0 = 15.0$ $[NH_4^+]_0 = 0$ $[OH^-]_0 \approx 0$	$\xrightarrow[\substack{H_2O \text{ to reach} \\ \text{equilibrium}}]{\substack{x \text{ mol/L} \\ NH_3 \text{ reacts with}}}$	$[NH_3] = 15.0 - x$ $[NH_4^+] = x$ $[OH^-] = x$

Substituting the equilibrium concentrations in the equilibrium expression and making the usual approximation gives

$$K_b = 1.8 \times 10^{-5} = \frac{[NH_4^+][OH^-]}{[NH_3]} = \frac{(x)(x)}{15.0 - x} \approx \frac{x^2}{15.0}$$

Thus

$$x \approx 1.6 \times 10^{-2}$$

The 5% rule validates the approximation (check it yourself), so

$$[OH^-] = 1.6 \times 10^{-2} \, M$$

Since we know that K_w must be satisfied for this solution, we can calculate $[H^+]$ as follows:

$$[H^+] = \frac{K_w}{[OH^-]} = \frac{1.0 \times 10^{-14}}{1.6 \times 10^{-2}} = 6.3 \times 10^{-13} \, M$$

Therefore,

$$pH = -\log(6.3 \times 10^{-13}) = 12.20$$

Sample Exercise 14.13 illustrates how a typical weak base equilibrium problem should be solved. Note two additional important points:

A table of K_b values for bases is also given in Appendix 5.3.

1. We calculated $[H^+]$ from K_w and then calculated the pH, but another method is available. The pOH could have been calculated from $[OH^-]$ and then used in Equation (14.3):

$$pK_w = 14.00 = pH + pOH$$
$$pH = 14.00 - pOH$$

2. In a 15.0 M NH_3 solution, the equilibrium concentrations of NH_4^+ and OH^- are each 1.6×10^{-2} M. Only a small percentage,

$$\frac{1.6 \times 10^{-2}}{15.0} \times 100 = 0.11\%$$

of the ammonia reacts with water. Bottles containing 15.0 M NH_3 solution are often labeled 15.0 M NH_4OH, but as you can see from these results, 15.0 M NH_3 is actually a much more accurate description of the solution contents.

Sample Exercise 14.14

Calculate the pH of a 1.0 M solution of methylamine ($K_b = 4.38 \times 10^{-4}$).

Solution

Since methylamine (CH_3NH_2) is a weak base, the major species in solution are

$$CH_3NH_2 \quad \text{and} \quad H_2O$$

Both are bases; however, water can be neglected as a source of OH^-, so the dominant equilibrium is

$$CH_3NH_2(aq) + H_2O(l) \rightleftharpoons CH_3NH_3^+(aq) + OH^-(aq)$$

and

$$K_b = 4.38 \times 10^{-4} = \frac{[CH_3NH_3^+][OH^-]}{[CH_3NH_2]}$$

The concentrations are as follows:

Initial Concentration (mol/L)		Equilibrium Concentration (mol/L)
$[CH_3NH_2]_0 = 1.0$ $[CH_3NH_3^+]_0 = 0$ $[OH^-]_0 \approx 0$	$\xrightarrow[\substack{\text{to reach} \\ \text{equilibrium}}]{\substack{x \text{ mol/L } CH_3NH_2 \\ \text{reacts with } H_2O}}$	$[CH_3NH_2] = 1.0 - x$ $[CH_3NH_3^+] = x$ $[OH^-] = x$

Substituting the equilibrium concentrations in the equilibrium expression and making the usual approximation give

$$K_b = 4.38 \times 10^{-4} = \frac{[CH_3NH_3^+][OH^-]}{[CH_3NH_2]} = \frac{(x)(x)}{1.0 - x} \approx \frac{x^2}{1.0}$$

and

$$x \approx 2.1 \times 10^{-2}$$

The approximation is valid by the 5% rule, so

$$[OH^-] = x = 2.1 \times 10^{-2} \ M$$

$$pOH = 1.68$$
$$pH = 14.00 - 1.68 = 12.32$$

14.7 Polyprotic Acids

Purpose

• To describe the dissociation equilibria of acids with more than one acidic proton.

Some important acids, such as sulfuric acid (H_2SO_4) and phosphoric acid (H_3PO_4), can furnish more than one proton and are called **polyprotic acids.** A polyprotic acid always dissociates in a *stepwise* manner, one proton at a time. For example, the diprotic (two-proton) acid carbonic acid (H_2CO_3), which is so important in maintaining a constant pH in human blood, dissociates in the following steps:

$$H_2CO_3(aq) \rightleftharpoons H^+(aq) + HCO_3^-(aq) \qquad K_{a_1} = \frac{[H^+][HCO_3^-]}{[H_2CO_3]} = 4.3 \times 10^{-7}$$

$$HCO_3^-(aq) \rightleftharpoons H^+(aq) + CO_3^{2-}(aq) \qquad K_{a_2} = \frac{[H^+][CO_3^{2-}]}{[HCO_3^-]} = 5.6 \times 10^{-11}$$

The successive K_a values for the dissociation equilibria are designated K_{a_1} and K_{a_2}. Note that the conjugate base HCO_3^- of the first dissociation equilibrium becomes the acid in the second step.

Carbonic acid is formed when carbon dioxide gas is dissolved in water. In fact, the first dissociation step for carbonic acid is best represented by the reaction

$$CO_2(aq) + H_2O(l) \rightleftharpoons H^+(aq) + HCO_3^-(aq)$$

since relatively little H_2CO_3 actually exists in solution. However, it is convenient to consider CO_2 in water as H_2CO_3 so that we can treat such solutions using the familiar dissociation reactions for weak acids.

Phosphoric acid is a **triprotic acid** (three protons) that dissociates in the following steps:

$$H_3PO_4(aq) \rightleftharpoons H^+(aq) + H_2PO_4^-(aq) \qquad K_{a_1} = \frac{[H^+][H_2PO_4^-]}{[H_3PO_4]} = 7.5 \times 10^{-3}$$

$$H_2PO_4^-(aq) \rightleftharpoons H^+(aq) + HPO_4^{2-}(aq) \qquad K_{a_2} = \frac{[H^+][HPO_4^{2-}]}{[H_2PO_4^-]} = 6.2 \times 10^{-8}$$

$$HPO_4^{2-}(aq) \rightleftharpoons H^+(aq) + PO_4^{3-}(aq) \qquad K_{a_3} = \frac{[H^+][PO_4^{3-}]}{[HPO_4^{2-}]} = 4.8 \times 10^{-13}$$

For a typical weak polyprotic acid,

$$K_{a_1} > K_{a_2} > K_{a_3}$$

That is, the acid involved in each step of the dissociation is successively weaker, as shown by the stepwise dissociation constants given in Table 14.4. These values indicate that the loss of a second or third proton occurs less readily than loss of the first proton. This is not surprising; as the negative charge on the acid increases, it becomes more difficult to remove the positively charged proton.

A table of K_a values for polyprotic acids is also given in Appendix 5.2.

Table 14.4

Stepwise Dissociation Constants for Several Common Polyprotic Acids

Name	Formula	K_{a_1}	K_{a_2}	K_{a_3}
Phosphoric acid	H_3PO_4	7.5×10^{-3}	6.2×10^{-8}	4.8×10^{-13}
Arsenic acid	H_3AsO_4	5×10^{-3}	8×10^{-8}	6×10^{-10}
Carbonic acid	H_2CO_3	4.3×10^{-7}	5.6×10^{-11}	
Sulfuric acid	H_2SO_4	Large	1.2×10^{-2}	
Sulfurous acid	H_2SO_3	1.5×10^{-2}	1.0×10^{-7}	
Hydrosulfuric acid*	H_2S	1.0×10^{-7}	$\sim 10^{-19}$	
Oxalic acid	$H_2C_2O_4$	6.5×10^{-2}	6.1×10^{-5}	
Ascorbic acid (vitamin C)	$H_2C_6H_6O_6$	7.9×10^{-5}	1.6×10^{-12}	

*The K_{a_2} value for H_2S is very uncertain. Because it is so small, the K_{a_2} value is very difficult to measure accurately.

Although we might expect the pH calculations for solutions of polyprotic acids to be complicated, the most common cases are surprisingly straightforward. To illustrate, we will consider a typical case, phosphoric acid, and a unique case, sulfuric acid.

Phosphoric Acid

Phosphoric acid is typical of most weak polyprotic acids in that the successive K_a values are very different. For example, the ratios of successive K_a values (from Table 14.4) are

$$\frac{K_{a_1}}{K_{a_2}} = \frac{7.5 \times 10^{-3}}{6.2 \times 10^{-8}} = 1.2 \times 10^5$$

$$\frac{K_{a_2}}{K_{a_3}} = \frac{6.2 \times 10^{-8}}{4.8 \times 10^{-13}} = 1.3 \times 10^5$$

Thus the relative acid strengths are

$$H_3PO_4 \gg H_2PO_4^- \gg HPO_4^{2-}$$

For a typical polyprotic acid in water, only the first dissociation step is important in determining the pH.

This means that in a solution prepared by dissolving H_3PO_4 in water, *only the first dissociation step makes an important contribution to [H^+]*. This greatly simplifies the pH calculations for phosphoric acid solutions, as is illustrated in Sample Exercise 14.15.

Sample Exercise 14.15

Calculate the pH of a 5.0 M H_3PO_4 solution and the equilibrium concentrations of the species H_3PO_4, $H_2PO_4^-$, HPO_4^{2-}, and PO_4^{3-}.

Solution

The major species in solution are

$$H_3PO_4 \quad \text{and} \quad H_2O$$

None of the dissociation products of H_3PO_4 is written, since the K_a values are all so small that they will be minor species. The dominant equilibrium is the dissociation of H_3PO_4:

$$H_3PO_4(aq) \rightleftharpoons H^+(aq) + H_2PO_4^-(aq)$$

where

$$K_{a_1} = 7.5 \times 10^{-3} = \frac{[H^+][H_2PO_4^-]}{[H_3PO_4]}$$

The concentrations are as follows:

Initial Concentration (mol/L)		Equilibrium Concentration (mol/L)
$[H_3PO_4]_0 = 5.0$	$\xrightarrow[\text{dissociates}]{\begin{array}{c} x \text{ mol/L} \\ H_3PO_4 \end{array}}$	$[H_3PO_4] = 5.0 - x$
$[H_2PO_4^-]_0 = 0$		$[H_2PO_4^-] = x$
$[H^+]_0 \approx 0$		$[H^+] = x$

Substituting the equilibrium concentrations into the expression for K_{a_1} and making the usual approximation gives

$$K_{a_1} = 7.5 \times 10^{-3} = \frac{[H^+][H_2PO_4^-]}{[H_3PO_4]} = \frac{(x)(x)}{5.0 - x} \approx \frac{x^2}{5.0}$$

Thus

$$x \approx 1.9 \times 10^{-1}$$

Since 1.9×10^{-1} is less than 5% of 5.0, the approximation is acceptable, and

$$[H^+] = x = 0.19 \, M$$
$$pH = 0.72$$

So far we have determined that

$$[H^+] = [H_2PO_4^-] = 0.19 \, M$$

and

$$[H_3PO_4] = 5.0 - x = 4.8 \, M$$

The concentration of HPO_4^{2-} can be obtained by using the expression for K_{a_2}:

$$K_{a_2} = 6.2 \times 10^{-8} = \frac{[H^+][HPO_4^{2-}]}{[H_2PO_4^-]}$$

where

$$[H^+] = [H_2PO_4^-] = 0.19 \, M$$

Thus

$$[HPO_4^{2-}] = K_{a_2} = 6.2 \times 10^{-8} \, M$$

To calculate $[PO_4^{3-}]$, we use the expression for K_{a_3} and the values of $[H^+]$ and $[HPO_4^{2-}]$ calculated previously:

$$K_{a_3} = \frac{[H^+][PO_4^{3-}]}{[HPO_4^{2-}]} = 4.8 \times 10^{-13} = \frac{0.19[PO_4^{3-}]}{(6.2 \times 10^{-8})}$$

$$[PO_4^{3-}] = \frac{(4.8 \times 10^{-13})(6.2 \times 10^{-8})}{0.19} = 1.6 \times 10^{-19} \, M$$

These results show that the second and third dissociation steps do not make an important contribution to $[H^+]$. This is apparent from the fact that $[HPO_4^{2-}]$ is $6.2 \times 10^{-8} \, M$, which means that only 6.2×10^{-8} mol/L $H_2PO_4^-$ has dissociated.

The value of $[PO_4^{3-}]$ shows that the dissociation of HPO_4^{2-} is even smaller. We must, however, use the second and third dissociation steps to calculate $[HPO_4^{2-}]$ and $[PO_4^{3-}]$, since these steps are the only sources of these ions.

Sulfuric Acid

Sulfuric acid is unique among the common acids in that it is *a strong acid in its first dissociation step and a weak acid in its second step:*

$$H_2SO_4(aq) \rightarrow H^+(aq) + HSO_4^-(aq) \qquad K_{a_1} \text{ is very large}$$
$$HSO_4^-(aq) \rightleftharpoons H^+(aq) + SO_4^{2-}(aq) \qquad K_{a_2} = 1.2 \times 10^{-2}$$

Sample Exercise 14.16 illustrates how to calculate the pH for sulfuric acid solutions.

Sample Exercise 14.16

Calculate the pH of a 1.0 M H_2SO_4 solution.

Solution

The major species in the solution are

$$H^+, \quad HSO_4^-, \quad \text{and} \quad H_2O$$

where the first two ions are produced by the complete first dissociation step of H_2SO_4. The concentration of H^+ in this solution will be at least 1.0 M, since this amount is produced by the first dissociation step of H_2SO_4. We must now answer this question: does the HSO_4^- ion dissociate enough to produce a significant contribution to the concentration of H^+? This question can be answered by calculating the equilibrium concentrations for the dissociation reaction of HSO_4^-:

$$HSO_4^-(aq) \rightleftharpoons H^+(aq) + SO_4^{2-}(aq)$$

where

$$K_{a_2} = 1.2 \times 10^{-2} = \frac{[H^+][SO_4^{2-}]}{[HSO_4^-]}$$

The concentrations are as follows:

Initial Concentration (mol/L)		Equilibrium Concentration (mol/L)
$[HSO_4^-]_0 = 1.0$	x mol/L HSO_4^- dissociates	$[HSO_4^-] = 1.0 - x$
$[SO_4^{2-}]_0 = 0$	$\xrightarrow{\hspace{2cm}}$	$[SO_4^{2-}] = x$
$[H^+]_0 = 1.0$	to reach equilibrium	$[H^+] = 1.0 + x$

Note that $[H^+]_0$ is not equal to zero, as it usually is for a weak acid, because the first dissociation step has already occurred. Substituting the equilibrium concentrations into the expression for K_{a_2} and making the usual approximation give

$$K_{a_2} = 1.2 \times 10^{-2} = \frac{[H^+][SO_4^{2-}]}{[HSO_4^-]} = \frac{(1.0 + x)(x)}{1.0 - x} \approx \frac{(1.0)(x)}{(1.0)}$$

Thus $$x \approx 1.2 \times 10^{-2}$$

Since 1.2×10^{-2} is 1.2% of 1.0, the approximation is valid according to the 5% rule. Note that x is not equal to $[H^+]$ in this case. Instead,

$$[H^+] = 1.0\ M + x = 1.0\ M + (1.2 \times 10^{-2})\ M$$
$$= 1.0\ M \quad \text{(to the correct number of significant figures)}$$

Thus the dissociation of HSO_4^- does not make a significant contribution to the concentration of H^+, and

$$[H^+] = 1.0\ M \quad \text{and} \quad pH = 0.00$$

Sample Exercise 14.16 illustrates the most common case for sulfuric acid in which only the first dissociation makes an important contribution to the concentration of H^+. In solutions more dilute than $1.0\ M$ (for example, $0.10\ M\ H_2SO_4$), the dissociation of HSO_4^- is important, and solving the problem requires use of the quadratic formula, as shown in Sample Exercise 14.17.

Only in dilute H_2SO_4 solutions does the second dissociation step contribute significantly to $[H^+]$.

Sample Exercise 14.17

Calculate the pH of a $1.00 \times 10^{-2}\ M\ H_2SO_4$ solution.

Solution

The major species in solution are

$$H^+, \quad HSO_4^-, \quad \text{and} \quad H_2O$$

Proceeding as in Sample Exercise 14.16, we consider the dissociation of HSO_4^-, which leads to the following concentrations:

Initial Concentration (mol/L)		Equilibrium Concentration (mol/L)
$[HSO_4^-]_0 = 0.0100$	x mol/L HSO_4^- dissociates	$[HSO_4^-] = 0.0100 - x$
$[SO_4^{2-}]_0 = 0$	$\xrightarrow{\text{to reach}}$	$[SO_4^{2-}] = x$
$[H^+]_0 = 0.0100$	equilibrium	$[H^+] = 0.0100 + x$
$\uparrow$		
From dissociation of H_2SO_4		

Substituting the equilibrium concentrations into the expression for K_{a_2} gives

$$1.2 \times 10^{-2} = K_{a_2} = \frac{[H^+][SO_4^{2-}]}{[HSO_4^-]} = \frac{(0.0100 + x)(x)}{(0.0100 - x)}$$

If we make the usual approximation, then $0.010 + x \approx 0.010$ and $0.010 - x \approx 0.010$, and we have

$$1.2 \times 10^{-2} = \frac{(0.0100 + x)(x)}{(0.0100 - x)} \approx \frac{(0.0100)x}{(0.0100)}$$

The calculated value of x is

$$x = 1.2 \times 10^{-2} = 0.012$$

This value is larger than 0.010, clearly a ridiculous result. Thus we cannot make the usual approximation and must instead solve the quadratic equation. The expression

$$1.2 \times 10^{-2} = \frac{(0.0100 + x)(x)}{(0.0100 - x)}$$

leads to

$$(1.2 \times 10^{-2})(0.0100 - x) = (0.0100 + x)(x)$$
$$(1.2 \times 10^{-4}) - (1.2 \times 10^{-2})x = (1.0 \times 10^{-2})x + x^2$$
$$x^2 + (2.2 \times 10^{-2})x - (1.2 \times 10^{-4}) = 0$$

This equation can be solved using the quadratic formula

$$x = \frac{-b \pm \sqrt{b^2 - 4ac}}{2a}$$

where $a = 1$, $b = 2.2 \times 10^{-2}$, and $c = -1.2 \times 10^{-4}$. Use of the quadratic formula gives one negative root (which cannot be correct) and one positive root,

$$x = 4.5 \times 10^{-3}$$

Thus

$$[H^+] = 0.0100 + x = 0.0100 + 0.0045 = 0.0145$$

and

$$pH = 1.84$$

Note that in this case the second dissociation step produces about half as many H^+ ions as the initial step does.

This problem also can be solved by successive approximations, a method illustrated in Appendix 1.4.

Characteristics of Weak Polyprotic Acids

- Typically, successive K_a values are so much smaller than the first value that only the first dissociation step makes a significant contribution to the equilibrium concentration of H^+. This means that the calculation of the pH for a solution of a typical weak polyprotic acid is identical to that for a solution of a weak monoprotic acid.

- Sulfuric acid is unique in being a strong acid in its first dissociation step and a weak acid in its second step. For relatively concentrated solutions of sulfuric acid (1.0 M or higher), the large concentration of H^+ from the first dissociation step represses the second step, which can be neglected as a contributor of H^+ ions. For dilute solutions of sulfuric acid, the second step does make a significant contribution, and the quadratic equation must be used to obtain the total H^+ concentration.

14.8 Acid–Base Properties of Salts

Purpose

- To explain why certain salts give acidic or basic solutions, and to show how to calculate the pH of these solutions.

Salt is simply another name for *ionic compound*. When a salt dissolves in water, we assume that it breaks up into its ions, which move about independently, at least in dilute solutions. Under certain conditions, these ions can behave as acids or bases. In this section we explore such reactions.

Salts That Produce Neutral Solutions

Recall that the conjugate base of a strong acid has virtually no affinity for protons in water. This is why strong acids completely dissociate in aqueous solution. Thus, when anions such as Cl^- and NO_3^- are placed in water, they do not combine with H^+ and have no effect on the pH. Cations such as K^+ and Na^+ from strong bases have no affinity for H^+ nor can they produce H^+, and so they too have no effect on the pH of an aqueous solution. *Salts that consist of the cations of strong bases and the anions of strong acids have no effect on [H^+] when dissolved in water.* This means that aqueous solutions of salts such as KCl, NaCl, NaNO$_3$, and KNO$_3$ are neutral (have a pH of 7).

The salt of a strong acid and a strong base gives a neutral solution.

Salts That Produce Basic Solutions

In an aqueous solution of sodium acetate (NaC$_2$H$_3$O$_2$), the major species are

$$Na^+, \quad C_2H_3O_2^-, \quad \text{and} \quad H_2O$$

What are the acid–base properties of each component? The Na^+ ion has neither acid nor base properties. The $C_2H_3O_2^-$ ion is the conjugate base of acetic acid, a weak acid. This means that $C_2H_3O_2^-$ has a significant affinity for a proton and is a base. Finally, water is a weakly amphoteric substance.

The pH of this solution will be determined by the $C_2H_3O_2^-$ ion. Since $C_2H_3O_2^-$ is a base, it will react with the best proton donor available. In this case, water is the *only* source of protons, and the reaction between the acetate ion and water is

$$C_2H_3O_2^-(aq) + H_2O(l) \rightleftharpoons HC_2H_3O_2(aq) + OH^-(aq) \qquad (14.7)$$

Note that this reaction, which yields a basic solution, involves a *base reacting with water to produce hydroxide ion and a conjugate acid*. We have defined K_b as the equilibrium constant for such a reaction. In this case,

$$K_b = \frac{[HC_2H_3O_2][OH^-]}{[C_2H_3O_2^-]}$$

The value of K_a for acetic acid is well known (1.8×10^{-5}). But how can we obtain the K_b value for the acetate ion? The answer lies in the relationships among K_a, K_b, and K_w. Note that when the expression for K_a for acetic acid is multiplied by the expression for K_b for the acetate ion, the result is K_w:

$$K_a \times K_b = \frac{[H^+][C_2H_3O_2^-]}{[HC_2H_3O_2]} \times \frac{[HC_2H_3O_2][OH^-]}{[C_2H_3O_2^-]} = [H^+][OH^-] = K_w$$

This is a very important result. For any weak acid and its conjugate base,

$$K_a \times K_b = K_w$$

Thus, when either K_a or K_b is known, the other can be calculated. For the acetate ion,

$$K_b = \frac{K_w}{K_a \text{ (for } HC_2H_3O_2)} = \frac{1.0 \times 10^{-14}}{1.8 \times 10^{-5}} = 5.6 \times 10^{-10}$$

A basic solution is formed if the anion of the salt is the conjugate base of a weak acid.

This is the K_b value for the reaction described by Equation (14.7). Note that it is obtained from the K_a value of the parent weak acid, in this case acetic acid. The sodium acetate solution is an example of an important general case. *For any salt whose cation has neutral properties (such as Na^+ or K^+) and whose anion is the conjugate base of a weak acid, the aqueous solution will be basic.* The K_b value for the anion can be obtained from the relationship $K_b = K_w/K_a$. Equilibrium calculations of this type are illustrated in Sample Exercise 14.18.

Sample Exercise 14.18

Calculate the pH of a 0.30 M NaF solution. The K_a value for HF is 7.2×10^{-4}.

Solution

The major species in solution are

$$Na^+, \quad F^-, \quad \text{and} \quad H_2O$$

Since HF is a weak acid, the F^- ion must have a significant affinity for protons, and the dominant reaction will be

$$F^-(aq) + H_2O(l) \rightleftharpoons HF(aq) + OH^-(aq)$$

which yields the K_b expression

$$K_b = \frac{[HF][OH^-]}{[F^-]}$$

The value of K_b can be calculated from K_w and the K_a value for HF:

$$K_b = \frac{K_w}{K_a \text{ (for HF)}} = \frac{1.0 \times 10^{-14}}{7.2 \times 10^{-4}} = 1.4 \times 10^{-11}$$

The concentrations are as follows:

Initial Concentration (mol/L)		Equilibrium Concentration (mol/L)
$[F^-]_0 = 0.30$ $[HF]_0 = 0$ $[OH^-]_0 \approx 0$	$\xrightarrow[\substack{\text{reacts with} \\ \text{H}_2\text{O to reach} \\ \text{equilibrium}}]{x \text{ mol/L } F^-}$	$[F^-] = 0.30 - x$ $[HF] = x$ $[OH^-] = x$

Thus

$$K_b = 1.4 \times 10^{-11} = \frac{[HF][OH^-]}{[F^-]} = \frac{(x)(x)}{0.30 - x} \approx \frac{x^2}{0.30}$$

$$x \approx 2.0 \times 10^{-6}$$

The approximation is valid by the 5% rule, so

$$[OH^-] = x = 2.0 \times 10^{-6} \, M$$

$$pOH = 5.69$$

$$pH = 14.00 - 5.69 = 8.31$$

As expected, the solution is basic.

Base Strength in Aqueous Solution

To emphasize the concept of base strength, let us consider the basic properties of the cyanide ion. One relevant reaction is the dissociation of hydrocyanic acid in water:

$$HCN(aq) + H_2O(l) \rightleftharpoons H_3O^+(aq) + CN^-(aq) \qquad K_a = 6.2 \times 10^{-10}$$

Since HCN is such a weak acid, CN^- appears to be a *strong* base, showing a very high affinity for H^+ *compared to H_2O*, with which it is competing. However, we also need to look at the reaction in which cyanide ion reacts with water:

$$CN^-(aq) + H_2O(l) \rightleftharpoons HCN(aq) + OH^-(aq)$$

where
$$K_b = \frac{K_w}{K_a} = \frac{1.0 \times 10^{-14}}{6.2 \times 10^{-10}} = 1.6 \times 10^{-5}$$

In this reaction CN^- appears to be a weak base; the K_b value is only 1.6×10^{-5}. What accounts for this apparent difference in base strength? The key idea is that in the reaction of CN^- with H_2O, *CN^- is competing with OH^- for H^+, instead of competing with H_2O,* as it does in the HCN dissociation reaction. These equilibria show the following relative base strengths:

$$OH^- > CN^- > H_2O$$

Similar arguments can be made for other "weak" bases, such as ammonia, the acetate ion, the fluoride ion, and so on.

Salts That Produce Acidic Solutions

Some salts produce acidic solutions when dissolved in water. For example, when solid NH_4Cl is dissolved in water, NH_4^+ and Cl^- ions are present, with NH_4^+ behaving as a weak acid:

$$NH_4^+(aq) \rightleftharpoons NH_3(aq) + H^+(aq)$$

The Cl^- ion, having virtually no affinity for H^+ in water, does not affect the pH of the solution.

In general, *salts in which the anion is not a base and the cation is the conjugate acid of a weak base produce acidic solutions.*

Sample Exercise 14.19

Calculate the pH of a 0.10 *M* NH_4Cl solution. The K_b value for NH_3 is 1.8×10^{-5}.

Solution

The major species in solution are

$$NH_4^+, \quad Cl^-, \quad \text{and} \quad H_2O$$

Note that both NH_4^+ and H_2O can produce H^+. The dissociation reaction for the NH_4^+ ion is

$$NH_4^+(aq) \rightleftharpoons NH_3(aq) + H^+(aq)$$

for which

$$K_a = \frac{[NH_3][H^+]}{[NH_4^+]}$$

Note that although the K_b value for NH_3 is given, the reaction corresponding to K_b is not appropriate here, since NH_3 is not a major species in the solution. Instead, the given value of K_b is used to calculate K_a for NH_4^+ from the relationship

$$K_a \times K_b = K_w$$

Thus $\quad K_a \text{ (for } NH_4^+\text{)} = \frac{K_w}{K_b \text{ (for } NH_3\text{)}} = \frac{1.0 \times 10^{-14}}{1.8 \times 10^{-5}} = 5.6 \times 10^{-10}$

Although NH_4^+ is a very weak acid, as indicated by its K_a value, it is stronger than H_2O and thus will dominate in the production of H^+. Thus we will focus on the dissociation reaction of NH_4^+ to calculate the pH in this solution.

We solve the weak acid problem in the usual way:

Initial Concentration (mol/L)		Equilibrium Concentration (mol/L)
$[NH_4^+]_0 = 0.10$	x mol/L NH_4^+ dissociates to reach equilibrium	$[NH_4^+] = 0.10 - x$
$[NH_3]_0 = 0$		$[NH_3] = x$
$[H^+]_0 \approx 0$		$[H^+] \approx x$

Thus $\quad 5.6 \times 10^{-10} = K_a = \frac{[H^+][NH_3]}{[NH_4^+]} = \frac{(x)(x)}{0.10 - x} \approx \frac{x^2}{0.10}$

$$x \approx 7.5 \times 10^{-6}$$

The approximation is valid by the 5% rule, so

$$[H^+] = x = 7.5 \times 10^{-6}\ M \quad \text{and} \quad pH = 5.13$$

A second type of salt that produces an acidic solution is one that contains a *highly charged metal ion*. For example, when solid aluminum chloride ($AlCl_3$) is dissolved in water, the resulting solution is significantly acidic. Although the Al^{3+} ion is not itself a Brønsted–Lowry acid, the hydrated ion $Al(H_2O)_6^{3+}$ formed in water is a weak acid:

$$Al(H_2O)_6^{3+}(aq) \rightleftharpoons Al(OH)(H_2O)_5^{2+}(aq) + H^+(aq)$$

The high charge on the metal ion polarizes the O—H bonds in the attached water molecules, making the hydrogens in these water molecules more acidic than those in free water molecules. Typically, the higher the charge on the metal ion, the stronger the acidity of the hydrated ion.

Section 14.9 contains a further discussion of the acidity of hydrated ions.

Sample Exercise 14.20

Calculate the pH of a 0.010 M $AlCl_3$ solution. The K_a value for $Al(H_2O)_6^{3+}$ is 1.4×10^{-5}.

Solution

The major species in solution are

$$Al(H_2O)_6^{3+}, \quad Cl^-, \quad \text{and} \quad H_2O$$

Since the $Al(H_2O)_6^{3+}$ ion is a stronger acid than water, the dominant equilibrium is

$$Al(H_2O)_6^{3+}(aq) \rightleftharpoons Al(OH)(H_2O)_5^{2+}(aq) + H^+(aq)$$

and

$$1.4 \times 10^{-5} = K_a = \frac{[Al(OH)(H_2O)_5^{2+}][H^+]}{[Al(H_2O)_6^{3+}]}$$

This is a typical weak acid problem, which we can solve with the usual procedures:

Initial Concentration (mol/L)		Equilibrium Concentration (mol/L)
$[Al(H_2O)_6^{3+}]_0 = 0.010$	$\xrightarrow[\substack{Al(OH_2)_6^{3+} \\ \text{dissociates} \\ \text{to reach} \\ \text{equilibrium}}]{x \text{ mol/L}}$	$[Al(H_2O)_6^{3+}] = 0.010 - x$
$[Al(OH)(H_2O)_5^{2+}]_0 = 0$		$[Al(OH)(H_2O)_5^{2+}] = x$
$[H^+]_0 \approx 0$		$[H^+] = x$

Thus $1.4 \times 10^{-5} = K_a = \dfrac{[Al(OH)(H_2O)_5^{2+}][H^+]}{[Al(H_2O)_6^{3+}]} = \dfrac{(x)(x)}{0.010 - x} \approx \dfrac{x^2}{0.010}$

$$x \approx 3.7 \times 10^{-4}$$

Since the approximation is valid by the 5% rule,

$$[H^+] = x = 3.7 \times 10^{-4} \ M \quad \text{and} \quad pH = 3.43$$

So far we have considered salts in which only one of the ions has acidic or basic properties. For many salts, such as ammonium acetate ($NH_4C_2H_3O_2$), both ions can affect the pH of the aqueous solution. Because the equilibrium calculations for these cases can be quite complicated, we will consider only the qualitative aspects of such problems. We can predict whether the solution will be basic, acidic, or neutral by comparing the K_a value for the acidic ion with the K_b value for the basic ion. If the K_a value for the acidic ion is larger than the K_b value for the basic ion, the solution will be acidic. If the K_b value is larger than the K_a value, the solution will be basic. Equal K_a and K_b values mean a neutral solution. These facts are summarized in Table 14.5.

Table 14.5

Qualitative Prediction of pH for Solutions of Salts for Which Both Cation and Anion Have Acidic or Basic Properties

$K_a > K_b$	pH < 7 (acidic)
$K_b > K_a$	pH > 7 (basic)
$K_a = K_b$	pH = 7 (neutral)

Sample Exercise 14.21

Predict whether an aqueous solution of each of the following salts will be acidic, basic, or neutral.

a. $NH_4C_2H_3O_2$
b. NH_4CN
c. $Al_2(SO_4)_3$

Solution

a. The ions in solution are NH_4^+ and $C_2H_3O_2^-$. As we mentioned previously, K_a for NH_4^+ is 5.6×10^{-10} and K_b for $C_2H_3O_2^-$ is 5.6×10^{-10}. Thus K_a for NH_4^+ is equal to K_b for $C_2H_3O_2^-$, and the solution will be neutral (pH = 7).

b. The solution will contain NH_4^+ and CN^- ions. The K_a value for NH_4^+ is 5.6×10^{-10} and

$$K_b \text{ (for } CN^-) = \frac{K_w}{K_a \text{ (for HCN)}} = 1.6 \times 10^{-5}$$

Since K_b for CN^- is much larger than K_a for NH_4^+, CN^- is a much stronger base than NH_4^+ is an acid. This solution will be basic.

c. The solution will contain $Al(H_2O)_6^{3+}$ and SO_4^{2-} ions. The K_a value for $Al(H_2O)_6^{3+}$ is 1.4×10^{-5}, as given in Sample Exercise 14.20. We must calculate K_b for SO_4^{2-}. The HSO_4^- ion is the conjugate acid of SO_4^{2-}, and its K_a value is K_{a_2} for sulfuric acid, or 1.2×10^{-2}. Therefore,

$$K_b \text{ (for } SO_4^{2-}) = \frac{K_w}{K_{a_2} \text{ (for sulfuric acid)}}$$
$$= \frac{1.0 \times 10^{-14}}{1.2 \times 10^{-2}} = 8.3 \times 10^{-13}$$

This solution will be acidic, since K_a for $Al(H_2O)_6^{3+}$ is much greater than K_b for SO_4^{2-}.

The acid–base properties of aqueous solutions of various salts are summarized in Table 14.6.

Table 14.6			
Acid–Base Properties of Various Types of Salts			
Type of Salt	Examples	Comment	pH of Solution
Cation is from strong base; anion is from strong acid	KCl, KNO_3, $NaCl$, $NaNO_3$	Neither acts as an acid or a base	Neutral
Cation is from strong base; anion is from weak acid	$NaC_2H_3O_2$, KCN, NaF	Anion acts as a base; cation has no effect on pH	Basic
Cation is conjugate acid of weak base; anion is from strong acid	NH_4Cl, NH_4NO_3	Cation acts as acid; anion has no effect on pH	Acidic
Cation is conjugate acid of weak base; anion is conjugate base of weak acid	$NH_4C_2H_3O_2$, NH_4CN	Cation acts as an acid; anion acts as a base	Acidic if $K_a > K_b$, basic if $K_b > K_a$, neutral if $K_a = K_b$
Cation is highly charged metal ion; anion is from strong acid	$Al(NO_3)_3$, $FeCl_3$	Hydrated cation acts as an acid; anion has no effect on pH	Acidic

14.9 The Effect of Structure on Acid–Base Properties

Purpose

• To show how bond strength and polarity affect acid–base properties.

We have seen that when a substance is dissolved in water, it produces an acidic solution if it can donate protons and produces a basic solution if it can accept protons. What structural properties of a molecule cause it to behave as an acid or as a base?

Any molecule containing a hydrogen atom is potentially an acid. However, many such molecules show no acidic properties. For example, molecules containing C—H bonds, such as chloroform ($CHCl_3$) and nitromethane (CH_3NO_2), do not produce acidic aqueous solutions because a C—H bond is both strong and nonpolar and thus there is no tendency to donate protons. On the other hand, although the H—Cl bond in gaseous hydrogen chloride is slightly stronger than a C—H bond, it is much more polar, and this molecule readily dissociates when dissolved in water.

Thus there are two main factors that determine whether a molecule containing an X—H bond will behave as a Brønsted-Lowry acid: the strength of the bond and the polarity of the bond.

The importance of these factors is clearly demonstrated by the relative acid strengths of the hydrogen halides. The bond polarities vary as shown

$$H—F > H—Cl > H—Br > H—I$$

↑   ↑
Most polar   Least polar

because electronegativity decreases going down the group. Based on the high polarity of the H—F bond, we might expect hydrogen fluoride to be a very strong acid. In fact, among HX molecules, HF is the only weak acid ($K_a = 7.2 \times 10^{-4}$) when dissolved in water. The H—F bond is unusually strong, as shown in Table 14.7, and thus is difficult to break. This contributes significantly to the reluctance of the HF molecules to dissociate in water.

Another important class of acids are the oxyacids, which as we saw in Section 14.2 characteristically contain the grouping H—O—X. Several series of oxyacids are listed with their K_a values in Table 14.8. Note from these data that for a given

Further aspects of acid strengths are discussed in Section 19.7.

Table 14.7		
Bond Strengths and Acid Strengths for Hydrogen Halides		
H—X Bond	Bond Strength (kJ/mol)	Acid Strength in Water
H—F	565	Weak
H—Cl	427	Strong
H—Br	363	Strong
H—I	295	Strong

Table 14.8

Several Series of Oxyacids and Their K_a Values

Oxyacid	Structure	K_a value
$HClO_4$	H—O—Cl with O above, O to right, O below	Large ($\sim 10^7$)
$HClO_3$	H—O—Cl with O above-right, O below-right	~ 1
$HClO_2$	H—O—Cl—O	1.2×10^{-2}
$HClO$	H—O—Cl	3.5×10^{-8}
H_2SO_4	H—O—S with O—H above-right, O to right, O below	Large
H_2SO_3	H—O—S with O—H above-right, O below-right	1.5×10^{-2}
HNO_3	H—O—N with O above-right, O below-right	Large
HNO_2	H—O—N—O	4.0×10^{-4}

Figure 14.6

The effect of the number of attached oxygens on the H—O bond in a series of chlorine oxyacids. As the number of oxygen atoms attached to the chlorine atom increases, they become more effective at withdrawing electron density from the H—O bond, thereby weakening and polarizing it. This increases the tendency for the molecule to produce a proton, and so its acid strength increases.

series the acid strength increases with an increase in the number of oxygen atoms attached to the central atom. For example, in the series containing chlorine and a varying number of oxygen atoms, HOCl is a weak acid, but the acid strength is successively greater as the number of oxygen atoms increases. This happens because the very electronegative oxygen atoms are able to draw electrons away from the chlorine atom and the O—H bond, as shown in Fig. 14.6. The net effect is to both polarize and weaken the O—H bond; this effect is more important as the number of attached oxygen atoms increases. This means that a proton is most readily produced by the molecule with the largest number of attached oxygen atoms ($HClO_4$).

This type of behavior is also observed for hydrated metal ions. Earlier in this chapter we saw that highly charged metal ions such as Al^{3+} produce acidic solutions. The acidity of the water molecules attached to the metal ion is increased by the attraction of electrons to the positive metal ion:

$$Al^{3+}—O \begin{matrix} H \\ H \end{matrix}$$

The greater the charge on the metal ion, the more acidic the hydrated ion becomes.

Table 14.9

		Comparison of Electronegativity of X and K_a Value for a Series of Oxyacids		
Acid	X	Electronegativity of X	K_a for Acid
HOCl	Cl	3.0	4×10^{-8}
HOBr	Br	2.8	2×10^{-9}
HOI	I	2.5	2×10^{-11}
HOCH$_3$	CH$_3$	2.3 (for carbon in CH$_3$)	$\sim 10^{-15}$

For acids containing the H—O—X grouping, the greater the ability of X to draw electrons toward itself, the greater is the acidity of the molecule. Since the electronegativity of X reflects its ability to attract the electrons involved in bonding, we might expect acid strength to depend on the electronegativity of X. In fact, there is an excellent correlation between the electronegativity of X and the acid strength for oxyacids, as shown in Table 14.9.

14.10 *Acid–Base Properties of Oxides*

Purpose

• To show how to predict whether an oxide will produce an acidic or a basic solution.

We have just seen that molecules containing the grouping H—O—X can behave as acids and that the acid strength depends on the electron-withdrawing ability of X. But substances with this grouping also can behave as bases if the hydroxide ion instead of a proton is produced. What determines which behavior will occur? The answer lies mainly in the nature of the O—X bond. If X has a relatively high electronegativity, the O—X bond will be covalent and strong. When the compound containing the H—O—X grouping is dissolved in water, the O—X bond will remain intact. It will be the polar and relatively weak H—O bond that will tend to break, releasing a proton. On the other hand, if X has a very low electronegativity, the O—X bond will be ionic and subject to being broken in polar water. Examples are the ionic substances NaOH and KOH that dissolve in water to give the metal cation and the hydroxide ion.

We can use these principles to explain the acid–base behavior of oxides when they are dissolved in water. For example, when a covalent oxide such as sulfur trioxide is dissolved in water, an acidic solution results because sulfuric acid is formed:

$$SO_3(g) + H_2O(l) \rightarrow H_2SO_4(aq)$$

A compound containing the H—O—X group will produce an acidic solution in water if the O—X bond is strong and covalent. If the O—X bond is ionic, the compound will produce a basic solution in water.

The structure of H_2SO_4 is shown in the margin. In this case, the strong, covalent O—S bonds remain intact and the H—O bonds break to produce protons. Other common covalent oxides that react with water to form acidic solutions are sulfur dioxide, carbon dioxide, and nitrogen dioxide, as shown by the following reactions:

$$SO_2(g) + H_2O(l) \rightarrow H_2SO_3(aq)$$
$$CO_2(g) + H_2O(l) \rightarrow H_2CO_3(aq)$$

$$2NO_2(g) + H_2O(l) \rightarrow HNO_3(aq) + HNO_2(aq)$$

Thus, when a covalent oxide dissolves in water, an acidic solution forms. These oxides are called **acidic oxides.**

On the other hand, when an ionic oxide dissolves in water, a basic solution results, as shown by the following reactions:

$$CaO(s) + H_2O(l) \rightarrow Ca(OH)_2(aq)$$
$$K_2O(s) + H_2O(l) \rightarrow 2KOH(aq)$$

These reactions can be explained by recognizing that the oxide ion has a high affinity for protons and reacts with water to produce hydroxide ions:

$$O^{2-}(aq) + H_2O(l) \rightarrow 2OH^{-}(aq)$$

Thus the most ionic oxides, such as those of the Group 1A and 2A metals, produce basic solutions when they are dissolved in water. As a result, these oxides are called **basic oxides.**

14.11 *The Lewis Acid–Base Model*

Purpose

• To define acids and bases in terms of electron pairs.

We have seen that the first successful conceptualization of acid–base behavior was proposed by Arrhenius. This useful but limited model was replaced by the more general Brønsted–Lowry model. An even more general model for acid–base behavior was suggested by G. N. Lewis in the early 1920s. A **Lewis acid** is an *electron-pair acceptor,* and a **Lewis base** is an *electron-pair donor.* Another way of saying this is that a Lewis acid has an empty atomic orbital that it can use to accept (share) an electron pair from a molecule that has a lone pair of electrons (Lewis base). The three models for acids and bases are summarized in Table 14.10.

Note that Brønsted–Lowry acid–base reactions (proton donor–proton acceptor reactions) are encompassed by the Lewis model. For example, the reaction between a proton and an ammonia molecule, that is,

$$H^+ \;+\; :N\!\!\begin{array}{c} H \\ | \\ \!\!-\!H \\ | \\ H \end{array} \longrightarrow \left[H\!-\!N\!\!\begin{array}{c} H \\ | \\ \!\!-\!H \\ | \\ H \end{array} \right]^+$$

Lewis acid   Lewis base

can be represented as a reaction between an electron-pair acceptor (H^+) and an electron-pair donor (NH_3). The same holds true for a reaction between a proton and a hydroxide ion:

$$H^+ \;+\; [:\!\overset{..}{\underset{..}{O}}\!-\!H]^- \longrightarrow \begin{array}{c} H \\ \diagdown \\ O: \\ \diagup \\ H \end{array}$$

Lewis acid   Lewis base

Table 14.10

Three Models for Acids and Bases

Model	Definition of Acid	Definition of Base
Arrhenius	H^+ producer	OH^- producer
Brønsted–Lowry	H^+ donor	H^+ acceptor
Lewis	Electron-pair acceptor	Electron-pair donor

The real value of the Lewis model for acids and bases is that it covers many reactions that do not involve Brønsted–Lowry acids. For example, consider the gas-phase reaction between boron trifluoride and ammonia:

The Lewis model encompasses the Brønsted–Lowry model, but the reverse is not true.

Here the electron-deficient BF_3 molecule (there are only six electrons around the boron) completes its octet by reacting with NH_3, which has a lone pair of electrons. In fact, as mentioned in Chapter 8, the electron deficiency of boron trifluoride makes it very reactive toward any electron-pair donor. That is, it is a strong Lewis acid.

The hydration of a metal ion, such as Al^{3+}, also can be viewed as a Lewis acid–base reaction:

Here the Al^{3+} ion accepts one electron pair from each of six water molecules.

In addition, the reaction between a covalent oxide and water to form a Brønsted–Lowry acid can be defined as a Lewis acid–base reaction. An example is the reaction between sulfur trioxide and water:

Note that as the water molecule attaches to sulfur trioxide, a proton shift occurs to form sulfuric acid.

Sample Exercise 14.22

For each reaction, identify the Lewis acid and base.

a. $Ni^{2+}(aq) + 6NH_3(aq) \rightarrow Ni(NH_3)_6{}^{2+}(aq)$
b. $H^+(aq) + H_2O(l) \rightleftharpoons H_3O^+(aq)$

Solution

a. Each NH_3 molecule donates an electron pair to the Ni^{2+} ion:

The nickel(II) ion is the Lewis acid, and ammonia is the Lewis base.
b. The proton is the Lewis acid and the water molecule is the Lewis base:

14.12 Strategy for Solving Acid–Base Problems: A Summary

In this chapter we have encountered many different situations involving aqueous solutions of acids and bases, and in the next chapter we will encounter still more. In solving for the equilibrium concentrations in these aqueous solutions, it is tempting to create a pigeonhole for each possible situation and to memorize the procedures necessary to deal with that particular case. This approach is just not practical and usually leads to frustration: too many pigeonholes are required—there seems to be an infinite number of cases. But you can handle any case successfully by taking a systematic, patient, and thoughtful approach. When analyzing an acid–base equilibrium problem, do *not* ask yourself how a memorized solution can be used to solve the problem. Instead, ask this question: *what are the major species in the solution and what is their chemical behavior?*

The most important part of doing a complicated acid–base equilibrium problem is the analysis you do at the beginning of a problem:

What major species are present?

Does a reaction occur that can be assumed to go to completion?

What equilibrium dominates the solution?

Let the problem guide you. Be patient.

◀ **CHEMICAL IMPACT** ▶

Self-Destructing Paper

The New York City Public Library has 88 miles of bookshelves, and on 36 miles of these shelves the books are quietly disintegrating between their covers. In fact, it is estimated that 40% of the books in the major research collections in the United States will soon be too fragile to handle.

This problem results from the acidic paper widely used in printing books in the last century. Ironically, books from the eighteenth, seventeenth, sixteenth, and even fifteenth century are in much better shape. Gutenberg Bibles contain paper that is in remarkably good condition. In those days, paper was made by hand from linen or rags, but in the nineteenth century demand for cheap paper skyrocketed. Paper manufacturers found that paper could be made economically, by machine, using wood pulp. To size the paper (that is, fill in microscopic holes to lower absorption of moisture and prevent seeping or spreading of inks), alum $[Al_2(SO_4)_3]$ was added in large amounts. Because the hydrated aluminum ion $[Al(OH_2)_6^{3+}]$ is an acid ($K_a \approx 10^{-5}$), paper manufactured using alum is quite acidic. Over time this acidity causes the paper fibers to disintegrate; the pages of books fall apart when they are used.

One could transfer the contents of the threatened books to microfilm, but that would be a very slow and expensive process. Can the books be chemically treated to neutralize the acid and stop the deterioration? Yes. In fact, you know enough chemistry at this point to design the treatment patented in 1936 by Otto Schierholz. He dipped individual pages in solutions of alkaline earth bicarbonate salts $[Mg(HCO_3)_2, Ca(HCO_3)_2,$ etc.]. The HCO_3^- ions present in these solutions react with the H^+ in the paper to give CO_2 and H_2O. This treatment works well and is used today to preserve especially important works, but it is slow and labor-intensive.

It would be much more economical if

A book ravaged by the decomposition of acidic paper.

large numbers of books could be treated at one time without disturbing the bindings. However, soaking entire books in an aqueous solution is out of the question. A logical question then is: are there gaseous bases that could be used to neutralize the acid? Certainly; the organic amines (general formula, RNH_2) are bases, and those with low molar masses are gases under normal conditions. Experiments in which books were treated using ammonia, butylamine ($CH_3CH_2CH_2CH_2NH_2$), and other amines have shown that the method works, but only for a short time. The amines do enter the paper and neutralize the acid, but being volatile, they gradually evaporate, leaving the paper in its original acidic condition.

A much more effective treatment involves diethylzinc $[(CH_3CH_2)_2Zn]$, which boils at 117°C and 1 atm. Diethylzinc (DEZ) reacts with oxygen or water to produce ZnO as follows:

$$(CH_3CH_2)_2Zn(g) + 7O_2(g) \rightarrow$$
$$ZnO(s) + 4CO_2(g) + 5H_2O(g)$$

$$(CH_3CH_2)_2Zn(g) + H_2O(g) \rightarrow$$
$$ZnO(s) + 2CH_3CH_3(g)$$

The solid zinc oxide produced in these reactions is deposited among the paper fibers, and being a basic oxide, it neutralizes the acid present as shown in the equation

$$ZnO + 2H^+ \rightarrow Zn^{2+} + H_2O$$

One major problem is that DEZ ignites spontaneously on contact with air. Therefore, this treatment must be carried out in a chamber filled mainly with $N_2(g)$, where the amount of O_2 present can be rigorously controlled. The pressure in the chamber must be maintained well below one atmosphere both to lower the boiling point of DEZ and to remove excess moisture from the book's pages. Several major DEZ fires have slowed its implementation as a book preservative. However, the Library of Congress has designed a new DEZ treatment plant that includes a chamber large enough for approximately 9000 books to be treated at one time.

The following steps outline a general strategy for solving problems involving acid–base equilibria.

SOLVING ACID–BASE PROBLEMS

STEP 1

List the major species in solution.

STEP 2

Look for reactions that can be assumed to go to completion, for example, a strong acid dissociating or H^+ reacting with OH^-.

STEP 3

For a reaction that can be assumed to go to completion:
a. Determine the concentrations of the products.
b. Write down the major species in solution after the reaction.

STEP 4

Look at each major component of the solution and decide if it is an acid or a base.

STEP 5

Pick the equilibrium that will control the pH. Use known values of the dissociation constants for the various species to help decide on the dominant equilibrium.
a. Write the equation for the reaction and the equilibrium expression.
b. Compute the initial concentrations (assuming the dominant equilibrium has not yet occurred, that is, no acid dissociation, etc.).
c. Define x.
d. Compute the equilibrium concentrations in terms of x.
e. Substitute the concentrations into the equilibrium expression, and solve for x.
f. Check the validity of the approximation.
g. Calculate the pH and other concentrations as required.

Although these steps may seem somewhat cumbersome, especially for simpler problems, they will become increasingly helpful as the aqueous solutions become more complicated. If you develop the habit of approaching acid–base problems systematically, the more complex cases will be much easier to manage.

Summary

In this chapter we have developed several models of acid–base behavior and have applied fundamental equilibrium principles to calculate the pH values for solutions of acids and bases.

Arrhenius postulated that acids produce H^+ ions in solutions and bases produce OH^- ions. The Brønsted–Lowry model is more general: an acid is a proton donor, and a base is a proton acceptor. Water acts as a Brønsted–Lowry base when it accepts a proton from an acid to form a hydronium ion:

$$HA(aq) + H_2O(l) \rightleftharpoons H_3O^+(aq) + A^-(aq)$$

Acid   Base   Conjugate   Conjugate
                        acid   base

A conjugate base is everything that remains of the acid molecule after the proton is lost. A conjugate acid is formed when a proton is transferred to the base. Two substances related in this way are called a conjugate acid–base pair.

The equilibrium expression for the dissociation of an acid in water is

$$K_a = \frac{[H^+][A^-]}{[HA]}$$

where H_3O^+ is simplified to H^+, $[H_2O]$ is not included because it is assumed to be constant, and K_a is called the acid dissociation constant. The strength of an acid is defined by the position of the dissociation equilibrium. A small value of K_a denotes a weak acid, one that does not dissociate to any great extent in aqueous solution. A strong acid is one for which the dissociation equilibrium lies far to the right—the K_a value is very large.

Strong acids such as nitric, hydrochloric, sulfuric, and perchloric acids have weak conjugate bases, which have a low affinity for a proton. The strength of an acid is inversely related to the strength of its conjugate base.

Water is an amphoteric substance—it can behave either as an acid or as a base. The autoionization of water demonstrates this property, since one water molecule transfers a proton to another water molecule to produce a hydronium ion and a hydroxide ion:

$$2H_2O(l) \rightleftharpoons H_3O^+(aq) + OH^-(aq)$$

This leads to the equilibrium expression

$$K_w = [H^+][OH^-]$$

where K_w is called the ion-product constant. It has been experimentally shown that at 25°C in pure water $[H^+] = [OH^-] = 1.0 \times 10^{-7} \, M$. Thus, at 25°C,

$$K_w = 1.0 \times 10^{-14}$$

In an acidic solution, $[H^+]$ is greater than $[OH^-]$. In a basic solution, $[OH^-]$ is greater than $[H^+]$. In a neutral solution, $[H^+]$ is equal to $[OH^-]$.

To describe $[H^+]$ in aqueous solutions, we often use the pH scale, where

$$pH = -\log[H^+]$$

Since pH is a log scale based on 10, the pH changes by 1 for every change by a power of 10 in $[H^+]$. Because pH is defined as $-\log[H^+]$, the pH decreases as $[H^+]$ increases.

The percent dissociation of a weak acid is defined as follows:

$$\text{Percent dissociation} = \frac{\text{amount dissociated (mol/L)}}{\text{initial concentration (mol/L)}} \times 100$$

This is another measure of the strength of an acid: the larger the percent dissociation, the stronger is the acid. As $[HA]_0$ decreases, $[H^+]$ decreases, but the percent dissociation increases. That is, dilution causes an increase in the percent dissociation.

Strong bases are hydroxide salts, such as NaOH or KOH, that dissociate completely in water. Bases do not have to contain the hydroxide ion; they can be species that remove a proton from water, producing the hydroxide ion. For example, ammonia is a base because it can accept a proton from water:

$$NH_3(aq) + H_2O(l) \rightleftharpoons NH_4^+(aq) + OH^-(aq)$$

The equilibrium expression is

$$K_b = \frac{[NH_4^+][OH^-]}{[NH_3]}$$

where K_b always refers to a reaction in which a base reacts with water to produce the conjugate acid and hydroxide ion. Because bases like ammonia must compete with the hydroxide ion for the proton, values of K_b for these bases are typically much less than 1, and these substances are called weak bases.

A polyprotic acid is an acid with more than one acidic proton, which dissociates in a stepwise fashion with a K_a value for each step. Typically, for a weak polyprotic acid,

$$K_{a_1} > K_{a_2} > K_{a_3}$$

Sulfuric acid is unique in that it is a strong acid in the first dissociation step and a weak acid in the second step.

Salts can exhibit neutral, acidic, or basic properties when dissolved in water. Salts that contain the cations of strong bases and the anions of strong acids produce neutral aqueous solutions. A basic solution is produced when the dissolved salt has a neutral cation and an anion that is the conjugate base of a weak acid. An acidic solution is produced when the dissolved salt has a neutral anion and a cation that is the conjugate acid of a weak base. Acidic solutions are also produced by salts containing a highly charged metal cation. For example, the hydrated ion $Al(H_2O)_6^{3+}$ is a weak acid.

Most substances that function as acids or bases contain the H—O—X grouping. Molecules where the O—X is a strong covalent bond tend to behave as acids, especially when X is highly electronegative, because the H—O bond is polarized and weakened. When X has low electronegativity (if X is a metal, for example), the O—X bond tends to be ionic and hydroxide ions form when these substances are dissolved in water.

The Lewis model for acids and bases generalizes the concept of acid–base behavior in terms of electron pairs. A Lewis acid is an electron-pair acceptor, and a Lewis base is an electron-pair donor. The value of the Lewis model is that it covers many reactions that do not involve Brønsted–Lowry acids and bases.

Key Terms

Section 14.1
Arrhenius concept
Brønsted–Lowry model
hydronium ion
conjugate base
conjugate acid
conjugate acid–base pair
acid dissociation constant

Section 14.2
strong acid
weak acid
diprotic acid

oxyacids
organic acids
carboxyl group
monoprotic acid
amphoteric substance
autoionization
ion-product constant

Section 14.3
pH scale

Section 14.4
major species

Section 14.5
percent dissociation

Section 14.6
strong bases
slaked lime
lime–soda process
weak base
amine

Section 14.7
polyprotic acid
triprotic acid

Section 14.8
salt

Section 14.10
acidic oxide
basic oxide

Section 14.11
Lewis acid
Lewis base

A blue question or exercise number indicates that the answer to that question or exercise appears at the back of this book and a solution appears in the Solutions Guide.

Questions

1. Define each of the following using the Arrhenius model.
   a. Strong acid   c. Weak acid
   b. Strong base   d. Weak base

2. Why is H_3O^+ the strongest acid and OH^- the strongest base that can exist in significant amounts in aqueous solutions?

3. Give the conditions for a neutral solution at 25°C, in terms of $[H^+]$, pH, and the relationship between $[H^+]$ and $[OH^-]$.

4. How many significant figures are there in the numbers: 10.78, 6.78, 0.78? If these were pH values, to how many significant figures can you express the $[H^+]$? Explain any discrepancies between your answers to the two questions.

5. Define each of the following.
   a. Arrhenius acid
   b. Brønsted–Lowry acid
   c. Lewis acid

6. Which of the definitions in Question 5 is most general? Write reactions to justify your answer.

7. The presence of what element most commonly results in basic properties for an organic compound?

8. For oxyacids, how does acid strength depend on
   a. Strength of the bond to the acidic hydrogen atom?
   b. Electronegativity of the element bonded to the oxygen atom that bears acidic hydrogen?
   c. The number of oxygen atoms?

9. How does the strength of a conjugate base depend on the factors listed in Question 8?

10. In terms of orbitals and electron arrangements, what must be present for a molecule or ion to act as a Lewis acid? What must be present for a molecule or ion to act as a Lewis base?

Exercises

In this section similar exercises are paired.

Nature of Acids and Bases

11. Classify each of the following as a strong acid, weak acid, strong base, or weak base in aqueous solution.
    a. HNO_2 d. $NaOH$
    b. H_3PO_4 e. NH_3
    c. CH_3NH_2 f. HF

12. Classify each of the following as a strong acid, weak acid, strong base, or weak base in aqueous solution.

    a. $HC{\overset{\displaystyle O}{\overset{\|}{-}}}OH$ d. HCN
    b. $H_2NCH_2CH_2NH_2$ e. HNO_3
    c. H_2SO_4 f. HBr

13. Use Table 14.2 to order the following from the strongest to the weakest acid.

$$HNO_3, \quad H_3O^+, \quad HOCl, \quad NH_4^+$$

Where would H_2O (acting as an acid) fit into this order?

14. Use Table 14.2 to order the following from the strongest to the weakest base.

$$NO_3^-, \quad OCl^-, \quad NH_3, \quad OH^-$$

Where would water (acting as a base) fit into this order?

15. You may need Table 14.2 to answer the following questions.
    a. Which is the stronger acid, HI or H_2O?
    b. Which is the stronger acid, H_2O or $HClO_2$?
    c. Which is the stronger acid, HF or HCN?

16. You may need Table 14.2 to answer the following questions.
    a. Which is the stronger base, I^- or H_2O?
    b. Which is the stronger base, H_2O or ClO_2^-?
    c. Which is the stronger base, F^- or CN^-?

17. For each of the following reactions, identify the acid, the base, the conjugate base, and the conjugate acid.
    a. $H_2O + H_2O \rightleftharpoons H_3O^+ + OH^-$
    b. $CH_3O^- + CH_3\overset{\overset{O}{\|}}{C}CH_3 \rightleftharpoons CH_3OH + CH_3\overset{\overset{O^-}{|}}{C}=CH_2$
    c. $H_2S + NH_3 \rightleftharpoons HS^- + NH_4^+$
    d. $H_2SO_4 + H_2O \rightleftharpoons H_3O^+ + HSO_4^-$
    e. $H_3O^+ + OH^- \rightleftharpoons 2H_2O$
    f. $H_2PO_4^- + H_2O \rightleftharpoons H_3PO_4 + OH^-$
    g. $HCN + H_2O \rightleftharpoons H_3O^+ + CN^-$

18. For each of the following reactions, identify the acid, the base, the conjugate base, and the conjugate acid.
    a. $H_2PO_4^- + H_2O \rightleftharpoons HPO_4^{2-} + H_3O^+$
    b. $H_2PO_4^- + H_2PO_4^- \rightleftharpoons H_3PO_4 + HPO_4^{2-}$
    c. $Fe(H_2O)_6^{3+} + H_2O \rightleftharpoons Fe(H_2O)_5(OH)^{2+} + H_3O^+$
    d. $HCN + CO_3^{2-} \rightleftharpoons CN^- + HCO_3^-$
    e. $CO_2 + 2H_2O \rightleftharpoons HCO_3^- + H_3O^+$
    f. $NH_3 + H_2O \rightleftharpoons NH_4^+ + OH^-$
    g. $C_5H_5N + H_2O \rightleftharpoons C_5H_5NH^+ + OH^-$

19. Write the dissociation reaction and the corresponding equilibrium expression for each of the following acids in water.
    a. H_3PO_4 d. HNO_2
    b. $H_2PO_4^-$ e. $Ti(H_2O)_6^{4+}$
    c. HPO_4^{2-}

20. Write the dissociation reaction and the corresponding equilibrium expression for each of the following acids in water.
    a. HCN
    b. Acetic acid, CH_3CO_2H ($HC_2H_3O_2$)
    c. Phenol, C_6H_5OH
    d. Benzoic acid, $C_6H_5CO_2H$
    e. Glycine, $H_2NCH_2CO_2H$

21. Write the reaction and the corresponding K_b equilibrium expression for each of the following substances acting as bases in water.
    a. PO_4^{3-} d. NH_3
    b. HPO_4^{2-} e. CN^-
    c. $H_2PO_4^-$

22. Write the reaction and the corresponding K_b equilibrium expression for each of the following substances acting as bases in water.
    a. Pyridine, C_5H_5N
    b. Glycine, $NH_2CH_2CO_2H$
    c. Ethylamine, $CH_3CH_2NH_2$
    d. Aniline, $C_6H_5NH_2$
    e. Dimethylamine, $(CH_3)_2NH$

23. Hydride ion (H^-) and methoxide ion (CH_3O^-) have much greater affinities for H^+ than the OH^- ion does. Write equations for the reactions that occur when NaH and $NaOCH_3$ are dissolved in water.

24. Write balanced equations that describe the following reactions.
    a. The dissociation of perchloric acid in water.
    b. The dissociation of propanoic acid ($CH_3CH_2CO_2H$) in water.
    c. The reaction between acetic acid and sodium hydroxide.
    d. The dissociation of ammonium ion in water.

Autoionization of Water and the pH Scale

25. Calculate the pH of each solution.
    a. $[H^+] = 1.4 \times 10^{-3} \, M$ e. $[OH^-] = 8 \times 10^{-11} \, M$
    b. $[H^+] = 2.5 \times 10^{-10} \, M$ f. $[OH^-] = 5.0 \, M$
    c. $[H^+] = 6.1 \, M$ g. pOH = 10.5
    d. $[OH^-] = 3.5 \times 10^{-2} \, M$ h. pOH = 2.3

26. Calculate the pH of each solution.
    a. $[H^+] = 1.0 \, M$ e. $[OH^-] = 6.2 \times 10^{-9} \, M$
    b. $[H^+] = 3.0 \times 10^{-2} \, M$ f. pOH = 2.6
    c. $[H^+] = 4.6 \times 10^{-8} \, M$ g. pOH = 9.1
    d. $[OH^-] = 6.2 \times 10^{-5} \, M$

27. Calculate $[H^+]$ and $[OH^-]$ for each solution.
    a. pH = 7.41 (the normal pH of blood)
    b. pH = 15.3
    c. pH = −1.0   e. pOH = 5.0
    d. pH = 3.2   f. pOH = 9.6

28. Calculate $[H^+]$ and $[OH^-]$ for each solution.
    a. pH = 2.66   d. pOH = 2.48
    b. pH = 8.66   e. pOH = 8.48
    c. pH = −0.34

29. Values of K_w as a function of temperature are as follows:

Temperature (°C)	K_w
0	1.14×10^{-15}
25	1.00×10^{-14}
35	2.09×10^{-14}
40	2.92×10^{-14}
50	5.47×10^{-14}

    a. Is the autoionization of water exothermic or endothermic?
    b. What is the pH of pure water at 50°C?
    c. Restate your answers to Question 3 for water at 50°C. Which of the three criteria for neutrality is most general?
    d. From a plot of $\ln(K_w)$ versus $1/T$ (using the Kelvin scale), estimate K_w at 37°C, normal physiologic temperature.
    e. What is the pH of a neutral solution at 37°C?

30. Supercritical water (water above the critical point, 218 atm and 374°C) has recently been studied as a medium for disposing of hazardous wastes. Assuming the pressure has no effect on K_w, determine the value of the autoionization constant for water at 374°C from the data in Exercise 29.

Solutions of Acids

31. What are the major species present in 0.250 *M* solutions of each of the following acids? Calculate the pH of each of these solutions.
    a. HCl   c. $HClO_4$
    b. HBr   d. HNO_3

32. What are the major species present in 0.250 *M* solutions of each of the following acids? Calculate the pH of each of these solutions.
    a. HNO_2 c. NH_4Cl
    b. CH_3CO_2H ($HC_2H_3O_2$)   d. HCN

33. Calculate the pH of each of the following solutions of a strong acid in water.
    a. 0.1 *M* HCl   c. 0.1 *M* $HClO_4$
    b. 0.1 *M* HNO_3

34. Calculate the pH of each of the following solutions containing a strong acid in water.
    a. 3.0×10^{-5} *M* HCl   c. 4.0 *M* HNO_3
    b. 2.0×10^{-2} *M* HNO_3

35. A solution is prepared by adding 50.0 mL of concentrated hydrochloric acid and 20.0 mL of concentrated nitric acid to 300 mL of water. Water is added until the final volume is 500.0 mL. Calculate $[H^+]$, $[OH^-]$, and pH for this solution. (See Exercise 21 in Chapter 11 for the composition of the concentrated reagents.)

36. A solution is prepared by mixing 90.0 mL of 5.00 *M* HCl and 30.0 mL of 8.00 *M* HNO_3. Water is then added until the final volume is 1.00 L. Calculate $[H^+]$, $[OH^-]$, and the pH for this solution.

37. Calculate $[H^+]$ and the pH for 0.050 *M*, 0.10 *M*, and 0.40 *M* solutions of acetic acid.

38. For propanoic acid (written $HC_3H_5O_2$ or $CH_3CH_2CO_2H$), $K_a = 1.3 \times 10^{-5}$. Calculate $[H^+]$ and the pH for 0.050 *M*, 0.10 *M*, and 0.40 *M* solutions of propanoic acid.

39. For trichlorophenol ($HC_6H_2Cl_3O$), $K_a = 1 \times 10^{-6}$. Calculate the concentrations of all species and the pH of a 0.05 M solution of trichlorophenol in water.

40. Using the K_a values given in Table 14.2, calculate the concentrations of all species present and the pH for each of the following.
    a. 0.20 M $HC_2H_3O_2$ c. 0.020 M HF
    b. 1.5 M HNO_2 d. 0.83 M lactic acid

    $$\left(\begin{array}{c} \text{OH} \\ | \\ CH_3CHCO_2H, \; K_a = 1.4 \times 10^{-4} \end{array} \right)$$

41. Boric acid (H_3BO_3) is commonly used in eyewash solutions in chemistry laboratories to neutralize bases splashed in the eye. It acts as a monoprotic acid, but the dissociation reaction is slightly different from that of other acids:

    $$B(OH)_3 + H_2O \rightleftharpoons B(OH)_4^- + H^+ \qquad K_a = 5.8 \times 10^{-10}$$

    Calculate the pH of a 0.50 M solution of boric acid.

42. Formic acid (HCO_2H) is secreted by ants. Calculate $[H^+]$ and the pH of a 0.025 M solution of formic acid ($K_a = 1.8 \times 10^{-4}$).

43. A solution is prepared by dissolving 0.56 g benzoic acid ($C_6H_5CO_2H$, $K_a = 6.4 \times 10^{-5}$) in enough water to make 1.0 L of solution. Calculate $[C_6H_5CO_2H]$, $[C_6H_5CO_2^-]$, $[H^+]$, $[OH^-]$, and the pH in this solution.

44. A solution with a volume of 250.0 mL is prepared by diluting 20.0 mL glacial acetic acid with water. Calculate $[H^+]$ and the pH of this solution. Assume that glacial acetic acid is pure liquid acetic acid, with a density of 1.05 g/cm^3.

45. Calculate the pH of a 0.50 M solution of iodic acid (HIO_3, $K_a = 0.17$).

46. Calculate the pH of a 0.0010 M solution of H_2SO_4.

47. Calculate the pH of a solution containing a mixture of 0.10 M HCl and 0.10 M HOCl.

48. Calculate the pH of a solution containing a mixture of 0.050 M HNO_3 and 0.50 M $HC_2H_3O_2$.

49. Calculate the percent dissociation for a 0.22 M solution of chlorous acid ($HClO_2$, $K_a = 1.2 \times 10^{-2}$).

50. In a 0.100 M solution of HF, the percent dissociation is 8.1%. Calculate K_a.

51. Calculate the percent dissociation of the acid in each of the following solutions.
    a. 0.50 M acetic acid
    b. 0.050 M acetic acid
    c. 0.0050 M acetic acid

52. Using the K_a values in Table 14.2, calculate the percent dissociation in a 0.100 M solution of each of the following acids.
    a. Hypochlorous acid (HOCl)
    b. Hydrocyanic acid (HCN)
    c. Hydrochloric acid (HCl)

53. The pH of a 0.063 M solution of hypobromous acid (HOBr but usually written HBrO) is 4.95. Calculate K_a.

54. Trichloroacetic acid (CCl_3CO_2H) is a corrosive acid that is used to precipitate proteins. The pH of a 0.050 M solution of trichloroacetic acid is 1.4. Calculate K_a.

55. Using the K_a values in Table 14.4 and only the first dissociation step, calculate the pH of 0.10 M solutions of each of the following polyprotic acids.
    a. H_3AsO_4 b. H_2CO_3

56. Calculate $[H^+]$, $[OH^-]$, $[H_3PO_4]$, $[H_2PO_4^-]$, $[HPO_4^{2-}]$, and $[PO_4^{3-}]$ for a 0.100 M solution of H_3PO_4.

Solutions of Bases

57. Use Table 14.3 to help to order the following bases from strongest to weakest.

    $$NO_3^-, \quad H_2O, \quad NH_3, \quad CH_3NH_2$$

58. Use Table 14.3 to help to order the following acids from strongest to weakest.

    $$HNO_3, \quad H_2O, \quad NH_4^+, \quad CH_3NH_3^+$$

59. Use Table 14.3 to help to answer the following questions.
   a. Which is the stronger base, NO_3^- or NH_3?
   b. Which is the stronger base, H_2O or NH_3?
   c. Which is the stronger base, OH^- or NH_3?
   d. Which is the stronger base, NH_3 or CH_3NH_2?

60. Use Table 14.3 to help to answer the following questions.
   a. Which is the stronger acid, HNO_3 or NH_4^+?
   b. Which is the stronger acid, H_2O or NH_4^+?
   c. Which is the stronger acid, NH_4^+ or $CH_3NH_3^+$?

61. Thallium(I) hydroxide is a strong base used in the synthesis of some organic compounds. Calculate the pH of a solution containing 2.48 g TlOH per liter.

62. Calculate $[OH^-]$, pOH, and pH for each of the following.
   a. 0.25 M NaOH
   b. 0.00040 M $Ba(OH)_2$
   c. A solution containing 25 g KOH per liter
   d. A solution containing 150.0 g NaOH per liter

63. What are the major species present in 0.150 M solutions of each of the following bases?
   a. KOH   d. Pyridine
   b. CsOH   e. Methylamine
   c. NH_3
   What is $[OH^-]$ and the pH of each of these solutions?

64. What are the major species present in the following mixtures of bases?
   a. 0.050 M NaOH and 0.050 M KOH
   b. 0.050 M NaOH and 0.50 M NH_3
   c. 0.0010 M $Ba(OH)_2$ and 0.020 M NaOH
   What is $[OH^-]$ and the pH of each of these solutions?

65. For the reaction of hydrazine (N_2H_4) in water,

$$H_2NNH_2 + H_2O \rightleftharpoons H_2NNH_3^+ + OH^-$$

K_b is 3.0×10^{-6}. Calculate the concentrations of all species and the pH of a 2.0 M solution of hydrazine in water.

66. Hydroxylamine ($HONH_2$) is a weak base with $K_b = 1.1 \times 10^{-8}$. Calculate the concentrations of all species and the pH of a 1.0 M aqueous solution of hydroxylamine.

67. Calculate $[OH^-]$, $[H^+]$, and pH of 0.20 M solutions of each of the following amines.
   a. Ethylamine ($C_2H_5NH_2$, $K_b = 5.6 \times 10^{-4}$)
   b. Diethylamine [$(C_2H_5)_2NH$, $K_b = 1.3 \times 10^{-3}$]
   c. Triethylamine [$(C_2H_5)_3N$, $K_b = 4.0 \times 10^{-4}$]

68. Calculate $[OH^-]$, $[H^+]$, and the pH of 0.20 M solutions of each of the following amines (the missing K_b values are found in Table 14.3).
   a. Aniline
   b. Pyridine
   c. Hydroxylamine ($HONH_2$, $K_b = 1.1 \times 10^{-8}$)

69. Calculate the percent ionization in each of the following solutions.
   a. 0.10 M NH_3
   b. 0.010 M NH_3

70. Calculate the percent ionization in each of the following solutions (see Table 14.3 for K_b values).
   a. 0.10 M hydroxylamine ($HONH_2$, $K_b = 1.1 \times 10^{-8}$)
   b. 0.10 M methylamine (CH_3NH_2)

71. Codeine is a derivative of morphine and is used as an analgesic, narcotic, or antitussive. It was once commonly used in cough syrups but is now available only by prescription because of its addictive properties. The formula for codeine is $C_{18}H_{21}NO_3$, and the pK_b is 6.05. Calculate the pH of a 10.0-mL solution containing 5.0 mg codeine.

72. Quinine ($C_{20}H_{24}N_2O_2$) is the most important alkaloid derived from cinchona bark. It is used as an antimalarial drug.

Quinine

For quinine, p$K_{b_1} = 5.1$ and p$K_{b_2} = 9.7$. (Recall that p$K_b = -\log K_b$.) A gram of quinine will dissolve in 1900.0 mL of water. Calculate the pH of a saturated aqueous solution of quinine. Consider only the reaction $Q + H_2O \rightleftharpoons QH^+ + OH^-$ described by pK_{b_1}.

73. The pH of a 0.016 M solution of p-toluidine ($CH_3C_6H_4NH_2$) in water is 8.60. Calculate K_b.

74. The pH of a 1.00×10^{-3} M solution of pyrrolidine is 10.82. Calculate K_b.

$$CH_2 \text{——} CH_2$$
$$CH_2 \qquad CH_2$$
$$NH$$

Pyrrolidine

Acid–Base Properties of Salts

75. Are solutions of the following salts acidic, basic, or neutral? For those which are not neutral, write balanced chemical equations for the reactions causing the solution to be acidic or basic. The relevant K_a and K_b values are found in Tables 14.2 to 14.4.
   a. $NaNO_3$ d. NH_4NO_2
   b. $NaNO_2$ e. Na_2CO_3
   c. NH_4NO_3 f. NaF

76. Are solutions of the following salts acidic, basic, or neutral? For those which are not neutral, write balanced equations for the reactions causing the solution to be acidic or basic. The relevant K_a and K_b values are found in Tables 14.2 to 14.4.
   a. KCl   d. $NaHCO_3$
   b. $NH_4C_2H_3O_2$ e. NH_4F
   c. CH_3NH_3Br

77. Arrange the following 0.10 M solutions in order from most acidic to most basic.

   KOH, KBr, KCN, NH_4Br, NH_4CN, HCN

78. Arrange the following 0.10 M solutions in order from most acidic to most basic.

   H_2O, KNO_2, HNO_3, HNO_2, NH_4NO_3, NH_4NO_2

79. Calculate the pH of each of the following solutions.
   a. 0.10 M CH_3NH_3Cl
   b. 0.050 M NaCN
   c. 0.20 M Na_2CO_3 (consider only the reaction CO_3^{2-} + $H_2O \rightleftharpoons HCO_3^- + OH^-$)

80. Calculate the pH of each of the following solutions.
   a. 0.12 M $NaNO_2$ c. 0.40 M NH_4I
   b. 0.45 M NaOCl

81. Sodium azide (NaN_3) is sometimes added to water to kill bacteria. Calculate the concentration of all species in a 0.010 M solution of NaN_3. The K_a value for hydrazoic acid (HN_3) is 1.9×10^{-5}.

82. Calculate the concentrations of all species present in a 0.25 M solution of ethylammonium chloride ($C_2H_5NH_3Cl$).

83. Given that the K_a value for acetic acid is 1.8×10^{-5} and the K_a value for hypochlorous acid is 3×10^{-8}, which is the stronger base, OCl^- or $C_2H_3O_2^-$?

84. The K_b values for ammonia and methylamine are 1.8×10^{-5} and 4.4×10^{-5}, respectively. Which is the stronger acid, NH_4^+ or $CH_3NH_3^+$?

Relationships Between Structure and Strengths of Acids and Bases

85. Place the species in each of the following groups in order of increasing acid strength. Explain the order you chose for each group.
   a. HBrO, $HBrO_2$, $HBrO_3$
   b. H_3AsO_4, $H_2AsO_4^-$, $HAsO_4^{2-}$

86. Order the following from the strongest to weakest acid.
   a. $HClO_2$, $HBrO_2$, HIO_2
   b. H_3PO_4, H_3AsO_4

87. Place the species in each of the following groups in order of increasing base strength. Give your reasoning in each case.
   a. BrO^-, BrO_2^-, BrO_3^-
   b. $H_2PO_4^-$, HPO_4^{2-}, PO_4^{3-}

88. Will the following oxides give acidic, basic, or neutral solutions when dissolved in water? Write reactions to justify your answers.
   a. CaO   d. Cl_2O
   b. Na_2O e. P_4O_{10}
   c. SO_2 f. NO_2

Lewis Acids and Bases

89. Identify the Lewis acid and the Lewis base in each of the following reactions.
  a. $B(OH)_3 + H_2O \rightleftharpoons B(OH)_4^- + H^+$
  b. $Ag^+ + 2NH_3 \rightleftharpoons Ag(NH_3)_2^+$
  c. $BF_3 + NH_3 \rightleftharpoons F_3BNH_3$

90. Identify the Lewis acid and the Lewis base in each of the following reactions.
  a. $I_2 + I^- \rightleftharpoons I_3^-$
  b. $Zn(OH)_2 + 2OH^- \rightleftharpoons Zn(OH)_4^{2-}$
  c. $Fe^{3+} + SCN^- \rightleftharpoons FeSCN^{2+}$

91. Aluminum hydroxide is an amphoteric substance. It can act as either a Brønsted–Lowry base or a Lewis acid. Write a reaction showing $Al(OH)_3$ acting as a base toward H^+ and as an acid toward OH^-.

92. Zinc hydroxide is an amphoteric substance. Write equations that describe $Zn(OH)_2$ acting as a Brønsted–Lowry base toward H^+ and as a Lewis acid toward OH^-.

93. Would you expect Fe^{3+} or Fe^{2+} to be the stronger Lewis acid? Explain.

94. $TiCl_4$ is a liquid at room temperature. It exists as discrete $TiCl_4$ molecules rather than as an ionic solid composed of Ti^{4+} and Cl^- ions. How can the Lewis acid–base model be used to rationalize these facts?

Additional Exercises

95. A solution is prepared by adding 50.0 mL of 0.050 M HCl to 150.0 mL of 0.10 M HNO_3. Calculate the concentrations of all species in this solution.

96. Calculate the pH of a 1.0×10^{-12} M solution of HCl in water. Before checking your answer, decide whether or not it makes sense.

97. Is an aqueous solution of $NaHSO_4$ acidic, basic, or neutral? What reaction with water occurs? If solid Na_2CO_3 is added to a solution of $NaHSO_4$, what reaction can occur between the CO_3^{2-} and HSO_4^- ions?

98. Derive an expression for the relationship between pK_a and pK_b for a conjugate acid–base pair. (Recall that $pK = -\log K$.)

99. At 25°C, a saturated solution of benzoic acid (see Exercise 43) has a pH of 2.8. Calculate the water solubility of benzoic acid in moles per liter and grams per 100 milliliters.

100. Calculate $[CO_3^{2-}]$ in a 0.010 M solution of CO_2 in water (H_2CO_3). If all the CO_3^{2-} in this solution comes from the reaction

$$HCO_3^- \rightleftharpoons H^+ + CO_3^{2-}$$

what percent of the H^+ ions in the solution are a result of the dissociation of HCO_3^-? When acid is added to a solution of sodium hydrogen carbonate ($NaHCO_3$), vigorous bubbling occurs. How is this reaction related to the existence of carbonic acid (H_2CO_3) molecules in aqueous solution?

101. Draw the structures of the conjugate acids of ephedrine and mescaline. See Section 14.6 for structures of the amines.

102. Calculate the value for the equilibrium constant for each of the following reactions.
  a. $NH_3 + H_3O^+ \rightleftharpoons NH_4^+ + H_2O$
  b. $NO_2^- + H_3O^+ \rightleftharpoons HNO_2 + H_2O$
  c. $NH_4^+ + CH_3CO_2^- \rightleftharpoons NH_3 + CH_3CO_2H$
  d. $H_3O^+ + OH^- \rightleftharpoons 2H_2O$
  e. $NH_4^+ + OH^- \rightleftharpoons NH_3 + H_2O$
  f. $HNO_2 + OH^- \rightleftharpoons H_2O + NO_2^-$

103. Hemoglobin (abbreviated Hb) is a protein that is responsible for the transport of oxygen in the blood of mammals. Each hemoglobin molecule contains four iron atoms that are the binding sites for O_2 molecules. The oxygen binding is pH dependent. The relevant equilibrium reaction is

$$HbH_4^{4+} + 4O_2 \rightleftharpoons Hb(O_2)_4 + 4H^+$$

Use Le Châtelier's principle to answer the following.
  a. What form of hemoglobin, HbH_4^{4+} or $Hb(O_2)_4$, is favored in the lungs? What form is favored in the cells?
  b. When a person hyperventilates, the concentration of CO_2 in the blood is decreased. How does this affect the oxygen-binding equilibrium? How does breathing into a paper bag help to counteract this effect?
  c. When a person has suffered a cardiac arrest, injection of a sodium bicarbonate solution is given. Why is this necessary?

Challenge Problems

104. Construct a thermochemical cycle for the following reaction in terms of bond energies, ionization energies, and electron affinities given in Chapters 7 and 8:

$$HX(g) \rightleftharpoons H^+(g) + X^-(g)$$

  a. Calculate ΔH for this reaction when X = F, Cl, Br, and I.
  b. How are the results of this thermochemical cycle consistent with statements in Section 14.9?

105. Use the results of Exercise 104 to explain two things that will increase the strength of an acid.

106. Using your conclusions from Exercise 105, place the species in each of the following groups in order of increasing acid strength.
    a. H_2O, H_2S, H_2Se (bond energies: H—O, 467 kJ/mol; H—S, 363 kJ/mol; H—Se, 276 kJ/mol)
    b. CH_3CO_2H, FCH_2CO_2H, F_2CHCO_2H, F_3CCO_2H
    c. NH_4^+, $CH_3NH_3^+$, $HONH_3^+$
    Give reasons for the orders you chose.

107. Using your conclusions from Exercise 106, place the species in each of the following groups in order of increasing base strength.
    a. OH^-, SH^-, SeH^-
    b. NH_3, PH_3 (bond energies: N—H, 391 kJ/mol; P—H, 322 kJ/mol)
    c. NH_3, $HONH_2$

108. Construct a thermochemical cycle for the reaction

$$HX(aq) \rightleftharpoons H^+(aq) + X^-(aq)$$

by adding hydration energies to the factors considered in Exercise 104. In what way can hydration energies affect the strength of an acid?

109. Liquid ammonia is sometimes used as a solvent for chemical reactions. It undergoes the autoionization reaction

$$2NH_3 \rightleftharpoons NH_4^+ + NH_2^-$$

    a. What species correspond to H^+ and OH^- in liquid ammonia?
    b. What is the condition for a neutral solution in liquid ammonia?
    c. Sodium metal reacts with liquid ammonia in a manner analogous to the reaction of sodium metal with water. Write a balanced chemical equation describing this reaction.
    d. What advantages might there be to using liquid ammonia as a solvent?

110. Alka-Seltzer employs the reaction between citric acid and sodium bicarbonate to generate its fizz [$CO_2(g)$]. The structure of citric acid and values of the acid dissociation constants are

$$\begin{array}{ll} CH_2-CO_2H & K_{a_1} = 8.4 \times 10^{-4} \\ HO-C-CO_2H & K_{a_2} = 1.8 \times 10^{-5} \\ CH_2-CO_2H & K_{a_3} = 4.0 \times 10^{-6} \end{array}$$

Calculate the value of the equilibrium constant for each of the following reactions (we abbreviate citric acid as H_3Cit) using the K_a values for citric acid and for carbonic acid.

$$H_3Cit + HCO_3^- \rightleftharpoons H_2Cit^- + H_2O + CO_2$$
$$H_3Cit + 3HCO_3^- \rightleftharpoons Cit^{3-} + 3H_2O + 3CO_2$$

Hint: When reactions are added, the corresponding equilibrium constants are multiplied.

111. a. The principal equilibrium in a solution of $NaHCO_3$ is

$$HCO_3^- + HCO_3^- \rightleftharpoons H_2CO_3 + CO_3^{2-}$$

Calculate the value of the equilibrium constant for this reaction.
    b. At equilibrium, what is the relationship between [H_2CO_3] and [CO_3^{2-}]?
    c. Using the equilibrium

$$H_2CO_3 \rightleftharpoons 2H^+ + CO_3^{2-}$$

derive an expression for the pH of the solution in terms of K_{a_1} and K_{a_2} using the result from part b.
    d. What is the pH of a solution of $NaHCO_3$?

112. Calculate the pH of a 1.0×10^{-7} *M* solution of NaOH in water. Consider the amount of hydroxide ion from the autoionization of water and the effect of the added hydroxide ion on the position of the autoionization equilibrium.

113. Making use of the assumptions we ordinarily make in calculating the pH of an aqueous solution of a weak acid, calculate the pH of a 1.0×10^{-6} *M* solution of hypobromous acid (HBrO, $K_a = 2 \times 10^{-9}$). What is wrong with your answer? Why is it wrong? Without trying to solve the problem, tell what has to be included to solve the problem correctly.

114. Concentrated HCl is added dropwise to 1.0 L of a 0.10 *M* solution of iodic acid (HIO_3) until the pH is 1.20. Calculate [HIO_3] and [IO_3^-] in this solution assuming the volume remains constant ($K_a = 1.7 \times 10^{-1}$).

115. A solution is made by mixing

5.0 mmol Na_3PO_4

5.0 mmol NaOH

5.0 mmol acetic acid

25.0 mL 2.00 *M* HCl

and enough water to make 250.0 mL of solution. Calculate the pH of this solution.

Marathon Problem*

116. Captain Kirk, of the Starship *Enterprise,* has been told by his superiors that only a chemist can be trusted with the combination to the safe containing the dilithium crystals that power the ship. The combination is the pH of solution A described below, followed by the pH of solution C. (Example: If the pH of solution A is 3.47 and that of solution C is 8.15, then the combination to the safe is 3-47-8-15.) The chemist must

*This Marathon Problem was developed by James H. Burness of Penn State University, York Campus.

find the combination using only the information below (all solutions are at 25°C):

Solution A is 50.0 ml of a 0.100 M solution of the weak monoprotic acid HX.

Solution B is a 0.0500 M solution of the salt NaX. It has a pH of 10.02.

Solution C is made by adding 15.0 ml of 0.250 M KOH to solution A.

What is the combination to the safe?

Applications of Aqueous Equilibria

M uch important chemistry, including almost all the chemistry of the natural world, occurs in aqueous solution. We have already introduced one very significant class of aqueous equilibria, acid–base reactions. In this chapter we consider more applications of acid–base chemistry and introduce two additional types of aqueous equilibria, those involving the solubility of salts and those involving the formation of complex ions.

The interplay of acid–base, solubility, and complex ion equilibria is often important in natural processes, such as the weathering of minerals, the uptake of nutrients by plants, and tooth decay. For example, limestone ($CaCO_3$) will dissolve in water made acidic by dissolved carbon dioxide:

$$CO_2(aq) + H_2O(l) \rightleftharpoons H^+(aq) + HCO_3^-(aq)$$
$$H^+(aq) + CaCO_3(s) \rightleftharpoons Ca^{2+}(aq) + HCO_3^-(aq)$$

This two-step process and its reverse account for the formation of limestone caves and the stalactites and stalagmites found therein. In the forward direction of the process the acidic water (containing carbon dioxide) dissolves the underground limestone deposits, thereby forming a cavern. The reverse process occurs as the water drips from the ceiling of the cave and the carbon dioxide is lost to the air. This causes solid calcium carbonate to form, producing stalactites on the ceiling and stalagmites where the drops hit the cave floor.

Before we consider the other types of aqueous equilibria, we will deal with acid–base equilibria in more detail.

< A room in Carlsbad Caverns in New Mexico. Limestone caves such as this one are formed when carbonate minerals dissolve in groundwater made acidic by dissolved carbon dioxide and then reform as the water evaporates.

Acid–Base Equilibria

15.1 Solutions of Acids or Bases Containing a Common Ion

Purpose

• To study the effect of a common ion on acid dissociation equilibria.

In Chapter 14 we were concerned with calculating the equilibrium concentrations of species (particularly H^+ ions) in solutions containing an acid or a base. In this section we discuss solutions that contain not only the weak acid HA, but also its salt NaA. Although this appears to be a new type of problem, we will see that this case can be handled rather easily using the procedures developed in Chapter 14.

Suppose we have a solution containing the weak acid hydrofluoric acid (HF, $K_a = 7.2 \times 10^{-4}$) and its salt sodium fluoride (NaF). Recall that when a salt dissolves in water, it breaks up completely into its ions—it is a strong electrolyte:

$$NaF(s) \xrightarrow{H_2O(l)} Na^+(aq) + F^-(aq)$$

Since hydrofluoric acid is a weak acid and only slightly dissociated, the major species in the solution are HF, Na^+, F^-, and H_2O. The **common ion** in this solution is F^-, since it is produced by both hydrofluoric acid and sodium fluoride. What effect does the presence of the dissolved sodium fluoride have on the dissociation equilibrium of hydrofluoric acid?

To answer this question, we compare the extent of dissociation of hydrofluoric acid in two different solutions, the first containing 1.0 M HF and the second containing 1.0 M HF and 1.0 M NaF. By Le Châtelier's principle, we would expect the dissociation equilibrium for HF

$$HF(aq) \rightleftharpoons H^+(aq) + F^-(aq)$$

in the second solution to be *driven to the left by the presence of F^- ions from the NaF*. Thus the extent of dissociation of HF will be *less* in the presence of dissolved NaF:

$$HF(aq) \rightleftharpoons H^+(aq) + F^-(aq)$$

Equilibrium shifts away from added component. Fewer H^+ ions present.

Added F^- ions from NaF

The common ion effect is an application of Le Châtelier's principle.

The shift in equilibrium position that occurs because of the addition of an ion already involved in the equilibrium reaction is called the **common ion effect.** This effect makes a solution of NaF and HF less acidic than a solution of HF alone.

The common ion effect is quite general. For example, solid NH_4Cl added to a 1.0 M NH_3 solution produces additional ammonium ions:

$$NH_4Cl(s) \xrightarrow{H_2O} NH_4^+(aq) + Cl^-(aq)$$

and this causes the position of the ammonia–water equilibrium to shift to the left:

$$NH_3(aq) + H_2O(l) \rightleftharpoons NH_4^+(aq) + OH^-(aq)$$

This reduces the equilibrium concentration of OH^- ions.

The common ion effect is also important in solutions of polyprotic acids. The production of protons by the first dissociation step greatly inhibits the succeeding dissociation steps, which, of course, also produce protons, the common ion in this case. We will see later in this chapter that the common ion effect is also important in dealing with the solubility of salts.

Equilibrium Calculations

The procedures for finding the pH of a solution containing a weak acid or base plus a common ion are very similar to the procedures, which we covered in Chapter 14, for solutions containing the acids or bases alone. For example, in the case of a weak acid, the only important difference is that the initial concentration of the anion A^- is not zero in a solution that also contains the salt NaA. Sample Exercise 15.1 illustrates a typical example using the same general approach we developed in Chapter 14.

Sample Exercise 15.1

In Section 14.5 we found that the equilibrium concentration of H^+ in a 1.0 M HF solution is 2.7×10^{-2} M and the percent dissociation of HF is 2.7%. Calculate $[H^+]$ and the percent dissociation of HF in a solution containing 1.0 M HF ($K_a = 7.2 \times 10^{-4}$) and 1.0 M NaF.

Solution

As the aqueous solutions we consider become more complex, it is more important than ever to be systematic and to *focus on the chemistry* occurring in the solution before thinking about mathematical procedures. The way to do this is *always* to write the major species first and consider the chemical properties of each one.

In a solution containing 1.0 M HF and 1.0 M NaF, the major species are

$$HF, \quad F^-, \quad Na^+, \quad \text{and} \quad H_2O$$

We know that Na^+ ions have neither acidic nor basic properties and that water is a very weak acid (or base). Therefore, the important species are HF and F^-, which participate in the acid dissociation equilibrium that controls $[H^+]$ in this solution. That is, the position of the equilibrium

$$HF(aq) \rightleftharpoons H^+(aq) + F^-(aq)$$

will determine $[H^+]$ in the solution. The equilibrium expression is

$$K_a = \frac{[H^+][F^-]}{[HF]} = 7.2 \times 10^{-4}$$

The important concentrations are shown in the following table.

Initial Concentration (mol/L)		Equilibrium Concentration (mol/L)
$[HF]_0 = 1.0$ (from dissolved HF)		$[HF] = 1.0 - x$
$[F^-]_0 = 1.0$ (from dissolved NaF)	x mol/L HF dissociates $\longrightarrow$	$[F^-] = 1.0 + x$
$[H^+]_0 = 0$ (neglect contribution from H_2O)		$[H^+] = x$

Note that $[F^-]_0 = 1.0\ M$ because of the dissolved sodium fluoride and that at equilibrium $[F^-] > 1.0\ M$ because when the acid dissociates it produces F^- as well as H^+. Then

$$K_a = 7.2 \times 10^{-4} = \frac{[H^+][F^-]}{[HF]} = \frac{(x)(1.0 + x)}{1.0 - x} \approx \frac{(x)(1.0)}{1.0}$$

(since x is expected to be small).

Solving for x gives

$$x = \frac{1.0}{1.0}(7.2 \times 10^{-4}) = 7.2 \times 10^{-4}$$

Noting that x is small compared to 1.0, we conclude that this result is acceptable. Thus

$$[H^+] = x = 7.2 \times 10^{-4}\ M \qquad \text{(The pH is 3.14.)}$$

The percent dissociation of HF in this solution is

$$\frac{[H^+]}{[HF]_0} \times 100 = \frac{7.2 \times 10^{-4}\ M}{1.0\ M} \times 100 = 0.072\%$$

Compare these values for $[H^+]$ and percent dissociation of HF with those for a 1.0 M HF solution, where $[H^+] = 2.7 \times 10^{-2}\ M$ and the percent dissociation is 2.7%. The large difference shows clearly that the presence of the F^- ions from the dissolved NaF greatly inhibits the dissociation of HF. The position of the acid dissociation equilibrium has been shifted to the left by the presence of F^- ions from NaF.

15.2 Buffered Solutions

Purpose

- To explain the characteristics of buffered solutions.
- To show how to calculate a buffer pH given the concentrations of the buffering materials.

The most important application of acid–base solutions containing a common ion is for buffering. A **buffered solution** is one that *resists a change in its pH* when either hydroxide ions or protons are added. The most important practical example of a buffered solution is our blood, which can absorb the acids and bases produced in biologic reactions without changing its pH. A constant pH for blood is vital because cells can survive only in a very narrow pH range.

A buffered solution may contain a *weak* acid and its salt (for example, HF and NaF) or a *weak* base and its salt (for example, NH_3 and NH_4Cl). By choosing the appropriate components, a solution can be buffered at virtually any pH.

In treating buffered solutions in this chapter, we will start by considering the equilibrium calculations. We will then use these results to show how buffering works. That is, we will answer the question: How does a buffered solution resist changes in pH when an acid or base is added?

As you do the calculations associated with buffered solutions, keep in mind that these are merely solutions containing weak acids or bases, and the procedures required are the same ones we have already developed. Be sure to use the systematic approach introduced in Chapter 14.

> The most important buffering system in the blood involves HCO_3^- and H_2CO_3.

> The systematic approach developed in Chapter 14 for weak acids and bases applies to buffered solutions.

Sample Exercise 15.2

A buffered solution contains 0.50 M acetic acid ($HC_2H_3O_2$, $K_a = 1.8 \times 10^{-5}$) and 0.50 M sodium acetate ($NaC_2H_3O_2$). Calculate the pH of this solution.

> Notice as you do this problem that it is exactly like examples you have seen in Chapter 14.

Solution

The major species in the solution are

$$HC_2H_3O_2, \quad Na^+, \quad C_2H_3O_2^-, \quad and \quad H_2O$$

| Weak acid | Neither acid nor base | Base (conjugate base of $HC_2H_3O_2$) | Very weak acid or base |

Examination of the solution components leads to the conclusion that the acetic acid dissociation equilibrium, which involves both $HC_2H_3O_2$ and $C_2H_3O_2^-$, will control the pH of the solution:

$$HC_2H_3O_2(aq) \rightleftharpoons H^+(aq) + C_2H_3O_2^-(aq)$$

$$K_a = 1.8 \times 10^{-5} = \frac{[H^+][C_2H_3O_2^-]}{[HC_2H_3O_2]}$$

The concentrations are as follows:

Initial Concentration (mol/L)		Equilibrium Concentration (mol/L)
$[HC_2H_3O_2]_0 = 0.50$ $[C_2H_3O_2^-]_0 = 0.50$ $[H^+]_0 \approx 0$	$\xrightarrow[\substack{\text{dissociates} \\ \text{to reach} \\ \text{equilibrium}}]{x \text{ mol/L of} \\ HC_2H_3O_2}$	$[HC_2H_3O_2] = 0.50 - x$ $[C_2H_3O_2^-] = 0.50 + x$ $[H^+] = x$

A digital pH meter shows the pH of the buffered solution to be 4.74.

Then

$$K_a = 1.8 \times 10^{-5} = \frac{[H^+][C_2H_3O_2^-]}{[HC_2H_3O_2]} = \frac{(x)(0.50 + x)}{0.50 - x} \approx \frac{(x)(0.50)}{0.50}$$

and
$$x \approx 1.8 \times 10^{-5}$$

The approximations are valid (by the 5% rule), so

$$[H^+] = x = 1.8 \times 10^{-5} \, M \quad \text{and} \quad pH = 4.74$$

Sample Exercise 15.3

Calculate the change in pH that occurs when 0.010 mol solid NaOH is added to 1.0 L of the buffered solution described in Sample Exercise 15.2. Compare this pH change with that which occurs when 0.010 mol solid NaOH is added to 1.0 L of water.

Solution

Since the added solid NaOH will completely dissociate, the major species in solution *before any reaction occurs* are $HC_2H_3O_2$, Na^+, $C_2H_3O_2^-$, OH^-, and H_2O. Note that the solution contains a relatively large amount of the very strong base hydroxide ion, which has a great affinity for protons. The best source of protons is the acetic acid, and the reaction that will occur is

$$OH^- + HC_2H_3O_2 \rightarrow H_2O + C_2H_3O_2^-$$

Although acetic acid is a weak acid, the hydroxide ion is such a strong base that the reaction above will *proceed essentially to completion* (until the OH^- ions are consumed).

The best approach to this problem involves two distinct steps: (1) assume that the reaction goes to completion and carry out the stoichiometric calculations; then (2) carry out the equilibrium calculations.

(1) *The stoichiometry problem.* The stoichiometry for the reaction is shown below.

	$HC_2H_3O_2$	+	OH^-	$\rightarrow$	$C_2H_3O_2^-$	+	H_2O
Before reaction:	1.0 L × 0.50 M = 0.50 mol		0.010 mol		1.0 L × 0.50 M = 0.50 mol		
After reaction:	0.50 − 0.01 = 0.49 mol		0.010 − 0.010 = 0 mol		0.50 + 0.01 = 0.51 mol		

Note that 0.01 mol $HC_2H_3O_2$ has been converted to 0.01 mol $C_2H_3O_2^-$ by the added OH^-.

(2) *The equilibrium problem.* After the reaction between OH^- and $HC_2H_3O_2$ is complete, the major species in solution are

$$HC_2H_3O_2, \quad Na^+, \quad C_2H_3O_2^-, \quad \text{and} \quad H_2O$$

The dominant equilibrium involves dissociation of acetic acid.

This problem is then very similar to that in Sample Exercise 15.2. The only difference is that the addition of 0.01 mol OH^- has consumed some $HC_2H_3O_2$ and produced some $C_2H_3O_2^-$, yielding the following concentrations:

Initial Concentration (mol/L)		Equilibrium Concentration (mol/L)
$[HC_2H_3O_2]_0 = 0.49$		$[HC_2H_3O_2] = 0.49 - x$
$[C_2H_3O_2^-]_0 = 0.51$	$\xrightarrow[\text{dissociates}]{x \text{ mol/L} \atop HC_2H_3O_2}$	$[C_2H_3O_2^-] = 0.51 + x$
$[H^+]_0 \approx 0$		$[H^+] = x$

Note that the initial concentrations are defined after the reaction with OH^- is complete but before the system adjusts to equilibrium. Following the usual procedure gives

$$K_a = 1.8 \times 10^{-5} = \frac{[H^+][C_2H_3O_2^-]}{[HC_2H_3O_2]} = \frac{(x)(0.51 + x)}{0.49 - x} \approx \frac{(x)(0.51)}{0.49}$$

and

$$x \approx 1.7 \times 10^{-5}$$

The approximations are valid (by the 5% rule), so

$$[H^+] = x = 1.7 \times 10^{-5} \quad \text{and} \quad pH = 4.76$$

The change in pH produced by the addition of 0.01 mol OH^- to this buffered solution is then

$$\underset{\substack{\uparrow \\ \text{New solution}}}{4.76} - \underset{\substack{\uparrow \\ \text{Original solution}}}{4.74} = +0.02$$

The pH increased by 0.02 pH units.

Now compare this with what happens when 0.01 mol solid NaOH is added to 1.0 L water to give 0.01 M NaOH. In this case $[OH^-] = 0.01\ M$ and

$$[H^+] = \frac{K_w}{[OH^-]} = \frac{1.0 \times 10^{-14}}{1.0 \times 10^{-2}} = 1.0 \times 10^{-12}$$
$$pH = 12.00$$

Thus the change in pH is

$$\underset{\substack{\uparrow \\ \text{New solution}}}{12.00} - \underset{\substack{\uparrow \\ \text{Pure water}}}{7.00} = +5.00$$

The increase is 5.00 pH units. Note how well the buffered solution resists a change in pH as compared with pure water.

(top) Pure water at pH 7.00.
(bottom) When 0.01 mol NaOH is added to 1.0 L of pure water, the pH jumps to 12.00.

Sample Exercises 15.2 and 15.3 represent typical buffer problems that involve all the concepts that you need to know to handle buffered solutions containing weak acids. Pay special attention to the following points:

1. Buffered solutions are simply solutions of weak acids or bases containing a common ion. The pH calculations on buffered solutions require exactly the same procedures introduced in Chapter 14. *This is not a new type of problem.*

2. When a strong acid or base is added to a buffered solution, it is best to deal with the stoichiometry of the resulting reaction first. After the stoichiometric calculations are completed, then consider the equilibrium calculations. This procedure can be represented as follows:

Buffering: How Does It Work?

Sample Exercises 15.2 and 15.3 demonstrate the ability of a buffered solution to absorb hydroxide ions without a significant change in pH. *But how does a buffer work?* Suppose a buffered solution contains relatively large quantities of a weak acid HA and its conjugate base A^-. When hydroxide ions are added to the solution, since the weak acid represents the best source of protons, the following reaction occurs:

$$OH^- + HA \rightarrow A^- + H_2O$$

The net result is that OH^- ions are not allowed to accumulate but are replaced by A^- ions.

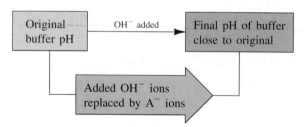

The stability of the pH under these conditions can be understood by examining the equilibrium expression for the dissociation of HA:

$$K_a = \frac{[H^+][A^-]}{[HA]}$$

or, rearranging,

$$[H^+] = K_a\frac{[HA]}{[A^-]}$$

In a buffered solution the pH is governed by the ratio [HA]/[A⁻].

In other words, the *equilibrium concentration of H^+, and thus the pH, is determined by the ratio [HA]/[A⁻].* When OH^- ions are added, HA is converted to A^-, and the ratio [HA]/[A⁻] decreases. However, *if the amounts of HA and A⁻ originally pres-*

ent are very large compared with the amount of OH⁻ added, the change in the [HA]/[A⁻] ratio will be small.

In Sample Exercises 15.2 and 15.3,

$$\frac{[HA]}{[A^-]} = \frac{0.50}{0.50} = 1.0 \qquad \text{Initially}$$

$$\frac{[HA]}{[A^-]} = \frac{0.49}{0.51} = 0.96 \qquad \text{After adding 0.01 mol/L OH}^-$$

The change in the ratio [HA]/[A⁻] is very small. Thus the [H⁺] and the pH remain essentially constant.

The essence of buffering, then, is that [HA] and [A⁻] are large compared with the amount of OH⁻ added. Thus when the OH⁻ is added, the concentrations of HA and A⁻ change, but only by small amounts. Under these conditions, the [HA]/[A⁻] ratio and thus the [H⁺] remain virtually constant.

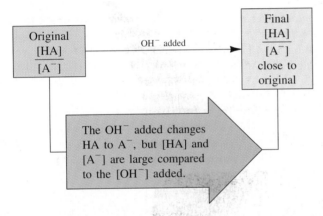

Similar reasoning applies when protons are added to a buffered solution of a weak acid and a salt of its conjugate base. Because the A⁻ ion has a high affinity for H⁺, the added H⁺ ions react with A⁻ to form the weak acid:

$$H^+ + A^- \rightarrow HA$$

and free H⁺ ions do not accumulate. In this case there will be a net change of A⁻ to HA. However, if [A⁻] and [HA] are large compared with the [H⁺] added, little change in the pH will occur.

The form of the acid dissociation equilibrium expression

$$[H^+] = K_a \frac{[HA]}{[A^-]} \tag{15.1}$$

is often useful for calculating [H⁺] in a buffered solution, since [HA] and [A⁻] are known. For example, to calculate [H⁺] in a buffered solution containing 0.10 M HF ($K_a = 7.2 \times 10^{-4}$) and 0.30 M NaF, we simply substitute into Equation (15.1):

$$[H^+] = (7.2 \times 10^{-4}) \frac{0.10}{0.30} = 2.4 \times 10^{-4}\ M$$

Another useful form of Equation (15.1) can be obtained by taking the negative log of both sides:

$$-\log[H^+] = -\log(K_a) - \log\left(\frac{[HA]}{[A^-]}\right)$$

That is,

$$pH = pK_a - \log\left(\frac{[HA]}{[A^-]}\right)$$

or, where inverting the log term reverses the sign:

$$pH = pK_a + \log\left(\frac{[A^-]}{[HA]}\right) = pK_a + \log\left(\frac{[base]}{[acid]}\right) \qquad (15.2)$$

This log form of the expression for K_a is called the **Henderson–Hasselbalch equation** and is useful for calculating the pH of solutions when the ratio $[HA]/[A^-]$ is known.

For a particular buffering system (acid–conjugate base pair), all solutions that have the same ratio $[A^-]/[HA]$ will have the same pH. For example, a buffered solution containing 5.0 M $HC_2H_3O_2$ and 3.0 M $NaC_2H_3O_2$ will have the same pH as one containing 0.050 M $HC_2H_3O_2$ and 0.030 M $NaC_2H_3O_2$. This can be shown as follows:

System	$[A^-]/[HA]$
5.0 M $HC_2H_3O_2$ and 3.0 M $NaC_2H_3O_2$	$\dfrac{3.0\ M}{5.0\ M} = 0.60$
0.050 M $HC_2H_3O_2$ and 0.030 M $NaC_2H_3O_2$	$\dfrac{0.030\ M}{0.050\ M} = 0.60$

Therefore,

$$pH = pK_a + \log\left(\frac{[C_2H_3O_2^-]}{[HC_2H_3O_2]}\right) = 4.74 + \log(0.60) - 4.74 - 0.22 = 4.52$$

Note that in using this equation we have assumed that the equilibrium concentrations of A^- and HA are equal to the initial concentrations. That is, we are assuming the validity of the approximations

$$[A^-] = [A^-]_0 + x \approx [A^-]_0 \quad \text{and} \quad [HA] = [HA]_0 - x \approx [HA]_0$$

where x is the amount of acid that dissociates. Since the initial concentrations of HA and A^- are relatively large in a buffered solution, this assumption is generally acceptable.

Sample Exercise 15.4

Calculate the pH of a solution containing 0.75 M lactic acid ($K_a = 1.4 \times 10^{-4}$) and 0.25 M sodium lactate. Lactic acid ($HC_3H_5O_3$) is a common constituent of biologic systems. For example, it is found in milk and is present in human muscle tissue during exertion.

Solution

The major species in solution are

$$HC_3H_5O_3, \quad Na^+, \quad C_3H_5O_3^-, \quad \text{and} \quad H_2O$$

Since Na^+ has no acid–base properties and H_2O is a weak acid or base, the pH will be controlled by the lactic acid dissociation equilibrium:

$$HC_3H_5O_3(aq) \rightleftharpoons H^+(aq) + C_3H_5O_3^-(aq)$$

$$K_a = \frac{[H^+][C_3H_5O_3^-]}{[HC_3H_5O_3]} = 1.4 \times 10^{-4}$$

Since $[HC_3H_5O_3]_0$ and $[C_3H_5O_3^-]_0$ are relatively large,

$$[HC_3H_5O_3] \approx [HC_3H_5O_3]_0 = 0.75 \ M$$

and

$$[C_3H_5O_3^-] \approx [C_3H_5O_3^-]_0 = 0.25 \ M$$

Thus, using the rearranged K_a expression, we have

$$[H^+] = K_a \frac{[HC_3H_5O_3]}{[C_3H_5O_3^-]} = (1.4 \times 10^{-4})\frac{(0.75 \ M)}{(0.25 \ M)} = 4.2 \times 10^{-4} \ M$$

and

$$pH = -\log(4.2 \times 10^{-4}) = 3.38$$

Alternatively, we could use the Henderson–Hasselbalch equation:

$$pH = pK_a + \log\left(\frac{[C_3H_5O_3^-]}{[HC_3H_5O_3]}\right) = 3.85 + \log\left(\frac{0.25 \ M}{0.75 \ M}\right) = 3.38$$

Buffered solutions also can be formed from a weak base and the corresponding conjugate acid. In these solutions, the weak base B reacts with any H^+ added

$$B + H^+ \rightarrow BH^+$$

and the conjugate acid BH^+ reacts with any added OH^-

$$BH^+ + OH^- \rightarrow B + H_2O$$

The approach needed to perform pH calculations for these systems is virtually identical to that used above. This makes sense because, as is true of all buffered solutions, a weak acid (BH^+) and a weak base (B) are present. A typical case is illustrated in Sample Exercise 15.5.

Sample Exercise 15.5

A buffered solution contains 0.25 M NH_3 ($K_b = 1.8 \times 10^{-5}$) and 0.40 M NH_4Cl. Calculate the pH of this solution.

Solution

The major species in solution are

$$NH_3, \quad \underbrace{NH_4^+, \quad Cl^-}_{\text{From the dissolved } NH_4Cl}, \quad \text{and} \quad H_2O$$

Since Cl^- is such a weak base and water is a weak acid or base, the important equilibrium is

$$NH_3(aq) + H_2O(l) \rightleftharpoons NH_4^+(aq) + OH^-(aq)$$

and

$$K_b = 1.8 \times 10^{-5} = \frac{[NH_4^+][OH^-]}{[NH_3]}$$

The appropriate concentrations are as follows:

Initial Concentration (mol/L)		Equilibrium Concentration (mol/L)
$[NH_3]_0 = 0.25$ $[NH_4^+]_0 = 0.40$ $[OH^-] \approx 0$	$\xrightarrow[\text{reacts with } H_2O]{x \text{ mol/L } NH_3}$	$[NH_3] = 0.25 - x$ $[NH_4^+] = 0.40 + x$ $[OH^-] = x$

Then

$$K_b = 1.8 \times 10^{-5} = \frac{[NH_4^+][OH^-]}{[NH_3]} = \frac{(0.40 + x)(x)}{0.25 - x} \approx \frac{(0.40)(x)}{0.25}$$

and

$$x \approx 1.1 \times 10^{-5}$$

The approximations are valid (by the 5% rule), so

$$[OH^-] = x = 1.1 \times 10^{-5}$$
$$pOH = 4.95$$
$$pH = 14.00 - 4.95 = 9.05$$

This case is typical of a buffered solution in that the initial and equilibrium concentrations of buffering materials are essentially the same.

ALTERNATIVE SOLUTION

There is another way of looking at this problem. Since the solution contains relatively large quantities of *both* NH_4^+ and NH_3, we can use the equilibrium

$$NH_3(aq) + H_2O(l) \rightleftharpoons NH_4^+(aq) + OH^-(aq)$$

to calculate $[OH^-]$ and then calculate $[H^+]$ from K_w as we have just done. Or we can use the dissociation equilibrium for NH_4^+, that is,

$$NH_4^+(aq) \rightleftharpoons NH_3(aq) + H^+(aq)$$

to calculate $[H^+]$ directly. *Either choice will give the same answer,* since the same equilibrium concentrations of NH_3 and NH_4^+ must satisfy both equilibria.

We can obtain the K_a value for NH_4^+ from the given K_b value for NH_3, since $K_a \times K_b = K_w$:

$$K_a = \frac{K_w}{K_b} = \frac{1.0 \times 10^{-14}}{1.8 \times 10^{-5}} = 5.6 \times 10^{-10}$$

Then, using the Henderson–Hasselbalch equation, we have

$$pH = pK_a + \log\left(\frac{[\text{base}]}{[\text{acid}]}\right)$$

$$= 9.25 + \log\left(\frac{0.25\ M}{0.40\ M}\right) = 9.25 - 0.20 = 9.05$$

Sample Exercise 15.6

Calculate the pH of the solution that results when 0.10 mol gaseous HCl is added to 1.0 L of the buffered solution from Sample Exercise 15.5.

Solution

Before any reaction occurs, the solution contains the following major species:

$$NH_3, \quad NH_4^+, \quad Cl^-, \quad H^+, \quad \text{and} \quad H_2O$$

What reaction can occur? We know that H^+ will not react with Cl^- to form HCl. In contrast to Cl^-, the NH_3 molecule has a great affinity for protons [this is demonstrated by the fact that NH_4^+ is such a weak acid ($K_a = 5.6 \times 10^{-10}$)]. Thus NH_3 will react with H^+ to form NH_4^+:

$$NH_3(aq) + H^+(aq) \rightarrow NH_4^+(aq)$$

Since this reaction can be assumed to go essentially to completion to form the very weak acid NH_4^+, we will do the stoichiometry calculations before we consider the equilibrium calculations. That is, we will let the reaction run to completion and then consider the equilibrium.

The stoichiometry calculations for this process are shown below.

Remember: Think about the chemistry first. Ask yourself if a reaction will occur among the major species.

	NH_3	$+$	H^+	$\rightarrow$	NH_4^+
Before reaction:	(1.0 L)(0.25 M) = 0.25 mol		0.10 mol ↑ Limiting reactant		(1.0 L)(0.40 M) = 0.40 mol
After reaction:	0.25 − 0.10 = 0.15 mol		0		0.40 + 0.10 = 0.50 mol

After the reaction goes to completion, the solution contains the major species

$$NH_3, \quad NH_4^+, \quad Cl^-, \quad \text{and} \quad H_2O$$

and

$$[NH_3]_0 = \frac{0.15\ \text{mol}}{1.0\ \text{L}} = 0.15\ M$$

$$[NH_4^+]_0 = \frac{0.50\ \text{mol}}{1.0\ \text{L}} = 0.50\ M$$

We can use the Henderson–Hasselbalch equation, where

$$[\text{Base}] = [NH_3] \approx [NH_3]_0 = 0.15\ M$$
$$[\text{Acid}] = [NH_4^+] \approx [NH_4^+]_0 = 0.50\ M$$

Then

$$pH = pK_a + \log\left(\frac{[NH_3]}{[NH_4^+]}\right)$$

$$= 9.25 + \log\left(\frac{0.15\ M}{0.50\ M}\right) = 9.25 - 0.52 = 8.73$$

Note that the addition of HCl only slightly decreases the pH, as we would expect in a buffered solution.

Summary of the Most Important Characteristics of Buffered Solutions

- Buffered solutions contain relatively large concentrations of a weak acid and the corresponding weak base. They can involve a weak acid HA and the conjugate base A^- or a weak base B and the conjugate acid BH^+.

- When H^+ is added to a buffered solution, it reacts essentially to completion with the weak base present:

$$H^+ + A^- \rightarrow HA \quad \text{or} \quad H^+ + B \rightarrow BH^+$$

- When OH^- is added to a buffered solution, it reacts essentially to completion with the weak acid present:

$$OH^- + HA \rightarrow A^- + H_2O \quad \text{or} \quad OH^- + BH^+ \rightarrow B + H_2O$$

- The pH in the buffered solution is determined by the ratio of the concentrations of the weak acid and weak base. As long as this ratio remains virtually constant, the pH will remain virtually constant. This will be the case as long as the concentrations of the buffering materials (HA and A^- or B and BH^+) are large compared with the amounts of H^+ or OH^- added.

15.3 Buffer Capacity

Purpose

- To describe the meaning of buffer capacity.

A buffer with a large capacity contains large concentrations of the buffering components.

The **buffering capacity** of a buffered solution represents the amount of protons or hydroxide ions the buffer can absorb without a significant change in pH. A buffer with a large capacity contains large concentrations of buffering components and so can absorb a relatively large amount of protons or hydroxide ions and show little pH change. *The pH of a buffered solution is determined by the ratio $[A^-]/[HA]$. The capacity of a buffered solution is determined by the magnitudes of $[HA]$ and $[A^-]$.*

Sample Exercise 15.7

Calculate the change in pH that occurs when 0.010 mol gaseous HCl is added to 1.0 L of each of the following solutions:

Solution A: 5.00 M $HC_2H_3O_2$ and 5.00 M $NaC_2H_3O_2$

Solution B: 0.050 M $HC_2H_3O_2$ and 0.050 M $NaC_2H_3O_2$

For acetic acid, $K_a = 1.8 \times 10^{-5}$.

Solution

For both solutions the initial pH can be determined from the Henderson–Hasselbalch equation:

$$pH = pK_a + \log\left(\frac{[C_2H_3O_2^-]}{[HC_2H_3O_2]}\right)$$

In each case, $[C_2H_3O_2^-] = [HC_2H_3O_2]$. Therefore, the initial pH for both A and B is

$$pH = pK_a + \log(1) = pK_a = -\log(1.8 \times 10^{-5}) = 4.74$$

After the addition of HCl to each of these solutions, the major species *before any reaction occurs* are

$$HC_2H_3O_2, \quad Na^+, \quad C_2H_3O_2^-, \quad \underbrace{H^+, \quad Cl^-}_{\text{From the added HCl}}, \quad \text{and} \quad H_2O$$

Will any reactions occur among these species? Note that we have a relatively large quantity of H^+, which will readily react with any effective base. We know that Cl^- will not react with H^+ to form HCl in water. However, $C_2H_3O_2^-$ will react with H^+ to form the weak acid $HC_2H_3O_2$:

$$H^+(aq) + C_2H_3O_2^-(aq) \rightarrow HC_2H_3O_2(aq)$$

Because $HC_2H_3O_2$ is a weak acid, we assume that this reaction runs to completion; the 0.010 mol of added H^+ will convert 0.010 mol $C_2H_3O_2^-$ to 0.010 mol $HC_2H_3O_2$.

For solution A (since the solution volume is 1.0 L, the number of moles equals the molarity) the following calculations apply:

	H^+	$+$	$C_2H_3O_2^-$	$\rightarrow$	$HC_2H_3O_2$
Before reaction:	0.010 M		5.00 M		5.00 M
After reaction:	0		4.99 M		5.01 M

The new pH can be obtained by substituting the new concentrations into the Henderson–Hasselbalch equation:

$$pH = pK_a + \log\left(\frac{[C_2H_3O_2^-]}{[HC_2H_3O_2]}\right)$$

$$= 4.74 + \log\left(\frac{4.99}{5.01}\right) = 4.74 - 0.0017 = 4.74$$

There is virtually no change in pH for solution A when 0.010 mol gaseous HCl is added.

For solution B the following calculations apply:

	H^+	$+$	$C_2H_3O_2^-$	$\rightarrow$	$HC_2H_3O_2$
Before reaction:	0.010 M		0.050 M		0.050 M
After reaction:	0		0.040 M		0.060 M

The new pH is

$$pH = 4.74 + \log\left(\frac{0.040}{0.060}\right)$$

$$= 4.74 - 0.18 = 4.56$$

Although the pH change for solution B is small, a change did occur, which is in contrast to solution A.

These results show that solution A, which contains much larger quantities of buffering components, has a much higher buffering capacity than solution B.

We have seen that the pH of a buffered solution depends on the ratio of the concentrations of buffering components. When this ratio is least affected by added protons or hydroxide ions, the solution is the most resistant to a change in pH. To find the ratio that gives optimal buffering, let's suppose we have a buffered solution containing a large concentration of acetate ion and only a small concentration of acetic acid. Addition of protons to form acetic acid will produce a relatively large *percent* change in the concentration of acetic acid and so will produce a relatively large change in the ratio $[C_2H_3O_2^-]/[HC_2H_3O_2]$ (see Table 15.1). Similarly, if hydroxide ions are added to remove some acetic acid, the percent change in the concentration of acetic acid is again large. The same effects are seen if the initial concentration of acetic acid is large and that of acetate ion is small.

Because large changes in the ratio $[A^-]/[HA]$ will produce large changes in pH, we want to avoid this situation for the most effective buffering. This type of reasoning leads us to the general conclusion that optimal buffering occurs when $[HA]$ is equal to $[A^-]$. It is for this condition that the ratio $[A^-]/[HA]$ is most resistant to change when H^+ or OH^- is added to the buffered solution. This means that when choosing the buffering components for a specific application, we want $[A^-]/[HA]$ to equal 1. It follows that since

$$pH = pK_a + \log\left(\frac{[A^-]}{[HA]}\right) = pK_a + \log(1) = pK_a$$

the *pK_a of the weak acid to be used in the buffer should be as close as possible to the desired pH*. For example, suppose we need a buffered solution with a pH of 4.00. The most effective buffering will occur when $[HA]$ is equal to $[A^-]$. From the

Solution A

Solution B

Table 15.1				
Change in $[C_2H_3O_2^-]/[HC_2H_3O_2]$ for Two Solutions When 0.01 mol H^+ is Added to 1.0 L of Each				
Solution	$\left(\dfrac{[C_2H_3O_2^-]}{[HC_2H_3O_2]}\right)_{orig}$	$\left(\dfrac{[C_2H_3O_2^-]}{[HC_2H_3O_2]}\right)_{new}$	Change	Percent Change
A	$\dfrac{1.00\ M}{1.00\ M} = 1.00$	$\dfrac{0.99\ M}{1.01\ M} = 0.98$	$1.00 \rightarrow 0.98$	2.00%
B	$\dfrac{1.00\ M}{0.01\ M} = 100$	$\dfrac{0.99\ M}{0.02\ M} = 49.5$	$100 \rightarrow 49.5$	50.5%

Henderson–Hasselbalch equation,

$$pH = pK_a + \log\left(\frac{[A^-]}{[HA]}\right)$$

<table>
<tr><td>4.00 is wanted</td><td></td><td>Ratio = 1 for most effective buffer</td></tr>
</table>

That is, $4.00 = pK_a + \log(1) = pK_a + 0$ and $pK_a = 4.00$

Thus the best choice of a weak acid is one that has $pK_a = 4.00$ or $K_a = 1.0 \times 10^{-4}$.

Sample Exercise 15.8

A chemist needs a solution buffered at pH 4.30 and can choose from the following acids (and their sodium salts):

a. Chloroacetic acid ($K_a = 1.35 \times 10^{-3}$)
b. Propanoic acid ($K_a = 1.3 \times 10^{-5}$)
c. Benzoic acid ($K_a = 6.4 \times 10^{-5}$)
d. Hypochlorous acid ($K_a = 3.5 \times 10^{-8}$)

Calculate the ratio $[HA]/[A^-]$ required for each system to yield a pH of 4.30. Which system will work best?

Solution

A pH of 4.30 corresponds to

$$[H^+] = 10^{-4.30} = \text{antilog}(-4.30) = 5.0 \times 10^{-5} \ M$$

Since K_a values rather than pK_a values are given for the various acids, we use Equation (15.1)

$$[H^+] = K_a\frac{[HA]}{[A^-]}$$

rather than the Henderson–Hasselbalch equation. We substitute the required $[H^+]$ and K_a for each acid into Equation (15.1) to calculate the ratio $[HA]/[A^-]$ needed in each case.

Acid	$[H^+] = K_a\dfrac{[HA]}{[A^-]}$	$\dfrac{[HA]}{[A^-]}$
a. Chloroacetic	$5.0 \times 10^{-5} = 1.35 \times 10^{-3}\left(\dfrac{[HA]}{[A^-]}\right)$	3.7×10^{-2}
b. Propanoic	$5.0 \times 10^{-5} = 1.3 \times 10^{-5}\left(\dfrac{[HA]}{[A^-]}\right)$	3.8
c. Benzoic	$5.0 \times 10^{-5} = 6.4 \times 10^{-5}\left(\dfrac{[HA]}{[A^-]}\right)$	0.78
d. Hypochlorous	$5.0 \times 10^{-5} = 3.5 \times 10^{-8}\left(\dfrac{[HA]}{[A^-]}\right)$	1.4×10^{-3}

Since [HA]/[A$^-$] for benzoic acid is closest to 1, the system of benzoic acid and its sodium salt will be the best choice among those given for buffering a solution at pH 4.3. This example demonstrates the principle that the optimal buffering system has a pK_a value close to the desired pH. The pK_a for benzoic acid is 4.19.

15.4 Titrations and pH Curves

Purpose

- To demonstrate how to calculate pH at any point in an acid–base titration.

As we saw in Chapter 4, a titration is commonly used to determine the amount of acid or base in a solution. This process involves a solution of known concentration (the titrant) delivered from a buret into the unknown solution until the substance being analyzed is just consumed. The stoichiometric (equivalence) point is often signaled by the color change of an indicator. In this section we will discuss the pH changes that occur during an acid–base titration. We will use this information later to show how an appropriate indicator can be chosen for a particular titration.

The progress of an acid–base titration is often monitored by plotting the pH of the solution being analyzed as a function of the amount of titrant added. Such a plot is called a **pH curve** or **titration curve.**

Strong Acid–Strong Base Titrations

The net ionic reaction for a strong acid–strong base titration is

$$H^+(aq) + OH^-(aq) \rightarrow H_2O(l)$$

To compute [H$^+$] at a given point in the titration, we must determine the amount of H$^+$ that remains at that point and divide by the total volume of the solution. Before we proceed, we need to consider a new unit, which is especially convenient for titrations. Since titrations usually involve small quantities (burets are typically graduated in milliliters), the mole is inconveniently large. Therefore, we will use the **millimole** (abbreviated **mmol**), which, as the prefix indicates, is a thousandth of a mole:

1 millimole = 1×10^{-3} mol

1 mL = 1×10^{-3} L

$\dfrac{\text{mmol}}{\text{mL}} = \dfrac{\text{mol}}{\text{L}} = M$

$$1 \text{ mmol} = \frac{1 \text{ mol}}{1000} = 10^{-3} \text{ mol}$$

So far we have defined molarity only in terms of moles per liter. We can now define it in terms of *millimoles per milliliter,* as shown below:

$$\text{Molarity} = \frac{\text{mol solute}}{\text{L solution}} = \frac{\dfrac{\text{mol solute}}{1000}}{\dfrac{\text{L solution}}{1000}} = \frac{\text{mmol solute}}{\text{mL solution}}$$

A 1.0 *M* solution thus contains 1.0 mole of solute per liter of solution or, *equivalently,* 1.0 millimole of solute per milliliter of solution. Just as we obtain the number of moles of solute from the product of the volume in liters and the molarity, we obtain the number of millimoles of solute from the product of the volume in milliliters and the molarity:

$$\text{Number of mmol} = \text{volume (in mL)} \times \text{molarity}$$

Case Study: Strong Acid–Strong Base Titration

We will illustrate the calculations involved in a strong acid–strong base titration by considering the titration of 50.0 mL of 0.200 M HNO_3 with 0.100 M NaOH. We will calculate the pH of the solution at selected points during the course of the titration, where specific volumes of 0.100 M NaOH have been added.

A. No NaOH has been added.

Since HNO_3 is a strong acid (is completely dissociated), the solution contains the major species

$$H^+, \quad NO_3^-, \quad \text{and} \quad H_2O,$$

and the pH is determined by the H^+ from the nitric acid. Since 0.20 M HNO_3 contains 0.20 M H^+,

$$[H^+] = 0.20 \ M \quad \text{and} \quad pH = 0.70$$

B. 10.0 mL of 0.100 M NaOH has been added.

In the mixed solution *before any reaction occurs,* the major species are

$$H^+, \quad NO_3^-, \quad Na^+, \quad OH^-, \quad \text{and} \quad H_2O$$

Note that large quantities of both H^+ and OH^- are present. The 1.0 mmol (10.0 mL × 0.10 M) of added OH^- will react with 1.0 mmol H^+ to form water:

	H^+	+	OH^-	→	H_2O
Before reaction:	50.0 mL × 0.200 M = 10.0 mmol		10.0 mL × 0.10 M = 1.00 mmol		
After reaction:	10.0 − 1.0 = 9.0 mmol		1.0 − 1.0 = 0		

After the reaction, the solution contains

$$H^+, \quad NO_3^-, \quad Na^+, \quad \text{and} \quad H_2O \text{ (the } OH^- \text{ ions have been consumed)}$$

and the pH will be determined by the H^+ remaining:

$$[H^+] = \frac{\text{mmol } H^+ \text{ left}}{\text{volume of solution (mL)}} = \frac{9.0 \text{ mmol}}{(50.0 + 10.0) \text{ mL}} = 0.15 \ M$$

Original volume of
HNO_3 solution

Volume of
NaOH added

The final solution volume is the sum of the original volume of HNO_3 and the volume of added NaOH.

$$pH = -\log(0.15) = 0.82$$

C. 20.0 mL (total) of 0.100 M NaOH has been added.

We consider this point from the perspective that a total of 20.0 mL NaOH has been added to the *original* solution, rather than that 10.0 mL has been added to the solution from point B. It is best to go back to the original solution each time so that a mistake made at an earlier point does not show up in each succeeding calculation. As before, the added OH^- will react with H^+ to form water:

	H^+	$+$	OH^-	$\rightarrow$	H_2O
Before reaction:	50.0 mL × 0.200 M = 10.0 mmol		20.0 mL × 0.10 M = 2.0 mmol		
After reaction:	10.0 − 2.0 = 8.0 mmol		2.0 − 2.0 = 0 mmol		

After the reaction

$$[H^+] = \frac{\overbrace{8.0 \text{ mmol}}^{(H^+ \text{ remaining})}}{(50.0 + 20.0) \text{ mL}} = 0.11 \ M$$

$$pH = 0.94$$

D. **50.0 mL (total) of 0.100 M NaOH has been added.**

Proceeding exactly as for points B and C, the pH is found to be 1.30.

E. **100.0 mL (total) of 0.100 M NaOH has been added.**

At this point the amount of NaOH that has been added is

$$100.0 \text{ mL} \times 0.100 \ M = 10.0 \text{ mmol}$$

The original amount of nitric acid was

$$50.0 \text{ mL} \times 0.200 \ M = 10.0 \text{ mmol}$$

Enough OH^- has been added to react exactly with the H^+ from the nitric acid. This is the **stoichiometric point,** or **equivalence point,** of the titration. At this point the major species in solution are

$$Na^+, \quad NO_3^-, \quad \text{and} \quad H_2O$$

Since Na^+ has no acid or base properties and NO_3^- is the anion of the strong acid HNO_3 and is therefore a very weak base, neither NO_3^- nor Na^+ affects the pH, and the solution is neutral (the pH is 7.00).

F. **150.0 mL (total) of 0.100 M NaOH has been added.**

The stoichiometric calculations for the titration reaction are as follows:

	H^+	$+$	OH^-	$\rightarrow$	H_2O
Before reaction:	50.0 mL × 0.200 M = 10.0 mmol		150.00 mL × 0.100 M = 15.0 mmol		
After reaction:	10.0 − 10.0 = 0 mmol		15.0 − 10.0 = 5.0 mmol ↑ Excess OH^- added		

Equivalence (stoichiometric) point: the point in the titration where an amount of base has been added to exactly react with all the acid originally present.

When 100.0 mL of 0.100 M sodium hydroxide is added to 50.0 mL of 0.200 M nitric acid, the equivalence (stoichiometric) point of the strong acid–strong base titration is reached, and the solution is neutral (pH = 7).

Now OH⁻ is *in excess* and will determine the pH:

$$[OH^-] = \frac{\text{mmol OH}^- \text{ in excess}}{\text{volume (mL)}} = \frac{5.0 \text{ mmol}}{(50.0 + 150.0) \text{ mL}} = \frac{5.0 \text{ mmol}}{200.0 \text{ mL}} = 0.025 \ M$$

Since $[H^+][OH^-] = 1.0 \times 10^{-14}$,

$$[H^+] = \frac{1.0 \times 10^{-14}}{2.5 \times 10^{-2}} = 4.0 \times 10^{-13} \ M \quad \text{and} \quad pH = 12.40$$

G. 200.0 mL (total) of 0.100 M NaOH has been added.

Proceeding as for point F, the pH is found to be 12.60.

The results of these calculations are summarized by the pH curve shown in Fig. 15.1. Note that the pH changes very gradually until the titration is close to the equivalence point, where a dramatic change occurs. This behavior is due to the fact that early in the titration there is a relatively large amount of H⁺ in the solution, and the addition of a given amount of OH⁻ thus produces a small change in pH. However, near the equivalence point [H⁺] is relatively small, and the addition of a small amount of OH⁻ produces a large change.

The pH curve in Fig. 15.1, typical of the titration of a strong acid with a strong base, has the following characteristics:

Before the equivalence point [H⁺] (and hence the pH) can be calculated by dividing the number of millimoles of H⁺ remaining by the total volume of the solution in milliliters.

At the equivalence point, the pH is 7.00.

After the equivalence point [OH⁻] can be calculated by dividing the number of millimoles of excess OH⁻ by the total volume of the solution. Then [H⁺] is obtained from K_w.

The titration of a strong base with a strong acid requires reasoning very similar to that used above, except, of course, that OH⁻ is in excess before the equivalence point and H⁺ is in excess after the equivalence point. The pH curve for the titration of 100.0 mL of 0.50 *M* NaOH with 1.0 *M* HCl is shown in Fig. 15.2.

After 200.0 mL of 0.100 M NaOH is added to 50.0 mL of 0.200 M nitric acid, the pH reaches a value of 12.60.

Figure 15.1

The pH curve for the titration of 50.0 mL of 0.200 M HNO₃ with 0.100 M NaOH. Note that the equivalence point occurs at 100.0 mL of NaOH added, the point where exactly enough OH⁻ has been added to react with all the H⁺ originally present. The pH of 7 at the equivalence point is characteristic of a strong acid–strong base titration.

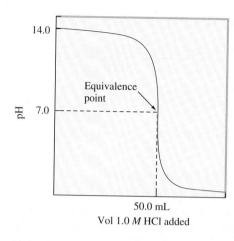

Figure 15.2

The pH curve for the titration of 100.0 mL of 0.50 M NaOH with 1.0 M HCl. The equivalence point occurs at 50.00 mL of HCl added, since at this point 5.0 mmol H^+ has been added to react with the original 5.0 mmol OH^-.

Titrations of Weak Acids with Strong Bases

We have seen that since strong acids and strong bases are completely dissociated, the calculations to obtain the pH curves for titrations involving the two are quite straightforward. However, when the acid being titrated is a weak acid, there is a major difference: to calculate $[H^+]$ after a certain amount of strong base has been added, we must deal with the weak acid dissociation equilibrium. We have dealt with this same situation earlier in this chapter when we treated buffered solutions. Calculation of the pH curve for a titration of a weak acid with a strong base really amounts to a series of buffer problems. In performing these calculations it is very important to remember that even though the acid is weak, it *reacts essentially to completion* with hydroxide ion, a very strong base.

Calculating the pH curve for a weak acid–strong base titration involves a two-step procedure:

Treat the stoichiometry and equilibrium problems separately.

STEP 1

A stoichiometry problem. The reaction of hydroxide ion with the weak acid is assumed to run to completion, and the concentrations of the acid *remaining* and the conjugate base *formed* are determined.

STEP 2

An equilibrium problem. The position of the weak acid equilibrium is determined, and the pH is calculated.

It is *essential* to do these steps *separately*. Note that the procedures necessary to do these calculations have all been used before.

Case Study: Weak Acid–Strong Base Titration

As an illustration, we will consider the titration of 50.0 mL of 0.10 M acetic acid ($HC_2H_3O_2$, $K_a = 1.8 \times 10^{-5}$) with 0.10 M NaOH. As before, we will calculate the pH at various points representing volumes of added NaOH.

A. **No NaOH has been added.**

This is a typical weak acid calculation of the type introduced in Chapter 14. The pH is 2.87. (Check this yourself.)

B. **10.0 mL of 0.10 M NaOH has been added.**

The major species in the mixed solution *before any reaction takes place* are

$$HC_2H_3O_2, \quad OH^-, \quad Na^+, \quad and \quad H_2O$$

The strong base OH^- will react with the strongest proton donor, which in this case is $HC_2H_3O_2$.

The Stoichiometry Problem.

	OH^-	$+$	$HC_2H_3O_2$	$\rightarrow$	$C_2H_3O_2^-$	$+$	H_2O
Before reaction:	$10 \text{ mL} \times 0.10 \ M$ $= 1.0 \text{ mmol}$		$50.0 \text{ mL} \times 0.10 \ M$ $= 5.0 \text{ mmol}$		0 mmol		
After reaction:	$1.0 - 1.0$ $= 0$ mmol $\uparrow$ Limiting reactant		$5.0 - 1.0$ $= 4.0$ mmol		1.0 mmol $\uparrow$ Formed by the reaction		

You are again doing exactly the same type of calculation already considered in Chapter 14.

The Equilibrium Problem We examine the major components left in the solution *after the reaction takes place* to decide on the dominant equilibrium. The major species are

$$HC_2H_3O_2, \quad C_2H_3O_2^-, \quad Na^+, \quad \text{and} \quad H_2O$$

Since $HC_2H_3O_2$ is a much stronger acid than H_2O, and since $C_2H_3O_2^-$ is the conjugate base of $HC_2H_3O_2$, the pH will be determined by the position of the acetic acid dissociation equilibrium:

$$HC_2H_3O_2(aq) \rightleftharpoons H^+(aq) + C_2H_3O_2^-(aq)$$

where

$$K_a = \frac{[H^+][C_2H_3O_2^-]}{[HC_2H_3O_2]}$$

We follow the usual steps to complete the equilibrium calculations:

Initial Concentration		Equilibrium Concentration
$[HC_2H_3O_2]_0 = \dfrac{4.0 \text{ mmol}}{(50.0 + 10.0) \text{ mL}} = \dfrac{4.0}{60.0}$	$\xrightarrow[\text{dissociates}]{\substack{x \text{ mmol/mL} \\ HC_2H_3O_2}}$	$[HC_2H_3O_2] = \dfrac{4.0}{60.0} - x$
$[C_2H_3O_2^-]_0 = \dfrac{1.0 \text{ mmol}}{(50.0 + 10.0) \text{ mL}} = \dfrac{1.0}{60.0}$		$[C_2H_3O_2^-] = \dfrac{1.0}{60.0} + x$
$[H^+]_0 \approx 0$		$[H^+] = x$

The initial concentrations are defined after the reaction with OH^- has gone to completion but before any dissociation of $HC_2H_3O_2$ occurs.

Therefore,

$$1.8 \times 10^{-5} = K_a = \frac{[H^+][C_2H_3O_2^-]}{[HC_2H_3O_2]} = \frac{x\left(\dfrac{1.0}{60.0} + x\right)}{\dfrac{4.0}{60.0} - x} \approx \frac{x\left(\dfrac{1.0}{60.0}\right)}{\dfrac{4.0}{60.0}} = \left(\frac{1.0}{4.0}\right)x$$

$$x = \left(\frac{4.0}{1.0}\right)(1.8 \times 10^{-5}) = 7.2 \times 10^{-5} = [H^+] \quad \text{and} \quad pH = 4.14$$

Note that the approximations made are well within the 5% rule.

C. 25.0 mL (total) of 0.10 M NaOH has been added.

The procedure here is very similar to that used at point B and will only be summarized briefly. The stoichiometry problem is summarized as follows:

	OH$^-$	+	HC$_2$H$_3$O$_2$	→	C$_2$H$_3$O$_2$$^-$	+	H$_2$O
Before reaction:	25.0 mL × 0.10 M = 2.5 mmol		50.0 mL × 0.10 M = 5.0 mmol		0 mmol		
After reaction:	2.5 − 2.5 = 0		5.0 − 2.5 = 2.5 mmol		2.5 mmol		

After the reaction, the major species in solution are

$$HC_2H_3O_2, \quad C_2H_3O_2^-, \quad Na^+, \quad \text{and} \quad H_2O$$

The equilibrium that will control the pH is

$$HC_2H_3O_2(aq) \rightleftharpoons H^+(aq) + C_2H_3O_2^-(aq)$$

and the pertinent concentrations are as follows:

Initial Concentration		Equilibrium Concentration
$[HC_2H_3O_2]_0 = \dfrac{2.5 \text{ mmol}}{(50.0 + 25.0) \text{ mL}}$		$[HC_2H_3O_2] = \dfrac{2.5}{75.0} - x$
$[C_2H_3O_2^-]_0 = \dfrac{2.5 \text{ mmol}}{(50.0 + 25.0) \text{ mL}}$	$\xrightarrow[\substack{x \text{ mmol/mL} \\ HC_2H_3O_2 \\ \text{dissociates}}]{}$	$[C_2H_3O_2^-] = \dfrac{2.5}{75.0} + x$
$[H^+]_0 \approx 0$		$[H^+] = x$

Therefore,

$$1.8 \times 10^{-5} = K_a = \frac{[H^+][C_2H_3O_2^-]}{[HC_2H_3O_2]} = \frac{x\left(\dfrac{2.5}{75.0} + x\right)}{\dfrac{2.5}{75.0} - x} \approx \frac{x\left(\dfrac{2.5}{75.0}\right)}{\dfrac{2.5}{75.0}}$$

$$x = 1.8 \times 10^{-5} = [H^+] \quad \text{and} \quad pH = 4.74$$

This is a special point in the titration because it is *halfway to the equivalence point*. The original solution, 50.0 mL of 0.10 M HC$_2$H$_3$O$_2$, contained 5.0 mmol HC$_2$H$_3$O$_2$. Thus 5.0 mmol OH$^-$ is required to reach the equivalence point. That is, 50 mL NaOH is required, since

$$(50.0 \text{ mL})(0.10 \ M) = 5.0 \text{ mmol}$$

After 25.0 mL NaOH has been added, half the original HC$_2$H$_3$O$_2$ has been converted to C$_2$H$_3$O$_2$$^-$. At this point in the titration [HC$_2$H$_3$O$_2$]$_0$ is equal to [C$_2$H$_3$O$_2$$^-$]$_0$. We can neglect the effect of dissociation; that is,

$$[HC_2H_3O_2] = [HC_2H_3O_2]_0 - x \approx [HC_2H_3O_2]_0$$
$$[C_2H_3O_2^-] = [C_2H_3O_2^-]_0 + x \approx [C_2H_3O_2^-]_0$$

At this point, half the acid has been used up, so

$$[HC_2H_3O_2] = [C_2H_3O_2^-]$$

The expression for K_a at the halfway point is

$$K_a = \frac{[H^+][C_2H_3O_2^-]}{[HC_2H_3O_2]} = \frac{[H^+][C_2H_3O_2^-]_0}{[HC_2H_3O_2]_0} = [H^+]$$

Equal at the halfway point

Then, *at the halfway point* in the titration,

$$[H^+] = K_a \quad \text{and} \quad pH = pK_a$$

D. 40.0 mL (total) of 0.10 M NaOH has been added.

The procedures required here are the same as those used for points B and C. The pH is 5.35. (Check this yourself.)

E. 50.0 mL (total) of 0.10 M NaOH has been added.

This is the equivalence point of the titration; 5.0 mmol OH^- has been added, which will just react with the 5.0 mmol $HC_2H_3O_2$ originally present. At this point the solution contains the major species

$$Na^+, \quad C_2H_3O_2^-, \quad \text{and} \quad H_2O$$

Note that the solution contains $C_2H_3O_2^-$, which is a base. Remember that a base wants to combine with a proton, and the only source of protons in this solution is water. Thus the reaction will be

$$C_2H_3O_2^-(aq) + H_2O(l) \rightleftharpoons HC_2H_3O_2(aq) + OH^-(aq)$$

This is a *weak base* reaction characterized by K_b:

$$K_b = \frac{[HC_2H_3O_2][OH^-]}{[C_2H_3O_2^-]} = \frac{K_w}{K_a} = \frac{1.0 \times 10^{-14}}{1.8 \times 10^{-5}} = 5.6 \times 10^{-10}$$

The relevant concentrations are as follows:

Initial Concentration (before any $C_2H_3O_2^-$ reacts with H_2O)		Equilibrium Concentration
$[C_2H_3O_2^-]_0 = \dfrac{5.0 \text{ mmol}}{(50.0 + 50.0) \text{ mL}}$ $= 0.050 \ M$	$\xrightarrow[\text{with } H_2O]{\substack{x \text{ mmol/mL} \\ C_2H_3O_2^- \text{ reacts}}}$	$[C_2H_3O_2^-] = 0.050 - x$
$[OH^-]_0 \approx 0$		$[OH^-] = x$
$[HC_2H_3O_2]_0 = 0$		$[HC_2H_3O_2] = x$

Therefore,

$$5.6 \times 10^{-10} = K_b = \frac{[HC_2H_3O_2][OH^-]}{[C_2H_3O_2^-]} = \frac{(x)(x)}{0.050 - x} \approx \frac{x^2}{0.050}$$

$$x \approx 5.3 \times 10^{-6}$$

The approximation is valid (by the 5% rule), so

$$[OH^-] = 5.3 \times 10^{-6} \ M$$

and

$$[H^+][OH^-] = K_w = 1.0 \times 10^{-14}$$

$$[H^+] = 1.9 \times 10^{-9} \ M$$

$$pH = 8.72$$

This is another important result: *the pH at the equivalence point of a titration of a weak acid with a strong base is always greater than 7.* This is so because the anion of the acid, which remains in solution at the equivalence point, is a base. In contrast, for the titration of a strong acid with a strong base, the pH at the equivalence point is 7.0, because the anion remaining in this case is *not* an effective base.

F. **60.0 mL (total) of 0.10 M NaOH has been added.**

At this point, excess OH^- has been added. The stoichiometric calculations are as follows:

	OH^-	+	$HC_2H_3O_2$	$\rightarrow C_2H_3O_2^- + H_2O$
Before reaction:	60.0 mL × 0.10 M = 6.0 mmol		50.0 mL × 0.10 M = 5.0 mmol	0 mmol
After reaction:	6.0 − 5.0 = 1.0 mmol in excess		5.0 − 5.0 = 0	5.0 mmol

After the reaction is complete, the solution contains the major species

$$Na^+, \quad C_2H_3O_2^-, \quad OH^-, \quad \text{and} \quad H_2O$$

There are two bases in this solution, OH^- and $C_2H_3O_2^-$. However, $C_2H_3O_2^-$ is a weak base compared with OH^-. Therefore, the amount of OH^- produced by reaction of $C_2H_3O_2^-$ with H_2O will be small compared with the excess OH^- already in solution. You can verify this conclusion by looking at point E, where only 5.3×10^{-6} M OH^- was produced by $C_2H_3O_2^-$. The amount in this case will be even smaller, since the excess OH^- will push the K_b equilibrium to the left.

Thus the pH is determined by the excess OH^-:

$$[OH^-] = \frac{\text{mmol of } OH^- \text{ in excess}}{\text{volume (in mL)}} = \frac{1.0 \text{ mmol}}{(50.0 + 60.0) \text{ mL}}$$
$$= 9.1 \times 10^{-3} \ M$$

and
$$[H^+] = \frac{1.0 \times 10^{-14}}{9.1 \times 10^{-3}} = 1.1 \times 10^{-12} \ M$$

$$pH = 11.96$$

G. **75.0 mL (total) of 0.10 M NaOH has been added.**

The procedure needed here is very similar to that for point F. The pH is 12.30. (Check this.)

The pH curve for this titration is shown in Fig. 15.3. It is important to note the differences between this curve and that in Fig. 15.1. For example, the shapes of the plots are quite different before the equivalence point, although they are very similar after that point. (The shapes of the strong and weak acid curves are the same after the equivalence points because excess OH^- controls the pH in this region in both cases.) Near the beginning of the titration of the weak acid, the pH increases more rapidly than it does in the strong acid case. It levels off near the halfway point and then increases rapidly again. The leveling off near the halfway point is caused by buffering effects. Earlier in this chapter we saw that optimal buffering occurs when [HA] is equal to

Figure 15.3

The pH curve for the titration of 50.0 mL of 0.100 M $HC_2H_3O_2$ with 0.100 M NaOH. Note that the equivalence point occurs at 50.0 mL of NaOH added, where the amount of added OH^- exactly equals the original amount of acid. The pH at the equivalence point is greater than 7.0 because the $C_2H_3O_2^-$ ion present at this point is a base and reacts with water to produce OH^-.

[A^-]. This is exactly the case at the halfway point of the titration. As we can see from the curve, the pH changes least rapidly in this region of the titration.

The other notable difference between the curves for strong and weak acids is the value of the pH at the equivalence point. For the titration of a strong acid, the equivalence point occurs at pH 7. For the titration of a weak acid, the pH at the equivalence point is greater than 7 because of the basicity of the conjugate base of the weak acid.

It is important to understand that the equivalence point in an acid–base titration is *defined by the stoichiometry, not by the pH*. The equivalence point occurs when enough titrant has been added to react exactly with all the acid or base being titrated.

The equivalence point is defined by the stoichiometry, not by the pH.

Sample Exercise 15.9

Hydrogen cyanide gas (HCN), a powerful respiratory inhibitor, is highly toxic. It is a very weak acid ($K_a = 6.2 \times 10^{-10}$) when dissolved in water. If a 50.0-mL sample of 0.100 M HCN is titrated with 0.100 M NaOH, calculate the pH of the solution

a. After 8.00 mL of 0.100 M NaOH has been added.
b. At the halfway point of the titration.
c. At the equivalence point of the titration.

Solution

a. *The stoichiometry problem.* After 8.00 mL of 0.100 M NaOH has been added, the following calculations apply:

	HCN	+	OH^-	$\rightarrow$	CN^-	+ H_2O
Before reaction:	50.0 mL $\times$ 0.100 M = 5.00 mmol		8.00 mL $\times$ 0.100 M = 0.800 mmol		0 mmol	
After reaction:	5.00 − 0.80 = 4.20 mmol		0.800 − 0.800 = 0		0.800 mmol	

The equilibrium problem. Since the solution contains the major species

$$HCN, \quad CN^-, \quad Na^+, \quad and \quad H_2O$$

the position of the acid dissociation equilibrium

$$HCN(aq) \rightleftharpoons H^+(aq) + CN^-(aq)$$

will determine the pH.

Initial Concentration		Equilibrium Concentration
$[HCN]_0 = \dfrac{4.2 \text{ mmol}}{(50.0 + 8.0) \text{ mL}}$		$[HCN] = \dfrac{4.2}{58.0} - x$
$[CN^-]_0 = \dfrac{0.800 \text{ mmol}}{(50.0 + 8.0) \text{ mL}}$	$\xrightarrow[\text{dissociates}]{\substack{x \text{ mmol/mL} \\ HCN}}$	$[CN^-] = \dfrac{0.80}{58.0} + x$
$[H^+]_0 \approx 0$		$[H^+] = x$

Substituting the equilibrium concentrations into the expression for K_a gives

$$6.2 \times 10^{-10} = K_a = \frac{[H^+][CN^-]}{[HCN]} = \frac{x\left(\dfrac{0.80}{58.0} + x\right)}{\dfrac{4.2}{58.0} - x} \approx \frac{x\left(\dfrac{0.80}{58.0}\right)}{\left(\dfrac{4.2}{58.0}\right)} = x\left(\dfrac{0.80}{4.2}\right)$$

$$x = 3.3 \times 10^{-9} \, M = [H^+] \quad and \quad pH = 8.49$$

b. *At the halfway point of the titration.* The amount of HCN originally present can be obtained from the original volume and molarity:

$$50.0 \text{ mL} \times 0.100 \, M = 5.00 \text{ mmol}$$

Thus the halfway point will occur when 2.50 mmol OH^- has been added:

$$\text{Volume of NaOH (in mL)} \times 0.100 \, M = 2.50 \text{ mmol OH}^-$$

or
$$\text{Volume of NaOH} = 25.0 \text{ mL}$$

As was pointed out previously, at the halfway point [HCN] is equal to $[CN^-]$ and pH is equal to pK_a. Thus, after 25.0 mL of 0.100 M NaOH has been added,

$$pH = pK_a = -\log(6.2 \times 10^{-10}) = 9.21$$

c. *At the equivalence point.* The equivalence point will occur when a total of 5.00 mmol OH^- has been added. Since the NaOH solution is 0.100 M, the equivalence point occurs when 50.0 mL NaOH has been added. This amount will form 5.00 mmol CN^-. The major species in solution at the equivalence point are

$$CN^-, \quad Na^+, \quad and \quad H_2O$$

Thus the reaction that will control the pH involves the basic cyanide ion extracting a proton from water:

$$CN^-(aq) + H_2O(l) \rightleftharpoons HCN(aq) + OH^-(aq)$$

and $\quad K_b = \dfrac{K_w}{K_a} = \dfrac{1.0 \times 10^{-14}}{6.2 \times 10^{-10}} = 1.6 \times 10^{-5} = \dfrac{[HCN][OH^-]}{[CN^-]}$

Initial Concentration	Equilibrium Concentration
$[CN^-]_0 = \dfrac{5.00 \text{ mmol}}{(50.0 + 50.0) \text{ mL}}$ $= 5.00 \times 10^{-2} \ M$	$[CN^-] = (5.00 \times 10^{-2}) - x$
$[HCN]_0 = 0$ $\xrightarrow[\text{with } H_2O]{x \text{ mmol/mL of} \atop CN^- \text{ reacts}}$	$[HCN] = x$
$[OH^-]_0 \approx 0$	$[OH^-] = x$

Substituting the equilibrium concentrations into the expression for K_b and solving in the usual way gives

$$[OH^-] = x = 8.9 \times 10^{-4}$$

Then, from K_w, we have

$$[H^+] = 1.1 \times 10^{-11} \quad \text{and} \quad pH = 10.96$$

Two important conclusions can be drawn from a comparison of the titration of 50.0 mL of 0.1 M acetic acid covered earlier in this section and that of 50.0 mL of 0.1 M hydrocyanic acid analyzed in Sample Exercise 15.9. First, the same amount of 0.1 M NaOH is required to reach the equivalence point in both cases. The fact that HCN is a much weaker acid than $HC_2H_3O_2$ has no bearing on the amount of base required. It is the *amount* of acid, not its strength, that determines the equivalence point. Second, the pH value at the equivalence point *is* affected by the acid strength. For the titration of acetic acid, the pH at the equivalence point is 8.72; for the titration of hydrocyanic acid, the pH at the equivalence point is 10.96. This difference occurs because the CN^- ion is a much stronger base than the $C_2H_3O_2^-$ ion. Also, the pH at the halfway point of the titration is much higher for HCN than for $HC_2H_3O_2$, again because of the greater base strength of the CN^- ion (or equivalently, the smaller acid strength of HCN).

The strength of a weak acid has a significant effect on the shape of its pH curve. Figure 15.4 shows pH curves for 50-mL samples of 0.10 M solutions of various acids titrated with 0.10 M NaOH. Note that the equivalence point occurs in each case when the same volume of 0.10 M NaOH has been added but that the shapes of the curves are dramatically different. The weaker the acid, the greater is the pH value at the equivalence point. In particular, note that the vertical region that surrounds the equivalence point becomes shorter as the acid being titrated becomes weaker. We will see in the next section that the choice of an indicator is more limited for such a titration.

Besides being used to analyze for the amount of acid or base in a solution, titrations also can be used to determine the values of equilibrium constants, as shown in Sample Exercise 15.10.

The amount of acid present, not its strength, determines the equivalence point.

Figure 15.4

The pH curves for the titrations of 50.0-mL samples of 0.10 M acids with various K_a values with 0.10 M NaOH.

Calculation of K_a

Sample Exercise 15.10

A chemist has synthesized a monoprotic weak acid and wants to determine its K_a value. To do so, the chemist dissolves 2.00 mmol of the solid acid in 100.0 mL water and titrates the resulting solution with 0.0500 M NaOH. After 20.0 mL NaOH has been added, the pH is 6.00. What is the K_a value for the acid?

Solution

The stoichiometry problem. We represent the monoprotic acid as HA. The stoichiometry for the titration reaction is shown below.

	HA	+	OH$^-$	$\rightarrow$	A$^-$	+	H$_2$O
Before reaction:	2.00 mmol		20.0 mL $\times$ 0.0500 M = 1.00 mmol		0 mmol		
After reaction:	2.00 $-$ 1.00 = 1.00 mmol		1.0 $-$ 1.0 = 0		1.00 mmol		

2.00 mmol HA

$\downarrow$ add OH$^-$

1.00 mmol HA
1.00 mmol A$^-$

The equilibrium problem. After the reaction the solution contains the major species

$$HA, \quad A^-, \quad Na^+, \quad and \quad H_2O$$

The pH will be determined by the equilibrium

$$HA(aq) \rightleftharpoons H^+(aq) + A^-(aq)$$

for which
$$K_a = \frac{[H^+][A^-]}{[HA]}$$

Initial Concentration	Equilibrium Concentration
$[HA]_0 = \dfrac{1.00 \text{ mmol}}{(100.0 + 20.0) \text{ mL}}$ $= 8.33 \times 10^{-3} M$	$[HA] = 8.33 \times 10^{-3} - x$
$[A^-]_0 = \dfrac{1.00 \text{ mmol}}{(100.0 + 20.0) \text{ mL}}$ $= 8.33 \times 10^{-3} M$	$[A^-] = 8.33 \times 10^{-3} + x$
$[H^+]_0 \approx 0$	$[H^+] = x$

$\xrightarrow{\substack{x \text{ mmol/mL HA} \\ \text{dissociates}}}$

Note that x is known here because the pH at this point is known to be 6.00. Thus

$$x = [H^+] = \text{antilog}(-pH) = 1.0 \times 10^{-6} M$$

Substituting the equilibrium concentrations into the expression for K_a allows calculation of the K_a value:

$$K_a = \frac{[H^+][A^-]}{[HA]} = \frac{x(8.33 \times 10^{-3} + x)}{(8.33 \times 10^{-3}) - x}$$

$$= \frac{(1.0 \times 10^{-6})(8.33 \times 10^{-3} + 1.0 \times 10^{-6})}{(8.33 \times 10^{-3}) - (1.0 \times 10^{-6})}$$

$$\approx \frac{(1.0 \times 10^{-6})(8.33 \times 10^{-3})}{8.33 \times 10^{-3}} = 1.0 \times 10^{-6}$$

There is an easier way to think about this problem. The original solution contained 2.00 mmol of HA, and since 20.0 mL of added 0.0500 M NaOH contains 1.00 mmol OH^-, this is the halfway point in the titration (where [HA] is equal to [A^-]). Thus

$$[H^+] = K_a = 1.0 \times 10^{-6}$$

Titrations of Weak Bases with Strong Acids

Titrations of weak bases with strong acids can be treated using the procedures we introduced previously. As always, you should *think first about the major species in solution* and decide whether a reaction occurs that runs essentially to completion. If such a reaction does occur, let it run to completion and do the stoichiometric calculations. Finally, choose the dominant equilibrium and calculate the pH.

Case Study: Weak Base–Strong Acid Titration

The calculations involved for the titration of a weak base with a strong acid will be illustrated by the titration of 100.0 mL of 0.050 M NH_3 with 0.10 M HCl.

Before the addition of any HCl.

1. Major species:

$$NH_3 \quad \text{and} \quad H_2O$$

NH_3 is a base and will seek a source of protons. In this case H_2O is the only available source.

2. No reactions occur that go to completion, since NH_3 cannot readily take a proton from H_2O. This is evidenced by the small K_b value for NH_3.

3. The equilibrium that controls the pH involves the reaction of ammonia with water:

$$NH_3(aq) + H_2O(l) \rightleftharpoons NH_4^+(aq) + OH^-(aq)$$

Use K_b to calculate [OH^-]. Although NH_3 is a weak base (compared with OH^-), it produces much more OH^- in this reaction than is produced from the autoionization of H_2O.

Before the equivalence point.

1. Major species (before any reaction occurs):

$$NH_3, \quad \underbrace{H^+, \quad Cl^-,}_{\text{From added HCl}} \quad \text{and} \quad H_2O$$

2. The NH_3 will react with H^+ from the added HCl:

$$NH_3(aq) + H^+(aq) \rightleftharpoons NH_4^+(aq)$$

This reaction proceeds essentially to completion because the NH_3 readily reacts with a free proton. This case is much different from the previous case, where H_2O was the only source of protons. The stoichiometric calculations are then carried out using the known volume of 0.10 M HCl added.

3. After the reaction of NH_3 with H^+ is run to completion, the solution contains the following major species:

$$NH_3, \quad \underset{\substack{\uparrow \\ \text{Formed in} \\ \text{titration reaction}}}{NH_4^+}, \quad Cl^-, \quad \text{and} \quad H_2O$$

Note that the solution contains NH_3 and NH_4^+, and the equilibria involving these species will determine $[H^+]$. You can use either the dissociation reaction of NH_4^+

$$NH_4^+(aq) \rightleftharpoons NH_3(aq) + H^+(aq)$$

or the reaction of NH_3 with H_2O

$$NH_3(aq) + H_2O(l) \rightleftharpoons NH_4^+(aq) + OH^-(aq)$$

At the equivalence point.

1. By definition, the equivalence point occurs when all the original NH_3 is converted to NH_4^+. Thus the major species in solution are

$$NH_4^+, \quad Cl^-, \quad \text{and} \quad H_2O$$

2. No reactions occur that go to completion.

3. The dominant equilibrium (the one that controls the $[H^+]$) will be the dissociation of the weak acid NH_4^+, for which

$$K_a = \frac{K_w}{K_b \text{ (for } NH_3)}$$

Beyond the equivalence point.

1. Excess HCl has been added, and the major species are

$$H^+, \quad NH_4^+, \quad Cl^-, \quad \text{and} \quad H_2O$$

2. No reaction occurs that goes to completion.

3. Although NH_4^+ will dissociate, it is such a weak acid that $[H^+]$ will be determined simply by the excess H^+:

$$[H^+] = \frac{\text{mmol } H^+ \text{ in excess}}{\text{mL solution}}$$

The results of these calculations are shown in Table 15.2. The pH curve is shown in Fig. 15.5.

Table 15.2

Summary of Results for the Titration of 100.0 mL 0.050 M NH$_3$ with 0.10 M HCl				
Volume of 0.10 M HCl Added (mL)	$[NH_3]_0$	$[NH_4^+]_0$	$[H^+]$	pH
0	0.05 M	0	1.1×10^{-11} M	10.96
10.0	$\dfrac{4.0\ \text{mmol}}{(100+10)\ \text{mL}}$	$\dfrac{1.0\ \text{mmol}}{(100+10)\ \text{mL}}$	1.4×10^{-10} M	9.85
25.0*	$\dfrac{2.5\ \text{mmol}}{(100+25)\ \text{mL}}$	$\dfrac{2.5\ \text{mmol}}{(100+25)\ \text{mL}}$	5.6×10^{-10} M	9.25
50.0†	0	$\dfrac{5.0\ \text{mmol}}{(100+50)\ \text{mL}}$	4.3×10^{-6} M	5.36
60.0‡	0	$\dfrac{5.0\ \text{mmol}}{(100+60)\ \text{mL}}$	$\dfrac{1.0\ \text{mmol}}{160\ \text{mL}}$ $= 6.2 \times 10^{-3}$ M	2.21

*Halfway point

†Equivalence point

‡$[H^+]$ determined by the 1.0 mmol of excess H^+

Figure 15.5

The pH curve for the titration of 100.0 mL of 0.050 M NH$_3$ with 0.10 M HCl. Note the pH at the equivalence point is less than 7, since the solution contains the weak acid NH$_4^+$.

15.5 Acid–Base Indicators

Purpose

• To explain how acid–base indicators work.

There are two common methods for determining the equivalence point of an acid–base titration:

1. Use a pH meter (see Fig. 14.4) to monitor the pH and then plot the titration curve. The center of the vertical region of the pH curve indicates the equivalence point (for example, see Figs. 15.1 through 15.5).

Methyl orange indicator is yellow in basic solution and red in acidic solution.

(Colorless acid form, HIn)

(Pink base form, In⁻)

Figure 15.6

The acid and base forms of the indicator phenolphthalein. In the acid form (HIn), the molecule is colorless. When a proton (plus H_2O) is removed to give the base form (In⁻), the color changes to pink.

2. Use an **acid–base indicator,** which marks the end point of a titration by changing color. Although the *equivalence point of a titration, defined by the stoichiometry, is not necessarily the same as the end point* (where the indicator changes color), careful selection of the indicator will ensure that the error is negligible.

The most common acid–base indicators are complex molecules that are themselves weak acids (represented by HIn). They exhibit one color when the proton is attached to the molecule and a different color when the proton is absent. For example, **phenolphthalein,** a commonly used indicator, is colorless in its HIn form and pink in its In⁻, or basic, form. The actual structures of the two forms of phenolphthalein are shown in Fig. 15.6.

To see how molecules such as phenolphthalein function as indicators, consider the following equilibrium for some hypothetical indicator HIn, a weak acid with $K_a = 1.0 \times 10^{-8}$.

$$HIn(aq) \rightleftharpoons H^+(aq) + In^-(aq)$$
$$\text{Red} \qquad\qquad\qquad \text{Blue}$$

$$K_a = \frac{[H^+][In^-]}{[HIn]}$$

By rearranging, we get

$$\frac{K_a}{[H^+]} = \frac{[In^-]}{[HIn]}$$

Suppose we add a few drops of this indicator to an acidic solution whose pH is 1.0 ($[H^+] = 1.0 \times 10^{-1}$). Then

$$\frac{K_a}{[H^+]} = \frac{1. \times 10^{-8}}{1.0 \times 10^{-1}} = 10^{-7} = \frac{1}{10,000,000} = \frac{[In^-]}{[HIn]}$$

This ratio shows that the predominant form of the indicator is HIn, resulting in a red solution. As OH⁻ is added to this solution in a titration, $[H^+]$ decreases and the

The indicator phenolphthalein is pink in basic solution and colorless in acidic solution.

equilibrium shifts to the right, changing HIn to In⁻. At some point in a titration, enough of the In⁻ form will be present in the solution so that a purple tint will be noticeable. That is, a color change from red to reddish purple will occur.

How much In⁻ must be present for the human eye to detect that the color is different from the original one? For most indicators, about a tenth of the initial form must be converted to the other form before a new color is apparent. We will assume, then, that in the titration of an acid with a base, the color change will occur at a pH where

$$\frac{[\text{In}^-]}{[\text{HIn}]} = \frac{1}{10}$$

The **end point** is defined by the change in color of the indicator. The **equivalence point** is defined by the reaction stoichiometry.

Sample Exercise 15.11

Bromthymol blue, an indicator with a K_a value of 1.0×10^{-7}, is yellow in its HIn form and blue in its In⁻ form. Suppose we put a few drops of this indicator in a strongly acidic solution. If the solution is then titrated with NaOH, at what pH will the indicator color change first be visible?

Solution

For bromthymol blue,

$$K_a = 1.0 \times 10^{-7} = \frac{[\text{H}^+][\text{In}^-]}{[\text{HIn}]}$$

We assume that the color change is visible when

$$\frac{[\text{In}^-]}{[\text{HIn}]} = \frac{1}{10}$$

(a)

(b)

(c)

Figure 15.7

(a) Yellow acid form of bromthymol blue; (b) a greenish tint is seen when the solution contains 1 part blue and 10 parts yellow; (c) blue basic form.

That is, we assume that we can see the first hint of a greenish tint (yellow plus a little blue) when the solution contains 1 part blue and 10 parts yellow (see Fig. 15.7). Thus

$$K_a = 1.0 \times 10^{-7} = \frac{[H^+](1)}{10}$$

$$[H^+] = 1.0 \times 10^{-6} \quad \text{or} \quad pH = 6.00.$$

The color change is first visible at pH 6.00.

The Henderson–Hasselbalch equation is very useful in determining the pH at which an indicator changes color. For example, application of Equation (15.2) to the K_a expression for the general indicator HIn yields

$$pH = pK_a + \log\left(\frac{[In^-]}{[HIn]}\right)$$

where K_a is the dissociation constant for the acid form of the indicator (HIn). Since we assume that the color change is visible when

$$\frac{[In^-]}{[HIn]} = \frac{1}{10}$$

we have the following equation for determining the pH at which the color change occurs:

$$pH = pK_a + \log(\tfrac{1}{10}) = pK_a - 1$$

For bromthymol blue ($K_a = 1 \times 10^{-7}$, or $pK_a = 7$), the pH at the color change is

$$pH = 7 - 1 = 6$$

as we calculated in Sample Exercise 15.11.

When a basic solution is titrated, the indicator HIn will initially exist as In^- in solution, but as acid is added, more HIn will be formed. In this case the color change will be visible when there is a mixture of 10 parts In^- and 1 part HIn. That is, a color change from blue to blue-green will occur (see Fig. 15.7) due to the presence of some of the yellow HIn molecules. This color change will be first visible when

$$\frac{[In^-]}{[HIn]} = \frac{10}{1}$$

Note that this is the reciprocal of the ratio for the titration of an acid. Substituting this ratio into the Henderson–Hasselbalch equation gives

$$pH = pK_a + \log(\tfrac{10}{1}) = pK_a + 1$$

For bromthymol blue ($pK_a = 7$), we have a color change at

$$pH = 7 + 1 = 8$$

In summary, when bromthymol blue is used for the titration of an acid, the starting form will be HIn (yellow), and the color change occurs at a pH of about 6. When bromthymol blue is used for the titration of a base, the starting form is In^-

Universal indicator paper can be used to estimate the pH of a solution.

(blue), and the color change occurs at a pH of about 8. Thus the useful pH range for bromthymol blue is

$$\text{p}K_a \text{ (bromthymol blue)} \pm 1 = 7 \pm 1$$

or from 6 to 8. This is a general result. For a typical acid–base indicator with dissociation constant K_a, the color transition occurs over a range of pH values given by $\text{p}K_a \pm 1$. The useful pH ranges for several common indicators are shown in Fig. 15.8.

When we choose an indicator for a titration, we want the indicator end point (where the color changes) and the titration equivalence point to be as close as possible. Choosing an indicator is easier if there is a large change in pH near the equivalence point of the titration. The dramatic change in pH near the equivalence point in a strong acid–strong base titration (Figs. 15.1 and 15.2) produces a sharp end point; that is, the complete color change (from the acid-to-base or base-to-acid colors) usually occurs over one drop of added titrant.

What indicator should we use for the titration of 100.00 mL of 0.100 M HCl with 0.100 M NaOH? We know that the equivalence point occurs at pH 7.00. In the initially acidic solution, the indicator will be predominantly in the HIn form. As OH^- ions are added, the pH increases rather slowly at first (Fig. 15.1) and then rises rapidly at the equivalence point. This sharp change causes the indicator dissociation equilibrium

$$\text{HIn} \rightleftharpoons \text{H}^+ + \text{In}^-$$

to shift suddenly to the right, producing enough In^- ions to give a color change. Since we are titrating an acid, the indicator is predominantly in the acid form initially. Therefore, the first observable color change will occur at a pH where

$$\frac{[\text{In}^-]}{[\text{HIn}]} = \frac{1}{10}$$

Figure 15.8

The useful pH ranges for several common indicators. Note that most indicators have a useful range of about two pH units, as predicted by the expression $pK_a \pm 1$.

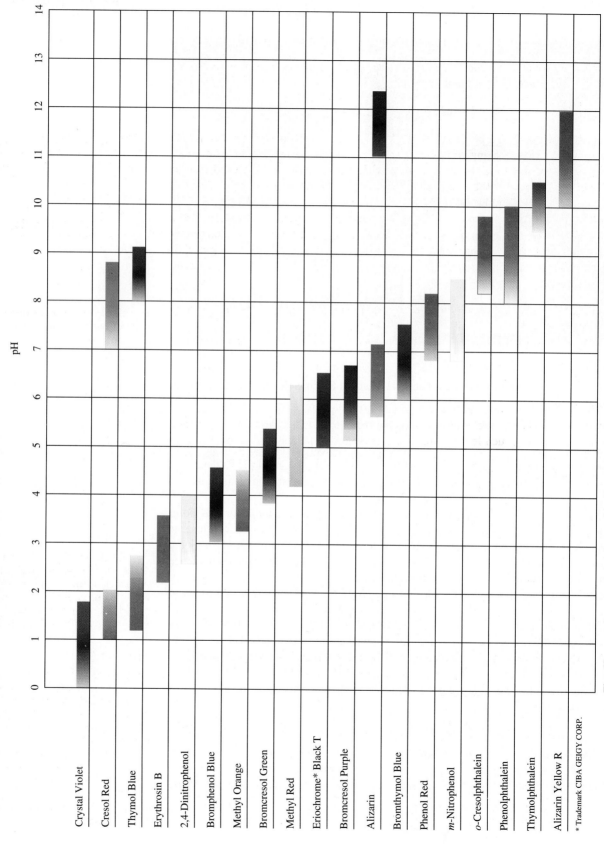

pH

| Crystal Violet |
| Cresol Red |
| Thymol Blue |
| Erythrosin B |
| 2,4-Dinitrophenol |
| Bromphenol Blue |
| Methyl Orange |
| Bromcresol Green |
| Methyl Red |
| Eriochrome* Black T |
| Bromcresol Purple |
| Alizarin |
| Bromthymol Blue |
| Phenol Red |
| m-Nitrophenol |
| o-Cresolphthalein |
| Phenolphthalein |
| Thymolphthalein |
| Alizarin Yellow R |

* Trademark CIBA GEIGY CORP.

The pH ranges shown are approximate. Specific transition ranges depend on the indicator solvent chosen.

Thus
$$\text{pH} = pK_a + \log(\tfrac{1}{10}) = pK_a - 1$$

If we want an indicator that changes color at pH 7, we can use this relationship to find the pK_a value for a suitable indicator:

$$\text{pH} = 7 = pK_a - 1 \quad \text{or} \quad pK_a = 7 + 1 = 8$$

Thus an indicator with a pK_a value of 8 ($K_a = 1 \times 10^{-8}$) changes color at about pH 7 and is ideal for marking the end point for a strong acid–strong base titration.

How crucial is it for a strong acid–strong base titration that the indicator change color exactly at pH 7? We can answer this question by examining the pH change near the equivalence point of the titration of 100 mL of 0.10 M HCl with 0.10 M NaOH. The data for a few points at or near the equivalence point are shown in Table 15.3. Note that in going from 99.99 to 100.01 mL of added NaOH solution (about half of a drop), the pH changes from 5.3 to 8.7—a very dramatic change. This behavior leads to the following general conclusions about indicators for a strong acid–strong base titration:

Indicator color changes will be sharp, occurring with the addition of a single drop of titrant.

There is a wide choice of suitable indicators. The results will agree within one drop of titrant, using indicators with end points as far apart as pH 5 and pH 9 (see Fig. 15.9).

The titration of weak acids is somewhat different. Figure 15.4 shows that the weaker the acid being titrated, the smaller is the vertical area around the equivalence point. This allows much less flexibility in choosing the indicator. We must choose an indicator whose useful pH range has a midpoint as close as possible to the pH at the equivalence point. For example, we saw earlier that in the titration of 0.1 M $HC_2H_3O_2$ with 0.1 M NaOH the pH at the equivalence point is 8.7 (see Fig. 15.3). A good indicator choice would be phenolphthalein, since its useful pH range is 8 to 10. Thymol blue also would be acceptable, but methyl red would not. The choice of an indicator is illustrated graphically in Fig. 15.10.

Table 15.3	
Selected pH Values Near the Equivalence Point in the Titration of 100.0 mL of 0.10 M HCl with 0.10 M NaOH	
NaOH Added (mL)	pH
99.99	5.3
100.00	7.0
100.01	8.7

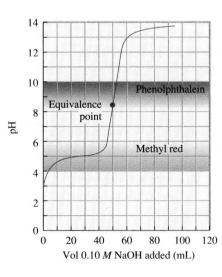

Figure 15.9 (left)

The pH curve for the titration of 100.0 mL of 0.10 M HCl with 0.10 M NaOH. Note that the end points of phenolphthalein and methyl red occur at virtually the same amounts of added NaOH.

Figure 15.10 (right)

The pH curve for the titration of 50 mL of 0.1 M $HC_2H_3O_2$ with 0.1 M NaOH. Phenolphthalein will give an end point very close to the equivalence point of the titration. Methyl red would change color well before the equivalence point (so the end point would be very different from the equivalence point) and would not be a suitable indicator for this titration.

Solubility Equilibria

15.6 *Solubility Equilibria and the Solubility Product*

Purpose

- To show how to calculate the solubility product of a salt given its solubility, and vice versa.
- To demonstrate the prediction of relative solubilities from K_{sp} values.
- To explain the effect of pH and a common ion on the solubility of a salt.

Adding F^- to drinking water is controversial. See Bette Hileman, "Fluoridation of Water," *Chem. Eng. News*, Aug. 1, 1988, p. 26.

An X ray of the lower gastro-intestinal tract using barium sulfate.

Solubility is a very important phenomenon. The fact that substances such as sugar and table salt dissolve in water allows us to flavor foods easily. The fact that calcium sulfate is less soluble in hot water than in cold water causes it to coat tubes in boilers, reducing thermal efficiency. Tooth decay involves solubility: when food lodges between the teeth, acids form that dissolve tooth enamel, which contains a mineral called hydroxyapatite, $Ca_5(PO_4)_3OH$. Tooth decay can be reduced by treating teeth with fluoride (see Chemical Impact, p. 756). Fluoride replaces the hydroxide in hydroxyapatite to produce the corresponding fluorapatite, $Ca_5(PO_4)_3F$, and calcium fluoride, CaF_2, both of which are less soluble in acids than the original enamel. Another important consequence of solubility involves the use of a suspension of barium sulfate to improve the clarity of X rays of the gastrointestinal tract. The very low solubility of barium sulfate, which contains the toxic ion Ba^{2+}, makes ingestion of the compound safe.

In this section we consider the equilibria associated with solids dissolving to form aqueous solutions. When a typical ionic solid dissolves in water, it dissociates completely into separate hydrated cations and anions. For example, calcium fluoride dissolves in water as follows:

$$CaF_2(s) \xrightarrow{\text{H}_2\text{O}} Ca^{2+}(aq) + 2F^-(aq)$$

When the solid salt is first added to the water, no Ca^{2+} and F^- ions are present. However, as the dissolution proceeds, the concentrations of Ca^{2+} and F^- increase, making it more and more likely that these ions will collide and re-form the solid phase. Thus two competing processes are occurring: the dissolution reaction and its reverse:

$$Ca^{2+}(aq) + 2F^-(aq) \rightarrow CaF_2(s)$$

Ultimately, dynamic equilibrium is reached:

$$CaF_2(s) \rightleftharpoons Ca^{2+}(aq) + 2F^-(aq)$$

At this point no more solid dissolves (the solution is said to be **saturated**).

We can write an equilibrium expression for this process according to the law of mass action:

$$K_{sp} = [Ca^{2+}][F^-]^2$$

where $[Ca^{2+}]$ and $[F^-]$ are expressed in mol/L. The constant K_{sp} is called the

solubility product constant or simply the **solubility product** for the equilibrium expression.

Since CaF_2 is a pure solid, it is not included in the equilibrium expression. The fact that the amount of excess solid present does not affect the position of the solubility equilibrium might seem strange at first; more solid means more surface area exposed to the solvent, which would seem to result in greater solubility. This is not the case, however. When the ions in solution re-form the solid, they do so on the surface of the solid. Thus doubling the surface area of the solid not only doubles the rate of dissolving, it also doubles the rate of re-formation of the solid. The amount of excess solid present therefore has no effect on the equilibrium position. Similarly, although either increasing the surface area by grinding up the solid or stirring the solution speeds up the attainment of equilibrium, neither procedure changes the amount of solid dissolved at equilibrium. Neither the amount of excess solid nor the size of the particles present will shift the *position* of the solubility equilibrium.

It is very important to distinguish between the *solubility* of a given solid and its *solubility product*. The solubility product is an *equilibrium constant* and has only *one* value for a given solid at a given temperature. Solubility, on the other hand, is an *equilibrium position*. In pure water at a specific temperature a given salt has a particular solubility. On the other hand, if a common ion is present in the solution, the solubility varies according to the concentration of the common ion. However, in all cases the product of the ion concentrations must satisfy the K_{sp} expression. The K_{sp} values at 25°C for many common ionic solids are listed in Table 15.4. The units are customarily omitted.

Solving solubility equilibria problems requires many of the same procedures we have used to deal with acid–base equilibria, as illustrated in Sample Exercises 15.12 and 15.13.

> Pure liquids and pure solids are never included in an equilibrium expression (Section 13.4).

> K_{sp} is an equilibrium constant; solubility is an equilibrium position.

Sample Exercise 15.12

Copper(I) bromide has a measured solubility of 2.0×10^{-4} mol/L at 25°C. Calculate its K_{sp} value.

Solution

In this experiment the solid was placed in contact with water. Thus, before any reaction occurred, the system contained solid CuBr and H_2O. The process that occurs is the dissolving of CuBr to form the separated Cu^+ and Br^- ions:

$$CuBr(s) \rightleftharpoons Cu^+(aq) + Br^-(aq)$$

where

$$K_{sp} = [Cu^+][Br^-]$$

Initially, the solution contains no Cu^+ or Br^-, so the initial concentrations are

$$[Cu^+]_0 = [Br^-]_0 = 0$$

The equilibrium concentrations can be obtained from the measured solubility of CuBr, which is 2.0×10^{-4} mol/L. This means that 2.0×10^{-4} mol solid CuBr dissolves per 1.0 L of solution to come to equilibrium with the excess solid. The reaction is

$$CuBr(s) \rightarrow Cu^+(aq) + Br^-(aq)$$

Thus

$$2.0 \times 10^{-4} \text{ mol/L CuBr}(s)$$
$$\rightarrow 2.0 \times 10^{-4} \text{ mol/L Cu}^+(aq) + 2.0 \times 10^{-4} \text{ mol/L Br}^-(aq)$$

We can now write the equilibrium concentrations:

$$[\text{Cu}^+] = [\text{Cu}^+]_0 + \text{change to reach equilibrium}$$
$$= 0 + 2.0 \times 10^{-4} \text{ mol/L}$$

and

$$[\text{Br}^-] = [\text{Br}^-]_0 + \text{change to reach equilibrium}$$
$$= 0 + 2.0 \times 10^{-4} \text{ mol/L}$$

These equilibrium concentrations allow us to calculate the value of K_{sp} for CuBr:

$$K_{sp} = [\text{Cu}^+][\text{Br}^-] = (2.0 \times 10^{-4} \text{ mol/L})(2.0 \times 10^{-4} \text{ mol/L})$$
$$= 4.0 \times 10^{-8} \text{ mol}^2/\text{L}^2 = 4.0 \times 10^{-8}$$

The units for K_{sp} values are usually omitted.

Table 15.4

K_{sp} Values at 25°C for Common Ionic Solids

Ionic Solid	K_{sp} (at 25°C)	Ionic Solid	K_{sp} (at 25°C)	Ionic Solid	K_{sp} (at 25°C)
Fluorides		Hg_2CrO_4*	2×10^{-9}	$Co(OH)_2$	2.5×10^{-16}
BaF_2	2.4×10^{-5}	$BaCrO_4$	8.5×10^{-11}	$Ni(OH)_2$	1.6×10^{-16}
MgF_2	6.4×10^{-9}	Ag_2CrO_4	9.0×10^{-12}	$Zn(OH)_2$	4.5×10^{-17}
PbF_2	4×10^{-8}	$PbCrO_4$	2×10^{-16}	$Cu(OH)_2$	1.6×10^{-19}
SrF_2	7.9×10^{-10}			$Hg(OH)_2$	3×10^{-26}
CaF_2	4.0×10^{-11}	Carbonates		$Sn(OH)_2$	3×10^{-27}
		$NiCO_3$	1.4×10^{-7}	$Cr(OH)_3$	6.7×10^{-31}
Chlorides		$CaCO_3$	8.7×10^{-9}	$Al(OH)_3$	2×10^{-32}
$PbCl_2$	1.6×10^{-5}	$BaCO_3$	1.6×10^{-9}	$Fe(OH)_3$	4×10^{-38}
$AgCl$	1.6×10^{-10}	$SrCO_3$	7×10^{-10}	$Co(OH)_3$	2.5×10^{-43}
Hg_2Cl_2*	1.1×10^{-18}	$CuCO_3$	2.5×10^{-10}		
		$ZnCO_3$	2×10^{-10}	Sulfides	
Bromides		$MnCO_3$	8.8×10^{-11}	MnS	2.3×10^{-13}
$PbBr_2$	4.6×10^{-6}	$FeCO_3$	2.1×10^{-11}	FeS	3.7×10^{-19}
$AgBr$	5.0×10^{-13}	Ag_2CO_3	8.1×10^{-12}	NiS	3×10^{-21}
Hg_2Br_2*	1.3×10^{-22}	$CdCO_3$	5.2×10^{-12}	CoS	5×10^{-22}
		$PbCO_3$	1.5×10^{-15}	ZnS	2.5×10^{-22}
Iodides		$MgCO_3$	1×10^{-15}	SnS	1×10^{-26}
PbI_2	1.4×10^{-8}	Hg_2CO_3*	9.0×10^{-15}	CdS	1.0×10^{-28}
AgI	1.5×10^{-16}			PbS	7×10^{-29}
Hg_2I_2*	4.5×10^{-29}	Hydroxides		CuS	8.5×10^{-45}
		$Ba(OH)_2$	5.0×10^{-3}	Ag_2S	1.6×10^{-49}
Sulfates		$Sr(OH)_2$	3.2×10^{-4}	HgS	1.6×10^{-54}
$CaSO_4$	6.1×10^{-5}	$Ca(OH)_2$	1.3×10^{-6}		
Ag_2SO_4	1.2×10^{-5}	$AgOH$	2.0×10^{-8}	Phosphates	
$SrSO_4$	3.2×10^{-7}	$Mg(OH)_2$	8.9×10^{-12}	Ag_3PO_4	1.8×10^{-18}
$PbSO_4$	1.3×10^{-8}	$Mn(OH)_2$	2×10^{-13}	$Sr_3(PO_4)_2$	1×10^{-31}
$BaSO_4$	1.5×10^{-9}	$Cd(OH)_2$	5.9×10^{-15}	$Ca_3(PO_4)_2$	1.3×10^{-32}
		$Pb(OH)_2$	1.2×10^{-15}	$Ba_3(PO_4)_2$	6×10^{-39}
Chromates		$Fe(OH)_2$	1.8×10^{-15}	$Pb_3(PO_4)_2$	1×10^{-54}
$SrCrO_4$	3.6×10^{-5}				

*Contains Hg_2^{2+} ions. $K_{sp} = [Hg_2^{2+}][X^-]^2$ for Hg_2X_2 salts, for example.

Sample Exercise 15.13

Calculate the K_{sp} value for bismuth sulfide (Bi_2S_3), which has a solubility of 1.0×10^{-15} mol/L at 25°C.

Solution

The system initially contains H_2O and solid Bi_2S_3, which dissolves as follows:

$$Bi_2S_3(s) \rightleftharpoons 2Bi^{3+}(aq) + 3S^{2-}(aq)$$

Therefore, $\quad\quad\quad\quad K_{sp} = [Bi^{3+}]^2[S^{2-}]^3$

Since no Bi^{3+} and S^{2-} ions were present in solution before the Bi_2S_3 dissolved,

$$[Bi^{3+}]_0 = [S^{2-}]_0 = 0$$

Thus the equilibrium concentrations of these ions will be determined by the amount of salt that dissolves to reach equilibrium, which in this case is 1.0×10^{-15} mol/L. Since each Bi_2S_3 unit contains $2Bi^{3+}$ and $3S^{2-}$ ions:

1.0×10^{-15} mol/L $Bi_2S_3(s)$
$\rightarrow 2(1.0 \times 10^{-15}$ mol/L$)\ Bi^{3+}(aq) + 3(1.0 \times 10^{-15}$ mol/L$)\ S^{2-}(aq)$

The equilibrium concentrations are

$$[Bi^{3+}] = [Bi^{3+}]_0 + \text{change} = 0 + 2.0 \times 10^{-15} \text{ mol/L}$$
$$[S^{2-}] = [S^{2-}]_0 + \text{change} = 0 + 3.0 \times 10^{-15} \text{ mol/L}$$

Then

$$K_{sp} = [Bi^{3+}]^2[S^{2-}]^3 = (2.0 \times 10^{-15})^2(3.0 \times 10^{-15})^3 = 1.1 \times 10^{-73}$$

Precipitation of bismuth sulfide.

Sulfide is a very basic anion and really exists in water as HS^-. We will not consider this complication.

Solubilities must be expressed in mol/L in K_{sp} calculations.

We have seen that the experimentally determined solubility of an ionic solid can be used to calculate its K_{sp} value.* The reverse is also possible: the solubility of an ionic solid can be calculated if its K_{sp} value is known.

Sample Exercise 15.14

The K_{sp} value for copper(II) iodate, $Cu(IO_3)_2$, is 1.4×10^{-7} at 25°C. Calculate its solubility at 25°C.

Solution

The system initially contains H_2O and solid $Cu(IO_3)_2$, which dissolves according to the following equilibrium:

$$Cu(IO_3)_2(s) \rightleftharpoons Cu^{2+}(aq) + 2IO_3^-(aq)$$

Therefore, $\quad\quad\quad\quad K_{sp} = [Cu^{2+}][IO_3^-]^2$

*This calculation assumes that all the dissolved solid is present as separated ions. In some cases, such as $CaSO_4$, large numbers of ion pairs exist in solution, so this method yields an incorrect value for K_{sp}.

To find the solubility of $Cu(IO_3)_2$, we must find the equilibrium concentrations of the Cu^{2+} and IO_3^- ions. We do this in the usual way by specifying the initial concentrations (before any solid has dissolved) and then defining the change required to reach equilibrium. Since in this case we do not know the solubility, we will assume that x mol/L of the solid dissolves to reach equilibrium. The 1:2 stoichiometry of the salt means that

$$x \text{ mol/L } Cu(IO_3)_2(s) \rightarrow x \text{ mol/L } Cu^{2+}(aq) + 2x \text{ mol/L } IO_3^-(aq)$$

The concentrations are as follows:

Initial Concentration (mol/L) [Before Any $Cu(IO_3)_2$ Dissolves]		Equilibrium Concentration (mol/L)
$[Cu^{2+}]_0 = 0$ $[IO_3^-]_0 = 0$	$\xrightarrow[\text{to reach}]{\substack{x \text{ mol/L} \\ \text{dissolves}}}$ equilibrium	$[Cu^{2+}] = x$ $[IO_3^-] = 2x$

Substituting the equilibrium concentrations into the expression for K_{sp} gives

$$1.4 \times 10^{-7} = K_{sp} = [Cu^{2+}][IO_3^-]^2 = (x)(2x)^2 = 4x^3$$

Then

$$x = \sqrt[3]{3.5 \times 10^{-8}} = 3.3 \times 10^{-3} \text{ mol/L}$$

Thus the solubility of solid $Cu(IO_3)_2$ is 3.3×10^{-3} mol/L.

Relative Solubilities

A salt's K_{sp} value gives us information about its solubility. However, we must be careful in using K_{sp} values to predict the *relative* solubilities of a group of salts. There are two possible cases:

1. The salts being compared produce the same number of ions. For example, consider

$$AgI(s) \qquad K_{sp} = 1.5 \times 10^{-16}$$
$$CuI(s) \qquad K_{sp} = 5.0 \times 10^{-12}$$
$$CaSO_4(s) \qquad K_{sp} = 6.1 \times 10^{-5}$$

Each of these solids dissolves to produce two ions:

$$\text{Salt} \rightleftharpoons \text{cation} + \text{anion}$$
$$K_{sp} = [\text{cation}][\text{anion}]$$

If x is the solubility in mol/L, then at equilibrium

$$[\text{Cation}] = x$$
$$[\text{Anion}] = x$$
$$K_{sp} = [\text{cation}][\text{anion}] = x^2$$
$$x = \sqrt{K_{sp}} = \text{solubility}$$

Therefore, in this case we can compare the solubilities for these solids by comparing the K_{sp} values:

$$CaSO_4(s) > CuI(s) > AgI(s)$$

Most soluble;   Least soluble;
largest K_{sp} smallest K_{sp}

2. The salts being compared produce different numbers of ions. For example, consider

$$CuS(s) \qquad K_{sp} = 8.5 \times 10^{-45}$$
$$Ag_2S(s) \qquad K_{sp} = 1.6 \times 10^{-49}$$
$$Bi_2S_3(s) \qquad K_{sp} = 1.1 \times 10^{-73}$$

Because these salts produce different numbers of ions when they dissolve, the K_{sp} values cannot be compared *directly* to determine relative solubilities. In fact, if we calculate the solubilities (using the procedure in Sample Exercise 15.14), we obtain the results summarized in Table 15.5. The order of solubilities is

$$Bi_2S_3(s) > Ag_2S(s) > CuS(s)$$

Most soluble   Least soluble

which is opposite to the order of the K_{sp} values.

Remember that relative solubilities can be predicted by comparing K_{sp} values *only* for salts that produce the same total number of ions.

Common Ion Effect

So far we have considered ionic solids dissolved in pure water. We will now see what happens when the water contains an ion in common with the dissolving salt. For example, consider the solubility of solid silver chromate (Ag_2CrO_4, $K_{sp} = 9.0 \times 10^{-12}$) in a 0.100 M solution of $AgNO_3$. Before any Ag_2CrO_4 dissolves, the solution contains the major species Ag^+, NO_3^-, and H_2O, with solid Ag_2CrO_4 on the bottom of the container. Since NO_3^- is not found in Ag_2CrO_4, we can ignore it. The relevant initial concentrations (before any Ag_2CrO_4 dissolves) are

$$[Ag^+]_0 = 0.100 \ M \text{ (from the dissolved } AgNO_3)$$
$$[CrO_4^{2-}]_0 = 0$$

The system comes to equilibrium as the solid Ag_2CrO_4 dissolves according to the reaction

$$Ag_2CrO_4(s) \rightleftharpoons 2Ag^+(aq) + CrO_4^{2-}(aq)$$

Table 15.5		
Calculated Solubilities for CuS, Ag₂S, and Bi₂S₃ at 25°C		
Salt	K_{sp}	Calculated Solubility (mol/L)
CuS	8.5×10^{-45}	9.2×10^{-23}
Ag₂S	1.6×10^{-49}	3.4×10^{-17}
Bi₂S₃	1.1×10^{-73}	1.0×10^{-15}

for which $\qquad K_{sp} = [Ag^+]^2[CrO_4^{2-}] = 9.0 \times 10^{-12}$

We assume that x mol/L of Ag_2CrO_4 dissolves to reach equilibrium, which means that

$$x \text{ mol/L } Ag_2CrO_4(s) \rightarrow 2x \text{ mol/L } Ag^+(aq) + x \text{ mol/L } CrO_4^{2-}$$

Now we can specify the equilibrium concentrations in terms of x:

$$[Ag^+] = [Ag^+]_0 + \text{change} = 0.100 + 2x$$
$$[CrO_4^{2-}] = [CrO_4^{2-}]_0 + \text{change} = 0 + x = x$$

Substituting these concentrations into the expression for K_{sp} gives

$$9.0 \times 10^{-12} = [Ag^+]^2[CrO_4^{2-}] = (0.100 + 2x)^2(x)$$

The mathematics required here appears to be complicated, since the multiplication of terms on the right-hand side produces an expression that contains an x^3 term. However, as is usually the case, we can make simplifying assumptions. Since the K_{sp} value for Ag_2CrO_4 is small (the position of the equilibrium lies far to the left), x is expected to be small compared with 0.100 M. Therefore, $0.100 + 2x \approx 0.100$, which allows simplification of the expression:

$$9.0 \times 10^{-12} = (0.100 + 2x)^2(x) \approx (0.100)^2(x)$$

Then $\qquad x \approx \dfrac{9.0 \times 10^{-12}}{(0.100)^2} = 9.0 \times 10^{-10}$ mol/L

Since x is much less than 0.100 M, the approximation is valid (by the 5% rule). Thus

Solubility of Ag_2CrO_4 in 0.100 M $AgNO_3 = x = 9.0 \times 10^{-10}$ mol/L

and the equilibrium concentrations are

$$[Ag^+] = 0.100 + 2x = 0.100 + 2(9.0 \times 10^{-10}) = 0.100 \ M$$
$$[CrO_4^{2-}] = x = 9.0 \times 10^{-10} \ M$$

Now we compare the solubilities of Ag_2CrO_4 in pure water and in 0.100 M $AgNO_3$:

Solubility of Ag_2CrO_4 in pure water $= 1.3 \times 10^{-4}$ mol/L
Solubility of Ag_2CrO_4 in 0.100 M $AgNO_3 = 9.0 \times 10^{-10}$ mol/L

Note that the solubility of Ag_2CrO_4 is much less in the presence of Ag^+ ions from $AgNO_3$. This is another example of the common ion effect. The solubility of a solid is lowered if the solution already contains ions common to the solid.

Silver chromate is a reddish-brown solid.

Sample Exercise 15.15

Calculate the solubility of solid CaF_2 ($K_{sp} = 4.0 \times 10^{-11}$) in a 0.025 M NaF solution.

Solution

Before any CaF_2 dissolves, the solution contains the major species Na^+, F^-, and H_2O. The solubility equilibrium for CaF_2 is

$$CaF_2(s) \rightleftharpoons Ca^{2+}(aq) + 2F^-(aq)$$

and
$$K_{sp} = 4.0 \times 10^{-11} = [Ca^{2+}][F^-]^2$$

Initial Concentration (mol/L) (Before any CaF$_2$ Dissolves)		Equilibrium Concentration (mol/L)
$[Ca^{2+}]_0 = 0$ $[F^-]_0 = 0.025\ M$ ↗ From 0.025 M NaF	$\xrightarrow[\text{to reach} \atop \text{equilibrium}]{x \text{ mol/L CaF}_2 \atop \text{dissolves}}$	$[Ca^{2+}] = x$ $[F^-] = 0.025 + 2x$ ↗ ↑ From NaF From CaF$_2$

Substituting the equilibrium concentrations into the expression for K_{sp} gives

$$K_{sp} = 4.0 \times 10^{-11} = [Ca^{2+}][F^-]^2 = (x)(0.025 + 2x)^2$$

Assuming that $2x$ is negligible compared with 0.025 (since K_{sp} is small) gives

$$4.0 \times 10^{-11} \approx (x)(0.025)^2$$
$$x \approx 6.4 \times 10^{-8}$$

The approximation is valid (by the 5% rule), and

$$\text{Solubility} = x = 6.4 \times 10^{-8} \text{ mol/L}$$

Thus 6.4×10^{-8} mol solid CaF$_2$ dissolves per liter of the 0.025 M NaF solution.

pH and Solubility

The pH of a solution can greatly affect a salt's solubility. For example, magnesium hydroxide dissolves according to the equilibrium

$$Mg(OH)_2(s) \rightleftharpoons Mg^{2+}(aq) + 2OH^-(aq)$$

Addition of OH^- ions (an increase in pH) will, by the common ion effect, force the equilibrium to the left, decreasing the solubility of $Mg(OH)_2$. On the other hand, an addition of H^+ ions (a decrease in pH) increases the solubility, because OH^- ions are removed from solution by reacting with the added H^+ ions. In response to the lower concentration of OH^-, the equilibrium position moves to the right. This is why a suspension of solid $Mg(OH)_2$, known as milk of magnesia, dissolves as required in the stomach to combat excess acidity.

This idea also applies to salts with other types of anions. For example, the solubility of silver phosphate (Ag_3PO_4) is greater in acid than in pure water because the PO_4^{3-} ion is a strong base that reacts with H^+ to form the HPO_4^{2-} ion. The reaction

$$H^+ + PO_4^{3-} \rightarrow HPO_4^{2-}$$

occurs in acidic solution, thus lowering the concentration of PO_4^{3-} and shifting the solubility equilibrium

$$Ag_3PO_4(s) \rightleftharpoons 3Ag^+(aq) + PO_4^{3-}(aq)$$

to the right. This, in turn, increases the solubility of silver phosphate.

Silver chloride (AgCl), however, has the same solubility in acid as in pure water. Why? Since the Cl^- ion is a very weak base (that is, HCl is a very strong acid), no

HCl molecules are formed. Thus the addition of H^+ to a solution containing Cl^- does not affect $[Cl^-]$ and has no effect on the solubility of a chloride salt.

The general rule is that if the anion X^- is an effective base—that is, if HX is a weak acid—the salt MX will show increased solubility in an acidic solution. Examples of common anions that are effective bases are OH^-, S^{2-}, CO_3^{2-}, $C_2O_4^{2-}$, and CrO_4^{2-}. Salts containing these anions are much more soluble in an acidic solution than in pure water.

As mentioned at the beginning of this chapter, one practical result of the increased solubility of carbonates in acid is the formation of huge limestone caves such as Mammoth Cave in Kentucky or Carlsbad Caverns in New Mexico. Carbon dioxide dissolved in groundwater makes it acidic, increasing the solubility of calcium carbonate and eventually producing huge caverns. As the carbon dioxide escapes to the air, the pH of the dripping water goes up and the calcium carbonate precipitates, forming stalactites and stalagmites.

15.7 Precipitation and Qualitative Analysis

Purpose

- To show how to predict if precipitation will occur when solutions are mixed.
- To describe the use of selective precipitation to separate a mixture of ions in solution.

So far we have considered solids dissolving in solutions. Now we will consider the reverse process—the formation of a solid from solution. When solutions are mixed, various reactions can occur. We have already considered acid base reactions in some detail. In this section we show how to predict whether a precipitate will form when two solutions are mixed. We will use the **ion product,** which is defined just like the expression for K_{sp} for a given solid except that *initial concentrations are used* instead of equilibrium concentrations. For solid CaF_2, the expression for the ion product Q is written

$$Q = [Ca^{2+}]_0[F^-]_0^2$$

If we add a solution containing Ca^{2+} ions to a solution containing F^- ions, a precipitate may or may not form, depending on the concentrations of these ions in the resulting mixed solution. To predict whether precipitation will occur, we consider the relationship between Q and K_{sp}:

Q is used here in a very similar way to the use of the reaction quotient in Chapter 13.

If Q is greater than K_{sp}, precipitation occurs and will continue until the concentrations are reduced to the point that they satisfy K_{sp}.

If Q is less than K_{sp}, no precipitation occurs.

Sample Exercise 15.16

A solution is prepared by adding 750.0 mL of 4.00×10^{-3} M $Ce(NO_3)_3$ to 300.0 mL of 2.00×10^{-2} M KIO_3. Will $Ce(IO_3)_3$ ($K_{sp} = 1.9 \times 10^{-10}$) precipitate from this solution?

Solution

First, we calculate $[Ce^{3+}]_0$ and $[IO_3^-]_0$ in the mixed solution before any reaction occurs:

$$[Ce^{3+}]_0 = \frac{(750.0 \text{ mL})(4.00 \times 10^{-3} \text{ mmol/mL})}{(750.0 + 300.0) \text{ mL}} = 2.86 \times 10^{-3} \text{ } M$$

$$[IO_3^-]_0 = \frac{(300.0 \text{ mL})(2.00 \times 10^{-2} \text{ mmol/mL})}{(750.0 + 300.0) \text{ mL}} = 5.71 \times 10^{-3} \text{ } M$$

The ion product for $Ce(IO_3)_3$ is

$$Q = [Ce^{3+}]_0[IO_3^-]_0^3 = (2.86 \times 10^{-3})(5.71 \times 10^{-3})^3 = 5.32 \times 10^{-10}$$

For $Ce(IO_3)_3(s)$, $K_{sp} = [Ce^{3+}][IO_3^-]^3$.

Since Q is greater than K_{sp}, $Ce(IO_3)_3$ will precipitate from the mixed solution.

Sometimes we want to do more than simply predict whether precipitation will occur; we may want to calculate the equilibrium concentrations in the solution after precipitation occurs. For example, let us calculate the equilibrium concentrations of Pb^{2+} and I^- ions in a solution formed by mixing 100.0 mL of 0.0500 M $Pb(NO_3)_2$ and 200.0 mL of 0.100 M NaI. First, we must determine whether solid PbI_2 ($K_{sp} = 1.4 \times 10^{-8}$) forms when the solutions are mixed. To do so, we need to calculate $[Pb^{2+}]_0$ and $[I^-]_0$ before any reaction occurs:

$$[Pb^{2+}]_0 = \frac{\text{mmol } Pb^{2+}}{\text{mL solution}} = \frac{(100.0 \text{ mL})(0.0500 \text{ mmol/mL})}{300.0 \text{ mL}} = 1.67 \times 10^{-2} \text{ } M$$

$$[I^-]_0 = \frac{\text{mmol } I^-}{\text{mL solution}} = \frac{(200.0 \text{ mL})(0.100 \text{ mmol/mL})}{300.0 \text{ mL}} = 6.67 \times 10^{-2} \text{ } M$$

The ion product for PbI_2 is

$$Q = [Pb^{2+}]_0[I^-]_0^2 = (1.67 \times 10^{-2})(6.67 \times 10^{-2})^2 = 7.43 \times 10^{-5}$$

Since Q is greater than K_{sp}, a precipitate of PbI_2 will form.

Note that since the K_{sp} for PbI_2 is quite small (1.4×10^{-8}), only very small quantities of Pb^{2+} and I^- can coexist in aqueous solution. In other words, when Pb^{2+} and I^- are mixed, most of these ions will precipitate out as PbI_2. That is, the reaction

$$Pb^{2+}(aq) + 2I^-(aq) \longrightarrow PbI_2(s)$$

The equilibrium constant for formation of solid PbI_2 is $1/K_{sp}$, or 7×10^7, so this equilibrium lies far to the right.

(which is the reverse of the dissolution reaction) goes essentially to completion.

If, when two solutions are mixed, a reaction occurs that goes virtually to completion, it is essential to do the stoichiometry calculations before considering the equilibrium calculations. Therefore, in this case we let the system go completely in the direction toward which it tends. Then we will let it adjust back to equilibrium. If we let Pb^{2+} and I^- react to completion, we have the following concentrations:

	Pb^{2+}	$+$	$2I^-$	$\longrightarrow$	PbI_2
Before reaction:	(100.0 mL)(0.0500 M) = 5.00 mmol		(200.0 mL)(0.100 M) = 20.0 mmol		The amount of PbI_2 formed does not influence the equilibrium
After reaction:	0 mmol		20.0 − 2(5.00) = 10.0 mmol		

In this reaction 10 mmol I^- is in excess.

Next we must allow the system to adjust to equilibrium. At equilibrium $[Pb^{2+}]$ is not actually zero because the reaction does not go quite to completion. The best way to think about this is that once the PbI_2 is formed, a very small amount redissolves to reach equilibrium. Since I^- is in excess, the PbI_2 is dissolving into a solution that contains 10.0 mmol I^- per 300.0 mL of solution, or $3.33 \times 10^{-2}\ M\ I^-$.

We could state this problem as follows: What is the solubility of solid PbI_2 in a $3.33 \times 10^{-2}\ M$ NaI solution? The lead iodide dissolves according to the equation

$$PbI_2(s) \rightleftharpoons Pb^{2+}(aq) + 2I^-(aq)$$

The concentrations are as follows:

Initial Concentration (mol/L)		Equilibrium Concentration (mol/L)
$[Pb^{2+}]_0 = 0$	$\xrightarrow[\text{dissolves}]{\substack{x\ \text{mol/L} \\ PbI_2(s)}}$	$[Pb^{2+}] = x$
$[I^-]_0 = 3.33 \times 10^{-2}$		$[I^-] = 3.33 \times 10^{-2} + 2x$

Substituting into the expression for K_{sp} gives

$$K_{sp} = 1.4 \times 10^{-8} = [Pb^{2+}][I^-]^2 = (x)(3.33 \times 10^{-2} + 2x)^2 \approx (x)(3.33 \times 10^{-2})^2$$

Then
$$[Pb^{2+}] = x = 1.3 \times 10^{-5}\ M$$

$$[I^-] = 3.33 \times 10^{-2}\ M$$

Note that $3.33 \times 10^{-2} \gg 2x$, so the approximation is valid. These Pb^{2+} and I^- concentrations thus represent the equilibrium concentrations present in a solution formed by mixing 100.0 mL of 0.0500 M $Pb(NO_3)_2$ and 200.0 mL of 0.100 M NaI.

Sample Exercise 15.17

A solution is prepared by mixing 150.0 mL of $1.00 \times 10^{-2}\ M$ $Mg(NO_3)_2$ and 250.0 mL of $1.00 \times 10^{-1}\ M$ NaF. Calculate the concentrations of Mg^{2+} and F^- at equilibrium with solid MgF_2 ($K_{sp} = 6.4 \times 10^{-9}$).

Solution

The first step is to determine whether solid MgF_2 forms. To do this, we need to calculate the concentrations of Mg^{2+} and F^- in the mixed solution and find Q:

$$[Mg^{2+}]_0 = \frac{\text{mmol } Mg^{2+}}{\text{mL solution}} = \frac{(150.0 \text{ mL})(1.00 \times 10^{-2}\ M)}{400.0 \text{ mL}} = 3.75 \times 10^{-3}\ M$$

$$[F^-]_0 = \frac{\text{mmol } F^-}{\text{mL solution}} = \frac{(250.0 \text{ mL})(1.00 \times 10^{-1}\ M)}{400.0 \text{ mL}} = 6.25 \times 10^{-2}\ M$$

For $MgF_2(s)$, $K_{sp} = [Mg^{2+}][F^-]^2$.

$$Q = [Mg^{2+}]_0[F^-]_0^2 = (3.75 \times 10^{-3})(6.25 \times 10^{-2})^2 = 1.46 \times 10^{-5}$$

Since Q is greater than K_{sp}, solid MgF_2 will form.

The next step is to run the precipitation reaction to completion:

	Mg^{2+}	+	$2F^-$	$\longrightarrow$ $MgF_2(s)$
Before reaction:	$(150.0)(1.00 \times 10^{-2})$ $= 1.5$ mmol		$(250.0)(1.00 \times 10^{-1})$ $= 25.0$ mmol	
After reaction:	$1.5 - 1.5 = 0$		$25.0 - 2(1.50)$ $= 22.0$ mmol	

Note that excess F^- remains after the precipitation reaction goes to completion. The concentration is

$$[F^-]_{excess} = \frac{22.0 \text{ mmol}}{400.0 \text{ mL}} = 5.50 \times 10^{-2} \, M$$

Although we have assumed that the Mg^{2+} is completely consumed, we know that $[Mg^{2+}]$ will not be zero at equilibrium. We can compute the equilibrium $[Mg^{2+}]$ by letting MgF_2 redissolve to satisfy the expression for K_{sp}. How much MgF_2 will dissolve in a $5.50 \times 10^{-2} \, M$ NaF solution? We proceed as usual:

$$MgF_2(s) \rightleftharpoons Mg^{2+}(aq) + 2F^-(aq)$$
$$K_{sp} = [Mg^{2+}][F^-]^2 = 6.4 \times 10^{-9}$$

Initial Concentration (mol/L)		Equilibrium Concentration (mol/L)
$[Mg^{2+}]_0 = 0$ $[F^-]_0 = 5.50 \times 10^{-2}$	$\xrightarrow[\text{dissolves}]{\substack{x \text{ mol/L} \\ MgF_2(s)}}$	$[Mg^{2+}] = x$ $[F^-] = 5.50 \times 10^{-2} + 2x$

$$K_{sp} = 6.4 \times 10^{-9} = [Mg^{2+}][F^-]^2$$
$$= (x)(5.50 \times 10^{-2} + 2x)^2 \approx (x)(5.50 \times 10^{-2})^2$$
$$[Mg^{2+}] = x = 2.1 \times 10^{-6} \, M$$
$$[F^-] = 5.50 \times 10^{-2} \, M$$

The approximations made here fall within the 5% rule.

Selective Precipitation

Mixtures of metal ions in aqueous solution are often separated by **selective precipitation,** that is, by using a reagent whose anion forms a precipitate with only one or a few of the metal ions in the mixture. For example, suppose we have a solution containing both Ba^{2+} and Ag^+ ions. If NaCl is added to the solution, AgCl precipitates as a white solid, but since $BaCl_2$ is soluble, the Ba^{2+} ions remain in solution.

Sample Exercise 15.18

A solution contains $1.0 \times 10^{-4} \, M$ Cu^+ and $2.0 \times 10^{-3} \, M$ Pb^{2+}. If a source of I^- is added gradually to this solution, will PbI_2 ($K_{sp} = 1.4 \times 10^{-8}$) or CuI ($K_{sp} = 5.3 \times 10^{-12}$) precipitate first? Specify the concentration of I^- necessary to begin precipitation of each salt.

Solution

For PbI_2, the K_{sp} expression is

$$1.4 \times 10^{-8} = K_{sp} = [Pb^{2+}][I^-]^2$$

Since $[Pb^{2+}]$ in this solution is known to be 2.0×10^{-3} M, the greatest concentration of I^- that can be present without causing precipitation of PbI_2 can be calculated from the K_{sp} expression:

$$1.4 \times 10^{-8} = [Pb^{2+}][I^-]^2 = (2.0 \times 10^{-3})[I^-]^2$$
$$[I^-] = 2.6 \times 10^{-3} \ M$$

Any I^- in excess of this concentration will cause solid PbI_2 to form.

Similarly, for CuI, the K_{sp} expression is

$$5.3 \times 10^{-12} = K_{sp} = [Cu^+][I^-] = (1.0 \times 10^{-4})[I^-]$$

and

$$[I^-] = 5.3 \times 10^{-8} \ M$$

A concentration of I^- in excess of 5.3×10^{-8} M will cause formation of solid CuI.

As I^- is added to the mixed solution, CuI will precipitate first, since the $[I^-]$ required is less. Therefore, Cu^+ could be separated from Pb^{2+} using this reagent.

Since metal sulfide salts differ dramatically in their solubilities, the sulfide ion is often used to separate metal ions by selective precipitation. For example, consider a solution containing a mixture of 10^{-3} M Fe^{2+} and 10^{-3} M Mn^{2+}. Since FeS ($K_{sp} = 3.7 \times 10^{-19}$) is much less soluble than MnS ($K_{sp} = 2.3 \times 10^{-13}$), careful addition of S^{2-} to the mixture will precipitate Fe^{2+} as FeS, leaving Mn^{2+} in solution.

> We can compare K_{sp} values to find relative solubilities because FeS and MnS produce the same number of ions in solution.

One real advantage of the sulfide ion as a precipitating reagent is that because it is basic, its concentration can be controlled by regulating the pH of the solution. H_2S is a diprotic acid that dissociates in two steps:

$$H_2S \rightleftharpoons H^+ + HS^- \qquad K_{a_1} = 1.0 \times 10^{-7}$$
$$HS^- \rightleftharpoons H^+ + S^{2-} \qquad K_{a_2} \approx 10^{-19}$$

Note from the small K_{a_2} value that S^{2-} ions have a high affinity for protons. In an acidic solution (large $[H^+]$), $[S^{2-}]$ will be relatively small, since under these conditions the dissociation equilibria will lie far to the left. On the other hand, in basic solutions $[S^{2-}]$ will be relatively large, since the very small value of $[H^+]$ will pull both equilibria to the right, producing S^{2-}.

This means that the most insoluble sulfide salts, such as CuS ($K_{sp} = 8.5 \times 10^{-45}$) and HgS ($K_{sp} = 1.6 \times 10^{-54}$), can be precipitated from an acidic solution, leaving the more soluble ones, such as MnS ($K_{sp} = 2.3 \times 10^{-13}$) and NiS ($K_{sp} = 3 \times 10^{-21}$), still dissolved. The manganese and nickel sulfides can then be precipitated by making the solution slightly basic. This procedure is diagrammed in Fig. 15.11.

Qualitative Analysis

The classic scheme for **qualitative analysis** of a mixture containing all the common cations (listed in Fig. 15.12) involves first separating them into five major groups based on solubilities. (These groups are not directly related to the groups of the periodic table.) Each group is then treated further to separate and identify the individual ions. We will be concerned here only with separation of the major groups.

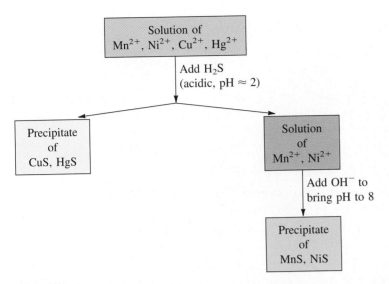

Figure 15.11

The separation of Cu^{2+} and Hg^{2+} from Ni^{2+} and Mn^{2+} using H_2S. At a low pH, $[S^{2-}]$ is relatively low and only the very insoluble HgS and CuS precipitate. When OH^- is added to lower $[H^+]$, the value of $[S^{2-}]$ increases, and MnS and NiS precipitate.

Figure 15.12

A schematic diagram of the classic method for separating the common cations by selective precipitation.

(*top*) Flame test for potassium.
(*bottom*) Flame test for sodium.

Group I—insoluble chlorides.

When dilute aqueous HCl is added to a solution containing a mixture of the common cations, only Ag^+, Pb^{2+}, and Hg_2^{2+} will precipitate out as insoluble chlorides. All

From left to right, cadmium sulfide, chromium(III) hydroxide, aluminum hydroxide, and nickel(II) hydroxide.

other chlorides are soluble and remain in solution. The Group I precipitate is removed, leaving the other ions in solution for treatment with sulfide ion.

Group II—sulfides insoluble in acid solution.

After the insoluble chlorides are removed, the solution is still acidic, since HCl was added. If H_2S is added to this solution, only the most insoluble sulfides (those of Hg^{2+}, Cd^{2+}, Bi^{3+}, Cu^{2+}, and Sn^{4+}) will precipitate, since $[S^{2-}]$ is relatively low because of the high concentration of H^+. The more soluble sulfides will remain dissolved under these conditions, and the precipitate of the insoluble salts is removed.

Group III—sulfides insoluble in basic solution.

The solution is made basic at this stage, and more H_2S is added. As we saw earlier, a basic solution produces a higher $[S^{2-}]$, which leads to precipitation of the more soluble sulfides. The cations precipitated as sulfides at this stage are Co^{2+}, Zn^{2+}, Mn^{2+}, Ni^{2+}, and Fe^{2+}. If any Cr^{3+} and Al^{3+} ions are present, they will also precipitate, but as insoluble hydroxides (remember the solution is now basic). The precipitate is separated from the solution containing the rest of the ions.

Group IV—insoluble carbonates.

At this point, all the cations have been precipitated except those from Groups 1A and 2A of the periodic table. The Group 2A cations form insoluble carbonates and can be precipitated by the addition of CO_3^{2-}. For example, Ba^{2+}, Ca^{2+}, and Mg^{2+} form solid carbonates and can be removed from the solution.

Group V—alkali metal and ammonium ions.

The only ions remaining in solution at this point are the Group 1A cations and the NH_4^+ ion, all of which form soluble salts with the common anions. The Group 1A cations are usually identified by the characteristic colors they produce when heated in a flame. These colors are due to the emission spectra of these ions.

The qualitative analysis scheme for cations based on the selective precipitation procedure described above is summarized in Fig. 15.12.

Complex Ion Equilibria

15.8 Equilibria Involving Complex Ions

Purpose

- To apply the principles of equilibrium to the formation of complex ions.
- To show how complex ion formation can increase the solubility of a salt.

A **complex ion** is a charged species consisting of a metal ion surrounded by **ligands.** A ligand is simply a Lewis base—a molecule or ion having a lone electron pair that can be donated to an empty orbital on the metal ion to form a covalent bond. Some common ligands are H_2O, NH_3, Cl^-, and CN^-. The number of ligands attached to a metal ion is called the **coordination number.** The most common coordination numbers are 6, for example, in $Co(H_2O)_6^{2+}$ and $Ni(NH_3)_6^{2+}$; 4, for example, in $CoCl_4^{2-}$ and $Cu(NH_3)_4^{2+}$; and 2, for example, in $Ag(NH_3)_2^+$; but others are known.

The properties of complex ions will be discussed in more detail in Chapter 20. For now, we will just look at the equilibria involving these species. Metal ions add ligands one at a time in steps characterized by equilibrium constants called **formation constants** or **stability constants.** For example, when solutions containing Ag^+ ions and NH_3 molecules are mixed, the following reactions take place:

$$Ag^+ + NH_3 \rightleftharpoons Ag(NH_3)^+ \qquad K_1 = 2.1 \times 10^3$$
$$Ag(NH_3)^+ + NH_3 \rightleftharpoons Ag(NH_3)_2^+ \qquad K_2 = 8.2 \times 10^3$$

where K_1 and K_2 are the formation constants for the two steps. In a solution containing Ag^+ and NH_3, all the species NH_3, Ag^+, $Ag(NH_3)^+$, and $Ag(NH_3)_2^+$ exist at equilibrium. Calculating the concentrations of all these components can be complicated. However, usually the total concentration of the ligand is much larger than the total concentration of the metal ion, and approximations can greatly simplify the problems.

For example, consider a solution prepared by mixing 100.0 mL of 2.0 M NH_3 with 100.0 mL of 1.0×10^{-3} M $AgNO_3$. *Before any reaction occurs,* the mixed solution contains the major species Ag^+, NO_3^-, NH_3, and H_2O. What reaction or reactions will occur in this solution? From our discussions of acid–base chemistry, we know that one reaction is

$$NH_3(aq) + H_2O(l) \rightleftharpoons NH_4^+(aq) + OH^-(aq)$$

However, we are interested in the reaction between NH_3 and Ag^+ to form complex ions, and since the position of the preceding equilibrium lies far to the left (K_b for NH_3 is 1.8×10^{-5}), we can neglect the amount of NH_3 used up in the reaction with water. Therefore, before any complex ion formation, the concentrations in the mixed solution are

$$[Ag^+]_0 = \frac{(100.0 \text{ mL})(1.0 \times 10^{-3} \, M)}{(200.0 \text{ mL})} = 5.0 \times 10^{-4} \, M$$

Total volume

$$[NH_3]_0 = \frac{(100.0 \text{ mL})(2.0 \, M)}{(200.0 \text{ mL})} = 1.0 \, M$$

As mentioned already, the Ag^+ ion reacts with NH_3 in a stepwise fashion to form $AgNH_3^+$ and then $Ag(NH_3)_2^+$:

$$Ag^+ + NH_3 \rightleftharpoons Ag(NH_3)^+ \qquad K_1 = 2.1 \times 10^3$$
$$Ag(NH_3)^+ + NH_3 \rightleftharpoons Ag(NH_3)_2^+ \qquad K_2 = 8.2 \times 10^3$$

Since both K_1 and K_2 are large, and since there is a large excess of NH_3, *both reactions can be assumed to go essentially to completion.* This is equivalent to writing the net reaction in the solution as follows:

$$Ag^+ + 2NH_3 \rightarrow Ag(NH_3)_2^+$$

The relevant stoichiometric calculations are as follows:

	Ag^+	$+$	$2NH_3$	$\longrightarrow$	$Ag(NH_3)_2^+$
Before reaction:	$5.0 \times 10^{-4} \, M$		$1.0 \, M$		0
After reaction:	0		$1.0 - 2(5.0 \times 10^{-4}) \approx 1.0 \, M$		$5.0 \times 10^{-4} \, M$

Twice as much NH_3 as Ag^+ is required

Note that in this case we have used molarities when performing the stoichiometry calculations and we have assumed this reaction to be complete, using all the original Ag^+ to form $Ag(NH_3)_2^+$. In reality, a *very small* amount of the $Ag(NH_3)_2^+$ formed will dissociate to produce small amounts of $Ag(NH_3)^+$ and Ag^+. However, since the amount of $Ag(NH_3)_2^+$ dissociating will be so small, we can safely assume that $[Ag(NH_3)_2^+]$ is $5.0 \times 10^{-4} \, M$ at equilibrium. Also, we know that since so little NH_3 has been consumed, $[NH_3]$ is $1.0 \, M$ at equilibrium. We can use these concentrations to calculate $[Ag^+]$ and $[Ag(NH_3)^+]$ using the K_1 and K_2 expressions.

To calculate the equilibrium concentration of $Ag(NH_3)^+$, we use

$$K_2 = 8.2 \times 10^3 = \frac{[Ag(NH_3)_2^+]}{[Ag(NH_3)^+][NH_3]}$$

since $[Ag(NH_3)_2^+]$ and $[NH_3]$ are known. Rearranging and solving for $[Ag(NH_3)^+]$ gives

$$[Ag(NH_3)^+] = \frac{[Ag(NH_3)_2^+]}{K_2[NH_3]} = \frac{5.0 \times 10^{-4}}{(8.2 \times 10^3)(1.0)} = 6.1 \times 10^{-8} \, M$$

Now the equilibrium concentration of Ag^+ can be calculated using K_1:

$$K_1 = 2.1 \times 10^3 = \frac{[Ag(NH_3)^+]}{[Ag^+][NH_3]} = \frac{6.1 \times 10^{-8}}{[Ag^+](1.0)}$$

$$[Ag^+] = \frac{6.1 \times 10^{-8}}{(2.1 \times 10^3)(1.0)} = 2.9 \times 10^{-11} \ M$$

So far we have assumed that $Ag(NH_3)_2^+$ is the dominant silver-containing species in solution. Is this a valid assumption? The calculated concentrations are

$$[Ag(NH_3)_2^+] = 5.0 \times 10^{-4} \ M$$
$$[Ag(NH_3)^+] = 6.1 \times 10^{-8} \ M$$
$$[Ag^+] = 2.9 \times 10^{-11} \ M$$

These values clearly support the conclusion that

$$[Ag(NH_3)_2^+] \gg [Ag(NH_3)^+] \gg [Ag^+]$$

Thus the assumption that $[Ag(NH_3)_2^+]$ is the dominant Ag^+-containing species is valid, and the calculated concentrations are correct.

This analysis shows that although complex ion equilibria have many species present and look complicated, the calculations are actually quite straightforward, especially if the ligand is present in large excess.

Essentially all the Ag^+ ions originally present end up in $Ag(NH_3)_2^+$.

Sample Exercise 15.19

Calculate the concentrations of Ag^+, $Ag(S_2O_3)^-$, and $Ag(S_2O_3)_2^{3-}$ in a solution prepared by mixing 150.0 mL of $1.00 \times 10^{-3} \ M$ $AgNO_3$ with 200.0 mL of 5.00 M $Na_2S_2O_3$. The stepwise formation equilibria are

$$Ag^+ + S_2O_3^{2-} \rightleftharpoons Ag(S_2O_3)^- \qquad K_1 = 7.4 \times 10^8$$
$$Ag(S_2O_3)^- + S_2O_3^{2-} \rightleftharpoons Ag(S_2O_3)_2^{3-} \qquad K_2 = 3.9 \times 10^4$$

Solution

The concentrations of the ligand and metal ion in the mixed solution *before any reaction occurs* are

$$[Ag^+]_0 = \frac{(150.0 \ \text{mL})(1.00 \times 10^{-3} \ M)}{(150.0 \ \text{mL} + 200.0 \ \text{mL})} = 4.29 \times 10^{-4} \ M$$

$$[S_2O_3^{2-}]_0 = \frac{(200.0 \ \text{mL})(5.0 \ M)}{(150.0 \ \text{mL} + 200.0 \ \text{mL})} = 2.86 \ M$$

Since $[S_2O_3^{2-}]_0 \gg [Ag^+]_0$, and since K_1 and K_2 are large, both formation reactions can be assumed to go to completion, and the net reaction in the solution is as follows:

	Ag^+	+	$2S_2O_3^{2-}$	$\rightarrow$	$Ag(S_2O_3)_2^{3-}$
Before reaction:	$4.29 \times 10^{-4} \ M$		$2.86 \ M$		0
After reaction:	~0		$2.86 - 2(4.29 \times 10^{-4})$ $\approx 2.86 \ M$		$4.29 \times 10^{-4} \ M$

Note that Ag^+ is limiting and that the amount of $S_2O_3^{2-}$ consumed is negligible. Also note that since all these species are in the same solution, the molarities can be used to do the stoichiometry problem.

Of course, the concentration of Ag^+ is not zero at equilibrium, and there is some $Ag(S_2O_3)^-$ in the solution. To calculate the concentrations of these species, we must use the K_1 and K_2 expressions. We can calculate the concentration of $Ag(S_2O_3)^-$ from K_2:

$$3.9 \times 10^4 = K_2 = \frac{[Ag(S_2O_3)_2^{3-}]}{[Ag(S_2O_3)^-][S_2O_3^{2-}]} = \frac{4.29 \times 10^{-4}}{[Ag(S_2O_3)^-](2.86)}$$

$$[Ag(S_2O_3)^-] = 3.8 \times 10^{-9} \ M$$

We can calculate $[Ag^+]$ from K_1:

$$7.4 \times 10^8 = K_1 = \frac{[Ag(S_2O_3)^-]}{[Ag^+][S_2O_3^{2-}]} = \frac{3.8 \times 10^{-9}}{[Ag^+](2.86)}$$

$$[Ag^+] = 1.8 \times 10^{-18} \ M$$

These results show that

$$[Ag(S_2O_3)_2^{3-}] \gg [Ag(S_2O_3)^-] \gg [Ag^+]$$

Thus the assumption is valid that essentially all the original Ag^+ is converted to $Ag(S_2O_3)_2^{3-}$ at equilibrium.

Complex Ions and Solubility

Often ionic solids that are very nearly water-insoluble must be dissolved somehow in aqueous solutions. For example, when the various qualitative analysis groups are precipitated out, the precipitates must be redissolved to separate the ions within each group. Consider a solution of cations that contains Ag^+, Pb^{2+}, and Hg_2^{2+}, among others. When dilute aqueous HCl is added to this solution, the Group I ions will form the insoluble chlorides $AgCl$, $PbCl_2$, and Hg_2Cl_2. Once this mixed precipitate is separated from the solution, it must be redissolved to identify the cations individually. How can this be done? We know that some solids are more soluble in acidic than in neutral solutions. What about chloride salts? For example, can $AgCl$ be dissolved by using a strong acid? The answer is no, because Cl^- ions have virtually no affinity for H^+ ions in aqueous solution. The position of the dissolution equilibrium

$$AgCl(s) \rightleftharpoons Ag^+(aq) + Cl^-(aq)$$

is not affected by the presence of H^+.

How can we pull the dissolution equilibrium to the right, even though Cl^- is an extremely weak base? The key is to lower the concentration of Ag^+ in solution by forming complex ions. For example, Ag^+ reacts with excess NH_3 to form the stable complex ion $Ag(NH_3)_2^+$. As a result, $AgCl$ is quite soluble in concentrated ammonia solutions. The relevant reactions are

(top) Aqueous ammonia is added to silver chloride (white). *(bottom)* Silver chloride, insoluble in water, dissolves to form $Ag(NH_3)_2^+(aq)$ and $Cl^-(aq)$.

$$
\begin{array}{ll}
AgCl(s) \rightleftharpoons Ag^+ + Cl^- & K_{sp} = 1.6 \times 10^{-10} \\
Ag^+ + NH_3 \rightleftharpoons Ag(NH_3)^+ & K_1 = 2.1 \times 10^3 \\
Ag(NH_3)^+ + NH_3 \rightleftharpoons Ag(NH_3)_2^+ & K_2 = 8.2 \times 10^3
\end{array}
$$

The Ag^+ ion produced by dissolving solid AgCl combines with NH_3 to form $Ag(NH_3)_2^+$, which causes more AgCl to dissolve, until the point at which

$$[Ag^+][Cl^-] = K_{sp} = 1.6 \times 10^{-10}$$

Here $[Ag^+]$ refers only to the Ag^+ ion that is present as a separate species in solution. It is *not* the total silver content of the solution, which is

$$[Ag]_{\text{total dissolved}} = [Ag^+] + [Ag(NH_3)^+] + [Ag(NH_3)_2^+]$$

For reasons discussed in the previous section, virtually all the Ag^+ from the dissolved AgCl ends up in the complex ion $Ag(NH_3)_2^+$. Thus we can represent the dissolving of solid AgCl in excess NH_3 by the equation

$$AgCl(s) + 2NH_3(aq) \rightleftharpoons Ag(NH_3)_2^+(aq) + Cl^-(aq)$$

Since this equation is the *sum of the three stepwise reactions* given above, the equilibrium constant for the reaction is the product of the constants for the three reactions. (Demonstrate this to yourself by multiplying together the three expressions for K_{sp}, K_1, and K_2.) The equilibrium expression is

> When reactions are added, the equilibrium constant for the overall process is the product of the constants for the individual reactions.

$$K = \frac{[Ag(NH_3)_2^+][Cl^-]}{[NH_3]^2}$$
$$= K_{sp} \times K_1 \times K_2 = (1.6 \times 10^{-10})(2.1 \times 10^3)(8.2 \times 10^3) = 2.8 \times 10^{-3}$$

Using this expression, we will now calculate the solubility of solid AgCl in a 10.0 M NH_3 solution. If we let x be the solubility (in mol/L) of AgCl in this solution, we can then write the following expressions for the equilibrium concentrations of the pertinent species:

$$[Cl^-] = x \longleftarrow$$

x mol/L of AgCl dissolves to produce x mol/L of Cl^- and x mol/L of $Ag(NH_3)_2^+$

$$[Ag(NH_3)_2^+] = x \longleftarrow$$

$$[NH_3] = 10.0 - 2x \longleftarrow$$

Formation of x mol/L of $Ag(NH_3)_2^+$ requires $2x$ mol/L of NH_3, since each complex ion contains two NH_3 ligands

Substituting these concentrations into the equilibrium expression gives

$$K = 2.8 \times 10^{-3} = \frac{[Ag(NH_3)_2^+][Cl^-]}{[NH_3]^2} = \frac{(x)(x)}{(10.0 - 2x)^2} = \frac{x^2}{(10.0 - 2x)^2}$$

No approximations are necessary here. Taking the square root of both sides of the equation gives

$$\sqrt{2.8 \times 10^{-3}} = \frac{x}{10.0 - 2x}$$

$$x = 0.48 \text{ mol/L} = \text{solubility of AgCl}(s) \text{ in } 10.0 \text{ } M \text{ } NH_3$$

Thus the solubility of AgCl in 10.0 M NH_3 is much greater than its solubility in pure water, which is

$$\sqrt{K_{sp}} = 1.3 \times 10^{-5} \text{ mol/L}$$

In this chapter we have considered two strategies for dissolving a water-insoluble ionic solid. If the *anion* of the solid is a good base, the solubility is greatly increased

---

◀ **C H E M I C A L   I M P A C T** ▶

The Chemistry of Teeth

If dental chemistry continues to progress at the present rate, tooth decay may soon be a thing of the past. Cavities are holes that develop in tooth enamel, which is composed of the mineral hydroxyapatite, $Ca_5(PO_4)_3OH$. Recent research has shown that there is constant dissolving and re-forming of the tooth mineral in the saliva at the tooth's surface. Demineralization (dissolving of tooth enamel) is mainly caused by weak acids in the saliva created by bacteria as they metabolize carbohydrates in food. (The solubility of $Ca_5(PO_4)_3OH$ in acidic saliva should come as no surprise to you if you understand how pH affects the solubility of a salt with basic anions.)

In the first stages of tooth decay, parts of the tooth surface become porous and spongy and develop swiss-cheese–like holes that, if untreated, eventually turn into cavities (see photo). However, recent results indicate that if the affected tooth is bathed in a solution containing appropriate amounts of Ca^{2+}, PO_4^{3-}, and F^-, it remineralizes. Because the F^- replaces OH^- in the tooth mineral [$Ca_5(PO_4)_3OH$ is changed to $Ca_5(PO_4)_3F$], the remineralized area is more resistant to future decay, since fluoride is a weaker base than hydroxide ion. In addition, it has been shown that the presence of Sr^{2+} in the remineralizing fluid significantly increases resistance to decay.

If these results hold up under further study, the work of dentists will change dramatically. Dentists will be much more involved in preventing damage to teeth than in repairing damage that has already occurred. One can picture the routine use of a remineralization rinse that will repair problem areas before they become cavi-

Tooth decay lesion.

ties. Dental drills could join leeches as a medical anachronism.

---

by acidifying the solution. In cases where the anion is not sufficiently basic, the ionic solid often can be dissolved in a solution containing a ligand that forms stable complex ions with its *cation*.

Sometimes solids are so insoluble that combinations of reactions are needed to dissolve them. For example, to dissolve the extremely insoluble HgS ($K_{sp} = 10^{-54}$), it is necessary to use a mixture of concentrated HCl and concentrated HNO_3, called **aqua regia.** The H^+ ions in the aqua regia react with the S^{2-} ions to form H_2S, and Cl^- reacts with Hg^{2+} to form various complex ions, including $HgCl_4^{2-}$. In addition, NO_3^- oxidizes S^{2-} to elemental sulfur. These processes lower the concentrations of Hg^{2+} and S^{2-} and thus promote the solubility of HgS.

Since the solubility of many salts increases with temperature, simple heating is sometimes enough to make a salt sufficiently soluble. For example, earlier in this section we considered the mixed chloride precipitates of the Group I ions—$PbCl_2$, AgCl, and Hg_2Cl_2. The effect of temperature on the solubility of $PbCl_2$ is such that we can precipitate $PbCl_2$ with cold aqueous HCl and then redissolve it by heating the solution to near boiling. The silver and mercury(I) chlorides remain precipitated, since they are not significantly soluble in hot water. However, solid AgCl can be dissolved using aqueous ammonia. The solid Hg_2Cl_2 reacts with NH_3 to form a mixture of elemental mercury and $HgNH_2Cl$:

$$Hg_2Cl_2(s) + 2NH_3(aq) \rightarrow HgNH_2Cl(s) + Hg(l) + NH_4^+(aq) + Cl^-(aq)$$
White   Black

The mixed precipitate appears gray. This is an oxidation–reduction reaction in which one mercury(I) ion in Hg_2Cl_2 is oxidized to Hg^{2+} in $HgNH_2Cl$ and the other mercury(I) ion is reduced to Hg, or elemental mercury.

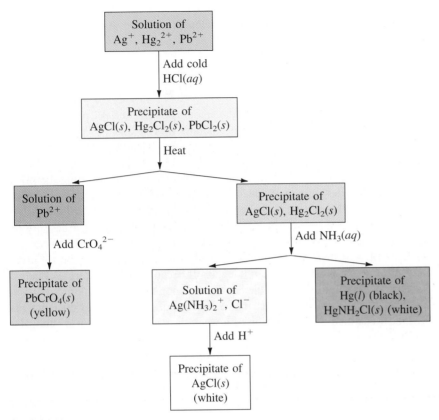

Figure 15.13

The separation of the Group I ions in the classic scheme of qualitative analysis.

The treatment of the Group I ions is summarized in Fig. 15.13. Note that the presence of Pb^{2+} is confirmed by adding CrO_4^{2-}, which forms bright yellow lead(II) chromate ($PbCrO_4$). Also note that H^+ added to a solution containing $Ag(NH_3)_2^+$ reacts with the NH_3 to form NH_4^+, destroying the $Ag(NH_3)_2^+$ complex. Silver chloride then re-forms:

$$2H^+(aq) + Ag(NH_3)_2^+(aq) + Cl^-(aq) \rightarrow 2NH_4^+(aq) + AgCl(s)$$

Note that the qualitative analysis of cations by selective precipitation involves all the types of reactions we have discussed and represents an excellent application of the principles of chemical equilibrium.

FOR REVIEW

Summary

When a weak acid HA and its salt NaA are dissolved in the same aqueous solution, a buffering effect is observed. A buffered solution is one that resists a change in pH when either hydroxide ions or protons are added. A buffer may contain a weak acid and its salt or a weak base and its salt. In a buffered solution the pH is governed by the ratio $[A^-]/[HA]$. The Henderson–Hasselbalch equation gives the relationship between pH, pK_a, and the ratio $[A^-]/[HA]$:

$$pH = pK_a + \log\left(\frac{[A^-]}{[HA]}\right)$$

The capacity of a buffer depends on the amounts of HA and A^- present. Buffering results because the relatively large amounts of HA and A^- cause the ratio $[A^-]/[HA]$ to be almost constant when H^+ or OH^- is added. Optimal buffering results when [HA] is equal to $[A^-]$.

The progress of an acid–base titration is often monitored by plotting the pH of the solution versus the volume of added titrant to give a pH curve or titration curve. Strong acid–strong base titrations have a very sharp change in pH near the stoichiometric, or equivalence, point, the point at which the original acid (or base) in the solution has been exactly consumed by the titrant base (or acid). When a weak acid is titrated with a strong base, the shape of the titration curve is quite different. Initially, the curve rises sharply; then it levels off because of the buffering effects of the weak acid and salt mixture. At the equivalence point of a titration of a weak acid with a strong base, the pH is greater than 7 because of the basicity of the conjugate base of the weak acid. For a titration of a weak base with a strong acid, the pH at the equivalence point is always less than 7 because of the acidity of the conjugate acid of the weak base. For a strong acid–strong base titration, the pH at the equivalence point equals 7. The equivalence point of a titration is determined by stoichiometry, not by pH.

Another way of following an acid–base titration is by the use of an indicator that marks the end point by changing color. Most commonly used indicators are themselves weak acids and exist in two forms, HIn and In^-, that exhibit different colors. For most indicators, the ratio of the minor form to the major form must be $\frac{1}{10}$ before a color change is apparent. The goal in choosing an indicator is to have the equivalence point and the end point coincide.

The principles of equilibrium also can be applied when a solid dissolves in water. The solubility product K_{sp} is an equilibrium constant defined by the law of mass action. Solubility is an equilibrium position. The K_{sp} value for a salt can be determined by measuring its solubility. The solubility of a salt can be calculated if its K_{sp} value is known.

Addition of an ion common to a salt will push the dissolution equilibrium to the left, reducing the salt's solubility. This is known as the common ion effect. The solubility of a salt MX that is only slightly soluble in pure water can be increased if the solubility equilibrium

$$MX(s) \rightleftharpoons M^+(aq) + X^-(aq)$$

can be shifted to the right by lowering $[M^+]$ or $[X^-]$. If X^- is a good base, addition of H^+ will form HX and lower $[X^-]$, thus increasing the salt's solubility. The equilibrium concentration of M^+ can be lowered by adding a ligand to form complex ions with it.

We can predict whether a precipitate will form when two solutions are mixed by using the ion product Q, which is defined just like K_{sp} except that initial concentrations of the ions are used. If Q is greater than K_{sp}, the salt will precipitate.

Mixtures of ions can be separated by selective precipitation, a process in which reagents are added to precipitate single ions or small groups of ions.

Key Terms

Section 15.1
common ion
common ion effect

Section 15.2
buffered solution
Henderson–Hasselbalch
  equation

Section 15.3
buffering capacity

Section 15.4
pH curve (titration curve)
millimole (mmol)
equivalence point
  (stoichiometric point)

Section 15.5
acid–base indicator
phenolphthalein

Section 15.6
solubility product
constant (solubility
  product)

Section 15.7
ion product
selective precipitation
qualitative analysis

Section 15.8
complex ion
formation constants

A blue question or exercise number indicates that the answer to that question or exercise appears at the back of this book and a solution appears in the Solutions Guide.

Questions

1. What is meant by a common ion? How does the presence of a common ion affect an equilibrium such as

$$HNO_2(aq) \rightleftharpoons H^+(aq) + NO_2^-(aq)$$

2. What components must be present in order to have a buffered solution? For what purposes are buffers used?

3. What is meant by the *capacity* of a buffer? How do the following buffers differ in capacity? How do they differ in pH?

   0.01 *M* acetic acid/0.01 *M* sodium acetate

   0.1 *M* acetic acid/0.1 *M* sodium acetate

   1.0 *M* acetic acid/1.0 *M* sodium acetate

4. Is it necessary that the concentration of the weak acid and weak base in a buffered solution be equal? Explain.

5. Show that the pH at the halfway point of the titration of a weak acid with a strong base is equal to pK_a.

6. Is it possible to determine the K_a of a weak acid from data at points other than the halfway point of a titration?

7. Is it possible for the indicator thymol blue to contain only a single —CO_2H group and no other acidic or basic functional group? Explain.

8. Define the equivalence (stoichiometric) point and the end point of a titration. Why does one choose an indicator so that the two points coincide? Is it necessary that the pH of the two points be within ±0.01 pH unit of each other? Explain.

9. Why does an indicator change from its acid to its base color over a range of pH values?

10. Under what circumstances can the relative solubilities of two salts be compared by directly comparing values of their solubility products?

Exercises

In this section similar exercises are paired.

Buffers

11. Write reactions to show how a solution containing acetic acid and sodium acetate acts as a buffer when a strong acid or base is added.

12. A buffer is made by dissolving $NaHCO_3$ and Na_2CO_3 in water. Write equations to show how this buffer neutralizes added H^+ and OH^-.

13. Calculate the pH of each of the following buffered solutions.
    a. 0.10 M acetic acid/0.25 M sodium acetate
    b. 0.25 M acetic acid/0.10 M sodium acetate
    c. 0.080 M acetic acid/0.20 M sodium acetate
    d. 0.20 M acetic acid/0.080 M sodium acetate

14. Using tabulated K_a and K_b values, calculate the pH of each of the following solutions.
    a. A solution containing 0.10 M HNO_2 and 0.15 M $NaNO_2$
    b. 25.0 g pure (glacial) acetic acid and 40.0 g sodium acetate diluted to 500. mL with water
    c. 50.0 mL of 1.0 M $HOCl$ and 30.0 mL of 0.80 M $NaOH$ diluted to 250 mL with water
    d. 100.0 g NH_4Cl and 65.0 g $NaOH$ diluted to 1.0 L with water
    e. 26.4 g sodium acetate and 50.0 mL of 6.00 M hydrochloric acid diluted to 5.00×10^2 mL with water
    Hint: In parts c, d, and e, reactions occur that go to completion.

15. Calculate the pH of each of the following solutions.
    a. 0.10 M propanoic acid ($HC_3H_5O_2$, $K_a = 1.3 \times 10^{-5}$)
    b. 0.10 M sodium propanoate ($NaC_3H_5O_2$)
    c. Pure H_2O
    d. A mixture containing 0.10 M $HC_3H_5O_2$ and 0.10 M $NaC_3H_5O_2$

16. Calculate the pH of each of the following solutions.
    a. 0.10 M NH_3
    b. 0.10 M NH_4Cl
    c. Pure H_2O
    d. A mixture containing 0.10 M NH_3 and 0.10 M NH_4Cl

17. Calculate the pH after 0.020 mol HCl is added to 1.0 L of each of the four solutions in Exercise 15.

18. Calculate the pH after 0.020 mol HCl is added to 1.0 L of each of the four solutions in Exercise 16.

19. Calculate the pH after 0.020 mol NaOH is added to 1.0 L of each of the four solutions in Exercise 15.

20. Calculate the pH after 0.020 mol NaOH is added to 1.0 L of each of the solutions in Exercise 16.

21. Which of the solutions in Exercise 15 shows the least change in pH upon the addition of acid or base? Explain.

22. Which of the solutions in Exercise 16 is a buffered solution?

23. Which of the following result in buffered solutions when equal volumes of the two solutions are mixed?
    a. 0.1 M HCl and 0.1 M NH_4Cl
    b. 0.1 M HCl and 0.1 M NH_3
    c. 0.2 M HCl and 0.1 M NH_3
    d. 0.1 M HCl and 0.2 M NH_3

24. Which of the following are buffers?
    a. A solution containing 0.1 M KNO_3 and 0.1 M HNO_3
    b. A solution containing 0.1 M $NaNO_2$ and 0.15 M HNO_2
    c. 250 mL of a solution that was originally 0.10 M acetic acid and has had 0.5 g KOH added
    d. A solution containing 0.10 M Na_2CO_3 and 0.05 M Na_3PO_4

25. Calculate the ratio $[NH_3]/[NH_4^+]$ in ammonia/ammonium chloride buffered solutions with the following pH values:
    a. pH = 9.00   c. pH = 10.00
    b. pH = 8.80   d. pH = 9.60

26. In blood the normal pH is 7.41. What is the ratio of CO_2 (usually written H_2CO_3) to HCO_3^- in blood?

$$H_2CO_3 \rightleftharpoons HCO_3^- + H^+ \qquad K_a = 4.3 \times 10^{-7}$$

27. What mass of solid NaOH must be added to 1.0 L of 2.0 M $HC_2H_3O_2$ to produce a solution buffered at each pH?
    a. pH = pK_a b. pH = 4.00   c. pH = 5.00

28. Calculate the number of moles of $HCl(g)$ that must be added to 1.0 L of 1.0 M $NaC_2H_3O_2$ to produce a solution buffered at each pH.
    a. pH = pK_a b. pH = 4.20   c. pH = 5.00

29. A buffered solution is made by adding 75.0 g sodium acetate to 500.0 mL of a 0.64 M solution of acetic acid. What is the pH of the final solution? (Assume no volume change.)

30. A buffered solution is made by adding 50.0 g NH_4Cl to 1.00 L of a 0.75 M solution of NH_3. Calculate the pH of the final solution?

31. Calculate the pH after 0.010 mol gaseous HCl is added to 250.0 mL of each of the following buffered solutions.
    a. 0.050 M NH_3/0.15 M NH_4Cl
    b. 0.50 M NH_3/1.5 M NH_4Cl
    Do the two original buffered solutions differ in their pH or their capacity? What advantage is there in having a buffer with a greater capacity?

32. Calculate the pH after 0.15 mol solid NaOH is added to 1.00 L of each of the following buffered solutions.
    a. 0.050 M propanoic acid ($HC_3H_5O_2$, $K_a = 1.3 \times 10^{-5}$)/0.080 M sodium propanoate
    b. 0.50 M propanoic acid/0.80 M sodium propanoate
    c. Is the solution in part a still a buffered solution after the NaOH has been added? Explain.

Acid–Base Titrations

33. Consider the titration of a generic weak acid HA with a strong base that gives the following titration curve:

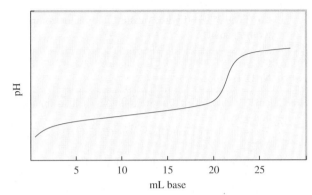

On the curve, indicate the points that correspond to the following:
a. The stoichiometric (equivalence) point
b. The region with maximum buffering
c. pH = pK_a
d. pH depends only on $[HA]_0$
e. pH depends only on $[A^-]$
f. pH depends only on the amount of excess strong base added

34. Sketch the titration curve for the titration of a generic weak base B with a strong acid. The titration reaction is

$$B + H^+ \rightleftharpoons BH^+$$

On this curve, indicate the points that correspond to the following:
a. The stoichiometric (equivalence) point
b. The region with maximum buffering
c. pH = pK_a
d. pH depends only on $[B]_0$
e. pH depends only on $[BH^+]_0$
f. pH depends only on the amount of excess strong acid added

35. A 25.0-mL sample of 0.100 M lactic acid (HC$_3$H$_5$O$_3$, pK_a = 3.86) is titrated with 0.100 M NaOH solution. Calculate the pH after the addition of 0.0 mL, 4.0 mL, 8.0 mL, 12.5 mL, 20.0 mL, 24.0 mL, 24.5 mL, 24.9 mL, 25.0 mL, 25.1 mL, 26 mL, 28 mL, and 30. mL of the NaOH. Plot the results of your calculations as pH versus milliliters of NaOH added.

36. Repeat the procedure in Exercise 35 but for the titration of 25.0 mL of 0.100 M propanoic acid (HC$_3$H$_5$O$_2$, K_a = 1.3 × 10^{-5}) with 0.100 M KOH.

37. Repeat the procedure in Exercise 35, but for the titration of 25.0 mL of 0.100 M NH$_3$ (K_b = 1.8 × 10^{-5}) with 0.100 M HCl.

38. Repeat the procedure in Exercise 35, but for the titration of 25.0 mL of 0.100 M pyridine with 0.100 M hydrochloric acid (K_b for pyridine is 1.7 × 10^{-9}). Do not do the points at 24.9 and 25.1 mL.

39. Calculate the pH at the equivalence point for each of the following titrations.
a. 0.104 g sodium acetate (K_b = 5.6 × 10^{-10}) is dissolved in 25 mL of water and titrated with 0.0996 M HCl.
b. 50.00 mL of 0.0426 M HOCl (K_a = 3.5 × 10^{-8}) is titrated with 0.1028 M NaOH.

40. Calculate the pH at the equivalence point for each of the following titrations.
a. 50.0 mL of 0.205 M HBr (a strong acid) is titrated with 0.356 M KOH.
b. 100.0 mL of a saturated solution of quinine is titrated with 0.0200 M HCl. (See Exercise 72 in Chapter 14 for information about quinine.)

41. Estimate the pH of a solution in which crystal violet is yellow and methyl orange is red. (See Fig. 15.8.)

42. Estimate the pH of a solution in which bromcresol green is blue and thymol blue is yellow. (See Fig. 15.8).

43. A solution has a pH of 9.0. What would be the color of the solution if each of the following indicators were added? (See Fig. 15.8.)
a. Methyl orange   c. Bromcresol green
b. Alizarin   d. Thymol blue

44. A solution has a pH of 4.5. What would be the color of the solution if each of the following indicators were added? (See Fig. 15.8).
a. Methyl orange   c. Bromcresol green
b. Alizarin   d. Phenolphthalein

45. Which of the indicators in Fig. 15.8 should be used for doing the titrations in Exercises 35, 37, and 39?

46. Which of the indicators in Fig. 15.8 should be used for doing the titrations in Exercises 36, 38, and 40?

Solubility Equilibria

47. Write balanced equations for the dissolution reactions and the corresponding expressions for the solubility products of the following.
   a. $AgC_2H_3O_2$ (silver acetate)   c. $Al(OH)_3$
   b. MnS d. $Ca_3(PO_4)_2$

48. Write balanced equations for the dissolution reactions and the corresponding expressions for the solubility products of the following.
   a. $Ca_5(PO_4)_3(OH)$ (hydroxyapatite, the major component of tooth enamel)
   b. PbI_2
   c. Cu_2S
   d. $Ni(OH)_2$

49. Calculate values of K_{sp} for the following salts using the information given.
   a. A sample of 4.8×10^{-5} mol calcium oxalate (CaC_2O_4) dissolves in 1.0 L of water to produce a saturated solution.

   $$CaC_2O_4(s) \rightleftharpoons Ca^{2+}(aq) + C_2O_4^{2-}(aq)$$

   b. The concentration of Pb^{2+} in a solution saturated with $PbBr_2$ is $2.14 \times 10^{-2}\ M$.
   c. The molar solubility of BiI_3 is 1.32×10^{-5} mol/L.

50. Calculate values of K_{sp} for the following salts using the information given.
   a. The solubility of iron(II) oxalate (FeC_2O_4) is 65.9 mg/L at 25°C.
   b. A 0.100-L sample of a saturated solution of copper(II) periodate $(Cu(IO_4)_2)$ contains 0.146 g of the dissolved salt.
   c. The solubility of lithium carbonate (Li_2CO_3) is 5.48 g/L.

51. Calculate the solubility of each of the following compounds in moles per liter and grams per liter.
   a. $Al(OH)_3$, $K_{sp} = 2 \times 10^{-32}$
   b. $Be(IO_4)_2$, $K_{sp} = 1.57 \times 10^{-9}$
   c. $CaSO_4$, $K_{sp} = 6.1 \times 10^{-5}$
   d. $CaCO_3$, $K_{sp} = 8.7 \times 10^{-9}$ (Neglect the basic properties of CO_3^{2-}.)
   e. $MgNH_4PO_4$, $K_{sp} = 3 \times 10^{-13}$ (Neglect the basic properties of PO_4^{3-}.)

52. Calculate the solubility of each of the following compounds in moles per liter and grams per liter.
   a. Hg_2Cl_2, $K_{sp} = 1.1 \times 10^{-18}$ (Hg_2^{2+} is the cation in solution.)
   b. $SrSO_4$, $K_{sp} = 3.2 \times 10^{-7}$
   c. Ag_2CO_3, $K_{sp} = 8.1 \times 10^{-12}$ (Neglect the basic properties of CO_3^{2-}.)
   d. $Ag_2Cl_2O_7$, $K_{sp} = 2 \times 10^{-7}$ ($Cl_2O_7^{2-}$ is the anion in solution.)
   e. Ag_2CrO_4, $K_{sp} = 9.0 \times 10^{-12}$

53. Which of the substances in Exercises 51 and 52 show increased solubility as the pH of the solution becomes more acidic? Write equations for the reactions that occur to increase the solubility.

54. For which salt in each of the following groups will the solubility depend on pH?
   a. AgF, $AgCl$, $AgBr$ c. $Sr(NO_3)_2$, $Sr(NO_2)_2$
   b. PbO, $PbCl_2$ d. $Ni(NO_3)_2$, $Ni(CN)_2$

55. Calculate the solubility (in moles per liter) of $Fe(OH)_3$ ($K_{sp} \approx 4 \times 10^{-38}$) in each of the following.
   a. Water (assume pH is 7.0 and constant)
   b. A solution buffered at pH = 5.0
   c. A solution buffered at pH = 11.0

56. The K_{sp} for lead iodide (PbI_2) is 1.4×10^{-8}. Calculate the solubility of lead iodide in each of the following.
   a. Water   b. 0.10 M $Pb(NO_3)_2$ c. 0.010 M NaI

57. What are the concentrations of all the ions in solution after 100.0 mL of 0.020 M $Pb(NO_3)_2$ and 100.0 mL of 0.020 M $NaCl$ are mixed?

58. A solution is prepared by mixing 75.0 mL of 0.020 M $BaCl_2$ and 125 mL of 0.040 M H_2SO_4. What are the concentrations of barium and sulfate ions in this solution? Assume only SO_4^{2-} ions (no HSO_4^-) are present.

Complex Ion Equilibria

59. Write equations for the stepwise and overall formation of each of the following complex ions.
   a. $Co(NH_3)_6^{2+}$ c. $Ag(NH_3)_2^+$
   b. $Fe(SCN)_6^{3-}$

60. Write equations for the stepwise and overall formation constants of each of the following complex ions.
   a. $Ni(CN)_4^{2-}$ c. $Mn(C_2O_4)_2^{2-}$
   b. $FeCl_4^-$

61. Concentrated ammonia is added to an aqueous solution of copper(II) sulfate. Initially, a white precipitate forms. As more ammonia is added, the precipitate dissolves and the solution becomes a deep bluish purple. Write equations describing the reactions that are occurring. [*Hint:* Cu^{2+} reacts with NH_3 to form $Cu(NH_3)_4^{2+}$.]

62. As sodium chloride solution is added to a solution of silver nitrate, a white precipitate forms. Ammonia is added to the mixture and the precipitate dissolves. When potassium bromide solution is then added, a pale yellow precipitate appears. When a solution of sodium thiosulfate is added, the yellow precipitate dissolves. Finally, potassium iodide is added to the solution and a yellow precipitate forms. Write reactions for all the changes mentioned above. What conclusions can you draw concerning the sizes of the K_{sp} values for AgCl, AgBr, and AgI? What can you say about the relative values of the formation constants of $Ag(NH_3)_2^+$ and $Ag(S_2O_3)_2^{3-}$?

63. The overall formation constant for HgI_4^{2-} is 1.0×10^{30}. That is,

$$1.0 \times 10^{30} = \frac{[HgI_4^{2-}]}{[Hg^{2+}][I^-]^4}$$

What is the concentration of Hg^{2+} in 500.0 mL of a solution that was originally 0.010 M Hg^{2+} and had 65 g KI added to it? The reaction is

$$Hg^{2+}(aq) + 4I^-(aq) \rightleftharpoons HgI_4^{2-}(aq)$$

64. A solution is prepared by adding 0.10 mol $Ni(NH_3)_6Cl_2$ to 0.50 L of 3.0 M NH_3. Calculate $[Ni(NH_3)_6^{2+}]$ and $[Ni^{2+}]$ in this solution [$K_{overall}$ for $Ni(NH_3)_6^{2+}$ is 5.5×10^8].

Additional Exercises

65. Derive an equation analogous to the Henderson–Hasselbalch equation but relating pOH and pK_b of a buffered solution composed of a weak base and its conjugate acid, such as NH_3 and NH_4^+.

66. Borax ($Na_2B_4O_7 \cdot 10H_2O$) dissolves in water according to the reaction

$$Na_2B_4O_7 \cdot 10H_2O(s)$$
$$\rightarrow 2Na^+ + 3H_2O + 2B(OH)_3 + 2B(OH)_4^-$$

Boric acid reacts with water according to the reaction

$$B(OH)_3 + H_2O \rightleftharpoons B(OH)_4^- + H^+ \qquad K_a = 5.8 \times 10^{-10}$$

a. Calculate the pH of the resulting solution when 28.6 g borax is dissolved to make 1.0 L of solution.
b. If 100. mL of 0.10 M NaOH is added to the solution in part a, what is the new pH?

67. Tris(hydroxymethyl)aminomethane, commonly called TRIS or Trizma, is often used as a buffer in biochemical studies. Its buffering range is pH 7 to 9, and K_b is 1.19×10^{-6} for the reaction

$$(HOCH_2)_3CNH_2 + H_2O \rightleftharpoons (HOCH_2)_3CNH_3^+ + OH^-$$
$$\text{TRIS} \qquad\qquad\qquad \text{TRISH}^+$$

a. What is the optimal pH for TRIS buffers?
b. Calculate the ratio $TRIS/TRISH^+$ at pH = 7.0 and at pH = 9.0.
c. A buffer is prepared by diluting 50.0 g TRIS base and 65.0 g TRIS hydrochloride (written as TRISHCl) to a total volume of 2.0 L. What is the pH of this buffer? What is

the pH after 0.50 mL of 12 M HCl is added to a 200.0-mL portion of the buffer?

68. Cacodylic acid, $(CH_3)_2AsO_2H$, a toxic compound that behaves as a weak acid, is used in preparing buffered solutions. For the following reaction $pK_a = 6.19$:

$$(CH_3)_2AsO_2H + H_2O \rightleftharpoons H_3O^+ + (CH_3)_2AsO_2^-$$

Calculate the masses of cacodylic acid and sodium cacodylate that should be used to prepare 500.0 mL of a buffer at pH = 6.60 that has a total concentration of all arsenic-containing species equal to 0.25 M; that is,

$$[(CH_3)_2AsO_2H] + [(CH_3)_2AsO_2^-] = 0.25 \, M$$

69. You have the following reagents on hand:

Solids (pK$_a$ of acid form is given)	
$(CH_3)_2AsO_2Na$ (6.19)	Sodium acetate (4.74)
TRISHCl (8.08)	Potassium fluoride (3.14)
Benzoic acid (4.19)	Ammonium chloride (9.26)
Solutions	
5.0 M HCl	2.6 M NaOH
Glacial acetic acid	

What combinations of reagents would you use to prepare buffers at the following pH values?
a. 3.0   d. 7.0
b. 4.0   e. 9.0
c. 5.0

70. a. Calculate the pH of a buffered solution that is 0.10 M in $C_6H_5CO_2H$ (benzoic acid, $K_a = 6.4 \times 10^{-5}$) and 0.10 M in $C_6H_5CO_2Na$.

b. Calculate the pH after 20.0% (by moles) of the benzoic acid is converted to benzoate anion by addition of base. Use the dissociation equilibrium

$$C_6H_5CO_2H \rightleftharpoons C_6H_5CO_2^- + H^+$$

to calculate the pH.

c. Do the same as in part b, but use the following equilibrium to calculate the pH:

$$C_6H_5CO_2^- + H_2O \rightleftharpoons C_6H_5CO_2H + OH^-$$

d. Do your answers in parts b and c agree? Explain.

71. Calculate the value of the equilibrium constant for each of the following reactions in aqueous solution.

a. $HC_2H_3O_2 + OH^- \rightleftharpoons C_2H_3O_2^- + H_2O$

b. $C_2H_3O_2^- + H^+ \rightleftharpoons HC_2H_3O_2$

c. $HC_2H_3O_2 + NH_3 \rightleftharpoons C_2H_3O_2^- + NH_4^+$

d. $HCl + NaOH \rightleftharpoons NaCl + H_2O$

Which of these reactions are useful for chemical analysis by titration?

72. One method for determining the purity of aspirin is to hydrolyze it with NaOH solution and then titrate the remaining NaOH. The reaction of aspirin with NaOH is as follows.

Aspirin (molar mass = 180.16 g/mol)

Salicylate ion   Acetate ion

A sample of aspirin with a mass of 1.427 g was boiled in 50.00 mL of 0.500 M NaOH. After the solution was cooled, it took 31.92 mL of 0.289 M HCl to titrate the excess NaOH. Calculate the purity of the aspirin. What indicator should be used for this titration? Why?

73. Potassium hydrogen phthalate, known as KHP (molar mass = 204.22 g/mol), can be obtained in high purity and is used to determine the concentration of solutions of strong bases by the reaction

$$HP^- + OH^- \rightarrow H_2O + P^{2-}$$

If a typical titration experiment begins with about 0.5 g KHP and has a final volume of about 100 mL, what would be an appropriate indicator to use? The pK_a for HP^- is 5.51.

74. Methyl red has the following structure:

$K_a = 5.0 \times 10^{-6}$

It undergoes a color change from red to yellow as a solution gets more basic. Calculate an approximate pH range for which methyl red is useful. What are the color change and the pH at the color change when a weak acid is titrated with a strong base using methyl red as an indicator? What are the color change and the pH at the color change when a weak base is titrated with a strong acid using methyl red as an indicator? For which of the titrations in Exercises 35 to 40 would methyl red be a suitable indicator?

75. The K_{sp} of hydroxyapatite, $Ca_5(PO_4)_3OH$, is 6.8×10^{-37}. Calculate the solubility of hydroxyapatite in pure water in moles per liter. How is the solubility of hydroxyapatite affected by adding acid? When hydroxyapatite is treated with fluoride, the mineral fluorapatite, $Ca_5(PO_4)_3F$, forms. The K_{sp} of this substance is 1×10^{-60}. Calculate the solubility of fluorapatite in water. How do these calculations provide a rationale for the fluoridation of drinking water?

76. Calculate the final concentrations of $K^+(aq)$, $C_2O_4^{2-}(aq)$, $Ba^{2+}(aq)$, and $Br^-(aq)$ in a solution prepared by adding 0.100 L of 0.20 M $K_2C_2O_4$ to 0.150 L of 0.25 M $BaBr_2$. (For BaC_2O_4, $K_{sp} = 2.3 \times 10^{-8}$.)

77. Calculate the concentration of Fe^{3+} in blood (pH = 7.41) using the solubility equilibrium of $Fe(OH)_3$ ($K_{sp} = 4 \times 10^{-38}$). Iron levels in blood serum range from 60 to 150 μg/100 mL. How can you account for the discrepancy between the two values?

78. Repeat the procedure in Exercise 35 but for the titration of 25.0 mL of 0.100 M HNO_3 with 0.100 M NaOH.

79. The equilibrium constant for the following reaction is 1.0×10^{23}.

$$Cr^{3+}(aq) + H_2EDTA^{2-}(aq) \rightleftharpoons CrEDTA^-(aq) + 2H^+(aq)$$

Ethylenediaminetetraacetate

EDTA is used as a complexing agent in chemical analysis. Solutions of EDTA, usually as the disodium salt Na_2H_2EDTA, are used to treat heavy metal poisoning. Calculate $[Cr^{3+}]$ at equilibrium in a solution originally 0.0010 M in Cr^{3+} and 0.050 M in H_2EDTA^{2-} and buffered at pH = 6.0.

Challenge Problems

80. Another way to treat data from a pH titration is to graph the absolute value of the change in pH per change in milliliters added versus milliliters added (ΔpH/ΔmL versus mL added). Make such graphs for the calculations you did in Exercise 35. What advantage might this method have over the traditional method for treating titration data?

81. Malonic acid ($HO_2CCH_2CO_2H$) is a diprotic acid. In the titration of malonic acid with NaOH, stoichiometric points occur at pH = 3.9 and 8.8. A 25.00-mL sample of malonic acid of unknown concentration is titrated with 0.0984 M NaOH, requiring 31.50 mL of the NaOH solution to reach the phenolphthalein endpoint. Calculate the concentration of malonic acid in the unknown solution.

82. A few drops of each of the indicators shown in the accompanying table were placed in separate portions of a 1.0 M solution of a weak acid, HX. The results are shown in the last column of the table. What is the approximate pH of the solution containing HX? Calculate the approximate value of K_a for HX.

Indicator	Color of HIn	Color of In⁻	pK_a of HIn	HX
Bromphenol blue	Yellow	Blue	4.0	Blue
Bromcresol purple	Yellow	Purple	6.0	Yellow
Bromcresol green	Yellow	Blue	4.8	Green
Alizarn	Yellow	Red	6.5	Yellow

83. Silica (SiO_2) can undergo the following reactions:

$$SiO_2(s) + 2H_2O(l) \rightleftharpoons H_4SiO_4(aq) \qquad K = 2 \times 10^{-3}$$
$$\text{Silicic acid}$$

$$H_4SiO_4(aq) \rightleftharpoons H_3SiO_4^-(aq) + H^+(aq) \qquad pK_a = 9.46$$

Will silica be more soluble in an acidic or basic solution? Why?

84. Use the equilibrium constants in Exercise 83 to calculate the molar solubility (in mol/L) of silica at a pH of 7.0 and a pH of 10.0.

85. In the chapter discussion of precipitate formation, we ran the precipitation reaction to completion and then let some of the precipitate redissolve to get back to equilibrium. To see why, redo Sample Exercise 15.17, where

Initial Concentration (mol/L)	Equilibrium Concentration (mol/L)
$[Mg^{2+}]_0 = 3.75 \times 10^{-3}$ $[F^-]_0 = 6.25 \times 10^{-2}$ $\xrightarrow[\text{reacts to form}]{y \text{ mol/L } Mg^{2+}} MgF_2$	$[Mg^{2+}] = 3.75 \times 10^{-3} - y$ $[F^-] = 6.25 \times 10^{-2} - 2y$

86. Calculate the concentration of Pb^{2+} in each of the following.
  a. Saturated solution of $Pb(OH)_2$; $K_{sp} = 1.2 \times 10^{-15}$
  b. Saturated solution of $Pb(OH)_2$ buffered at pH = 13.0
  c. 0.010 mol $Pb(NO_3)_2$ added to 1.0 L of aqueous solution, buffered at pH = 13.0 and containing 0.050 M Na_4EDTA. Does $Pb(OH)_2$ precipitate from this solution? For the reaction

$$Pb^{2+} + EDTA^{4-} \rightleftharpoons PbEDTA^{2-} \qquad K = 1.1 \times 10^{18}$$

87. Using the K_{sp} for $Cu(OH)_2$ (1.6×10^{-19}) and the overall formation constant for $Cu(NH_3)_4^{2+}$ (1.0×10^{13}), calculate the value of the equilibrium constant for the reaction

$$Cu(OH)_2(s) + 4NH_3(aq) \rightleftharpoons Cu(NH_3)_4^{2+}(aq) + 2OH^-(aq)$$

88. Use the value of the equilibrium constant you calculated in Exercise 87 to calculate the solubility (in mol/L) of $Cu(OH)_2$ in 5.0 M NH_3. In 5.0 M NH_3 the concentration of OH^- is about 0.010 M.

89. Will a precipitate of $Cd(OH)_2$ form if 1.0 mL of 1.0 M $Cd(NO_3)_2$ is added to 1.0 L of 5.0 M NH_3?

$$Cd^{2+} + 4NH_3 \rightleftharpoons Cd(NH_3)_4^{2+} \qquad K = 1.0 \times 10^7$$
$$Cd(OH)_2 \rightleftharpoons Cd^{2+} + 2OH^- \qquad K_{sp} = 5.9 \times 10^{-15}$$

Marathon Problem*

90. A 225-mg sample of a diprotic acid is dissolved in enough water to make 250. mL of solution. The pH of this solution is 2.06. A saturated solution of calcium hydroxide ($K_{sp} = 5.5 \times 10^{-6}$) is prepared by adding excess calcium hydroxide to pure water and then removing the undissolved solid by filtration. Enough of the calcium hydroxide solution is added to the solution of the acid to reach the second equivalence point. The pH at the second equivalence point (as determined by a pH meter) is 7.96. The first dissociation constant for the acid (K_{a_1}) is 5.90×10^{-2}. Assume that the volumes of the solutions are additive, all solutions are at 25°C, and that K_{a_1} is at least 1000 times greater than K_{a_2}.

  1. Calculate the molar mass of the acid.

  2. Calculate the second dissociation constant for the acid (K_{a_2}).

*This Marathon Problem was developed by James H. Burness of Penn State University, York Campus.

CHAPTER 16

Spontaneity, Entropy, and Free Energy

T he **first law of thermodynamics** is a statement of the law of conservation of energy: energy can be neither created nor destroyed. In other words, *the energy of the universe is constant.* Although the total energy is constant, the various forms of energy can be interchanged in physical and chemical processes. For example, if you drop a book, some of the initial potential energy of the book is changed to kinetic energy, which is then transferred to the atoms in the air and the floor as random motion. The net effect of this process is to change a given quantity of potential energy to exactly the same quantity of thermal energy. Energy has been converted from one form to another, but the same quantity of energy exists before and after the process.

Now let's consider a chemical example. When methane is burned in excess oxygen, the major reaction is

$$CH_4(g) + 2O_2(g) \rightarrow CO_2(g) + 2H_2O(g) + \text{energy}$$

This reaction produces a quantity of energy, which is released as heat. This energy flow results from the lowering of the potential energy stored in the bonds of CH_4 and O_2 as they react to form CO_2 and H_2O. This is illustrated in Fig. 16.1. Potential energy has been converted to thermal energy, but the energy content of the universe has remained constant in accordance with the first law of thermodynamics.

Figure 16.1

When methane and oxygen react to form carbon dioxide and water, the products have lower potential energy than the reactants. This change in potential energy results in energy flow (heat) to the surroundings.

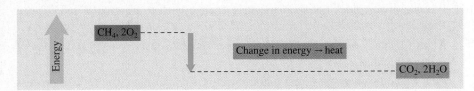

< Solid carbon dioxide (dry ice), when placed in water, causes violent bubbling as gaseous CO_2 is released. The "fog" is moisture condensed from the cold air.

The first law of thermodynamics is used mainly for energy bookkeeping, that is, to answer such questions as

How much energy is involved in the change?

Does energy flow into or out of the system?

What form does the energy finally assume?

The first law of thermodynamics: the energy of the universe is constant.

Although the first law of thermodynamics provides the means for accounting for energy, it gives no hint as to *why* a particular process occurs in a given direction. This is the main question to be considered in this chapter.

16.1 Spontaneous Processes and Entropy

Purpose

- To define a spontaneous process.
- To define entropy in terms of positional probability.

Spontaneous does not mean fast.

A process is said to be **spontaneous** if it *occurs without outside intervention*. **Spontaneous processes** may be fast or slow. As we will see in this chapter, thermodynamics can tell us the *direction* in which a process will occur but can say nothing about the *speed* of the process. As we saw in Chapter 12, the rate of a reaction depends on many factors, such as activation energy, temperature, concentration, and catalysts, and we were able to explain these effects using a simple collision model. In describing a chemical reaction, the discipline of chemical kinetics focuses on the pathway between reactants and products; thermodynamics only considers the initial and final states and does not require knowledge of the pathway between reactants and products (see Fig. 16.2).

In summary, thermodynamics lets us predict whether a process will occur but gives no information about the amount of time required for the process. For example, according to the principles of thermodynamics, a diamond should change spontaneously to graphite. The fact that we do not observe this process does not mean the prediction is wrong; it simply means the process is very slow. Thus we need both thermodynamics and kinetics to describe reactions fully.

To explore the idea of spontaneity, consider the following physical and chemical processes:

A ball rolls down a hill but never spontaneously rolls back up the hill.

If exposed to air and moisture, steel rusts spontaneously. However, the iron oxide in rust does not spontaneously change back to iron metal and oxygen gas.

A gas fills its container uniformly. It never spontaneously collects at one end of the container.

Heat flow always occurs from a hot object to a cooler one. The reverse process never occurs spontaneously.

Wood burns spontaneously in an exothermic reaction to form carbon dioxide and water, but wood is not formed when carbon dioxide and water are heated together.

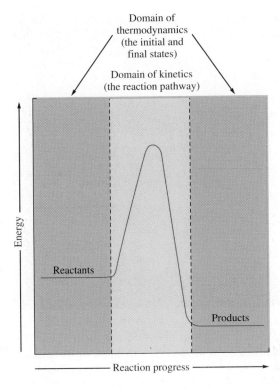

Domain of
thermodynamics
(the initial and
final states)

Domain of kinetics
(the reaction pathway)

Energy

Reactants

Products

Reaction progress

Figure 16.2

The rate of a reaction depends on the pathway from reactants to products; this is the domain of kinetics. Thermodynamics tells us whether or not a reaction is spontaneous based only on the properties of the reactants and products. The predictions of thermodynamics do not require knowledge of the pathway between reactants and products.

At temperatures below 0°C, water spontaneously freezes, and at temperatures above 0°C, ice spontaneously melts.

What thermodynamic principle will provide an explanation of why, under a given set of conditions, each of these diverse processes occurs in one direction and never in the reverse? In searching for an answer, we could explain the behavior of a ball on a hill in terms of gravity. But what does gravity have to do with the rusting of a nail or the freezing of water? Early developers of thermodynamics thought that exothermicity might be the key—that a process would be spontaneous if it were exothermic. Although this factor does appear to be important, since many spontaneous processes are exothermic, it is not the total answer. For example, the melting of ice, which occurs spontaneously at temperatures greater than 0°C, is an endothermic process.

What common characteristic causes the processes listed above to be spontaneous in one direction only? After many years of observation, scientists have concluded that the characteristic common to all spontaneous processes is an increase in a property called **entropy**, denoted by the symbol **S**. *The driving force for a spontaneous process is an increase in the entropy of the universe.*

What is entropy? Although there is no simple definition that is completely accurate, *entropy can be viewed as a measure of randomness or disorder*. The natural progression of things is from order to disorder, from lower entropy to higher entropy. You only have to think about the condition of your room to be convinced of this. Your room naturally tends to get messy (disordered), because an ordered room requires everything to be in its place. There are simply many more ways for things to be out of place than for them to be in their places.

Plant materials burn to form carbon dioxide and water.

As another example, suppose you have a deck of playing cards ordered in some particular way. You throw these cards into the air and pick them all up at random. Looking at the new sequence of the cards, you would be very surprised to find that it matched the original order. Such an event would be possible, but *very improbable*. There are billions of ways for the deck to be disordered, but only one way to be ordered according to your definition. Thus the chances of picking the cards up out of order are much greater than the chance of picking them up in order. It is natural for disorder to increase.

Entropy is a thermodynamic function that describes the *number of arrangements* (positions and/or energy levels) that are *available to a system* existing in a given state. Entropy is closely associated with probability. The key concept is that the more ways a particular state can be achieved, the greater is the likelihood (probability) of finding that state. In other words, *nature spontaneously proceeds toward the states that have the highest probabilities of existing*. This conclusion is not surprising at all. The difficulty comes in connecting this concept to real-life processes. For example, what does the spontaneous rusting of steel have to do with probability? Understanding the connection between entropy and spontaneity will allow us to answer such questions. We will begin to explore this connection by considering a very simple process, the expansion of an ideal gas into a vacuum, as represented in Fig. 16.3. Why is this process spontaneous? The driving force is probability. Because there are more ways of having the gas evenly spread throughout the container than there are ways for it to be in any other possible state, the gas spontaneously attains the uniform distribution.

To understand this conclusion, we will greatly simplify the system and consider some of the possible arrangements of only four gas molecules in the two-bulbed container (Fig. 16.4). How many ways can each arrangement (state) be achieved? Arrangement I can be achieved in only one way—all the molecules must be in one end. Arrangement II can be achieved in four ways, as shown in Table 16.1. Each configuration that gives a particular arrangement is called a **microstate.** Arrangement I has one microstate, and arrangement II has four microstates. Arrangement III

Probability refers to likelihood.

A disordered pile of playing cards.

Ideal gas   Vacuum

Figure 16.3

The expansion of an ideal gas into an evacuated bulb.

can be achieved in six ways (six microstates), as shown in Table 16.1. *Which arrangement is most likely to occur?* The one that can be achieved in the greatest number of ways. Thus arrangement III is most probable. The relative probabilities of arrangements III, II, and I are 6:4:1. We have discovered an important principle: the probability of occurrence of a particular arrangement (state) depends on the number of ways (microstates) in which that arrangement can be achieved.

The consequences of this principle are dramatic for large numbers of molecules. One gas molecule in the flask in Fig. 16.4 has one chance in two of being in the left bulb. We say that the probability of finding the molecule in the left bulb is $\frac{1}{2}$. For

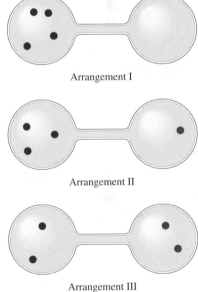

Arrangement I

Arrangement II

Arrangement III

Figure 16.4

Three possible arrangements (states) of four molecules in a two-bulbed flask.

Table 16.1		
The Microstates That Give a Particular Arrangement (State)		
Arrangement		Microstates

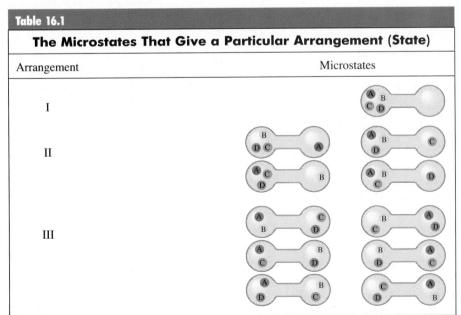

For two molecules in the flask, there are four possible microstates:

Thus there is one chance in four of finding

two molecules in the flask, there is one chance in two of finding each molecule in the left bulb, so there is one chance in four ($\frac{1}{2} \times \frac{1}{2} = \frac{1}{4}$) that *both* molecules will be in the left bulb. As the number of molecules increases, the relative probability of finding all of them in the left bulb decreases, as shown in Table 16.2. For 1 mole of gas, the probability of finding all the molecules in the left bulb is so small that this arrangement would "never" occur.

Thus a gas placed in one end of a container will spontaneously expand to fill the entire vessel evenly because, for a large number of gas molecules, there is a huge number of microstates in which equal numbers of molecules are in both ends. On the other hand, the opposite process,

although not impossible, is *highly* improbable, since only one microstate leads to this arrangement. Therefore, this process does not occur spontaneously.

The type of probability we have been considering in this example is called **positional probability** because it depends on the number of configurations in space (positional microstates) that yield a particular state. A gas expands into a vacuum to give a uniform distribution because the expanded state has the highest positional probability, that is, the largest entropy, of the states available to the system.

Table 16.2

Probability of Finding All the Molecules in the Left Bulb as a Function of the Total Number of Molecules	
Number of Molecules	Relative Probability of Finding All Molecules in the Left Bulb
1	$\dfrac{1}{2}$
2	$\dfrac{1}{2} \times \dfrac{1}{2} = \dfrac{1}{2^2} = \dfrac{1}{4}$
3	$\dfrac{1}{2} \times \dfrac{1}{2} \times \dfrac{1}{2} = \dfrac{1}{2^3} = \dfrac{1}{8}$
5	$\dfrac{1}{2} \times \dfrac{1}{2} \times \dfrac{1}{2} \times \dfrac{1}{2} \times \dfrac{1}{2} = \dfrac{1}{2^5} = \dfrac{1}{32}$
10	$\dfrac{1}{2^{10}} = \dfrac{1}{1024}$
n	$\dfrac{1}{2^n} = \left(\dfrac{1}{2}\right)^n$
6×10^{23} (1 mole)	$\left(\dfrac{1}{2}\right)^{6 \times 10^{23}} \approx 10^{-(2 \times 10^{23})}$

Positional probability is also illustrated by changes of state. In general, positional entropy increases in going from solid to liquid to gas. A mole of a substance has a much smaller volume in the solid state than it does in the gaseous state. In the solid state, the molecules are close together, with relatively few positions available to them; in the gaseous state, the molecules are far apart, with many more positions available to them. The liquid state is closer to the solid state than it is to the gaseous state in these terms. We can summarize these comparisons as follows:

$$S_{\text{solid}} < S_{\text{liquid}} \ll S_{\text{gas}}$$

Positional entropy is also very important in the formation of solutions. In Chapter 11 we saw that solution formation is favored by the natural tendency for substances to mix. We can now be more precise. The entropy change associated with the mixing of two pure substances is expected to be positive. An increase in entropy is expected because there are many more microstates for the mixed condition than for the separated condition. This effect is due principally to the increased volume available to a given "particle" after mixing occurs. For example, when two liquids are mixed to form a solution, the molecules of each liquid have more available volume and thus more available positions. Therefore, the increase in positional entropy associated with mixing favors the formation of solutions.

> Solid, liquid, and gaseous states were compared in Chapter 10.
>
> Solids are more ordered than liquids or gases and thus have lower entropy.
>
> The tendency to mix is due to the increased volume available to the particles of each component of the mixture. For example, when two liquids are mixed, the molecules of each liquid have more available volume and thus more available positions.

Sample Exercise 16.1

For each of the following pairs, choose the substance with the higher positional entropy (per mole) at a given temperature.

a. Solid CO_2 and gaseous CO_2
b. N_2 gas at 1 atm and N_2 gas at 1.0×10^{-2} atm

Solution

a. Since a mole of gaseous CO_2 has the greater volume by far, the molecules have many more available positions than in a mole of solid CO_2. Thus gaseous CO_2 has the higher positional entropy.
b. A mole of N_2 gas at 1×10^{-2} atm has a volume 100 times that (at a given temperature) of a mole of N_2 gas at 1 atm. Thus N_2 gas at 1×10^{-2} atm has the higher positional entropy.

A "steaming" piece of dry ice (solid carbon dioxide).

Sample Exercise 16.2

Predict the sign of the entropy change for each of the following processes.

a. Solid sugar is added to water to form a solution.
b. Iodine vapor condenses on a cold surface to form crystals.

Solution

a. The sugar molecules become randomly dispersed in the water when the solution forms and thus have access to a larger volume and a larger number of possible positions. The positional disorder is increased, and there will be an increase in entropy. ΔS is positive, since the final state has a larger entropy than the initial state, and $\Delta S = S_{final} - S_{initial}$.

b. Gaseous iodine is forming a solid. This process involves a change from a relatively large volume to a much smaller volume, which results in lower positional disorder. For this process ΔS is negative (the entropy decreases).

16.2 Entropy and the Second Law of Thermodynamics

Purpose

- To state the second law of thermodynamics in terms of entropy.

The total energy of the universe is constant, but the entropy is increasing.

We have seen that processes are spontaneous when they result in an increase in disorder. Nature always moves toward the most probable state available to it. We can state this principle in terms of entropy: *in any spontaneous process there is always an increase in the entropy of the universe*. This is the **second law of thermodynamics.** Contrast this with the first law of thermodynamics, which tells us that the energy of the universe is constant. Energy is conserved in the universe, but entropy is not. In fact, the second law can be paraphrased as follows: *the entropy of the universe is increasing*.

As in Chapter 6, we find it convenient to divide the universe into a system and the surroundings. Thus we can represent the change in the entropy of the universe as

$$\Delta S_{univ} = \Delta S_{sys} + \Delta S_{surr}$$

where ΔS_{sys} and ΔS_{surr} represent the changes in entropy that occur in the system and surroundings, respectively.

To predict whether a given process will be spontaneous, we must know the sign of ΔS_{univ}. If ΔS_{univ} is positive, the entropy of the universe increases, and the process is spontaneous in the direction written. If ΔS_{univ} is negative, the process is spontaneous in the *opposite* direction. If ΔS_{univ} is zero, the process has no tendency to occur and the system is at equilibrium. To predict whether a process is spontaneous, we must consider the entropy changes that occur both in the system and also in the surroundings and then take their sum.

Sample Exercise 16.3

In a living cell, large molecules are assembled from simple ones. Is this process consistent with the second law of thermodynamics?

Solution

To reconcile the operation of an order-producing cell with the second law of thermodynamics, we must remember that ΔS_{univ}, not ΔS_{sys}, must be positive for a process to be spontaneous. A process for which ΔS_{sys} is negative can be spontaneous if the associated ΔS_{surr} is both larger and positive. The operation of a cell is such a process.

A colony of Volvox, a genus of minute unicellular organisms, formerly classified in the animal kingdom but now regarded as vegetables.

16.3 *The Effect of Temperature on Spontaneity*

Purpose

- To discuss the important characteristics of entropy changes in the surroundings.
- To apply the relationship between ΔS_{surr}, ΔH, and T (K).

To explore the interplay of ΔS_{sys} and ΔS_{surr} in determining the sign of ΔS_{univ}, we will first discuss the change of state for one mole of water from liquid to gas,

$$H_2O(l) \rightarrow H_2O(g)$$

considering the water to be the system and everything else the surroundings.

What happens to the entropy of water in this process? A mole of liquid water (18 grams) has a volume of approximately 18 mL. A mole of gaseous water at 1 atmosphere and 100°C occupies a volume of approximately 31 liters. Clearly there are many more positions available to the water molecules in a volume of 31 L than in 18 mL, and the vaporization of water is favored by this increase in positional probability. That is, for this process the entropy of the system increases; ΔS_{sys} has a positive sign.

What about the entropy change in the surroundings? Although we will not prove it here, entropy changes in the surroundings are determined primarily by the flow of energy into or out of the system as heat. To understand this, suppose an exothermic process transfers 50 J of energy as heat to the surroundings, where it becomes thermal energy, that is, kinetic energy associated with the random motions of atoms. Thus this flow of energy into the surroundings increases the random motions of atoms there and thereby increases the entropy of the surroundings. The sign of ΔS_{surr} is positive. When an endothermic process occurs in the system, it produces the opposite effect. Heat flows from the surroundings to the system, and the random motions of the atoms in the surroundings decrease, decreasing the entropy of the surroundings. The vaporization of water is an endothermic process. Thus for this change of state, ΔS_{surr} is negative.

Remember it is the sign of ΔS_{univ} that tells us whether the vaporization of water is spontaneous or not. We have seen that ΔS_{sys} is positive and favors the process and that ΔS_{surr} is negative and unfavorable. Thus the components of ΔS_{univ} are in opposition. Which one controls the situation? The answer *depends on the temperature.* We know that at a pressure of 1 atmosphere, water changes spontaneously from liquid to gas at all temperatures above 100°C. Below 100°C, the opposite process (condensation) is spontaneous.

Since ΔS_{sys} and ΔS_{surr} are in opposition for the vaporization of water, the temperature must have an effect on the relative importance of these two terms. To understand why this is so, we must discuss in more detail the factors that control the entropy changes in the surroundings. The central idea is that *the entropy changes in the surroundings are primarily determined by heat flow.* An exothermic process in the system increases the entropy of the surroundings, because the resulting energy flow increases the random motions in the surroundings. This means that exothermicity is an important driving force for spontaneity. In earlier chapters we have seen that a system tends to undergo changes that lower its energy. We now understand the reason for this tendency. When a system at constant temperature moves to a lower energy, the energy it gives up is transferred to the surroundings, leading to an increase in entropy there.

In an endothermic process, heat flows from the surroundings into the system. In an exothermic process, heat flows into the surroundings from the system.

The significance of exothermicity as a driving force *depends on the temperature at which the process occurs*. That is, the magnitude of ΔS_{surr} depends on the temperature at which the heat is transferred. We will not attempt to prove this fact here. Instead, we offer an analogy. Suppose that you have $50 to give away. Giving it to a millionaire would not create much of an impression—a millionaire has money to spare. However, to a poor college student, $50 would represent a significant sum and would be received with considerable joy. The same principle can be applied to energy transfer via the flow of heat. If 50 J of energy is transferred to the surroundings, the impact of that event depends greatly on the temperature. If the temperature of the surroundings is very high, the atoms there are in rapid motion. The 50 J of energy will not make a large percent change in these motions. On the other hand, if 50 J of energy is transferred to the surroundings at a very low temperature, where atomic motion is slow, the energy will cause a large percent change in these motions. *The impact of the transfer of a given quantity of energy as heat to or from the surroundings will be greater at lower temperatures.*

For our purposes, there are two important characteristics of the entropy changes that occur in the surroundings:

In a process occurring at constant temperature, the tendency for the system to lower its energy results from the positive value of ΔS_{surr}.

1. *The sign ΔS_{surr} depends on the direction of the heat flow*. At constant temperature, an exothermic process in the system causes heat to flow into the surroundings, increasing the random motions and thus the entropy of the surroundings. For this case, ΔS_{surr} is positive. The opposite is true for an endothermic process in a system at constant temperature. Note that although the driving force described here really results from the change in entropy, it is often described in terms of energy: nature tends to seek the lowest possible energy.

2. *The magnitude of ΔS_{surr} depends on the temperature*. The transfer of a given quantity of energy as heat produces a much greater percent change in the randomness of the surroundings at a low temperature than it does at a high temperature. Thus ΔS_{surr} depends directly on the quantity of heat transferred and inversely on temperature. In other words, the tendency for the system to lower its energy becomes a more important driving force at lower temperatures.

$$\begin{array}{c} \text{Driving force} \\ \text{provided by} \\ \text{the energy flow} \\ \text{(heat)} \end{array} = \begin{array}{c} \text{magnitude of the} \\ \text{entropy change of} \\ \text{the surroundings} \end{array} = \frac{\text{quantity of heat (J)}}{\text{temperature (K)}}$$

These ideas are summarized as follows:

Exothermic process: $\quad \Delta S_{surr} = + \dfrac{\text{quantity of heat (J)}}{\text{temperature (K)}}$

Endothermic process: $\quad \Delta S_{surr} = - \dfrac{\text{quantity of heat (J)}}{\text{temperature (K)}}$

We can express ΔS_{surr} in terms of the change in enthalpy ΔH for a process occurring at constant pressure, since

$$\text{Heat flow (constant } P) = \text{change in enthalpy} = \Delta H$$

Exothermic process:
ΔS_{surr} = positive
Endothermic process:
ΔS_{surr} = negative

When no subscript is present, the quantity (for example, ΔH) refers to the system.

Recall that ΔH consists of two parts: a sign and a number. The *sign* indicates the direction of flow, where a plus sign means into the system (endothermic) and a minus sign means out of the system (exothermic). The *number* indicates the quantity of energy.

Combining all these concepts produces the following definition of ΔS_{surr} for a reaction that takes place under conditions of constant temperature (Kelvin) and pressure:

$$\Delta S_{surr} = -\frac{\Delta H}{T}$$

The minus sign is necessary because the sign of ΔH is determined with respect to the reaction system, and this equation expresses a property of the surroundings. This means that if the reaction is exothermic, ΔH has a negative sign, but since heat flows into the surroundings, ΔS_{surr} is positive.

The negative sign changes the point of view from the system to the surroundings.

Sample Exercise 16.4

In the metallurgy of antimony, the pure metal is recovered via different reactions, depending on the composition of the ore. For example, iron is used to reduce antimony in sulfide ores:

$$Sb_2S_3(s) + 3Fe(s) \rightarrow 2Sb(s) + 3FeS(s) \qquad \Delta H = -125 \text{ kJ}$$

Carbon is used as the reducing agent for oxide ores:

$$Sb_4O_6(s) + 6C(s) \rightarrow 4Sb(s) + 6CO(g) \qquad \Delta H = 778 \text{ kJ}$$

Calculate ΔS_{surr} for each of these reactions at 25°C and 1 atm.

The mineral stibnite contains Sb_2S_3.

Solution

We use

$$\Delta S_{surr} = -\frac{\Delta H}{T}$$

where

$$T = 25 + 273 = 298 \text{ K}$$

For the sulfide ore reaction,

$$\Delta S_{surr} = -\frac{-125 \text{ kJ}}{298 \text{ K}} = 0.419 \text{ kJ/K} = 419 \text{ J/K}$$

Note that ΔS_{surr} is positive, as it should be, since this reaction is exothermic and heat flow occurs to the surroundings, increasing the randomness of the surroundings.

For the oxide ore reaction,

$$\Delta S_{surr} = -\frac{778 \text{ kJ}}{298} = -2.61 \text{ kJ/K} = -2.61 \times 10^3 \text{ J/K}$$

In this case ΔS_{surr} is negative because heat flow occurs from the surroundings to the system.

We have seen that the spontaneity of a process is determined by the entropy change it produces in the universe. We have also seen that ΔS_{univ} has two components, ΔS_{sys} and ΔS_{surr}. If for some process both ΔS_{sys} and ΔS_{surr} are positive, then

Table 16.3

Interplay of ΔS_{sys} and ΔS_{surr} in Determining the Sign of ΔS_{univ}			
Signs of Entropy Changes			
ΔS_{sys}	ΔS_{surr}	ΔS_{univ}	Process Spontaneous?
+	+	+	Yes
−	−	−	No (reaction will occur in opposite direction)
+	−	?	Yes, if ΔS_{sys} has a larger magnitude than ΔS_{surr}
−	+	?	Yes, if ΔS_{surr} has a larger magnitude than ΔS_{sys}

ΔS_{univ} is positive, and the process is spontaneous. If, on the other hand, both ΔS_{sys} and ΔS_{surr} are negative, the process does not occur in the direction indicated but is spontaneous in the opposite direction. Finally, if ΔS_{sys} and ΔS_{surr} have opposite signs, the spontaneity of the process depends on the sizes of the opposing terms. These cases are summarized in Table 16.3.

We can now understand why spontaneity is often dependent on temperature and thus why water spontaneously freezes below 0°C and melts above 0°C. The term ΔS_{surr} is temperature-dependent. Since

$$\Delta S_{surr} = -\frac{\Delta H}{T}$$

at constant pressure, the value of ΔS_{surr} changes markedly with temperature. The magnitude of ΔS_{surr} will be very small at high temperatures and will increase as the temperature decreases. That is, exothermicity is most important as a driving force at low temperatures.

16.4 Free Energy

Purpose

• To define free energy and relate it to spontaneity.

So far we have used ΔS_{univ} to predict the spontaneity of a process. However, another thermodynamic function is also related to spontaneity and is especially useful in dealing with the temperature dependence of spontaneity. This function is called the **free energy,** which is symbolized by G and defined by the relationship

$$G = H - TS$$

where H is the enthalpy, T is the Kelvin temperature, and S is the entropy.

The symbol G for free energy honors Josiah Willard Gibbs (1839–1903) who was Professor of Mathematical Physics at Yale University from 1871 to 1903. He laid the foundations of many areas of thermodynamics, particularly as they apply to chemistry.

For a process that occurs at constant temperature, the change in free energy (ΔG) is given by the equation

$$\Delta G = \Delta H - T\Delta S$$

Note that all quantities here refer to the system. From this point on we will follow the usual convention that when no subscript is included, the quantity refers to the system.

To see how this equation relates to spontaneity, we divide both sides of the equation by $-T$ to produce

$$-\frac{\Delta G}{T} = -\frac{\Delta H}{T} + \Delta S$$

Remember that at constant temperature and pressure

$$\Delta S_{surr} = -\frac{\Delta H}{T}$$

So we can write

$$-\frac{\Delta G}{T} = -\frac{\Delta H}{T} + \Delta S = \Delta S_{surr} + \Delta S = \Delta S_{univ}$$

We have shown that

$$\Delta S_{univ} = -\frac{\Delta G}{T} \qquad \text{at constant } T \text{ and } P$$

This result is very important. It means that a process carried out at constant temperature and pressure will be spontaneous only if ΔG is negative. That is, *a process (at constant T and P) is spontaneous in the direction in which the free energy decreases* ($-\Delta G$ means $+\Delta S_{univ}$).

Now we have two functions that can be used to predict spontaneity: the entropy of the universe, which applies to all processes; and free energy, which can be used for processes carried out at constant temperature and pressure. Since so many chemical reactions occur under the latter conditions, free energy is the more useful to chemists.

Let's use the free energy equation to predict the spontaneity of the melting of ice:

$$H_2O(s) \rightarrow H_2O(l)$$

for which $\Delta H° = 6.03 \times 10^3$ J/mol and $\Delta S° = 22.1$ J/K · mol

Results of the calculations of ΔS_{univ} and $\Delta G°$ at $-10°C$, $0°C$, and $10°C$ are shown in Table 16.4. These data predict that the process is spontaneous at $10°C$; that is, ice melts at this temperature because ΔS_{univ} is positive and $\Delta G°$ is negative. The opposite is true at $-10°C$, where water freezes spontaneously.

The superscript degree symbol (°) indicates all substances are in their standard states.

Why is this so? The answer lies in the fact that ΔS_{sys} ($\Delta S°$) and ΔS_{surr} oppose each other. The term $\Delta S°$ favors the melting of ice because of the increase in positional entropy, and ΔS_{surr} favors the freezing of water because it is an exothermic process. At temperatures below $0°C$, the change of state occurs in the exothermic direction because ΔS_{surr} is larger in magnitude than ΔS_{sys}. But above $0°C$ the change occurs in the direction in which ΔS_{sys} is favorable, since in this case ΔS_{sys} is larger in magnitude than ΔS_{surr}. At $0°C$ the *opposing tendencies just balance,* and

Table 16.4

Results of the Calculation of ΔS_{univ} and $\Delta G°$ for the Process $H_2O(s) \rightarrow H_2O(l)$ at $-10°C$, $0°C$, and $10°C$*

T ($°C$)	T (K)	$\Delta H°$ (J/mol)	$\Delta S°$ (J/K · mol)	$\Delta S_{surr} = -\dfrac{\Delta H°}{T}$ (J/K · mol)	$\Delta S_{univ} = \Delta S° + \Delta S_{surr}$ (J/K · mol)	$T\Delta S°$ (J/mol)	$\Delta G° = \Delta H° - T\Delta S°$ (J/mol)
-10	263	6.03×10^3	22.1	-22.9	-0.8	5.81×10^3	$+2.2 \times 10^2$
0	273	6.03×10^3	22.1	-22.1	0	6.03×10^3	0
10	283	6.03×10^3	22.1	-21.3	$+0.8$	6.25×10^3	-2.2×10^2

*Note that at 10°C, $\Delta S°$ (ΔS_{sys}) controls, and the process occurs even though it is endothermic. At $-10°C$, the magnitude of ΔS_{surr} is larger than that of $\Delta S°$, so the process is spontaneous in the opposite (exothermic) direction.

the two states coexist; there is no driving force in either direction. An equilibrium exists between the two states of water. Note that ΔS_{univ} is equal to 0 at 0°C.

We can reach the same conclusions by examining $\Delta G°$. At $-10°C$, $\Delta G°$ is positive because the $\Delta H°$ term is larger than the $T\Delta S°$ term. The opposite is true at 10°C. At 0°C, $\Delta H°$ is equal to $T\Delta S°$ and $\Delta G°$ is equal to 0. This means that solid H_2O and liquid H_2O have the same free energy at 0°C ($\Delta G° = G_{liquid} - G_{solid}$), and the system is at equilibrium.

We can understand the temperature dependence of spontaneity by examining the behavior of ΔG. For a process occurring at constant temperature and pressure,

$$\Delta G = \Delta H - T\Delta S$$

If ΔH and ΔS favor opposite processes, spontaneity will depend on temperature in such a way that the exothermic direction will be favored at low temperatures. For example, for the process

$$H_2O(s) \rightarrow H_2O(l)$$

ΔH is positive and ΔS is positive. The natural tendency for this system to lower its energy is in opposition to its natural tendency to increase its positional randomness. At low temperatures, ΔH dominates, and at high temperatures, ΔS dominates. The various possible cases are summarized in Table 16.5.

Table 16.5

Various Possible Combinations of ΔH and ΔS for a Process and the Resulting Dependence of Spontaneity on Temperature

Case	Result
ΔS positive, ΔH negative	Spontaneous at all temperatures
ΔS positive, ΔH positive	Spontaneous at high temperatures (where exothermicity is relatively unimportant)
ΔS negative, ΔH negative	Spontaneous at low temperatures (where exothermicity is dominant)
ΔS negative, ΔH positive	Process not spontaneous at *any* temperature (reverse process is spontaneous at *all* temperatures)

Sample Exercise 16.5

At what temperatures is the following process spontaneous at 1 atm?

$$Br_2(l) \rightarrow Br_2(g)$$
$$\Delta H° = 31.0 \text{ kJ/mol} \quad \text{and} \quad \Delta S° = 93.0 \text{ J/K} \cdot \text{mol}$$

What is the normal boiling point of liquid Br_2?

Solution

The vaporization process will be spontaneous at all temperatures where $\Delta G°$ is negative. Note that $\Delta S°$ favors the vaporization process because of the increase in positional entropy, and $\Delta H°$ favors the *opposite* process, which is exothermic. These opposite tendencies will exactly balance at the boiling point of liquid Br_2, since at this temperature liquid and gaseous Br_2 are in equilibrium ($\Delta G° = 0$). We can find this temperature by setting $\Delta G° = 0$ in the equation

$$\Delta G° = \Delta H° - T\Delta S°$$
$$0 = \Delta H° - T\Delta S°$$
$$\Delta H° = T\Delta S°$$

Then
$$T = \frac{\Delta H°}{\Delta S°} = \frac{3.10 \times 10^4 \text{ J/mol}}{93.0 \text{ J/K} \cdot \text{mol}} = 333 \text{ K}$$

At temperatures above 333 K, $T\Delta S°$ has a larger magnitude than $\Delta H°$, and $\Delta G°$ (or $\Delta H° - T\Delta S°$) is negative. Above 333 K, the vaporization process is spontaneous; the opposite process occurs spontaneously below this temperature. At 333 K, liquid and gaseous Br_2 coexist in equilibrium. These observations can be summarized as follows (the pressure is 1 atm in each case):

1. $T > 333$ K. The term $\Delta S°$ controls. The increase in entropy when liquid Br_2 is vaporized is dominant.

2. $T < 333$ K. The process is spontaneous in the direction in which it is exothermic. The term $\Delta H°$ controls.

3. $T = 333$ K. The opposing driving forces are just balanced ($\Delta G° = 0$), and the liquid and gaseous phases of bromine coexist. This is the normal boiling point.

16.5 Entropy Changes in Chemical Reactions

Purpose

- To apply positional probability to chemical reactions.
- To relate molecular complexity to entropy.

The second law of thermodynamics tells us that a process will be spontaneous if the entropy of the universe increases when the process occurs. We saw in Section 16.4 that for a process at constant temperature and pressure, we can use the change in free energy of the system to predict the sign of ΔS_{univ} and thus the direction in which it is spontaneous. So far we have applied these ideas only to physical processes, such as changes of state and the formation of solutions. However, the main business of chemistry is studying chemical reactions, and therefore, we want to apply the second law to reactions.

First, we will consider the entropy changes accompanying chemical reactions that occur under conditions of constant temperature and pressure. As for the other types of processes we have considered, the entropy changes in the *surroundings* are determined by the heat flow that occurs as the reaction takes place. However, the entropy changes in the *system* (the reactants and products of the reaction) are determined by positional probability.

For example, in the ammonia synthesis reaction

$$N_2(g) + 3H_2(g) \rightarrow 2NH_3(g)$$

four reactant molecules become two product molecules, lowering the number of independent units in the system, which leads to less positional disorder. *Fewer molecules mean fewer possible configurations.* To help clarify this, consider a special container with a million compartments, each large enough to hold a hydrogen molecule. Thus there are a million ways one H_2 molecule can be placed in this container. But suppose we break the H—H bond and place the two independent H atoms in the same container. A little thought will convince you that there are *many* more than a million ways to place the two separate atoms. The number of arrangements possible for the two independent atoms is much greater than the number for the molecule. Thus for the process

$$H_2 \rightarrow 2H$$

positional entropy increases.

Does positional entropy increase or decrease when the following reaction takes place?

$$4NH_3(g) + 5O_2(g) \rightarrow 4NO(g) + 6H_2O(g)$$

In this case 9 gaseous molecules are changed to 10 gaseous molecules, and the positional entropy increases. There are more independent units as products than as reactants. In general, when a reaction involves gaseous molecules, *the change in positional entropy is dominated by the relative numbers of molecules of gaseous reactants and products.* If the number of molecules of the gaseous products is greater than the number of molecules of the gaseous reactants, positional entropy typically increases, and ΔS will be positive for the reaction.

Sample Exercise 16.6

Predict the sign of $\Delta S°$ for each of the following reactions.

a. The thermal decomposition of solid calcium carbonate:

$$CaCO_3(s) \rightarrow CaO(s) + CO_2(g)$$

b. The oxidation of SO_2 in air:

$$2SO_2(g) + O_2(g) \rightarrow 2SO_3(g)$$

Solution

a. Since in this reaction a gas is produced from a solid reactant, the positional entropy increases, and $\Delta S°$ is positive.

b. Here three molecules of gaseous reactants become two molecules of gaseous products. Since the number of gas molecules decreases, positional entropy decreases, and $\Delta S°$ is negative.

In thermodynamics it is the *change* in a certain function that is usually important. The change in enthalpy determines if a reaction is exothermic or endothermic at constant pressure. The change in free energy determines if a process is spontaneous at constant temperature and pressure. It is fortunate that changes in thermodynamic functions are sufficient for most purposes, since absolute values for many thermodynamic characteristics of a system, such as enthalpy or free energy, cannot be determined.

However, we can assign absolute entropy values. Consider a solid at 0 K, where molecular motion virtually ceases. If the substance is a perfect crystal, its internal arrangement is absolutely regular [see Fig. 16.5(a)]. There is only *one way* to achieve this perfect order: every particle must be in its place. For example, with *N* coins there is only one way to achieve the state of all heads. Thus a perfect crystal represents the lowest possible entropy; that is, *the entropy of a perfect crystal at 0 K is zero.* This is a statement of the **third law of thermodynamics.**

As the temperature of a perfect crystal is increased, the random vibrational motions increase, and disorder increases within the crystal [see Fig. 16.5(b)]. Thus the entropy of a substance increases with temperature. Since *S* is zero for a perfect crystal at 0 K, the entropy value for a substance at a particular temperature can be calculated by knowing the temperature dependence of entropy. (We will not show such calculations here.)

The *standard entropy values* $S°$ of many common substances at 298 K and 1 atm are listed in Appendix 4. From these values you will see that the entropy of a substance does indeed increase in going from solid to liquid to gas. One especially interesting feature of this table is the very low $S°$ value for diamond. The structure of diamond is highly ordered, with each carbon strongly bound to a tetrahedral arrangement of four other carbon atoms (see Section 10.5, Fig. 10.22). This type of structure allows very little disorder and has a very low entropy, even at 298 K. Graphite has a slightly higher entropy because its layered structure allows for a little more disorder.

A perfect crystal at 0 K is an unattainable ideal, taken as a standard but never actually observed.

The standard entropy values represent the increase in entropy that occurs when a substance is heated from 0 K to 298 K at 1 atm pressure.

Figure 16.5

(a) A perfect crystal of hydrogen chloride at 0 K; the dipolar HCl molecules are represented by ⊕+|−. The entropy is zero ($S = 0$) for this perfect crystal at 0 K. (b) As the temperature rises above 0 K, lattice vibrations allow some dipoles to change their orientations, producing some disorder and an increase in entropy ($S > 0$).

(a)

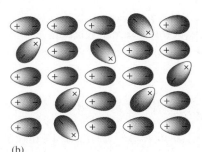

(b)

Because *entropy is a state function of the system* (it is not pathway-dependent), the entropy change for a given chemical reaction can be calculated by taking the difference between the standard entropy values of products and those of the reactants:

$$\Delta S^{\circ}_{\text{reaction}} = \Sigma n_p S^{\circ}_{\text{products}} - \Sigma n_r S^{\circ}_{\text{reactants}}$$

where, as usual, Σ represents the sum of the terms. It is important to note that entropy is an extensive property (it depends on the amount of substance present). This means that the number of moles of a given reactant (n_r) or product (n_p) must be taken into account.

Sample Exercise 16.7

Calculate ΔS° at 25°C for the reaction

$$2NiS(s) + 3O_2(g) \rightarrow 2SO_2(g) + 2NiO(s)$$

given the following standard entropy values:

Substance	S° (J/K · mol)
$SO_2(g)$	248
$NiO(s)$	38
$O_2(g)$	205
$NiS(s)$	53

Solution

Since

$$\Delta S^{\circ} = \Sigma n_p S^{\circ}_{\text{products}} - \Sigma n_r S^{\circ}_{\text{reactants}}$$

$$= 2S^{\circ}_{SO_2(g)} + 2S^{\circ}_{NiO(s)} - 2S^{\circ}_{NiS(s)} - 3S^{\circ}_{O_2(s)}$$

$$= 2 \text{ mol}\left(248\frac{J}{K \cdot mol}\right) + 2 \text{ mol}\left(38\frac{J}{K \cdot mol}\right)$$

$$- 2 \text{ mol}\left(53\frac{J}{K \cdot mol}\right) - 3 \text{ mol}\left(205\frac{J}{K \cdot mol}\right)$$

$$= 496 \text{ J/K} + 76 \text{ J/K} - 106 \text{ J/K} - 615 \text{ J/K}$$

$$= -149 \text{ J/K}$$

We would expect ΔS° to be negative because the number of gaseous molecules decreases in this reaction.

Sample Exercise 16.8

Calculate ΔS° for the reduction of aluminum oxide by hydrogen gas:

$$Al_2O_3(s) + 3H_2(g) \rightarrow 2Al(s) + 3H_2O(g)$$

Use the following standard entropy values:

Substance	$S°$ (J/K · mol)
$Al_2O_3(s)$	51
$H_2(g)$	131
$Al(s)$	28
$H_2O(g)$	189

Solution

$$\Delta S° = \Sigma n_p S°_{products} - \Sigma n_r S°_{reactants}$$

$$= 2S°_{Al(s)} + 3S°_{H_2O(g)} - 3S°_{H_2(g)} - S°_{Al_2O_3(s)}$$

$$= 2 \text{ mol}\left(28\frac{J}{K \cdot mol}\right) + 3 \text{ mol}\left(189\frac{J}{K \cdot mol}\right)$$

$$- 3 \text{ mol}\left(131\frac{J}{K \cdot mol}\right) - 1 \text{ mol}\left(51\frac{J}{K \cdot mol}\right)$$

$$= 56 \text{ J/K} + 567 \text{ J/K} - 393 \text{ J/K} - 51 \text{ J/K}$$

$$= 179 \text{ J/K}$$

Vibrations

Rotation

Figure 16.6

The H_2O molecule can vibrate and rotate in several ways, some of which are shown here. This freedom of motion leads to a higher entropy for water than for a substance like hydrogen, a simple diatomic molecule with fewer possible motions.

The reaction considered in Sample Exercise 16.8 involves 3 moles of hydrogen gas on the reactant side and 3 moles of water vapor on the product side. Would you expect ΔS to be large or small for such a case? We have assumed that ΔS depends on the relative numbers of molecules of gaseous reactants and products. Based on this assumption, ΔS should be near zero for this reaction. However, ΔS is large and positive. Why is this so? The large value for ΔS results from the difference in the entropy values for hydrogen gas and water vapor. The reason for this difference can be traced to the difference in molecular structure. Because it is a nonlinear, triatomic molecule, H_2O has more rotational and vibrational motions (see Fig. 16.6) than does the diatomic H_2 molecule. Thus the standard entropy value for $H_2O(g)$ is greater than that for $H_2(g)$. Generally, *the more complex the molecule, the higher is the standard entropy value*.

16.6 Free Energy and Chemical Reactions

Purpose

- To show how to calculate the standard free energy change in a chemical reaction.
- To define the standard free energy of formation and show how to use it to predict spontaneity.

For chemical reactions we are often interested in the **standard free energy change ($\Delta G°$),** *the change in free energy that will occur if the reactants in their standard states are converted to the products in their standard states*. For example, for the ammonia synthesis reaction at 25°C,

$$N_2(g) + 3H_2(g) \rightleftharpoons 2NH_3(g) \qquad \Delta G° = -33.3 \text{ kJ} \qquad (16.1)$$

This $\Delta G°$ value represents the change in free energy when 1 mol nitrogen gas at 1 atm reacts with 3 mol hydrogen gas at 1 atm to produce 2 mol gaseous NH_3 at 1 atm.

It is important to recognize that the standard free energy change for a reaction is not measured directly. For example, we can measure heat flow in a calorimeter to determine $\Delta H°$, but we cannot measure $\Delta G°$ this way. The value of $\Delta G°$ for the ammonia synthesis in Equation (16.1) was *not* obtained by mixing 1 mol N_2 and 3 mol H_2 in a flask and measuring the change in free energy as 2 mol NH_3 formed. For one thing, if we mixed 1 mol N_2 and 3 mol H_2 in a flask, the system would go to equilibrium rather than to completion. Also, we have no instrument that measures free energy. However, while we cannot directly measure $\Delta G°$ for a reaction, we can calculate it from other measured quantities, as we will see later in this section.

> The value of $\Delta G°$ tells us nothing about the rate of a reaction, only its eventual equilibrium position.

Why is it useful to know $\Delta G°$ for a reaction? As we will see in more detail later in this chapter, knowing the $\Delta G°$ values for several reactions allows us to compare the relative tendency of these reactions to occur. The more negative the value of $\Delta G°$, the further a reaction will go to the right to reach equilibrium. We must use standard-state free energies to make this comparison because free energy varies with pressure or concentration. Thus, to get an accurate comparison of reaction tendencies, we must compare all reactions under the same pressure or concentration conditions. We will have more to say about the significance of $\Delta G°$ later.

There are several ways to calculate $\Delta G°$. One common method uses the equation

$$\Delta G° = \Delta H° - T\Delta S°$$

which applies to a reaction carried out at constant temperature. For example, for the reaction

$$C(s) + O_2(g) \rightarrow CO_2(g)$$

the values of $\Delta H°$ and $\Delta S°$ are known to be -393.5 kJ and 3.05 J/K, respectively, and $\Delta G°$ can be calculated at 298 K as follows:

$$\begin{aligned} \Delta G° &= \Delta H° - T\Delta S° \\ &= -3.935 \times 10^5 \text{ J} - (298 \text{ K})(3.05 \text{ J/K}) \\ &= -3.944 \times 10^5 \text{ J} \\ &= -394.4 \text{ kJ (per mole of } CO_2) \end{aligned}$$

Sample Exercise 16.9

Consider the reaction

$$2SO_2(g) + O_2(g) \rightarrow 2SO_3(g)$$

carried out at 25°C and 1 atm. Calculate $\Delta H°$, $\Delta S°$, and $\Delta G°$ using the following data:

Substance	$\Delta H_f°$ (kJ/mol)	$S°$ (J/K · mol)
$SO_2(g)$	−297	248
$SO_3(g)$	−396	257
$O_2(g)$	0	205

Solution

The value of $\Delta H°$ can be calculated from the enthalpies of formation using the equation we discussed in Section 6.4:

$$\Delta H° = \Sigma n_p \Delta H°_{f \text{ (products)}} - \Sigma n_r \Delta H°_{f \text{ (reactants)}}$$

Then
$$\Delta H° = 2\Delta H°_{f \text{ (SO}_3(g))} - 2\Delta H°_{f \text{ (SO}_2(g))} - \Delta H°_{f \text{ (O}_2(g))}$$
$$= 2 \text{ mol}(-396 \text{ kJ/mol}) - 2 \text{ mol}(-297 \text{ kJ/mol}) - 0$$
$$= -792 \text{ kJ} + 594 \text{ kJ}$$
$$= -198 \text{ kJ}$$

The value of $\Delta S°$ can be calculated using the standard entropy values and the equation discussed in Section 16.5:

$$\Delta S° = \Sigma n_p S°_{\text{products}} - \Sigma n_r S°_{\text{reactants}}$$

Thus

$$\Delta S° = 2S°_{\text{SO}_3(g)} - 2S°_{\text{SO}_2(g)} - S°_{\text{O}_2(g)}$$
$$= 2 \text{ mol}(257 \text{ J/K} \cdot \text{mol}) - 2 \text{ mol}(248 \text{ J/K} \cdot \text{mol}) - 1 \text{ mol}(205 \text{ J/K} \cdot \text{mol})$$
$$= 514 \text{ J/K} - 496 \text{ J/K} - 205 \text{ J/K}$$
$$= -187 \text{ J/K}$$

We would expect $\Delta S°$ to be negative since three molecules of gaseous reactants give two molecules of gaseous products.

The value of $\Delta G°$ can now be calculated from the equation

$$\Delta G° = \Delta H° - T\Delta S°$$
$$= -198 \text{ kJ} - (298 \text{ K})\left(-187\frac{\text{J}}{\text{K}}\right)\left(\frac{1 \text{ kJ}}{1000 \text{ J}}\right)$$
$$= -198 \text{ kJ} + 55.7 \text{ kJ} = -142 \text{ kJ}$$

A second method for calculating ΔG for a reaction takes advantage of the fact that, like enthalpy, *free energy is a state function*. Therefore, we can use procedures for finding ΔG that are similar to those for finding ΔH using Hess's law.

To illustrate this method for calculating the free energy change, we will obtain $\Delta G°$ for the reaction

$$2CO(g) + O_2(g) \rightarrow 2CO_2(g) \qquad (16.2)$$

from the following data:

$$2CH_4(g) + 3O_2(g) \rightarrow 2CO(g) + 4H_2O(g) \qquad \Delta G° = -1088 \text{ kJ} \quad (16.3)$$
$$CH_4(g) + 2O_2(g) \rightarrow CO_2(g) + 2H_2O(g) \qquad \Delta G° = -801 \text{ kJ} \quad (16.4)$$

Note that $CO(g)$ is a reactant in Equation (16.2). This means that Equation (16.3) must be reversed, since $CO(g)$ is a product in that reaction as written. When a reaction is reversed, the sign of $\Delta G°$ is also reversed. In Equation (16.4), $CO_2(g)$ is a product, as it is in Equation (16.2), but only one molecule of CO_2 is formed. Thus Equation (16.4) must be multiplied by 2, which means the $\Delta G°$ value for Equation (16.4) also must be multiplied by 2. Free energy is an extensive property, since it is defined by two extensive properties, H and S.

Reversed Equation (16.3)
$$2CO(g) + 4H_2O(g) \rightarrow 2CH_4(g) + 3O_2(g) \qquad \Delta G° = -(-1088 \text{ kJ})$$

2 × Equation (16.4)
$$\underline{2CH_4(g) + 4O_2(g) \rightarrow 2CO_2(g) + 4H_2O(g) \qquad \Delta G° = 2(-801 \text{ kJ})}$$
$$2CO(g) + O_2(g) \rightarrow 2CO_2(g) \qquad \Delta G° = -(-1088 \text{ kJ})$$
$$+2(-801 \text{ kJ})$$
$$= -514 \text{ kJ}$$

This example shows that the ΔG values for reactions are manipulated in exactly the same way as the ΔH values.

Sample Exercise 16.10

Using the following data (at 25°C)

$$C_{diamond}(s) + O_2(g) \rightarrow CO_2(g) \qquad \Delta G° = -397 \text{ kJ} \qquad (16.5)$$

$$C_{graphite}(s) + O_2(g) \rightarrow CO_2(g) \qquad \Delta G° = -394 \text{ kJ} \qquad (16.6)$$

calculate $\Delta G°$ for the reaction

$$C_{diamond}(s) \rightarrow C_{graphite}(s)$$

Solution

We reverse Equation (16.6) to make graphite a product, as required, and then add the new equation to Equation (16.5):

$$C_{diamond}(s) + O_2(g) \rightarrow CO_2(g) \qquad \Delta G° = -397 \text{ kJ}$$

Reversed Equation (16.6)
$$\underline{CO_2(g) \rightarrow C_{graphite}(s) + O_2(g) \qquad \Delta G° = -(-394 \text{ kJ})}$$
$$C_{diamond}(s) \rightarrow C_{graphite}(s) \qquad \Delta G° = -397 \text{ kJ} + 394 \text{ kJ}$$
$$= -3 \text{ kJ}$$

Since $\Delta G°$ is negative for this process, diamond should spontaneously change to graphite at 25°C and 1 atm. However, the reaction is so slow under these conditions that we do not observe the process. This is another example of kinetic rather than thermodynamic control of a reaction. We can say that diamond is kinetically stable with respect to graphite even though it is thermodynamically unstable.

In Sample Exercise 16.10 we saw that the process

$$C_{diamond}(s) \rightarrow C_{graphite}(s)$$

is spontaneous but very slow at 25°C and 1 atm. The reverse process can be made to occur at high temperatures and pressures. Diamond has a more compact structure and thus a higher density than graphite, so exerting very high pressure causes it to become thermodynamically favored. If high temperatures are also used to make the process fast enough to be feasible, diamonds can be made from graphite. The conditions usually used involve temperatures greater than 1000°C and pressures of about 10^5 atm. About half of all industrial diamonds are made this way.

A third method for calculating the free energy change for a reaction uses standard free energies of formation. The **standard free energy of formation (ΔG_f°)** of a substance is defined as the *change in free energy that accompanies the formation of 1 mole of that substance from its constituent elements with all reactants and products in their standard states.* For the formation of glucose ($C_6H_{12}O_6$), the appropriate reaction is

The standard state of an element is its most stable state at 25°C and 1 atm.

$$6C(s) + 6H_2(g) + 3O_2(g) \rightarrow C_6H_{12}O_6(s)$$

The standard free energy associated with this process is called the *free energy of formation of glucose.* Values of the standard free energy of formation are useful in calculating ΔG° for specific chemical reactions using the equation

Calculating ΔG° is very similar to calculating ΔH°, as shown in Section 6.4.

$$\Delta G^\circ = \Sigma n_p \Delta G_f^\circ \text{ (products)} - \Sigma n_r \Delta G_f^\circ \text{ (reactants)}$$

Values of ΔG_f° for many common substances are listed in Appendix 4. Note that, analogous to the enthalpy of formation, *the standard free energy of formation of an element in its standard state is zero.* Also note that the number of moles of each reactant (n_r) and product (n_p) must be used when calculating ΔG° for a reaction.

Sample Exercise 16.11

Methanol is a high-octane fuel used in high-performance racing engines. Calculate ΔG° for the reaction

$$2CH_3OH(g) + 3O_2(g) \rightarrow 2CO_2(g) + 4H_2O(g)$$

given the following free energies of formation:

Substance	ΔG_f° (kJ/mol)
$CH_3OH(g)$	−163
$O_2(g)$	0
$CO_2(g)$	−394
$H_2O(g)$	−229

Solution

We use the equation

$$\Delta G^\circ = \Sigma n_p \Delta G_f^\circ \text{ (products)} - \Sigma n_r \Delta G_f^\circ \text{ (reactants)}$$

$$= 2\Delta G_f^\circ {}_{(CO_2(g))} + 4\Delta G_f^\circ {}_{(H_2O(g))} - 3\Delta G_f^\circ {}_{(O_2(g))} - 2\Delta G_f^\circ {}_{(CH_3OH(g))}$$

$$= 2 \text{ mol}(-394 \text{ kJ/mol}) + 4 \text{ mol}(-229 \text{ kJ/mol}) - 3(0) - 2 \text{ mol}(-163 \text{ kJ/mol})$$

$$= -1378 \text{ kJ}$$

The large magnitude and the negative sign of ΔG° indicate that this reaction is very favorable thermodynamically.

Sample Exercise 16.12

A chemical engineer wants to determine the feasibility of making ethanol (C_2H_5OH) by reacting water with ethylene (C_2H_4) according to the equation

$$C_2H_4(g) + H_2O(l) \rightarrow C_2H_5OH(l)$$

Is this reaction spontaneous under standard conditions?

Solution

To determine the spontaneity of this reaction under standard conditions, we must determine $\Delta G°$ for the reaction. We can do this using standard free energies of formation at 25°C from Appendix 4:

$$\Delta G°_{f\,(C_2H_5OH(l))} = -175 \text{ kJ/mol}$$
$$\Delta G°_{f\,(H_2O(l))} = -237 \text{ kJ/mol}$$
$$\Delta G°_{f\,(C_2H_4(g))} = 68 \text{ kJ/mol}$$

Then
$$\Delta G° = \Delta G°_{f\,(C_2H_5OH(l))} - \Delta G°_{f\,(H_2O(l))} - \Delta G°_{f\,(C_2H_4(g))}$$
$$= -175 \text{ kJ} - (-237 \text{ kJ}) - 68 \text{ kJ}$$
$$= -6 \text{ kJ}$$

Thus the process is spontaneous under standard conditions at 25°C.

Although the reaction considered in Sample Exercise 16.12 is spontaneous, other features of the reaction must be studied to see if the process is feasible. For example, the chemical engineer will need to study the kinetics of the reaction to determine whether it is fast enough to be useful and, if it is not, whether a catalyst can be found to enhance the rate. In doing these studies, the engineer must remember that $\Delta G°$ depends on temperature:

$$\Delta G° = \Delta H° - T\Delta S°$$

Thus, if the process must be carried out at high temperatures to be fast enough to be feasible, $\Delta G°$ must be recalculated at that temperature from the $\Delta H°$ and $\Delta S°$ values for the reaction.

16.7 The Dependence of Free Energy on Pressure

Purpose

• To relate free energy to pressure.

In this chapter we have seen that a system at constant temperature and pressure will proceed spontaneously in the direction that lowers its free energy. This is why reactions proceed until they reach equilibrium. As we will see later in this section, *the equilibrium position represents the lowest free energy value available to a particular reaction system.* The free energy of a reaction system changes as the reaction proceeds, because free energy is dependent on the pressure of a gas or on the concentration of species in solution. We will deal only with the pressure dependence of the free energy of an ideal gas. The dependence of free energy on concentration can be developed using similar reasoning.

To understand the pressure dependence of free energy, we need to know how pressure affects the thermodynamic functions that comprise free energy, that is, enthalpy and entropy (recall that $G = H - TS$). For an ideal gas, enthalpy is not pressure-dependent. However, entropy *does* depend on pressure because of its dependence on volume. Consider 1 mole of an ideal gas at a given temperature. At a volume of 10.0 L, the gas has many more positions available for its molecules than if its volume is 1.0 L. The positional entropy is greater in the larger volume. In summary, at a given temperature for 1 mole of ideal gas

$$S_{\text{large volume}} > S_{\text{small volume}}$$

or, since pressure and volume are inversely related,

$$S_{\text{low pressure}} > S_{\text{high pressure}}$$

We have shown qualitatively that the entropy and therefore the free energy of an ideal gas depend on its pressure. Using a more detailed argument, which we will not consider here, it can be shown that

$$G = G° + RT \ln(P)$$

where $G°$ is the free energy of the gas at a pressure of 1 atm, G is the free energy of the gas at a pressure of P atm, R is the universal gas constant, and T is the Kelvin temperature.

To see how the change in free energy for a reaction depends on pressure, we will consider the ammonia synthesis reaction

$$N_2(g) + 3H_2(g) \rightarrow 2NH_3(g)$$

In general,
$$\Delta G = \Sigma n_p G_{\text{products}} - \Sigma n_r G_{\text{reactants}}$$

For this reaction
$$\Delta G = 2G_{\text{NH}_3} - G_{\text{N}_2} - 3G_{\text{H}_2}$$

where
$$G_{\text{NH}_3} = G°_{\text{NH}_3} + RT \ln(P_{\text{NH}_3})$$
$$G_{\text{N}_2} = G°_{\text{N}_2} + RT \ln(P_{\text{N}_2})$$
$$G_{\text{H}_2} = G°_{\text{H}_2} + RT \ln(P_{\text{H}_2})$$

See Appendix 1.2 if you need a review of logarithms.

Substituting these values into the equation gives

$$\Delta G = 2[G°_{\text{NH}_3} + RT \ln(P_{\text{NH}_3})] - [G°_{\text{N}_2} + RT \ln(P_{\text{N}_2})] - 3[G°_{\text{H}_2} + RT \ln(P_{\text{H}_2})]$$
$$= 2G°_{\text{NH}_3} - G°_{\text{N}_2} - 3G°_{\text{H}_2} + 2RT \ln(P_{\text{NH}_3}) - RT \ln(P_{\text{N}_2}) - 3RT \ln(P_{\text{H}_2})$$
$$= \underbrace{(2G°_{\text{NH}_3} - G°_{\text{N}_2} - 3G°_{\text{H}_2})}_{\Delta G° \text{ reaction}} + RT[2 \ln(P_{\text{NH}_3}) - \ln(P_{\text{N}_2}) - 3 \ln(P_{\text{H}_2})]$$

The first term in parentheses is $\Delta G°$ for the reaction. Thus we have

$$\Delta G = \Delta G°_{\text{reaction}} + RT[2 \ln(P_{\text{NH}_3}) - \ln(P_{\text{N}_2}) - 3 \ln(P_{\text{H}_2})]$$

and since
$$2 \ln(P_{\text{NH}_3}) = \ln(P_{\text{NH}_3}{}^2)$$

$$-\ln(P_{N_2}) = \ln\left(\frac{1}{P_{N_2}}\right)$$

$$-3 \ln(P_{H_2}) = \ln\left(\frac{1}{P_{H_2}{}^3}\right)$$

the equation becomes

$$\Delta G = \Delta G^\circ + RT \ln\left(\frac{P_{NH_3}{}^2}{(P_{N_2})(P_{H_2}{}^3)}\right)$$

But the term
$$\frac{P_{NH_3}{}^2}{(P_{N_2})(P_{H_2}{}^3)}$$

is the reaction quotient Q discussed in Section 13.5. Therefore, we have

$$\Delta G = \Delta G^\circ + RT \ln(Q)$$

where Q is the reaction quotient (from the law of mass action), T is the temperature (K), R is the gas law constant and is equal to $8.3145 \text{ J/K} \cdot \text{mol}$, ΔG° is the free energy change for the reaction with all reactants and products at a pressure of 1 atm, and ΔG is the free energy change for the reaction for the specified pressures of reactants and products.

Sample Exercise 16.13

One method for synthesizing methanol (CH_3OH) involves reacting carbon monoxide and hydrogen gases:

$$CO(g) + 2H_2(g) \rightarrow CH_3OH(l)$$

Calculate ΔG at 25°C for this reaction where carbon monoxide gas at 5.0 atm and hydrogen gas at 3.0 atm are converted to liquid methanol.

Solution

To calculate ΔG for this process, we use the equation

$$\Delta G = \Delta G^\circ + RT \ln(Q)$$

We must first compute ΔG° from standard free energies of formation (see Appendix 4). Since

$$\Delta G^\circ_{f\ (CH_3OH(l))} = -166 \text{ kJ}$$
$$\Delta G^\circ_{f\ (H_2(g))} = 0$$
$$\Delta G^\circ_{f\ (CO(g))} = -137 \text{ kJ}$$
$$\Delta G^\circ = -166 \text{ kJ} - (-137 \text{ kJ}) - 0 = -29 \text{ kJ} = -2.9 \times 10^4 \text{ J}$$

Note that this is the value of ΔG° for the reaction of 1 mol CO with 2 mol H_2 to produce 1 mol CH_3OH. We might call this the value of ΔG° for one "round" of the reaction or for one mole of the reaction. Thus the ΔG° value might better be written as -2.9×10^4 J/mol of reaction or -2.9×10^4 J/mol rxn.

We can now calculate ΔG using

$$\Delta G^\circ = -2.9 \times 10^4 \text{ J/mol rxn}$$

$$R = 8.3145 \text{ J/K} \cdot \text{mol}$$

$$T = 273 + 25 = 298 \text{ K}$$

$$Q = \frac{1}{(P_{CO})(P_{H_2}^2)} = \frac{1}{(5.0)(3.0)^2} = 2.2 \times 10^{-2}$$

Note in this case that ΔG is defined for "one mole of the reaction," that is, for 1 mol $CO(g)$ reacting with 2 mol $H_2(g)$ to form 1 mol $CH_3OH(l)$. Thus ΔG, $\Delta G°$, and $RT \ln(Q)$ all have units of J/mol of reaction. In this case the units of R are actually J/K · mol of reaction, although they are usually not written this way.

Note that the pure liquid methanol is not included in the calculation of Q. Then

$$\Delta G = \Delta G° + RT \ln(Q)$$

$$= (-2.9 \times 10^4 \text{ J/mol rxn}) + (8.3145 \text{ J/K} \cdot \text{mol rxn})(298 \text{ K}) \ln(2.2 \times 10^{-2})$$

$$= (-2.9 \times 10^4 \text{ J/mol rxn}) - (9.4 \times 10^3 \text{ J/mol rxn}) = -3.8 \times 10^4 \text{ J/mol rxn}$$

$$= -38 \text{ kJ/mol rxn}$$

Note that ΔG is significantly more negative than $\Delta G°$, implying that the reaction is more spontaneous at reactant pressures greater than 1 atm. We might expect this result from Le Châtelier's principle.

The Meaning of ΔG for a Chemical Reaction

In this section we have learned to calculate ΔG for chemical reactions under various conditions. For example, in Sample Exercise 16.13 the calculations show that the formation of $CH_3OH(l)$ from $CO(g)$ at 5.0 atm reacting with $H_2(g)$ at 3.0 atm is spontaneous. What does this result mean? Does it mean that if we mixed 1.0 mol $CO(g)$ and 2.0 mol $H_2(g)$ together at pressures of 5.0 and 3.0 atm, respectively, that 1.0 mol $CH_3OH(l)$ would form in the reaction flask? The answer is no. This answer may surprise you in view of what has been said in this section. It is true that 1.0 mol $CH_3OH(l)$ has a lower free energy than 1.0 mol $CO(g)$ at 5.0 atm plus 2.0 mol $H_2(g)$ at 3.0 atm. However, when $CO(g)$ and $H_2(g)$ are mixed under these conditions, there is *an even lower free energy available to this system than 1.0 mol pure $CH_3OH(l)$*. For reasons we will discuss shortly, *the system can achieve the lowest possible free energy by going to equilibrium, not by going to completion.* At the equilibrium position, some of the $CO(g)$ and $H_2(g)$ will remain in the reaction flask. So even though 1.0 mol pure $CH_3OH(l)$ is at a lower free energy than 1.0 mol $CO(g)$ and 2.0 mol $H_2(g)$ at 5.0 and 3.0 atm, respectively, the reaction system will stop short of forming 1.0 mol $CH_3OH(l)$. The reaction stops short of completion because the equilibrium mixture of $CH_3OH(l)$, $CO(g)$, and $H_2(g)$ exists at the lowest possible free energy available to the system.

To illustrate this point, we will explore a mechanical example. Consider balls rolling down the two hills shown in Fig. 16.7. Note that in both cases point B has a lower potential energy than point A.

In Fig 16.7(a) the ball will roll to point B. This diagram is analogous to a phase change. For example, at 25°C ice will spontaneously change completely to liquid water, because the latter has the lowest free energy. In this case liquid water is the only choice. There is no intermediate substance with lower free energy.

The situation is different for a chemical reaction system, as illustrated in Fig. 16.7(b). In Fig. 16.7(b) the ball will not get to point B because there is a lower potential energy at point C. Like the ball, a chemical system will seek the *lowest possible* free energy, which, for reasons we will discuss below, is the equilibrium position.

Figure 16.7

Schematic representations of balls rolling down two types of hills.

(a)

(b)

Therefore, although the value of ΔG for a given reaction system tells us whether the products or reactants are favored under a given set of conditions, it does not mean that the system will proceed to pure products (if ΔG is negative) or remain at pure reactants (if ΔG is positive). Instead, the system will spontaneously go to the equilibrium position, the lowest possible free energy available to it. In the next section we will see that the value of $\Delta G°$ for a particular reaction tells us exactly where this position will be.

16.8 Free Energy and Equilibrium

Purpose

- To define equilibrium in terms of minimum free energy.
- To show how the value of K is related to $\Delta G°$.

When the components of a given chemical reaction are mixed, they will proceed, rapidly or slowly depending on the kinetics of the process, to the equilibrium position. In Chapter 13 we defined the equilibrium position as the point at which the forward and reverse reaction rates are equal. In this chapter we look at equilibrium from a thermodynamic point of view, and we find that *the equilibrium point occurs at the lowest value of free energy available to the reaction system*. As it turns out, the two definitions give the same equilibrium state, which must be the case for both the kinetic and thermodynamic models to be valid.

To understand the relationship of free energy to equilibrium, let's consider the following simple hypothetical reaction:

$$A(g) \rightleftharpoons B(g)$$

where 1.0 mole of gaseous A is initially placed in a reaction vessel at a pressure of 2.0 atm. The free energies for A and B are diagrammed as shown in Fig. 16.8(a). As A reacts to form B, the total free energy of the system changes, yielding the following results:

$$\text{Free energy of A} = G_A = G_A° + RT \ln(P_A)$$
$$\text{Free energy of B} = G_B = G_B° + RT \ln(P_B)$$
$$\text{Total free energy of system} = G = G_A + G_B$$

As A changes to B, G_A will decrease because P_A is decreasing [Fig. 16.8(b)]. In contrast, G_B will increase because P_B is increasing. The reaction will proceed to the

(a)

(b)

(c)

Figure 16.8

(a) The initial free energies of A and B. (b) As A(g) changes to B(g), the free energy of A decreases and that of B increases. (c) Eventually, pressures of A and B are achieved such that $G_A = G_B$, the equilibrium position.

right as long as the total free energy of the system decreases (as long as G_B is less than G_A). At some point the pressures of A and B reach the values P_A^e and P_B^e that make G_A equal to G_B. *The system has reached equilibrium* [Fig. 16.8(c)]. Since A at pressure P_A^e and B at pressure P_B^e have the same free energy (G_A equals G_B), ΔG is zero for A at pressure P_A^e changing to B at pressure P_B^e. *The system has reached minimum free energy.* There is no longer any driving force to change A to B or B to A, so the system remains at this position (the pressures of A and B remain constant).

Suppose that for the experiment described above the plot of free energy versus the mole fraction of A reacted is defined as shown in Fig. 16.9(a). In this experiment, minimum free energy is reached when 75% of A has been changed to B. At this point, the pressure of A is 0.25 times the original pressure, or

$$(0.25)(2.0 \text{ atm}) = 0.50 \text{ atm}$$

The pressure of B is

$$(0.75)(2.0 \text{ atm}) = 1.5 \text{ atm}$$

Since this is the equilibrium position, we can use the equilibrium pressures to calculate a value for K for the reaction in which A is converted to B at this temperature:

$$K = \frac{P_B^e}{P_A^e} = \frac{1.5 \text{ atm}}{0.50 \text{ atm}} = 3.0$$

Exactly the same equilibrium point would be achieved if we placed 1.0 mol pure B(g) in the flask at a pressure of 2.0 atm. In this case B would change to A until equilibrium ($G_B = G_A$) is reached. This is shown in Fig. 16.9(b).

The overall free energy curve for this system is shown in Fig. 16.9(c). Note that any mixture of A(g) and B(g) containing 1.0 mol (A plus B) at a total pressure of 2.0 atm will react until it reaches the minimum in the curve.

In summary, when substances undergo a chemical reaction, the reaction proceeds to the minimum free energy (equilibrium), which corresponds to the point where $G_{\text{products}} = G_{\text{reactants}}$ or

$$\Delta G = G_{\text{products}} - G_{\text{reactants}} = 0$$

For the reaction A(g) $\rightleftharpoons$ B(g), the pressure is always constant during the reaction, since the same number of gas molecules is always present.

(a)   (b)   (c)

Figure 16.9

(a) The change in free energy to reach equilibrium beginning with 1.0 mol A(g) at P_A = 2.0 atm. (b) The change in free energy to reach equilibrium, beginning with 1.0 mol B(g) at P_B = 2.0 atm. (c) The free energy profile for A(g) $\rightleftharpoons$ B(g) in a system containing 1.0 mol (A plus B) at P_{TOTAL} = 2.0 atm. Each point on the curve corresponds to the total free energy of the system for a given combination of A and B.

We can now establish a quantitative relationship between free energy and the value of the equilibrium constant. We have seen that

$$\Delta G = \Delta G° + RT \ln(Q)$$

and at equilibrium ΔG equals 0 and Q equals K.

So

$$\Delta G = 0 = \Delta G° + RT \ln(K)$$

or

$$\Delta G° = -RT \ln(K)$$

We must note the following characteristics of this very important equation.

Case 1: $\Delta G° = 0$. When $\Delta G°$ equals zero for a particular reaction, the free energies of the reactants and products are equal when all components are in the standard states (1 atm for gases). The system is at equilibrium when the pressures of all reactants and products are 1 atm, which means that K equals 1.

Case 2: $\Delta G° < 0$. In this case $\Delta G°$ ($G°_{products} - G°_{reactants}$) is negative, which means that

$$G°_{products} < G°_{reactants}$$

If a flask contains the reactants and products, all at 1 atm, the system will *not* be at equilibrium. Since $G°_{products}$ is less than $G°_{reactants}$, the system will adjust to the right to reach equilibrium. In this case K will be *greater than 1,* since the pressures of the products at equilibrium will be greater than 1 atm and the pressures of the reactants at equilibrium will be less than 1 atm.

Case 3: $\Delta G° > 0$. Since $\Delta G°$ ($G°_{products} - G°_{reactants}$) is positive,

$$G°_{reactants} < G°_{products}$$

If a flask contains the reactants and products, all at 1 atm, the system will *not* be at equilibrium. In this case the system will adjust to the left (toward the reactants, which have a lower free energy) to reach equilibrium. The value of K will be *less than 1,* since at equilibrium the pressures of the reactants will be greater than 1 atm and the pressures of the products will be less than 1 atm.

These results are summarized in Table 16.6. The value of K for a specific reaction can be calculated from the equation

$$\Delta G° = -RT \ln(K)$$

as is shown in Sample Exercises 16.14 and 16.15.

Table 16.6	
Qualitative Relationship between the Change in Standard Free Energy and the Equilibrium Constant for a Given Reaction	
$\Delta G°$	K
$\Delta G° = 0$	$K = 1$
$\Delta G° < 0$	$K > 1$
$\Delta G° > 0$	$K < 1$

Sample Exercise 16.14

Consider the ammonia synthesis reaction

$$N_2(g) + 3H_2(g) \rightleftharpoons 2NH_3(g)$$

where $\Delta G° = -33.3$ kJ per mole of N_2 consumed at 25°C. For each of the following mixtures of reactants and products at 25°C, predict the direction in which the system will shift to reach equilibrium.

a. $P_{NH_3} = 1.00$ atm, $P_{N_2} = 1.47$ atm, $P_{H_2} = 1.00 \times 10^{-2}$ atm
b. $P_{NH_3} = 1.00$ atm, $P_{N_2} = 1.00$ atm, $P_{H_2} = 1.00$ atm

Solution

a. We can predict the direction of reaction to equilibrium by calculating the value of ΔG using the equation

$$\Delta G = \Delta G° + RT \ln(Q)$$

where

$$Q = \frac{P_{NH_3}{}^2}{(P_{N_2})(P_{H_2}{}^3)} = \frac{(1.00)^2}{(1.47)[(1.00 \times 10^{-2})^3]} = 6.80 \times 10^5$$

$$T = 25 + 273 = 298 \text{ K}$$

$$R = 8.3145 \text{ J/K} \cdot \text{mol}$$

and

$$\Delta G° = -33.3 \text{ kJ/mol} = -3.33 \times 10^4 \text{ J/mol}$$

Then

$$\Delta G = (-3.33 \times 10^4 \text{ J}) + (8.3145 \text{ J/K} \cdot \text{mol})(298 \text{ K}) \ln(6.8 \times 10^5)$$

$$= (-3.33 \times 10^4 \text{ J/mol}) + (3.33 \times 10^4 \text{ J/mol}) = 0$$

Since $\Delta G = 0$, the reactants and products have the same free energies at these partial pressures. The system is already at equilibrium, and no shift will occur.

The units of ΔG, $\Delta G°$, and $RT \ln(Q)$ all refer to the balanced reaction with all amounts expressed in moles. We might say that the units are joules per "mole of reaction," although only the "per mole" is indicated for R (as is customary).

b. The partial pressures given here are all 1.00 atm, which means that the system is in the standard state. That is,

$$\Delta G = \Delta G° + RT \ln(Q) = \Delta G° + RT \ln\frac{(1.00)^2}{(1.00)(1.00)^3}$$

$$= \Delta G° + RT \ln(1.00) = \Delta G° + 0 = \Delta G°$$

For this reaction at 25°C,

$$\Delta G° = -33.3 \text{ kJ/mol}$$

The negative value for $\Delta G°$ means that in their standard states the products have a lower free energy than the reactants. Thus the system will move to the right to reach equilibrium. That is, K is greater than 1.

Sample Exercise 16.15

The overall reaction for the corrosion (rusting) of iron by oxygen is

$$4Fe(s) + 3O_2(g) \rightleftharpoons 2Fe_2O_3(s)$$

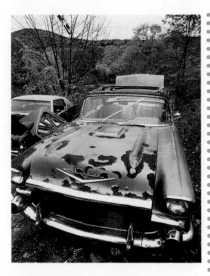

Formation of rust on bare steel is a spontaneous process.

Using the following data, calculate the equilibrium constant for this reaction at 25°C.

Substance	ΔH_f° (kJ/mol)	S° (J/K · mol)
$Fe_2O_3(s)$	−826	90
$Fe(s)$	0	27
$O_2(g)$	0	205

Solution

To calculate K for this reaction we will use the equation

$$\Delta G^\circ = -RT \ln(K)$$

We must first calculate ΔG° from

$$\Delta G^\circ = \Delta H^\circ - T\Delta S^\circ$$

where

$$\begin{aligned}
\Delta H^\circ &= 2\Delta H_{f\,(Fe_2O_3(s))}^\circ - 3\Delta H_{f\,(O_2(g))}^\circ - 4\Delta H_{f\,(Fe(s))}^\circ \\
&= 2 \text{ mol}(-826 \text{ kJ/mol}) - 0 - 0 \\
&= -1652 \text{ kJ} = -1.652 \times 10^6 \text{ J} \\
\Delta S^\circ &= 2S_{Fe_2O_3}^\circ - 3S_{O_2}^\circ - 4S_{Fe}^\circ \\
&= 2 \text{ mol}(90 \text{ J/K} \cdot \text{mol}) - 3 \text{ mol}(205 \text{ J/K} \cdot \text{mol}) - 4 \text{ mol}(27 \text{ J/K} \cdot \text{mol}) \\
&= -543 \text{ J/K}
\end{aligned}$$

and $T = 273 + 25 = 298$ K

Then $\Delta G^\circ = \Delta H^\circ - T\Delta S^\circ = (-1.652 \times 10^6 \text{ J}) - (298 \text{ K})(-543 \text{ J/K})$
$$= -1.490 \times 10^6 \text{ J}$$

and

$$\Delta G^\circ = -RT \ln(K) = -1.490 \times 10^6 \text{ J} = -(8.3145 \text{ J/K} \cdot \text{mol})(298 \text{ K}) \ln(K)$$

Thus $$\ln(K) = \frac{1.490 \times 10^6}{2.48 \times 10^3} = 601$$

and $K = e^{601}$

In terms of base 10, $K = 10^{261}$

This is a very large equilibrium constant. The rusting of iron is clearly very favorable from a thermodynamic point of view.

The Temperature Dependence of K

In Chapter 13 we used Le Châtelier's principle to predict qualitatively how the value of K for a given reaction would change with a change in temperature. Now we can specify the quantitative dependence of the equilibrium constant on temperature from the relationship

$$\Delta G^\circ = -RT \ln(K) = \Delta H^\circ - T\Delta S^\circ$$

We can rearrange this equation to give

$$\ln(K) = -\frac{\Delta H°}{RT} + \frac{\Delta S°}{R} = -\frac{\Delta H°}{R}\left(\frac{1}{T}\right) + \frac{\Delta S°}{R}$$

Note that this is a linear equation of the form $y = mx + b$, where $y = \ln(K)$, $m = -\Delta H°/R$ = slope, $x = 1/T$, and $b = \Delta S°/R$ = intercept. This means that if values of K for a given reaction are determined at various temperatures, a plot of $\ln(K)$ versus $1/T$ will be linear, with slope $-\Delta H°/R$ and intercept $\Delta S°/R$. This result assumes that both $\Delta H°$ and $\Delta S°$ are independent of temperature over the temperature range considered. This assumption is a good approximation over a relatively small temperature range.

16.9 Free Energy and Work

Purpose

• To relate work done to the change in free energy.

One of the main reasons we are interested in physical and chemical processes is that we want to use them to do work for us, and we want this work done as efficiently and economically as possible. We have already seen that at constant temperature and pressure, the sign of the change in free energy tells us whether a given process is spontaneous or not. This is very useful information because it prevents us from wasting effort on a process that has no inherent tendency to occur. Although a thermodynamically favorable chemical reaction may not occur to any appreciable extent because it is too slow, it makes sense in this case to try to find a catalyst to speed up the reaction. On the other hand, if the reaction is prevented from occurring by its thermodynamic characteristics, we would be wasting our time looking for a catalyst.

In addition to its qualitative usefulness (telling us whether a process is spontaneous), the change in free energy is important quantitatively because it can tell us how much work can be done with a given process. In fact, the *maximum possible useful work obtainable from a process at constant temperature and pressure is equal to the change in free energy:*

$$w_{\max} = \Delta G$$

This relationship explains why this function is called the *free* energy. Under certain conditions, ΔG for a spontaneous process represents the energy that is *free to do useful work*. On the other hand, for a process that is not spontaneous, the value of ΔG tells us the minimum amount of work that must be *expended* to make the process occur.

Knowing the value of ΔG for a process thus gives us valuable information about how close the process is to 100% efficiency. For example, when gasoline is burned in a car's engine, the work produced is about 20% of the maximum work available.

For reasons we will only briefly introduce in this book, the amount of work we actually obtain from a spontaneous process is *always* less than the maximum possible amount.

To explore this idea more fully, let's consider an electric current flowing through the starter motor of a car. The current is generated from a chemical change in a battery, and we can calculate ΔG for the battery reaction and so determine the energy available to do work. Can we use all this energy to do work? No, because a current flowing through a wire causes frictional heating, and the greater the current, the greater the heat. This heat represents wasted energy—it is not useful for running the starter motor. We can minimize this energy waste by running very low currents through the motor circuit. However, zero current flow would be necessary to eliminate frictional heating entirely, and we cannot derive any work from the motor if no current flows. This represents the difficulty in which nature places us. Using a process to do work requires that some of the energy be wasted, and usually the faster we run the process, the more energy we waste.

Achieving the maximum work available from a spontaneous process can only occur via a hypothetical pathway. Any real pathway wastes energy. If we could discharge the battery infinitely slowly by an infinitesimal current flow, we would achieve the maximum useful work. Also, if we could then recharge the battery using an infinitesimally small current, exactly the same amount of energy would be used to return the battery to its original state. After we cycle the battery in this way, the universe (the system and surroundings) is exactly the same as it was before the cyclic process. This is a **reversible process** (see Fig. 16.10).

However, if the battery is discharged to run the starter motor and then recharged using a *finite* current flow, as is the case in reality, *more* work will always be required to recharge the battery than the battery produces as it discharges. This means that even though the battery (the system) has returned to its original state, the surroundings has not, because the surroundings had to furnish a net amount of work as the battery was cycled. The *universe is different* after this cyclic process is performed, and this function is called an **irreversible process.** *All real processes are irreversible.*

Figure 16.10

A battery can do work by sending current to a starter motor. The battery can then be recharged by forcing current through it in the opposite direction. If the current flow in both processes is infinitesimally small, $w_1 = w_2$. This is a *reversible process.* But if the current flow is finite, as it would be in any real case, $w_2 > w_1$. This is an *irreversible process* (the *universe is different* after the cyclic process occurs). All real processes are irreversible.

In general, after any real cyclic process is carried out in a system, the surroundings have less ability to do work and contain more thermal energy. In other words, *in any real cyclic process in the system, work is changed to heat in the surroundings, and the entropy of the universe increases*. This is another way of stating the second law of thermodynamics.

Thus thermodynamics tells us the work potential of a process and then tells us that we can never achieve this potential. In this spirit, thermodynamicist Henry Bent has paraphrased the first two laws of thermodynamics as follows:

First law: You can't win, you can only break even.

Second law: You can't break even.

The ideas we have discussed in this section are applicable to the energy crisis that will probably increase in severity over the next 25 years. The crisis is obviously not one of supply; the first law tells us that the universe contains a constant supply of energy. The problem is the availability of *useful* energy. *As we use energy, we degrade its usefulness.* For example, when gasoline reacts with oxygen in the combustion reaction, the change in potential energy results in heat flow. Thus the energy concentrated in the bonds of the gasoline and oxygen molecules ends up *spread* over the surroundings as thermal energy, where it is much more difficult to harness for useful work. This is a way in which the entropy of the universe increases: concentrated energy becomes spread out—more disordered and less useful. Thus the crux of the energy problem is that we are rapidly consuming the concentrated energy found in fossil fuels. It took millions of years to concentrate the sun's energy in these fuels, and we will consume these same fuels in a few hundred years. Thus we must consider carefully our use of these energy sources and use them as wisely as possible.

> When energy is used to do work, it becomes less organized and less concentrated, and thus less useful.

FOR REVIEW

Summary

The first law of thermodynamics, which states that the energy of the universe is constant, gives us no clue as to why a particular process occurs in a given direction. A process is said to be spontaneous if it occurs without outside intervention. The driving force for a spontaneous process is described in terms of entropy (S). Entropy is a thermodynamic function that can be viewed as a measure of randomness, or disorder. It describes the number of arrangements (positions and/or energy levels) available to a system existing in a given state. Nature spontaneously proceeds toward states that have the highest probabilities of occurring. The second law of thermodynamics states that for any spontaneous process there is always an increase in the entropy of the universe. Using entropy, thermodynamics predicts the direction in which a process will occur. However, it cannot predict the rate at which the process will occur; this must be done using the principles of kinetics.

We can predict whether a process is spontaneous by considering the entropy changes that occur in the system and the surroundings:

$$\Delta S_{univ} = \Delta S_{sys} + \Delta S_{surr}$$

For a process at constant temperature and pressure, ΔS_{sys} is dominated by changes in positional entropy, and ΔS_{surr} is determined by heat flow:

$$\Delta S_{surr} = -\frac{\Delta H}{T}$$

The sign of ΔS_{surr} depends on the direction of the heat flow: ΔS_{surr} is positive for an exothermic process and negative for an endothermic process. The magnitude of ΔS_{surr}, however, depends on both the quantity of energy that flows as heat and the temperature at which the energy is transferred. Thus the significance of exothermicity as a driving force for a process depends on the temperature at which the process occurs.

For a chemical reaction, entropy changes in the system are dominated by the change in the number of gaseous molecules. Fewer gaseous molecules on the product side means a decrease in entropy, and vice versa. Molecular structure also plays a role. In general, a complex molecule has a higher standard entropy than a simpler one.

The third law of thermodynamics states that the entropy of a perfect crystal at 0 K is zero. Above this temperature the molecules will begin to vibrate, and disorder will occur.

Free energy (G) is a thermodynamic function defined by the relationship

$$G = H - TS$$

A process occurring at constant temperature and pressure is spontaneous in the direction in which the free energy decreases.

The standard free energy change ($\Delta G°$) is the change in free energy that will occur if the reactants in their standard states are converted to the products in their standard states. Since free energy is a state function, we can use procedures similar to those used with Hess's law to calculate $\Delta G°$, for example,

$$\Delta G° = \Sigma n_p \Delta G°_{f \text{ (products)}} - \Sigma n_r \Delta G°_{f \text{ (reactants)}}$$

where $\Delta G°_f$, the standard free energy of formation of a substance, is the change in free energy accompanying the formation of one mole of that substance from its constituent elements with all reactants and products in their standard states. The standard free energy of formation of an element in its standard state is zero.

Free energy depends on pressure according to the equation

$$G = G° + RT \ln(P)$$

The ΔG value for a reaction at conditions other than standard conditions can be calculated from

$$\Delta G = \Delta G° + RT \ln(Q)$$

where Q is the reaction quotient.

The equilibrium position for a chemical reaction occurs where the free energy is the minimum value available to the system. The relationship between $\Delta G°$ and the equilibrium constant K is

$$\Delta G° = -RT \ln(K)$$

When $\Delta G°$ is equal to zero, the system is at equilibrium with the products and reactants in their standard states ($K = 1$). When $\Delta G°$ is less than zero, then $G°_{products}$

is less than $G°_{reactants}$, and the system will adjust to the right from standard conditions to attain equilibrium (K is greater than 1). When $\Delta G°$ is greater than zero, $G°_{reactants}$ is less than $G°_{products}$, and the system will shift to the left from standard conditions to attain equilibrium (K is less than 1).

The maximum possible useful work obtainable from a process at constant temperature and pressure is equal to the change in free energy:

$$w_{max} = \Delta G$$

In any real process, the actual work obtained is less than w_{max}. When energy is used to do work, the total energy of the universe remains constant, but it is rendered less useful. After being used to do work, concentrated energy is spread out in the surroundings as thermal energy, and this is the crux of our energy problem.

Key Terms

Section 16.1
spontaneous process
entropy
positional probability

Section 16.2
second law of thermodynamics

Section 16.4
free energy

Section 16.5
third law of thermodynamics

Section 16.6
standard free energy change
standard free energy of formation

Section 16.8
equilibrium (thermodynamic definition)

Section 16.9
reversible process
irreversible process

A blue question or exercise number indicates that the answer to that question or exercise appears at the back of this book and a solution appears in the Solutions Guide.

Questions

1. Define what is meant by a spontaneous process.

2. a. Define entropy.
   b. Is entropy a form of energy?

3. Describe how the following changes affect the positional entropy of a substance.
   a. Increase in volume of a gas at constant T
   b. Increase in temperature of a gas at constant V
   c. Increase in pressure of a gas at constant T

4. Define the following:
   a. System
   b. Surroundings

5. The synthesis of glucose directly from CO_2 and H_2O and the synthesis of proteins directly from amino acids are both nonspontaneous processes under standard conditions. Yet it is necessary for these to occur in order for life to exist. In light of the second law of thermodynamics, how can life exist?

6. If you calculate a value for $\Delta G°$ for a reaction using the values of $\Delta G°_f$ in Appendix 4 and get a negative number, is it correct to say that the reaction is always spontaneous?

7. When the environment is contaminated by a toxic or potentially toxic substance (for example, from a chemical spill or the use of insecticides), the substance tends to disperse. How is this consistent with the second law of thermodynamics? In terms of the second law, which requires the least work: cleaning the environment after it has been contaminated or trying to prevent the contamination before it occurs? Explain.

8. Entropy has been described as "time's arrow." Interpret this view of entropy.

Exercises

In this section similar exercises are paired.

Spontaneity and Entropy

9. Which of the following processes require energy as they occur?
   a. Salt dissolves in H_2O.
   b. A clear solution becomes a uniform color after a few drops of dye are added.
   c. A cell produces proteins from amino acids.
   d. Iron rusts.

10. Which of the following processes require energy as they occur?
   a. A house is built.
   b. A satellite is launched into orbit.
   c. A satellite falls back to earth.
   d. Natural gas is burned in the air.

11. Consider the following energy levels, each capable of holding two objects:

   $$E = 2 \text{ kJ} \underline{\hspace{2cm}}$$

   $$E = 1 \text{ kJ} \underline{\hspace{2cm}}$$

   $$E = 0 \quad \underline{\text{ XX }}$$

   Draw all the possible arrangements of the two identical particles (represented by X) in the three energy levels. What total energy is most likely, that is, occurs the greatest number of times? Assume that the particles are indistinguishable from each other.

12. Do Exercise 11 with two particles, A and B, which can be distinguished from each other.

13. Do Exercise 11 assuming that each level can hold three indistinguishable particles, X.

14. Do Exercise 11 assuming that each level can hold three objects and that there are three particles (A, B, and C), which can be distinguished from each other.

15. Which of the following involve an increase in the entropy of the system?
   a. Melting of a solid
   b. Evaporation of a liquid
   c. Sublimation
   d. Freezing

16. Which of the following involve an increase in the entropy of the system?
   a. Mixing
   b. Separation
   c. Diffusion
   d. Precipitation of a solid from a solution

17. Choose the compound with the greatest positional entropy in each case.
   a. 1 mol H_2 (at STP) or 1 mol N_2O (at STP)
   b. 1 mol H_2 (at STP) or 1 mol H_2 (at 100°C, 0.5 atm)
   c. 1 mol N_2 (at STP) or 1 mol N_2 (at 100 K, 2.0 atm)
   d. 1 mol $H_2O(s)$ (at 0°C) or 1 mol $H_2O(l)$ (at 20°C)

18. Choose the substance with the greater positional entropy in each case.
   a. 1 mol He (at 10 K, 1 atm) or 1 mol He (at 10°C, 1 atm)
   b. 1 mol He (at 500°C, 1 atm) or 1 mol He (at 500°C, 2 atm)
   c. 1 mol He (at STP) or 1 mol He (at 200 K, 2 atm)
   d. 1 mol He(s) (at 0 K) or 1 mol He(g) (at 5 K)

Entropy and the Second Law of Thermodynamics: Free Energy

19. For each of the following pairs of substances, which substance has the greater value of $S°$?
   a. Glucose ($C_6H_{12}O_6$) or sucrose ($C_{12}H_{22}O_{11}$)
   b. H_2O (at 0 K) or H_2O (at 0°C)
   c. $H_2O(l)$ (at 25°C) or $H_2S(g)$ (at 25°C)

20. For each of the following pairs, which substance has the greater value of $S°$?
   a. N_2O (at 0 K) or He (at 10 K)
   b. $N_2O(g)$ (at 1 atm, at 25°C) or He(g) (at 1 atm, at 25°C)
   c. HF(g) (at 1 atm, at 25°C) or HCl(g) (at 1 atm, at 25°C)

21. Predict the sign of $\Delta S°$ for each of the following changes.
    a.

    b. $AgCl(s) \rightarrow Ag^+(aq) + Cl^-(aq)$
    c. $2H_2(g) + O_2(g) \rightarrow 2H_2O(l)$

22. Predict the sign of $\Delta S°$ for each of the following changes.
    a. $Na(s) + \frac{1}{2}Cl_2(g) \rightarrow NaCl(s)$
    b. $N_2(g) + 3H_2(g) \rightarrow 2NH_3(g)$
    c. $NaCl(s) \rightarrow Na^+(aq) + Cl^-(aq)$

23. Calculate $\Delta S°$ for each of the following reactions.
    a. $H_2(g) + \frac{1}{2}O_2(g) \rightarrow H_2O(g)$
    b. $3O_2(g) \rightarrow 2O_3(g)$
    c. $N_2(g) + O_2(g) \rightarrow 2NO(g)$

24. Calculate $\Delta S°$ for each of the following reactions.
    a. $H_2(g) + \frac{1}{2}O_2(g) \rightarrow H_2O(l)$
    b. $N_2(g) + 3H_2(g) \rightarrow 2NH_3(g)$
    c. $HCl(g) \rightarrow H^+(aq) + Cl^-(aq)$

25. For the reaction

    $$CS_2(g) + 3O_2(g) \rightarrow CO_2(g) + 2SO_2(g)$$

    $\Delta S°$ is equal to -143 J/K. Use this value and data from Appendix 4 to calculate the value of $S°$ for $CS_2(g)$.

26. For the reaction

    $$2Al(s) + 3Br_2(l) \rightarrow 2AlBr_3(s)$$

    $\Delta S°$ is equal to -144 J/K. Use this value and data from Appendix 4 to calculate the value of $S°$ for solid aluminum bromide.

27. Given the values of ΔH and ΔS, which of the following changes will be spontaneous at constant T and P?
    a. $\Delta H = +25$ kJ, $\Delta S = +5$ J/K, $T = 300$ K
    b. $\Delta H = +25$ kJ, $\Delta S = +100$ J/K, $T = 300$ K
    c. $\Delta H = -10$ kJ, $\Delta S = +5$ J/K, $T = 298$ K
    d. $\Delta H = -10$ kJ, $\Delta S = -40$ J/K, $T = 200$ K

28. Given the values of ΔH and ΔS, which of the following changes will be spontaneous at constant temperature and pressure?
    a. $\Delta H = -10$ kJ, $\Delta S = -40$ J/K, $T = 300$ K
    b. $\Delta H = -10$ kJ, $\Delta S = -40$ J/K, $T = 500$ K
    c. $\Delta H = +5$ kJ, $\Delta S = -5$ J/K, $T = 10$ K
    d. $\Delta H = +5$ kJ, $\Delta S = -5$ J/K, $T = 1000$ K

29. The boiling point of chloroform ($CHCl_3$) is 61.7°C. The enthalpy of vaporization is 31.4 kJ/mol. Calculate the entropy of vaporization.

30. For mercury, the enthalpy of vaporization is 58.51 kJ/mol and the entropy of vaporization is 92.92 J/K · mol. What is the normal boiling point of mercury?

Free Energy and Chemical Reactions

31. From data in Appendix 4, calculate $\Delta H°$, $\Delta S°$, and $\Delta G°$ for each of the following reactions at 25°C.
    a. $CH_4(g) + 2O_2(g) \rightarrow CO_2(g) + 2H_2O(g)$
    b. $6CO_2(g) + 6H_2O(l) \rightarrow C_6H_{12}O_6(s) + 6O_2(g)$
       Glucose
    c. $P_4O_{10}(s) + 6H_2O(l) \rightarrow 4H_3PO_4(s)$
    d. $HCl(g) + NH_3(g) \rightarrow NH_4Cl(s)$

32. Acrylonitrile is the starting material used in the manufacture of acrylic fibers (U.S. production capacity is more than 2 million pounds). Three industrial processes for the production of acrylonitrile are given below. Using data from Appendix 4, calculate $\Delta S°$, $\Delta H°$, and $\Delta G°$ for each process. For part a, assume that $T = 25°C$; for part b, $T = 70°C$; and for part c, $T = 700°C$.
    a. $CH_2{-}CH_2(g) + HCN(g) \rightarrow CH_2{=}CHCN(g) + H_2O(l)$
       $\backslash_{O}\diagup$
       Ethylene oxide   Acrylonitrile

    b. $HC{\equiv}CH(g) + HCN(g) \xrightarrow[70-90°C]{CaCl_2 \cdot HCl} CH_2{=}CHCN(g)$

    c. $4CH_2{=}CHCH_3(g) + 6NO(g)$

       $\xrightarrow[Ag]{700°C} 4CH_2{=}CHCN(g) + 6H_2O(g) + N_2(g)$

33. For the reaction

$$SF_4(g) + F_2(g) \rightarrow SF_6(g)$$

the value of $\Delta G°$ is -374 kJ. Use this value and data from Appendix 4 to calculate the value of $\Delta G_f°$ for $SF_4(g)$.

34. The value of $\Delta G°$ for the reaction

$$2Al(OH)_3(s) \rightarrow Al_2O_3(s) + 3H_2O(g)$$

is $+7$ kJ. Use this value and data from Appendix 4 to calculate the value of the standard free energy of formation of aluminum hydroxide.

35. Two crystalline forms of white phosphorus are known. Both forms contain P_4 molecules, but the molecules are packed together in different ways. The α form is always obtained when the liquid freezes. However, below $-76.9°C$, the α form spontaneously converts to the β form:

$$P_4(s, \alpha) \rightarrow P_4(s, \beta)$$

a. Predict the signs of ΔH and ΔS for this process.
b. Predict which form of phosphorus has the more ordered crystalline structure.

36. When most biologic enzymes are heated they lose their catalytic activity. The change

Original enzyme $\rightarrow$ new form

that occurs upon heating is endothermic and spontaneous. Is the structure of the original enzyme or its new form more ordered? Explain.

37. For the reaction

$$H_2(g) \rightarrow 2H(g)$$

a. Predict the signs of ΔH and ΔS.
b. Would the reaction be more spontaneous at high or low temperatures?

38. Hydrogen cyanide is produced industrially by the following reaction:

$$2NH_3(g) + 3O_2(g) + 2CH_4(g) \xrightarrow[\text{Pt-Rh}]{1000°C}$$
$$2HCN(g) + 6H_2O(g)$$

Is the high temperature needed for thermodynamic, or kinetic, reasons?

39. One of the reactions that destroys ozone in the upper atmosphere is

$$NO(g) + O_3(g) \rightleftharpoons NO_2(g) + O_2(g)$$

Using data from Appendix 4, calculate $\Delta G°$ and K (at 298 K) for this reaction.

40. Hydrogen sulfide can be removed from natural gas by the reaction

$$2H_2S(g) + SO_2(g) \rightleftharpoons 3S(s) + 2H_2O(g)$$

Calculate $\Delta G°$ and K (at 298 K) for this reaction. Would this reaction be favored at a high or low temperature?

41. a. The autoionization of water at $25°C$,

$$H_2O(l) \rightleftharpoons H^+(aq) + OH^-(aq)$$

has the equilibrium constant 1.00×10^{-14}. Calculate $\Delta G°$ for this process at $25°C$.
b. At $40°C$, $K_w = 2.92 \times 10^{-14}$. Calculate $\Delta G°$ at $40.°C$.

42. The Ostwald process for the commercial production of nitric acid involves three steps:

$$4NH_3(g) + 5O_2(g) \xrightarrow[825°C]{Pt} 4NO(g) + 6H_2O(g)$$
$$2NO(g) + O_2(g) \rightarrow 2NO_2(g)$$
$$3NO_2(g) + H_2O(l) \rightarrow 2HNO_3(l) + NO(g)$$

a. Calculate $\Delta H°$, $\Delta S°$, $\Delta G°$, and K (at 298 K) for each of the three steps in the Ostwald process (see Appendix 4).
b. Calculate the equilibrium constant for the first step at $825°C$.
c. What is the reason for the high temperature in the first step?

Free Energy and Pressure

43. Calculate ΔG for the reaction

$$NO(g) + O_3(g) \rightarrow NO_2(g) + O_2(g)$$

for these conditions:

$$T = 298 \text{ K}$$

$$P_{NO} = 1.00 \times 10^{-6} \text{ atm}, \; P_{O_3} = 2.00 \times 10^{-6} \text{ atm}$$

$$P_{NO_2} = 1.00 \times 10^{-7} \text{ atm}, \; P_{O_2} = 1.00 \times 10^{-3} \text{ atm}$$

For $\Delta G°$ use your answer from Exercise 39.

44. Calculate ΔG for the reaction

$$2H_2S(g) + SO_2(g) \rightleftharpoons 3S(s) + 2H_2O(g)$$

for the following conditions at 25°C:

$$P_{H_2S} = 1.0 \times 10^{-4} \text{ atm}$$

$$P_{SO_2} = 1.0 \times 10^{-2} \text{ atm}$$

$$P_{H_2O} = 3.0 \times 10^{-2} \text{ atm}$$

See Exercise 40 for $\Delta G°$.

45. Using data from Appendix 4, calculate $\Delta H°$, $\Delta S°$, and K (at 298 K) for the synthesis of ammonia by the Haber process:

$$N_2(g) + 3H_2(g) \rightleftharpoons 2NH_3(g)$$

Calculate ΔG for this reaction under the following conditions (assume an uncertainty of ± 1 in all quantities):
a. $T = 298$ K, $P_{N_2} = P_{H_2} = 200$ atm, $P_{NH_3} = 50$ atm
b. $T = 298$ K, $P_{N_2} = 200$ atm, $P_{H_2} = 600$ atm, $P_{NH_3} = 200$ atm
c. $T = 100$ K, $P_{N_2} = 50$ atm, $P_{H_2} = 200$ atm, $P_{NH_3} = 10$ atm
d. $T = 700$ K, $P_{N_2} = 50$ atm, $P_{H_2} = 200$ atm, $P_{NH_3} = 10$ atm

46. Consider the following reaction:

$$H_2O(g) + Cl_2O(g) \rightleftharpoons 2HOCl(g) \qquad K_{298} = 0.090$$

For $Cl_2O(g)$,

$$\Delta G_f° = 97.9 \text{ kJ/mol}$$

$$\Delta H_f° = 80.3 \text{ kJ/mol}$$

$$S° = 266.1 \text{ J/K} \cdot \text{mol}$$

a. Calculate $\Delta G°$ for the reaction using the equation $\Delta G° = -RT \ln(K)$.
b. Use bond energy values (Table 8.4) to estimate $\Delta H°$ for the reaction.
c. Use the results from parts a and b to estimate $\Delta S°$ for the reaction.
d. Estimate $\Delta H_f°$ and $S°$ for $HOCl(g)$. (Assume that these values are unavailable from tabulated data.)
e. Estimate the value of K at 500 K.
f. Estimate ΔG at 25°C when $P_{H_2O} = 18$ torr, $P_{Cl_2O} = 2.0$ torr, and $P_{HOCl} = 0.10$ torr.

47. A rough rule of thumb is that for a chemical reaction

$$\Delta S° \approx 100(\Delta n)$$

where Δn is the change in the number of moles of gaseous components and $\Delta S°$ has units of J/K.
a. Use this approximation and the values of bond energies (Table 8.4) to estimate $\Delta S°$, $\Delta H°$, and $\Delta G°$ for the reaction

$$CO(g) + 2H_2(g) \rightleftharpoons CH_3OH(g)$$

b. Compare the above values with those calculated from thermodynamic data in Appendix 4.
c. If you were to propose using this reaction on an industrial scale, would you choose a high or low temperature?

48. Acrylic acid ($CH_2{=}CHCO_2H$) is an important monomer in the chemical industry. One method for the production of acrylic acid is the reaction of carbon monoxide with ethylene oxide:

a. Use bond energies (Table 8.4) and the approximation given in Exercise 47 to estimate $\Delta H°$, $\Delta S°$, and $\Delta G°$ for this reaction.
b. Under what temperature conditions should this reaction be run?

Additional Exercises

49. In rolling two dice, what *total* number is the most likely to occur? Is there an energy reason why this number is favored? Would energy have to be spent to increase the probability of getting a particular number (that is, to cheat)?

50. Using the second law of thermodynamics and the following relationships

$$\Delta S_{univ} = \Delta S_{sys} + \Delta S_{surr}$$

$$\Delta S_{surr} = -\frac{\Delta H}{T}$$

$$\Delta G = \Delta H - T\Delta S$$

show that $\Delta G < 0$ for a spontaneous process at constant temperature and pressure. (The unlabeled quantities refer to the system as usual.)

51. The melting point of tungsten is the second highest among the elements (only that of carbon is higher). The melting point of tungsten is 3650 K. The enthalpy of fusion is 35.23 kJ/mol. What is the entropy of fusion?

52. Elemental sulfur can exist in two crystalline forms, rhombic and monoclinic. Calculate the temperature for the conversion of monoclinic sulfur to rhombic sulfur given the following data:

	ΔH_f° (kJ/mol)	S° (J/K · mol)
S (rhombic)	0	31.88
S (monoclinic)	0.30	32.55

53. A green plant synthesizes glucose by photosynthesis, as shown in the reaction

$$6CO_2(g) + 6H_2O(l) \rightarrow C_6H_{12}O_6(s) + 6O_2(g)$$

Animals use glucose as a source of energy:

$$C_6H_{12}O_6(s) + 6O_2(g) \rightarrow 6CO_2(g) + 6H_2O(l)$$

If we were to assume that both these processes occur to the same extent in a cyclic process, what thermodynamic property must have a nonzero value?

54. Consider two reactions for the production of ethanol:

$$C_2H_4(g) + H_2O(g) \rightarrow CH_3CH_2OH(l)$$
$$C_2H_6(g) + H_2O(g) \rightarrow CH_3CH_2OH(l) + H_2(g)$$

Which would be the more thermodynamically feasible? Why?

55. Using data from Appendix 4, calculate ΔH°, ΔS°, and ΔG° for the following reactions that produce acetic acid:

$$CH_4(g) + CO_2(g) \rightarrow CH_3\overset{\overset{\displaystyle O}{\|}}{C}-OH(l)$$

$$CH_3OH(g) + CO(g) \rightarrow CH_3\overset{\overset{\displaystyle O}{\|}}{C}-OH(l)$$

Which reaction would you choose as a commercial method for producing acetic acid (CH_3CO_2H)? What temperature conditions would you choose for the reaction?

56. In the text we derived the equation

$$\Delta G = \Delta G^\circ + RT \ln(Q)$$

for gaseous reactions where the quantities in Q were expressed in units of pressure. We can also use units of mol/L for the quantities in Q. With this in mind, calculate ΔG for the reaction

$$H_2O(l) \rightleftharpoons H^+(aq) + OH^-(aq)$$

under the following conditions at 25°C.
a. $[H^+] = [OH^-] = 1.00 \times 10^{-7}$ M
b. $[H^+] = 1.00 \times 10^{-5}$ M, $[OH^-] = 1.00 \times 10^{-9}$ M
c. $[H^+] = [OH^-] = 1.00 \times 10^{-10}$ M
d. $[H^+] = 10.0$ M, $[OH^-] = 1.00 \times 10^{-7}$ M
e. $[H^+] = 1.00$ M, $[OH^-] = 1.00$ M

See Exercise 41 for the ΔG° value. Based on the calculated ΔG values, in what direction will the system shift to equilibrium for each of the five sets of conditions? Are these results consistent with Le Châtelier's principle?

57. Many biochemical reactions that occur in cells require relatively high concentrations of potassium ion (K^+). The concentration of K^+ in muscle cells is about 0.15 M. The concentration of K^+ in blood plasma is about 0.0050 M. The high internal concentration in cells is maintained by pumping K^+ from the plasma. How much work must be done to transport 1.0 mol K^+ from the blood to the inside of a muscle cell at 37°C, normal body temperature? When 1.0 mol K^+ is transferred from blood to the cells, do any other ions have to be transported? Why or why not? Much of the ATP (see Exercise 65) formed from metabolic processes is used in providing energy for transport of cellular components. How much ATP must be hydrolyzed to provide the energy for the transport of 1.0 mol K^+?

58. Comment on how this refrain from a popular song might be taken as a statement of the second law of thermodynamics.

> And the seasons they go 'round and 'round,
> And the painted ponies go up and down.
> We're captive on the carousel of time.
> We can't return; we can only look behind
>   from where we came,
> And go 'round and 'round and 'round in the
>   circle game.

("The Circle Game" by Joni Mitchell, © 1966 & 1974 Siquomb Publishing Corp. All rights reserved. Used by permission.)

59. The lines from T. S. Eliot's "The Hollow Men" (V)

> . . . this is the way the world ends—
>   not with a bang, but a whimper

have been said by some to describe the eventual heat death of the universe. Comment on this view.
(Excerpt from "The Hollow Men" in *Collected Poems 1909–1962* by T. S. Eliot, copyright 1936 by Harcourt Brace Jovanovich, Inc.; copyright © 1963, 1964 by T. S. Eliot. Reprinted by permission of the publisher.)

60. Human DNA contains almost twice as much information as is needed to code for all the substances produced in the body.

Likewise, the digital data sent from Voyager II contained one redundant bit out of every two bits of information. The Hubble space telescope transmits three redundant bits for every bit of information. How is entropy related to the transmission of information? What do you think is accomplished by having so many redundant bits of information in both DNA and the space probes?

Challenge Problems

61. Entropy can be calculated by a relationship proposed by Ludwig Boltzmann:

$$S = k \ln(W)$$

where $k = 1.38 \times 10^{-23}$ J/K and W is the number of ways a particular state can be obtained. (This equation is engraved on Boltzmann's tombstone.) Calculate S for the three arrangements of particles in Table 16.1.

62. Using the relationships $\Delta G° = \Delta H° - T\Delta S° = -RT \ln(K)$ derive the equation

$$\ln(K) = -\frac{\Delta H°}{RT} + \frac{\Delta S°}{R}$$

Show that for a system at equilibrium the equilibrium will shift to the right for an endothermic process when the temperature is increased.

63. Use the equation you derived in Exercise 62 to determine $\Delta H°$ and $\Delta S°$ for the autoionization of water:

$$H_2O(l) \rightleftharpoons H^+(aq) + OH^-(aq)$$

T (°C)	K_w
0	1.14×10^{-15}
25	1.00×10^{-14}
35	2.09×10^{-14}
40	2.92×10^{-14}
50	5.47×10^{-14}

64. a. Using the free energy profile for a simple one-step reaction, show that at equilibrium $K = k_f/k_r$, where k_f and k_r are the rate constants for the forward and reverse reactions. *Hint:* Use the relationship $\Delta G° = -RT \ln(K)$ and represent k_f and k_r using the Arrhenius equation ($k = Ae^{-E_a/RT}$).

b. Why is the following statement false? "A catalyst can increase the rate of a forward reaction but not the rate of the reverse reaction."

65. Cells use the hydrolysis of adenosine triphosphate, abbreviated as ATP, as a source of energy. Symbolically, this reaction can be written as

$$ATP + H_2O \rightarrow ADP + H_2PO_4^-$$

where ADP represents adenosine diphosphate. For this reaction, $\Delta G° = -30.5$ kJ/mol.
a. Calculate K at 25°C.
b. If all the free energy from the metabolism of glucose

$$C_6H_{12}O_6(s) + 6O_2(g) \rightarrow 6CO_2(g) + 6H_2O(l)$$

goes into ATP, how many ATP molecules can be produced for every molecule of glucose?

66. Carbon monoxide is toxic because it binds much more strongly to the iron in hemoglobin than does O_2. The equilibrium constant for the binding of CO is about two hundred times that for the binding of O_2. That is, for the reactions

$$(heme)Fe + O_2 \underset{}{\overset{K_{O_2}}{\rightleftharpoons}} (heme)Fe - O_2$$

$$(heme)Fe + CO \underset{}{\overset{K_{CO}}{\rightleftharpoons}} (heme)Fe - CO$$

$K_{CO}/K_{O_2} = 2.1 \times 10^2$. Calculate the difference in $\Delta G°$ for the binding of CO and O_2 to hemoglobin at 25°C.

67. For the dissociation of the hydrogen halides in aqueous solution:

$$HX(aq) \rightarrow H^+(aq) + X^-(aq)$$

the following entropy changes apply:

HX	ΔS_{diss} (J/K · mol)
HF	−88
HCl	−54
HBr	−38
HI	−13

Explain why ΔS_{diss} is negative in all cases, and rationalize the observed order.

68. The standard entropy of vaporization of water is greater than that of a "typical" liquid. Give a possible explanation.

69. Consider the reaction

$$H_2(g) + Br_2(g) \rightleftharpoons 2HBr(g)$$

where $\Delta H° = -103.8$ kJ/mol. In a particular experiment, equal moles of $H_2(g)$ at 1.0 atm and $Br_2(g)$ at 1.0 atm were mixed in a 1.0-L flask at 25°C and allowed to reach equilibrium. Then the molecules of H_2 at equilibrium were counted using a very sensitive technique, and 1.10×10^{13} molecules were found. For this reaction, calculate the values of K, $\Delta G°$, and $\Delta S°$.

CHAPTER 17

Electrochemistry

E lectrochemisty constitutes one of the most important interfaces between chemistry and everyday life. Every time you start your car, turn on your calculator, look at your digital watch, or listen to a radio at the beach, you are depending on electrochemical reactions. Our society sometimes seems to run almost entirely on batteries. Certainly the advent of small, dependable batteries along with silicon-chip technology has made possible the tiny calculators, tape recorders, and clocks that we take for granted.

Electrochemistry is important in other less obvious ways. For example, the corrosion of iron, which has tremendous economic implications, is an electrochemical process. In addition, many important industrial materials such as aluminum, chlorine, and sodium hydroxide are prepared by electrolytic processes. In analytical chemistry, electrochemical techniques employ electrodes that are specific for a given molecule or ion, such as H^+ (pH meters), F^-, Cl^-, and many others. These increasingly important methods are used to analyze for trace pollutants in natural waters or for the tiny quantities of chemicals in human blood that may signal the development of a specific disease.

Electrochemistry is best defined as *the study of the interchange of chemical and electrical energy*. It is primarily concerned with two processes that involve oxidation–reduction reactions: the generation of an electric current from a spontaneous chemical reaction and the opposite process, the use of a current to produce chemical change.

< The electrolysis of water produces elemental hydrogen and oxygen.

811

17.1 Galvanic Cells

Purpose

- To review oxidation and reduction.
- To define the components of an electrochemical cell.
- To distinguish between a galvanic and an electrolytic cell.
- To define cell potentials.

As we discussed in detail in Section 4.9, an **oxidation–reduction (redox) reaction** involves a transfer of electrons from the **reducing agent** to the **oxidizing agent.** Recall that **oxidation** involves a *loss of electrons* (an increase in oxidation number) and that **reduction** involves a *gain of electrons* (a decrease in oxidation number).

To understand how a redox reaction can be used to generate a current, let's consider the reaction between MnO_4^- and Fe^{2+}:

$$8H^+(aq) + MnO_4^-(aq) + 5Fe^{2+}(aq) \rightarrow Mn^{2+}(aq) + 5Fe^{3+}(aq) + 4H_2O(l)$$

In this reaction, Fe^{2+} is oxidized and MnO_4^- is reduced; electrons are transferred from Fe^{2+} (the reducing agent) to MnO_4^- (the oxidizing agent).

It is useful to break a redox reaction into **half-reactions,** one involving oxidation and one involving reduction. For the reaction above, the half-reactions are

Reduction: $\qquad 8H^+ + MnO_4^- + 5e^- \rightarrow Mn^{2+} + 4H_2O$

Oxidation: $\qquad 5(Fe^{2+} \rightarrow Fe^{3+} + e^-)$

Balancing half-reactions is discussed in Section 4.10.

The multiplication of the second half-reaction by 5 indicates that this reaction must occur five times for each time the first reaction occurs. The balanced overall reaction is the sum of the half-reactions.

When MnO_4^- and Fe^{2+} are present in the same solution, the electrons are transferred directly when the reactants collide. Under these conditions, no useful work is obtained from the chemical energy involved in the reaction, which instead is released as heat. How can we harness this energy? The key is to separate the oxidizing agent from the reducing agent, thus requiring the electron transfer to occur through a wire. The current produced in the wire by the electron flow can then be directed through a device, such as an electric motor, to provide useful work.

For example, consider the system illustrated in Fig. 17.1. If our reasoning has been correct, electrons should flow through the wire from Fe^{2+} to MnO_4^-. How-

Figure 17.1

Schematic of a method to separate the oxidizing and reducing agents of a redox reaction. (The solutions also contain counter ions to balance the charge.)

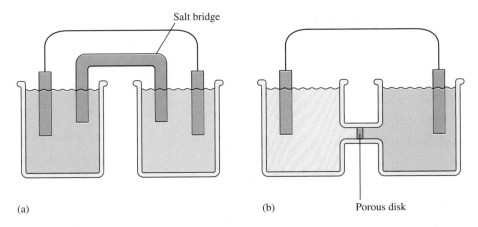

ever, when we construct the apparatus as shown, no flow of electrons is apparent. Why? Careful observation shows that when we connect the wires from the two compartments, current flows for an instant and then ceases. The current stops flowing because of charge buildups in the two compartments. If electrons flowed from the right to the left compartment in the apparatus as shown, the left compartment (receiving electrons) would become negatively charged, and the right compartment (losing electrons) would become positively charged. Creating a charge separation of this type requires a large amount of energy. Thus sustained electron flow cannot occur under these conditions.

However, we can solve this problem very simply. The solutions must be connected so that ions can flow to keep the net charge in each compartment zero. This connection might involve a **salt bridge** (a U-tube filled with an electrolyte) or a **porous disk** in a tube connecting the two solutions (see Fig. 17.2). Either of these devices allows ion flow without extensive mixing of the solutions. When we make the provision for ion flow, the circuit is complete. Electrons flow through the wire from reducing agent to oxidizing agent, and ions flow from one compartment to the other to keep the net charge zero.

We now have covered all the essential characteristics of a **galvanic cell,** *a device in which chemical energy is changed to electrical energy*. (The opposite process is called **electrolysis** and will be considered in Section 17.7.)

The reaction in an electrochemical cell occurs at the interface between the electrode and the solution where the electron transfer occurs. The electrode compartment in which *oxidation* occurs is called the **anode;** the electrode compartment in which *reduction* occurs is called the **cathode** (see Fig. 17.3).

A galvanic cell uses a spontaneous redox reaction to produce a current that can be used to do work.

Oxidation occurs at the anode. Reduction occurs at the cathode.

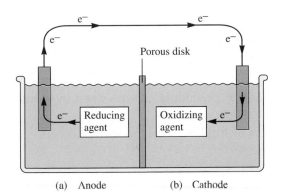

Figure 17.3

An electrochemical process involves electron transfer at the interface between the electrode and the solution. (a) The species in solution acting as the reducing agent supplies electrons to the anode. (b) The species in solution acting as the oxidizing agent receives electrons from the cathode.

Digital
voltmeter

Figure 17.4
Digital voltmeters draw only a negligible current and are convenient to use.

A volt is 1 joule of work per coulomb of charge transferred: 1 V = 1 J/C.

Cell Potential

A galvanic cell consists of an oxidizing agent in one compartment that pulls electrons through a wire from a reducing agent in the other compartment. The "pull," or driving force, on the electrons is called the **cell potential** ($\mathscr{E}_{cell}$), or the **electromotive force** (emf) of the cell. The unit of electrical potential is the **volt** (abbreviated V), which is defined as 1 joule of work per coulomb of charge transferred.

How can we measure the cell potential? One possible instrument is a crude **voltmeter,** which works by drawing current through a known resistance. However, when current flows through a wire, the frictional heating that occurs wastes some of the potentially useful energy of the cell. A traditional voltmeter will therefore measure a potential that is less than the maximum cell potential. The key to determining the maximum potential is to do the measurement under conditions of zero current so that no energy is wasted. Traditionally, this has been accomplished by inserting a variable-voltage device (powered from an external source) in *opposition* to the cell potential. The voltage on this instrument (called a **potentiometer**) is adjusted until no current flows in the cell circuit. Under such conditions, the cell potential is equal in magnitude and opposite in sign to the voltage setting of the potentiometer. This value represents the *maximum* cell potential, since no energy is wasted heating the wire. More recently, advances in electronic technology have allowed the design of *digital voltmeters* that draw only a negligible amount of current (see Fig. 17.4). Since these instruments are more convenient to use, they have replaced potentiometers in the modern laboratory.

17.2 Standard Reduction Potentials

Purpose

- To describe how standard reduction potentials are assigned in terms of the standard hydrogen electrode.
- To demonstrate the combination of half-reactions to form the cell reaction.
- To characterize a galvanic cell.

(a)

Figure 17.5

(a) A galvanic cell involving the reactions $Zn \rightarrow Zn^{2+} + 2e^-$ (at the anode) and $2H^+ + 2e^- \rightarrow H_2$ (at the cathode) has a potential of 0.76 V. (b) The standard hydrogen electrode where $H_2(g)$ at 1 atm is passed over a platinum electrode in contact with 1 M H^+ ions. This electrode process (assuming ideal behavior) is arbitrarily assigned a value of exactly zero volts.

The reaction in a galvanic cell is always an oxidation–reduction reaction that can be broken down into two half-reactions. It would be convenient to assign a potential to *each* half-reaction so that when we construct a cell from a given pair of half-reactions, we can obtain the cell potential by summing the half-cell potentials. For example, the observed potential for the cell shown in Fig. 17.5(a) is 0.76 V, and the cell reaction* is

$$2H^+(aq) + Zn(s) \rightarrow Zn^{2+}(aq) + H_2(g)$$

For this cell, the anode compartment contains a zinc metal electrode with Zn^{2+} and SO_4^{2-} ions in aqueous solution. The anode reaction is the oxidation half-reaction:

$$Zn \rightarrow Zn^{2+} + 2e^-$$

The zinc metal, in producing Zn^{2+} ions that go into solution, is giving up electrons, which flow through the wire. For now, we will assume that all cell components are in their standard states, so in this case the solution in the anode compartment will contain 1 M Zn^{2+}. The cathode reaction of this cell is the reduction half-reaction:

$$2H^+ + 2e^- \rightarrow H_2$$

The cathode consists of a platinum electrode (used because it is a chemically inert conductor) in contact with 1 M H^+ ions and bathed by hydrogen gas at 1 atm. Such an electrode, called the **standard hydrogen electrode,** is shown in Fig. 17.5(b).

Although we can measure the *total* potential of this cell (0.76 V), there is no way to measure the potentials of the individual electrode processes. Thus, if we want potentials for the half-reactions (half-cells), we must arbitrarily divide the total cell potential. For example, if we assign the reaction

$$2H^+ + 2e^- \rightarrow H_2$$

where

$$[H^+] = 1 \ M \quad \text{and} \quad P_{H_2} = 1 \text{ atm}$$

The name **galvanic cell** honors Luigi Galvani (1737–1798), an Italian scientist generally credited with the discovery of electricity. These cells are sometimes called **voltaic cells** after Alessandro Volta (1745–1827), another Italian, who first constructed cells of this type around 1800.

*In this text we will follow the convention of indicating the physical states of the reactants and products only in the overall redox reaction. For simplicity, half-reactions will *not* include the physical states.

Copper being plated onto the copper metal cathode on the right, and zinc dissolving from the zinc metal anode on the left. Note the porous disk in the tube connecting the two solutions, which allows the ion flow to balance the electron flow through the wire.

a potential of exactly zero volts, then the reaction

$$Zn \rightarrow Zn^{2+} + 2e^-$$

will have a potential of 0.76 V because

$$\mathscr{E}^\circ_{cell} = \mathscr{E}^\circ_{H^+ \rightarrow H_2} + \mathscr{E}^\circ_{Zn \rightarrow Zn^{2+}}$$
$$\quad\quad 0.76\ V \quad\quad 0\ V \quad\quad 0.76\ V$$

Standard states were discussed in Section 6.4.

where the superscript ° indicates that *standard states* are employed. In fact, by setting the standard potential for the half-reaction $2H^+ + 2e^- \rightarrow H_2$ equal to zero, we can assign values to all other half-reactions.

For example, the measured potential for the cell shown in Fig. 17.6 is 1.10 V. The cell reaction is

$$Zn(s) + Cu^{2+}(aq) \rightarrow Zn^{2+}(aq) + Cu(s)$$

which can be divided into the half-reactions

Anode: $\quad Zn \rightarrow Zn^{2+} + 2e^-$

Cathode: $\quad Cu^{2+} + 2e^- \rightarrow Cu$

Then $\quad\quad \mathscr{E}^\circ_{cell} = \mathscr{E}^\circ_{Zn \rightarrow Zn^{2+}} + \mathscr{E}^\circ_{Cu^{2+} \rightarrow Cu}$

Figure 17.6

A galvanic cell involving the half-reactions $Zn \rightarrow Zn^{2+} + 2e^-$ (anode) and $Cu^{2+} + 2e^- \rightarrow Cu$ (cathode), with $\mathscr{E}^\circ_{cell} = 1.10$ V.

Since $\mathcal{E}^{\circ}_{Zn\rightarrow Zn^{2+}}$ was earlier assigned a value of 0.76 V, the value of $\mathcal{E}^{\circ}_{Cu^{2+}\rightarrow Cu}$ must be 0.34 V because

$$1.10 \text{ V} = 0.76 \text{ V} + 0.34 \text{ V}$$

The scientific community has universally accepted the half-reaction potentials based on the assignment of zero volts to the process $2H^+ + 2e^- \rightarrow H_2$ (under standard conditions where ideal behavior is assumed). However, before we can use these values to calculate cell potentials, we need to understand several essential characteristics of half-cell potentials.

The accepted convention is to give the potentials of half-reactions as *reduction* processes, for example:

$$2H^+ + 2e^- \rightarrow H_2$$
$$Cu^{2+} + 2e^- \rightarrow Cu$$
$$Zn^{2+} + 2e^- \rightarrow Zn$$

The $\mathcal{E}^{\circ}$ values corresponding to reduction half-reactions with all solutes at 1 M and all gases at 1 atm are called **standard reduction potentials.** Standard reduction potentials for the most common half-reactions are given in Table 17.1 and Appendix 5.5.

Combining two half-reactions to obtain a balanced oxidation–reduction reaction often requires two manipulations:

1. One of the reduction half-reactions must be reversed (since redox reactions must involve a substance being oxidized and a substance being reduced), which means that the *sign* of the potential for the reversed half-reaction also must be *reversed*.

2. Since the number of electrons lost must equal the number gained, the half-reactions must be multiplied by integers as necessary to achieve the balanced equation. However, the *value of $\mathcal{E}^{\circ}$ is not changed* when a half-reaction is multiplied by an integer. Since a standard reduction potential is an *intensive property* (it does not depend on how many times the reaction occurs), the potential is *not* multiplied by the integer required to balance the cell reaction.

Consider a galvanic cell based on the redox reaction

$$Fe^{3+}(aq) + Cu(s) \rightarrow Cu^{2+}(aq) + Fe^{2+}(aq)$$

The pertinent half-reactions are

$$Fe^{3+} + e^- \rightarrow Fe^{2+} \qquad \mathcal{E}^{\circ} = 0.77 \text{ V} \qquad (1)$$
$$Cu^{2+} + 2e^- \rightarrow Cu \qquad \mathcal{E}^{\circ} = 0.34 \text{ V} \qquad (2)$$

To balance the cell reaction and calculate the standard cell potential, reaction (2) must be reversed:

$$Cu \rightarrow Cu^{2+} + 2e^- \qquad -\mathcal{E}^{\circ} = -0.34 \text{ V}$$

Note the change in sign for the $\mathcal{E}^{\circ}$ value. Now, since each Cu atom produces two electrons but each Fe^{3+} ion accepts only one electron, reaction (1) must be multiplied by 2:

$$2Fe^{3+} + 2e^- \rightarrow 2Fe^{2+} \qquad \mathcal{E}^{\circ} = 0.77 \text{ V}$$

Note that $\mathcal{E}^{\circ}$ is not changed in this case.

The standard hydrogen potential is the reference potential against which all half-reaction potentials are assigned.

All half-reactions are given as reduction processes in standard tables.

When a half-reaction is reversed, the sign of $\mathcal{E}^{\circ}$ is reversed.

When a half-reaction is multiplied by an integer, $\mathcal{E}^{\circ}$ remains the same.

Table 17.1

Standard Reduction Potentials at 25°C (298 K) for Many Common Half-reactions

Half-reaction	$\mathscr{E}°$ (V)	Half-reaction	$\mathscr{E}°$ (V)
$F_2 + 2e^- \rightarrow 2F^-$	2.87	$O_2 + 2H_2O + 4e^- \rightarrow 4OH^-$	0.40
$Ag^{2+} + e^- \rightarrow Ag^+$	1.99	$Cu^{2+} + 2e^- \rightarrow Cu$	0.34
$Co^{3+} + e^- \rightarrow Co^{2+}$	1.95	$Hg_2Cl_2 + 2e^- \rightarrow 2Hg + 2Cl^-$	0.34
$H_2O_2 + 2H^+ + 2e^- \rightarrow 2H_2O$	1.78	$AgCl + e^- \rightarrow Ag + Cl^-$	0.22
$Ce^{4+} + e^- \rightarrow Ce^{3+}$	1.70	$SO_4^{2-} + 4H^+ + 2e^- \rightarrow H_2SO_3 + H_2O$	0.20
$PbO_2 + 4H^+ + SO_4^{2-} + 2e^- \rightarrow PbSO_4 + 2H_2O$	1.69	$Cu^{2+} + e^- \rightarrow Cu^+$	0.16
$MnO_4^- + 4H^+ + 3e^- \rightarrow MnO_2 + 2H_2O$	1.68	$2H^+ + 2e^- \rightarrow H_2$	0.00
$2e^- + 2H^+ + IO_4^- \rightarrow IO_3^- + H_2O$	1.60	$Fe^{3+} + 3e^- \rightarrow Fe$	-0.036
$MnO_4^- + 8H^+ + 5e^- \rightarrow Mn^{2+} + 4H_2O$	1.51	$Pb^{2+} + 2e^- \rightarrow Pb$	-0.13
$Au^{3+} + 3e^- \rightarrow Au$	1.50	$Sn^{2+} + 2e^- \rightarrow Sn$	-0.14
$PbO_2 + 4H^+ + 2e^- \rightarrow Pb^{2+} + 2H_2O$	1.46	$Ni^{2+} + 2e^- \rightarrow Ni$	-0.23
$Cl_2 + 2e^- \rightarrow 2Cl^-$	1.36	$PbSO_4 + 2e^- \rightarrow Pb + SO_4^{2-}$	-0.35
$Cr_2O_7^{2-} + 14H^+ + 6e^- \rightarrow 2Cr^{3+} + 7H_2O$	1.33	$Cd^{2+} + 2e^- \rightarrow Cd$	-0.40
$O_2 + 4H^+ + 4e^- \rightarrow 2H_2O$	1.23	$Fe^{2+} + 2e^- \rightarrow Fe$	-0.44
$MnO_2 + 4H^+ + 2e^- \rightarrow Mn^{2+} + 2H_2O$	1.21	$Cr^{3+} + e^- \rightarrow Cr^{2+}$	-0.50
$IO_3^- + 6H^+ + 5e^- \rightarrow \frac{1}{2}I_2 + 3H_2O$	1.20	$Cr^{3+} + 3e^- \rightarrow Cr$	-0.73
$Br_2 + 2e^- \rightarrow 2Br^-$	1.09	$Zn^{2+} + 2e^- \rightarrow Zn$	-0.76
$VO_2^+ + 2H^+ + e^- \rightarrow VO^{2+} + H_2O$	1.00	$2H_2O + 2e^- \rightarrow H_2 + 2OH^-$	-0.83
$AuCl_4^- + 3e^- \rightarrow Au + 4Cl^-$	0.99	$Mn^{2+} + 2e^- \rightarrow Mn$	-1.18
$NO_3^- + 4H^+ + 3e^- \rightarrow NO + 2H_2O$	0.96	$Al^{3+} + 3e^- \rightarrow Al$	-1.66
$ClO_2 + e^- \rightarrow ClO_2^-$	0.954	$H_2 + 2e^- \rightarrow 2H^-$	-2.23
$2Hg^{2+} + 2e^- \rightarrow Hg_2^{2+}$	0.91	$Mg^{2+} + 2e^- \rightarrow Mg$	-2.37
$Ag^+ + e^- \rightarrow Ag$	0.80	$La^{3+} + 3e^- \rightarrow La$	-2.37
$Hg_2^{2+} + 2e^- \rightarrow 2Hg$	0.80	$Na^+ + e^- \rightarrow Na$	-2.71
$Fe^{3+} + e^- \rightarrow Fe^{2+}$	0.77	$Ca^{2+} + 2e^- \rightarrow Ca$	-2.76
$O_2 + 2H^+ + 2e^- \rightarrow H_2O_2$	0.68	$Ba^{2+} + 2e^- \rightarrow Ba$	-2.90
$MnO_4^- + e^- \rightarrow MnO_4^{2-}$	0.56	$K^+ + e^- \rightarrow K$	-2.92
$I_2 + 2e^- \rightarrow 2I^-$	0.54	$Li^+ + e^- \rightarrow Li$	-3.05
$Cu^+ + e^- \rightarrow Cu$	0.52		

Now we can obtain the balanced cell reaction by summing the appropriately modified half-reactions:

$$Cu \rightarrow Cu^{2+} + 2e^- \qquad\qquad -\mathscr{E}° = -0.34 \text{ V}$$

$$\underline{2Fe^{3+} + 2e^- \rightarrow 2Fe^{2+} \qquad\qquad \mathscr{E}° = 0.77 \text{ V}}$$

Cell reaction: $\quad Cu(s) + 2Fe^{3+}(aq) \rightarrow Cu^{2+}(aq) + 2Fe^{2+}(aq) \qquad \mathscr{E}°_{cell} = -0.34 \text{ V} + 0.77 \text{ V}$

$$= 0.43 \text{ V}$$

Sample Exercise 17.1

a. Consider a galvanic cell based on the reaction

$$Al^{3+}(aq) + Mg(s) \rightarrow Al(s) + Mg^{2+}(aq)$$

The half-reactions are

$$Al^{3+} + 3e^- \rightarrow Al \qquad \mathscr{E}° = -1.66 \text{ V} \qquad (1)$$

$$Mg^{2+} + 2e^- \rightarrow Mg \qquad \mathscr{E}° = -2.37 \text{ V} \qquad (2)$$

Give the balanced cell reaction, and calculate $\mathscr{E}°$ for the cell.

b. A galvanic cell is based on the reaction

$$MnO_4^-(aq) + H^+(aq) + ClO_3^-(aq) \rightarrow ClO_4^-(aq) + Mn^{2+}(aq) + H_2O(l)$$

The half-reactions are

$$MnO_4^- + 5e^- + 8H^+ \rightarrow Mn^{2+} + 4H_2O \qquad \mathscr{E}° = 1.51 \text{ V} \qquad (1)$$
$$ClO_4^- + 2H^+ + 2e^- \rightarrow ClO_3^- + H_2O \qquad \mathscr{E}° = 1.19 \text{ V} \qquad (2)$$

Give the balanced cell reaction, and calculate $\mathscr{E}°$ for the cell.

Solution

a. The half-reaction involving magnesium must be reversed:

$$Mg \rightarrow Mg^{2+} + 2e^- \qquad -\mathscr{E}° = -(-2.37 \text{ V}) = 2.37 \text{ V}$$

Also, since the two half-reactions involve different numbers of electrons, they must be multiplied by integers as follows:

$$
\begin{array}{ll}
2(Al^{3+} + 3e^- \rightarrow Al) & \mathscr{E}° = -1.66 \text{ V} \\
3(Mg \rightarrow Mg^{2+} + 2e^-) & -\mathscr{E}° = 2.37 \text{ V} \\
\hline
2Al^{3+}(aq) + 3Mg(s) \rightarrow 2Al(s) + 3Mg^{2+}(aq) & \mathscr{E}°_{\text{cell}} = -1.66 \text{ V} + 2.37 \text{ V} \\
& \phantom{\mathscr{E}°_{\text{cell}}} = 0.71 \text{ V}
\end{array}
$$

b. Half-reaction (2) must be reversed, and both half-reactions must be multiplied by integers to make the number of electrons equal:

$$
\begin{array}{ll}
2(MnO_4^- + 5e^- + 8H^+ \rightarrow Mn^{2+} + 4H_2O) & \mathscr{E}° = 1.51 \text{ V} \\
5(ClO_3^- + H_2O \rightarrow ClO_4^- + 2H^+ + 2e^-) & -\mathscr{E}° = -1.19 \text{ V} \\
\hline
2MnO_4^-(aq) + 6H^+(aq) + 5ClO_3^-(aq) \rightarrow 2Mn^{2+}(aq) + 3H_2O(l) + 5ClO_4^-(aq) & \mathscr{E}°_{\text{cell}} = 1.51 \text{ V} - 1.19 \text{ V} \\
& \phantom{\mathscr{E}°_{\text{cell}}} = 0.32 \text{ V}
\end{array}
$$

Line Notation

We now will introduce a handy line notation used to describe electrochemical cells. In this notation the anode components are listed on the left and the cathode components are listed on the right, separated by double vertical lines (indicating the salt bridge or porous disk). For example, the line notation for the cell described in Sample Exercise 17.1(a) is:

$$Mg(s)|Mg^{2+}(aq)\,\|\,Al^{3+}(aq)|Al(s)$$

In this notation a phase difference (boundary) is indicated by a single vertical line. Thus, in this case, vertical lines occur between the solid Mg metal and the Mg^{2+} in aqueous solution and between solid Al and Al^{3+} in aqueous solution. Also note that the substance constituting the anode is listed at the far left and the substance constituting the cathode is listed at the far right.

For the cell described in Sample Exercise 17.1(b), all the components involved in the oxidation–reduction reaction are ions. Since none of these dissolved ions can serve as an electrode, a nonreacting (inert) conductor must be used. The usual choice is platinum. Thus, for the cell described in Sample Exercise 17.1(b), the line notation is

$$Pt(s)|ClO_3^-(aq),\ ClO_4^-(aq)\,\|\,MnO_4^-(aq),\ Mn^{2+}(aq)|Pt(s)$$

Complete Description of a Galvanic Cell

Next we want to consider how to describe a galvanic cell fully, given just its half-reactions. This description will include the cell reaction, the cell potential, and the physical setup of the cell. Let's consider a galvanic cell based on the following half-reactions:

$$Fe^{2+} + 2e^- \rightarrow Fe \qquad \qquad \mathscr{E}° = -0.44 \text{ V}$$
$$MnO_4^- + 5e^- + 8H^+ \rightarrow Mn^{2+} + 4H_2O \qquad \mathscr{E}° = 1.51 \text{ V}$$

In a working galvanic cell, one of these reactions must run in reverse. Which one?

We can answer this question by considering the sign of the potential of a working cell: *a cell will always run spontaneously in the direction that produces a positive cell potential.* Thus, in the present case, it is clear that the half-reaction involving iron must be reversed, since this choice leads to a positive cell potential:

$$Fe \rightarrow Fe^{2+} + 2e^- \qquad \qquad -\mathscr{E}° = 0.44 \text{ V}$$
$$MnO_4^- + 5e^- + 8H^+ \rightarrow Mn^{2+} + 4H_2O \qquad \mathscr{E}° = 1.51 \text{ V}$$

where

$$\mathscr{E}°_{cell} = 0.44 \text{ V} + 1.51 \text{ V} = 1.95 \text{ V}$$

The balanced cell reaction is obtained as follows:

$$5(Fe \rightarrow Fe^{2+} + 2e^-)$$
$$\underline{2(MnO_4^- + 5e^- + 8H^+ \rightarrow Mn^{2+} + 4H_2O)}$$
$$2MnO_4^-(aq) + 5Fe(s) + 16H^+(aq) \rightarrow 5Fe^{2+}(aq) + 2Mn^{2+}(aq) + 8H_2O(l)$$

Now consider the physical setup of the cell, shown schematically in Fig. 17.7. In the left compartment the active components in their standard states are pure metallic iron (Fe) and 1.0 M Fe^{2+}. The anion present depends on the iron salt used. In this compartment the anion does not participate in the reaction, but simply balances the charge. The half-reaction that takes place at this electrode is

$$Fe \rightarrow Fe^{2+} + 2e^-$$

which is an oxidation reaction, so this compartment is the anode. The electrode consists of pure iron metal.

In the right compartment the active components in their standard states are 1.0 M MnO_4^-, 1.0 M H^+, and 1.0 M Mn^{2+}, with appropriate unreacting ions (often called counter ions) to balance the charge. The half-reaction in this compartment is

$$MnO_4^- + 5e^- + 8H^+ \rightarrow Mn^{2+} + 4H_2O$$

which is a reduction reaction, so this compartment is the cathode. Since neither MnO_4^- nor Mn^{2+} ions can serve as the electrode, a nonreacting conductor such as platinum must be employed.

The next step is to determine the direction of electron flow. In the left compartment the half-reaction involves the oxidation of iron:

$$Fe \rightarrow Fe^{2+} + 2e^-$$

In the right compartment the half-reaction is the reduction of MnO_4^-:

$$MnO_4^- + 5e^- + 8H^+ \rightarrow Mn^{2+} + 4H_2O$$

Thus the electrons flow from Fe to MnO_4^- in this cell, or from the anode to the

> A galvanic cell runs spontaneously in the direction that gives a positive value for $\mathscr{E}_{cell}$.

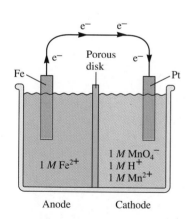

Figure 17.7

The schematic of a galvanic cell based on the half-reactions:

$$Fe \rightarrow Fe^{2+} + 2e^-$$
$$MnO_4^- + 5e^- + 8H^+$$
$$\rightarrow Mn^{2+} + 4H_2O.$$

cathode, as is always the case. The line notation for this cell is

$$Fe(s)|Fe^{2+}(aq)\|MnO_4^-(aq),\ Mn^{2+}(aq)|Pt(s)$$

A complete description of a galvanic cell usually includes four items:

- The cell potential (always positive for a galvanic cell) and the balanced cell reaction.

- The direction of electron flow, obtained by inspecting the half-reactions and using the directions that give a positive $\mathscr{E}_{cell}$.

- Designation of the anode and cathode.

- The nature of each electrode and the ions present in each compartment. A chemically inert conductor is required if none of the substances participating in the half-reaction is a conducting solid.

Sample Exercise 17.2

Describe completely the galvanic cell based on the following half-reactions under standard conditions:

$$Ag^+ + e^- \rightarrow Ag \qquad \mathscr{E}° = 0.80\ V \qquad (1)$$
$$Fe^{3+} + e^- \rightarrow Fe^{2+} \qquad \mathscr{E}° = 0.77\ V \qquad (2)$$

Solution

ITEM 1

Since a positive $\mathscr{E}°_{cell}$ value is required, reaction (2) must run in reverse:

$$
\begin{array}{lrr}
Ag^+ + e^- \rightarrow Ag & \mathscr{E}° = & 0.80\ V \\
Fe^{2+} \rightarrow Fe^{3+} + e^- & -\mathscr{E}° = & -0.77\ V \\
\hline
\text{Cell reaction:}\quad Ag^+(aq) + Fe^{2+}(aq) \rightarrow Fe^{3+}(aq) + Ag(s) & \mathscr{E}°_{cell} = & 0.03\ V
\end{array}
$$

ITEM 2

Since Ag^+ receives electrons and Fe^{2+} loses electrons in the cell reaction, the electrons will flow from the compartment containing Fe^{2+} to the compartment containing Ag^+.

ITEM 3

Oxidation occurs in the compartment containing Fe^{2+} (electrons flow from Fe^{2+} to Ag^+). Hence this compartment functions as the anode. Reduction occurs in the compartment containing Ag^+, so this compartment functions as the cathode.

ITEM 4

The electrode in the Ag/Ag^+ compartment is silver metal, and an inert conductor, such as platinum, must be used in the Fe^{2+}/Fe^{3+} compartment. Appropriate counter ions are assumed to be present. The diagram for this cell is shown in Fig. 17.8. The line notation for this cell is

$$Pt(s)|Fe^{2+}(aq),\ Fe^{3+}(aq)\|Ag^+(aq)|Ag(s)$$

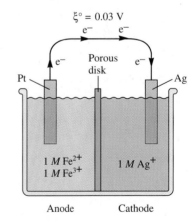

Figure 17.8

Schematic diagram for the galvanic cell based on the half-reactions

$$Ag^+ + e^- \rightarrow Ag$$
$$Fe^{2+} \rightarrow Fe^{3+} + e^-.$$

17.3 Cell Potential, Electrical Work, and Free Energy

Purpose

• To relate the maximum cell potential to the free energy difference between cell reactants and products.

So far we have considered electrochemical cells in a very practical fashion without much theoretical background. The next step will be to explore the relationship between thermodynamics and electrochemistry.

The work that can be accomplished when electrons are transferred through a wire depends on the "push" (the thermodynamic driving force) behind the electrons. This driving force (the emf) is defined in terms of a *potential difference* (in volts) between two points in the circuit. Recall that a volt represents a joule of work per coulomb of charge transferred:

$$\text{emf} = \text{potential difference (V)} = \frac{\text{work (J)}}{\text{charge (C)}}$$

Thus 1 joule of work is produced or required (depending on the direction) when 1 coulomb of charge is transferred between two points in the circuit that differ by a potential of 1 volt.

In this book, *work is viewed from the point of view of the system*. Thus work flowing out of the system is indicated by a minus sign. When a cell produces a current, the cell potential is positive, and the current can be used to do work—to run a motor, for instance. Thus the cell potential $\mathscr{E}$ and the work w have opposite signs:

$$\mathscr{E} = \frac{-w \quad \longleftarrow \text{Work}}{q \quad \longleftarrow \text{Charge}}$$

Therefore,
$$-w = q\mathscr{E}$$

From this equation it can be seen that the maximum work in a cell would be obtained at the maximum cell potential:

$$-w_{\text{max}} = q\mathscr{E}_{\text{max}} \quad \text{or} \quad w_{\text{max}} = -q\mathscr{E}_{\text{max}}$$

Work is never the maximum possible if any current is flowing.

However, there is a problem. To obtain electrical work, current must flow. When current flows, some energy is inevitably wasted through frictional heating, and the maximum work is not obtained. This reflects the important general principle introduced in Section 16.9: *in any real, spontaneous process some energy is always wasted—the actual work realized is always less than the calculated maximum*. This is a consequence of the fact that the entropy of the universe must increase in any spontaneous process. Recall from Section 16.9 that the only process from which maximum work could be realized is the hypothetical reversible process. For a galvanic cell this would involve an infinitesimally small current flow and thus an infinite amount of time to do the work. Even though we can never achieve the maximum work through the actual discharge of a galvanic cell, we can measure the maximum potential. There is negligible current flow when a cell potential is measured with a potentiometer or an efficient digital voltmeter. No current flow implies no waste of energy, so the potential measured is the maximum.

Although we can never actually realize the maximum work from a cell reaction, the value for it is still useful in evaluating the efficiency of a real process based on the cell reaction. For example, suppose a certain galvanic cell has a maximum potential (at zero current) of 2.50 V. In a particular experiment 1.33 moles of electrons were passed through this cell at an average actual potential of 2.10 V. The actual work done is

$$w = -q\mathscr{E}$$

where $\mathscr{E}$ represents the actual potential difference at which the current flowed (2.10 V or 2.10 J/C) and q is the quantity of charge in coulombs transferred. The charge on 1 mole of electrons is a constant called the **faraday** (abbreviated F), which has the value *96,485 coulombs of charge per mole of electrons*. Thus q equals the number of moles of electrons times the charge per mole of electrons:

$$q = nF = 1.33 \text{ mol e}^- \times 96,485 \text{ C/mol e}^-$$

Then, for the experiment above, the actual work is

$$w = -q\mathscr{E} = -(1.33 \text{ mol e}^- \times 96,485 \text{ C/mol e}^-) \times (2.10 \text{ J/C})$$
$$= -2.69 \times 10^5 \text{ J}$$

For the maximum possible work, the calculation is similar, except that the maximum potential is used:

$$w_{max} = -q\mathscr{E}_{max}$$
$$= -\left(1.33 \text{ mol e}^- \times 96,485 \frac{\text{C}}{\text{mol e}^-}\right)\left(2.50 \frac{\text{J}}{\text{C}}\right)$$
$$= -3.21 \times 10^5 \text{ J}$$

Thus, in its actual operation, the efficiency of this cell is

$$\frac{w}{w_{max}} \times 100 = \frac{-2.69 \times 10^5 \text{ J}}{-3.21 \times 10^5 \text{ J}} \times 100 = 83.8\%$$

Next we want to relate the potential of a galvanic cell to free energy. In Section 16.9 we saw that for a process carried out at constant temperature and pressure, the change in free energy equals the maximum useful work obtainable from that process.

$$w_{max} = \Delta G$$

For a galvanic cell,

$$w_{max} = -q\mathscr{E}_{max} = \Delta G$$

Since

$$q = nF$$

we have

$$\Delta G = -q\mathscr{E}_{max} = -nF\mathscr{E}_{max}$$

From now on the subscript on $\mathscr{E}_{max}$ will be deleted, with the understanding that any potential given in this book is the maximum potential. Thus

$$\Delta G = -nF\mathscr{E}$$

For standard conditions,

$$\Delta G^\circ = -nF\mathscr{E}^\circ$$

The faraday was named in honor of Michael Faraday (1791–1867), an Englishman who may have been the greatest experimental scientist of the nineteenth century. Among his many achievements were the invention of the electric motor and generator and the development of the principles of electrolysis.

This equation states that *the maximum cell potential is directly related to the free energy difference between the reactants and the products in the cell.* This relationship is important because it provides an experimental means to obtain ΔG for a reaction. It also confirms that a galvanic cell will run in the direction that gives a positive value for $\mathscr{E}_{cell}$; a positive $\mathscr{E}_{cell}$ value corresponds to a negative ΔG value, which is the condition for spontaneity.

Sample Exercise 17.3

Using the data in Table 17.1, calculate $\Delta G°$ for the reaction

$$Cu^{2+}(aq) + Fe(s) \rightarrow Cu(s) + Fe^{2+}(aq)$$

Is this reaction spontaneous?

Solution

The half-reactions are

$$Cu^{2+} + 2e^- \rightarrow Cu \qquad \mathscr{E}° = 0.34 \text{ V}$$
$$\underline{Fe \rightarrow Fe^{2+} + 2e^- \qquad -\mathscr{E}° = 0.44 \text{ V}}$$
$$Cu^{2+} + Fe \rightarrow Fe^{2+} + Cu \qquad \mathscr{E}°_{cell} = 0.78 \text{ V}$$

We can calculate $\Delta G°$ from the equation

$$\Delta G° = -nF\mathscr{E}°$$

Since two electrons are transferred per atom in the reaction, 2 moles of electrons are required per mole of reactants and products. Thus $n = 2$ mol e$^-$, $F = 96{,}485$ C/mol e$^-$, and $\mathscr{E}° = 0.78$ V $= 0.78$ J/C. Therefore,

$$\Delta G° = -(2 \text{ mol e}^-)\left(96{,}485 \frac{C}{\text{mol e}^-}\right)\left(0.78 \frac{J}{C}\right)$$
$$= -1.5 \times 10^5 \text{ J}$$

The process is spontaneous, as indicated both by the negative sign of $\Delta G°$ and the positive sign of $\mathscr{E}°_{cell}$.

This reaction is used industrially to deposit copper metal from solutions resulting from the dissolving of copper ores.

Sample Exercise 17.4

Using the data from Table 17.1, predict whether 1 M HNO$_3$ will dissolve gold metal to form a 1 M Au^{3+} solution.

Solution

The half-reaction for HNO$_3$ acting as an oxidizing agent is

$$NO_3^- + 4H^+ + 3e^- \rightarrow NO + 2H_2O \qquad \mathscr{E}° = 0.96 \text{ V}$$

The reaction for the oxidation of solid gold to Au^{3+} ions is

$$Au \rightarrow Au^{3+} + 3e^- \qquad -\mathscr{E}° = -1.50 \text{ V}$$

The sum of these half-reactions gives the required reaction:

$$Au(s) + NO_3^-(aq) + 4H^+(aq) \rightarrow Au^{3+}(aq) + NO(g) + 2H_2O(l)$$

and $\qquad\qquad \mathscr{E}°_{cell} = 0.96 \text{ V} - 1.50 \text{ V} = -0.54 \text{ V}$

Since the $\mathscr{E}°$ value is negative, the process will *not* occur under standard conditions. That is, gold will not dissolve in 1 M HNO_3 to give 1 M Au^{3+}. In fact, a mixture (1:3 by volume) of concentrated nitric and hydrochloric acids, called **aqua regia,** is required to dissolve gold.

17.4 Dependence of Cell Potential on Concentration

Purpose

- To discuss the driving force in concentration cells.
- To quantify the relationship between cell potential and cell concentration.
- To show how to calculate equilibrium constants from cell potentials.

So far we have described cells under standard conditions. In this section we consider the dependence of the cell potential on concentration. Under standard conditions (all concentrations 1 M) the cell with the reaction

$$Cu(s) + 2Ce^{4+}(aq) \rightarrow Cu^{2+}(aq) + 2Ce^{3+}(aq)$$

has a potential of 1.36 V. What will the cell potential be if $[Ce^{4+}]$ is greater than 1.0 M? This question can be answered qualitatively in terms of Le Châtelier's principle. An increase in the concentration of Ce^{4+} will favor the forward reaction and thus increase the driving force on the electrons. The cell potential will increase. On the other hand, an increase in the concentration of a product (Cu^{2+} or Ce^{3+}) will oppose the forward reaction, thus decreasing the cell potential.

These ideas are illustrated in Sample Exercise 17.5.

Sample Exercise 17.5

For the cell reaction

$$2Al(s) + 3Mn^{2+}(aq) \rightarrow 2Al^{3+}(aq) + 3Mn(s) \qquad \mathscr{E}°_{cell} = 0.48 \text{ V}$$

predict whether $\mathscr{E}_{cell}$ is larger or smaller than $\mathscr{E}°_{cell}$ for the following cases.

a. $[Al^{3+}] = 2.0 \text{ } M, [Mn^{2+}] = 1.0 \text{ } M$

b. $[Al^{3+}] = 1.0 \text{ } M, [Mn^{2+}] = 3.0 \text{ } M$

Solution

a. A product concentration has been raised above 1.0 M. This will oppose the cell reaction and will cause $\mathcal{E}_{cell}$ to be less than $\mathcal{E}_{cell}^{\circ}$ ($\mathcal{E}_{cell} < 0.48$ V).

b. A reactant concentration has been increased above 1.0 M, and $\mathcal{E}_{cell}$ will be greater than $\mathcal{E}_{cell}^{\circ}$ ($\mathcal{E}_{cell} > 0.48$ V).

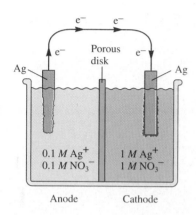

Figure 17.9

A concentration cell that contains a silver electrode and aqueous silver nitrate in both compartments. Because the right compartment contains 1 M Ag⁺ and the left compartment contains 0.1 M Ag⁺, there will be a driving force to transfer electrons from left to right. Silver will be deposited on the right electrode, thus lowering the concentration of Ag⁺ in the right compartment. In the left compartment the silver electrode dissolves (producing Ag⁺ ions) to raise the concentration of Ag⁺ in solution.

Concentration Cells

Because cell potentials depend on concentration, we can construct galvanic cells where both compartments contain the same components but at different concentrations. For example, in the cell in Fig. 17.9, both compartments contain aqueous $AgNO_3$, but with different molarities. Let's consider the potential of this cell and the direction of electron flow. The half-reaction relevant to both compartments of this cell is

$$Ag^{+} + e^{-} \rightarrow Ag \qquad \mathcal{E}^{\circ} = 0.80 \text{ V}$$

If the cell had 1 M Ag^{+} in both compartments,

$$\mathcal{E}_{cell}^{\circ} = 0.80 \text{ V} - 0.80 \text{ V} = 0 \text{ V}$$

However, in the cell described here, the concentrations of Ag^{+} in the two compartments are 1 M and 0.1 M. Because the concentrations of Ag^{+} are unequal, the half-cell potentials will not be identical, and the cell will exhibit a positive voltage. In which direction will the electrons flow in this cell? The best way to think about this question is to recognize that nature will try to equalize the concentrations of Ag^{+} in the two compartments. This can be done by transferring electrons from the compartment containing 0.1 M Ag^{+} to the one containing 1 M Ag^{+} (left to right in Fig. 17.9). This electron transfer will produce more Ag^{+} in the left compartment and consume Ag^{+} (to form Ag) in the right compartment.

A cell in which both compartments have the same components but at different concentrations is called a **concentration cell.** The difference in concentration is the only factor that produces a cell potential in this case, and the voltages are typically small.

Sample Exercise 17.6

Determine the direction of electron flow and designate the anode and cathode for the cell represented in Fig. 17.10.

Solution

The concentrations of Fe^{2+} ion in the two compartments can (eventually) be equalized by transferring electrons from the left compartment to the right. This will cause Fe^{2+} to be formed in the left compartment, and iron metal will be deposited (by reducing Fe^{2+} ions to Fe) on the right electrode. Since electron flow is from left to right, oxidation occurs in the left compartment (the anode) and reduction occurs in the right (the cathode).

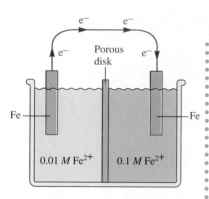

Figure 17.10

A concentration cell containing iron electrodes and different concentrations of Fe^{2+} ion in the two compartments.

The Nernst Equation

The dependence of the cell potential on concentration results directly from the dependence of free energy on concentration. Recall from Chapter 16 that the equation

$$\Delta G = \Delta G^\circ + RT \ln(Q)$$

where Q is the reaction quotient, was used to calculate the effect of concentration on ΔG. Since $\Delta G = -nF\mathscr{E}$ and $\Delta G^\circ = -nF\mathscr{E}^\circ$, the equation becomes

$$-nF\mathscr{E} = -nF\mathscr{E}^\circ + RT \ln(Q)$$

Dividing each side of the equation by $-nF$ gives

$$\mathscr{E} = \mathscr{E}^\circ - \frac{RT}{nF}\ln(Q) \qquad (17.1)$$

Equation (17.1), which gives the relationship between the cell potential and the concentrations of the cell components, is commonly called the **Nernst equation,** after the German chemist Walther Hermann Nernst (1864–1941).

The Nernst equation is often given in a form that is valid at 25°C:

$$\mathscr{E} = \mathscr{E}^\circ - \frac{0.0592}{n}\log(Q)$$

Nernst was one of the pioneers in the development of electrochemical theory and is generally given credit for first stating the third law of thermodynamics. He won the Nobel Prize in chemistry in 1920.

Using this relationship, we can calculate the potential of a cell in which some or all of the components are not in their standard states.

For example, $\mathscr{E}^\circ_{cell}$ is 0.48 V for the galvanic cell based on the reaction

$$2Al(s) + 3Mn^{2+}(aq) \rightarrow 2Al^{3+}(aq) + 3Mn(s)$$

Consider a cell in which

$$[Mn^{2+}] = 0.50\ M \quad \text{and} \quad [Al^{3+}] = 1.50\ M$$

The cell potential at 25°C for these concentrations can be calculated using the Nernst equation:

$$\mathscr{E}_{cell} = \mathscr{E}^\circ_{cell} - \frac{0.0592}{n}\log(Q)$$

We know that $$\mathscr{E}^\circ_{cell} = 0.48\ V$$

and $$Q = \frac{[Al^{3+}]^2}{[Mn^{2+}]^3} = \frac{(1.50)^2}{(0.50)^3} = 18$$

Since the half-reactions are

$$\text{Oxidation:} \quad 2Al \rightarrow 2Al^{3+} + 6e^-$$
$$\text{Reduction:} \quad 3Mn^{2+} + 6e^- \rightarrow 3Mn$$

we know that $$n = 6$$

Thus $$\mathscr{E}_{cell} = 0.48 - \frac{0.0592}{6}\log(18)$$

$$= 0.48 - \frac{0.0592}{6}(1.26) = 0.48 - 0.01 = 0.47\ V$$

Note that the cell voltage decreases slightly because of the nonstandard concentrations. This change is consistent with the predictions of Le Châtelier's principle (see Sample Exercise 17.5). In this case, since the reactant concentration is lower than 1.0 M and the product concentration is higher than 1.0 M, $\mathscr{E}_{cell}$ is less than $\mathscr{E}^{\circ}_{cell}$.

The potential calculated from the Nernst equation is the maximum potential before any current flow has occurred. As the cell discharges and current flows from anode to cathode, the concentrations will change, and as a result, $\mathscr{E}_{cell}$ will change. In fact, *the cell will spontaneously discharge until it reaches equilibrium,* at which point

$$Q = K \text{ (the equilibrium constant)} \quad \text{and} \quad \mathscr{E}_{cell} = 0$$

A "dead" battery is one in which the cell reaction has reached equilibrium, and there is no longer any chemical driving force to push electrons through the wire. In other words, *at equilibrium the components in the two cell compartments have the same free energy,* and $\Delta G = 0$ for the cell reaction at the equilibrium concentrations. The cell no longer has the ability to do work.

Sample Exercise 17.7

Describe the cell based on the following half-reactions:

$$VO_2^+ + 2H^+ + e^- \rightarrow VO^{2+} + H_2O \qquad \mathscr{E}^{\circ} = 1.00 \text{ V} \qquad (1)$$

$$Zn^{2+} + 2e^- \rightarrow Zn \qquad \mathscr{E}^{\circ} = -0.76 \text{ V} \qquad (2)$$

where
$$T = 25°C$$
$$[VO_2^+] = 2.0 \ M$$
$$[H^+] = 0.50 \ M$$
$$[VO^{2+}] = 1.0 \times 10^{-2} \ M$$
$$[Zn^{2+}] = 1.0 \times 10^{-1} \ M$$

Solution

The balanced cell reaction is obtained by reversing reaction (2) and multiplying reaction (1) by 2:

2 × reaction (1)	$2VO_2^+ + 4H^+ + 2e^- \rightarrow 2VO^{2+} + 2H_2O$	$\mathscr{E}^{\circ} = 1.00$ V
Reaction (2) reversed	$Zn \rightarrow Zn^{2+} + 2e^-$	$-\mathscr{E}^{\circ} = 0.76$ V

Cell reaction: $2VO_2^+(aq) + 4H^+(aq) + Zn(s) \rightarrow 2VO^{2+}(aq) + 2H_2O(l) + Zn^{2+}(aq)$ $\mathscr{E}^{\circ}_{cell} = 1.76$ V

Since the cell contains components at concentrations other than 1 M, we must use the Nernst equation, where $n = 2$ (since two electrons are transferred), to calculate the cell potential. At 25°C we can use the equation

$$\mathscr{E} = \mathscr{E}^{\circ}_{cell} - \frac{0.0592}{n} \log(Q)$$

$$= 1.76 - \frac{0.0592}{2} \log\left(\frac{[Zn^{2+}][VO^{2+}]^2}{[VO_2^+]^2[H^+]^4}\right)$$

$$= 1.76 - \frac{0.0592}{2} \log \left(\frac{(1.0 \times 10^{-1})(1.0 \times 10^{-2})^2}{(2.0)^2 (0.50)^4} \right)$$

$$= 1.76 - \frac{0.0592}{2} \log(4 \times 10^{-5}) = 1.76 + 0.13 = 1.89 \text{ V}$$

The cell diagram is given in Fig. 17.11.

Figure 17.11

Schematic diagram of the cell described in Sample Exercise 17.7.

Ion-Selective Electrodes

Because the cell potential is sensitive to the concentrations of the reactants and products involved in the cell reaction, measured potentials can be used to determine the concentration of an ion. A pH meter (see Fig. 14.4) is a familiar example of an instrument that measures concentration using an observed potential. The pH meter has three main components: a standard electrode of known potential, a special **glass electrode** that changes potential depending on the concentration of H^+ ions in the solution into which it is dipped, and a potentiometer that measures the potential between the two electrodes. The potentiometer reading is automatically converted electronically to a direct reading of the pH of the solution being tested.

The glass electrode (see Fig. 17.12) contains a reference solution of dilute hydrochloric acid in contact with a thin glass membrane. The electrical potential of the glass electrode depends on the difference in $[H^+]$ between the reference solution and the solution into which the electrode is dipped. Thus the electrical potential varies with the pH of the solution being tested.

Electrodes that are sensitive to the concentration of a particular ion are called **ion-selective electrodes,** of which the glass electrode for pH measurement is just one example. Glass electrodes can be made sensitive to such ions as Na^+, K^+, or NH_4^+ by changing the composition of the glass. Other ions can be detected if an appropriate crystal replaces the glass membrane. For example, a crystal of lanthanum(III) fluoride (LaF_3) can be used in an electrode to measure $[F^-]$. Solid

Reference solution of dilute hydrochloric acid

Silver wire coated with silver chloride

Thin-walled membrane

Figure 17.12

A glass electrode contains a reference solution of dilute hydrochloric acid in contact with a thin glass membrane in which a silver wire coated with silver chloride has been embedded. When the electrode is dipped into a solution containing H^+ ions, the electrode potential is determined by the difference in $[H^+]$ between the two solutions.

silver sulfide (Ag_2S) can be used to measure $[Ag^+]$ and $[S^{2-}]$. Some of the ions that can be detected by ion-selective electrodes are listed in Table 17.2.

Calculation of Equilibrium Constants for Redox Reactions

The quantitative relationship between $\mathscr{E}°$ and $\Delta G°$ allows calculation of equilibrium constants for redox reactions. For a cell at equilibrium,

$$\mathscr{E}_{cell} = 0 \quad \text{and} \quad Q = K$$

Applying these conditions to the Nernst equation valid at 25°C,

$$\mathscr{E} = \mathscr{E}° - \frac{0.0592}{n}\log(Q)$$

gives

$$0 = \mathscr{E}° - \frac{0.0592}{n}\log(K)$$

or

$$\log(K) = \frac{n\mathscr{E}°}{0.0592} \quad \text{at 25°C}$$

The blue solution on the left contains Cr^{2+} ions and the green solution contains Cr^{3+} ions.

Sample Exercise 17.8

For the oxidation–reduction reaction

$$S_4O_6^{2-}(aq) + Cr^{2+}(aq) \rightarrow Cr^{3+}(aq) + S_2O_3^{2-}(aq)$$

the appropriate half-reactions are

$$S_4O_6^{2-} + 2e^- \rightarrow 2S_2O_3^{2-} \qquad \mathscr{E}° = 0.17 \text{ V} \qquad (1)$$
$$Cr^{3+} + e^- \rightarrow Cr^{2+} \qquad \mathscr{E}° = -0.50 \text{ V} \qquad (2)$$

Balance the redox reaction, and calculate $\mathscr{E}°$ and K (at 25°C).

Solution

To obtain the balanced reaction, we must reverse reaction (2), multiply it by 2, and add it to reaction (1):

2 × reaction (2) reversed
$$2(Cr^{2+} \rightarrow Cr^{3+} + e^-) \qquad\qquad -\mathscr{E}° = -(-0.50) \text{ V}$$
Reaction (1)
$$\underline{S_4O_6^{2-} + 2e^- \rightarrow 2S_2O_3^{2-} \qquad\qquad \mathscr{E}° = 0.17 \text{ V}}$$
Cell reaction:
$$2Cr^{2+}(aq) + S_4O_6^{2-}(aq) \rightarrow 2Cr^{3+}(aq) + 2S_2O_3^{2-}(aq) \qquad \mathscr{E}° = 0.67 \text{ V}$$

In this reaction, 2 moles of electrons are transferred for every unit of reaction, that is, for every 2 mol Cr^{2+} reacting with 1 mol $S_4O_6^{2-}$ to form 2 mol Cr^{3+} and 2 mol $S_2O_3^{2-}$. Thus $n = 2$. Then

$$\log(K) = \frac{n\mathscr{E}°}{0.0592} = \frac{2(0.67)}{0.0592} = 22.6$$

The value of K is found by taking the antilog of 22.6:

$$K = 10^{22.6} = 4 \times 10^{22}$$

This very large equilibrium constant is not unusual for a redox reaction.

17.5 Batteries

Purpose

- To discuss the composition and operation of commonly used batteries.

A **battery** is a galvanic cell or, more commonly, a group of galvanic cells connected in series, where the potentials of the individual cells add to give the total battery potential. Batteries are a source of direct current and have become an essential source of portable power in our society. In this section we examine the most common types of batteries. Some new batteries currently being developed are described at the end of the chapter.

Lead Storage Battery

Since about 1915 when self-starters were first used in automobiles, the **lead storage battery** has been a major factor in making the automobile a practical means of transportation. This type of battery can function for several years under temperature extremes from $-30°F$ to $100°F$ and under incessant punishment from rough roads.

In this battery, lead serves as the anode, and lead coated with lead dioxide serves as the cathode. Both electrodes dip into an electrolyte solution of sulfuric acid. The electrode reactions are

Anode reaction:	$Pb + HSO_4^- \rightarrow PbSO_4 + H^+ + 2e^-$
Cathode reaction:	$PbO_2 + HSO_4^- + 3H^+ + 2e^- \rightarrow PbSO_4 + 2H_2O$
Cell reaction:	$Pb(s) + PbO_2(s) + 2H^+(aq) + 2HSO_4^-(aq) \rightarrow 2PbSO_4(s) + 2H_2O(l)$

The typical automobile lead storage battery has six cells connected in series. Each cell contains multiple electrodes in the form of grids (Fig. 17.13) and produces approximately 2 V, to give a total battery potential of about 12 V. Note from the cell reaction that sulfuric acid is consumed as the battery discharges. This lowers the density of the electrolyte solution from its initial value of about 1.28 g/cm^3 in the fully charged battery. As a result, the condition of the battery can be monitored by measuring the density of the sulfuric acid solution. The solid lead sulfate formed in the cell reaction during discharge adheres to the grid surfaces of the electrodes. The battery is recharged by forcing current through the battery in the opposite direction to reverse the cell reaction. A car's battery is continuously charged by an alternator driven by the automobile engine.

An automobile with a dead battery can be "jump-started" by connecting its battery to the battery in a running automobile. This process can be dangerous, however, because the resulting flow of current causes electrolysis of water in the

H_2SO_4 electrolyte solution

Anode (lead grid filled with spongy lead)

Cathode (lead grid filled with spongy PbO_2)

Figure 17.13

One of the six cells in a 12-V lead storage battery. The anode consists of a lead grid filled with spongy lead, and the cathode is a lead grid filled with lead dioxide. The cell also contains 38% (by mass) sulfuric acid.

Using jumper cables to start a car with a dead battery. Notice the ground cable on the dead car is attached at a point away from the battery to avoid a possible explosion.

dead battery, producing hydrogen and oxygen gases (see Section 17.7 for details). Disconnecting the jumper cables after the disabled car starts causes an arc that can ignite the gaseous mixture. If this happens, the battery may explode, ejecting corrosive sulfuric acid. This problem can be avoided by connecting the ground jumper cable to a part of the engine remote from the battery. Any arc produced when this cable is disconnected will then be harmless.

Traditional types of storage batteries require periodic "topping off," because the water in the electrolyte solution is depleted by the electrolysis that accompanies the charging process. Recent types of batteries have electrodes made of an alloy of calcium and lead that inhibits the electrolysis of water. These batteries can be sealed, since they require no addition of water.

It is rather amazing that in the 75 years in which lead storage batteries have been used, no better system has been found. Although a lead storage battery does provide excellent service, it has a useful lifetime of 3 to 5 years in an automobile. While it might seem that the battery could undergo an indefinite number of discharge/charge cycles, physical damage from road shock and chemical side-reactions eventually cause it to fail.

Other Batteries

The calculators, electronic watches, portable radios, and tape players that are so familiar to us are all powered by small, efficient batteries. The common **dry cell battery** was invented more than 100 years ago by George Leclanché (1839–1882), a French chemist. In its *acid version,* the dry cell battery contains a zinc inner case that acts as the anode and a carbon rod in contact with a moist paste of solid MnO_2, solid NH_4Cl, and carbon that acts as the cathode (Fig. 17.14). The half-reactions are complex but can be approximated as follows:

— Anode (zinc inner case)

— Cathode (graphite rod)

— Paste of MnO_2, NH_4Cl, and carbon

Figure 17.14

A common dry cell battery.

Anode reaction: $\qquad\qquad Zn \rightarrow Zn^{2+} + 2e^-$

Cathode reaction: $\quad 2NH_4^+ + 2MnO_2 + 2e^- \rightarrow Mn_2O_3 + 2NH_3 + H_2O$

This cell produces a potential of about 1.5 V.

In the *alkaline version* of the dry cell battery, the solid NH_4Cl is replaced with KOH or NaOH. In this case the half-reactions can be approximated as follows:

Anode reaction: $\qquad\qquad Zn + 2OH^- \rightarrow ZnO + H_2O + 2e^-$

Cathode reaction: $\quad 2MnO_2 + H_2O + 2e^- \rightarrow Mn_2O_3 + 2OH^-$

The alkaline dry cell lasts longer mainly because the zinc anode corrodes less rapidly under basic conditions than under acidic conditions.

Other types of useful batteries include the *silver cell,* which has a Zn anode and a cathode that employs Ag_2O as the oxidizing agent in a basic environment. *Mercury cells,* often used in calculators, have a Zn anode and a cathode involving HgO as the oxidizing agent in a basic medium (see Fig. 17.15).

An especially important type of battery is the *nickel–cadmium battery,* in which the electrode reactions are

Anode reaction: $\qquad\qquad Cd + 2OH^- \rightarrow Cd(OH)_2 + 2e^-$

Cathode reaction: $\quad NiO_2 + 2H_2O + 2e^- \rightarrow Ni(OH)_2 + 2OH^-$

As in the lead storage battery, the products adhere to the electrodes. Therefore, a nickel–cadmium battery can be recharged an indefinite number of times.

Batteries for electronic watches are, by necessity, very tiny.

Insulation
Cathode (steel)
Anode (zinc container)

Solution of HgO (oxidizing agent) in a basic medium (KOH and $Zn(OH)_2$)

Figure 17.15

A mercury battery of the type used in small calculators.

Fuel Cells

A **fuel cell** is *a galvanic cell for which the reactants are continuously supplied*. To illustrate the principles of fuel cells, let's consider the exothermic redox reaction of methane with oxygen:

$$CH_4(g) + 2O_2(g) \rightarrow CO_2(g) + 2H_2O(g) + \text{energy}$$

Usually the energy from this reaction is released as heat to warm homes and to run machines. However, in a fuel cell designed to use this reaction, the energy is used to produce an electric current: the electrons flow from the reducing agent (CH_4) to the oxidizing agent (O_2) through a conductor.

The U.S. space program has supported extensive research to develop fuel cells. The Apollo missions used a fuel cell based on the reaction of hydrogen and oxygen to form water:

$$2H_2(g) + O_2(g) \rightarrow 2H_2O(l)$$

A schematic of a fuel cell that employs this reaction is shown in Fig. 17.16. The half-reactions are

Anode reaction: $\quad\quad 2H_2 + 4OH^- \rightarrow 4H_2O + 4e^-$

Cathode reaction: $\quad 4e^- + O_2 + 2H_2O \rightarrow 4OH^-$

A cell of this type weighing about 500 pounds has been designed for space vehicles, but neither this nor any other type of fuel cell is practical enough for general use as a source of portable power. Current research on portable electrochemical power sources seems mainly focused on rechargeable storage batteries with high power-to-weight ratios.

Fuel cells are finding some use, however, as permanent power sources. For example, a power plant built in New York City contains stacks of hydrogen–oxygen fuel cells, which can be rapidly put on-line in response to fluctuating power demands. The hydrogen gas is obtained by decomposing the methane in natural gas. A plant of this type also has been constructed in Tokyo.

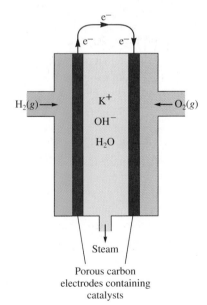

$H_2(g) \rightarrow$
K^+
OH^-
H_2O
$\leftarrow O_2(g)$

Steam

Porous carbon electrodes containing catalysts

Figure 17.16

Schematic of the hydrogen–oxygen fuel cell.

17.6 Corrosion

Purpose

- To explain the electrochemical nature of corrosion and describe some means for preventing it.

Corrosion can be viewed as the process of returning metals to their natural state—the ores from which they were originally obtained. Corrosion involves oxidation of the metal. Since corroded metal often loses its structural integrity and attractiveness, this spontaneous process has great economic impact. Approximately one-fifth of the iron and steel produced annually is used to replace rusted metal.

Metals corrode because they oxidize easily. Table 17.1 shows that, with the exception of gold, those metals commonly used for structural and decorative purposes all have standard reduction potentials less positive than that of oxygen gas. When any of these half-reactions is reversed (to show oxidation of the metal) and combined with the reduction half-reaction for oxygen, the result is a positive $\mathscr{E}°$ value. Thus the oxidation of most metals by oxygen is spontaneous (although we cannot tell from the potential how fast it will occur).

In view of the large difference in reduction potentials between oxygen and most metals, it is surprising that the problem of corrosion does not completely prevent the use of metals in air. However, most metals develop a thin oxide coating, which tends to protect their internal atoms against further oxidation. The metal that best demonstrates this phenomenon is aluminum. With a reduction potential of -1.7 V, aluminum should be easily oxidized by O_2. According to the apparent thermodynamics of the reaction, an aluminum airplane could dissolve in a rainstorm. The fact that this very active metal can be used as a structural material is due to the formation of a thin, adherent layer of aluminum oxide (Al_2O_3), more properly represented as $Al_2(OH)_6$, which greatly inhibits further corrosion. The potential of the "passive," oxide-coated aluminum is -0.6 V, a value that causes it to behave much like a noble metal.

Iron also can form a protective oxide coating. This is not an infallible shield against corrosion, however; when steel is exposed to oxygen in moist air, the oxide that forms tends to scale off and expose new metal surfaces to corrosion.

The corrosion products of noble metals such as copper and silver are complex and affect the use of these metals as decorative materials. Under normal atmospheric conditions, copper forms an external layer of greenish copper carbonate called **patina.** *Silver tarnish* is silver sulfide (Ag_2S), which in thin layers gives the silver surface a richer appearance. Gold, with a positive standard reduction potential of 1.50 V, significantly larger than that for oxygen (1.23 V), shows no appreciable corrosion in air.

Corrosion of Iron

Since steel is the main structural material for bridges, buildings, and automobiles, controlling its corrosion is extremely important. To do this, we must understand the corrosion mechanism. Instead of being a direct oxidation process as we might expect, the corrosion of iron is an electrochemical reaction, as shown in Fig. 17.17.

Steel has a nonuniform surface because the chemical composition is not completely homogeneous. Also, physical strains leave stress points in the metal. These

Some metals, such as copper, gold, silver, and platinum, are relatively difficult to oxidize. These are often called **noble metals.**

(Anode reaction: Fe ⟶ Fe²⁺ + 2e⁻)   (Cathode reaction: $O_2 + 2H_2O + 4e^- \longrightarrow 4OH^-$)

Figure 17.17

The electrochemical corrosion of iron.

nonuniformities cause areas where the iron is more easily oxidized (*anodic regions*) than it is at others (*cathodic regions*). In the anodic regions each iron atom gives up two electrons to form the Fe^{2+} ion:

$$Fe \rightarrow Fe^{2+} + 2e^-$$

The electrons that are released flow through the steel, as they do through the wire of a galvanic cell, to a cathodic region, where they react with oxygen:

$$O_2 + 2H_2O + 4e^- \rightarrow 4OH^-$$

The Fe^{2+} ions formed in the anodic regions travel to the cathodic regions through the moisture on the surface of the steel, just as ions travel through a salt bridge in a galvanic cell. In the cathodic regions Fe^{2+} ions react with oxygen to form rust, which is hydrated iron(III) oxide of variable composition:

$$4Fe^{2+}(aq) + O_2(g) + (4 + 2n)H_2O(l) \rightarrow 2Fe_2O_3 \cdot nH_2O(s) + 8H^+(aq)$$
Rust

Because of the migration of ions and electrons, rust often forms at sites that are remote from those where the iron dissolved to form pits in the steel. The degree of hydration of the iron oxide affects the color of the rust, which may vary from black to yellow to the familiar reddish brown.

The electrochemical nature of the rusting of iron explains the importance of moisture in the corrosion process. Moisture must be present to act as a kind of salt bridge between anodic and cathodic regions. Steel does not rust in dry air, a fact that explains why cars last much longer in the arid Southwest than in the relatively humid Midwest. Salt also accelerates rusting, a fact all too easily recognized by car owners in the colder parts of the United States, where salt is used on roads to melt snow and ice. The severity of rusting is greatly increased because the dissolved salt on the moist steel surface increases the conductivity of the aqueous solution formed there and thus accelerates the electrochemical corrosion process. Chloride ions also form very stable complex ions with Fe^{3+}, and this factor tends to encourage the dissolving of the iron, again accelerating the corrosion.

A rusty shipwreck.

Prevention of Corrosion

Prevention of corrosion is an important way of conserving our natural resources of energy and metals. The primary means of protection is the application of a coating, most commonly paint or metal plating, to protect the metal from oxygen and moisture. Chromium and tin are often used to plate steel (see Section 17.8) because they

◀ **CHEMICAL IMPACT** ▶

Refurbishing the Lady

The recent restoration of the Statue of Liberty in New York harbor represents a fascinating blend of science, technology, and art. The statue consists of copper sheets attached to a framework of iron, which had become so weakened by corrosion during 100 years of exposure to the elements that the statue was in danger of collapsing.

Gustave Eiffel, who designed the ingenious support structure, knew from experience that if the copper touched the iron framework, the more active iron would corrode very rapidly. Why does this happen? It is apparent from the reduction potentials

$$Cu^{2+} + 2e^- \rightarrow Cu$$
$$\mathscr{E}° = 0.34 \text{ V}$$
$$Fe^{2+} + 2e^- \rightarrow Fe$$
$$\mathscr{E}° = -0.44 \text{ V}$$

that Cu^{2+} will spontaneously oxidize iron. However, as with many electrochemical processes, the situation is more complex than it first appears. Since we are talking about two metal strips touching each other, the question is: Where do the Cu^{2+} ions (the oxidizing agents) come from? In fact, research on this process suggests that the copper simply acts as a conductor for electrons and that the oxidizing agent is not Cu^{2+} at all but probably O_2 or oxides of N or S.

Whatever the mechanism, Eiffel attempted to combat the corrosion problem by inserting asbestos pads between the copper sheets and the frame. However, this idea did not work, probably because copper is such a good conductor that *any* contact between the two metals anywhere on the statue totally thwarted the effect of the insulation. In fact, the iron framework was found to be so corroded it had to be completely replaced with stainless steel, which is much more corrosion-resistant.

Stainless steel has its own problems, however. In being bent to achieve the intricate shapes needed, the steel bars often became brittle. Flexibility was restored by heating each bar to a very high temperature using a current of 30,000 amperes and then cooling the bar suddenly. (See Section 20.9, for more on the heat treatment of steel.) Unfortunately, this process also destroyed the resistance to corrosion of the stainless steel. That resistance had to be restored by soaking the bars in nitric acid, an oxidizing acid that re-forms the protective oxide coating removed by heating the stainless steel.

Another problem faced by the restorers was the removal of layers of coal tar and paint, which had been applied in vain attempts to protect the statue's interior. Although the iron could be cleaned by blasting with aluminum oxide powder, the more fragile copper sheets required a gentler treatment. The restorers discovered that liquid nitrogen (77 K) cracked the paint and caused it to peel off. The coal-tar layer under the paint was removed by blasting with baking soda ($NaHCO_3$), a substance sometimes used by museum curators for polishing dinosaur bones. While this worked very well, it created another chemical problem: where the baking soda seeped between the seams in the copper plates onto the exterior, the statue turned from green to light blue when it rained. After this phenomenon was observed for the first time, workers stationed on the exterior scaffolding immediately cleaned off any leaking $NaHCO_3$.

One of the most interesting aspects of the chemistry of the Statue of Liberty is the green patina on its surface. Copper metal exposed to the atmosphere changes from its bright reddish brown metallic luster first to an almost black color and then to the familiar green patina. The initial blackening is due mainly to the formation of copper oxide and copper sulfide. The green patina that then forms consists of thin layers of two types of basic copper sulfates: brochantite, $CuSO_4 \cdot 3Cu(OH)_2$, and antlerite, $CuSO_4 \cdot 2Cu(OH)_2$. Crystals of these compounds seem to be cemented onto the copper surface by organic molecules from the air.

In recent years, large areas of the stat-

The Statue of Liberty in New York harbor.

ue's left side have been observed to darken as if the patina were being removed. Scientists speculated that this may be the result of acid rain that converts brochantite to the more soluble antlerite, which is then washed off by rainwater.

To make any new copper sheets look like the old ones, the restorers transplanted the patina from a weathered piece of copper to the new surface. Applying acetone, an organic solvent, to the weathered surface and scraping with an abrasive cloth caused tiny flakes of patina to fall off. These flakes, applied to the new copper, attached themselves permanently in one to three weeks of exposure to the atmosphere.

The restoration of the Statue of Liberty made use of the latest advances in chemisty as well as facts known to most general chemistry students. It's an example of the fascinating and varied problems faced by chemists in their profession.

Suggested Reading
Ivars Peterson, ''Lessons Learned from a Lady,'' *Science News* **130** (1986): 392.

◀ **C H E M I C A L   I M P A C T** ▶

Paint That Stops Rust—Completely

Traditionally, paint has provided the most economical method for protecting steel against corrosion. However, as people who live in the Midwest know well, paint cannot prevent a car from rusting indefinitely. Eventually, flaws develop in the paint that allow the ravages of rusting to take place.

This situation may soon change. Chemists at Glidden Research Center in Ohio have developed a paint called Rustmaster Pro that worked so well to prevent rusting in its initial tests that the scientists did not believe their results. Steel coated with the new paint showed no signs of rusting after an astonishing 10,000 hours of exposure in a salt spray chamber at 38°C.

Rustmaster is a water-based polymer formulation that prevents corrosion in two different ways. First, the polymer layer that cures in air forms a barrier impenetrable to both oxygen and water vapor. Second, the chemicals in the coating react with the steel surface to produce an interlayer between the metal and the polymer coating. This interlayer is a complex mineral called pyroaurite that contains cations of the form $[M_{1-x}Z_x(OH)_2]^{x+}$, where M is a 2+ ion (Mg^{2+}, Fe^{2+}, Zn^{2+}, Co^{2+}, or Ni^{2+}), Z is a 3+ ion (Al^{3+}, Fe^{3+}, Mn^{3+}, Co^{3+}, or Ni^{3+}), and x is a number between 0 and 1. The anions in pyroaurite are typically CO_3^{2-}, Cl^-, and/or SO_4^{2-}.

This pyroaurite interlayer is the real secret of the paint's effectiveness. Because the corrosion of steel has an electrochemical mechanism, motion of ions must be possible between the cathodic and anodic areas on the surface of the steel for rusting to occur. However, the pyroaurite interlayer grows into the neighboring polymer layer, thus preventing this crucial movement of ions. In effect, this layer prevents corrosion in the same way that removing the salt bridge prevents current from flowing in a galvanic cell.

In addition to having an extraordinary corrosion-fighting ability, Rustmaster yields an unusually small quantity of volatile solvents as it dries. A typical paint can produce from 1 to 5 kg of volatiles per gallon; Rustmaster produces only 0.05 kg. This paint may signal a new era in corrosion prevention.

---

oxidize to form a durable, effective oxide coating. Zinc, also used to coat steel in a process called **galvanizing,** does not form an oxide coating. However, since it is a more active metal than iron, as the potentials for the oxidation half-reactions show:

$$Fe \rightarrow Fe^{2+} + 2e^- \qquad -\mathscr{E}° = 0.44 \text{ V}$$
$$Zn \rightarrow Zn^{2+} + 2e^- \qquad -\mathscr{E}° = 0.76 \text{ V}$$

any oxidation that occurs dissolves zinc rather than iron. Recall that the reaction with the most positive standard potential has the greatest thermodynamic tendency to occur. Thus zinc acts as a "sacrificial" coating on steel.

Alloying is also used to prevent corrosion. *Stainless steel* contains chromium and nickel, both of which form oxide coatings that change steel's reduction potential to one characteristic of the noble metals. In addition, a new technology is now being developed to create surface alloys. That is, instead of forming a metal alloy such as stainless steel, which has the same composition throughout, a cheaper carbon steel is treated by ion bombardment to produce a thin layer of stainless steel or other desirable alloy on the surface. In this process, a "plasma" or "ion gas" of the alloying ions is formed at high temperatures and is then directed onto the surface of the metal.

Cathodic protection is a method most often employed to protect steel in buried fuel tanks and pipelines. An active metal, such as magnesium, is connected by a wire to the pipeline or tank to be protected [Fig. 17.18(a)]. Because the magnesium is a better reducing agent than iron, electrons are furnished by the magnesium rather than by the iron, keeping the iron from being oxidized. As oxidation occurs, the magnesium anode dissolves, and so it must be replaced periodically. Ships' hulls are protected in a similar way by attaching bars of titanium metal to the steel hull [Fig. 17.18(b)]. In salt water the titanium acts as the anode and is oxidized instead of the steel hull (the cathode).

(a)

Figure 17.18

(a) Cathodic protection of an underground pipe. (b) Cathodic protection is also used to prevent corrosion of the hulls of ships, such as this one belonging to the U.S. Navy.

(b)

17.7 Electrolysis

Purpose

- To describe the stoichiometry of electrolysis reactions.
- To show how to predict the order of electrolysis of the components of a mixture.

An electrolytic cell uses electrical energy to produce a chemical change that would otherwise not occur spontaneously.

A galvanic cell produces current when an oxidation–reduction reaction proceeds spontaneously. A similar apparatus, an **electrolytic cell,** uses electrical energy to produce chemical change. The process of **electrolysis** involves *forcing a current through a cell to produce a chemical change for which the cell potential is negative;* that is, electrical work causes an otherwise nonspontaneous chemical reaction to occur. Electrolysis has great practical importance; for example, charging a battery, producing aluminum metal, and chrome plating an object are all done electrolytically.

To illustrate the difference between a galvanic cell and an electrolytic cell, consider the cell shown in Fig. 17.19(a) as it runs spontaneously to produce 1.10 V. In this *galvanic* cell the reaction at the anode is

$$Zn \rightarrow Zn^{2+} + 2e^-$$

whereas at the cathode the reaction is

$$Cu^{2+} + 2e^- \rightarrow Cu$$

Figure 17.19(b) shows an external power source forcing electrons through the cell in the *opposite* direction to that in (a). This requires an external potential greater than 1.10 V, which must be applied in opposition to the natural cell potential. This device is an *electrolytic cell*. Notice that since electron flow is opposite in the two

(a)

(b)

Figure 17.19

(a) A standard galvanic cell based on the spontaneous reaction

$$Zn + Cu^{2+} \rightarrow Zn^{2+} + Cu$$

(b) A standard electrolytic cell. A power source forces the reaction $Cu + Zn^{2+} \rightarrow Cu^{2+} + Zn$ to occur.

cases, the anode and cathode are reversed between (a) and (b). Also, ion flow through the salt bridge is opposite in the two cells.

Now we will consider the stoichiometry of electrolytic processes, that is, *how much chemical change occurs with the flow of a given current for a specified time.* Suppose we wish to determine the mass of copper that is plated out when a current of 10.0 amps [an **ampere** (amp), abbreviated A, is *1 coulomb of charge per second*] is passed for 30.0 minutes through a solution containing Cu^{2+}. **Plating** means depositing the neutral metal on the electrode by reducing the metal ions in solution. In this case each Cu^{2+} ion requires two electrons to become an atom of copper metal:

$$Cu^{2+}(aq) + 2e^- \rightarrow Cu(s)$$

This reduction process will occur at the cathode of the electrolytic cell.

To solve this stoichiometry problem, we need the following steps:

current and time	$\xrightarrow{1}$	quantity of charge in coulombs	$\xrightarrow{2}$	moles of electrons	$\xrightarrow{3}$	moles of copper	$\xrightarrow{4}$	grams of copper

1 A = 1 C/s

STEP 1

Since an amp is a coulomb of charge per second, we multiply the current by the time in seconds to obtain the total coulombs of charge passed into the Cu^{2+} solution at the cathode:

$$\text{Coulombs of charge} = \text{amps} \times \text{seconds} = \frac{C}{s} \times s$$

$$= 10.0\frac{C}{s} \times 30.0 \text{ min} \times 60.0\frac{s}{\text{min}}$$

$$= 1.80 \times 10^4 \text{ C}$$

STEP 2

Since 1 mole of electrons carries a charge of 1 faraday, or 96,485 coulombs, we can calculate the number of moles of electrons required to carry 1.80×10^4 coulombs of charge:

$$1.80 \times 10^4 \text{ C} \times \frac{1 \text{ mol e}^-}{96,485 \text{ C}} = 1.87 \times 10^{-1} \text{ mol e}^-$$

This means that 0.187 mole of electrons flowed into the Cu^{2+} solution.

STEP 3

Each Cu^{2+} ion requires two electrons to become a copper atom. Thus each mole of electrons produces $\frac{1}{2}$ mole of copper metal:

$$1.87 \times 10^{-1} \text{ mol e}^- \times \frac{1 \text{ mol Cu}}{2 \text{ mol e}^-} = 9.35 \times 10^{-2} \text{ mol Cu}$$

STEP 4

We now know the moles of copper metal plated onto the cathode, and we can calculate the mass of copper formed:

$$9.35 \times 10^{-2} \text{ mol Cu} \times \frac{63.546 \text{ g}}{\text{mol Cu}} = 5.94 \text{ g Cu}$$

Sample Exercise 17.9

How long must a current of 5.00 A be applied to a solution of Ag^+ to produce 10.5 g silver metal?

Solution

In this case, we must use the steps given earlier in reverse:

$$\boxed{\begin{array}{c}\text{grams} \\ \text{of} \\ \text{silver}\end{array}} \longrightarrow \boxed{\begin{array}{c}\text{moles} \\ \text{of} \\ \text{silver}\end{array}} \longrightarrow \boxed{\begin{array}{c}\text{moles of} \\ \text{electrons} \\ \text{required}\end{array}} \longrightarrow \boxed{\begin{array}{c}\text{coulombs} \\ \text{of charge} \\ \text{required}\end{array}} \longrightarrow \boxed{\begin{array}{c}\text{time} \\ \text{required} \\ \text{for plating}\end{array}}$$

$$10.5 \text{ g Ag} \times \frac{1 \text{ mol Ag}}{107.868 \text{ g Ag}} = 9.73 \times 10^{-2} \text{ mol Ag}$$

Each Ag^+ ion requires one electron to become a silver atom:

$$Ag^+ + e^- \rightarrow Ag$$

Thus 9.73×10^{-2} mol of electrons is required, and we can calculate the quantity of charge carried by these electrons:

$$9.73 \times 10^{-2} \text{ mol e}^- \times \frac{96,485 \text{ C}}{\text{mol e}^-} = 9.39 \times 10^3 \text{ C}$$

The 5.00 A (5.00 C/s) of current must produce 9.39×10^3 C of charge. Thus

$$\left(5.00\frac{\text{C}}{\text{s}}\right) \times (\text{time, in s}) = 9.39 \times 10^3 \text{ C}$$

Sample Exercise 17.9 describes only the half cell of interest. There also must be an anode at which oxidation is occurring.

$$\text{Time} = \frac{9.39 \times 10^3}{5.00}\,s = 1.88 \times 10^3\ s = 31.3\ \text{min}$$

Electrolysis of Water

We have seen that hydrogen and oxygen combine spontaneously to form water and that the accompanying decrease in free energy can be used to run a fuel cell to produce electricity. The reverse process, which is of course nonspontaneous, can be forced by electrolysis:

Anode reaction:	$2H_2O \rightarrow O_2 + 4H^+ + 4e^-$	$-\mathscr{E}° = -1.23$ V
Cathode reaction:	$4H_2O + 4e^- \rightarrow 2H_2 + 4OH^-$	$\mathscr{E}° = -0.83$ V
Net reaction:	$6H_2O \rightarrow 2H_2 + O_2 + \underset{4H_2O}{4(H^+ + OH^-)}$	$\mathscr{E}° = -2.06$ V

or

$$2H_2O \rightarrow 2H_2 + O_2$$

Note that these potentials assume an anode chamber with 1 M H^+ and a cathode chamber with 1 M OH^-. In pure water, where $[H^+] = [OH^-] = 10^{-7}\ M$, the potential for the overall process is -1.23 V.

In practice, however, if platinum electrodes connected to a 6-V battery are dipped into pure water, no reaction is observed because pure water contains so few ions that only a negligible current can flow. However, addition of even a small amount of a soluble salt causes an immediate evolution of bubbles of hydrogen and oxygen, as illustrated in Fig. 17.20.

Electrolysis of Mixtures of Ions

Suppose a solution in an electrolytic cell contains the ions Cu^{2+}, Ag^+, and Zn^{2+}. If the voltage is initially very low and is gradually turned up, in which order will the metals be plated out onto the cathode? This question can be answered by looking at the standard reduction potentials of these ions:

$$Ag^+ + e^- \rightarrow Ag \qquad \mathscr{E}° = 0.80\ \text{V}$$
$$Cu^{2+} + 2e^- \rightarrow Cu \qquad \mathscr{E}° = 0.34\ \text{V}$$
$$Zn^{2+} + 2e^- \rightarrow Zn \qquad \mathscr{E}° = -0.76\ \text{V}$$

Figure 17.20
The electrolysis of water produces hydrogen gas at the cathode (*on the right*) and oxygen gas at the anode (*on the left*).

Remember that the more *positive* the $\mathscr{E}°$ value, the more the reaction has a tendency to proceed in the direction indicated. Of the three reactions listed, the reduction of Ag^+ occurs most easily, and the order of oxidizing ability is

$$Ag^+ > Cu^{2+} > Zn^{2+}$$

This means that silver will plate out first as the potential is increased, followed by copper, and finally zinc.

Sample Exercise 17.10

An acidic solution contains the ions Ce^{4+}, VO_2^+, and Fe^{3+}. Using the $\mathscr{E}°$ values listed in Table 17.1, give the order of oxidizing ability of these species and predict which one will be reduced at the cathode of an electrolytic cell at the lowest voltage.

Solution

The half-reactions and $\mathscr{E}°$ values are

$$Ce^{4+} + e^- \rightarrow Ce^{3+} \qquad\qquad \mathscr{E}° = 1.70 \text{ V}$$
$$VO_2^+ + 2H^+ + e^- \rightarrow VO^{2+} + H_2O \qquad \mathscr{E}° = 1.00 \text{ V}$$
$$Fe^{3+} + e^- \rightarrow Fe^{2+} \qquad\qquad \mathscr{E}° = 0.77 \text{ V}$$

The order of oxidizing ability is therefore

$$Ce^{4+} > VO_2^+ > Fe^{3+}$$

The Ce^{4+} ion will be reduced at the lowest voltage in an electrolytic cell.

◀ **CHEMICAL IMPACT** ▶

The Chemistry of Sunken Treasure

When the galleon *Atocha* was destroyed on a reef by a hurricane in 1622, it was bound for Spain carrying approximately 47 tons of copper, gold, and silver from the New World. The bulk of the treasure was silver bars and coins packed in wooden chests. When treasure hunter Mel Fisher salvaged the silver in 1985, corrosion and marine growth had transformed the shiny metal into something that looked like coral. Restoring the silver to its original condition required an understanding of the chemical changes that had occurred in 350 years of being submerged in the ocean. Much of this chemistry we have already considered at various places in this text.

As the wooden chests containing the silver decayed, the oxygen supply was depleted, favoring the growth of certain bacteria that use the sulfate ion rather than oxygen as an oxidizing agent to generate energy. As these bacteria consume sulfate ions, they release hydrogen sulfide gas that reacts with silver to form black silver sulfide:

$$2Ag(s) + H_2S(aq) \rightarrow Ag_2S(s) + H_2(g)$$

Thus, over the years, the surface of the silver became covered with a tightly adhering layer of corrosion, which fortunately protected the silver underneath and thus prevented total conversion of the silver to silver sulfide.

Another change that took place as the wood decomposed was the formation of carbon dioxide. This shifted the equilibrium that is present in the ocean,

$$CO_2(aq) + H_2O(l) \rightleftharpoons HCO_3^-(aq) + H^+$$

to the right, producing higher concentrations of HCO_3^-. In turn, the HCO_3^- reacted with Ca^{2+} ions present in the seawater to form calcium carbonate:

$$Ca^{2+}(aq) + HCO_3^-(aq) \rightleftharpoons$$
$$CaCO_3(s) + H^+(aq)$$

Calcium carbonate is the main component of limestone. Thus, over time, the corroded silver coins and bars became encased in limestone.

Both the limestone formation and the corrosion had to be dealt with. Since $CaCO_3$ contains the basic anion CO_3^{2-}, acid dissolves limestone:

$$2H^+(aq) + CaCO_3(s) \rightarrow$$
$$Ca^{2+}(aq) + CO_2(g) + H_2O(l)$$

Soaking the mass of coins in a buffered acidic bath for several hours allowed the individual pieces to be separated, and the black Ag_2S on the surfaces was revealed. An abrasive could not be used to remove this corrosion; it would have destroyed the details of the engraving—a very valuable feature of the coins to a historian or a collector—and it would have washed away some of the silver. Instead, the corrosion reaction was reversed through electrolytic reduction. The coins were connected to the cathode of an electrolytic cell in a di-

lute sodium hydroxide solution as represented in the figure.

As electrons flow, the Ag^+ ions in the silver sulfide are reduced to silver metal:

$$Ag_2S + 2e^- \rightarrow Ag + S^{2-}$$

As a by-product, bubbles of hydrogen gas from the reduction of water form on the surface of the coins:

$$2H_2O + 2e^- \rightarrow H_2(g) + 2OH^-$$

The agitation caused by the bubbles loosens the flakes of metal sulfide and helps clean the coins.

Using these procedures, it has been possible to restore the treasure to very nearly its condition when the *Atocha* sailed many years ago.

The principle described in this section is very useful, but it must be applied with some caution. For example, in the electrolysis of an aqueous solution of sodium chloride, we should be able to use $\mathscr{E}°$ values to predict the products. Of the major species in the solution (Na^+, Cl^-, and H_2O), only Cl^- and H_2O can be readily oxidized. The half-reactions (written as oxidization processes) are

$$2Cl^- \rightarrow Cl_2 + 2e^- \qquad -\mathscr{E}° = -1.36 \text{ V}$$
$$2H_2O \rightarrow O_2 + 4H^+ + 4e^- \qquad -\mathscr{E}° = -1.23 \text{ V}$$

Since water has the more positive potential, we would expect to see O_2 produced at the anode because it is easier (thermodynamically) to oxidize H_2O than Cl^-. Actually, this does not happen. As the voltage is increased in the cell, the Cl^- ion is the first to be oxidized. A much higher potential than expected is required to oxidize water. The voltage required in excess of the expected value (called the **overvoltage**) is much greater for the production of O_2 than for Cl_2, which explains why chlorine is produced first.

The causes of overvoltage are very complex. Basically, the phenomenon is caused by difficulties in transferring electrons from the species in the solution to the atoms on the electrode across the electrode–solution interface. Because of this situation, $\mathscr{E}°$ values must be used cautiously in predicting the actual order of oxidation or reduction of species in an electrolytic cell.

17.8 Commercial Electrolytic Processes

Purpose

- To discuss the manufacture of aluminum, the chlor–alkali process, and other industrial applications of electrolysis.

The chemistry of metals is characterized by their ability to donate electrons to form ions. Because metals are typically such good reducing agents, most are found in nature in *ores,* mixtures of ionic compounds often containing oxide, sulfide, and silicate anions. The noble metals, such as gold, silver, and platinum, are more difficult to oxidize and are often found as pure metals.

Production of Aluminum

Aluminum is one of the most abundant elements on earth, ranking third behind oxygen and silicon. Since aluminum is a very active metal, it is found in nature as its oxide in an ore called **bauxite** (named after Les Baux, France, where it was discovered in 1821). Production of aluminum metal from its ore proved to be more difficult than production of most other metals. In 1782 Lavoisier recognized aluminum to be a metal "whose affinity for oxygen is so strong that it cannot be overcome by any known reducing agent." As a result, pure aluminum metal remained unknown. Finally, in 1854 a process was found for producing metallic aluminum using sodium, but aluminum remained a very expensive rarity. In fact, it is said that Napoleon III served his most honored guests with aluminum forks and spoons, while the others had to settle for gold and silver utensils.

The breakthrough came in 1886 when two men, Charles M. Hall in the United States and Paul Heroult in France, almost simultaneously discovered a practical

Figure 17.21

Charles Martin Hall (1863–1914) was a student at Oberlin College in Ohio when he first became interested in aluminum. One of his professors commented that anyone who could manufacture aluminum cheaply would make a fortune, and Hall decided to give it a try. The 21-year-old Hall worked in a wooden shed near his house with an iron frying pan as a container, a blacksmith's forge as a heat source, and galvanic cells constructed from fruit jars. Using these crude galvanic cells, Hall found that he could produce aluminum by passing a current through a molten Al_2O_3/Na_3AlF_6 mixture. By a strange coincidence, Paul Heroult, a Frenchman who was born and died in the same years as Hall, made the same discovery at about the same time.

electrolytic process for producing aluminum (see Fig. 17.21). The key factor in the **Hall–Heroult process** is the use of molten cryolite (Na_3AlF_6) as the solvent for the aluminum oxide.

Electrolysis is possible only if ions can move to the electrodes. A common method for producing ion mobility is dissolving the substance to be electrolyzed in water. This is not possible in the case of aluminum because water is more easily reduced than Al^{3+}, as the following standard reduction potentials show:

$$Al^{3+} + 3e^- \rightarrow Al \qquad \mathscr{E}° = -1.66 \text{ V}$$
$$2H_2O + 2e^- \rightarrow H_2 + 2OH^- \qquad \mathscr{E}° = -0.83 \text{ V}$$

Thus aluminum metal cannot be plated out of an aqueous solution of Al^{3+}.

Ion mobility also can be produced by melting the salt. But the melting point of solid Al_2O_3 is much too high (2050°C) to allow practical electrolysis of the molten oxide. A mixture of Al_2O_3 and Na_3AlF_6, however, has a melting point of 1000°C, and the resulting molten mixture can be used to obtain aluminum metal electrolytically. Because of this discovery by Hall and Heroult, the price of aluminum plunged (see Table 17.3), and its use became economically feasible.

Bauxite is not pure aluminum oxide (called **alumina**) but also contains the oxides of iron, silicon, and titanium, and various silicate materials. To obtain the pure hydrated alumina ($Al_2O_3 \cdot nH_2O$), the crude bauxite is treated with aqueous sodium hydroxide. Being amphoteric, alumina dissolves in the basic solution:

$$Al_2O_3(s) + 2OH^-(aq) \rightarrow 2AlO_2^-(aq) + H_2O(l)$$

The other metal oxides, which are basic, remain as solids. The solution containing the aluminate ion (AlO_2^-) is separated from the sludge of other oxides and is acidified with carbon dioxide gas, causing the hydrated alumina to reprecipitate:

$$2CO_2(g) + 2AlO_2^-(aq) + (n + 1)H_2O(l) \rightarrow 2HCO_3^-(aq) + Al_2O_3 \cdot nH_2O(s)$$

The purified alumina is then mixed with cryolite and melted, and the aluminum ion is reduced to aluminum metal in an electrolytic cell of the type shown in Fig. 17.22. Because the electrolyte solution contains a large number of aluminum-containing ions, the chemistry is not completely clear. However, the alumina probably reacts with the cryolite anion as follows:

$$Al_2O_3 + 4AlF_6^{3-} \rightarrow 3Al_2OF_6^{2-} + 6F^-$$

The electrode reactions are thought to be

Cathode reaction: $\qquad AlF_6^{3-} + 3e^- \rightarrow Al + 6F^-$

Anode reaction: $\qquad 2Al_2OF_6^{2-} + 12F^- + C \rightarrow 4AlF_6^{3-} + CO_2 + 4e^-$

The overall cell reaction can be written as

$$2Al_2O_3 + 3C \rightarrow 4Al + 3CO_2$$

The aluminum produced in this electrolytic process is 99.5% pure. To be useful as a structural material, aluminum is alloyed with metals such as zinc (used for trailer and aircraft construction) and manganese (used for cooking utensils, storage tanks, and highway signs). The production of aluminum consumes about almost 5% of all the electricity used in the United States.

Electrodes of
graphite rods

To external
power source

Carbon
dioxide
formed at
the anodes

Molten Al_2O_3/Na_3AlF_6
mixture

Carbon-lined iron tank

Molten
aluminum

Plug

Table 17.3

The Price of Aluminum over the Last Century

Date	Price of aluminum ($/lb)*
1855	100,000
1885	100
1890	2
1895	0.50
1970	0.30
1980	0.80

*Note the precipitous drop in price after the discovery of the Hall–Heroult process.

Figure 17.22

A schematic diagram of an electrolytic cell for producing aluminum by the Hall–Heroult process. Because molten aluminum is more dense than the mixture of molten cryolite and alumina, it settles to the bottom of the cell and is drawn off periodically. The graphite electrodes are gradually eaten away and must be replaced from time to time. The cell operates at a current flow of up to 250,000 A.

Electrorefining of Metals

Purification of metals is another important application of electrolysis. For example, impure copper from the chemical reduction of copper ore is cast into large slabs that serve as the anodes for electrolytic cells. Aqueous copper sulfate is the electrolyte, and thin sheets of ultrapure copper function as the cathodes (see Fig. 17.23).

The main reaction at the anode is

$$Cu \rightarrow Cu^{2+} + 2e^-$$

Figure 17.23

Ultrapure copper sheets that serve as the cathodes are lowered between slabs of impure copper that serve as the anodes into a tank containing an aqueous solution of copper sulfate ($CuSO_4$). It takes about four weeks for the anodes to dissolve and for the pure copper to be deposited on the cathodes.

◀ C H E M I C A L   I M P A C T ▶

Batteries of the Future

A possible alternative to the internal combustion engine used in present-day automobiles is an electric motor powered by batteries. This and many other applications have stimulated research into new types of efficient batteries. In fact, some types being developed are capable of producing five to ten times as much power per unit of weight as the lead storage battery.

Ion mobility is needed in a battery to prevent charge polarization. Usually this is accomplished with an aqueous electrolyte. But there is now considerable interest in solid ceramic materials that transport ions very efficiently. For example, in the **beta,** or **sodium–sulfur, battery,** a solid electrolyte, called **beta alumina,** composed of a mixture of sodium, aluminum, lithium, and magnesium oxides, separates the electrode compartments. Liquid sodium is the reducing agent (the anode), and liquid sulfur is the oxidizing agent (the cathode). Although the beta battery must be operated at 350°C to keep the reactants liquid, the system shows promise because it can store approximately four times as much energy per unit of weight and can undergo approximately three times as many discharge/charge cycles as the lead storage battery. Asea Brown Boveri, a German battery manufacturer, has recently teamed with the automaker BMW to assemble a car powered by a 584-pound liquid sodium–sulfur battery. This car has a top speed of 60 mi/h, a cruising range of about 100 miles on a full charge, and a battery life projected to be as much as 125,000 miles.

Another promising power source is the **aluminum–air battery,** which is under development by chemist John Cooper at Lawrence Livermore National Laboratory in California. This is really a combination battery and fuel cell, since it uses a stored quantity of aluminum metal and requires a continuous supply of humid air from the atmosphere. A diagram of the cell is shown in Fig. 17.24. The aluminum–air battery is a flow system, since air and the

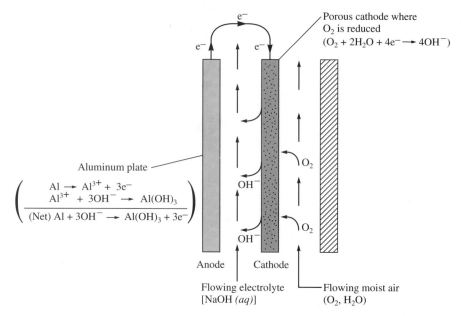

Figure 17.24

The aluminum–air battery. Aluminum is the reducing agent, and oxygen gas from the air is the oxidizing agent. As the aluminum loses electrons and dissolves, it forms aluminum hydroxide in the flowing aqueous sodium hydroxide solution.

aqueous sodium hydroxide electrolyte flow past the electrodes. As the cell runs, aluminum and water are consumed, and aluminum hydroxide is produced. Periodically, the aluminum plate must be replaced, water added, and the aluminum hydroxide removed. It is estimated that a small car with an aluminum–air battery weighing approximately 500 pounds could travel about 3000 miles before the aluminum needed to be replaced. Every 250 miles during the trip, 6 gallons of water would be needed and the solid aluminum hydroxide would have to be removed.

One new type of battery being studied has no metal electrodes or metal ions [Fig. 17.25(a)]. The electrodes are thin films of giant **polyacetylene** molecules (polymers) of the form shown below:

The battery is charged by attaching it to a power source, which forces electrons from one polyacetylene electrode to the other. As one electrode gains electrons, positive ions from the electrolyte diffuse into the film to balance the charge. The other electrode, which has given up electrons, absorbs anions to balance the charge [see Fig. 17.25(b)]. The battery discharges, generating a current to run an electric motor, as the excess electrons flow from the electron-rich anode to the electron-deficient cathode [see Fig. 17.25(c)].

◀ **C H E M I C A L   I M P A C T** ▶

Figure 17.25

A battery with polyacetylene electrodes. (a) The uncharged battery. (b) The charging process using an external power source. (c) The discharging battery running an electric motor.

Suggested Reading

1. Mercouri Kanatzidis, "Conductive Polymers," *Chem. Eng. News* (Dec. 3, 1990): 36.

2. Richard C. Alkire, "Electrochemical Engineering," *J. Chem. Ed.* **60** (1983): 274.

3. Jacob Jorné, "Flow Batteries," *Am. Sci.* **71** (1983): 507.

4. Anthony F. Sammells, "Fuel Cells and Electrochemical Energy Storage," *J. Chem. Ed.* **60** (1983): 320.

Other metals such as iron and zinc are also oxidized from the impure anode:

$$Zn \rightarrow Zn^{2+} + 2e^-$$
$$Fe \rightarrow Fe^{2+} + 2e^-$$

Noble metal impurities in the anode are not oxidized at the voltage used; they fall to the bottom of the cell to form a sludge, which is processed to remove the valuable silver, gold, and platinum.

The Cu^{2+} ions from the solution are deposited onto the cathode

$$Cu^{2+} + 2e^- \rightarrow Cu$$

producing copper that is 99.95% pure.

Metal Plating

Metals that readily corrode can often be protected by the application of a thin coating of a metal that resists corrosion. Examples are "tin" cans, which are actually steel cans with a thin coating of tin, and chrome-plated steel bumpers for automobiles.

An object can be plated by making it the cathode in a tank containing ions of the plating metal. The silver plating of a spoon is shown schematically in Fig. 17.26(b). In an actual plating process, the solution also contains ligands that form complexes

Figure 17.26

(a) A silver-plated teapot. Silver plating is often used to beautify and protect cutlery and items of table service. (b) Schematic of the electroplating of a spoon. The item to be plated is the cathode, and the anode is a silver bar. Silver is plated out at the cathode: $Ag^+ + e^- \rightarrow Ag$. Note that a salt bridge is not needed here because Ag^+ ions are involved at both electrodes.

with the silver ion. By lowering the concentration of Ag^+ in this way, a smooth, even coating of silver is obtained.

Electrolysis of Sodium Chloride

Sodium metal is mainly produced by the electrolysis of molten sodium chloride. Because solid NaCl has a rather high melting point (800°C), it is usually mixed with solid $CaCl_2$ to lower the melting point to about 600°C. The mixture is then electrolyzed in a **Downs cell,** as illustrated in Fig. 17.27, where the reactions are

Anode reaction: $2Cl^- \rightarrow Cl_2 + 2e^-$

Cathode reaction: $Na^+ + e^- \rightarrow Na$

At the temperatures in the Downs cell, the sodium is liquid and is drained off, then cooled, and cast into blocks. Because it is so reactive, sodium must be stored in an inert solvent, such as mineral oil, to prevent its oxidation.

Electrolysis of aqueous sodium chloride (brine) is an important industrial process for the production of chlorine and sodium hydroxide. In fact, this process is the second largest consumer of electricity in the United States, after the production of aluminum. Sodium is not produced in this process under normal circumstances because H_2O is more easily reduced than Na^+, as the standard reduction potentials show:

$$Na^+ + e^- \rightarrow Na \qquad \mathscr{E}° = -2.71 \text{ V}$$
$$2H_2O + 2e^- \rightarrow H_2 + 2OH^- \qquad \mathscr{E}° = -0.83 \text{ V}$$

Hydrogen, not sodium, is produced at the cathode.

For the reasons we discussed in Section 17.7, chlorine gas is produced at the anode. Thus the electrolysis of brine produces hydrogen and chlorine:

Addition of a nonvolatile solute lowers the melting point of the solvent, molten NaCl in this case.

Figure 17.27

The Downs cell for the electrolysis of molten sodium chloride. The cell is designed so that the sodium and chlorine produced cannot come into contact with each other to reform NaCl.

Anode reaction: $2Cl^- \rightarrow Cl_2 + 2e^-$

Cathode reaction: $2H_2O + 2e^- \rightarrow H_2 + 2OH^-$

It leaves a solution containing dissolved NaOH and NaCl.

The contamination of the sodium hydroxide by NaCl can be virtually eliminated using a special **mercury cell** for electrolyzing brine (see Fig. 17.28). In this cell, mercury is the conductor at the cathode, and because hydrogen gas has an extremely high overvoltage with a mercury electrode, Na^+ is reduced instead of H_2O. The

Figure 17.28

The mercury cell for production of chlorine and sodium hydroxide. The large overvoltage required to produce hydrogen at a mercury electrode means that Na^+ ions are reduced rather than water. The sodium formed dissolves in the liquid mercury and is pumped to a chamber where it reacts with water.

resulting sodium metal dissolves in the mercury, forming a liquid alloy, which is then pumped to a chamber where the dissolved sodium reacts with water to produce hydrogen:

$$2Na(s) + 2H_2O(l) \rightarrow 2Na^+(aq) + 2OH^-(aq) + H_2(g)$$

Relatively pure solid NaOH can be recovered from the aqueous solution, and the regenerated mercury is then pumped back to the electrolysis cell. This process, called the **chlor–alkali process,** has been replaced by a process employing a semi-permeable membrane between the anode and the cathode that prevents mixing of the chloride and hydroxide ions.

FOR REVIEW

Summary

Electrochemistry is the study of the interchange of chemical and electrical energy that occurs through oxidation–reduction (redox) reactions, in which electrons are transferred from a reducing agent to an oxidizing agent. Oxidation is the loss of electrons, and reduction is the gain of electrons. It is useful to break a redox reaction into half-reactions, one involving oxidation and one involving reduction.

When a redox reaction occurs in solution, the electrons are transferred directly, and no useful work can be obtained from the chemical energy involved in the reaction. However, if the oxidizing agent is physically separated from the reducing agent so that the electrons must flow through a wire from one to the other, the chemical energy can produce useful work. A galvanic cell is a device in which chemical energy is transformed to electrical energy. The opposite process, where electrical energy is used to produce chemical change, is called electrolysis and is accomplished in an electrolytic cell by forcing current through the cell.

Oxidation occurs at the anode of a cell; reduction occurs at the cathode. The driving force on the electrons is called the cell potential ($\mathscr{E}_{cell}$). A galvanic cell always runs in the direction that gives a positive value for $\mathscr{E}_{cell}$. Standard reduction potentials are assigned to half-reactions written as reduction processes by arbitrarily assigning a potential of zero volts to the half-reaction $2H^+ + 2e^- \rightarrow H_2$ under standard conditions.

The unit of electrical potential is the volt (V), defined as a joule of work per coulomb of charge:

$$\mathscr{E} \text{ (V)} = \frac{-\text{work (J)}}{\text{charge (C)}} = \frac{-w}{q}$$

where the sign for work is determined from the point of view of the system (cell). The maximum work can be calculated from the equation

$$-w_{max} = q\mathscr{E}_{max}$$

where $\mathscr{E}_{max}$ represents the cell potential when no current flows. Actual work is always less than the maximum possible work, since energy is wasted through frictional heating when a current flows through a wire.

For a process carried out at constant temperature and pressure, the change in free energy equals the maximum useful work obtainable from that process:

$$\Delta G = w_{max} = -q\mathscr{E}_{max} = -nF\mathscr{E}$$

where F (the faraday) is the charge of 1 mole of electrons (96,485 coulombs) and n is the number of moles of electrons transferred in the reaction.

A concentration cell is a galvanic cell in which both compartments have the same components but at different concentrations. The electrons flow in the direction that tends to equalize the concentrations.

The Nernst equation gives the relationship between the cell potential and the concentrations of the cell components:

$$\mathscr{E} = \mathscr{E}° - \frac{RT}{nF} \ln(Q)$$

When the cell is at 25°C, the Nernst equation can be written

$$\mathscr{E} = \mathscr{E}° - \frac{0.0592}{n} \log(Q)$$

When the cell is at equilibrium, $Q = K$ and $\mathscr{E}_{cell} = 0$. Thus the Nernst equation can be used to calculate the values of equilibrium constants for oxidation–reduction reactions.

A battery is a galvanic cell or group of cells connected in series, which serves as a source of direct current. The lead storage battery has a lead anode, a cathode of lead coated with PbO_2, and an electrolyte of sulfuric acid. Dry cell batteries do not have liquid electrolytes but a moist paste of either solid manganese dioxide, carbon, and ammonium chloride (the acid version) or potassium hydroxide or sodium hydroxide (the alkaline version). A case of zinc acts as the anode, and a carbon rod acts as the electrode for the cathode reaction.

Fuel cells are galvanic cells in which the reactants are continuously supplied. For example, a hydrogen–oxygen fuel cell is based on the reaction of hydrogen and oxygen gases to form water.

Corrosion involves the oxidation of metals to form mainly oxides and sulfides. Some metals, such as aluminum, form a thin protective coating of oxide that inhibits further corrosion. The corrosion of iron is an electrochemical process; different parts of the iron surface form anodic and cathodic regions. The Fe^{2+} ions formed in the anodic regions migrate through the moisture on the iron surface to the cathodic regions, and the electrons flow through the metal to the cathodic regions, where they react with oxygen in the air. Corrosion can be prevented by coating the iron with paint or a layer of a metal such as chromium, tin, or zinc; by alloying; and by cathodic protection.

Aluminum is commercially produced by the electrolysis of a molten alumina–cryolite mixture in the Hall–Heroult process. Metals such as copper can be refined electrolytically. The chlor–alkali process is used to manufacture chlorine and sodium hydroxide by electrolysis.

Key Terms

electrochemistry

Section 17.1
oxidation–reduction
   (redox) reaction
reducing agent
oxidizing agent
oxidation
reduction
half-reactions

salt bridge
porous disk
galvanic cell
anode
cathode
cell potential
   (electromotive force)
volt
voltmeter

potentiometer

Section 17.2
standard hydrogen electrode
standard reduction potential

Section 17.3
faraday

Section 17.4
concentration cell

Nernst equation
glass electrode
ion-selective electrode

Section 17.5
battery
lead storage battery
dry cell battery
fuel cell

Section 17.6
corrosion
galvanizing

cathodic protection
Section 17.7
electrolytic cell

electrolysis
ampere

Section 17.8
Downs cell

mercury cell
chlor–alkali process

A blue question or exercise number indicates that the answer to that question or exercise appears at the back of this book and a solution appears in the Solutions Guide.

Review of Oxidation–Reduction Reactions

If you have trouble with these exercises, you should review Sections 4.9 to 4.11.

1. Define *oxidation* and *reduction* both in terms of change in oxidation number and electron loss or gain.

2. Assign oxidation numbers to all the atoms in each of the following.
   a. HNO_3
   b. $CuCl_2$
   c. O_2
   d. H_2O_2
   e. $MgSO_4$
   f. Ag
   g. $PbSO_4$
   h. PbO_2
   i. $Na_2C_2O_4$
   j. CO_2
   k. $(NH_4)_2Ce(SO_4)_3$
   l. Cr_2O_3

3. Specify which of the following equations represent oxidation–reduction reactions, and indicate the oxidizing agent, the reducing agent, the species being oxidized, and the species being reduced.
   a. $CH_4(g) + H_2O(g) \rightarrow CO(g) + 3H_2(g)$
   b. $2AgNO_3(aq) + Cu(s) \rightarrow Cu(NO_3)_2(aq) + 2Ag(s)$
   c. $AgCl(s) + 2NH_3(aq) \rightarrow Ag(NH_3)_2^+(aq) + Cl^-(aq)$
   d. $Zn(s) + 2HCl(aq) \rightarrow ZnCl_2(aq) + H_2(g)$
   e. $2H^+(aq) + 2CrO_4^{2-}(aq) \rightarrow Cr_2O_7^{2-}(aq) + H_2O(l)$
   f. $2Fe(s) + 8HCl(aq) \rightarrow 2HFeCl_4(aq) + 3H_2(g)$

4. Balance each of the following equations by the half-reaction method for the pH conditions specified.
   a. $Cr(s) + NO_3^-(aq) \rightarrow Cr^{3+}(aq) + NO(g)$ (acidic)
   b. $Al(s) + MnO_4^-(aq) \rightarrow Al^{3+}(aq) + Mn^{2+}(aq)$ (acidic)
   c. $CH_3OH(aq) + Ce^{4+}(aq) \rightarrow CO_2(aq) + Ce^{3+}(aq)$
      (acidic)
   d. $SO_3^{2-}(aq) + MnO_4^-(aq) \rightarrow SO_4^{2-}(aq) + Mn^{2+}(aq)$
      (acidic)

   e. $PO_3^{3-}(aq) + MnO_4^-(aq) \rightarrow PO_4^{3-}(aq) + MnO_2(s)$
      (basic)
   f. $Mg(s) + OCl^-(aq) \rightarrow Mg(OH)_2(s) + Cl^-(aq)$ (basic)
   g. $Ni(CN)_4^{2-}(aq) + Ce^{4+}(aq)$
      $\rightarrow Ce(OH)_3(s) + Ni(OH)_2(s) + CO_3^{2-}(aq) + NO_3^-(aq)$
      (basic)
   h. $H_2CO(aq) + Ag(NH_3)_2^+(aq)$
      $\rightarrow HCO_3^-(aq) + Ag(s) + NH_3(aq)$ (basic)

Questions

5. Explain the difference between a galvanic and an electrolytic cell.

6. Why is it necessary to use a salt bridge or a porous disk in a galvanic cell?

7. Define the following.
   a. Cathode
   b. Anode
   c. Oxidation half-reaction
   d. Reduction half-reaction

8. Describe each of the following.
   a. Purification of a metal by electrolysis
   b. Cathodic protection

9. Give three methods by which metals are protected against corrosion.

10. What happens to $\mathscr{E}_{cell}$ as a battery discharges? Does a battery represent a system at equilibrium? Explain. What is $\mathscr{E}_{cell}$ when a battery reaches equilibrium?

Exercises

In this section similar exercises are paired.

Galvanic Cells

11. Sketch the galvanic cells based on the following overall reactions. Show the direction of electron flow, the direction of ion migration through the porous disk, and identify the cathode and anode. Give the overall balanced reaction. Assume that all concentrations are 1.0 M and that all partial pressures are 1.0 atm.
    a. $Cr^{3+}(aq) + Cl_2(g) \rightleftharpoons Cr_2O_7^{2-}(aq) + Cl^-(aq)$
    b. $Cu^{2+}(aq) + Mg(s) \rightleftharpoons Mg^{2+}(aq) + Cu(s)$

12. Sketch the galvanic cells based on the following reactions. Show the direction of electron flow and the direction of ion migration through the porous disk, and identify the cathode and anode. Give the overall balanced reaction. Assume that all concentrations are 1.0 M and that all partial pressures are 1.0 atm.
    a. $IO_3^-(aq) + Fe^{2+}(aq) \rightleftharpoons Fe^{3+}(aq) + I_2(s)$
    b. $Zn(s) + Ag^+(aq) \rightleftharpoons Zn^{2+}(aq) + Ag(s)$

13. Sketch the diagrams for galvanic cells (standard conditions) utilizing the following half-cells. Write balanced equations for the overall cell reaction.

Cathode	Anode
a. Cl_2/Cl^-	Br^-/Br_2
b. IO_4^-/IO_3^-	Mn^{2+}/MnO_4^-

14. Sketch the diagrams for galvanic cells (standard conditions) utilizing the following half-cells. Write balanced equations for the overall cell reaction.

Cathode	Anode
a. Ni^{2+}/Ni	Al/Al^{3+}
b. Co^{2+}/Co^{3+}	Fe^{3+}/Fe^{2+}

15. Give the standard line notation for each cell in Exercises 11 and 13.

16. Give the standard line notation for each cell in Exercises 12 and 14.

Cell Potentials, Standard Reduction Potentials, and Free Energy

17. Calculate $\mathscr{E}°$ values for the cells in Exercises 11 and 13. Standard reduction potentials are found in Table 17.1.

18. Calculate $\mathscr{E}°$ for the cells in Exercises 12 and 14. Standard reduction potentials are found in Table 17.1.

19. Calculate $\mathscr{E}°$ values for the following cells. Which reactions are spontaneous as written (under standard conditions)? Balance the reactions that are not already balanced. Standard reduction potentials are found in Table 17.1.
    a. $2Ag^+(aq) + Cu(s) \rightleftharpoons Cu^{2+}(aq) + 2Ag(s)$
    b. $Zn^{2+}(aq) + Ni(s) \rightleftharpoons Ni^{2+}(aq) + Zn(s)$

20. Calculate $\mathscr{E}°$ values for the following cells. Which reactions are spontaneous as written (under standard conditions)? Balance the reactions. Standard reduction potentials are found in Table 17.1.
    a. $MnO_4^-(aq) + I^-(aq) \rightleftharpoons I_2(aq) + Mn^{2+}(aq)$
    b. $MnO_4^-(aq) + F^-(aq) \rightleftharpoons F_2(g) + Mn^{2+}(aq)$

21. Answer the following questions using data from Table 17.1 (all under standard conditions).
    a. Is $H^+(aq)$ capable of oxidizing $Cu(s)$ to $Cu^{2+}(aq)$?
    b. Is $H^+(aq)$ capable of oxidizing $Mg(s)$?
    c. Is $Fe^{3+}(aq)$ capable of oxidizing $I^-(aq)$?
    d. Is $Fe^{3+}(aq)$ capable of oxidizing $Br^-(aq)$?

22. Answer the following questions using data from Table 17.1 (all under standard conditions).
    a. Is $H_2(g)$ capable of reducing $Ag^+(aq)$?
    b. Is $H_2(g)$ capable of reducing $Ni^{2+}(aq)$?
    c. Is $Fe^{2+}(aq)$ capable of reducing $VO_2^+(aq)$?
    d. Is $Fe^{2+}(aq)$ capable of reducing $Cr^{3+}(aq)$ to $Cr^{2+}(aq)$?
    e. Is $Fe^{2+}(aq)$ capable of reducing $Cr^{3+}(aq)$ to $Cr(s)$?
    f. Is $Fe^{2+}(aq)$ capable of reducing $Sn^{2+}(aq)$ to $Sn(s)$?

23. Using data from Table 17.1, place the following in order of increasing strength as oxidizing agents (all under standard conditions).

    MnO_4^-, Cl_2, $Cr_2O_7^{2-}$, Mg^{2+}, Fe^{2+}, Fe^{3+}

24. Using data from Table 17.1, place the following in order of increasing strength as reducing agents (all under standard conditions).

    Cr^{3+}, H_2, Zn, Li, F^-, Fe^{2+}

25. Consider only the species (standard conditions)

    Br^-, Br_2, H^+, H_2, La^{3+}, Ca, Cd

    in answering the following questions. Give reasons for your answers.
    a. Which is the strongest oxidizing agent?
    b. Which is the strongest reducing agent?
    c. Which species can be oxidized by MnO_4^- in acid?
    d. Which species can be reduced by $Zn(s)$?

26. Consider only the species (standard conditions)

    Ce^{4+}, Ce^{3+}, Fe^{2+}, Fe^{3+}, Fe, Mg^{2+}, Mg, Ni^{2+}, Sn

    in answering the following questions. Give reasons for your answers. (Use data from Table 17.1.)
    a. Which is the strongest oxidizing agent?
    b. Which is the strongest reducing agent?
    c. Will iron dissolve in a 1.0 M solution of Ce^{4+}? If so, will there be Fe^{2+} or Fe^{3+} ions resulting in the solution?
    d. Which of the species can be oxidized by $H^+(aq)$?
    e. Which of the species can be reduced by $H_2(g)$?
    f. Would you use Mg or Sn to reduce Fe^{3+} to Fe^{2+}?

27. Use the table of standard reduction potentials (Table 17.1) to pick a reagent that is capable of each of the following oxidations (under standard conditions in acid solution).
    a. Oxidize Hg to Hg_2^{2+} but not oxidize Hg_2^{2+} to Hg^{2+}
    b. Oxidize Br^- to Br_2 but not oxidize Cl^- to Cl_2
    c. Oxidize Mn to Mn^{2+} but not oxidize Ni to Ni^{2+}

28. Use the table of standard reduction potentials (Table 17.1) to pick a reagent that is capable of each of the following reductions (under standard conditions in acidic solution).
    a. Reduce Fe^{3+} to Fe^{2+} but not reduce Fe^{2+} to Fe
    b. Reduce Ag^+ to Ag but not reduce O_2 to H_2O_2

29. Is it possible for a reagent to reduce I_2 to I^- but not to reduce Cu^{2+} to Cu? What range of standard reduction potentials could such a reagent have?

30. The standard reduction potential for the half-reaction

    $$Sn^{4+} + 2e^- \rightarrow Sn^{2+}$$

    is +0.15 V. Use data from Table 17.1 to answer the following questions.
    a. Is it possible to find a reducing agent that will reduce Sn^{4+} to Sn^{2+} and not reduce Sn^{2+} to Sn? If so, name a reducing agent that can accomplish this.
    b. Is it possible to find an oxidizing agent that will oxidize Sn to Sn^{2+} but not oxidize Sn^{2+} to Sn^{4+}? If so, name an oxidizing agent that can do this.

31. Chlorine dioxide (ClO_2), which is produced by the reaction

    $$2NaClO_2(aq) + Cl_2(g) \rightarrow 2ClO_2(g) + 2NaCl(aq)$$

    has been tested as a disinfectant for municipal water treatment.
    a. Using data from Table 17.1, calculate $\mathscr{E}°$, $\Delta G°$, and K at 25°C for the production of ClO_2.
    b. One of the concerns in using ClO_2 as a disinfectant is that the carcinogenic chlorate ion (ClO_3^-) might be a by-product. It can be formed from the reaction

    $$ClO_2(g) \rightleftharpoons ClO_3^-(aq) + Cl^-(aq)$$

    Balance the equation for the decomposition of ClO_2.

32. The amount of manganese in steel is determined by changing it to permanganate ion. The steel is first dissolved in nitric acid, producing Mn^{2+} ions. These ions are then oxidized to the deeply colored MnO_4^- ions by periodate ion (IO_4^-) in acid solution.
    a. Complete and balance an equation describing each of the above reactions.
    b. Calculate $\mathscr{E}°$, $\Delta G°$, and K at 25°C for each reaction.

33. Calculate $\Delta G°$ and K at 25°C for the reactions in Exercises 11 and 13.

34. Calculate $\Delta G°$ and K at 25°C for the reactions in Exercises 12 and 14.

35. The equation $\Delta G° = -nF\mathscr{E}°$ also can be applied to half-reactions. For the half-reaction

    $$Ag^+ + e^- \rightarrow Ag \qquad \mathscr{E}° = 0.80 \text{ V}$$

    calculate the value of $\Delta G_f°$ for $Ag^+(aq)$.

36. Use standard reduction potentials to estimate $\Delta G_f°$ for $Fe^{2+}(aq)$ and $Fe^{3+}(aq)$.

37. Estimate $\mathscr{E}°$ for the half-reaction

    $$2H_2O + 2e^- \rightarrow H_2 + 2OH^-$$

    given the following values of $\Delta G_f°$:

    $$H_2O(l) = -237 \text{ kJ/mol}$$
    $$H_2(g) = 0.0$$
    $$OH^-(aq) = -157 \text{ kJ/mol}$$

    Compare this value of $\mathscr{E}°$ with the value of $\mathscr{E}°$ given in Table 17.1.

38. Calculate $\mathscr{E}°$ for the reaction

    $$CH_3OH(l) + \tfrac{3}{2}O_2(g) \rightarrow CO_2(g) + 2H_2O(l)$$

    using values of $\Delta G_f°$ in Appendix 4.

---

39. Use the half-reactions

$$PbSO_4 + 2e^- \rightarrow Pb + SO_4^{2-} \qquad \mathscr{E}° = -0.35 \text{ V}$$
$$Pb^{2+} + 2e^- \rightarrow Pb \qquad \mathscr{E}° = -0.13 \text{ V}$$

to calculate the value of the solubility product for $PbSO_4(s)$.

40. The solubility product for $CuI(s)$ is 1.1×10^{-12}. Calculate the value of $\mathscr{E}°$ for the half-reaction

$$CuI + e^- \rightarrow Cu + I^-$$

The Nernst Equation

41. Consider the concentration cell shown below. Calculate the cell potential at 25°C when the concentration of Ag^+ in the compartment on the right is the following.
    a. 1.0 M
    b. 2.0 M
    c. 0.10 M
    d. 4.0×10^{-5} M
    e. Calculate the potential when both solutions are 0.10 M in Ag^+.

    For each case, also identify the cathode, the anode, and the direction in which electrons flow.

42. Consider a concentration cell similar to the one shown in Exercise 41, except that both electrodes are made of Zn and in the left-hand compartment $[Zn^{2+}] = 1.0$ M. Calculate the cell potential at 25°C when the concentration of Zn^{2+} in the compartment on the right has each of the following values.
    a. 1.0 M
    b. 2.0 M
    c. 0.10 M
    d. 4.0×10^{-5} M
    e. Calculate the potential when both solutions are 2.5 M in Zn^{2+}.

    For each case, also identify the cathode, the anode, and the direction in which electrons flow.

43. Can permanganate ion oxidize Fe^{2+} to Fe^{3+} at 25°C under the following conditions?

$$[Mn^{2+}] = 1 \times 10^{-6} \text{ } M$$
$$[MnO_4^-] = 0.01 \text{ } M$$
$$[Fe^{2+}] = 1 \times 10^{-3} \text{ } M$$
$$[Fe^{3+}] = 1 \times 10^{-6} \text{ } M$$
$$pH = 4.0$$

44. Can cobalt metal be oxidized to Co^{2+} by air at 25°C under each of the following conditions?
    a. Under standard conditions in 1.0 M OH^- [For $Co(OH)_2(s)$, $K_{sp} = 2.5 \times 10^{-16}$.]
    b. Under standard conditions in 1.0 M H^+
    c. At pH = 7.00

$$Co^{2+} + 2e^- \rightarrow Co \qquad \mathscr{E}° = -0.277 \text{ V}$$

45. An electrochemical cell consists of a standard hydrogen electrode and a copper metal electrode.
    a. What is the potential of the cell at 25°C if the copper electrode is placed in a solution in which $[Cu^{2+}] = 2.5 \times 10^{-4}$ M?
    b. If the copper electrode is placed in a solution of 0.10 M NaOH that is saturated with $Cu(OH)_2$, what is the cell potential at 25°C? [For $Cu(OH)_2$, $K_{sp} = 1.6 \times 10^{-19}$.]
    c. The copper electrode is placed in a solution of unknown $[Cu^{2+}]$. The measured potential at 25°C is 0.195 V. What is $[Cu^{2+}]$?
    d. If you wished to construct a calibration curve for how the cell potential varies with $[Cu^{2+}]$, what would you plot in order to have a straight line? What would be the slope of this line?

46. An electrochemical cell consists of a silver metal electrode immersed in a solution with $[Ag^+] = 1.0$ M separated by a porous disk from a copper metal electrode.
    a. What is the potential of this cell at 25°C if the copper electrode is placed in a solution in which $[Cu^{2+}] = 1.3 \times 10^{-5}$ M?
    b. If the copper electrode is placed in a solution of 5.0 M NH_3 that is also 0.010 M in $Cu(NH_3)_4^{2+}$, what is the cell potential at 25°C?

$$[K_f \text{ for } Cu(NH_3)_4^{2+} \text{ is } 1.0 \times 10^{13}.]$$

    c. When the copper electrode is placed in a certain solution in which $[Cu^{2+}]$ is unknown, the measured cell potential at 25°C is 0.58 V. Calculate $[Cu^{2+}]$ in the unknown solution.

47. Consider the following half-reactions:

$$Pt^{2+} + 2e^- \rightarrow Pt \qquad \mathscr{E}° = 1.188 \text{ V}$$
$$PtCl_4^{2-} + 2e^- \rightarrow Pt + 4Cl^- \qquad \mathscr{E}° = 0.755 \text{ V}$$
$$NO_3^- + 4H^+ + 3e^- \rightarrow NO + 2H_2O \qquad \mathscr{E}° = 0.96 \text{ V}$$

Explain why platinum metal will dissolve in aqua regia (a mixture of hydrochloric and nitric acids) but not in either concentrated nitric or concentrated hydrochloric acid individually.

48. A cleaning solution for glassware is prepared by dissolving potassium dichromate in concentrated sulfuric acid. (This solution is becoming much less commonly used because of the carcinogenic properties of chromium(VI) compounds.) An unthinking chemist tried to prepare some cleaning solution from some waste potassium dichromate that had been contaminated by sodium chloride. On adding the solid to some sulfuric acid, he was driven from the lab by pungent fumes. What happened?

Electrolysis

49. How long will it take to plate out each of the following with a current of 100.0 A?
  a. 1.0 kg Al from aqueous Al^{3+}
  b. 1.0 g Ni from aqueous Ni^{2+}
  c. 5.0 mol Ag from aqueous Ag^+

50. What mass of each of the following substances can be produced in 1.0 hour with a current of 15 A?
  a. Co from aqueous Co^{2+}
  b. Hf from aqueous Hf^{4+}
  c. I_2 from aqueous KI
  d. Cr from molten CrO_3

51. What reaction will take place at the cathode and the anode when each of the following is electrolyzed?
  a. Molten KF
  b. 0.10 M KF solution
  c. 1.0 M H_2O_2 solution containing 1.0 M H_2SO_4

52. What reaction will take place at the cathode and the anode when each of the following is electrolyzed?
  a. Molten $CuCl_2$
  b. 1.0 M $CuCl_2$ solution
  c. Molten $MgCl_2$

53. A solution containing a 3+ metal ion is electrolyzed by a current of 5.0 A for 10.0 minutes. What is the identity of the metal if 1.18 g of metal was plated out in this electrolysis?

54. It took 74.6 seconds for a 2.50-A current to plate 0.1086 g of a metal from a solution containing M^{2+} ions. What is the metal?

55. What volume of F_2 gas, at 25°C and 1.00 atm, is produced when molten KF is electrolyzed by a current of 10.0 A for 2.00 hours? What mass of potassium metal is produced? At which electrode does each reaction occur?

56. What volumes of $H_2(g)$ and $O_2(g)$ at STP are produced from the electrolysis of water by a current of 2.50 A in 15.0 minutes?

57. Gold is produced electrochemically from a basic solution of $Au(CN)_4^-$. Gold metal and oxygen gas are produced at the electrodes. Write the overall cell reaction. What volume of pure oxygen gas is produced at 25°C and 740 torr for every kilogram of gold produced?

58. In the electrolysis of a sodium chloride solution, what volume of Cl_2 is produced in the same time it takes to produce 6.00 L of $H_2(g)$, both volumes measured at 0°C and 1 atm?

59. One of the few industrial-scale processes that produce organic compounds electrochemically is used by the Monsanto Company to produce 1,4-dicyanobutane. The reduction reaction is

$$2CH_2{=}CHCN + 2H^+ + 2e^- \rightarrow NC{-}(CH_2)_4{-}CN$$

The NC—$(CH_2)_4$—CN is then chemically reduced using hydrogen gas to H_2N—$(CH_2)_6$—NH_2, which is used in the production of nylon. What current must be used to produce 1.0×10^3 kg of NC—$(CH_2)_4$—CN per hour?

60. A single Hall–Heroult cell (as shown in Fig. 17.22) produces about 1 ton of aluminum in 24 hours. What current must be used to accomplish this?

61. It took 2.30 minutes using a current of 2.00 A to plate out all the silver from 0.250 L of a solution containing Ag^+. What was the original concentration of Ag^+ in the solution?

62. A solution containing Pt^{4+} is electrolyzed with a current of 4.00 A. How long will it take to plate out 99% of the platinum in 0.50 L of a 0.010 M solution of Pt^{4+}?

Additional Exercises

63. The saturated calomel electrode, abbreviated SCE, is often used as a reference electrode in making electrochemical measurements. The SCE is composed of mercury in contact with a saturated solution of calomel (Hg_2Cl_2). The electrolyte solution is saturated KCl. $\mathscr{E}_{SCE}$ is +0.242 V with respect to the standard hydrogen electrode. What will be the measured potential for each of the following cells (standard conditions), containing an SCE and the given half-cell components? In each case, indicate whether the SCE is the cathode or the anode. Standard reduction potentials are found in Table 17.1.
    a. Cu^{2+}/Cu ($Cu^{2+} + 2e^- \rightarrow Cu$)
    b. Fe^{3+}/Fe^{2+} ($Fe^{3+} + e^- \rightarrow Fe^{2+}$)
    c. $Ag/AgCl$ ($AgCl + e^- \rightarrow Ag + Cl^-$)
    d. Al/Al^{3+} ($Al^{3+} + 3e^- \rightarrow Al$)
    e. Ni/Ni^{2+} ($Ni^{2+} + 2e^- \rightarrow Ni$)

64. A disproportionation reaction involves a substance that acts as both an oxidizing and reducing agent, producing higher and lower oxidation states of the same element in the products. Which of the following disproportionation reactions are spontaneous under standard conditions?
    a. $2Cu^+(aq) \rightarrow Cu^{2+}(aq) + Cu(s)$
    b. $2Sn^{2+}(aq) \rightarrow Sn^{4+}(aq) + Sn(aq)$
       (See Exercise 30 for the Sn^{4+} reduction potential.)
    c. $3Fe^{2+}(aq) \rightarrow 2Fe^{3+}(aq) + Fe(s)$
    d. $HClO_2(aq) \rightarrow ClO_3^-(aq) + HClO(aq)$ (unbalanced)
    Use the half-reactions

    $ClO_3^- + 3H^+ + 2e^- \rightarrow HClO_2 + H_2O$ $\mathscr{E}^\circ = +1.21$ V
    $HClO_2 + 2H^+ + 2e^- \rightarrow HClO + H_2O$ $\mathscr{E}^\circ = +1.65$ V

65. A 1.0 M solution of Cu^+ ion spontaneously decomposes even if it is protected from the oxygen in the air. Use data from Table 17.1 to predict what reaction occurs. Calculate $\mathscr{E}^\circ$, ΔG°, and K for this reaction at 25°C.

66. Calculate ΔG° and K at 25°C for those reactions from Exercise 64 that are spontaneous under standard conditions.

67. Hydrogen peroxide can function either as an oxidizing agent or as a reducing agent. Referring to Table 17.1, write half-reactions for H_2O_2 acting in these roles. Calculate $\mathscr{E}^\circ$ for the reaction

    $$2H_2O_2 \rightarrow 2H_2O + O_2$$

68. Under standard conditions, what reaction occurs, if any, when each of the following operations is performed?
    a. Crystals of I_2 are added to a solution of NaCl.
    b. Cl_2 gas is bubbled into a solution of NaI.
    c. A silver wire is placed in a solution of $CuCl_2$.
    d. A lead wire is placed in a solution of $CuCl_2$.
    e. A solution of $FeSO_4$ is allowed to sit exposed to air.

69. For the reactions that occur in Exercise 68, write a balanced equation and calculate $\mathscr{E}^\circ$, ΔG°, and K at 25°C.

70. Calculate $\mathscr{E}^\circ$, ΔG°, and K at 25°C for each of the following reactions.

    a. $2Cu^+(aq) \rightarrow Cu(s) + Cu^{2+}(aq)$
    b. $2Na(s) + 2H_2O(l) \rightleftharpoons 2NaOH(aq) + H_2(g)$
    c. $Al(s) + 3H^+(aq) \rightleftharpoons Al^{3+}(aq) + \frac{3}{2}H_2(g)$
    d. $Br_2(l) + 2I^-(aq) \rightleftharpoons I_2(s) + 2Br^-(aq)$

71. In 1973 the wreckage of the Civil War ironclad USS *Monitor* was discovered near Cape Hatteras, North Carolina. [The *Monitor* and the CSS *Virginia* (formerly the USS *Merrimack*) fought the first battle between iron-armored ships.] In 1987 investigations were begun to see if the ship could be salvaged. It was reported in *Time* (June 22, 1987) that scientists were considering adding sacrificial anodes of zinc to the rapidly corroding metal hull of the *Monitor*. Describe how attaching zinc to the hull would protect the *Monitor* from further corrosion.

72. For the following half-reaction, $\mathscr{E}^\circ = -2.07$ V:

    $$AlF_6^{3-} + 3e^- \rightarrow Al + 6F^-$$

    Calculate the equilibrium constant at 25°C for the reaction

    $$Al^{3+}(aq) + 6F^-(aq) \rightleftharpoons AlF_6^{3-}(aq)$$

73. The standard reduction potential for the reaction

    $$2D^+ + 2e^- \rightarrow D_2$$

    where D is deuterium, is −0.0034 V at 25°C. Calculate $\mathscr{E}^\circ$, ΔG°, and K at 25°C for the reaction

    $$2H^+(aq) + D_2(g) \rightleftharpoons 2D^+(aq) + H_2(g)$$

74. The Nernst equation also can be applied to half-reactions. Calculate the reduction potential at 25°C of each of the following half-cells.
    a. Cu/Cu^{2+} (0.10 M)
       (The half-reaction is $Cu^{2+} + 2e^- \rightarrow Cu$)
    b. Cu/Cu^{2+} (2.0 M)
    c. Cu/Cu^{2+} (1.0×10^{-4} M)
    d. MnO_4^- (0.10 M)/Mn^{2+} (0.010 M) at pH = 3.00 (The half-reaction is $MnO_4^- + 8H^+ + 5e^- \rightarrow Mn^{2+} + 4H_2O$)
    e. MnO_4^- (0.10 M)/Mn^{2+} (0.010 M) at pH = 1.00

75. A crude pH meter is constructed at 25°C using a saturated calomel electrode (SCE; see Exercise 63) and a standard hydrogen electrode (SHE).
    a. What is $\mathscr{E}_{cell}$ when the half cells are the SCE and SHE?
    b. Is the hydrogen electrode the cathode or the anode under these conditions?
    c. Write the Nernst equation showing how this cell is dependent on $[H^+]$.
    d. What is the measured cell potential when the 1.0 M H^+ solution in the hydrogen electrode is replaced by each of the following solutions?

       i. $[H^+] = 1.0 \times 10^{-3}$ M
       ii. $[H^+] = 2.5$ M
       iii. $[H^+] = 1.0 \times 10^{-9}$ M

e. When an unknown acid solution is measured, the observed potential is 0.285 V. What is the pH of the solution?

f. Why is the glass electrode more commonly used than the standard hydrogen electrode to measure pH?

76. Write the Nernst equation for the corrosion of iron by oxygen. Will corrosion be a greater problem under acidic or basic conditions?

77. A solution at 25°C is 1.0 M in Fe^{2+} and 0.010 M in Ag^+. Which metal will be plated on the cathode first as the voltage is gradually increased when this solution is electrolyzed? (*Hint:* Use the Nernst equation to calculate $\mathscr{E}$ for each half-reaction.)

78. A solution at 25°C contains the metal ions

$$Au^{3+}, \ 1.0 \times 10^{-6} \ M$$
$$Fe^{3+}, \ 0.50 \ M$$
$$Ni^{2+}, \ 1.0 \times 10^{-3} \ M$$

What metal will plate out first as the voltage is gradually increased when this solution is electrolyzed?

79. Is it feasible to separate the ions Pt^{2+}, Pd^{2+}, and Ni^{2+} from each other by plating out each one in succession if each is present at a concentration of 1.0 M in the mixture at 25°C?

$$Ni^{2+} + 2e^- \rightarrow Ni \qquad \mathscr{E}° = -0.23 \ V$$
$$Pt^{2+} + 2e^- \rightarrow Pt \qquad \mathscr{E}° = 1.2 \ V$$
$$Pd^{2+} + 2e^- \rightarrow Pd \qquad \mathscr{E}° = 0.99 \ V$$

80. Can NO be produced electrochemically at 25°C by the electrolysis of a 5.0 M aqueous solution of $NaNO_3$?

81. It takes 15 kWh (kilowatthours) of electrical energy to produce 1.0 kg of aluminum metal from aluminum oxide by the Hall–Heroult process. Compare this to the amount of energy necessary to melt 1.0 kg of aluminum metal. Why is it economically feasible to recycle aluminum cans? [The enthalpy of fusion for aluminum metal is 10.7 kJ/mol (1 watt = 1 J/s).]

82. A patent attorney has asked for your advice concerning the merits of a patent application that describes a single aqueous galvanic cell capable of producing a 12-V potential. Comment.

83. What is the maximum work that can be obtained from a hydrogen–oxygen fuel cell that produces 1.00 kg of water at 25°C? Why do we say that this is the maximum work that can be obtained? What are the advantages and disadvantages in using fuel cells rather than the corresponding combustion reactions to produce electricity?

Challenge Problems

84. Combine the equations

$$\Delta G° = -nF\mathscr{E}° \quad \text{and} \quad \Delta G° = \Delta H° - T\Delta S°$$

to derive an expression for $\mathscr{E}°$ as a function of temperature. Describe how one can graphically determine $\Delta H°$ and $\Delta S°$ from measurements of $\mathscr{E}°$ at different temperatures. What property would you look for in designing a reference half-cell that would produce a potential relatively stable with respect to temperature?

85. a. Calculate $\mathscr{E}°$ and $\Delta G°$ for the following reaction at 298 K:

$$2H_2O(l) \rightleftharpoons 2H_2(g) + O_2(g)$$

b. Calculate $\Delta H°$ and $\Delta S°$ for the reaction from thermodynamic data in Appendix 4.

c. Calculate the values of $\mathscr{E}°$ and $\Delta G°$ at temperatures of 90°C and 0°C.

86. The overall reaction in the lead storage battery is

$$Pb(s) + PbO_2(s) + 2H^+(aq) + 2HSO_4^-(aq)$$
$$\rightarrow 2PbSO_4(s) + 2H_2O(l)$$

a. Calculate $\mathscr{E}$ at 25°C for this battery when $[H_2SO_4] = 4.5 \ M$, that is, $[H^+] = [HSO_4^-] = 4.5 \ M$. At 25°C, $\mathscr{E}° = 2.04$ V for the lead storage battery.

b. For the cell reaction, $\Delta H° = -315.9$ kJ and $\Delta S° = 263.5$ J/K. Calculate $\mathscr{E}°$ at $-20°C$. (See Exercise 84.)

c. Calculate $\mathscr{E}$ at $-20°C$ when $[H_2SO_4] = 4.5 \ M$.

87. For the following half-reaction, $\mathscr{E}° = +0.017$ V:

$$Ag(S_2O_3)_2^{3-} + e^- \rightarrow Ag + 2S_2O_3^{2-}$$

Calculate the value of the equilibrium constant at 25°C for the reaction

$$Ag^+(aq) + 2S_2O_3^{2-}(aq) \rightleftharpoons Ag(S_2O_3)_2^{3-}(aq)$$

(*Hint:* Find a half-reaction that can be added to the one above to give the required reaction.)

88. Beginning with the half-reaction

$$O_2 + 4H^+ + 4e^- \rightarrow 2H_2O \qquad \mathscr{E}° = 1.23 \ V$$

show that $\mathscr{E}° = 0.40$ V at 25°C for the half-reaction

$$O_2 + 2H_2O + 4e^- \rightarrow 4OH^-$$

(*Hint:* Write the Nernst equation for the first half-reaction, and use the expression for K_w to get the Nernst equation for the second half-reaction.)

89. The physiologic properties of chromium depend on its oxidation state. Chromium(III) ion is essential for an enzyme cofactor called the glucose tolerance factor. Chromium deficiency gives symptoms similar to diabetes. The chromium(VI) ion, on the other hand, is toxic and a potent carcinogen. This is mainly a result of the strength of chromium(VI) as an oxidizing agent.

a. Consider the half-reaction

$$CrO_4^{2-} + 4H_2O + 3e^- \rightarrow Cr(OH)_3 + 5OH^-$$
$$\mathscr{E}° = -0.13 \ V$$

Note: $Cr(OH)_3$ is a solid. Using the Nernst equation, calculate the potential for this half-reaction at 25°C, where pH = 7.40 and

$$[CrO_4^{2-}] = 1.0 \times 10^{-6} \, M$$

b. In acidic solution chromium(VI) exists as $Cr_2O_7^{2-}$. Calculate the potential at 25°C for the half-reaction

$$Cr_2O_7^{2-} + 14H^+ + 6e^- \rightarrow 2Cr^{3+} + 7H_2O$$
$$\mathscr{E}° = 1.33 \, V$$

under conditions where pH = 2.00 and

$$[Cr_2O_7^{2-}] = [Cr^{3+}] = 1.0 \times 10^{-6} \, M$$

90. A chemist wishes to determine the concentration of CrO_4^{2-} electrochemically. A cell is constructed consisting of a saturated calomel electrode (SCE, see Exercise 63) and a silver wire coated with Ag_2CrO_4. The $\mathscr{E}°$ value for the following half-reaction is +0.446 V with respect to the standard hydrogen electrode:

$$Ag_2CrO_4 + 2e^- \rightarrow 2Ag + CrO_4^{2-}$$

a. Calculate $\mathscr{E}_{cell}$ and ΔG at 25°C for the cell reaction when $[CrO_4^{2-}] = 1.0 \, mol/L$.
b. Write the Nernst equation for the cell.
c. If the coated silver wire is placed in a solution at 25°C in which $[CrO_4^{2-}] = 1.0 \times 10^{-5} \, M$, what is the expected cell potential?
d. The measured cell potential at 25°C is 0.504 V when the coated wire is dipped into a solution of unknown $[CrO_4^{2-}]$. What is the $[CrO_4^{2-}]$ for this solution?

91. The measurement of pH using a glass electrode obeys the Nernst equation. The typical response of a pH meter at 25°C is given by the equation

$$\mathscr{E}_{meas} = \mathscr{E}_{ref} + 0.05916 \, pH$$

where $\mathscr{E}_{ref}$ contains the potential of the reference electrode and all other potentials that arise in the cell that are not related to the hydrogen ion concentration. Assume that $\mathscr{E}_{ref} = 0.250 \, V$ and that $\mathscr{E}_{meas} = 0.480 \, V$.
a. What is the uncertainty in the values of pH and $[H^+]$ if the uncertainty in the measured potential is $\pm 1 \, mV$ ($\pm 0.001 \, V$)?
b. To what accuracy must the potential be measured for the uncertainty in pH to be ± 0.02 pH unit?

92. The measurement of F^- ion concentration by ion selective electrodes at 25°C obeys the equation

$$\mathscr{E}_{meas} = \mathscr{E}_{ref} - 0.05916 \, \log[F^-]$$

a. For a given solution, $\mathscr{E}_{meas}$ is 0.4462 V. If $\mathscr{E}_{ref}$ is 0.2420 V, what is the concentration of F^- in the solution?
b. Hydroxide ion interferes with the measurement of F^-. Taking this into account, the response of a fluoride electrode is

$$\mathscr{E}_{meas} = \mathscr{E}_{ref} - 0.05916 \, \log([F^-] + k[OH^-])$$

where $k = 1.00 \times 10^1$ and is called the selectivity factor for the electrode response. Calculate $[F^-]$ for the data in part a if the pH is 9.00. What is the percentage error introduced in the $[F^-]$ if the hydroxide interference is ignored?
c. For the $[F^-]$ in part b, what is the maximum pH such that $[F^-]/k[OH^-] = 50.$?
d. At low pH, F^- is mostly converted to HF. The fluoride electrode does not respond to HF. What is the minimum pH at which 99% of the fluoride is present as F^- and only 1% is present as HF?
e. Buffering agents are added to solutions containing fluoride before making measurements with a fluoride selective electrode. Why?

Marathon Problem*

93. The addition of aqueous ammonia to the cathode compartment of the cell described below reduces the cell potential. Likewise, addition of aqueous ammonia to the anode compartment increases the cell potential.

$$Zn(s)|Zn^{2+}(aq)\|Cu^{2+}(aq)|Cu(s)$$

Assume that $[Cu^{2+}(aq)]_0 = [Zn^{2+}(aq)]_0 = 0.10 \, M$ and that both Cu^{2+} and Zn^{2+} form very stable complexes with ammonia (overall formation constants $> 10^{10}$), each with a coordination number of 4.

1. Show how to estimate the ratio of the overall formation constant for $[Zn(NH_3)_4]^{2+}$ to the overall formation constant for $[Cu(NH_3)_4]^{2+}$ if the cell potential is observed to be 0.96 V after adding equal amounts (assume a large excess) of 6 M NH_3 to each compartment (assume that $T = 298 \, K$).

2. Which of the two transition metal complexes is more thermodynamically stable? How much more stable is it than the other complex?

*This Marathon Problem was developed by James H. Burness of Penn State University, York Campus.

CHAPTER 18

The Representative Elements: Groups 1A Through 4A

So far in this book we have covered the major principles and explored the most important models of chemistry. In particular, we have seen that the chemical properties of the elements can be explained very successfully by the quantum mechanical model of the atom. In fact, the most convincing evidence of that model's validity is its ability to relate the observed periodic properties of the elements to the number of valence electrons in their atoms.

We have learned many properties of the elements and their compounds, but we have not discussed in detail the relationship between the chemical properties of a particular element and its position on the periodic table. In this chapter and the next we will explore the chemical similarities and differences among the elements in the several groups of the periodic table and will try to interpret these data using the quantum mechanical model of the atom. In the process we will illustrate a great variety of chemical properties and further demonstrate the practical importance of chemistry.

< In a popular lecture demonstration hydrogen gas is used to blow large soap bubbles, which are ignited (by a candle on a long pole) as they float upward.

18.1 A Survey of the Representative Elements

Purpose

- To give an overview of the representative elements.
- To discuss the relationship of the first member to the rest of the group.
- To give a general introduction to the commercial preparation of some elements.

The traditional form of the periodic table is shown in Fig. 18.1. Recall that the **representative elements,** whose chemical properties are determined by the valence-level s and p electrons, are designated Groups 1A through 8A. The **transition metals,** in the center of the table, result from the filling of d orbitals. The elements that correspond to the filling of the $4f$ and $5f$ orbitals are listed separately as the **lanthanides** and **actinides,** respectively.

The heavy black line in Fig. 18.1 divides the metals from the nonmetals. Some elements just on either side of this line, such as silicon and germanium, exhibit both metallic and nonmetallic properties and are often called **metalloids** or **semimetals.** The fundamental chemical difference between a metal and a nonmetal is that metals tend to lose their valence electrons to form *cations,* usually with the valence-electron configuration of the noble gas from the preceding period, and nonmetals tend to gain electrons to form *anions* that exhibit the electron configuration of the noble gas in the same period. Metallic character is observed to increase going down a given group, which is consistent with the trends in ionization energy, electron affinity, and electronegativity discussed earlier (see Sections 7.13 and 8.2).

Metallic character increases going down a group in the periodic table.

Atomic Size and Group Anomalies

Although the chemical properties of the members of a group show many similarities, there are also important differences. In fact, the relatively large increase in atomic radius in going from the first to the second member of a group causes the

Figure 18.1

The periodic table. The elements in the A groups are the representative elements. The elements shown in red are called transition metals. The dark line approximately divides the nonmetals from the metals. The elements that have both metallic and nonmetallic properties (semimetals) are shaded in blue.

first element to show properties that are often quite different from the others. Consequently, hydrogen, beryllium, boron, carbon, nitrogen, oxygen, and fluorine all have some properties that distinguish them from the other members of their groups. For example, in Group 1A hydrogen is a nonmetal and lithium is a very active metal. This extreme difference results primarily from the very large difference in the atomic radii of hydrogen and lithium, as shown in Fig. 18.2. The small hydrogen atom has a much greater attraction for electrons than do the larger members of Group 1A and forms covalent bonds with nonmetals; the other members of Group 1A lose their valence electrons to nonmetals to form 1+ cations in ionic compounds.

This effect of size is also evident in other groups. For example, the oxides of the metals in Group 2A are all quite basic except for the first member of the series; beryllium oxide (BeO) is amphoteric. Recall from Section 14.10 that the basicity of an oxide depends on its ionic character. Ionic oxides contain the O^{2-} ion, which reacts with water to form two OH^- ions. All the oxides of the Group 2A metals are highly ionic except for beryllium oxide, which has considerable covalent character. The small Be^{2+} ion can effectively polarize the electron "cloud" of the O^{2-} ion, producing significant electron sharing. We see the same pattern in Group 3A, where only the small boron atom behaves as a nonmetal, or sometimes as a semimetal, and aluminum and the other members are active metals.

In Group 4A the effect of size is reflected in the dramatic differences between the chemistry of carbon and that of silicon. The chemistry of carbon is dominated by molecules containing chains of C—C bonds, but silicon compounds mainly contain Si—O bonds rather than Si—Si bonds. Carbon forms a wide variety of stable compounds with strong C—C single bonds. Silicon also forms compounds with chains of Si—Si bonds, but these compounds are much more reactive than the corresponding carbon compounds. The reasons for the difference in reactivity between the carbon and silicon compounds are quite complex but are likely related to the differences in the sizes of the carbon and silicon atoms.

Carbon and silicon differ markedly in their abilities to form π bonds. As we discussed in Section 9.1, carbon dioxide is composed of discrete CO_2 molecules with the Lewis structure

$$\ddot{O}=C=\ddot{O}$$

Figure 18.2

The atomic radii of some atoms in picometers.

where the carbon and oxygen atoms achieve the [Ne] configuration by forming π bonds. In contrast, the structure of silica (empirical formula SiO_2) is based on SiO_4 tetrahedra with Si—O—Si bridges, as shown in Fig. 18.3. The silicon $3p$ valence orbitals do not overlap very effectively with the smaller oxygen $2p$ orbitals to form π bonds; therefore, discrete SiO_2 molecules with the Lewis structure

$$\ddot{O}=Si=\ddot{O}$$

are not stable. Instead, the silicon atoms achieve a noble gas configuration by forming several Si—O single bonds.

The importance of π bonding for the relatively small elements of the second period also explains the different elemental forms of the members of Groups 5A and 6A. For example, elemental nitrogen consists of very stable N_2 molecules with the Lewis structure

$$:N\equiv N:$$

Elemental phosphorus forms larger aggregates of atoms, the simplest being the tetrahedral P_4 molecules found in white phosphorus (see Fig. 19.12). Like silicon atoms, the relatively large phosphorus atoms do not form strong π bonds and prefer to achieve a noble gas configuration by forming single bonds to several other phosphorus atoms. In contrast, its very strong π bonds make the N_2 molecule the most stable form of elemental nitrogen. Similarly, in Group 6A the most stable form of elemental oxygen is the O_2 molecule with a double bond, but the larger sulfur atom forms bigger aggregates, such as the cyclic S_8 molecule (see Fig. 19.16), which contains only single bonds.

The relatively large change in size in going from the first to second member of a group also has important consequences for the Group 7A elements. For example, fluorine has a smaller electron affinity than chlorine. This reversal of the expected trend can be attributed to the small fluorine $2p$ orbitals, which result in unusually large electron repulsions. The relative weakness of the bond in the F_2 molecule can be explained in terms of the repulsions among the lone pairs, shown in the Lewis structure:

$$: \ddot{F} - \ddot{F} :$$

The small size of the fluorine atoms allows close approach of the lone pairs, which leads to much greater repulsions than are found in the Cl_2 molecule with its much larger atoms.

Abundance and Preparation

Table 18.1 shows the distribution of elements in the earth's crust, oceans, and atmosphere. The major element is, of course, oxygen, which is found in the atmosphere as O_2, in the oceans in H_2O, and in the earth's crust primarily in silicate and carbonate minerals. The second most abundant element, silicon, is found throughout the earth's crust in the silica and silicate minerals that form the basis of most sand, rocks, and soil. The most abundant metals, aluminum and iron, are found in ores in which they are combined with nonmetals, most commonly oxygen. One notable fact revealed by Table 18.1 is the small incidence of most transition metals. Since many of these relatively rare elements are assuming increasing importance in

Figure 18.3

The structure of quartz, which has the empirical formula SiO_2. Note that the structure is based on interlocking SiO_4 tetrahedra, where each oxygen atom is shared by two silicon atoms.

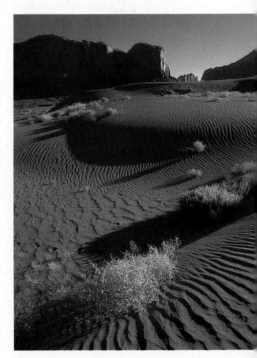

Sand dunes in Monument Valley, Arizona.

Table 18.1			
Distribution (Mass Percent) of the 18 Most Abundant Elements in the Earth's Crust, Oceans, and Atmosphere			
Element	Mass Percent	Element	Mass Percent
Oxygen	49.2	Titanium	0.58
Silicon	25.7	Chlorine	0.19
Aluminum	7.50	Phosphorus	0.11
Iron	4.71	Manganese	0.09
Calcium	3.39	Carbon	0.08
Sodium	2.63	Sulfur	0.06
Potassium	2.40	Barium	0.04
Magnesium	1.93	Nitrogen	0.03
Hydrogen	0.87	Fluorine	0.03
		All others	0.49

Table 18.2

Abundance of Elements in the Human Body

Major Elements	Mass Percent	Trace Elements (in alphabetical order)
Oxygen	65.0	Arsenic
Carbon	18.0	Chromium
Hydrogen	10.0	Cobalt
Nitrogen	3.0	Copper
Calcium	1.4	Fluorine
Phosphorus	1.0	Iodine
Magnesium	0.50	Manganese
Potassium	0.34	Molybdenum
Sulfur	0.26	Nickel
Sodium	0.14	Selenium
Chlorine	0.14	Silicon
Iron	0.004	Vanadium
Zinc	0.003	

our high-technology society, it is possible that the control of transition metal ores may ultimately have more significance for world politics than the control of petroleum supplies.

The distribution of elements in living materials is very different from that found in the earth's crust. Table 18.2 shows the relative abundance of elements in the human body. Oxygen, carbon, hydrogen, and nitrogen form the basis for all biologically important molecules. The other elements, even though they are found in relatively small amounts, are often crucial for life. For example, zinc is found in over 150 different biomolecules in the human body.

Only about one-fourth of the elements occur naturally in the free state. Most are found in a combined state. The *process of obtaining a metal from its ore* is called **metallurgy.** Since the metals in ores are found in the form of cations, the chemistry of *metallurgy always involves reduction of the ions to the elemental metal (with an oxidation state of zero).* A variety of reducing agents can be used, but carbon is the usual choice because of its wide availability and relatively low cost. As we will see in Chapter 20, carbon is the primary reducing agent in the production of steel. Carbon also can be used to produce tin and lead from their oxides:

Metallurgy is discussed in more detail in Chapter 20.

Carbon is the cheapest and most readily available industrial reducing agent for metallic ions.

$$2SnO(s) + C(s) \xrightarrow{\text{Heat}} 2Sn(s) + CO_2(g)$$

$$2PbO(s) + C(s) \xrightarrow{\text{Heat}} 2Pb(s) + CO_2(g)$$

Hydrogen gas also can be used as a reducing agent for metal oxides, as in the production of tin:

$$SnO(s) + H_2(g) \xrightarrow{\text{Heat}} Sn(s) + H_2O(g)$$

Electrolysis is often used to reduce the most active metals. In Chapter 17 we considered the electrolytic production of aluminum metal. The alkali metals are also produced by electrolysis, usually of their molten halide salts.

The preparation of nonmetals varies widely. Elemental nitrogen and oxygen are usually obtained from the **liquefaction** of air, which is based on the principle that a real gas cools when it expands. After each expansion, part of the cooler gas is compressed, while the rest is used to carry away the heat of the compression. The compressed gas is then allowed to expand again. This cycle is repeated many times. Eventually, the remaining gas becomes cold enough to form the liquid state. Because liquid nitrogen and liquid oxygen have different boiling points, they can be separated by the distillation of liquid air. Both substances are important industrial chemicals, nitrogen ranking second in amount manufactured in the United States (~60 billion pounds per year) and oxygen ranking fourth (over 40 billion pounds per year). Hydrogen can be obtained from the electrolysis of water, but more commonly it is obtained from the decomposition of the methane in natural gas. Sulfur is found underground in its elemental form and is recovered using the Frasch process (see Section 19.6). The halogens are obtained by oxidation of the anions from halide salts (see Section 19.7).

The preparation of sulfur and the halogens is discussed in Chapter 19.

18.2 *The Group 1A Elements*

Purpose

- To consider the thermodynamics and rates of the reactions of alkali metals with water.
- To discuss the oxides of alkali metals.

The Group 1A elements with their ns^1 valence-electron configurations are all very active metals (they lose their valence electrons very readily), except for hydrogen, which behaves as a nonmetal. We will discuss the chemistry of hydrogen in the next section. Many of the properties of the **alkali metals** have been described previously (see Section 7.14). The sources and methods of preparation of pure alkali metals are given in Table 18.3. The ionization energies, standard reduction potentials, ionic radii, and melting points for the alkali metals are listed in Table 18.4.

In Section 7.14 we saw that the alkali metals all react vigorously with water to release hydrogen gas:

$$2M(s) + 2H_2O(l) \rightarrow 2M^+(aq) + 2OH^-(aq) + H_2(g)$$

1A
H
Li
Na
K
Rb
Cs
Fr

Several properties of the alkali metals are given in Table 7.8.

Table 18.3

Sources and Methods of Preparation of the Pure Alkali Metals

Element	Source	Method of Preparation
Lithium	Silicate minerals such as spodumene, $LiAl(Si_2O_6)$	Electrolysis of molten LiCl
Sodium	NaCl	Electrolysis of molten NaCl
Potassium	KCl	Electrolysis of molten KCl
Rubidium	Impurity in lepidolite, $Li_2(F,OH)_2Al_2(SiO_3)_3$	Reduction of RbOH with Mg and H_2
Cesium	Pollucite $(Cs_4Al_4Si_9O_{26} \cdot H_2O)$ and an impurity in lepidolite (see Fig. 18.4)	Reduction of CsOH with Mg and H_2

Figure 18.4

Lepidolite is composed mainly of lithium, aluminum, silicon, and oxygen, but it also contains significant amounts of rubidium and cesium.

Table 18.4				
Selected Physical Properties of the Alkali Metals				
Element	Ionization Energy (kJ/mol)	Standard Reduction Potential (V) for $M^+ + e^- \rightarrow M$	Radius of M^+ (pm)	Melting Point (°C)
Lithium	520	−3.05	60	180
Sodium	495	−2.71	95	98
Potassium	419	−2.92	133	63
Rubidium	409	−2.99	148	39
Cesium	382	−3.02	169	29

We will reconsider this process briefly because it illustrates several important concepts. Based on the ionization energies, we might expect lithium to be the weakest of the alkali metals as a reducing agent in water. However, the standard reduction potentials indicate that it is the strongest. This reversal results mainly from the very large energy of hydration of the small Li^+ ion. Because of its relatively high charge density, the Li^+ ion very effectively attracts water molecules. A large quantity of energy is released in the process, favoring the formation of the Li^+ ion and making lithium a strong reducing agent in aqueous solution.

We also saw in Section 7.14 that lithium, although it is the strongest reducing agent, reacts more slowly with water than does sodium or potassium. From the discussions in Chapters 12 and 16, we know that the *equilibrium position* for a reaction (in this case indicated by the $\mathscr{E}°$ values) is controlled by thermodynamic factors but that the *rate* of a reaction is controlled by kinetic factors. There is *no* direct connection between these factors. Lithium reacts more slowly with water than does sodium or potassium because as a solid it has a higher melting point than either of them. It does not become molten from the heat of reaction with water as sodium and potassium do, and thus it has a smaller area of contact with the water.

The relative ease with which the alkali metals lose electrons to form M^+ cations means that they react with nonmetals to form ionic compounds. Although we might expect the alkali metals to react with oxygen to form regular oxides of the general formula M_2O, lithium is the only one that does so in the presence of excess oxygen gas:

$$4Li(s) + O_2(g) \rightarrow 2Li_2O(s)$$

Sodium forms solid Na_2O if the oxygen supply is limited, but in excess oxygen it forms *sodium peroxide:*

$$2Na(s) + O_2(g) \rightarrow Na_2O_2(s)$$

Sodium peroxide contains the basic O_2^{2-} anion and reacts with water to form hydrogen peroxide and hydroxide ions:

$$Na_2O_2(s) + 2H_2O(l) \rightarrow 2Na^+(aq) + H_2O_2(aq) + 2OH^-(aq)$$

Hydrogen peroxide is a strong oxidizing agent often used as a bleach for hair and as a disinfectant.

Potassium, rubidium, and cesium react with oxygen to produce **superoxides** of the general formula MO_2, which contain the O_2^- anion. For example, potassium reacts with oxygen as follows:

$$K(s) + O_2(g) \rightarrow KO_2(s)$$

Sodium reacts violently with water.

Hydrogen peroxide has the structure

Table 18.5

Types of Compounds Formed by the Alkali Metals with Oxygen

General Formula	Name	Examples
M_2O	Oxide	Li_2O, Na_2O
M_2O_2	Peroxide	Na_2O_2
MO_2	Superoxide	KO_2, RbO_2, CsO_2

The superoxides release oxygen gas in reactions with water or carbon dioxide:

$$2MO_2(s) + 2H_2O(l) \rightarrow 2M^+(aq) + 2OH^-(aq) + O_2(g) + H_2O_2(aq)$$
$$4MO_2(s) + 2CO_2(g) \rightarrow 2M_2CO_3(s) + 3O_2(g)$$

This chemistry makes superoxides very useful in the self-contained breathing apparatuses used by firefighters. These "airpacks" are also used as emergency equipment in labs and production facilities in case toxic fumes are released.

The types of compounds formed by the alkali metals with oxygen are summarized in Table 18.5.

Lithium is the only alkali metal that reacts with gaseous nitrogen to form a **nitride salt** containing the N^{3-} anion:

$$6Li(s) + N_2(g) \rightarrow 2Li_3N(s)$$

Table 18.6 summarizes some important reactions of the alkali metals.

The alkali metal ions are very important for the proper functioning of biologic systems, such as nerves and muscles, and Na^+ and K^+ ions are present in all body cells and fluids. In human blood plasma the concentrations are

$$[Na^+] \approx 0.15\ M \quad \text{and} \quad [K^+] \approx 0.005\ M$$

For the fluids *inside* the cells the concentrations are reversed:

$$[Na^+] \approx 0.005\ M \quad \text{and} \quad [K^+] \approx 0.16\ M$$

Since the concentrations are so different inside and outside the cells, an elaborate mechanism is needed to transport Na^+ and K^+ ions through the cell membranes.

Recently, studies have been carried out concerning the role of the Li^+ ion in the human brain, and lithium carbonate has been used extensively in the treatment of

The effect of lithium on human behavior is discussed in a Chemical Impact in Chapter 7.

Table 18.6

Selected Reactions of the Alkali Metals

Reaction	Comment
$2M + X_2 \rightarrow 2MX$	X_2 = any halogen molecule
$4Li + O_2 \rightarrow 2Li_2O$	Excess oxygen
$2Na + O_2 \rightarrow Na_2O_2$	
$M + O_2 \rightarrow MO_2$	M = K, Rb, or Cs
$2M + S \rightarrow M_2S$	
$6Li + N_2 \rightarrow 2Li_3N$	Li only
$12M + P_4 \rightarrow 4M_3P$	
$2M + H_2 \rightarrow 2MH$	
$2M + 2H_2O \rightarrow 2MOH + H_2$	
$2M + 2H^+ \rightarrow 2M^+ + H_2$	Violent reaction!

manic–depressive patients. The Li^+ ion apparently affects the levels of neurotransmitters, molecules that assist the transmission of messages along the nerve networks. Incorrect concentrations of these molecules can lead to depression or mania.

Sample Exercise 18.1

Predict the products formed by the following reactants.

a. $Li_3N(s)$ and $H_2O(l)$
b. $KO_2(s)$ and $H_2O(l)$

Solution

a. Solid Li_3N contains the N^{3-} anion, which has a strong attraction for three H^+ ions to form NH_3. Thus the reaction is

$$Li_3N(s) + 3H_2O(l) \rightarrow NH_3(g) + 3Li^+(aq) + 3OH^-(aq)$$

b. Solid KO_2 is a superoxide that characteristically reacts with water to produce O_2, H_2O_2, and OH^-:

$$2KO_2(s) + 2H_2O(l) \rightarrow 2K^+(aq) + 2OH^-(aq) + O_2(g) + H_2O_2(aq)$$

18.3 Hydrogen

Purpose

- To describe the production and uses of hydrogen.
- To discuss types of hydrides.

Under ordinary conditions of temperature and pressure, hydrogen is a colorless, odorless gas composed of H_2 molecules. Because of its low molar mass and nonpolarity, hydrogen has a very low boiling point ($-253°C$) and melting point ($-260°C$). Hydrogen gas is highly flammable, and mixtures of air containing from 18% to 60% hydrogen by volume are explosive. In a common lecture demonstration hydrogen and oxygen gases are bubbled into soapy water. The resulting bubbles can be ignited with a candle on a long stick, giving a loud explosion.

The major industrial source of hydrogen gas is the reaction of methane and water at high temperatures (800–1000°C) and high pressures (10–50 atm) with a metallic catalyst, often nickel:

$$CH_4(g) + H_2O(g) \xrightarrow[\text{Catalyst}]{\text{Heat, pressure}} CO(g) + 3H_2(g)$$

Large quantities of hydrogen are also formed as a by-product of gasoline production, in which hydrocarbons with high molar masses are broken down (or **cracked**) to produce smaller molecules more suitable for use as a motor fuel (see Section 22.4).

(left) Hydrogen gas being used to blow soap bubbles. *(right)* As the bubbles float upward, they are lighted using a candle on a long pole. The orange flame is due to the reaction of hydrogen with the oxygen in the air.

Very pure hydrogen can be produced by electrolysis of water (see Section 17.7), but this method is currently not economically feasible for large-scale production because of the relatively high cost of electricity.

The major industrial use of hydrogen is in the production of ammonia by the Haber process. Large quantities of hydrogen are also used for hydrogenating unsaturated vegetable oils (those containing carbon–carbon double bonds) to produce solid shortenings that are saturated (containing carbon–carbon single bonds):

$$\text{\footnotesize $\sim\!\!\sim\!\!\sim$} \underset{\underset{\displaystyle H}{|}}{\overset{\overset{\displaystyle H}{|}}{C}}\!=\!\underset{\underset{\displaystyle H}{|}}{\overset{\overset{\displaystyle H}{|}}{C}} \text{\footnotesize $\sim\!\!\sim$} \xrightarrow{\;H_2\;} \text{\footnotesize $\sim\!\!\sim\!\!\sim$} \underset{\underset{\displaystyle H}{|}}{\overset{\overset{\displaystyle H}{|}}{C}}\!-\!\underset{\underset{\displaystyle H}{|}}{\overset{\overset{\displaystyle H}{|}}{C}} \text{\footnotesize $\sim\!\!\sim$}$$

The catalysis of this process was discussed in Section 12.8.

Chemically, hydrogen behaves as a typical nonmetal, forming covalent compounds with other nonmetals and forming salts with very active metals. Binary compounds containing hydrogen are called **hydrides,** of which there are three classes. The **ionic (or saltlike) hydrides** are formed when hydrogen combines with the most active metals, those from Groups 1A and 2A. Examples are LiH and CaH_2, which can best be characterized as containing hydride ions (H^-) and metal cations. Because the presence of two electrons in the small $1s$ orbital produces large electron–electron repulsions and the nucleus only has a 1^+ charge, the hydride ion is a strong reducing agent (easily loses electrons). For example, when ionic hydrides are placed in water, a violent reaction takes place. This reaction results in the formation of hydrogen gas, as seen in the equation

$$\text{LiH}(s) + \text{H}_2\text{O}(l) \rightarrow \text{H}_2(g) + \text{Li}^+(aq) + \text{OH}^-(aq)$$

Covalent hydrides are formed when hydrogen combines with other nonmetals. We have encountered many of these compounds already: HCl, CH_4, NH_3, H_2O,

◀ C H E M I C A L   I M P A C T ▶

Light Produces Hydrogen from Seawater

As it becomes increasingly clear that the greenhouse effect (the warming of the earth due to the accumulation of CO_2 and other gases in the atmosphere) is a serious environmental problem, the search for non-carbon-based fuels is being intensified. One such fuel is hydrogen gas, which produces only water as a combustion product. One of the drawbacks of hydrogen as a fuel is its high cost. In recent years, considerable research has been performed on ways to use solar energy to liberate hydrogen from water. Pioneering work to develop semiconductors for the solar electrolysis of water was carried out at the University of Texas by A. J. Bard and coworkers, who found that a bipolar photoelectrode consisting of CdSe deposited on titanium foil could produce hydrogen from water using visible light. Another approach to this problem was recently described by H. Ti Tien of Michigan State University. The heart of Tien's

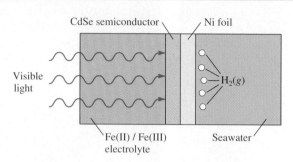

hydrogen-producing solar cell is a cadmium selenide *n*-type semiconductor deposited on nickel foil. This semiconducting foil is then used as a barrier between an electrolyte solution containing Fe(II) and Fe(III) complex ions and a compartment containing seawater. When visible light shines on the semiconductor, electrons are excited into conduction bands, leaving behind holes (low-energy elec-

tron vacancies). The electrons in the conduction bands move to the metal foil–seawater interface, where they reduce water to form H_2 gas. The holes, on the other hand, travel to the semiconductor–electrolyte interface, where they are filled with electrons from Fe^{2+} ions (see the accompanying figure), which are regenerated by an external energy source (not shown).

○ Oxygen

○ Hydrogen

Figure 18.5

The structure of ice, showing the hydrogen bonding.

Boiling points of covalent hydrides are discussed in Section 10.1.

and so on. The most important covalent hydride is water. The polarity of the H_2O molecule leads to many of water's unusual properties. Water has a much higher boiling point than is expected from its molar mass. It has a large heat of vaporization and a large heat capacity, both of which make it a very useful coolant. Water has a higher density as a liquid than as a solid. This is due to the open structure of ice, which results from maximizing the hydrogen bonding (see Fig. 18.5). Because water is an excellent solvent for ionic and polar substances, it provides an effective medium for life processes. In fact, water is one of the few covalent hydrides that is nontoxic to organisms.

The third class of hydrides, the **metallic** (or **interstitial**) **hydrides,** are formed when transition metal crystals are treated with hydrogen gas. The hydrogen molecules dissociate at the metal's surface, and the small hydrogen atoms migrate into the crystal structure to occupy holes, or interstices. These metal–hydrogen mixtures are more like solid solutions than true compounds. Palladium can absorb about *900 times* its own volume of hydrogen gas. In fact, hydrogen can be purified by placing it under slight pressure in a vessel containing a thin wall of palladium. The hydrogen diffuses into and through the metal wall, leaving the impurities behind.

Although hydrogen can react with transition metals to form compounds of constant composition, most of the interstitial hydrides have variable compositions (often called nonstoichiometric compositions) with formulas such as $LaH_{2.76}$ and $VH_{0.56}$. The compositions of the nonstoichiometric hydrides vary with the length of exposure of the metal to hydrogen gas and other factors.

When interstitial hydrides are heated, much of the absorbed hydrogen is expelled as hydrogen gas. Because of this behavior, these materials offer possibilities for storing hydrogen for use as a portable fuel. The internal combustion engines in current automobiles can burn hydrogen gas with little modification, but storage of enough hydrogen to provide an acceptable mileage range remains a problem. One possible solution might be to use a fuel tank containing a porous solid that includes a transition metal into which the hydrogen gas could be pumped to form the interstitial hydride. The hydrogen gas could then be released as required by the engine.

See Section 6.6 for a discussion of the feasibility of using hydrogen gas as a fuel.

18.4 The Group 2A Elements

Purpose

* To describe the general chemical properties of the alkaline earth metals.
* To discuss three-center bonding in beryllium compounds.

The Group 2A elements (with valence-electron configuration ns^2) are very reactive, losing their two valence electrons to nonmetals to form ionic compounds containing M^{2+} cations. These elements are commonly called the **alkaline earth metals** because of the basicity of their oxides:

$$MO(s) + H_2O(l) \rightarrow M^{2+}(aq) + 2OH^-(aq)$$

Only beryllium oxide (BeO) also shows some acidic properties, such as dissolving in aqueous solutions containing hydroxide ions:

An amphoteric oxide displays both acidic and basic properties.

$$BeO(s) + 2OH^-(aq) + H_2O(l) \rightarrow Be(OH)_4{}^{2-}(aq)$$

The more active alkaline earth metals react with water as the alkali metals do, producing hydrogen gas:

$$M(s) + 2H_2O(l) \rightarrow M^{2+}(aq) + 2OH^-(aq) + H_2(g)$$

Calcium, strontium, and barium react vigorously at 25°C. The less easily oxidized beryllium and magnesium show no observable reaction with water at 25°C, although magnesium reacts with boiling water. Table 18.7 summarizes various properties, sources, and preparations of the alkaline earth metals.

The heavier alkaline earth metals react with nitrogen or hydrogen at high temperatures to produce ionic nitride or hydride salts, for example:

$$3Ca(s) + N_2(g) \rightarrow Ca_3N_2(s)$$
$$Ca(s) + H_2(g) \rightarrow CaH_2(s)$$

Magnesium, strontium, and barium form similar compounds. Beryllium hydride cannot be formed by direct combination of the elements but can be prepared by the following reaction:

$$BeCl_2 + 2LiH \rightarrow BeH_2 + 2LiCl$$

Hydrogen bridges between the beryllium atoms produce a polymeric structure for BeH_2, as shown in Fig. 18.6. The localized electron model describes this bonding by assuming only one electron pair is available to bind each Be—H—Be cluster.

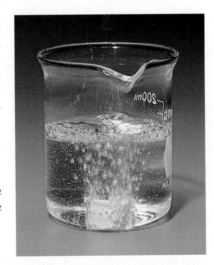

Calcium metal reacting with water to form bubbles of hydrogen gas.

Table 18.7

Selected Physical Properties, Sources, and Methods of Preparation for the Group 2A Elements

Element	Radius of M^{2+} (pm)	Ionization Energy (kJ/mol)		$\mathscr{E}°$ (V) for $M^{2+} + 2e^- \rightarrow M$	Source	Method of Preparation
		First	Second			
Beryllium	~30	900	1760	−1.70	Beryl ($Be_3Al_2Si_6O_{18}$)	Electrolysis of molten $BeCl_2$
Magnesium	65	738	1450	−2.37	Magnesite ($MgCO_3$), dolomite ($MgCO_3 \cdot CaCO_3$), carnallite ($MgCl_2 \cdot KCl \cdot 6H_2O$)	Electrolysis of molten $MgCl_2$
Calcium	99	590	1146	−2.76	Various minerals containing $CaCO_3$	Electrolysis of molten $CaCl_2$
Strontium	113	549	1064	−2.89	Celestite ($SrSO_4$), strontianite ($SrCO_3$)	Electrolysis of molten $SrCl_2$
Barium	135	503	965	−2.90	Baryte ($BaSO_4$), witherite ($BaCO_3$)	Electrolysis of molten $BaCl_2$
Radium	140	509	979	−2.92	Pitchblende (1 g of Ra/7 tons of ore)	Electrolysis of molten $RaCl_2$

Figure 18.6

The structure of solid BeH_2.

Figure 18.7

(a) Solid $BeCl_2$ can be visualized as being formed from many $BeCl_2$ molecules, where lone pairs on the chlorine atoms are used to bond to the beryllium atoms in adjacent $BeCl_2$ molecules. (b) The extended structure of solid $BeCl_2$.

This is called a **three-center bond,** since one electron pair is shared among three atoms. Three-center bonds also have been postulated to explain the bonding in other electron-deficient compounds (compounds where there are fewer electron pairs than bonds) such as the boron hydrides (see Section 18.5).

As we saw in Section 18.1, the small size and relatively high electronegativity of the beryllium atom cause its bonds to be more covalent than is usual for a metal. For example, beryllium chloride with the Lewis structure

$$:\ddot{C}l—Be—\ddot{C}l:$$

exists as a linear molecule, as predicted by the VSEPR model. The Be—Cl bonds are covalent, and beryllium is best described as being sp hybridized. Since the beryllium atom in $BeCl_2$ is very electron-deficient (only four valence electrons surround it), it is very reactive toward electron-pair donors (Lewis bases) such as ammonia:

As a solid, $BeCl_2$ achieves an octet of electrons around each beryllium atom by forming an extended structure containing Be in a tetrahedral environment, as shown in Fig. 18.7. The lone pairs on the chlorine atoms are used to form Be—Cl bonds.

The alkaline earth metals have great practical importance. Calcium and magnesium ions are essential for human life. Calcium is found primarily in the structural minerals comprising bones and teeth; magnesium (as the Mg^{2+} ion) plays a vital role in metabolism and muscle functions. Also, magnesium is commonly used to produce the bright light for photographic flash units from its reaction with oxygen:

$$2Mg(s) + O_2(g) \rightarrow 2MgO(s) + light$$

Table 18.8

Selected Reactions of the Group 2A Elements

Reaction	Comment
$M + X_2 \rightarrow MX_2$	X_2 = any halogen molecule
$2M + O_2 \rightarrow 2MO$	Ba gives BaO_2 as well
$M + S \rightarrow MS$	
$3M + N_2 \rightarrow M_3N_2$	High temperatures
$6M + P_4 \rightarrow 2M_3P_2$	High temperatures
$M + H_2 \rightarrow MH_2$	M = Ca, Sr or Ba; high temperatures; Mg at high pressure
$M + 2H_2O \rightarrow M(OH)_2 + H_2$	M = Ca, Sr, or Ba
$M + 2H^+ \rightarrow M^{2+} + H_2$	
$Be + 2OH^- + 2H_2O \rightarrow Be(OH)_4{}^{2-} + H_2$	

Because magnesium metal has a relatively low density and moderate strength, it is a useful structural material, especially if alloyed with aluminum.

Table 18.8 summarizes some important reactions of the alkaline earth metals.

Relatively large concentrations of Ca^{2+} and Mg^{2+} ions are often found in natural water supplies. These ions in this **hard water** interfere with the action of detergents and form precipitates with soap. In Section 14.6 we saw that Ca^{2+} is often removed by precipitation as $CaCO_3$ in large-scale water softening. In individual homes Ca^{2+}, Mg^{2+}, and other cations are removed by **ion exchange.** An **ion-exchange resin** consists of large molecules (polymers) that have many ionic sites. A **cation-exchange resin** is represented schematically in Fig. 18.8(a), showing Na^+ ions bound ionically to the SO_3^- groups that are covalently attached to the resin polymer. When hard water is passed over the resin, Ca^{2+} and Mg^{2+} bind to the resin in place of Na^+, which is released into the solution [Fig. 18.8(b)]. Replacing Mg^{2+} and Ca^{2+} by Na^+ [Fig. 18.8(c)] ''softens'' the water because the sodium ions interfere much less with the action of soaps and detergents.

Sample Exercise 18.2

Calculate the amount of time required to produce 1.00×10^3 kg of magnesium metal by the electrolysis of molten $MgCl_2$ using a current of 1.00×10^2 A.

Solution

The reaction for plating magnesium is

$$Mg^{2+} + 2e^- \rightarrow Mg$$

which means that 2 moles of electrons are required for each mole of Mg produced. The number of moles of magnesium in 1.00×10^3 kg is

$$1.00 \times 10^3 \text{ kg} \times \frac{1000 \text{ g}}{\text{kg}} \times \frac{1 \text{ mol Mg}}{24.31 \text{ g}} = 4.11 \times 10^4 \text{ mol Mg}$$

Thus

$$\frac{2 \text{ mol e}^-}{1 \text{ mol Mg}} \times 4.11 \times 10^4 \text{ mol Mg} = 8.22 \times 10^4 \text{ mol e}^-$$

(a)

(b)

(c)

Figure 18.8

(a) A schematic representation of a typical cation-exchange resin. (b) and (c) When hard water is passed over the cation-exchange resin, the Ca^{2+} and Mg^{2+} bind to the resin.

Using the faraday (96,485 C/mol e$^-$), we can calculate the coulombs of charge:

$$8.22 \times 10^4 \text{ mol e}^- \times \frac{96,485 \text{ C}}{\text{mol e}^-} = 7.93 \times 10^9 \text{ C}$$

Since an ampere is a coulomb of charge per second, we can now calculate the time required:

$$\frac{7.93 \times 10^9 \text{ C}}{1.00 \times 10^2 \text{ C/s}} = 7.93 \times 10^7 \text{ s} \quad \text{or} \quad 918 \text{ days}$$

18.5 The Group 3A Elements

3A
B
Al
Ga
In
Tl

Purpose

• To show the general trend from nonmetallic to metallic behavior in Group 3A.

The Group 3A elements (valence-electron configuration ns^2np^1) generally show the increase in metallic character in going down the group that is characteristic of the representative elements. Some physical properties, sources, and methods of preparation for the Group 3A elements are summarized in Table 18.9.

Boron is a nonmetal, and most of its compounds are covalent. The most interesting compounds of boron are the covalent hydrides called **boranes.** We might expect BH_3 to be the simplest hydride, since boron has three valence electrons to share with three hydrogen atoms. However, this compound is unstable, and the simplest known member of the series is diborane (B_2H_6), with the structure shown in Fig. 18.9(a). In this molecule the terminal B—H bonds are normal covalent bonds, each involving one electron pair. The bridging bonds are three-center bonds similar to those in solid BeH_2. Another interesting borane contains the square pyramidal B_5H_9

Table 18.9

Selected Physical Properties, Sources, and Methods of Preparation for the Group 3A Elements

Element	Radius of M^{3+} (pm)	Ionization Energy (kJ/mol)	$\mathscr{E}°$ (V) for M^{3+} + 3e$^-$ → M	Sources	Method of Preparation
Boron	20	798	—	Kernite, a form of borax ($Na_2B_4O_7 \cdot 4H_2O$)	Reduction by Mg or H$_2$
Aluminum	51	581	−1.71	Bauxite (Al_2O_3)	Electrolysis of Al_2O_3 in molten Na_3AlF_6
Gallium	62	577	−0.53	Traces in various minerals	Reduction with H$_2$ or electrolysis
Indium	81	556	−0.34	Traces in various minerals	Reduction with H$_2$ or electrolysis
Thallium	95	589	0.72	Traces in various minerals	Electrolysis

(a)   (b)

Figure 18.9

(a) The structure of B_2H_6 with its two three-center B—H—B bridging bonds and four "normal" B—H bonds. (b) The structure of B_5H_9. There are five "normal" B—H bonds to terminal hydrogens and four three-center bridging bonds around the base.

molecule [Fig. 18.9(b)], which has four three-center bonds around the base of the pyramid. Because the boranes are extremely electron-deficient, they are highly reactive. The boranes react very exothermically with oxygen and were once evaluated as potential fuels for rockets in the U.S. space program.

Aluminum, the most abundant metal on earth, has metallic physical properties, such as high thermal and electrical conductivities and a lustrous appearance, but its bonds to nonmetals are significantly covalent. This covalency is responsible for the amphoteric nature of Al_2O_3, which dissolves in acidic or basic solution, and for the acidity of $Al(H_2O)_6^{3+}$ (see Section 14.8):

$$Al(H_2O)_6^{3+}(aq) \rightleftharpoons Al(OH)(H_2O)_5^{2+}(aq) + H^+(aq)$$

One especially interesting property of *gallium* is its unusually low melting point of 29.8°C, which is in contrast to the 660°C melting point of aluminum. Gallium's boiling point is approximately 2400°C. This gives gallium the largest liquid range of any metal, which makes it useful for thermometers, especially to measure high temperatures. Gallium, like water, expands when it freezes. The chemistry of gallium is quite similar to that of aluminum. For example, Ga_2O_3 is amphoteric.

The chemistry of *indium* is similar to that of aluminum and gallium except that compounds containing the 1+ ion are known, such as InCl and In_2O, in addition to those with the more common 3+ ion.

The chemistry of *thallium* is completely metallic. For example, Tl_2O_3 is a basic oxide. Both the +1 and +3 oxidation states are quite common for thallium; Tl_2O_3 and Tl_2O and $TlCl_3$ and $TlCl$ are all well-known compounds. The tendency for the heavier members of Group 3A to exhibit the +1 as well as the expected +3 oxidation state is often called the **inert-pair effect.** This effect is also found in Group 4A, where lead and tin exhibit both +4 and +2 oxidation states.

Table 18.10 summarizes some important reactions of the Group 3A elements.

Gallium metal melts in the hand.

The explanation for the inert-pair effect is very complex, involving a relativistic treatment of the atom, and will not be considered here.

Table 18.10	
Selected Reactions of the Group 3A Elements	
Reaction	Comment
$2M + 3X_2 \rightarrow 2MX_3$	X_2 = any halogen molecule; Tl gives TlX as well, but no TlI_3
$4M + 3O_2 \rightarrow 2M_2O_3$	High temperatures; Tl gives Tl_2O as well
$2M + 3S \rightarrow M_2S_3$	High temperatures; Tl gives Tl_2S as well
$2M + N_2 \rightarrow 2MN$	M = Al only
$2M + 6H^+ \rightarrow 2M^{3+} + 3H_2$	M = Al, Ga, or In; Tl gives Tl^+
$2M + 2OH^- + 6H_2O \rightarrow 2M(OH)_4^- + 3H_2$	M = Al or Ga

The practical importance of the Group 3A elements centers on aluminum. Since the discovery of the electrolytic production process by Hall and Heroult (see Section 17.8), aluminum has become a highly important structural material in a wide variety of applications from aircraft bodies to bicycle components. Aluminum is especially valuable because it has a high strength-to-weight ratio and because it protects itself from corrosion by developing a tough, adherent oxide coating.

18.6 The Group 4A Elements

Purpose

4A
C
Si
Ge
Sn
Pb

- To contrast the chemistry of carbon with that of silicon and the other members of Group 4A.
- To describe carbon oxides.
- To discuss the characteristics of the +2 and +4 oxidation states of tin and lead.

Group 4A (with the valence-electron configuration ns^2np^2) contains two of the most important elements on earth: carbon, the fundamental constituent of the molecules necessary for life; and silicon, which forms the basis of the geologic world. The change from nonmetallic to metallic properties seen in Group 3A is also apparent in going down Group 4A from carbon, a typical nonmetal, to silicon and germanium, usually considered semimetals, to the metals tin and lead. Table 18.11 summarizes some physical properties, sources, and methods of preparation for the elements in this group.

All the Group 4A elements can form four covalent bonds to nonmetals, for example: CH_4, SiF_4, $GeBr_4$, $SnCl_4$, and $PbCl_4$. In each of these tetrahedral molecules, the central atom is described as sp^3 hybridized by the localized electron model. All these compounds, except those of carbon, can react with Lewis bases to

Table 18.11

Selected Physical Properties, Sources, and Methods of Preparation for the Group 4A Elements

Element	Electronegativity	Melting Point (°C)	Boiling Point (°C)	Sources	Method of Preparation
Carbon	2.5	3727 (sublimes)	—	Graphite, diamond, petroleum, coal	
Silicon	1.8	1410	2355	Silicate minerals, silica	Reduction of K_2SiF_6 with Al, or reduction of SiO_2 with Mg
Germanium	1.8	937	2830	Germanite (mixture of copper, iron, and germanium sulfides)	Reduction of GeO_2 with H_2 or C
Tin	1.8	232	2270	Cassiterite (SnO_2)	Reduction of SnO_2 with C
Lead	1.9	327	1740	Galena (PbS)	Roasting of PbS with O_2 to form PbO_2 and then reduction with C

form two additional covalent bonds. For example, $SnCl_4$, which is a fuming liquid (bp = 114°C), can add two chloride ions:

$$SnCl_4 + 2Cl^- \rightarrow SnCl_6^{2-}$$

Carbon compounds cannot react in this way because of the small atomic size of carbon and because there are no d orbitals on carbon to accommodate the extra electrons, as there are on the other elements in the group.

We have seen that carbon also differs markedly from the other members of Group 4A in its ability to form π bonds. This accounts for the completely different structures and properties of CO_2 and SiO_2. Note from Table 18.12 that C—C bonds and Si—O bonds are stronger than Si—Si bonds. This partly explains why the chemistry of carbon is dominated by C—C bonds, whereas that of silicon is dominated by Si—O bonds.

Carbon occurs in the earth's crust in two allotropic forms—graphite and diamond. In addition, new forms of elemental carbon, including buckminsterfullerene (C_{60}) and other related substances, have recently been characterized. The structures of graphite and diamond are given in Section 10.5.

Carbon monoxide (CO), one of three oxides of carbon, is an odorless, colorless, and toxic gas formed as a by-product of the combustion of carbon-containing compounds when there is a limited oxygen supply. Incidents of carbon monoxide poisoning are especially common in the winter in cold areas of the world when blocked furnace vents limit the availability of oxygen. The bonding in carbon monoxide, which has the Lewis structure

$$:C\equiv O:$$

is described in terms of sp hybridized carbon and oxygen atoms that interact to form one σ and two π bonds.

Carbon dioxide, a linear molecule with the Lewis structure

$$\ddot{O}=C=\ddot{O}$$

and an sp hybridized carbon atom, is a product of human and animal respiration and of the combustion of fossil fuels. It is also produced by fermentation, a process by which the sugar in fruits and grains is changed to ethanol (C_2H_5OH) and carbon dioxide (see Section 22.5):

$$C_6H_{12}O_6(aq) \xrightarrow{\text{Enzymes}} 2C_2H_5OH(aq) + 2CO_2(g)$$
Glucose

Carbon dioxide dissolves in water to produce an acidic solution:

$$CO_2(aq) + H_2O(l) \rightleftharpoons H^+(aq) + HCO_3^-(aq)$$

Carbon suboxide, the third carbon oxide, is a linear molecule with the Lewis structure

$$\ddot{O}=C=C=C=\ddot{O}$$

which contains sp hybridized carbon atoms.

Silicon, the second most abundant element in the earth's crust, is a semimetal found widely distributed in silica and silicates (see Section 10.5). Approximately 85% of the earth's crust is composed of these substances. Although silicon is found in some steel and aluminum alloys, its major use is in semiconductors for electronic devices (see the Chemical Impact on page 484).

Table 18.12

Strengths of C—C, Si—Si, and Si—O Bonds

Bond	Bond Energy (kJ/mol)
C—C	347
Si—Si	340
Si—O	452

The organic chemistry of carbon is discussed in Chapter 22.

Although graphite is thermodynamically more stable than diamond, the transformation of diamond to graphite is not observed under normal conditions.

Fullerenes have recently been discovered by geologists in ancient rocks in Russia.

◀ **C H E M I C A L   I M P A C T** ▶

Concrete Learning

Concrete has literally paved the way for civilization over the past 5000 years, tracing its roots to the ancient Egyptians. At a cost of about a penny per pound, concrete is ubiquitous in today's world—used in houses, factories, roads, dams, cooling towers, pipes, skyscrapers, and countless other places. In the United States alone there are an estimated $6 trillion worth of concrete-based structures.

Most concretes are based on portland cement, patented in 1824 by an English bricklayer named J. Aspdin and so named because it forms a product that resembles the natural limestone on the Isle of Portland in England. Portland cement is a powder containing a mixture of calcium silicates [Ca_2SiO_4 (26%) and Ca_3SiO_5 (51%)], calcium aluminate [$Ca_3Al_2O_6$ (11%)], and calcium iron aluminate [$Ca_4Al_2Fe_2O_{10}$ (1%)]. Portland cement is made from a mixture of limestone, sand, shale, clay, and gypsum ($CaSO_4 \cdot 2H_2O$). When the cement is mixed with sand, gravel, and water, it turns into a muddy substance that eventually hardens into the familiar concrete that finds so many uses in our world. The hardening of concrete occurs not through drying but through hydration. The material becomes dry and hard as the water is consumed in building the complex silicate structures present in cured concrete. Although many of the details of this process are poorly understood, the main "glue" that holds the components of concrete together is calcium silicate hydrate, which forms a three-dimensional network mainly responsible for concrete's strength.

Despite its strength when newly produced, concrete contains pockets of air and water dispersed throughout, making it porous and subject to deterioration. Thus despite all the advantages of concrete, it cracks and deteriorates seriously over time.

Much research is now being carried out to improve the durability of concrete. Most of these efforts are directed toward lowering the porosity of concrete and making it less brittle. One group of additives aimed at solving this problem consists of molecules with carbon atom backbones that have sulfate groups attached. These so-called "superplasticizers" allow the formation of concrete using much less water, and these chemicals have doubled the strength of ready-mix concrete over the past 20 years.

Researchers also have found that the properties of concrete can be greatly improved by adding fibers of various kinds, including those made of steel, glass, and carbon-based polymers. One type of fiber concrete—called slurry infiltrated fiber concrete (SIFCON), which is tough enough to be used to make missile silos and can be formed into complex shapes—may be especially useful for structures in earthquake-prone areas.

Other efforts to improve concrete center on replacing portland cement with other binders such as carbon-based polymers. Although these polymer-based concretes will burn and do lose their shapes at high temperatures, they are much more resistant to the effects of water, acids, and salts than those made with portland cement.

Despite the fact that most concrete now used is very similar to that used by the Romans to build the Pantheon, progress is being made, and revolutionary improvements may be just around the corner.

Germanium, a relatively rare element, is a semimetal used mainly in the manufacture of semiconductors for transistors and similar electronic devices.

Tin is a soft silvery metal that can be rolled into thin sheets (tin foil) and has been used for centuries in various alloys such as bronze (~20% Sn and ~80% Cu), solder (~33% Sn and ~67% Pb), and pewter (~85% Sn, ~7% Cu, ~6% Bi, and ~2% Sb). Tin exists as three allotropes: *white tin,* stable at normal temperatures; *gray tin,* stable at temperatures below 13.2°C; and *brittle tin,* found at temperatures above 161°C. When tin is exposed to low temperatures, it gradually changes to the powdery gray tin and crumbles away; this process is known as **tin disease.**

The major current use for tin is as a protective coating for steel, especially for cans used as food containers. The thin layer of tin, applied electrolytically, forms a protective oxide coating that prevents further corrosion.

Tin forms compounds in the +2 and +4 oxidation states. For example, all the possible tin(II) and tin(IV) halides are known. The tin(IV) halides, except for SnF_4, are all relatively volatile (see Table 18.13) and generally behave much more like molecular than ionic compounds. This is no doubt due to the high charge-to-radius ratio that would be characteristic of Sn^{4+} if it existed. Thus, instead of containing Sn^{4+} and X^- ions, the tin(IV) halides contain covalent Sn—X bonds. The Sn^{4+} ion almost certainly does not exist in these or any other known compounds. The com-

The compositions of these alloys vary significantly. For example, the tin content of bronze varies from 5% to 30%, and the tin content of pewter is often as high as 95%.

Table 18.13

Boiling Points of the Tin(IV) Halides

Compound	Boiling Point (°C)
SnF_4	705 (sublimes)
$SnCl_4$	114
$SnBr_4$	202
SnI_4	364

pound SnF_4 is relatively nonvolatile, not because it contains Sn^{4+} and F^- ions, but because it consists of a mixture of SnF_6^{2-} and SnF_2^{2+} ions.

The tin(II) halides are much less volatile than the corresponding tin(IV) compounds; in fact, they are probably ionic, containing Sn^{2+} and X^- ions. Tin(II) chloride in aqueous solution is commonly used as a reducing agent. Tin(II) fluoride (stannous fluoride) was formerly added to toothpaste to help prevent tooth decay.

Lead is easily obtained from its ore, galena (PbS). Because lead melts at such a low temperature, it may have been the first pure metal obtained from its ore. We know that lead was used as early as 3000 B.C. by the Egyptians and was later used by the Romans to make eating utensils, glazes on pottery, and even intricate plumbing systems. Lead is very toxic, however. In fact, the Romans had so much contact with lead that it may have contributed to the demise of their civilization. Analysis of bones from that era shows significant levels of lead.

Although lead poisoning has been known since at least the second century B.C., the incidences of this problem have been relatively isolated. However, the widespread use of tetraethyl lead, $(C_2H_5)_4Pb$, as an antiknock agent in gasoline has increased the lead levels in our environment in this century. Concern about the effects of this lead pollution has caused the U.S. government to require the gradual replacement of the lead in gasoline with other antiknock agents. The largest commercial use of lead (about 1.3 million tons annually) is for electrodes in the lead storage batteries used in automobiles (see Section 17.5).

Lead forms compounds in the +2 and +4 oxidation states. The lead(II) halides, all of which are known, exhibit ionic properties and thus can be assumed to contain Pb^{2+} ions. Only PbF_4 and $PbCl_4$ are known among the possible lead(IV) halides, presumably because lead(IV) oxidizes bromide and iodide ions to give the lead(II) halide and the free halogen:

$$PbX_4 \rightarrow PbX_2 + X_2$$

Lead(IV) chloride decomposes in this fashion at temperatures above 100°C.

A Persian bronze bottle used to hold eye makeup, circa the first century B.C.

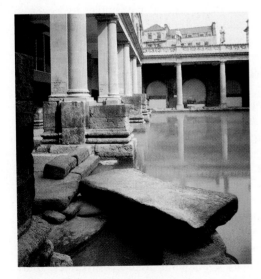

Roman baths such as these in Bath, England, used lead pipes for water.

Lead(II) oxide, known as litharge.

Table 18.14

Selected Reactions of the Group 4A Elements

Reaction	Comment
$M + 2X_2 \rightarrow MX_4$	X_2 = any halogen molecule; M = Ge or Sn; Pb gives PbX_2
$M + O_2 \rightarrow MO_2$	M = Ge or Sn; high temperatures; Pb gives PbO or Pb_3O_4
$M + 2H^+ \rightarrow M^{2+} + H_2$	M = Sn or Pb

Yellow lead(II) oxide, known as **litharge,** is widely used to glaze ceramic ware. Lead(IV) oxide does not exist in nature, but a substance with the formula $PbO_{1.9}$ can be produced in the laboratory by oxidation of lead(II) compounds in basic solution. The nonstoichiometric nature of this compound is caused by defects in the crystal structure. The crystal has some vacancies in positions where there should be oxide ions. These imperfections in the crystal (lattice defects) make lead(IV) oxide an electrical conductor, since the oxide ions can jump from hole to hole. This makes possible the use of lead(IV) oxide as an electrode (the cathode) in the lead storage battery.

Table 18.14 summarizes some important reactions of the Group 4A elements.

FOR REVIEW

Summary

The representative elements have chemical properties determined by their valence s and p electrons. Although the chemical properties of the members of a group are similar in many ways, there is usually a dramatic difference between the first member and the rest of the group due to size differences. For example, hydrogen in Group 1A is much smaller than lithium and forms covalent bonds because it has a much greater attraction for electrons than do the larger members of Group 1A. The first member of a group forms the strongest π bonds, causing elemental nitrogen and oxygen to exist as N_2 and O_2 molecules, while phosphorus and sulfur exist as P_4 and S_8 molecules.

The most abundant element is oxygen, followed by silicon. The most abundant metals are aluminum and iron, which are found as ores in which they are combined with nonmetals, most commonly oxygen.

The Group 1A elements have the valence-electron configuration ns^1 and lose the one electron readily to form M^+ ions, except for hydrogen, which is a nonmetal. The alkali metals all react vigorously with water to form M^+ and OH^- ions and hydrogen gas. With oxygen they form a series of oxides. The regular oxide is formed by lithium (Li_2O). Sodium forms the peroxide Na_2O_2 in excess oxygen, and potassium, rubidium, and cesium form the superoxides of general formula MO_2.

Hydrogen can form covalent compounds with other nonmetals and can form salts with very active metals. Hydrogen's binary compounds are called hydrides. Ionic hydrides are formed when hydrogen combines with the Group 1A and Group 2A metals. The hydride ion (H^-) is a strong reducing agent. Covalent hydrides are formed when hydrogen combines with other nonmetals. Metallic hydrides are formed when hydrogen atoms migrate into transition metal crystals.

The Group 2A elements (with the valence-electron configuration ns^2) are called the alkaline earth metals because of the basicity of their oxides. Only the smallest (first) member of the group, beryllium, has an amphoteric oxide. The alkaline earth metals react less vigorously with water than do the alkali metals, beryllium and magnesium showing no reaction at all at 25°C. The heavier alkaline earth metals form ionic nitrides and hydrides. Solid BeH_2 is a polymeric compound that contains three-center bonds in which one electron pair is shared among three atoms.

Hard water contains Ca^{2+} and Mg^{2+} ions, which can be removed by precipitation of $CaCO_3$ or by ion-exchange resins. These polymeric molecules have many ionic sites, usually with Na^+ ions bound to them. When hard water is passed over the resin, the Ca^{2+} and Mg^{2+} ions replace Na^+ on the resin, and are removed from the water.

The Group 3A elements (with the valence-electron configuration ns^2np^1) show increasing metallic character going down the group. Boron is a nonmetal that forms covalent hydrides called boranes; these are highly electron-deficient with three-center bonds and are therefore very reactive. Aluminum, a metal, has some covalent characteristics, as do gallium and indium. The chemistry of thallium is completely metallic.

The Group 4A elements (with the valence-electron configuration ns^2np^2) also show a change from nonmetallic to metallic properties in going down the group. However, all these elements can form covalent bonds to nonmetals. The MX_4 compounds, except those of carbon, can react with Lewis bases to form two additional covalent bonds; CX_4 compounds cannot react in this way because carbon has no $2d$ orbitals and the $3d$ orbitals are too high in energy to be used.

Key Terms

Section 18.1

representative elements
transition metals
lanthanides
actinides
metalloids (semimetals)
metallurgy
liquefaction

Section 18.2

alkali metals
hydrogen peroxide
superoxide
nitride salt

Section 18.3

hydride

ionic hydride
covalent hydride
metallic (interstitial) hydride

Section 18.4

alkaline earth metals
hard water
ion exchange

ion-exchange resin

Section 18.5

boranes
inert-pair effect

A blue question or exercise number indicates that the answer to that question or exercise appears at the back of this book and a solution appears in the Solutions Guide.

Questions

1. Although the earth was formed from the same interstellar material as the sun, there is little elemental hydrogen (H_2) in the earth's atmosphere. Explain.

2. List two major industrial uses of hydrogen.

3. Name the three types of hydrides. How do they differ?

4. Many lithium salts are hygroscopic (absorb water), whereas the corresponding salts of the other alkali metals are not. Explain.

5. What evidence supports putting hydrogen in Group 1A of the periodic table? In some periodic tables hydrogen is listed sep-

arately from any of the groups. In what ways is hydrogen unlike a typical Group 1A element?

6. Describe how potassium superoxide is used in a self-contained breathing apparatus.

7. All the Group 1A and 2A metals are produced by electrolysis of molten salts. Why?

8. How do the acidities of the aqueous solutions of the alkaline earth metal ions (M^{2+}) change in going down the group?

9. Why is graphite a good lubricant? What advantages does it have over grease- or oil-based lubricants?

10. What are some of the structural differences between quartz and amorphous SiO_2?

11. Why are the tin(IV) halides more volatile than the tin(II) halides?

12. What type of semiconductor is formed when a Group 3A element is added as an impurity to Si or Ge?

13. Diagonal relationships in the periodic table exist as well as the vertical relationships. For example, Be and Al are similar in some of their properties as are B and Si. Rationalize why these diagonal relationships hold for properties such as size, ionization energy, and electron affinity.

14. What is the inert-pair effect? How is it important in the properties of thallium and lead?

Exercises

In this section similar exercises are paired.

Group 1A Elements

15. Hydrogen is produced commercially by the reaction of methane with steam:

$$CH_4(g) + H_2O(g) \rightleftharpoons CO(g) + 3H_2(g)$$

a. Calculate $\Delta H°$ and $\Delta S°$ for this reaction (use the data in Appendix 4).
b. What conditions of temperature and pressure would favor the products of this reaction at equilibrium?

16. Hydrogen is also produced commercially by the following reactions:

$$3Fe(s) + 4H_2O(g) \rightleftharpoons Fe_3O_4(s) + 4H_2(g)$$
$$C(s) + H_2O(g) \rightleftharpoons CO(g) + H_2(g)$$

a. Using the data in Appendix 4, calculate $\Delta H°$ and $\Delta S°$ for these reactions.
b. Under what temperature conditions are each of these reactions spontaneous at standard conditions?

17. Write formulas for each of the following: sodium oxide, sodium superoxide, and sodium peroxide.

18. Give a formula for each binary compound.
a. Rubidium nitride
b. Potassium peroxide

19. Complete and balance the following reactions.
a. $Li_3N(s) + HCl(aq) \rightarrow$
b. $Rb_2O(s) + H_2O(l) \rightarrow$
c. $Cs_2O_2(s) + H_2O(l) \rightarrow$
d. $NaH(s) + H_2O(l) \rightarrow$

20. Write balanced equations describing the reaction of potassium metal with each of the following: O_2, S_8, P_4, H_2, and H_2O.

21. Lithium reacts with acetylene in liquid ammonia to produce LiC_2H (lithium acetylide, $LiC{\equiv}CH$) and hydrogen gas. Write a balanced equation for this reaction. What type of reaction is this?

22. Show how the reaction of NaH with water

$$NaH(s) + H_2O(l) \rightarrow Na^+(aq) + OH^-(aq) + H_2(g)$$

can be described as both an oxidation–reduction and an acid–base reaction.

Group 2A Elements

23. Write the formulas for barium oxide and barium peroxide.

24. Write the formulas for strontium carbonate and magnesium sulfate.

25. Magnesium nitride and magnesium phosphide are expected to react with water in a fashion similar to lithium nitride. Write equations describing the reactions of magnesium nitride and magnesium phosphide with water.

26. Write balanced equations describing the reactions of Ca with each of the following: O_2, S_8, N_2, P_4, H_2, and H_2O.

27. Predict the geometry about beryllium in the compound Cl_2BeNH_3. What hybrid orbitals are predicted for beryllium and nitrogen in this compound? What type of acid is $BeCl_2$?

28. Would you expect $BeCl_2NH_3$ or another compound to form from the reaction of $BeCl_2$ with an excess of ammonia? Draw Lewis structures of other products that might be produced.

29. Beryllium is amphoteric, in contrast with its fellow Group 2A metals. Beryllium metal reacts with aqueous NaOH to produce hydrogen gas and the $Be(OH)_4^{2-}$ ion. Write a balanced equation for this reaction, and name the oxidizing agent and the reducing agent.

30. Calculate the solubility of $Mg(OH)_2$ in an aqueous solution buffered at pH = 8.0. (See Table 15.4.)

Group 3A Elements

31. Name each of the following.
    a. TlOH   c. Ga_2O_3
    b. In_2S_3

32. Name each of the following.
    a. InP   c. GaAs
    b. TlF_3

33. Boron hydrides were once evaluated for possible use as rocket fuels. Complete and balance the following equation for the combustion of diborane.

$$B_2H_6 + O_2 \rightarrow B(OH)_3$$

34. Elemental boron is produced by reduction of boron oxide with magnesium to give boron and magnesium oxide. Write a balanced equation for this reaction.

35. Ga_2O_3 is an amphoteric oxide, and In_2O_3 is a basic oxide. Write equations for the reactions that illustrate these properties.

36. Is Al_2O_3 an acidic, basic, or amphoteric oxide? Write balanced chemical equations to support your answer.

37. Write balanced equations describing the reactions of In with each of the following: F_2, Cl_2, O_2, and HCl.

38. Write a balanced equation describing the reaction of aluminum metal with concentrated aqueous sodium hydroxide.

Group 4A Elements

39. Carbon suboxide (C_3O_2) has the following Lewis structure:

$$\ddot{O}{=}C{=}C{=}C{=}\ddot{O}$$

a. What is the molecular geometry of C_3O_2?
b. What hybrid orbitals are used by the carbon atoms in C_3O_2?

40. Carbon and sulfur form compounds with the formulas CS_2 and C_3S_2. Draw Lewis structures and predict the shapes of these two compounds.

41. Elemental silicon was not isolated until 1823 when J. J. Berzelius succeeded in reducing K_2SiF_6 with molten potassium.
    a. Write a balanced equation for this reaction.
    b. Describe the bonding in K_2SiF_6.

42. Hydrofluoric acid (HF) cannot be stored in glass because it reacts with silica (SiO_2) to form the volatile SiF_4. Write a balanced equation for the reaction of HF with glass.

43. Calculate $\mathscr{E}°$ for the reaction

$$2H_2O(l) + 2Pb(s) + O_2(g) \rightarrow 2Pb(OH)_2(s)$$

which is analogous to the corrosion of iron by O_2 (see Chapter 17). Are lead pipes more easily corroded by oxygen than iron pipes? For $Pb(OH)_2 + 2e^- \rightarrow Pb + 2OH^-$, $\mathscr{E}° = -0.57$ V.

44. Calculate the solubility of $Pb(OH)_2$ ($K_{sp} = 1.2 \times 10^{-15}$) in water.

45. Stannous fluoride (SnF_2) is a compound that was formerly used to introduce F^- ions into toothpaste. Give another name for stannous fluoride.

46. Name the compounds PbO and PbO_2.

47. The resistivity (a measure of electrical resistance) of graphite is $(0.4 \text{ to } 5.0) \times 10^{-4}$ ohm · cm in the basal plane. (The basal plane is the plane of the six-membered rings of carbon atoms.) The resistivity is 0.2 to 1.0 ohm · cm along the axis perpendicular to the plane. The resistivity of diamond is 10^{14} to 10^{16} ohm · cm and is independent of direction. How can you account for this behavior in terms of the structures of graphite and diamond?

48. Silicon carbide (SiC) is an extremely hard substance. Propose a structure for SiC.

Additional Exercises

49. The Group 1A metals are readily soluble in liquid ammonia, releasing hydrogen gas on dissolution. As the metal begins to dissolve, a deep blue solution forms. The color is attributed to the presence of solvated electrons, or $e(NH_3)_x^-$. The metal amide (MNH_2) can be isolated by allowing the ammonia to evaporate.
   a. Write a balanced equation for the reaction for the formation of $NaNH_2$.
   b. The solubility of sodium in liquid ammonia at $-33.5°C$ is 251.4 g/kg. Calculate the mass percent, mole fraction, and molality of sodium in this solution.

50. Use the Nernst equation (see Section 17.4) to calculate the amount of work that must be done to transport 1.0 mol K^+ ions from the outside of a cell to the inside. Inside muscle cells $[K^+]$ is about 0.15 mol/L and in blood plasma $[K^+]$ is about 5.0×10^{-3} mol/L.

51. Graph the melting points (see Table 18.4) of the alkali metals versus atomic number. Predict the melting point for francium. Would you predict francium to be a solid or a liquid at room temperature?

52. Predict the structure of BeF_2 in the gas phase. What structure would you predict for $BeF_2(s)$?

53. What current is needed to produce 1.00×10^3 kg of Ca metal in 8.00 hours from the electrolysis of molten $CaCl_2$? What mass of Cl_2 is produced?

54. The compound $BeSO_4 \cdot 4H_2O$ cannot be dehydrated easily by heating. It dissolves in water to give an acidic solution. Explain these observations.

55. The compound $AlCl_3$ is quite volatile and appears to exist as a dimer in the gas phase. Propose a structure for this dimer.

56. Assume that element 113 is produced. Predict the radius of its 3+ ion and the first ionization energy using the information in Table 18.9.

57. Lithium aluminum hydride ($LiAlH_4$) is a powerful reducing agent used in the synthesis of organic compounds. Assign oxidation states to all atoms in $LiAlH_4$.

58. The compound with the formula TlI_3 is a black solid. Given the following standard reduction potentials:

$$Tl^{3+} + 2e^- \rightarrow Tl^+ \qquad \mathscr{E}° = +1.25 \text{ V}$$
$$I_3^- + 2e^- \rightarrow 3I^- \qquad \mathscr{E}° = +0.55 \text{ V}$$

would you formulate this compound as thallium(III) iodide or thallium(I) triiodide?

59. The compound Ga_2Cl_4 is brown. How could you determine experimentally whether this compound contains two gallium(II) ions or one gallium(I) and one gallium(III) ion? (*Hint:* Consider the electron configurations of the three possible ions.)

60. Tricalcium aluminate, an important component of Portland cement, is 44.4% calcium and 20.0% aluminum by mass. The remainder is oxygen.
   a. Calculate the empirical formula of tricalcium aluminate.
   b. The structure of tricalcium aluminate was not determined until 1975. The $Al_6O_{18}^{18-}$ anion has the following structure:

   What is the molecular formula of tricalcium aluminate?
   c. How would you describe the bonding in the $Al_6O_{18}^{18-}$ anion?

61. Use bond energies (see Table 8.4) to estimate ΔH for the following reaction.

$$\underset{HO}{\overset{O}{\underset{\displaystyle \parallel}{C}}}\overset{}{OH} \longrightarrow CO_2 + H_2O$$

Why is it better to write carbonic acid as $CO_2(aq)$ rather than as H_2CO_3?

62. What is the ratio of lead(II) to lead(IV) in red lead (Pb_3O_4)?

63. Which Group 4A elements are capable of reducing H^+ to H_2? Write balanced equations describing the reactions.

64. Dioctyltin compounds are used as stabilizers for polyvinyl chloride polymers. (See Chapter 22.) They can be produced by this reaction:

$$2CH_3CH_2CH_2CH_2CH_2CH_2CH_2CH_2X + Sn$$
$$\rightarrow (C_8H_{17})_2SnX_2$$

where X is a halogen. Predict the structure of $(C_8H_{17})_2SnCl_2$.

Challenge Problems

65. Compounds containing the sodide ion (Na^-) have recently been made.

$$2Na + Crypt \rightarrow [Na(Crypt)]^+Na^-$$

where Crypt represents a cryptand $N[(C_2H_4O)_2C_2H_4]_3N$.

The cryptand encapsulates the Na^- ion. Why is it necessary to encapsulate Na^-? (See Exercise 83 in Chapter 7.)

66. Ionic compounds, such as $KMnO_4$, can be dissolved in nonpolar solvents by adding *crown ethers*. The structure of a typical crown ether is as follows:

Suggest how crown ethers make $KMnO_4$ soluble in nonpolar solvents.

67. From the information on the temperature stability of white and gray tin given in this chapter, which form would you expect to have the more ordered structure?

68. The compounds CCl_4 and H_2O do not react with each other. On the other hand, silicon tetrachloride reacts with water according to the equation

$$SiCl_4(l) + 2H_2O(l) \rightarrow SiO_2(s) + 4HCl(aq)$$

Discuss the importance of thermodynamics and kinetics in the reactivity of water with $SiCl_4$ as compared with its lack of reactivity with CCl_4.

69. One reason suggested to account for the instability of long chains of silicon atoms is that the decomposition involves the transition state shown below:

The activation energy for such a process is 210 kJ/mol, which is less than either the Si—Si or Si—H bond energy. Why would a similar mechanism not be expected to be very important in the decomposition of long carbon chains?

CHAPTER 19

The Representative Elements: Groups 5A Through 8A

I n Chapter 18 we saw that vertical groups of elements tend to show similar chemical characteristics because they have identical valence-electron configurations. Generally, metallic character increases going down a group, as the valence electrons are found further from the nucleus. Also, recall that the most dramatic change in properties occurs after the first group member, mainly because the most dramatic change in size occurs between the first and second group members.

As we proceed from Group 1A to Group 7A, the elements change from active metals (electron donors) to strong nonmetals (electron acceptors). Thus it is not surprising that the middle groups show the most varied chemistry: some group members behave principally as metals, others behave mainly as nonmetals, and some show both tendencies. The elements in Groups 5A and 6A show great chemical variety and form many compounds of considerable practical value. The halogens (Group 7A) are nonmetals that are also found in many everyday substances such as household bleach, photographic films, and "automatic" sunglasses. The elements in Group 8A (the noble gases) are most useful in their elemental forms, but their ability to form compounds, discovered only within the past 30 years, has provided important tests for the theories of chemical bonding.

In this chapter we give an overview of the elements in Groups 5A through 8A, concentrating on the chemistry of the most important elements in these groups: nitrogen, phosphorus, oxygen, sulfur, and the halogens.

◁ Lightning, which furnishes the energy to disrupt the bonds in N_2 and O_2 molecules, is a major source of fixed nitrogen.

19.1 *The Group 5A Elements*

Purpose

• To give an overview of the characteristics of the Group 5A elements, with emphasis on bonding.

The Group 5A elements (with the valence-electron configuration ns^2np^3) are prepared as shown in Table 19.1, and they show remarkably varied chemical properties. As usual, metallic character increases going down the group, as is apparent from the electronegativity values (Table 19.1). *Nitrogen* and *phosphorus* are non-

5A
N
P
As
Sb
Bi

Table 19.1

Selected Physical Properties, Sources, and Methods of Preparation for the Group 5A Elements

Element	Electro-negativity	Sources	Method of Preparation
Nitrogen	3.0	Air	Liquefaction of air
Phosphorus	2.1	Phosphate rock $(Ca_3(PO_4)_2)$, Fluorapatite $(Ca_5(PO_4)_3F)$	$2Ca_3(PO_4)_2 + 6SiO_2 \rightarrow$ $6CaSiO_3 + P_4O_{10}$ $P_4O_{10} + 10C \rightarrow$ $4P + 10CO$
Arsenic	2.0	Arsenopyrite (Fe_3As_2, FeS)	Heating arsenopyrite in the absence of air
Antimony	1.9	Stibnite (Sb_2S_3)	Roasting Sb_2S_3 in air to form Sb_2O_3 and then reduction with carbon
Bismuth	1.9	Bismite (Bi_2O_3), bismuth glance (Bi_2S_3)	Roasting Bi_2S_3 in air to form Bi_2O_3 and then reduction with carbon

metals that can gain three electrons to form $3-$ anions in salts with active metals, for example, magnesium nitride (Mg_3N_2) and beryllium phosphide (Be_3P_2). The chemistry of these two important elements is discussed in the next two sections.

Bismuth and *antimony* tend to be metallic, readily losing electrons to form cations. Although these elements have five valence electrons, so much energy is required to remove all five that no ionic compounds containing Bi^{5+} or Sb^{5+} ions are known. Three pentahalides (BiF_5, $SbCl_5$, and SbF_5) are known, but these are molecular rather than ionic compounds. The fact that no other pentahalides of these elements are known no doubt results from the strong oxidizing ability of bismuth and antimony in the $+5$ oxidation state. In fact, BiF_5 is an excellent fluorinating agent, readily decomposing to bismuth trifluoride and fluorine:

$$BiF_5 \rightarrow BiF_3 + F_2$$

Salts containing the Bi^{3+} or Sb^{3+} ions, such as $Sb_2(SO_4)_3$ and $Bi(NO_3)_3$, are quite common. When these salts are dissolved in water, the resulting hydrated cations are very acidic. For example, the reaction of the Bi^{3+} ion with water can be represented as

$$Bi^{3+}(aq) + H_2O(l) \rightarrow BiO^+(aq) + 2H^+(aq)$$

where BiO^+ is called the **bismuthyl ion.** If chloride ion is added to this solution, a white salt, bismuthyl chloride ($BiOCl$), precipitates. Antimony exhibits similar chemistry in aqueous solution.

The Group 5A elements can form molecules or ions that involve three, five, or six covalent bonds to the Group 5A atom. Examples involving three single bonds are NH_3, PH_3, NF_3, and $AsCl_3$. Each of these molecules has a lone pair of electrons (and thus can behave as a Lewis base) and a pyramidal shape as predicted by the VSEPR model (see Fig. 19.1).

All the Group 5A elements except nitrogen can form molecules with five covalent bonds (of general formula MX_5). Nitrogen cannot form such molecules because of its small size and lack of available d orbitals. The MX_5 molecules have a trigonal bipyramidal shape (see Fig. 19.1) as predicted by the VSEPR model, and the central atom is described as dsp^3 hybridized. The MX_5 molecules can accept an additional electron pair to form ionic species containing six covalent bonds. An example is

$$PF_5 + F^- \rightarrow PF_6^-$$

where the PF_6^- anion has an octahedral shape (see Fig. 19.1) and the phosphorus atom is described as d^2sp^3 hybridized.

Although the MX_5 molecules have a trigonal bipyramidal structure in the gas phase, the solids of many of these compounds contain the ions MX_4^+ and MX_6^- (Fig. 19.2), where the MX_4^+ cation is tetrahedral (the atom represented by M is sp^3 hybridized) and the MX_6^- anion is octahedral (the atom represented by M is d^2sp^3 hybridized). Examples are PCl_5, which in the solid state contains PCl_4^+ and PCl_6^-, and AsF_3Cl_2, which in the solid state contains $AsCl_4^+$ and AsF_6^-.

As discussed in Section 18.1, the ability of the Group 5A elements to form π bonds decreases dramatically after nitrogen. This explains why elemental nitrogen exists as N_2 molecules, whereas the other elements in the group exist as larger aggregates containing single bonds. For example, in the gas phase, the elements phosphorus, arsenic, and antimony consist of P_4, As_4, and Sb_4 molecules, respectively.

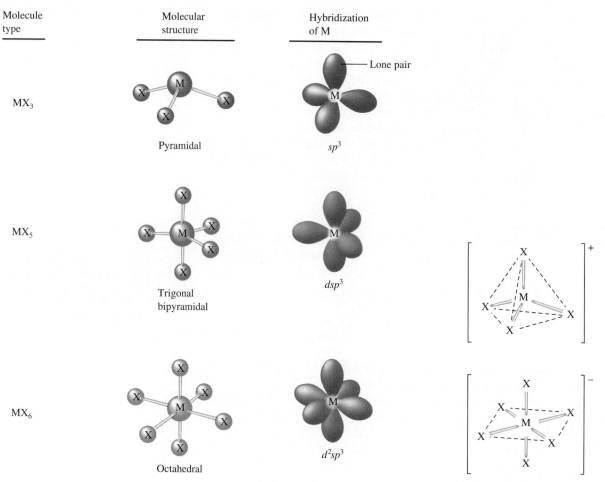

Molecule type	Molecular structure	Hybridization of M
MX_3	Pyramidal	sp^3
MX_5	Trigonal bipyramidal	dsp^3
MX_6	Octahedral	d^2sp^3

Figure 19.1

The molecules of the types MX_3, MX_5, and MX_6 formed by Group 5A elements.

Figure 19.2

The structures of the tetrahedral MX_4^+ and octahedral MX_6^- ions.

19.2 The Chemistry of Nitrogen

Purpose

- To discuss the kinetic and thermodynamic importance of the strength of the triple bond in the nitrogen molecule.
- To introduce the nitrogen cycle.
- To describe the structures and uses of major nitrogen-containing compounds.

At the earth's surface, virtually all elemental nitrogen exists as the N_2 molecule with its very strong triple bond (941 kJ/mol). Because of this high bond strength, the N_2 molecule is so unreactive that it can coexist with most other elements under normal conditions without undergoing any appreciable reaction. This property makes nitrogen gas very useful as a medium for experiments involving substances

Figure 19.3
An inert atmosphere box used when working with oxygen- or water-sensitive materials. The box is filled with an inert gas such as nitrogen, and work is done through the ports fitted with large rubber gloves.

that react with oxygen or water. Such experiments can be done using an inert-atmosphere box of the type shown in Fig. 19.3.

The strength of the triple bond in the N_2 molecule is important both thermodynamically and kinetically. Thermodynamically, the great stability of the $N\equiv N$ bond means that most binary compounds containing nitrogen decompose exothermically to the elements, for example:

$$N_2O(g) \rightarrow N_2(g) + \tfrac{1}{2}O_2(g) \qquad \Delta H° = -82 \text{ kJ}$$
$$NO(g) \rightarrow \tfrac{1}{2}N_2(g) + \tfrac{1}{2}O_2(g) \qquad \Delta H° = -90 \text{ kJ}$$
$$NO_2(g) \rightarrow \tfrac{1}{2}N_2(g) + O_2(g) \qquad \Delta H° = -34 \text{ kJ}$$
$$N_2H_4(g) \rightarrow N_2(g) + 2H_2(g) \qquad \Delta H° = -95 \text{ kJ}$$
$$NH_3(g) \rightarrow \tfrac{1}{2}N_2(g) + \tfrac{3}{2}H_2(g) \qquad \Delta H° = +46 \text{ kJ}$$

Of these compounds, only ammonia is thermodynamically more stable than its component elements. That is, only for ammonia is energy required (endothermic process, positive value of $\Delta H°$) to decompose the molecule to its elements. For the remaining molecules, energy is released when decomposition to the elements occurs as a result of the great stability of N_2.

The importance of the thermodynamic stability of N_2 can be seen clearly in the power of nitrogen-based explosives, such as nitroglycerin ($C_3H_5N_3O_9$), which has the structure

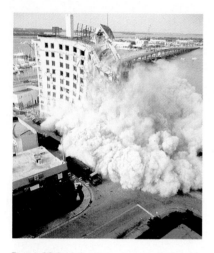

Figure 19.4

Chemical explosives are used to demolish a building in Miami, Florida.

When ignited or subjected to sudden impact, nitroglycerin decomposes very rapidly and exothermically:

$$4C_3H_5N_3O_9(l) \rightarrow 6N_2(g) + 12CO_2(g) + 10H_2O(g) + O_2(g) + \text{energy}$$

An explosion occurs; that is, large volumes of gas are produced in a fast, highly exothermic reaction. Note that 4 moles of liquid nitroglycerin produce 29 (6 + 12 + 10 + 1) moles of gaseous products. This alone produces a large increase in volume. However, also note that the products, including N_2, are very stable molecules with strong bonds. Their formation is therefore accompanied by the release of large quantities of energy as heat, which increases the gaseous volume. The hot, rapidly expanding gases produce a pressure surge and damaging shock wave.

Pure nitroglycerin is quite dangerous because it explodes with little provocation. However, in 1867 the Swedish inventor Alfred Nobel found that if nitroglycerin is absorbed in porous silica, it can be handled quite safely. This tremendously important explosive (see Fig. 19.4), which he called **dynamite,** earned Nobel a great fortune, which he subsequently used to establish the Nobel Prizes.

Most high explosives are organic compounds that, like nitroglycerin, contain nitro (—NO_2) groups and produce nitrogen and other gases as products. Another example is *trinitrotoluene,* or TNT, a solid at normal temperatures, which decomposes as follows:

$$2C_7H_5N_3O_6(s) \rightarrow 12CO(g) + 5H_2(g) + 3N_2(g) + 2C(s) + \text{energy}$$

Note that 2 moles of solid TNT produce 20 moles of gaseous products plus energy.

Sample Exercise 19.1

When ammonium nitrite is heated, it decomposes to nitrogen gas and water. Calculate the volume of N_2 gas produced from 1.00 g of solid NH_4NO_2 at 250°C and 1.00 atm.

Solution

The decomposition reaction is

$$NH_4NO_2(s) \xrightarrow{\text{Heat}} N_2(g) + 2H_2O(g)$$

Using the molar mass of NH_4NO_2 (64.05 g/mol), we first calculate the moles of NH_4NO_2:

$$1.00 \text{ g } NH_4NO_2 \times \frac{1 \text{ mol } NH_4NO_2}{64.05 \text{ g } NH_4NO_2} = 1.56 \times 10^{-2} \text{ mol } NH_4NO_2$$

Since 1 mol N_2 is produced for each mole of NH_4NO_2, 1.56×10^{-2} mol N_2 will be produced in the given experiment. We can calculate the volume of N_2 from the ideal gas law:

$$PV = nRT$$

In this case we have

$$P = 1.00 \text{ atm}$$
$$n = 1.56 \times 10^{-2} \text{ mol}$$

$$R = 0.08206 \text{ L} \cdot \text{atm/K} \cdot \text{mol}$$

$$T = 250 + 273 = 523 \text{ K}$$

and the volume of N_2 is

$$V = \frac{nRT}{P} = \frac{(1.56 \times 10^{-2} \text{ mol})\left(0.08206\dfrac{\text{L} \cdot \text{atm}}{\text{K} \cdot \text{mol}}\right)(523 \text{ K})}{1.00 \text{ atm}}$$

$$= 0.670 \text{ L}$$

The effect of bond strength on the kinetics of reactions involving the N_2 molecule is illustrated by the synthesis of ammonia from nitrogen and hydrogen, a reaction we have discussed many times before. Because a large quantity of energy is required to disrupt the $N \equiv N$ bond, the ammonia synthesis reaction has a negligible rate at room temperature, even though the equilibrium constant is very large ($K \approx 10^6$) at 25°C. Of course, the most direct way to increase the rate is to raise the temperature, but since the reaction is very exothermic, that is,

$$N_2(g) + 3H_2(g) \rightarrow 2NH_3(g) \qquad \Delta H° = -92 \text{ kJ}$$

the value of K decreases significantly with a temperature increase (at 500°C, $K \approx 10^{-2}$).

Obviously, the kinetics and the thermodynamics of this reaction are in opposition. A compromise must be reached: high pressure to force the equilibrium to the right and high temperature to produce a reasonable rate. The **Haber process** for manufacturing ammonia illustrates this compromise (see Fig. 19.5). The process is carried out at a pressure of about 250 atm and a temperature of approximately 400°C. Even higher temperatures would be required except that a catalyst, consisting of a solid iron oxide mixed with small amounts of potassium oxide and aluminum oxide, is used to facilitate the reaction.

Nitrogen is essential to living systems. The problem with nitrogen is not one of supply—we are surrounded by it—but of changing it from inert N_2 molecules to a form usable by plants and animals. The process of transforming N_2 to other nitrogen-containing compounds is called **nitrogen fixation.** The Haber process is one example of nitrogen fixation. The ammonia produced can be applied to the soil as a fertilizer, since plants can readily employ the nitrogen in ammonia to make the nitrogen-containing biomolecules essential for their growth.

Nitrogen fixation also results from the high-temperature combustion process in automobile engines. The nitrogen in the air drawn into the engine reacts at a significant rate with oxygen to form nitric oxide (NO), which further reacts with oxygen from the air to form nitrogen dioxide (NO_2). This nitrogen dioxide, which is an important contributor to photochemical smog in many urban areas (see Section 12.8), eventually reacts with moisture in the air and reaches the soil to form nitrate salts, which are plant nutrients.

Nitrogen fixation also occurs naturally. For example, lightning provides the energy to disrupt N_2 and O_2 molecules in the air, producing highly reactive nitrogen and oxygen atoms that attack other N_2 and O_2 molecules to form nitrogen oxides that eventually become nitrates. Although lightning traditionally has been credited with forming about 10% of the total fixed nitrogen, recent studies indicate that

Figure 19.5

A schematic diagram of the Haber process for the manufacture of ammonia.

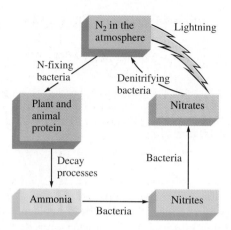

Figure 19.6

The nitrogen cycle. To be used by plants and animals, nitrogen must be converted from N_2 to nitrogen-containing compounds, such as nitrates, ammonia, and proteins. The nitrogen is returned to the atmosphere by natural decay processes.

Nodules on the roots of pea plants contain nitrogen-fixing bacteria.

lightning may account for as much as half the fixed nitrogen available on earth. Another natural nitrogen fixation process is provided by bacteria that reside in the root nodules of plants such as beans, peas, and alfalfa. These **nitrogen-fixing bacteria** readily allow the conversion of nitrogen to ammonia and other nitrogen-containing compounds useful to plants. The efficiency of these bacteria is intriguing: they produce ammonia at soil temperature and 1 atm of pressure, whereas the Haber process requires severe conditions of 400°C and 250 atm. For obvious reasons, researchers are studying these bacteria intensively.

When plants and animals die, they decompose, and the elements they consist of are returned to the environment. In the case of nitrogen, the return of the element to the atmosphere as nitrogen gas, called **denitrification,** is carried out by bacteria that change nitrates to nitrogen. The complex **nitrogen cycle** is summarized in Fig. 19.6. It has been estimated that as much as 10 million tons per year more nitrogen is currently being fixed by natural and human processes than is being returned to the atmosphere. This fixed nitrogen is accumulating in the soil, lakes, rivers, and oceans, where it can promote the growth of algae and other undesirable organisms.

Nitrogen Hydrides

By far the most important hydride of nitrogen is **ammonia** (NH_3). A toxic, colorless gas with a pungent odor, ammonia is manufactured in huge quantities ($\sim$30 billion pounds per year), mainly for use in fertilizers.

The pyramidal ammonia molecule (see Fig. 19.1) has a lone pair of electrons on the nitrogen atom and polar N—H bonds. This structure leads to a high degree of intermolecular interaction by hydrogen bonding in the liquid state and produces an unusually high boiling point (-33.4°C) for a substance of such low molar mass. Note, however, that the hydrogen bonding in liquid ammonia is clearly not so important as that in liquid water, which has about the same molar mass but a much higher boiling point. The water molecule has two polar bonds involving hydrogen and two lone pairs—the right combination for optimal hydrogen bonding—in contrast to the one lone pair and three polar bonds of the ammonia molecule.

As we saw in Chapter 14, ammonia behaves as a base and reacts with acids to produce ammonium salts, for example,

$$NH_3(g) + HCl(g) \rightarrow NH_4Cl(s)$$

◀ **CHEMICAL IMPACT** ▶

A Blanket of Nitrogen

Inert gases play a very important role as blanketing agents to prevent unwanted chemical reactions. Nitrogen gas, because of its ready availability and low reactivity at normal temperatures, has been the leader in this market. For example, nitrogen is finding increasing use for blanketing fruit after it has been picked to protect it from deterioration until the consumer buys it. Apples that receive no protective treatment deteriorate to the point of being unmarketable within about six weeks after picking (of which four weeks are required for ripening). However, the marketable range of apples can be extended to nearly thirty months by storing them at temperatures just above freezing and by controlling the storage atmosphere. As apples ripen, they consume oxygen and emit carbon dioxide and ethylene (C_2H_4). Ethylene is a ripening hormone that rapidly accelerates the ripening, and thus the deterioration of the fruit.

State-of-the-art cold-storage facilities for apples have purging and recycling systems to lower the oxygen content of the gas in the room to below 5% within two days. Optimal long-term storage conditions involve oxygen concentrations of ~1.5% by volume, carbon dioxide concentrations of ~3% by volume, and ethylene concentrations below 1 ppm.

One relatively expensive method for producing the nitrogen gas used in these storage facilities is the vaporization of liquid nitrogen stored in cryogenic tanks. A less expensive source of nitrogen gas is the exhaust gas from the combustion reaction of propane and air. The carbon dioxide in the exhaust is removed with activated charcoal. In Europe nitrogen gas is commonly produced by catalytically decomposing ammonia to nitrogen and hydrogen and then removing the hydrogen gas by reaction with oxygen.

However, recent advances in high-volume gas separation technology in the United States have made direct separation of nitrogen from air economically feasible. One separation method is called the *pressure-swing adsorption process,* in which carbon molecular sieves (substances with precisely sized passages) are used to selectively adsorb the oxygen from air while allowing the nitrogen to pass through. When the molecular sieves become saturated with oxygen, the O_2 molecules are dislodged by a sudden jump in pressure—thus the name of the process. Using more than one bed of molecular sieves in parallel permits a steady flow of nitrogen for controlled-atmosphere applications.

Another gas separation process employs special hollow fiber membranes designed to allow the oxygen and water vapor in a stream of air to "leak" through the walls of the fibers as the air flows through, producing a stream of nitrogen at the end of the tube.

One major advantage of these latter two processes is that they can be used to generate a controlled atmosphere for a product such as fruit while it is in transport by ship, rail, or truck. These gas separation processes also have been adapted for use in other industries. For example, the Fetzer Winery in Redwood Valley, California, uses a membrane separator to produce a nitrogen-rich atmosphere for its fermentation tanks to prevent oxygen-driven decomposition of the wine.

The future of the gas-blanketing market appears anything but inert.

A second nitrogen hydride of major importance is **hydrazine** (N_2H_4). The Lewis structure of hydrazine is

$$\text{H} \quad \overset{\cdot\cdot}{\underset{\text{H}}{\text{N}}} \!-\! \overset{\cdot\cdot}{\underset{\text{H}}{\text{N}}} \quad \text{H}$$

indicating that each nitrogen atom should be sp^3 hybridized with bond angles close to 109.5 degrees (the tetrahederal angle), since the nitrogen atom is surrounded by four electron pairs. The observed structure with bond angles of 112 degrees (see Fig. 19.7) agrees reasonably well with these predictions. Hydrazine, a colorless liquid with an ammoniacal odor, freezes at 2°C and boils at 113.5°C. This boiling point is quite high for a compound with a molar mass of 32 g/mol; this suggests that considerable hydrogen bonding must occur among the polar hydrazine molecules.

Hydrazine is a powerful reducing agent that has been used widely as a rocket propellant. For example, its reaction with oxygen is highly exothermic:

$$N_2H_4(l) + O_2(g) \rightarrow N_2(g) + 2H_2O(g) \qquad \Delta H° = -622 \text{ kJ}$$

Figure 19.7

The molecular structure of hydrazine (N_2H_4). This arrangement minimizes the repulsion between the lone pairs on the nitrogen atoms by placing them on opposite sides.

The space shuttle Endeavour being launched from the Kennedy Space Center in Florida. The space shuttle orbiter uses monomethylhydrazine mixed with an oxidizer as fuel.

Since hydrazine also reacts vigorously with the halogens, fluorine is often used instead of oxygen as the oxidizer in rocket engines. Substituted hydrazines, where one or more of the hydrogen atoms are replaced by other groups, are also useful rocket fuels. For example, monomethylhydrazine,

$$CH_3 \quad\quad\quad H$$
$$N{-}N$$
$$H \quad\quad\quad H$$

is used with the oxidizer dinitrogen tetroxide (N_2O_4) to power the U.S. space shuttle orbiter. The reaction is

$$5N_2O_4(l) + 4N_2H_3(CH_3)(l) \rightarrow 12H_2O(g) + 9N_2(g) + 4CO_2(g)$$

Because of the large number of gaseous molecules produced and the exothermic nature of this reaction, a very high thrust per mass of fuel is achieved. The reaction is also self-starting—it begins immediately when the fuels are mixed—which is a useful property for rocket engines that must be started and stopped frequently.

Sample Exercise 19.2

Using the bond energies in Table 8.4 (Chapter 8), calculate the approximate value of ΔH for the reaction between gaseous monomethylhydrazine and dinitrogen tetroxide:

$$5N_2O_4(g) + 4N_2H_3(CH_3)(g) \rightarrow 12H_2O(g) + 9N_2(g) + 4CO_2(g)$$

The bonding in N_2O_4 is described by resonance structures that predict that the N—O bonds are intermediate in strength between single and double bonds (assume an average N—O bond energy of 440 kJ/mol).

Solution

To calculate ΔH for this reaction, we must compare the energy necessary to break the bonds of the reactants and the energy released by formation of the bonds in the products

$$5 \begin{array}{c} O \quad\quad O \\ N \\ | \\ N \\ O \quad\quad O \end{array} + 4 \begin{array}{c} H \quad C{-}H \\ N \quad H \\ | \\ N \\ H \quad H \end{array} \longrightarrow 12 \begin{array}{c} H \\ O \\ H \end{array} + 9N{\equiv}N + 4O{=}C{=}O$$

Breaking bonds requires energy (positive sign), and forming bonds releases energy (negative sign). As summarized in the following table,

$$\Delta H = (21.1 \times 10^3 \text{ kJ}) - (26.1 \times 10^3 \text{ kJ}) = -5.0 \times 10^3 \text{ kJ}$$

The reaction is highly exothermic.

Bonds Broken	Energy Required (kJ/mol)	Bonds Formed	Energy Released (kJ/mol)
$5 \times 4 = 20$ N$=$O	$20 \times 440 = 8.8 \times 10^3$	$12 \times 2 = 24$ O—H	$24 \times 467 = 1.12 \times 10^4$
$5 + 4 = 9$ N—N	$9 \times 160 = 1.4 \times 10^3$	9 N$\equiv$N	$9 \times 941 = 8.5 \times 10^3$
$4 \times 3 = 12$ N—H	$12 \times 391 = 4.7 \times 10^3$	$4 \times 2 = 8$ C$=$O	$8 \times 799 = 6.4 \times 10^3$
$4 \times 3 = 12$ C—H	$12 \times 413 = 5.0 \times 10^3$		
$4 \times 1 = 4$ C—N	$4 \times 305 = 1.2 \times 10^3$		
Total	21.1×10^3	Total	26.1×10^3

The use of hydrazine as a rocket propellant is a rather specialized application. The main industrial use of hydrazine is as a "blowing" agent in the manufacture of plastics. Hydrazine decomposes to form nitrogen gas, which causes foaming in the liquid plastic, which results in a porous texture. Another major use of hydrazine is in the production of agricultural pesticides. Of the many hundreds of hydrazine derivatives (substituted hydrazines) that have been tested, 40 are used as fungicides, herbicides, insecticides, and plant growth regulators.

The manufacture of hydrazine involves the oxidation of ammonia by the hypochlorite ion in basic solution:

$$2NH_3(aq) + OCl^-(aq) \rightarrow N_2H_4(aq) + Cl^-(aq) + H_2O(l)$$

Although this reaction looks straightforward, the actual process involves many steps and requires high pressure, high temperature, and catalysis to optimize the yield of hydrazine in the face of many competing reactions.

Blowing agents such as hydrazine, which forms nitrogen gas on decomposition, are used to produce porous plastics like these styrofoam "peanuts."

Nitrogen Oxides

Nitrogen forms a series of oxides in which it has an oxidation state from +1 to +5, as shown in Table 19.2.

Dinitrogen monoxide (N_2O), more commonly called **nitrous oxide** or laughing gas, has an inebriating effect and is often used as a mild anesthetic by dentists. Because of its high solubility in fats, nitrous oxide is used widely as a propellant in aerosol cans of whipped cream. It is dissolved in the liquid in the can at high pressure and forms bubbles that produce foaming as the liquid is released from the can. A significant amount of N_2O exists in the atmosphere, mostly produced by soil microorganisms, and its concentration appears to be gradually increasing. Because it can strongly absorb infrared radiation, nitrous oxide plays a small but probably significant role in controlling the earth's temperature in the same way that atmospheric carbon dioxide and water vapor do (see the discussion of the greenhouse effect in Section 6.5). Some scientists fear that the rapid decrease of tropical rain forests resulting from development in countries such as Brazil will significantly affect the rate of production of N_2O by soil organisms and thus will have important effects on the earth's temperature.

In the laboratory, nitrous oxide is prepared by the thermal decomposition of ammonium nitrate:

$$NH_4NO_3(s) \xrightarrow{\text{Heat}} N_2O(g) + 2H_2O(g)$$

Table 19.2			
Some Common Nitrogen Compounds			
Oxidation State of Nitrogen	Compound	Formula	Lewis Structure*
−3	Ammonia	NH_3	H—N—H with H below and lone pair on N
−2	Hydrazine	N_2H_4	H—N—N—H with H below each N and lone pairs
−1	Hydroxylamine	NH_2OH	H—N—O—H with H below N and lone pairs
0	Nitrogen	N_2	$:N \equiv N:$
+1	Dinitrogen monoxide (nitrous oxide)	N_2O	$:N = N = O:$
+2	Nitrogen monoxide (nitric oxide)	NO	$:N = O:$
+3	Dinitrogen trioxide	N_2O_3	O₂N—N=O structure with lone pairs
+4	Nitrogen dioxide	NO_2	$:O—N = O$
+5	Nitric acid	HNO_3	O—N—O—H with double-bonded O below

*In some cases, additional resonance structures are needed to fully describe the electron distribution.

Do not attempt this experiment unless you have the proper safety equipment.

This experiment must be done carefully because ammonium nitrate can explode. In fact, one of the greatest industrial disasters in U.S. history occurred in 1947 in Texas, when a ship loaded with ammonium nitrate for use as fertilizer exploded and killed nearly 600 people.

Nitrogen monoxide (NO), commonly called **nitric oxide,** is a colorless gas under normal conditions that can be produced in the laboratory by reaction of 6 *M* nitric acid with copper metal:

$$8H^+(aq) + 2NO_3^-(aq) + 3Cu(s) \rightarrow 3Cu^{2+}(aq) + 4H_2O(l) + 2NO(g)$$

When this reaction is run in the air, the nitric oxide is immediately oxidized to brown nitrogen dioxide (NO_2).

Since the NO molecule has an odd number of electrons, it is most conveniently described in terms of the molecular orbital model. The molecular orbital energy-level diagram is shown in Fig. 19.8. Note that the NO molecule is paramagnetic and should have a bond order of 2.5, a prediction that is supported by experimental observations. Since the NO molecule has one high-energy electron, it is not surprising that it can be rather easily oxidized to form NO^+, the *nitrosyl ion*. Because an

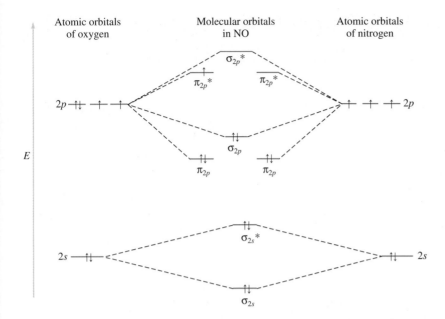

Atomic orbitals of oxygen ... Molecular orbitals in NO ... Atomic orbitals of nitrogen

Figure 19.8
The molecular orbital energy-level diagram for nitric oxide (NO). The bond order is 2.5, or $(8 - 3)/2$.

antibonding electron is removed in going from NO to NO^+, the ion should have a stronger bond (the predicted bond order is 3) than the molecule. This is borne out by experiment. The bond lengths and bond energies for nitric oxide and the nitrosyl ion are shown in Table 19.3. The nitrosyl ion is formed when nitric oxide and nitrogen dioxide are dissolved in concentrated sulfuric acid:

$$NO(g) + NO_2(g) + 3H_2SO_4(aq) \rightarrow 2NO^+(aq) + 3HSO_4^-(aq) + H_3O^+(aq)$$

The ionic compound $NO^+HSO_4^-$ can be isolated from this solution.

Nitric oxide is thermodynamically unstable and decomposes to nitrous oxide and nitrogen dioxide:

$$3NO(g) \rightarrow N_2O(g) + NO_2(g)$$

Nitrogen dioxide (NO_2) is also an odd-electron molecule and has a V-shaped structure. The brown, paramagnetic NO_2 molecule readily dimerizes to form dinitrogen tetroxide,

$$2NO_2(g) \rightleftharpoons N_2O_4(g)$$

which is diamagnetic and colorless. The value of the equilibrium constant is ~1 for this process at 55°C, and since the dimerization is exothermic, K decreases as the temperature increases.

A copper penny reacts with nitric acid to produce NO gas, which is immediately oxidized in air to brown NO_2.

Production of NO_2 by power plants and automobiles leads to smog (see Section 12.8).

Table 19.3		
Comparison of the Bond Lengths and Bond Energies for Nitric Oxide and the Nitrosyl Ion		
	NO	NO^+
Bond length (pm)	115	109
Bond energy (kJ/mol)	630	1020
Bond order (predicted by MO model)	2.5	3

◀ **CHEMICAL IMPACT** ▶

Nitrous Oxide: Laughing Gas that Propels Whipped Cream and Cars

Nitrous oxide (N_2O), more properly called dinitrogen monoxide, is a compound with many interesting uses. It was discovered in 1772 by Joseph Priestly (who is also given credit for discovering oxygen gas), and its intoxicating effects were noted almost immediately. In 1798 the 20-year-old Humphry Davy became director of the Pneumatic Institute, which was set up to investigate the medical effects of various gases. Davy tested the effects of N_2O on himself, reporting that after inhaling 16 quarts of the gas in 7 minutes, he became "absolutely intoxicated."

Over the next century "laughing gas," as nitrous oxide became known, was developed as an anesthetic, particularly for dental procedures. Nitrous oxide is still used as an anesthetic, although it has been largely replaced by more modern drugs.

One major use of nitrous oxide today is as the propellant in cans of "instant" whipped cream. The high solubility of N_2O in the whipped cream mixture makes it an excellent candidate for pressurizing the cans of whipping cream.

Another current use of nitrous oxide is to produce "instant horsepower" for hot rods and street racers. Because the reaction of N_2O with O_2 to form NO actually absorbs heat, this reaction has a cooling effect when placed in the fuel mixture in an automobile engine. This cooling effect lowers combustion temperatures, thus allowing the fuel/air mixture to be significantly more dense (the density of a gas is inversely proportional to temperature). This effect can produce a burst of additional power in excess of 200 horsepower. Because engines are not designed to run steadily at such high power levels, the nitrous oxide is injected from a tank when extra power is desired.

Sample Exercise 19.3

Use the molecular orbital model to predict the bond order and magnetism of the NO^- ion.

Solution

Using the energy-level diagram for the NO molecule in Fig. 19.8, we can see that NO^- has one more antibonding electron than NO. Thus there will be unpaired electrons in the two $\pi_{2p}*$ orbitals, and NO^- will be paramagnetic with a bond order of $(8 - 4)/2$, or 2. Note that the bond in the NO^- ion is weaker than that in the NO molecule.

The least common of the nitrogen oxides are *dinitrogen trioxide* (N_2O_3), a blue liquid that readily dissociates into gaseous nitric oxide and nitrogen dioxide, and *dinitrogen pentoxide* (N_2O_5), which under normal conditions is a solid that is best viewed as a mixture of NO_2^+ and NO_3^- ions. Although N_2O_5 molecules do exist in the gas phase, they readily dissociate to nitrogen dioxide and oxygen:

$$2N_2O_5(g) \rightleftharpoons 4NO_2(g) + O_2(g)$$

This reaction follows first-order kinetics, as was discussed in Section 12.4.

Oxyacids of Nitrogen

Nitric acid is an important industrial chemical (~8 million tons are produced annually) used in the manufacture of many products, such as nitrogen-based explosives and ammonium nitrate for use as fertilizer.

Nitric acid is produced commercially by the oxidation of ammonia in the **Ostwald process** (see Fig. 19.9). In the first step of this process, ammonia is oxidized to nitric oxide:

$$4NH_3(g) + 5O_2(g) \rightarrow 4NO(g) + 6H_2O(g) \qquad \Delta H° = -905 \text{ kJ}$$

Although this reaction is highly exothermic, it is very slow at 25°C. There is also a side reaction between nitric oxide and ammonia:

$$4NH_3(g) + 6NO(g) \rightarrow 5N_2(g) + 6H_2O(g)$$

which is particularly undesirable because it traps the nitrogen as very unreactive N_2 molecules. To speed up the desired reaction and minimize the effects of the competing reaction, the ammonia oxidation is carried out using a catalyst of a platinum–rhodium alloy heated to 900°C. Under these conditions, there is a 97% conversion of the ammonia to nitric oxide.

In the second step, nitric oxide reacts with oxygen to produce nitrogen dioxide:

$$2NO(g) + O_2(g) \rightarrow 2NO_2(g) \qquad \Delta H° = -113 \text{ kJ}$$

This oxidation reaction has a rate that *decreases* with increasing temperature. Because of this very unusual behavior, the reaction is carried out at ~25°C and is kept at this temperature by cooling with water.

The third step in the Ostwald process is the absorption of nitrogen dioxide by water:

$$3NO_2(g) + H_2O(l) \rightarrow 2HNO_3(aq) + NO(g) \qquad \Delta H° = -139 \text{ kJ}$$

The gaseous NO produced in this reaction is recycled to be oxidized to NO_2. The aqueous nitric acid from this process is about 50% HNO_3 by mass, which can be increased to 68% by distillation to remove some of the water. The maximum concentration attainable this way is 68% because nitric acid and water form an **azeotrope** at this concentration. The solution can be further concentrated to 95% HNO_3

Figure 19.9
The Ostwald process.

An azeotrope is a solution that, like a pure liquid, distills at a constant temperature without a change in composition.

(left) Preparation of a platinum-rhodium gauze for use in the manufacture of nitric acid. (right) A photomicrograph of the gauze.

Figure 19.10

(a) The molecular structure of HNO_3. (b) The resonance structures of HNO_3.

by treatment with concentrated sulfuric acid, which strongly absorbs water; H_2SO_4 is often used as a dehydrating (water-removing) agent.

Nitric acid is a colorless, fuming liquid (bp = 83°C) with a pungent odor; it decomposes in sunlight via the following reaction:

$$4HNO_3(l) \xrightarrow{h\nu} 4NO_2(g) + 2H_2O(l) + O_2(g)$$

As a result, nitric acid turns yellow as it ages because of the dissolved nitrogen dioxide. The common laboratory reagent known as concentrated nitric acid is 15.9 M HNO_3 (70.4% HNO_3 by mass) and is a very strong oxidizing agent. The resonance structures and molecular structure of HNO_3 are shown in Fig. 19.10. Note that the hydrogen is bound to an oxygen atom rather than to nitrogen, as the formula suggests.

Nitric acid reacts with metal oxides, hydroxides, and carbonates and with other ionic compounds containing basic anions to form nitrate salts. For example,

$$Ca(OH)_2(s) + 2HNO_3(aq) \rightarrow Ca(NO_3)_2(aq) + 2H_2O(l)$$

Nitrate salts are generally very soluble in water.

Nitrous acid (HNO_2) is a weak acid

$$HNO_2(aq) \rightleftharpoons H^+(aq) + NO_2^-(aq) \qquad K_a = 4.0 \times 10^{-4}$$

that forms pale yellow nitrite (NO_2^-) salts. In contrast to nitrates, which are often used as explosives, nitrites are quite stable even at high temperatures. Nitrites are usually prepared by bubbling equal numbers of moles of nitric oxide and nitrogen dioxide into the appropriate aqueous solution of a metal hydroxide, for example,

$$NO(g) + NO_2(g) + 2NaOH(aq) \rightarrow 2NaNO_2(aq) + H_2O(l)$$

19.3 *The Chemistry of Phosphorus*

Purpose

- To characterize the forms of elemental phosphorus.
- To describe the preparation and structure of the major compounds of phosphorus.

Although phosphorus lies directly below nitrogen in Group 5A of the periodic table, its chemical properties are significantly different from those of nitrogen. The differences arise mainly from four factors: nitrogen's ability to form much stronger π bonds, the greater electronegativity of nitrogen, the larger size of the phosphorus atom, and the availability of empty valence d orbitals on phosphorus.

(a)   (b)   (c)

Figure 19.11

(a) The P_4 molecule found in white phosphorus. (b) The crystalline network structure of black phosphorus. (c) The chain structure of red phosphorus.

The chemical differences are apparent in the elemental forms of nitrogen and phosphorus. In contrast to the diatomic form of elemental nitrogen, which is stabilized by strong π bonds, there are several solid forms of phosphorus, all containing aggregates of atoms. *White phosphorus,* which contains discrete tetrahedral P_4 molecules [see Fig. 19.11(a)], is very reactive and bursts into flames on contact with air (it is said to be **pyrophoric**). To prevent this, white phosphorus is commonly stored under water. White phosphorus is quite toxic, and the P_4 molecules are very damaging to tissue, particularly the cartilage and bones of the nose and jaw. The much less reactive forms known as *black phosphorus* and *red phosphorus* are network solids (see Section 10.5). Black phosphorus has a regular crystalline structure [Fig. 19.11(b)], but red phosphorus is amorphous and is thought to consist of chains of P_4 units [Fig. 19.11(c)]. Red phosphorus can be obtained by heating white phosphorus in the absence of air at 1 atm. Black phosphorus is obtained from either white or red phosphorus by heating at high pressures.

Even though phosphorus has a lower electronegativity than nitrogen, it will form phosphides (ionic substances containing the P^{3-} anion) such as Na_3P and Ca_3P_2. Phosphide salts react vigorously with water to produce *phosphine* (PH_3), a toxic, colorless gas:

$$2Na_3P(s) + 6H_2O(l) \rightarrow 2PH_3(g) + 6Na^+(aq) + 6OH^-(aq)$$

Phosphine is analogous to ammonia, although it is a much weaker base ($K_b \approx 10^{-26}$) and much less soluble in water. Because phosphine has a relatively small affinity for protons, phosphonium (PH_4^+) salts are very uncommon and not very stable—only PH_4I, PH_4Cl, and PH_4Br are known.

Phosphine has the Lewis structure

$$\left[\begin{array}{c} \overset{\displaystyle ..}{H-P-H} \\ | \\ H \end{array} \right]$$

and a pyramidal molecular structure, as we would predict from the VSEPR model. However, it has bond angles of 94 degrees, rather than 107 degrees as found in the ammonia molecule. The reasons for this are complex, and we will simply regard phosphine as an exception to the simple version of the VSEPR model that we use.

Phosphorus Oxides and Oxyacids

Phosphorus reacts with oxygen to form oxides in which it has oxidation states of +5 and +3. The oxide P_4O_6 is formed when elemental phosphorus is burned in a limited supply of oxygen, and P_4O_{10} is produced when the oxygen is in excess. These oxides, as shown in Fig. 19.12, can be pictured as being constructed by adding oxygen atoms to the fundamental P_4 structure. The intermediate states, P_4O_7, P_4O_8, and P_4O_9, which contain one, two, and three terminal oxygen atoms, respectively, are also known.

The terminal oxygens are the nonbridging oxygen atoms.

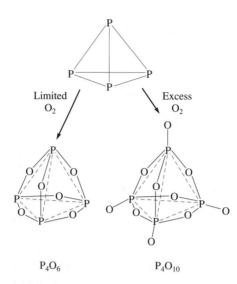

Figure 19.12

The structures of P_4O_6 and P_4O_{10}.

P_4O_6 P_4O_{10}

Tetraphosphorus decaoxide (P_4O_{10}), which was formerly represented as P_2O_5, has a great affinity for water and thus is a powerful dehydrating agent. For example, it can be used to convert HNO_3 and H_2SO_4 to their parent oxides, N_2O_5 and SO_3, respectively.

When tetraphosphorus decaoxide dissolves in water, **phosphoric acid** (H_3PO_4), also called **orthophosphoric acid,** is produced:

$$P_4O_{10}(s) + 6H_2O(l) \rightarrow 4H_3PO_4(aq)$$

Pure phosphoric acid is a white solid that melts at 42°C. Aqueous phosphoric acid is a much weaker acid ($K_{a_1} \approx 10^{-2}$) than nitric acid or sulfuric acid and is a poor oxidizing agent.

Phosphate minerals are the main source of phosphoric acid. Unlike nitrogen, phosphorus is found in nature exclusively in a combined state, principally as the PO_4^{3-} ion in phosphate rock, which is mainly calcium phosphate, $Ca_3(PO_4)_2$, and fluorapatite, $Ca_5(PO_4)_3F$. Fluorapatite can be converted to phosphoric acid by grinding up the phosphate rock and forming a slurry with sulfuric acid:

$$Ca_5(PO_4)_3F(s) + 5H_2SO_4(aq) + 10H_2O(l)$$
$$\rightarrow HF(aq) + 5CaSO_4 \cdot 2H_2O(s) + 3H_3PO_4(aq)$$

(A similar reaction can be written for the conversion of calcium phosphate.) The solid product $CaSO_4 \cdot 2H_2O$, called **gypsum,** is used to manufacture wallboard for the construction of buildings.

The process just described, called the **wet process,** produces only impure phosphoric acid. In another procedure, phosphate rock, sand (SiO_2), and coke are heated in an electric furnace to form white phosphorus:

$$12Ca_5(PO_4)_3F + 43SiO_2 + 90C \rightarrow 9P_4 + 90CO + 20(3CaO \cdot 2SiO_2) + 3SiF_4$$

The white phosphorus obtained is burned in air to form tetraphosphorous decoxide, which is then combined with water to give phosphoric acid.

Phosphoric acid easily undergoes **condensation reactions,** where a molecule of water is eliminated in the joining of two molecules of acid:

The mineral hydroxyapatite, $Ca_5(PO_4)_3OH$, the principal component of tooth enamel, can be converted to fluorapatite by reaction with fluoride. Fluoride ions added to drinking water and toothpaste help prevent tooth decay because fluorapatite is less soluble in the acids of the mouth than hydroxyapatite.

The product ($H_4P_2O_7$) is called **pyrophosphoric acid.** Further heating produces polymers, such as *tripolyphosphoric acid* ($H_5P_3O_{10}$), which has the structure

The sodium salt of tripolyphosphoric acid is widely used in detergents because the $P_3O_{10}{}^{5-}$ anion can form complexes with metal ions such as Mg^{2+} and Ca^{2+}, which would otherwise interfere with detergent action.

Sample Exercise 19.4

What are the molecular structure and the hybridization of the central atom of the phosphoric acid molecule?

Solution

In the phosphoric acid molecule, the hydrogen atoms are attached to oxygens, and the Lewis structure is as shown below. Thus the phosphorus atom is surrounded by four effective pairs, which are arranged tetrahedrally. The atom is sp^3 hybridized.

Lewis structure

Molecular structure

When P_4O_6 is placed in water, **phosphorous acid** (H_3PO_3) is formed [Fig. 19.13(a)]. Although the formula suggests a triprotic acid, phosphorous acid is a *diprotic* acid. The hydrogen atom bonded directly to the phosphorus atom is not acidic in aqueous solution; only those hydrogen atoms bonded to the oxygen atoms in H_3PO_3 can be released as protons.

A third oxyacid of phosphorus is *hypophosphorous acid* (H_3PO_2) [Fig. 19.13(b)], which is a monoprotic acid.

Figure 19.13

(a) The structure of phosphorous acid (H_3PO_3). (b) The structure of hypophosphorous acid (H_3PO_2).

Phosphorus in Fertilizers

Phosphorus is essential for plant growth. Although most soil contains large amounts of phosphorus, it is often present as insoluble minerals, which makes it inaccessible to the plants. Soluble phosphate fertilizers are manufactured by treating phosphate rock with sulfuric acid to make **superphosphate of lime,** a mixture of $CaSO_4 \cdot 2H_2O$ and $Ca(H_2PO_4)_2 \cdot H_2O$. If phosphate rock is treated with phosphoric acid, $Ca(H_2PO_4)_2$, or *triple phosphate,* is produced. The reaction of ammonia and phosphoric acid gives *ammonium dihydrogen phosphate* ($NH_4H_2PO_4$), a very efficient fertilizer because it furnishes both phosphorus and nitrogen.

Phosphorus Halides

Phosphorus forms all possible halides of the general formulas PX_3 and PX_5, with the exception of PI_5. The PX_3 molecule has the expected pyramidal structure [Fig. 19.14(a)]. Under normal conditions of temperature and pressure, PF_3 is a colorless gas, PCl_3 is a liquid (bp = 74°C), PBr_3 is a liquid (bp = 175°C), and PI_3 is an unstable red solid (mp = 61°C). All the PX_3 compounds react with water to produce phosphorous acid:

$$PX_3 + 3H_2O(l) \rightarrow H_3PO_3(aq) + 3HX(aq)$$

In the gaseous and liquid states, the PX_5 compounds have molecules with a trigonal bipyramidal structure [Fig. 19.14(b)]. However, PCl_5 and PBr_5 form ionic solids: solid PCl_5 contains a mixture of octahedral PCl_6^- ions and tetrahedral PCl_4^+ ions, and solid PBr_5 appears to consist of PBr_4^+ and Br^- ions.

The PX_5 compounds react with water to form phosphoric acid:

$$PX_5 + 4H_2O(l) \rightarrow H_3PO_4(aq) + 5HX(aq)$$

(a)

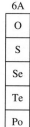

(b)

Figure 19.14

Structures of the phosphorus halides. (a) The PX_3 compounds have pyramidal molecules. (b) The gaseous and liquid phases of the PX_5 compounds are composed of trigonal bipyramidal molecules.

19.4 The Group 6A Elements

Purpose

• To discuss trends in the chemistry of the Group 6A elements.

Although in Group 6A (Table 19.4) there is the usual tendency for metallic properties to increase going down the group, none of the Group 6A elements (valence-electron configuration n^2np^4) behaves as a typical metal. The most common chemical behavior of a Group 6A atom is to achieve a noble gas electron configuration by adding two electrons to become a 2− anion in ionic compounds with metals. In fact, for most metals, the oxides and sulfides constitute the most common minerals.

The Group 6A elements can form covalent bonds with other nonmetals. For example, they combine with hydrogen to form a series of covalent hydrides of the general formula H_2X. Those members of the group which have valence d orbitals available (all except oxygen) commonly form molecules in which they are surrounded by more than eight electrons. Examples are SF_4, SF_6, TeI_4, and $SeBr_4$.

The two heaviest members of Group 6A can lose electrons to form cations. Although they do not lose all six valence electrons because of the high energies that

6A
O
S
Se
Te
Po

Table 19.4				
Selected Physical Properties, Sources, and Methods of Preparation for the Group 6A Elements				
Element	Electro-negativity	Radius of X^{2-} (pm)	Source	Method of Preparation
Oxygen	3.5	140	Air	Distillation from liquid air
Sulfur	2.5	184	Sulfur deposits	Melted with hot water and pumped to the surface
Selenium	2.4	198	Impurity in sulfide ores	Reduction of H_2SeO_4 with SO_2
Tellurium	2.1	221	Nagyagite (mixed sulfide and telluride)	Reduction of ore with SO_2
Polonium	2.0	230	Pitchblende	

would be required, tellurium and polonium appear to exhibit some chemistry involving their 4+ cations. However, the chemistry of these Group 6A cations is much more limited than that of the Group 5A elements bismuth and antimony.

In recent years there has been a growing interest in the chemistry of selenium, an element found throughout the environment in trace amounts. Selenium's toxicity has long been known, but recent medical studies have shown an *inverse* relationship between the incidence of cancer and the selenium levels in soil. It has been suggested that the resulting greater dietary intake of selenium by people living in areas of relatively high levels of selenium somehow furnishes protection from cancer. These studies are only preliminary, but selenium is known to be physiologically important (it is involved in the activity of vitamin E and certain enzymes). Also of importance is the fact that selenium (and tellurium) are semiconductors and therefore find some application in the electronics industry.

Polonium was discovered in 1898 by Marie and Pierre Curie in their search for the sources of radioactivity in pitchblende. Polonium has 27 isotopes and is highly toxic and very radioactive. It has been suggested that the isotope ^{210}Po, a natural contaminant of tobacco and an α-particle emitter (see Section 21.1), might be at least partly responsible for the incidence of cancer in smokers.

19.5 The Chemistry of Oxygen

Purpose

• To characterize the forms of elemental oxygen.

It is hard to overstate the importance of oxygen, the most abundant element in and near the earth's crust. Oxygen is present in the atmosphere as oxygen gas and ozone; in soil and rocks in oxide, silicate, and carbonate minerals; in the oceans in water; and in our bodies in water and in a myriad of molecules. In addition, most of the energy we need to live and to run our civilization comes from the exothermic reactions of oxygen and carbon-containing molecules.

The most common elemental form of oxygen (O_2) comprises 21% of the volume of the earth's atmosphere. Since nitrogen has a lower boiling point than oxygen, nitrogen can be boiled away from liquid air, leaving oxygen and small amounts of argon, another component of air. Liquid oxygen is a pale blue liquid that freezes at $-219°C$ and boils at $-183°C$. The paramagnetism of the O_2 molecule can be demonstrated by pouring liquid oxygen between the poles of a strong magnet, where it "sticks" as it boils away (see Fig. 9.40). The paramagnetism of the O_2 molecule can be accounted for by the molecular orbital model (see Fig. 9.39), which also explains its bond strength.

The other form of elemental oxygen is **ozone** (O_3), a molecule that can be represented by the resonance structures

The bond angle in the O_3 molecule is 117 degrees, in reasonable agreement with the prediction of the VSEPR model (three effective pairs require a trigonal planar arrangement). That the bond angle is slightly less than 120 degrees can be explained by concluding that more space is required for the lone pair than for the bonding pairs.

Ozone can be prepared by passing an electric discharge through pure oxygen gas. The electrical energy disrupts the bonds in some O_2 molecules to give oxygen atoms, which react with other O_2 molecules to form O_3. Ozone is much less stable than oxygen at 25°C and 1 atm. For example, $K \approx 10^{-57}$ for the equilibrium

$$3O_2(g) \rightleftharpoons 2O_3(g)$$

A pale blue, highly toxic gas, ozone is a much more powerful oxidizing agent than oxygen. Because of its oxidizing ability, ozone is being considered as a replacement for chlorine in municipal water purification. Chlorine leaves residues of chloro compounds, such as chloroform ($CHCl_3$), which may cause cancer after long-term exposure. Although ozone effectively kills the bacteria in water, one problem with **ozonolysis** is that the water supply is not protected against recontamination, since virtually no ozone remains after the initial treatment. In contrast, for chlorination, significant residual chlorine remains after treatment.

The oxidizing ability of ozone can be highly detrimental, especially when it is formed in the pollution from automobile exhausts (see Section 5.9).

Ozone exists naturally in the upper atmosphere of the earth. The **ozone layer** is especially important because it absorbs ultraviolet light and thus acts as a screen to prevent this radiation, which can cause skin cancer, from penetrating to the earth's surface. When an ozone molecule absorbs this energy, it splits into an oxygen molecule and an oxygen atom.

$$O_3 \xrightarrow{hv} O_2 + O$$

Recently, scientists have become concerned that Freons and nitrogen dioxide are promoting the destruction of the ozone layer (see Section 12.8), which is why Freons have been banned by the U.S. government for use in aerosol cans and why Freons are being phased out of use for air-conditioning systems and refrigerators.

If the oxygen molecule and atom collide, they will not stay together as ozone unless a "third body," such as a nitrogen molecule, is present to help absorb the energy released in the bond formation. The third body absorbs the energy as kinetic energy; its temperature is increased. Therefore, the energy originally absorbed as ultraviolet radiation is eventually changed to thermal energy. Thus the ozone prevents the harmful high-energy ultraviolet light from reaching the earth.

19.6 The Chemistry of Sulfur

Purpose

- To characterize the elemental forms of sulfur.
- To describe the bonding and structure of the oxycompounds of sulfur.

Sulfur is found in nature both in large deposits of the free element and in widely distributed ores, such as galena (PbS), cinnabar (HgS), pyrite (FeS_2), gypsum ($CaSO_4 \cdot 2H_2O$), epsomite ($MgSO_4 \cdot 7H_2O$), and glauberite ($Na_2SO_4 \cdot CaSO_4$).

About 60% of the sulfur produced in the United States comes from the underground deposits of elemental sulfur found in Texas and Louisiana. This sulfur is recovered using the **Frasch process** developed by Herman Frasch in the 1890s. Superheated water is pumped into the deposit to melt the sulfur (mp = 113°C), which is then forced to the surface by air pressure (see Fig. 19.15). The remaining 40% of sulfur produced in the United States is either a by-product of the purification of fossil fuels before combustion to prevent pollution or from the sulfur dioxide (SO_2) scrubbed from the exhaust gases when sulfur-containing fuels are burned.

In contrast to oxygen, elemental sulfur exists as S_2 molecules only in the gas phase at high temperatures. Because sulfur atoms form much stronger σ bonds than π bonds, S_2 is less stable at 25°C than larger aggregates such as S_6 and S_8 rings and S_n chains (Fig. 19.16). The most stable form of sulfur at 25°C and 1 atm is called **rhombic sulfur** [see Fig. 19.17(a)], which contains stacked S_8 rings. If rhombic sulfur is melted and heated to 120°C, it forms *monoclinic sulfur* as it cools slowly [Fig. 19.17(b)]. This form also contains S_8 rings, but the rings are stacked differently than they are in rhombic sulfur.

Pouring liquid sulfur into water to produce plastic sulfur.

The scrubbing of sulfur dioxide from exhaust gases was discussed in Section 5.9.

Figure 19.15

The Frasch method for recovering sulfur from underground deposits.

(a)

(b)

Figure 19.16

(a) The S_8 molecule. (b) Chains of sulfur atoms in viscous liquid sulfur. The chains may contain as many as 10,000 atoms.

(left) A sulfur deposit. (right) Melted sulfur obtained from underground deposits by the Frasch process.

As sulfur is heated beyond its melting point, a relatively nonviscous liquid containing S_8 rings forms initially. With continued heating, the liquid becomes highly viscous as the rings first break and then link up to form long chains. Further heating lowers the viscosity because the long chains are broken down as the energetic sulfur atoms break loose. If the liquid is suddenly cooled, a substance called **plastic sulfur,** which contains S_n chains and has rubber-like qualities, is formed. Eventually, this form reverts back to the more stable S_8 rings.

Sulfur Oxides

From its position below oxygen in the periodic table, we might expect the simplest stable oxide of sulfur to have the formula SO. However, *sulfur monoxide,* which can be produced in small amounts when gaseous sulfur dioxide (SO_2) is subjected to an electrical discharge, is very unstable. The difference in the stabilities of the O_2 and SO molecules probably reflects the stronger π bonding between oxygen atoms than between sulfur and oxygen atoms.

Figure 19.17

(left) Crystals of rhombic sulfur. (right) Crystals of monoclinic sulfur.

Sulfur burns in air with a bright blue flame to give *sulfur dioxide* (SO_2), a colorless gas with a pungent odor, which condenses to a liquid at $-10°C$ and 1 atm. Sulfur dioxide is a very effective antibacterial agent and is often used to preserve stored fruit. Its structure is given in Fig. 19.18.

Sulfur dioxide reacts with oxygen to produce *sulfur trioxide* (SO_3):

$$2SO_2(g) + O_2(g) \rightarrow 2SO_3(g)$$

However, this reaction is very slow in the absence of a catalyst. One of the mysteries during early research on air pollution was how the sulfur dioxide produced from the combustion of sulfur-containing fuels is so rapidly converted to sulfur trioxide. It is now known that dust and other particles can act as heterogeneous catalysts for this process (see Section 12.8). In the preparation of sulfur trioxide for the manufacture of sulfuric acid, a platinum or vanadium(V) oxide (V_2O_5) catalyst is used, and the reaction is carried out at ~$500°C$, even though this temperature decreases the value of the equilibrium constant for this exothermic reaction.

The bonding in the SO_3 molecule is usually described in terms of the resonance structures shown in Fig. 19.19. The molecule is trigonal planar, as predicted by the VSEPR model. Sulfur trioxide is a corrosive gas with a choking odor that forms white fumes of sulfuric acid when it reacts with moisture in the air. Thus sulfur trioxide and nitrogen dioxide, which reacts with water to form a mixture of nitrous and nitric acids, are the major culprits in the formation of acid rain.

Sulfur trioxide condenses to a colorless liquid at $44.5°C$ and freezes at $16.8°C$ to give three solid forms, one containing S_3O_9 rings and the other two containing $(SO_3)_x$ chains (Fig. 19.20).

Oxyacids of Sulfur

Sulfur dioxide dissolves in water to form an acidic solution. The reaction is often represented as

$$SO_2(g) + H_2O(l) \rightarrow H_2SO_3(aq)$$

The preparation of sulfur trioxide provides an example of the compromise that often must be made between thermodynamics and kinetics.

(a)

(b)

Figure 19.20

Different structures for solid SO_3. (a) S_3O_9 rings. (b) $(SO_3)_x$ chains. In both cases the sulfur atoms are surrounded by a tetrahedral arrangement of oxygen atoms.

Figure 19.18

(a) Two of the resonance structures for SO_2. (b) SO_2 is a bent molecule with a 119° bond angle, as predicted by the VSEPR model.

Figure 19.19

(a) Three of the resonance structures of SO_3. (b) A resonance structure with three double bonds. (c) SO_3 is a planar molecule with 120° bond angles.

where H_2SO_3 is called **sulfurous acid.** However, very little H_2SO_3 actually exists in the solution. The major form of sulfur dioxide in water is SO_2, and the acid dissociation equilibria are best represented as

$$SO_2(aq) + H_2O(l) \rightleftharpoons H^+(aq) + HSO_3^-(aq) \qquad K_{a_1} = 1.5 \times 10^{-2}$$
$$HSO_3^-(aq) \rightleftharpoons H^+(aq) + SO_3^{2-}(aq) \qquad K_{a_2} = 1.0 \times 10^{-7}$$

This situation is analogous to the behavior of carbon dioxide in water (see Section 14.7). Although H_2SO_3 cannot be isolated, salts of SO_3^{2-} (*sulfites*) and HSO_3^- (*hydrogen sulfites*) are well known.

Sulfur trioxide reacts violently with water to produce the diprotic acid **sulfuric acid:**

$$SO_3(g) + H_2O(l) \rightarrow H_2SO_4(aq)$$

Manufactured in greater amounts than any other chemical, sulfuric acid is usually produced by the **contact process,** which is described at the end of Chapter 3. About 60% of the sulfuric acid manufactured in the United States is used to produce fertilizers from phosphate rock (see Section 19.3). The other 40% is used in lead storage batteries and in petroleum refining, steel manufacturing, and for various purposes in most of the chemical industries.

Because sulfuric acid has a high affinity for water, it is often used as a dehydrating agent. Gases that do not react with sulfuric acid, such as oxygen, nitrogen, and carbon dioxide, are often dried by bubbling them through concentrated solutions of the acid. Sulfuric acid is such a powerful dehydrating agent that it will remove hydrogen and oxygen from a substance in a 2:1 ratio even when the substance contains no molecular water. For example, concentrated sulfuric acid reacts vigorously with common table sugar (sucrose), leaving a charred mass of carbon (see Fig. 19.21):

$$\underset{\text{Sucrose}}{C_{12}H_{22}O_{11}(s)} + 11H_2SO_4(conc) \rightarrow 12C(s) + 11H_2SO_4 \cdot H_2O(l)$$

Figure 19.21

(a) A beaker of sucrose (table sugar). (b) Concentrated sulfuric acid reacts with the sucrose to produce a column of carbon (c), accompanied by an intense burnt-sugar odor.

(a)

(b)

(c)

Sulfuric acid is a moderately strong oxidizing agent, especially at high temperatures. Hot concentrated sulfuric acid oxidizes bromide or iodide ions to elemental bromine or iodine, for example,

$$2I^-(aq) + 3H_2SO_4(aq) \rightarrow I_2(aq) + SO_2(aq) + 2H_2O(l) + 2HSO_4^-(aq)$$

Hot sulfuric acid attacks copper metal:

$$Cu(s) + 2H_2SO_4(aq) \rightarrow CuSO_4(aq) + 2H_2O(l) + SO_2(aq)$$

The cold acid does not react with copper.

The acidic properties of sulfuric acid solutions are discussed in Section 14.7.

Other Compounds of Sulfur

Sulfur reacts with both metals and nonmetals to form a wide variety of compounds in which it has a $+6$, $+4$, $+2$, 0, or -2 oxidation state (see Table 19.5). The -2 oxidation state occurs in the metal sulfides and in *hydrogen sulfide* (H_2S), a toxic, foul-smelling gas that acts as a diprotic acid when dissolved in water. Hydrogen sulfide is a strong reducing agent in aqueous solution, producing a milky looking suspension of finely divided sulfur as one of the products. For example, hydrogen sulfide reacts with chlorine in aqueous solution as follows:

$$H_2S(g) + Cl_2(aq) \rightarrow 2H^+(aq) + 2Cl^-(aq) + S(s)$$

Milky suspension of sulfur

Sulfur also forms the **thiosulfate ion** ($S_2O_3^{2-}$), which has the Lewis structure

$$\left[\begin{array}{c} :\!\ddot{O}\!: \\ | \\ :\!\ddot{O}\!-\!S\!-\!\ddot{S}\!: \\ | \\ :\!\ddot{O}\!: \end{array} \right]^{2-}$$

The prefix thio *means sulfur.*

Note that this anion can be viewed as a sulfate ion in which one of the oxygen atoms has been replaced by sulfur, which is reflected in the name *thio*sulfate. The thiosulfate ion can be formed by heating sulfur with a sulfite salt in aqueous solution:

$$S(s) + SO_3^{2-}(aq) \rightarrow S_2O_3^{2-}(aq)$$

One important use of thiosulfate ion is in photography, where $S_2O_3^{2-}$ dissolves solid silver bromide by forming a complex with the Ag^+ ion (see the Chemical

Table 19.5

Common Compounds of Sulfur with Various Oxidation States

Oxidation State of Sulfur	Compounds
$+6$	SO_3, H_2SO_4, SO_4^{2-}, SF_6
$+4$	SO_2, HSO_3^-, SO_3^{2-}, SF_4
$+2$	SCl_2
0	S_8 and all other forms of elemental sulfur
-2	H_2S, S^{2-}

Figure 19.22

The structures of (a) SF_4, (b) SF_6, (c) S_2F_{10}, and (d) S_2Cl_2.

Impact in Section 19.7). Thiosulfate ion is also a good reducing agent and is often used to analyze for iodine:

$$S_2O_3^{2-}(aq) + I_2(aq) \rightarrow S_4O_6^{2-}(aq) + 2I^-(aq)$$

where $S_4O_6^{2-}$ is called the **tetrathionate ion.**

Sulfur reacts with the halogens to form a variety of compounds, such as S_2Cl_2, SF_4, SF_6, and S_2F_{10}. The structures of these molecules are shown in Fig. 19.22.

19.7 The Group 7A Elements

Purpose

- To describe the bonding in compounds of halogens with other nonmetals.
- To explain the acid strengths of the hydrogen halides.
- To discuss the chemistry of oxyhalogen compounds.
- To give the structures of interhalogen compounds.

In our coverage of the representative elements we have progressed from groups of metallic elements (Groups 1A and 2A), through groups in which the lighter members are nonmetals and the heavier members are metals (Groups 3A, 4A, and 5A), to a group of all nonmetals (Group 6A—although some might prefer to call polonium a metal). The Group 7A elements, the **halogens** (with the valence-electron configuration ns^2np^5), are also all nonmetals whose properties generally vary smoothly going down the group. The only notable exceptions are the unexpectedly low values for the electron affinity of fluorine and the bond energy of the F_2 molecule (see Section 18.1). Table 19.6 summarizes the trends in some physical properties of the halogens.

Because of their high reactivities, the halogens are not found as the free elements in nature. Instead, they are found as halide ions (X^-) in various minerals and in seawater (see Table 19.7).

Although astatine is a member of Group 7A, its chemistry is of no practical importance because all its known isotopes are radioactive. The longest-lived isotope, ^{210}At, has a half-life of only 8.3 hours.

The halogens, particularly fluorine, have very high electronegativity values (Table 19.6). They tend to form polar covalent bonds with other nonmetals and ionic bonds with metals in their lower oxidation states. When a metal ion is in a higher oxidation state, such as +3 or +4, the metal–halogen bonds are polar cova-

Chlorine, iodine, and bromine.

A candle burning in an atmosphere of $Cl_2(g)$. The exothermic reaction, which involves breaking C—C and C—H bonds in the wax and forming C—Cl bonds in their places, produces enough heat to make the gases in the region incandescent (a flame results).

Table 19.6

Trends in Selected Physical Properties of the Group 7A Elements

Element	Electro-negativity	Radius of X^- (pm)	$\mathscr{E}°$ (V) for $X_2 + 2e \rightarrow 2X^-$	Bond Energy of X_2 (kJ/mol)
Fluorine	4.0	136	2.87	154
Chlorine	3.0	181	1.36	239
Bromine	2.8	185	1.09	193
Iodine	2.5	216	0.54	149
Astatine	2.2	—	—	—

Table 19.7

Some Physical Properties, Sources, and Methods of Preparation for the Group 7A Elements

Element	Color and State	Percentage of Earth's Crust	Melting Point (°C)	Boiling Point (°C)	Sources	Method of Preparation
Fluorine	Pale yellow gas	0.07	−220	−188	Fluorospar (CaF_2), cryolite (Na_3AlF_6), fluorapatite $(Ca_5(PO_4)_3F)$	Electrolysis of molten KHF_2
Chlorine	Yellow-green gas	0.14	−101	−34	Rock salt (NaCl), halite (NaCl), sylvite (KCl)	Electrolysis of aqueous NaCl
Bromine	Red-brown liquid	2.5×10^{-4}	−7.3	59	Seawater, brine wells	Oxidation of Br^- by Cl_2
Iodine	Violet-black solid	3×10^{-5}	113	184	Seaweed, brine wells	Oxidation of I^- by electrolysis or MnO_2

◀ **CHEMICAL IMPACT** ▶

Photography

In black-and-white photography, light from an object is focused onto a special paper containing an emulsion of solid silver bromide. Silver salts turn dark when exposed to light because the radiant energy stimulates the transfer of an electron to the Ag^+ ion, forming an atom of elemental silver. When photographic paper (film) is exposed to light, the areas exposed to the brightest light form the most silver atoms. The next step is the application of a chemical reducing agent to the film, a process called **developing.** The real advantage of silver-based films is that the silver atoms already present from exposure to light catalyze the reduction of millions of Ag^+ ions in the immediate vicinity in the developing process. Thus the effect of exposure to light is greatly intensified in this chemical reduction process. Once the image has been developed, the unchanged solid silver bromide must be removed so that the film is no longer

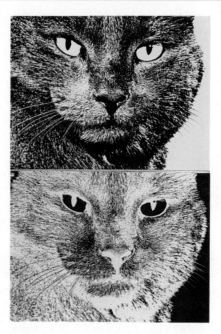

Positive and negative images.

light-sensitive and the image is fixed. A solution of sodium thiosulfate (called **hypo**) is used in this **fixing process:**

$$AgBr(s) + 2S_2O_3{}^{2-}(aq)$$
$$\rightarrow Ag(S_2O_3)_2{}^{3-}(aq) + Br^-(aq)$$

After the excess silver bromide is dissolved and washed away, the fixed image (the **negative**) is ready to produce the positive print. By shining light through the negative onto a fresh sheet of film and repeating the developing and fixing processes, a black-and-white photograph can be produced.

---

lent ones. For example, $TiCl_4$ and $SnCl_4$ are both covalent compounds that are liquids under normal conditions.

Hydrogen Halides

The hydrogen halides can be prepared by a reaction of the elements:

$$H_2(g) + X_2(g) \rightarrow 2HX(g)$$

This reaction occurs with explosive vigor when fluorine and hydrogen are mixed. On the other hand, hydrogen and chlorine can coexist with little apparent reaction for relatively long periods in the dark. However, ultraviolet light causes an explosively fast reaction, and this is the basis of a popular lecture demonstration, the "hydrogen–chlorine cannon." Bromine and iodine also react with hydrogen, but more slowly.

The hydrogen halides also can be prepared by treating halide salts with acid. For example, hydrogen fluoride and hydrogen chloride can be prepared as follows:

$$CaF_2(s) + H_2SO_4(aq) \rightarrow CaSO_4(s) + 2HF(g)$$
$$2NaCl(s) + H_2SO_4(aq) \rightarrow Na_2SO_4(s) + 2HCl(g)$$

Sulfuric acid is capable of oxidizing Br^- to Br_2 and I^- to I_2 and so cannot be used to prepare hydrogen bromide and hydrogen iodide. However, phosphoric acid, a non-oxidizing acid, can be used to treat bromides and iodides to form the corresponding hydrogen halides.

Table 19.8			
Some Physical Properties of the Hydrogen Halides			
HX	Melting Point (°C)	Boiling Point (°C)	H—X Bond Energy (kJ/mol)
HF	−83	20	565
HCl	−114	−85	427
HBr	−87	−67	363
HI	−51	−35	295

Some physical properties of the hydrogen halides are listed in Table 19.8. Note the very high boiling point for hydrogen fluoride, which results from extensive hydrogen bonding among the very polar HF molecules (Fig. 19.23). Fluoride ion has such a high affinity for protons that in concentrated aqueous solutions of hydrogen fluoride, the ion [F—H—F]$^-$ exists, in which an H$^+$ ion is centered between two F$^-$ ions.

When dissolved in water, the hydrogen halides behave as acids, and all except hydrogen fluoride are completely dissociated. Because water is a much stronger base than Cl$^-$, Br$^-$, or I$^-$ ion, the acid strengths of HCl, HBr, and HI cannot be differentiated in water. However, in a less basic solvent, such as glacial (pure) acetic acid, the acids show different strengths of the order

$$\text{H—I} > \text{H—Br} > \text{H—Cl} \gg \text{H—F}$$

Strongest   Weakest
acid   acid

To see why hydrogen fluoride is the only weak acid in water among the HX molecules, let's consider the dissociation equilibrium

$$\text{HX}(aq) \rightleftharpoons \text{H}^+(aq) + \text{X}^-(aq)$$

where

$$K_a = \frac{[\text{H}^+][\text{X}^-]}{[\text{HX}]}$$

from a thermodynamic point of view. Recall that acid strength is reflected by the magnitude of K_a—a small K_a value means a weak acid. Also recall that the value of an equilibrium constant depends on the standard free energy change for the reaction as follows:

$$\Delta G° = -RT \ln(K)$$

As $\Delta G°$ becomes more negative, K becomes larger; a *decrease* in free energy favors a given reaction. As we saw in Chapter 16, free energy depends on enthalpy, entropy, and temperature. For a process at constant temperature,

$$\Delta G° = \Delta H° - T\Delta S°$$

Thus, to explain the various acid strengths of the hydrogen halides, we must focus on the factors that determine $\Delta H°$ and $\Delta S°$ for the acid dissociation reaction.

What energy terms are important in determining $\Delta H°$ for the dissociation of HX in water? (Keep in mind that large positive contributions to the value of $\Delta H°$ will

Figure 19.23

The hydrogen bonding among HF molecules in liquid hydrogen fluoride.

Table 19.9		
The Enthalpies and Entropies of Hydration for the Halide Ions		
$X^-(g) \xrightarrow{H_2O} X^-(aq)$		
X^-	$\Delta H°$ (kJ/mol)	$\Delta S°$ (J/K · mol)
F^-	−510	−159
Cl^-	−366	−96
Br^-	−334	−81
I^-	−291	−64

Hydration becomes more exothermic as the charge density of an ion increases. Thus, for ions of a given charge, the smallest is most strongly hydrated.

tend to make $\Delta G°$ more highly positive, K_a smaller, and the acid weaker.) One important factor is certainly the H—X bond strength. Note from Table 19.8 that the H—F bond is much stronger than the other H—X bonds. This factor tends to make HF a weaker acid than the others.

Another important contribution to $\Delta H°$ is the enthalpy of hydration (see Section 11.2) of X^- (see Table 19.9). As we would expect, the smallest of the halide ions, F^-, has the most negative value—its hydration is the most exothermic. This term favors the dissociation of HF into its ions more so than it does for the other HX molecules.

So far we have two conflicting factors: the large HF bond energy tends to make HF a weaker acid than the other hydrogen halides, but the enthalpy of hydration favors the dissociation of HF more than that of the others. In comparing data for HF and HCl, the difference in bond energy (138 kJ/mol) is slightly smaller than the difference in the enthalpies of hydration for the anions (144 kJ/mol). If these were the *only* important factors, HF should be a stronger acid than HCl because the large enthalpy of hydration of F^- more than makes up the large HF bond strength.

As it turns out, the *deciding factor is entropy*. Note from Table 19.9 that the entropy of hydration for F^- is much more negative than for the other halides because of the high degree of ordering that occurs as the water molecules associate with the small F^- ion. Remember that a negative change in entropy is unfavorable. Thus, although the enthalpy of hydration favors dissociation of HF, the *entropy* of hydration strongly opposes it.

When H_2O molecules cluster around an ion, an ordering effect occurs, and $\Delta S°_{hyd}$ is negative.

When all these factors are taken into account, $\Delta G°$ for the dissociation of HF in water is positive; that is, K_a is small. In contrast, $\Delta G°$ for dissociation of the other HX molecules in water is negative (K_a is large). This example illustrates the complexity of the processes that occur in aqueous solutions and the importance of entropy effects in that medium.

In practical terms, **hydrochloric acid** is the most important of the **hydrohalic acids,** the aqueous solutions of the hydrogen halides. About 3 million tons of hydrochloric acid are produced annually for use in cleaning steel before galvanizing and in the manufacture of many other chemicals.

Stomach acid is 0.1 M HCl.

Hydrofluoric acid is used to etch glass by reacting with the silica in glass to form the volatile gas SiF_4:

$$SiO_2(s) + 4HF(aq) \rightarrow SiF_4(g) + 2H_2O(l)$$

Oxyacids and Oxyanions

All the halogens except fluorine combine with various numbers of oxygen atoms to form a series of oxyacids, as shown in Table 19.10. The strengths of these acids vary in direct proportion to the number of oxygen atoms attached to the halogen, as we discussed in Section 14.9.

The only member of the chlorine series that has been obtained in the pure state is *perchloric acid* ($HOClO_3$), a strong acid and powerful oxidizing agent. Because perchloric acid reacts explosively with many organic materials, it must be handled with great caution. The other oxyacids of chlorine are known only in solution, although salts containing their anions are well-known (Fig. 19.24).

Hypochlorous acid (HOCl) is formed when chlorine gas is dissolved in cold water:

$$Cl_2(aq) + H_2O(l) \rightleftharpoons HOCl(aq) + H^+(aq) + Cl^-(aq)$$

Note that in this reaction chlorine is both oxidized (from 0 in Cl_2 to +1 in HOCl) and reduced (from 0 in Cl_2 to −1 in Cl^-). Such a reaction, *where a given element is both oxidized and reduced,* is called a **disproportionation reaction.** Hypochlorous acid and its salts are strong oxidizing agents, and solutions of them are widely used as household bleaches and disinfectants.

Chlorate salts, such as $KClO_3$, are also strong oxidizing agents and are used as weed killers and as oxidizers in fireworks (see Chapter 7) and explosives.

Fluorine only forms one oxyacid, hypofluorous acid (HOF), but at least two oxides. When fluorine gas is bubbled into a dilute solution of sodium hydroxide, the compound *oxygen difluoride* (OF_2) is formed:

$$4F_2(g) + 3H_2O(l) \rightarrow 6HF(aq) + OF_2(g) + O_2(g)$$

Oxygen difluoride is a pale yellow gas (bp = −145°C), which is a strong oxidizing agent. The oxide *dioxygen difluoride* (O_2F_2) is an orange solid that can be prepared by passing an electric discharge through an equimolar mixture of fluorine and oxygen gases:

$$F_2(g) + O_2(g) \xrightarrow{\text{Electric discharge}} O_2F_2(s)$$

The name for OF_2 is oxygen difluoride rather than difluorine oxide because fluorine has a higher electronegativity than oxygen and thus is named as if it were an anion.

Table 19.10						
The Known Oxyacids of the Halogens*						
Oxidation State of Halogen	Fluorine	Chlorine	Bromine	Iodine*	General Name of Acids	General Name of Salts
+1	HOF	HOCl	HOBr	HOI	Hypohalous acid	Hypohalites, MOX
+3	**	HOClO	**	**	Halous acid	Halites, MXO₂
+5	**	HOClO₂	HOBrO₂	HOIO₂	Halic acid	Halates, MXO₃
+7	**	HOClO₃	HOBrO₃	HOIO₃	Perhalic acid	Perhalates, MXO₄

*Iodine also forms $H_4I_2O_9$ (mesodiperiodic acid) and H_5IO_6 (paraperiodic acid).
**Compound is unknown.

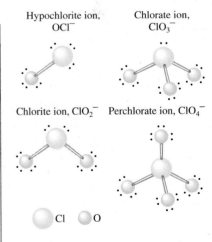

Hypochlorite ion, OCl^-
Chlorate ion, ClO_3^-
Chlorite ion, ClO_2^-
Perchlorate ion, ClO_4^-
Cl   O

Figure 19.24

The structures of the oxychloro anions.

Sample Exercise 19.5

Give the Lewis structure, molecular structure, and hybridization of the oxygen atom for OF_2.

Solution

The OF_2 molecule has 20 valence electrons and the Lewis structure is

The four effective pairs around the oxygen are arranged tetrahedrally. Therefore, the oxygen atom is sp^3 hybridized. The molecule is bent (V-shaped), and the bond angle is predicted to be smaller than 109.5 degrees because of the lone-pair repulsions.

Sample Exercise 19.6

Using the half-reactions

$$I_2 + 2e^- \rightarrow 2I^- \qquad \mathscr{E}° = 0.54 \text{ V}$$
$$2H^+ + 2HOI + 2e^- \rightarrow I_2 + 2H_2O \qquad \mathscr{E}° = 1.45 \text{ V}$$

predict whether I_2 will disproportionate to HOI and I^- in acidic solution.

Solution

We need to determine whether the disproportionation reaction

$$I_2 \rightleftharpoons HOI + I^-$$

is spontaneous. The balanced equation for this process can be obtained by reversing the second half-reaction and adding the two:

$$
\begin{array}{lr}
I_2 + 2e^- \rightarrow 2I^- & \mathscr{E}° = \quad 0.54 \text{ V} \\
\underline{I_2 + 2H_2O \rightarrow 2H^+ + 2HOI + 2e^-} & \underline{-\mathscr{E}° = -1.45 \text{ V}} \\
2I_2 + 2H_2O \rightarrow 2I^- + 2H^+ + 2HOI & \mathscr{E}° = -0.91 \text{ V}
\end{array}
$$

or $\qquad I_2 + H_2O \rightarrow I^- + H^+ + HOI \qquad \mathscr{E}° = -0.91 \text{ V}$

Since the $\mathscr{E}°$ value for this reaction is negative, the reaction is not spontaneous under standard conditions.

Other Halogen Compounds

The halogens react readily with most nonmetals to form a variety of compounds, some of which are shown in Table 19.11.

Halogens react with each other to form **interhalogen compounds** with the general formula AB_n, where n is typically 1, 3, 5, or 7 and A is the larger of the two halogens. The structures of these compounds (see Fig. 19.25) are predicted accu-

Table 19.11				
Some Compounds of the Halogens with Nonmetals				
Compounds with Group 3A Nonmetals	Compounds with Group 4A Nonmetals	Compounds with Group 5A Nonmetals	Compounds with Group 6A Nonmetals	Compounds with Group 7A Nonmetals
BX_3 (X = F,Cl,Br,I) BF_4^-	CX_4 (X = F,Cl,Br,I)	NX_3 (X = F,Cl,Br,I) N_2F_4	OF_2 O_2F_2 OCl_2 OBr_2	ICl IBr BrF BrCl ClF
	SiF_4 SiF_6^{2-} $SiCl_4$	PX_3 (X = F,Cl,Br,I) PF_5 PCl_5	SF_2 SCl_2 S_2F_2	ClF_3 BrF_3 ICl_3
	GeF_4 GeF_6^{2-} $GeCl_4$	PBr_5 AsF_3 AsF_5	S_2Cl_2 SF_4 SCl_4 SF_6	IF_3
		SbF_3 SbF_5	SeF_4 SeF_6 $SeCl_2$ $SeCl_4$ $SeBr_4$	ClF_5 BrF_5 IF_5 IF_7
			TeF_4 TeF_6 $TeCl_4$ $TeBr_4$ TeI_4	

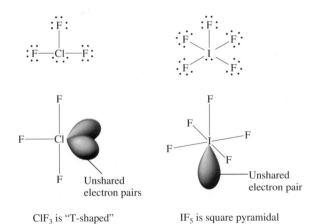

ClF_3 is "T-shaped" IF_5 is square pyramidal

Figure 19.25

The idealized structures of the interhalogens ClF_3 and IF_5. In reality, the lone pairs cause the bond angles to be slightly less than 90°.

rately by the VSEPR model. The interhalogens are volatile, highly reactive compounds that act as strong oxidizing agents. They react readily with water, forming the halide ion of the more electronegative halogen and the hypohalous acid of the less electronegative halogen, for example,

$$ICl(s) + H_2O(l) \rightarrow H^+(aq) + Cl^-(aq) + HOI(aq)$$

◀ **CHEMICAL IMPACT** ▶

Automatic Sunglasses

Sunglasses can be troublesome. It seems they are always getting lost or sat on. One solution to this problem for people who wear glasses is photochromic glass—glass that darkens in response to intense light. Recall that glass is a complex, noncrystalline material that is composed of polymeric silicates (see Chapter 10). Of course, glass transmits visible light—its transparency is its most useful property.

Glass can be made photochromic by adding tiny silver chloride crystals that get trapped in the glass matrix as the glass solidifies. Silver chloride has the unusual property of darkening when struck by light—the property that makes the silver halide salts so useful for photographic films. This darkening occurs because light causes an electron transfer from Cl^- to Ag^+ in the silver chloride crystal, forming a silver atom and a chlorine atom. The silver atoms formed in this way tend to migrate to the surface of the silver chloride crystal, where they aggregate to form a tiny crystal of silver metal, which is opaque to light.

In photography the image defined by the grains of silver is fixed by chemical treatment so that it remains permanent. However, in photochromic glass this process must be reversible—the glass must become fully transparent again when the person goes back indoors. The secret to the reversibility of photochromic glass is the presence of Cu^+ ions. The added Cu^+ ions serve two important functions. First, they reduce the Cl atoms formed in the light-induced reaction. This prevents them from escaping from the crystal:

$$Ag^+ + Cl^- \xrightarrow{h\nu} Ag + Cl$$
$$Cl + Cu^+ \longrightarrow Cu^{2+} + Cl^-$$

Second, when the exposure to intense light ends (the person goes indoors), the Cu^{2+} ions migrate to the surface of the silver chloride crystal, where they accept electrons from silver atoms as the tiny crystal of silver atoms disintegrates:

$$Cu^{2+} + Ag \longrightarrow Cu^+ + Ag^+$$

The Ag^+ ions are re-formed in this way then return to their places in the silver chloride crystal, making the glass transparent once again.

Typical photochromic glass decreases to about 20% transmittance (transmits 20% of the light that strikes it) in strong sunlight, and then over a period of a few minutes returns to about 80% transmittance indoors (normal glass has 92% transmittance).

The halogens react with carbon to form many commercially important compounds. Especially significant are a group of polymers, or long-chain compounds (see Section 22.6), made from ethylene molecules:

For example, the compound perfluoroethylene

can react with itself to give the polymer

or **Teflon,** a substance with high thermal stability and resistance to chemical attack, used as a coating in many different applications.

The **Freons,** compounds of the general formula CCl_xF_{4-x}, are very stable compounds that are used as coolant fluids in refrigerators and air conditioners.

Chlorine is found in many other useful carbon compounds. For example, the molecule

called **vinyl chloride,** can be polymerized to form *polyvinyl chloride,* or PVC:

Chlorine is also found in many pesticides.

Bromine is used in silver bromide–based photographic films. It is also used to make NaBr and KBr, two chemicals used in sedatives and soporifics (sleeping aids). Bromine-containing compounds are also used as flame retardants for cloth (see Section 22.7).

19.8 The Group 8A Elements

Purpose

- To describe the uses of the noble gases.
- To discuss the structures of xenon compounds.

The Group 8A elements, the **noble gases,** are characterized by filled s and p valence orbitals (electron configuration of $2s^2$ for helium and ns^2np^6 for the others). Because of this, these elements are very unreactive. In fact, no noble gas compounds were known 30 years ago. Selected properties of the Group 8A elements are summarized in Table 19.12.

Helium was identified by its characteristic emission spectrum as a component of the sun before it was found on earth. The major sources of helium on earth are natural gas deposits, where helium was formed from α-particle decay of radioactive

8A
He
Ne
Ar
Kr
Xe
Rn

Table 19.12				
Selected Properties of Group 8A Elements				
Element	Melting Point (°C)	Boiling Point (°C)	Atmospheric Abundance (% by Volume)	Examples of Compounds
Helium	−272	−269	5×10^{-4}	None
Neon	−249	−246	1×10^{-3}	None
Argon	−189	−186	9×10^{-1}	None
Krypton	−157	−153	1×10^{-4}	KrF_2
Xenon	−112	−107	9×10^{-6}	XeF_4, XeO_3, XeF_6

Blimps are often used by companies as floating billboards.

elements. The α particle is a helium nucleus that can easily pick up electrons from the environment to form a helium atom. Although helium forms no compounds, it is an important substance that is used as a coolant, as a pressurizing gas for rocket fuels, as a diluent in the gases used for deep-sea diving and spaceship atmospheres, and as the gas in lighter-than-air airships (blimps).

Like helium, *neon* and *argon* form no compounds but are used extensively. For example, neon is employed in luminescent lighting (neon signs), and argon is used to provide the noncorrosive atmosphere in incandescent light bulbs, which prolongs the life of the tungsten filament.

Of the Group 8A elements, only *krypton* and *xenon* have been observed to form chemical compounds. The first of these was prepared in 1962 by Neil Bartlett (b. 1932), an English chemist who used $Xe(g)$ and $PtF_6(g)$ to make the ionic compound with the empirical formula $XePtF_6$.

Less than a year after Barlett's report of $XePtF_6$, a group at Argonne National Laboratory near Chicago prepared xenon tetrafluoride by reaction of xenon and fluorine gases in a nickel reaction vessel at 400°C and 6 atm:

$$Xe(g) + 2F_2(g) \rightarrow XeF_4(s)$$

Xenon tetrafluoride forms stable colorless crystals. Two other xenon fluorides, XeF_2 and XeF_6, were synthesized by the group at Argonne, and a highly explosive xenon oxide (XeO_3) also was found. The xenon fluorides react with water to form hydrogen fluoride and oxycompounds, for example:

$$XeF_6(s) + 3H_2O(l) \rightarrow XeO_3(aq) + 6HF(aq)$$
$$XeF_6(s) + H_2O(l) \rightarrow XeOF_4(aq) + 2HF(g)$$

In the past 20 years, other xenon compounds have been prepared, for example, XeO_4 (explosive), $XeOF_4$, $XeOF_2$, and XeO_3F_2. These compounds contain discrete molecules with covalent bonds between the xenon and the other atoms. The structures of some of these xenon compounds are summarized in Fig. 19.26. A few compounds of krypton, such as KrF_2 and KrF_4, also have been observed. There is

Figure 19.26

The structures of several known xenon compounds.

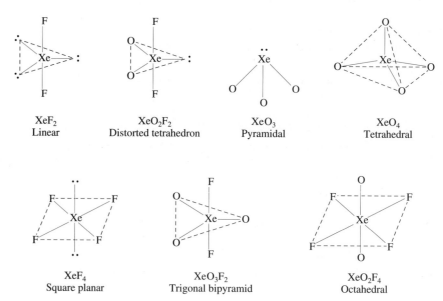

evidence that radon also reacts with fluorine, but the radioactivity of radon makes its chemistry very difficult to study.

Sample Exercise 19.7

Use the VSEPR model to predict whether XeF_6 has an octahedral structure.

Solution

The XeF_6 molecule contains 50 [8 + 6(7)] valence electrons and the Lewis structure is

The xenon atom has seven effective pairs of electrons around it (one lone pair and six bonding pairs), one more pair than can be accommodated in an octahedral arrangement. Thus XeF_6 will not have an octahedral structure, but should be distorted from this geometry by the extra electron pair. There is experimental evidence that the structure of XeF_6 is not octahedral.

FOR REVIEW

Summary

The Group 5A elements show remarkably varied chemical properties. Nitrogen and phosphorus are nonmetals and can form 3− anions in salts with active metals. Antimony and bismuth tend to be metallic, although no ionic compounds with their 5+ ions are known. The compounds containing bismuth(V) or antimony(V) are molecular rather than ionic. All the Group 5A members except nitrogen form molecules with five covalent bonds. The ability of these elements to form π bonds decreases dramatically after nitrogen. Thus phosphorus, arsenic, and antimony exist in the gas phase as aggregates of more than two atoms.

The strength of the triple bond in the N_2 molecule is of great importance both thermodynamically and kinetically. Most binary nitrogen-containing compounds decompose exothermically to the elements, a fact that explains the power of nitrogen-based explosives.

The nitrogen cycle is composed of a series of steps describing how nitrogen is cycled in the natural environment. One step involves the transformation of nitrogen gas in the atmosphere into nitrogen-containing compounds useful to plants, a process called nitrogen fixation. The Haber process is one example of nitrogen fixation; another is provided by nitrogen-fixing bacteria in the root nodules of certain plants. Denitrification is the reverse process—the release of nitrogen gas back into the atmosphere.

Ammonia, the most important nitrogen hydride, has pyramidal molecules with polar bonds. Hydrazine (N_2H_4) is a powerful reducing agent. Nitrogen forms a series of oxides in which it has an oxidation state ranging from 1 to 5; the most important are nitric oxide and nitrogen dioxide. Nitric acid (HNO_3) is an important strong acid made by the Ostwald process, in which ammonia is first oxidized to nitric oxide, which is then oxidized to nitrogen dioxide, which is dissolved in water to form nitric acid. Nitrous acid (HNO_2) is a weak acid.

Phosphorus exists in three elemental forms: white, black, and red. Although it has a lower electronegativity than nitrogen, phosphorus forms the P^{3-} anion in phosphides. Phosphine (PH_3) has a structure analogous to that of ammonia but with bond angles close to $90°$. Phosphorus reacts with oxygen to form P_4O_6 (oxidation state of $+3$) and P_4O_{10} (oxidation state of $+5$). When P_4O_{10} dissolves in water, it forms phosphoric acid (H_3PO_4), a weak acid. Phosphoric acid readily undergoes condensation reactions, giving up water molecules to form polymeric acids.

The Group 6A elements show the usual tendency of increasing metallic properties going down the group. However, none behave as typical metals. Most commonly, these elements achieve noble gas configurations by adding two electrons to form $2-$ anions. Group 6A elements also can form covalent bonds with other nonmetals.

Oxygen exists in two elemental forms, O_2 and ozone (O_3), a V-shaped molecule. Ozone is a powerful oxidizing agent with important environmental implications.

Sulfur also exists in two elemental forms, rhombic and monoclinic, both of which contain stacks of S_8 rings. Sulfur occurs in nature both as the free element and in ores as sulfides and sulfates. Sulfur forms three oxides. Sulfur monoxide (SO) is unstable. When sulfur dioxide (SO_2) is dissolved in water, sulfurous acid (H_2SO_3) forms, which is analogous in many respects to carbonic acid as a weak acid. Sulfur trioxide (SO_3) dissolves in water to form sulfuric acid (H_2SO_4), an extremely important industrial chemical and a strong acid that is a powerful dehydrating agent. Sulfur forms a variety of compounds in which it has a $+6$, $+4$, $+2$, 0, or -2 oxidation state.

The Group 7A elements, the halogens, are all nonmetals. The halogens form hydrogen halides (HX) that behave as strong acids in water, except for hydrogen fluoride. Hydrofluoric acid is a weak acid because of the strong H—F bond and because the entropy of hydration for the F^- ion is much more negative than it is for the other halide ions. The oxyacids of the halogens become stronger as the number of oxygen atoms attached to the halogen increases. Interhalogens are compounds of two different halogens. Halogen–carbon compounds are important industrially; examples are Teflon, PVC, and the Freons.

The noble gases of Group 8A are characterized by filled valence shells and are generally unreactive. Krypton, xenon, and radon do, however, form compounds with the highly electronegative atoms fluorine and oxygen.

Key Terms

Section 19.2
Haber process
nitrogen fixation
nitrogen-fixing bacteria
denitrification
nitrogen cycle
ammonia

hydrazine
nitric acid
Ostwald process

Section 19.3
phosphoric acid
condensation reactions

phosphorous acid
superphosphate of lime

Section 19.5
ozone
ozonolysis

Section 19.6
Frasch process
sulfuric acid
thiosulfate ion

Section 19.7
halogens
hydrochloric acid

hydrohalic acids
disproportionation reaction
interhalogen compounds
Freons

Section 19.8
noble gases

A blue question or exercise number indicates that the answer to that question or exercise appears at the back of this book and a solution appears in the Solutions Guide.

Questions

1. What trade-offs must be made between kinetics and thermodynamics in the Haber process for the production of ammonia? How did the discovery of an appropriate catalyst make the process feasible?

2. Account for the reactivity of oxygen with white phosphorus, red phosphorus, and black phosphorus in terms of their structures.

3. In many natural waters, nitrogen and phosphorus are the least abundant nutrients available for plant life. Some waters that become polluted from agricultural runoff or municipal sewage become infested with algae. The algae consume most of the dissolved oxygen in the water, and fish life dies off as a result. Describe how these events are chemically related.

4. Ozone is desirable in the upper atmosphere and undesirable in the lower atmosphere. A dictionary states that ozone has the scent of a fresh spring day. How can these seemingly conflicting statements be reconciled in terms of the chemical properties of ozone?

5. Describe the structural changes that occur when plastic sulfur becomes brittle.

6. Sulfur dissolves in an aqueous solution that contains sulfide ion. Sulfur will then precipitate from this solution if nitric acid is added. Explain.

7. Give two reasons why F_2 is the most reactive of the halogens.

8. The noble gases were among the latest elements discovered; their existence was not predicted by Mendeleev when he published his first periodic table. Explain.

9. Although He is the second most abundant element in the universe, it is very rare on earth. Why?

10. In chemistry textbooks written before 1962 the noble gases were referred to as the inert gases. Why do we no longer use this term?

Exercises

In this section similar exercises are paired.

Group 5A Elements

11. The oxyanion of nitrogen in which it has the highest oxidation state is the nitrate ion (NO_3^-). The corresponding oxyanion of phosphorus is PO_4^{3-}. The NO_4^{3-} ion is known but not very stable. The PO_3^- ion is not known. Account for these differences in terms of the bonding in the four anions.

12. In each of the following pairs of substances, one is stable and known, the other is unstable. For each pair, choose the stable substance, and explain why the other is unstable.
    a. NF_5 or PF_5 c. NF_3 or NBr_3
    b. AsF_5 or AsI_5

13. Write balanced equations that describe how the following can be produced.
    a. $NO(g)$ c. $KNO_2(s)$
    b. $N_2O(g)$

14. Complete and balance each of the following reactions.
    a. $P_4O_6(s) + O_2(g) \rightarrow$ c. $PCl_5(l) + H_2O(l) \rightarrow$
    b. $P_4O_{10}(s) + H_2O(l) \rightarrow$

15. Predict the hybridization of the nitrogen atoms in the compounds listed in Table 19.2.

16. Name the compounds in Table 19.2 that exhibit resonance, and draw the corresponding resonance structures.

17. Using data from Appendix 4 calculate $\Delta H°$, $\Delta S°$, and $\Delta G°$ for the reaction

$$N_2(g) + O_2(g) \rightarrow 2NO(g)$$

Why does NO form in an automobile engine but then does not readily decompose back to N_2 and O_2 in the atmosphere?

18. Write an equation for the reaction of hydrazine with fluorine gas to produce nitrogen gas and hydrogen fluoride gas. Estimate $\Delta H°$ for this reaction using bond energies from Table 8.4.

19. Predict the relative acid strengths of the following compounds.
    a. H_3PO_4 and H_3PO_3
    b. H_3PO_4, $H_2PO_4^-$, HPO_4^{2-}

20. Isohypophosphonic acid ($H_4P_2O_6$) and diphosphonic acid ($H_4P_2O_5$) are tri- and diprotic acids, respectively. Draw Lewis structures for these acids that are consistent with these facts.

21. Write balanced equations for the reactions described in Table 19.1 for the production of Bi and Sb.

22. Arsenic reacts with oxygen to form oxides (analogous to the phosphorus oxides) that react with water in a manner analogous to that of the phosphorus oxides. Write balanced chemical equations describing the reaction of arsenic with oxygen and the reaction of the resulting oxide with water.

Group 6A Elements

23. Use bond energies to estimate the maximum wavelength of light that will cause the reaction

$$O_3 \xrightarrow{h\nu} O_2 + O$$

24. The xerographic (dry writing) process was invented in 1938 by C. Carlson. In xerography, an image is produced on a photoconductor by exposing it to light. Selenium is commonly used, since its conductivity increases three orders of magnitude upon exposure to light in the range from 400 to 500 nm. What color light should be used to cause selenium to become conductive? (See Figure 20.24.)

25. When nitric acid is added to a solution of sodium sulfide, elemental sulfur forms.
    a. What type of reaction is this?
    b. Use standard reduction potentials (Table 17.1) to predict the product in the reaction that comes from HNO_3.
    c. Write a balanced equation for this process.

26. Write a balanced equation describing the reduction of H_2SeO_4 by SO_2 to produce selenium.

27. The SF_5^- ion can be formed by the reaction

$$CsF + SF_4 \rightarrow Cs^+ + SF_5^-$$

Predict the molecular structure of the SF_5^- ion.

28. The teflate anion ($OTeF_5^-$) often acts like a halide ion. For example, $P(OTeF_5)_3$ has a structure similar to that of PF_3. Draw Lewis structures for $OTeF_5^-$ and $P(OTeF_5)_3$.

Group 7A Elements

29. Write the Lewis structures and predict the geometries for each of the following compounds.
    a. ClF_5 c. Cl_2O_7 (has a Cl—O—Cl bond)
    b. IF_3 d. $FBrO_2$

30. Write the Lewis structure for O_2F_2. Assign oxidation numbers and formal charges to the atoms in O_2F_2. The compound O_2F_2 is a vigorous and potent oxidizing and fluorinating agent. Are oxidation numbers or formal charges more useful in accounting for these properties of O_2F_2?

31. Although the perchlorate and periodate ions have been known for a long time, the perbromate ion proved to be quite elusive and was not synthesized until 1965. Perbromate was synthesized by oxidizing bromate ion with aqueous xenon difluoride, producing xenon, hydrofluoric acid, and perbromate ion. Write a balanced equation for this reaction.

32. Hypofluorous acid is the most recently prepared of the halogen oxyacids. Weighable amounts were first obtained in 1971 by M. H. Studies and E. N. Appelman using the fluorination of ice. Hypofluorous acid is exceedingly unstable, decomposing spontaneously (with a half-life of 30 min) to HF and O_2 in a Teflon container at room temperature. It reacts rapidly with water to produce HF, H_2O_2, and O_2. In dilute acid, H_2O_2 is the major product; in dilute base, O_2 is the major product.

a. Write balanced equations for the reactions described above.

b. Assign oxidation states to the elements in hypofluorous acid. Does this suggest why hypofluorous acid is so unstable?

33. Chlorine is used as a disinfectant in the treatment of water supplies.

a. Calculate $\mathscr{E}°$ for the reaction

$$Cl_2(aq) \rightarrow OCl^-(aq) + Cl^-(aq) \qquad \text{(not balanced)}$$

b. Is the reaction spontaneous under standard conditions?

c. What will be the effect of pH on $\mathscr{E}$ for this reaction? *Hint:* HOCl is a weak acid.

Note: For the half-reaction $2OCl^- + 4H^+ + 2e^- \rightarrow 2H_2O + Cl_2$, $\mathscr{E} = 1.63$ V.

34. What is a disproportionation reaction? Use the following reduction potentials

$$ClO_3^- + 3H^+ + 2e^- \rightarrow HClO_2 + H_2O \qquad \mathscr{E}° = 1.21 \text{ V}$$
$$HClO_2 + 2H^+ + 2e^- \rightarrow HClO + H_2O \qquad \mathscr{E}° = 1.65 \text{ V}$$

to predict whether $HClO_2$ will disproportionate.

Group 8A Elements

35. The xenon halides, oxyhalides, and oxides are isoelectronic with many other compounds and ions containing halogens. Give a molecule or ion, in which iodine is the central atom, that is isoelectronic with each of the following.

a. XeO_4 d. XeF_4

b. XeO_3 e. XeF_6

c. XeF_2 f. $XeOF_3$

36. Write the Lewis structures and predict the molecular structures for XeO_3, XeO_4, $XeOF_4$, $XeOF_2$, and XeO_3F_2.

37. Xenon difluoride has proven to be a versatile fluorinating agent. For example, in the reaction

$$C_6H_6(l) + XeF_2(g) \rightarrow C_6H_5F(l) + Xe(g) + HF(g)$$

the by-products Xe and HF are easily removed, leaving pure C_6H_5F. Xenon difluoride is stored in an inert atmosphere free from oxygen and water. Why is this necessary?

38. Using the data in Table 19.12, calculate the mass of xenon at 25°C and 1.0 atm in a room 10.0 m × 5.0 m × 3.0 m. How many Xe atoms are in this room? How many Xe atoms do you inhale in one breath (approximately 2 L) of air?

Additional Exercises

39. The compound NF_3 is quite stable, but NCl_3 is very unstable (NCl_3 was first synthesized in 1811 by P. L. Dulong, who lost three fingers and an eye studying its properties). The compounds NBr_3 and NI_3 are unknown, although the explosive compound $NI_3 \cdot NH_3$ is known. Account for the instability of these halides of nitrogen.

40. Many structures of phosphorus- and sulfur-containing compounds are drawn with some P═O and P═S bonds. These bonds are not the typical π bonds we've considered, involving the overlap of two p orbitals. They result instead from the overlap of a d orbital on the phosphorus or sulfur atom and a p orbital on oxygen. This is sometimes used as an explanation for why H_3PO_3 has the first structure below rather than the second:

$$
\begin{array}{cc}
\text{O} & \text{OH} \\
\parallel & \vert \\
\text{H—P—OH} & \text{HO—P:} \\
\vert & \vert \\
\text{OH} & \text{OH}
\end{array}
$$

Draw a picture showing how a *d* orbital and a *p* orbital overlap to form a π bond.

41. Use data in Appendix 4 to calculate $\Delta H°$, $\Delta S°$, and $\Delta G°$ for the reaction

$$3NO(g) \rightleftharpoons N_2O(g) + NO_2(g)$$

Under what temperature conditions is this reaction spontaneous?

42. Given the information about N_2O_5 in Section 19.2, draw a possible structure for this molecule in the gas phase.

43. Oxidation of the cyanide ion produces the stable cyanate ion, OCN^-. The fulminate ion, CNO^-, on the other hand, is very unstable. Fulminate salts explode when struck; $Hg(CNO)_2$ is used in blasting caps. Write the Lewis structures and assign formal charges for the cyanate and fulminate ions. Why is the fulminate ion so unstable?

44. Write the Lewis structures for the $AsCl_4^+$ and $AsCl_6^-$ ions. What type of reaction (acid–base, oxidation–reduction, etc.) is the following?

$$2AsCl_5(g) \rightarrow AsCl_4AsCl_6(s)$$

45. Compare the Lewis structures with the molecular orbital view of the bonding in NO, NO^+, and NO^-. Account for any discrepancies between the two models.

46. Sodium tripolyphosphate ($Na_5P_3O_{10}$) is used in many synthetic detergents to soften the water by complexing Mg^{2+} and Ca^{2+} ions. It also increases the efficiency of surfactants (wetting agents) that lower a liquid's surface tension. The pK value for the formation of $MgP_3O_{10}^{3-}$ is -8.6. The reaction is

$$Mg^{2+} + P_3O_{10}^{5-} \rightleftharpoons MgP_3O_{10}^{3-}$$

Calculate the concentration of Mg^{2+} in a solution that was originally 50 ppm of Mg^{2+} (50 mg/L of solution) after 40 g $Na_5P_3O_{10}$ is added to 1.0 L of the solution.

47. Sodium bismuthate ($NaBiO_3$) is used to test for the presence of Mn^{2+} in solution by the reaction

$$Mn^{2+}(aq) + NaBiO_3(s) \rightarrow MnO_4^-(aq) + BiO_3^{3-}(aq)$$

a. Balance this equation.
b. Given that bismuth does not form double bonds with oxygen in BiO_3^- and that $NaBiO_3$ is relatively insoluble in water, what type of structure must $NaBiO_3$ have that accounts for this behavior?

48. What experiments can be done to verify that bismuthyl chloride (BiOCl) is composed of BiO^+ and Cl^- ions and not Bi^+ and OCl^- ions?

49. Cadmium sulfide, which has recently been tested as a photoconductor for xerography, is a semiconducting material with a band gap of 2.42 eV. (1 eV, or electronvolt, equals 96.5 kJ/mol.) What is the minimum wavelength of light needed to promote electrons from the valence band to the conduction band in CdS? What color of light is this? (See Figure 20.24.)

50. The structure of TeF_5^- is

Draw a complete Lewis structure for TeF_5^-, and explain the distortion from the ideal square pyramidal geometry.

51. Sodium perchlorate is produced by the electrolytic oxidation of aqueous $NaClO_3$:

$$ClO_3^- + H_2O \rightarrow ClO_4^- + H_2$$

More than half the annual U.S. production is converted to NH_4ClO_4 for use as a rocket fuel. The two booster rockets on the space shuttle use NH_4ClO_4 (70% by mass) as an oxidizer and powdered aluminum (30% by mass) as fuel. About 7×10^5 kg of NH_4ClO_4 is required for each launch.

a. What is the minimum electrical potential that must be applied to produce $NaClO_4$? For the half-reaction $ClO_4^- + 2H^+ + 2e^- \rightarrow ClO_3^- + H_2O$, $\mathscr{E}° = +1.19$ V.
b. A possible reaction in the booster rocket is

$$3Al(s) + 3NH_4ClO_4(s) \\ \rightarrow Al_2O_3(s) + AlCl_3(s) + 3NO(g) + 6H_2O(g)$$

Estimate the total energy generated by the booster rocket during a space shuttle launch.

Challenge Problems

52. Use bond energies (Table 8.4) to show that the preferred products for the decomposition of N_2O_3 are NO_2 and NO rather than O_2 and N_2O. (The N—O single bond energy is 201 kJ/mol.) *Hint:* Consider the reaction kinetics.

53. The energy to break a particular bond is not always constant. It takes about 200 kJ/mol less energy to break the N—Cl bond

in NOCl as compared with NCl_3:

$$NOCl \rightarrow NO + Cl \qquad \Delta H° = 158 \text{ kJ/mol}$$

$$NCl_3 \rightarrow NCl_2 + Cl \qquad \Delta H° \approx 375 \text{ kJ/mol}$$

Why is there such a great discrepancy in the apparent N—Cl bond energies? *Hint:* Consider what happens to the nitrogen–oxygen bond in the first reaction.

54. One of the most strongly acidic solutions known is a mixture of antimony pentafluoride (SbF_5) and fluorosulfonic acid (HSO_3F). The important equilibria are

$$SbF_5 + HSO_3F \rightleftharpoons F_5SbOSO_2FH$$

$$F_5SbOSO_2FH + HSO_3F \rightleftharpoons H_2SO_3F^+ + F_5SbOSO_2F^-$$

a. Write the Lewis structures for all the species shown in the preceding reactions.

b. Such *superacid* solutions are capable of protonating (adding H^+ to) virtually every known organic compound. What is the active protonating agent in these solutions?

55. The first acid dissociation constants of H_2S, H_2Se, and H_2Te are 1.03×10^{-7}, 1.3×10^{-4}, and 2.3×10^{-3}, respectively.

a. To what do you attribute this trend? (See the data in the following table.)

b. To the nearest power of 10, predict K_a for H_2Po.

Bond Energy (kJ/mol)		Electron Affinity (kJ/mol)	
H—S	363	S	−200.4
H—Se	276	Se	−195
H—Te	238	Te	−190

56. Photogray lenses contain small embedded crystals of solid silver chloride. Silver chloride is light-sensitive because of the reaction

$$AgCl(s) \xrightarrow{h\nu} Ag(s) + Cl$$

Small particles of metallic silver cause the lenses to darken. In the lenses this process is reversible. When the light is removed, the reverse reaction occurs. However, when pure white silver chloride is exposed to sunlight it darkens; the reverse reaction does not occur in the dark.

a. How do you explain this difference?

b. Photogray lenses do become permanently dark in time. How do you account for this?

CHAPTER 20

Transition Metals and Coordination Chemistry

CONTENTS

Transition metals have many uses in our society. Iron is used for steel; copper for electrical wiring and water pipes; titanium for paint; silver for photographic paper; manganese, chromium, vanadium, and cobalt as additives to steel; platinum for industrial and automotive catalysts; and so on.

One indication of the importance of transition metals is the great concern shown by the U.S. government for continuing the supply of these elements. In recent years the United States has been a net importer of about 60 "strategic and critical" minerals, including cobalt, manganese, platinum, palladium, and chromium. All these metals play a vital role in the U.S. economy and defense, and approximately 90% of the required amounts must be imported (see Table 20.1).

In addition to being important in industry, transition metal ions also play a vital role in living organisms. For example, complexes of iron provide for the transport and storage of oxygen, molybdenum and iron compounds are catalysts in nitrogen fixation, zinc is found in more than 150 biomolecules in humans, copper and iron play a crucial role in the respiratory cycle, and cobalt is found in essential biomolecules such as vitamin B_{12}.

In this chapter we explore the general properties of transition metals, paying particular attention to the bonding, structure, and properties of the complex ions of these metals.

< A gold Byzantine cup from near Durazzo, Albania, c. A.D. 600. It is decorated with female personifications of imperial cities and the metropolitan sees of Constantinople, Cyprus, Rome, and Alexandria, which are identified by Greek inscriptions.

Table 20.1		
Some Transition Metals Important to the U.S. Economy and Defense		
Metal	Uses	Percentage Imported
Chromium	Stainless steel (especially for parts exposed to corrosive gases and high temperatures)	~91%
Cobalt	High-temperature alloys in jet engines, magnets, catalysts, drill bits	~93%
Manganese	Steelmaking	~97%
Platinum and palladium	Catalysts	~87%

20.1 The Transition Metals: A Survey

Purpose

- To discuss electron configurations and general trends in the properties of the first-row transition metals.
- To introduce the 4d and 5d transition series.

General Properties

One striking characteristic of the representative elements is that their chemistry changes markedly across a given period as the number of valence electrons changes. The chemical similarities occur mainly within the vertical groups. In contrast, *the transition metals show great similarities within a given period as well as within a given vertical group*. This difference occurs because the last electrons added for transition metals are inner electrons: *d* electrons for the *d*-block transition metals and *f* electrons for the lanthanides and actinides. These inner *d* and *f* electrons cannot participate as easily in bonding as can the valence *s* and *p* electrons. Thus the chemistry of transition elements is not affected as greatly by the gradual change in the number of electrons as is the chemistry of the representative elements.

Group designations are traditionally given on the periodic table for the *d*-block transition metals (see Fig. 20.1 on p. 938). However, these designations do not relate as directly to the chemical behavior of these elements as they do for the representative elements (the A groups), so we will not use them.

As a class, the transition metals behave as typical metals, possessing metallic luster and relatively high electrical and thermal conductivities. Silver is the best conductor of heat and electric current. However, copper is a close second, which explains copper's wide use in the electrical systems of homes and factories.

Despite their many similarities, the transition metals do vary considerably in certain properties. For example, tungsten has a melting point of 3400°C and is used for filaments in light bulbs; mercury is a liquid at 25°C. Some transition metals such as iron and titanium are hard and strong and make very useful structural materials; others such as copper, gold, and silver are relatively soft. The chemical reactivity of the transition metals also varies significantly. Some react readily with

Sc	Ti	V	Cr	Mn	Fe	Co	Ni	Cu	Zn
Y	Zr	Nb	Mo	Tc	Ru	Rh	Pd	Ag	Cd
La	Hf	Ta	W	Re	Os	Ir	Pt	Au	Hg
Ac	Unq	Unp	Unh	Uns	Uno	Une			

Ce	Pr	Nd	Pm	Sm	Eu	Gd	Tb	Dy	Ho	Er	Tm	Yb	Lu
Th	Pa	U	Np	Pu	Am	Cm	Bk	Cf	Es	Fm	Md	No	Lr

(clockwise from upper left) Calcite stalactites colored by traces of iron. Quartz is often colored by the presence of transition metals such as Mn, Fe, and Ni. Wulfenite contains $PbMoO_4$. Rhodochrosite is a mineral containing $MnCO_3$.

d-block transition elements

Figure 20.1

The position of the transition elements on the periodic table. The d-block elements correspond to filling the 3d, 4d, 5d, or 6d orbitals. The inner transition metals correspond to filling the 4f (lanthanides) or 5f (actinides) orbitals.

f-block transition elements

	Ce	Pr	Nd	Pm	Sm	Eu	Gd	Tb	Dy	Ho	Er	Tm	Yb	Lu
*Lanthanides														
†Actinides	Th	Pa	U	Np	Pu	Am	Cm	Bk	Cf	Es	Fm	Md	No	Lr

oxygen to form oxides. Of these metals, some, such as chromium, nickel, and cobalt, form oxides that adhere tightly to the metallic surface, protecting the metal from further oxidation. Others, such as iron, form oxides that scale off, constantly exposing new metal to the corrosion process. On the other hand, the noble metals—primarily gold, silver, platinum, and palladium—do not readily form oxides.

In forming ionic compounds with nonmetals, the transition metals exhibit several typical characteristics:

More than one oxidation state is often found. For example, iron combines with chlorine to form $FeCl_2$ and $FeCl_3$.

The cations are often **complex ions,** species where *the transition metal ion is surrounded by a certain number of ligands* (molecules or ions that behave as Lewis bases). For example, the compound $[Co(NH_3)_6]Cl_3$ contains the $Co(NH_3)_6^{3+}$ cation and Cl^- anions.

The $Co(NH_3)_6^{3+}$ ion

Most compounds are colored, because the transition metal ion in the complex ion can absorb visible light of specific wavelengths.

Many compounds are paramagnetic (they contain unpaired electrons).

Table 20.2										
Selected Properties of the First-Row Transition Metals										
	Scandium	Titanium	Vanadium	Chromium	Manganese	Iron	Cobalt	Nickel	Copper	Zinc
Atomic number	21	22	23	24	25	26	27	28	29	30
Electron configuration*	$4s^23d^1$	$4s^23d^2$	$4s^23d^3$	$4s^13d^5$	$4s^23d^5$	$4s^23d^6$	$4s^23d^7$	$4s^23d^8$	$4s^13d^{10}$	$4s^23d^{10}$
Atomic radius (pm)	162	147	134	130	135	126	125	124	128	138
Ionization energies (eV/atom)										
First	6.54	6.82	6.74	6.77	7.44	7.87	7.86	7.64	7.73	9.39
Second	12.80	13.58	14.65	16.50	15.64	16.18	17.06	18.17	20.29	17.96
Third	24.76	27.49	29.31	30.96	33.67	30.65	33.50	35.17	36.83	39.72
Reduction potential† (V)	−2.08	−1.63	−1.2	−0.91	−1.18	−0.44	−0.28	−0.23	+0.34	−0.76
Common oxidation states	+3	+2,+3, +4	+2,+3, +4,+5	+2,+3, +6	+2,+3, +4,+7	+2,+3	+2,+3	+2	+1,+2	+2
Melting point (°C)	1397	1672	1710	1900	1244	1530	1495	1455	1083	419
Density (g/cm³)	2.99	4.49	5.96	7.20	7.43	7.86	8.9	8.90	8.92	7.14
Electrical conductivity‡	—	2	3	10	2	17	24	24	97	27

*Each atom has an argon inner-core configuration.
†For the reduction process $M^{2+} + 2e^- \rightarrow M$ (except for scandium, where the ion is Sc^{3+}).
‡Compared with an arbitrarily assigned value of 100 for silver.

In this chapter we will concentrate on the **first-row transition metals** (scandium through zinc) because they are representative of the other transition series and because they have great practical significance. Some important properties of these elements are summarized in Table 20.2 and are discussed below.

Electron Configurations

The electron configurations of the first-row transition metals were discussed in Section 7.11. The $3d$ orbitals begin to fill after the $4s$ orbital is complete, that is, after calcium ($[Ar]4s^2$). The first transition metal, *scandium,* has one electron in the $3d$ orbitals; the second, *titanium,* has two; and the third, *vanadium,* has three. We would expect *chromium,* the fourth transition metal, to have the electron configuration $[Ar]4s^23d^4$. However, the actual configuration is $[Ar]4s^13d^5$, which shows a half-filled $4s$ orbital and a half-filled set of $3d$ orbitals (one electron in each of the five $3d$ orbitals). It is tempting to say that the configuration results because half-filled "shells" are especially stable. Although there are some reasons to think that this explanation might be valid, it is an oversimplification. For instance, tungsten, which is in the same vertical group as chromium, has the configuration

(from left to right) Aqueous solutions containing the metal ions Co^{2+}, Mn^{2+}, Cr^{3+}, Fe^{3+}, and Ni^{2+}.

Chromium has the electron configuration $[Ar]4s^13d^5$.

A set of orbitals with the same energy is said to be degenerate.

$[Xe]6s^24f^{14}5d^4$, where half-filled s and d shells are not found. There are several similar cases.

Basically, the chromium configuration occurs because the energies of the $3d$ and $4s$ orbitals are very similar for the first-row transition elements. We saw in Section 7.11 that when electrons are placed in a set of degenerate orbitals, they first occupy each orbital singly to minimize electron repulsions. Since the $4s$ and $3d$ orbitals are virtually degenerate in the chromium atom, we would expect the configuration

$$4s \uparrow \qquad 3d \uparrow \uparrow \uparrow \uparrow \uparrow$$

rather than $\qquad 4s \uparrow\downarrow \qquad 3d \uparrow \uparrow \uparrow \uparrow \underline{}$

since the second arrangement has greater electron–electron repulsions and thus a higher energy.

The only other unexpected configuration among the first-row transition metals is that of copper, which is $[Ar]4s^13d^{10}$ rather than the expected $[Ar]4s^23d^9$.

Copper has the electron configuration $[Ar]4s^13d^{10}$.

In transition metal *ions*, the $3d$ orbitals are lower in energy than the $4s$ orbitals.

In contrast to the neutral transition metals, where the $3d$ and $4s$ orbitals have very similar energies, the *energy of the 3d orbitals in transition metal ions is significantly less than that of the 4s orbital*. This means that the electrons remaining after the ion is formed occupy the $3d$ orbitals, since they are lower in energy. *First-row transition metal ions do not have 4s electrons.* For example, manganese has the configuration $[Ar]4s^23d^5$, while that of Mn^{2+} is $[Ar]3d^5$. The neutral titanium atom has the configuration $[Ar]4s^23d^2$, while that of Ti^{3+} is $[Ar]3d^1$.

Oxidation States and Ionization Energies

The transition metals can form a variety of ions by losing one or more electrons. The common oxidation states of these elements are shown in Table 20.2. Note that for the first five metals the maximum possible oxidation state corresponds to the loss of all the $4s$ and $3d$ electrons. For example, the maximum oxidation state of chromium ($[Ar]4s^13d^5$) is $+6$. Toward the right end of the period, the maximum oxidation states are not observed; in fact, the $2+$ ions are the most common. The higher oxidation states are not seen for these metals because the $3d$ orbitals become lower in energy as the nuclear charge increases, and the electrons become increasingly difficult to remove. From Table 20.2 we see that ionization energy increases gradually going from left to right across the period. However, the third ionization energy (when an electron is removed from a $3d$ orbital) increases faster than the first ionization energy, clear evidence of the significant decrease in the energy of the $3d$ orbital going across the period (see Fig. 20.2).

Standard Reduction Potentials

When a metal acts as a *reducing agent,* the half-reaction is

$$M \rightarrow M^{n+} + ne^-$$

This is the reverse of the conventional listing for half-reactions in tables. Thus, to rank the transition metals in order of reducing ability, it is most convenient to reverse the reactions and the signs given in Table 20.2. The metal with the most positive potential is then the best reducing agent. The transition metals are listed in order of reducing ability in Table 20.3.

Table 20.3	
Relative Reducing Abilities of the First-Row Transition Metals in Aqueous Solution	
Reaction	Potential (V)
$Sc \rightarrow Sc^{3+} + 3e^-$	2.08
$Ti \rightarrow Ti^{2+} + 2e^-$	1.63
$V \rightarrow V^{2+} + 2e^-$	1.2
$Mn \rightarrow Mn^{2+} + 2e^-$	1.18
$Cr \rightarrow Cr^{2+} + 2e^-$	0.91
$Zn \rightarrow Zn^{2+} + 2e^-$	0.76
$Fe \rightarrow Fe^{2+} + 2e^-$	0.44
$Co \rightarrow Co^{2+} + 2e^-$	0.28
$Ni \rightarrow Ni^{2+} + 2e^-$	0.23
$Cu \rightarrow Cu^{2+} + 2e^-$	−0.34

Reducing ability ↑

Figure 20.2

Plots of the first (red dots) and third (blue dots) ionization energies for the first-row transition metals.

Since $\mathscr{E}°$ is zero for the process

$$2H^+ + 2e^- \rightarrow H_2$$

all the metals except copper can reduce H^+ ions to hydrogen gas in 1 *M* aqueous solutions of strong acid:

$$M(s) + 2H^+(aq) \rightarrow H_2(g) + M^{2+}(aq)$$

As Table 20.3 shows, the reducing abilities of the first-row transition metals generally decrease going from left to right across the period. Only chromium and zinc do not follow this trend.

The 4d and 5d Transition Series

In comparing the $3d$, $4d$, and $5d$ transition series, it is instructive to consider the atomic radii of these elements (Fig. 20.3). Note that there is a general, although not regular, decrease in size going from left to right for each of the series. Also note that although there is a significant increase in radius in going from the $3d$ to the $4d$

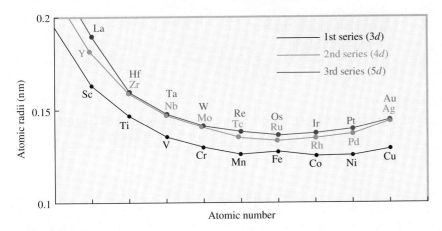

Figure 20.3

Atomic radii of the 3d, 4d, and 5d transition series.

◀ **C H E M I C A L   I M P A C T** ▶

Transition Metals in Action

Transition metals are important in many aspects. The following three applications show the varied nature of the contributions transition metals make to everyday life and research. (See also the Chemical Impact on cancer therapy in Section 20.4.)

Nitinol is a nickel–titanium alloy that "remembers" a preset shape after it has been deformed; it can be made to return to its original shape by heating. This property of nitinol is being exploited to repair arteries that are partially blocked by plaque or that have weaknesses in their walls.

A nitinol wire is first coiled around a pipe whose outside diameter is identical to the inside diameter of the artery to be repaired. The coil of wire is then heated until its original straw color turns to a deep blue. This sets the "memory" of the alloy for the coiled structure. The wire is subsequently cooled and straightened so that it can be fed into the artery through a catheter (a thin tube) containing a cool saline solution.

When the wire is in place, the body heat causes it to return to its original coiled shape, pushing apart the restricted area in a partially blocked artery or acting as reinforcement for an artery with a weak, bulging wall. Within a few weeks the wire coils are completely incorporated into the arterial walls.

Although overshadowed by gold for making jewelry, platinum has great industrial value. In fact, it is used in the production of perhaps one out of five products in modern society (see Fig. 20.4). Approximately 75 tons of platinum are produced annually, the major portion from the Republic of South Africa. Platinum catalysts are used in the manufacture of nitric acid (see Section 19.2), but the largest single use of the metal is for the platinum-coated ceramic honeycomb catalyst used in automobile exhaust systems to help convert unburned fuel and carbon monoxide to carbon dioxide and water. Also, many airliners use platinum catalysts to convert the harmful ozone found at high altitudes to oxygen.

Because of its durability, malleability, resistance to corrosion, and stability at high temperatures (mp = 1769°C), platinum has many other uses, including jewelry, dies for the manufacture of glass strands for fiberglass, thin protective coatings (100 atoms in thickness) for razor blades, and electrodes in body implant devices such as heart pacemakers. Also, the kilogram is defined by a cylinder of platinum–iridium alloy stored in a special vault in Paris.

Why did the dinosaurs suddenly disappear from the earth about 65 million years ago? Although many hypotheses have been suggested, none has seemed very convincing until recently. Geologists examining core samples containing material that was on the earth's surface when the dinosaurs lived have found an unusually high concentration of iridium. Since this metal is often found in relatively high concentrations in extraterrestrial bodies such as meteorites and comets, it has been suggested that one of these objects may have collided with the earth about 65 million years ago, upsetting the earth's atmosphere and leading to the extinction of many species.

Subsequently, the ratios of niobium isotopes in the same core samples were investigated and found to be much more characteristic of extraterrestrial bodies than of the normal distribution on earth. These niobium studies thus support the iridium data and lend further credence to this hypothesis for the extinction of the vast number of dinosaurs.

United States demand for platinum (1981)
873,000 troy ounces

- 51.2% Automotive industry
- 12.9% Electrical
- 10.1% Petroleum refining
- 8.9% Chemicals
- 3.3% Ceramics, glass
- 3.2% Jewelry, arts
- 2.2% Dentistry
- 8.2% Other

Figure 20.4

Uses of platinum in the U.S. (From *National Geographic* **164**(5) (1983): 686. Reprinted by courtesy of National Geographic Magazine.)

metals, the $4d$ and $5d$ metals are remarkably similar in size. This latter phenomenon is the result of the **lanthanide contraction.** In the **lanthanide series,** consisting of the elements between lanthanum and hafnium (see Fig. 20.1), electrons are filling the $4f$ orbitals. Since the $4f$ orbitals are buried in the interior of these atoms, the additional electrons do not add to the atomic size. In fact, the increasing nuclear charge (remember that a proton is added to the nucleus for each electron) causes the radii of the lanthanide elements to decrease significantly going from left to right. This lanthanide contraction just offsets the normal increase in size due to going from one principal quantum level to another. Thus the $5d$ elements, instead of being significantly larger than the $4d$ elements, are almost identical to them in size. This leads to a great similarity in the chemistry of the $4d$ and $5d$ elements in a given vertical group. For example, the chemical properties of hafnium and zirconium are remarkably similar, and they always occur together in nature. Their separation, which is probably more difficult than the separation of any other pair of elements, often requires fractional distillation of their compounds.

In general, the differences between the $4d$ and $5d$ elements in a group increase gradually going from left to right. For example, niobium and tantalum are also quite similar, but less so than zirconium and hafnium.

Although generally less well-known than the $3d$ elements, the $4d$ and $5d$ transition metals have certain very useful properties. For example, zirconium and zirconium oxide (ZrO_2) have great resistance to high temperatures and are used, along with niobium and molybdenum alloys, for space vehicle parts that are exposed to high temperatures during reentry into the earth's atmosphere. Niobium and molybdenum are also important alloying materials for certain types of steel. Tantalum, which has a high resistance to attack by body fluids, is often used for replacement of bones. The *platinum group metals*—ruthenium, osmium, rhodium, iridium, palladium, and platinum—are all quite similar and are widely used as catalysts for many types of industrial processes.

Niobium was originally called columbium and is still occasionally referred to by that name.

20.2 *The First-Row Transition Metals*

Purpose

- To discuss some chemistry of the $3d$ transition metals.

We have seen that the transition metals are similar in many ways but also show important differences. We will now explore some of the specific properties of each of the $3d$ transition metals.

Scandium is a rare element that exists in compounds mainly in the $+3$ oxidation state, for example, in $ScCl_3$, Sc_2O_3, and $Sc_2(SO_4)_3$. The chemistry of scandium strongly resembles that of the lanthanides, with most of its compounds being colorless and diamagnetic. This is not surprising; as we will see in Section 20.6, the color and magnetism of transition metal compounds usually arise from the d electrons on

A hip joint constructed from tantalum metal.

the metal ion, and Sc^{3+} has no d electrons. Scandium metal, which can be prepared by electrolysis of molten $ScCl_3$, is not widely used because of its rarity, but it is found in some electronic devices, such as high-intensity lamps.

Titanium is widely distributed in the earth's crust (0.6% by mass). Because of its relatively low density and high strength, titanium is an excellent structural material, especially in jet engines, where light weight and stability at high temperatures are required. Nearly 5000 kg of titanium alloys are used in each engine of a Boeing 747 jetliner. In addition, the resistance of titanium to chemical attack makes it a useful material for pipes, pumps, and reaction vessels in the chemical industry.

The most familiar compound of titanium is no doubt responsible for the white color of this paper. Titanium dioxide, or more correctly, *titanium(IV) oxide* (TiO_2), is a highly opaque substance used as the white pigment in paper, paint, linoleum, plastics, synthetic fibers, whitewall tires, and cosmetics (sunscreens, for example). Approximately 700,000 tons are used annually in these and other products. Titanium(IV) oxide is widely dispersed in nature, but the main ores are rutile (impure TiO_2) and ilmenite ($FeTiO_3$). Rutile is processed by treatment with chlorine to form volatile $TiCl_4$, which is separated from the impurities and burned to form TiO_2:

$$TiCl_4(g) + O_2(g) \rightarrow TiO_2(s) + 2Cl_2(g)$$

Ilmenite is treated with sulfuric acid to form a soluble sulfate:

$$FeTiO_3(s) + 2H_2SO_4(aq) \rightarrow Fe^{2+}(aq) + TiO^{2+}(aq) + 2SO_4^{2-}(aq) + 2H_2O(l)$$

When this aqueous mixture is allowed to stand, under vacuum, solid $FeSO_4 \cdot 7H_2O$ forms first and is removed. The mixture is then heated, and the insoluble titanium(IV) oxide hydrate ($TiO_2 \cdot H_2O$) forms. The water of hydration is driven off by heating to form pure TiO_2:

$$TiO_2 \cdot H_2O(s) \xrightarrow{\text{Heat}} TiO_2(s) + H_2O(g)$$

In its compounds, titanium is most often found in the +4 oxidation state. Examples are TiO_2 and $TiCl_4$, the latter a colorless liquid (bp = 137°C) that fumes in moist air to produce TiO_2:

$$TiCl_4(l) + 2H_2O(l) \rightarrow TiO_2(s) + 4HCl(g)$$

Ti(H$_2$O)$_6^{3+}$ is purple in solution.

Titanium(III) compounds can be produced by reduction of the +4 state. In aqueous solution, Ti^{3+} exists as the purple $Ti(H_2O)_6^{3+}$ ion, which is slowly oxidized to titanium(IV) by air. Titanium(II) is not stable in aqueous solution but does exist in the solid state in compounds such as TiO and the dihalides of general formula TiX_2.

Vanadium is widely spread throughout the earth's crust (0.02% by mass). It is used mostly in alloys with other metals such as iron (80% of vanadium is used in steel) and titanium. Vanadium(V) oxide (V_2O_5) is used as an industrial catalyst in the production of materials such as sulfuric acid.

The manufacture of sulfuric acid was discussed at the end of Chapter 3.

The most common oxidation state for vanadium is +5.

Pure vanadium can be obtained from the electrolytic reduction of fused salts, such as VCl_2, to produce a metal similar to titanium that is steel-gray, hard, and corrosion resistant. Often the pure element is not required for alloying. For example, *ferrovanadium,* produced by the reduction of a mixture of V_2O_5 and Fe_2O_3 with aluminum, is added to iron to form *vanadium steel,* a hard steel used for engine parts and axles.

◀ CHEMICAL IMPACT ▶

Titanium Makes Great Bicycles

A titanium bicycle.

One of the most interesting characteristics of the world of bicycling is the competition among various frame materials. Bicycle frames are now built from steel, aluminum, carbon fiber composites, and titanium, with each material having advantages and disadvantages. Steel is strong, economical, adaptable, and (unfortunately) "rustable." Aluminum is light and stiff but has relatively low fatigue limits (resistance to repeated stresses). Carbon fiber composites have amazing strength-to-mass ratios and have shock- and vibration-dampening properties superior to any metal; however, they are very expensive. Titanium has a density approximately 43% less than that of steel, a yield strength (when alloyed with metals such as aluminum and tin) that is 30% greater than that of steel, an extraordinary resistance to fatigue, and a high resistance to corrosion, but it is expensive and difficult to work.

Of all these materials, titanium gives the bicycle that fanatics seem to love the most. After their first ride on a bicycle with a titanium frame, most experienced cyclists find themselves shaking their heads and searching hard for the right words to describe the experience. Typically, the word *magic* is used a great deal in the ensuing description.

The magic of titanium results from its combination of toughness, stretchability, and resilience. A bicycle that is built stiff to resist pedaling loads usually responds by giving a harsh, uncomfortable ride. A titanium bike is very stiff against high pedaling torques, but it seems to transmit much less road shock than bikes made of competitive materials. Why titanium excels in dampening vibrations is not entirely clear. Despite titanium's significantly lower density than steel's, shock waves travel more slowly in titanium than in steel. Whatever the explanation for its shock-absorbing abilities, titanium provides three things that cyclists find crucial: light weight, stiffness, and a smooth ride—magic.

Titanium is quite abundant in the earth's crust, ranking ninth of all the elements and second among the transition elements. The metallurgy of titanium presents special challenges. Carbon, the reducing agent most commonly used to obtain metals from their oxides ores, cannot be used because it forms intractable interstitial carbides with titanium. These carbides are extraordinarily hard and have melting points close to 3000°C. However, if chlorine gas is used in conjunction with carbon to treat the ore, volatile $TiCl_4$ is formed, which can be distilled off and then reduced with magnesium or sodium at approximately 1000°C to form a titanium "sponge." This sponge is then ground up, cleaned with aqua regia (a 1:3 mixture of concentrated HNO_3 and concentrated HCl), melted under a blanket of inert gas (to prevent reaction with oxygen), and cast into ingots. Titanium, a lustrous, silvery metal with a high melting point (1667°C), crystallizes in a hexagonal closest packed structure. Because titanium tends to become quite brittle when trace impurities such as C, N, and O are present, it must be fabricated with great care.

Titanium's unusual ability to stretch makes it hard to machine. It tends to push away even from a very sharp cutting blade, giving a rather unpredictable final dimension. Also, because titanium is embrittled by reaction with oxygen, all welding operations must be carried out under a shielding gas such as argon.

However, the bicycle that results is worth all these difficulties. One woman described a titanium bicycle as "the one God rides on Sunday."

The principal oxidation state of vanadium is +5, found in compounds such as the orange V_2O_5 (mp = 650°C) and the colorless VF_5 (mp = 19.5°C). The oxidation states from +5 to +2 all exist in aqueous solution (see Table 20.4). The higher oxidation states, +5 and +4, do not exist as hydrated ions of the type $V^{n+}(aq)$ because the highly charged ion causes the attached water molecules to be very acidic. The H^+ ions are lost to give the oxycations VO_2^+ and VO^{2+}. The hydrated V^{3+} and V^{2+} ions are easily oxidized and thus can function as reducing agents in aqueous solution.

Although *chromium* is relatively rare, it is a very important industrial material. The chief ore of chromium is chromite ($FeCr_2O_4$), which can be reduced by carbon to give *ferrochrome*,

$$FeCr_2O_4(s) + 4C(s) \rightarrow \underbrace{Fe(s) + 2Cr(s)}_{\text{Ferrochrome}} + 4CO(g)$$

which can be added directly to iron in the steelmaking process. Chromium metal, which is often used to plate steel, is hard and brittle and maintains a bright surface by developing a tough invisible oxide coating.

Chromium commonly forms compounds in which it has the oxidation state +2, +3, or +6, as shown in Table 20.5. The Cr^{2+} (chromous) ion is a powerful reducing agent in aqueous solution. In fact, traces of O_2 in other gases can be removed by bubbling through a Cr^{2+} solution:

$$4Cr^{2+}(aq) + O_2(g) + 4H^+(aq) \rightarrow 4Cr^{3+}(aq) + 2H_2O(l)$$

The chromium(VI) species are excellent oxidizing agents, especially in acidic solution, where chromium(VI) as the dichromate ion ($Cr_2O_7^{2-}$) is reduced to the Cr^{3+} ion:

$$Cr_2O_7^{2-}(aq) + 14H^+(aq) + 6e^- \rightarrow 2Cr^{3+}(aq) + 7H_2O(l) \qquad \mathscr{E}° = 1.33 \text{ V}$$

The oxidizing ability of the dichromate ion is strongly pH-dependent, increasing as $[H^+]$ increases, as predicted by Le Châtelier's principle. In basic solution, chromium(VI) exists as the chromate ion, a much less powerful oxidizing agent:

$$CrO_4^{2-}(aq) + 4H_2O(l) + 3e^- \rightarrow Cr(OH)_3(s) + 5OH^-(aq) \qquad \mathscr{E}° = -0.13 \text{ V}$$

The structures of the $Cr_2O_7^{2-}$ and CrO_4^{2-} ions are shown in Fig. 20.5.

Red chromium(VI) oxide (CrO_3) dissolves in water to give a strongly acidic, red-orange solution:

$$2CrO_3(s) + H_2O(l) \rightarrow 2H^+(aq) + Cr_2O_7^{2-}(aq)$$

It is possible to precipitate bright orange dichromate salts, such as $K_2Cr_2O_7$, from these solutions. When made basic, the solution turns yellow, and chromate salts such as Na_2CrO_4 can be obtained. A mixture of chromium(VI) oxide and concentrated sulfuric acid, commonly called **cleaning solution,** is a powerful oxidizing

Table 20.4

Oxidation States and Species for Vanadium in Aqueous Solution

Oxidation State of Vanadium	Species in Aqueous Solution
+5	VO_2^+ (yellow)
+4	VO^{2+} (blue)
+3	$V^{3+}(aq)$ (blue-green)
+2	$V^{2+}(aq)$ (violet)

Table 20.5

Typical Chromium Compounds

Oxidation State of Chromium	Examples of Compounds (X = halogen)
+2	CrX_2
+3	CrX_3
	Cr_2O_3 (green)
	$Cr(OH)_3$ (blue-green)
+6	$K_2Cr_2O_7$ (orange)
	Na_2CrO_4 (yellow)
	CrO_3 (red)

Figure 20.5

The structures of the chromium(VI) anions: (a) $Cr_2O_7^{2-}$, which exists in acidic solution; and (b) CrO_4^{2-}, which exists in basic solution.

medium that can remove organic materials from analytical glassware, yielding a very clean surface.

Manganese is relatively abundant (0.1% of the earth's crust), although no significant sources are found in the United States. The most common use of manganese is in the production of an especially hard steel used for rock crushers, bank vaults, and armor plate. One interesting source of manganese is from *manganese nodules* found on the ocean floor. These roughly spherical "rocks" contain mixtures of manganese and iron oxides as well as smaller amounts of other metals such as cobalt, nickel, and copper. Apparently the nodules were formed at least partly by the action of marine organisms. Because of the abundance of these nodules, there is much interest in developing economical methods for their recovery and processing.

Manganese can exist in all oxidation states from +2 to +7, although +2 and +7 are the most common. Manganese(II) forms an extensive series of salts with all the common anions. In aqueous solution Mn^{2+} forms $Mn(H_2O)_6^{2+}$, which has a light pink color. Manganese(VII) is found in the intensely purple permanganate ion (MnO_4^-). Widely used as an analytical reagent in acidic solution, the MnO_4^- ion behaves as a strong oxidizing agent, and the manganese becomes Mn^{2+}:

$$MnO_4^-(aq) + 8H^+(aq) + 5e^- \rightarrow Mn^{2+}(aq) + 4H_2O(l) \qquad \mathscr{E}° = 1.51 \text{ V}$$

Several typical compounds of manganese are shown in Table 20.6.

Iron is the most abundant heavy metal (4.7% of the earth's crust) and the most important to our civilization. It is a white, lustrous, not particularly hard metal that is very reactive toward oxidizing agents. For example, in moist air it is rapidly oxidized by oxygen to form rust, a mixture of iron oxides.

The chemistry of iron mainly involves its +2 and +3 oxidation states. Typical compounds are shown in Table 20.7. In aqueous solutions iron(II) salts are generally light green because of the presence of $Fe(H_2O)_6^{2+}$. Although the $Fe(H_2O)_6^{3+}$ ion is colorless, aqueous solutions of iron(III) salts are usually yellow to brown in color due to the presence of $Fe(OH)(H_2O)_5^{2+}$, which results from the acidity of $Fe(H_2O)_6^{3+}$ ($K_a = 6 \times 10^{-3}$):

$$Fe(H_2O)_6^{3+}(aq) \rightleftharpoons Fe(OH)(H_2O)_5^{2+}(aq) + H^+(aq)$$

Although *cobalt* is relatively rare, it is found in ores such as smaltite ($CoAs_2$) and cobaltite (CoAsS) in large enough concentrations to make its production economically feasible. Cobalt is a hard, bluish white metal mainly used in alloys such as stainless steel and stellite, an alloy of iron, copper, and tungsten that is used in surgical instruments.

The chemistry of cobalt involves mainly its +2 and +3 oxidation states, although compounds containing cobalt in the 0, +1, or +4 oxidation state are known. Aqueous solutions of cobalt(II) salts contain the $Co(H_2O)_6^{2+}$ ion, which has a characteristic rose color. Cobalt forms a wide variety of coordination compounds, many of which will be discussed in later sections of this chapter. Some typical cobalt compounds are shown in Table 20.8.

Nickel, which ranks twenty-fourth in elemental abundance in the earth's crust, is found in ores, where it is combined mainly with arsenic, antimony, and sulfur. Nickel metal, a silvery white substance with high electrical and thermal conductivities, is quite resistant to corrosion and is often used for plating more active metals. Nickel is also widely used in the production of alloys such as steel.

Nickel in compounds is almost exclusively in the +2 oxidation state. Aqueous solutions of nickel(II) salts contain the $Ni(H_2O)_6^{2+}$ ion, which has a characteristic

Table 20.6

Some Compounds of Manganese in Its Most Common Oxidation States	
Oxidation State of Manganese	Examples of Compounds
+2	$Mn(OH)_2$ (pink) MnS (salmon) $MnSO_4$ (reddish) $MnCl_2$ (pink)
+4	MnO_2 (dark brown)
+7	$KMnO_4$ (purple)

Table 20.7

Typical Compounds of Iron	
Oxidation State of Iron	Examples of Compounds
+2	FeO (black) FeS (brownish black) $FeSO_4 \cdot 7H_2O$ (green) $K_4Fe(CN)_6$ (yellow)
+3	$FeCl_3$ (brownish black) Fe_2O_3 (reddish brown) $K_3Fe(CN)_6$ (red) $Fe(SCN)_3$ (red)
+2, +3 (mixture)	Fe_3O_4 (black) $KFe[Fe(CN)_6]$ (deep blue, "Prussian blue")

Table 20.8	
Typical Compounds of Cobalt	
Oxidation State	Examples of Compounds
+2	$CoSO_4$ (dark blue)
	$[Co(H_2O)_6]Cl_2$ (pink)
	$[Co(H_2O)_6](NO_3)_2$ (red)
	CoS (black)
	CoO (greenish brown)
+3	CoF_3 (brown)
	Co_2O_3 (charcoal)
	$K_3[Co(CN)_6]$ (yellow)
	$[Co(NH_3)_6]Cl_3$ (yellow)

Table 20.9	
Typical Compounds of Nickel	
Oxidation State of Nickel	Examples of Compounds
+2	$NiCl_2$ (yellow)
	$[Ni(H_2O)_6]Cl_2$ (green)
	NiO (greenish black)
	NiS (black)
	$[Ni(H_2O)_6]SO_4$ (green)
	$[Ni(NH_3)_6](NO_3)_2$ (blue)

emerald green color. Coordination compounds of nickel(II) will be discussed later in this chapter. Some typical nickel compounds are shown in Table 20.9.

Copper, widely distributed in nature in ores containing sulfides, arsenides, chlorides, and carbonates, is valued for its high electrical conductivity and its resistance to corrosion. It is widely used for plumbing, and 50% of all copper produced annually is used for electrical applications. Copper is a major constituent in several well-known alloys (see Table 20.10).

Although copper is not highly reactive (it will not reduce H^+ to H_2, for example), the reddish metal does slowly corrode in air, producing the characteristic green *patina* consisting of basic copper sulfate

$$3Cu(s) + 2H_2O(l) + SO_2(g) + 2O_2(g) \rightarrow Cu_3(OH)_4SO_4$$

Basic copper sulfate

and other similar compounds.

The chemistry of copper principally involves the +2 oxidation state, but many compounds containing copper(I) are also known. Aqueous solutions of copper(II) salts are a characteristic bright blue color due to the presence of the $Cu(H_2O)_6^{2+}$ ion. Table 20.11 lists some typical copper compounds.

Copper roofs and bronze statues, such as the Statue of Liberty (see Chemical Impact in Section 17.6), turn green in air because $Cu_3(OH)_4SO_4$ and $Cu_4(OH)_6SO_4$ form.

Table 20.11	
Typical Compounds of Copper	
Oxidation State of Copper	Examples of Compounds
+1	Cu_2O (red)
	Cu_2S (black)
	$CuCl$ (white)
+2	CuO (black)
	$CuSO_4 \cdot 5H_2O$ (blue)
	$CuCl_2 \cdot 2H_2O$ (green)
	$[Cu(H_2O)_6](NO_3)_2$ (blue)

Table 20.10	
Alloys Containing Copper	
Alloy	Composition (% by Mass in Parentheses)
Brass	Cu (20–97), Zn (2–80), Sn (0–14), Pb (0–12), Mn (0–25)
Bronze	Cu (50–98), Sn (0–35), Zn (0–29), Pb (0–50), P (0–3)
Sterling silver	Cu (7.5), Ag (92.5)
Gold (18-karat)	Cu (5–15), Au (75), Ag (10–20)
Gold (14-karat)	Cu (12–28), Au (58), Ag (4–30)

Although trace amounts of copper are essential for life, copper in large amounts is quite toxic; copper salts are used to kill bacteria, fungi, and algae. For example, paints containing copper are used on ship hulls to prevent fouling by marine organisms.

Widely dispersed in the earth's crust, *zinc* is mainly refined from sphalerite (ZnS), which often occurs with galena (PbS). Zinc is a white, lustrous, very active metal that behaves as an excellent reducing agent and tarnishes rapidly. About 90% of the zinc produced is used for galvanizing steel. Zinc forms colorless salts in which it is in the $+2$ oxidation state.

20.3 Coordination Compounds

Purpose

- To define terms used in coordination chemistry.
- To discuss some common chelates.
- To give rules for naming coordination compounds.

Transition metal ions characteristically form coordination compounds, which are usually colored and often paramagnetic. A **coordination compound** typically consists of a *complex ion,* a transition metal ion with its attached ligands (see Section 15.8), and **counter ions,** anions or cations as needed to produce a compound with no net charge. The substance $[Co(NH_3)_5Cl]Cl_2$ is a typical coordination compound. The brackets indicate the composition of the complex ion, in this case $Co(NH_3)_5Cl^{2+}$, and the two Cl^- counter ions are shown outside the brackets. Note that in this compound one Cl^- acts as a ligand along with the five NH_3 molecules. In the solid state this compound consists of the large $Co(NH_3)_5Cl^{2+}$ cations and twice as many Cl^- anions, all packed together as efficiently as possible. When dissolved in water, the solid behaves like any ionic solid; the cations and anions are assumed to separate and move about independently:

$$[Co(NH_3)_5Cl]Cl_2(s) \xrightarrow{\text{H}_2\text{O}} Co(NH_3)_5Cl^{2+}(aq) + 2Cl^-(aq)$$

Coordination compounds have been known since about 1700, but their true nature was not understood until the 1890s when a young Swiss chemist named Alfred Werner (1866–1919) proposed that transition metal ions have two types of valence (combining ability). One type of valence, which Werner called the *secondary valence,* refers to the ability of a metal ion to bind to Lewis bases (ligands) to form complex ions. The other type, the *primary valence,* refers to the ability of the metal ion to form ionic bonds with oppositely charged ions. Thus Werner explained that the compound, originally written as $CoCl_3 \cdot 5NH_3$, was really $[Co(NH_3)_5Cl]Cl_2$, where the Co^{3+} ion has a primary valence of 3, satisfied by the three Cl^- ions, and a secondary valence of 6, satisfied by the six ligands (five NH_3 and one Cl^-). We now call the primary valence the **oxidation state** and the secondary valence the **coordination number,** which reflects the number of bonds formed between the metal ion and the ligands in the complex ion.

Coordination Number

The number of bonds formed by metal ions to ligands in complex ions varies from two to eight depending on the size, charge, and electron configuration of the transi-

Table 20.12

Typical Coordination Numbers for Some Common Metal Ions

M^+	Coordination Numbers	M^{2+}	Coordination Numbers	M^{3+}	Coordination Numbers
Cu^+	2, 4	Mn^{2+}	4, 6	Sc^{3+}	6
Ag^+	2	Fe^{2+}	6	Cr^{3+}	6
Au^+	2, 4	Co^{2+}	4, 6	Co^{3+}	6
		Ni^{2+}	4, 6		
		Cu^{2+}	4, 6	Au^{3+}	4
		Zn^{2+}	4, 6		

Coordination number	Geometry
2	Linear
4	Tetrahedral Square planar
6	Octahedral

Figure 20.6

The ligand arrangements for coordination numbers 2, 4, and 6.

tion metal ion. As shown in Table 20.12, 6 is the most common coordination number, followed closely by 4, with a few metal ions showing a coordination number of 2. Many metal ions show more than one coordination number, and there is really no simple way to predict what the coordination number will be in a particular case. The typical geometries for the various common coordination numbers are shown in Fig. 20.6. Note that six ligands produce an octahedral arrangement around the metal ion. Four ligands can form either a tetrahedral or a square planar arrangement, and two ligands give a linear structure.

Ligands

A **ligand** is a *neutral molecule or ion having a lone electron pair that can be used to form a bond to a metal ion.* The formation of a metal–ligand bond therefore can be described as the interaction between a Lewis base (the ligand) and a Lewis acid (the metal ion). The resulting bond is often called a **coordinate covalent bond.**

A *ligand that can form one bond to a metal ion* is called a **monodentate ligand,** or a **unidentate ligand** (from root words meaning "one tooth"). Examples of unidentate ligands are shown in Table 20.13.

Some ligands have more than one atom with a lone electron pair that can be used to bond to a metal ion. Such ligands are said to be **chelating ligands,** or **chelates** (from the Greek word *chele* for "claw"). A ligand that can form two bonds to a metal ion is called a **bidentate ligand.** A very common bidentate ligand is ethylenediamine (abbreviated en), which is shown coordinating to a metal ion in Fig. 20.7(a). Note the relationship between this ligand and the unidentate ligand ammonia [Fig. 20.7(b)]. Oxalate, another typical bidentate ligand, is shown in Table 20.13.

Ligands that can form more than two bonds to a metal ion are called **polydentate ligands.** Some ligands can form as many as six bonds to a metal ion. The best known example is ethylenediaminetetraacetate (abbreviated EDTA), which is shown in Table 20.13. This ligand virtually surrounds the metal ion (Fig. 20.8), coordinating through six atoms (a **hexadentate ligand**). As might be expected from the large number of coordination sites, EDTA forms very stable complex ions with most metal ions and is used as a "scavenger" to remove toxic heavy metals such as lead from the human body. It is also used as a reagent to analyze solutions for the metal ion content. EDTA is found in countless consumer products, such as soda, beer, salad dressings, bar soaps, and most cleaners. In these products EDTA ties up trace metal ions that would otherwise catalyze decomposition and produce unwanted precipitates.

Table 20.13

	Some Common Ligands	
Type	Examples	
Unidentate/monodentate	H_2O CN^- SCN^- (thiocyanate) X^- (halides) NH_3 NO_2^- (nitrite) OH^-	
Bidentate	Oxalate Ethylenediamine (en)	
Polydentate	Diethylenetriamine (dien) $H_2N-(CH_2)_2-NH-(CH_2)_2-NH_2$ Three coordinating atoms Ethylenediaminetetraacetate (EDTA) Six coordinating atoms	

(a)

(b)

Figure 20.7

(a) The bidentate ligand ethylenediamine can bond to the metal ion through the lone pair on each nitrogen atom, thus forming two coordinate covalent bonds. (b) Ammonia is a monodentate ligand.

Figure 20.8

The coordination of EDTA with a 2+ metal ion.

Some even more complicated ligands are found in biologic systems, where metal ions play crucial roles in catalyzing reactions, transferring electrons, and transporting and storing oxygen. A discussion of these complex ligands will follow in Section 20.8.

Nomenclature

In Werner's lifetime, no system was used to name coordination compounds. Names of the compounds were commonly based on colors and names of discoverers. As the field expanded and more coordination compounds were identified, an orderly system of nomenclature became necessary. A simplified version of this system is summarized by the following rules.

Rules for Naming Coordination Compounds

- As with any ionic compound, *the cation is named before the anion*.
- In naming a complex ion, *the ligands are named before the metal ion*.
- In naming ligands, *an o is added to the root name of an anion*. For example, the halides as ligands are called *fluoro, chloro, bromo,* and *iodo;* hydroxide is

◀ **C H E M I C A L   I M P A C T** ▶

Alfred Werner: Coordination Chemist

During the early and middle parts of the nineteenth century, chemists prepared a large number of colored compounds containing transition metals and other substances such as ammonia, chloride ion, cyanide ion, and water. These compounds were very interesting to chemists who were trying to understand the nature of bonding (Dalton's atomic theory of 1808 was very new at this time), and many theories were suggested to explain these substances. The most widely accepted early theory was the *chain theory,* championed by Sophus Mads Jorgensen (1837–1914), professor of chemistry at the University of Copenhagen. The chain theory got its name from the postulate that metal ammine* complexes contain chains of NH_3 molecules. For example, Jorgensen proposed the structure

$$Co \underset{NH_3—Cl}{\overset{NH_3—Cl}{—NH_3—NH_3—NH_3—NH_3—Cl}}$$

*Ammine is the name for NH_3 as a ligand.

for the compound $Co(NH_3)_6Cl_3$. In the late nineteenth century this theory was used in classrooms around the world to explain the nature of metal–ammine compounds.

However, in 1890 a young Swiss chemist named Alfred Werner, who had just obtained a Ph.D. in the field of organic chemistry, became so interested in these compounds that he apparently even dreamed about them. In the middle of one night Werner awoke realizing that he had the correct explanation for the constitution of these compounds. Writing furiously the rest of that night and into the late afternoon of the following day, he constructed a scientific paper containing his now famous *coordination theory.* This model postulates an octahedral arrangement of ligands around the Co^{3+} ion, producing the $Co(NH_3)_6^{3+}$ complex ion with three Cl^- ions as counter ions. Thus Werner's picture of $Co(NH_3)_6Cl_3$ varied greatly from the chain theory.

In his paper on the coordination theory, Werner explained not only the metal–ammine compounds but most of the other known transition metal compounds, and

the importance of his contribution was recognized immediately. He was appointed professor at the University of Zurich, where he spent the rest of his life studying coordination compounds and refining his theory. Alfred Werner was a confident, impulsive man of seemingly boundless energy, who was known for his inspiring lectures, his intolerance of incompetence (he once threw a chair at a student who performed poorly on an oral exam), and his intuitive scientific brilliance. For example, he was the first to show that stereochemistry is a general phenomenon, not one exhibited only by carbon, as was previously thought. He also recognized and named many types of isomerism.

In 1913, for his work on coordination chemistry and stereochemistry, Werner became the fourteenth Nobel Prize winner in chemistry and the first Swiss chemist to be so honored. Werner's work is even more remarkable when one realizes that his ideas preceded by many years any real understanding of the nature of covalent bonds.

hydroxo; cyanide is *cyano;* etc. *For a neutral ligand the name of the molecule is used,* with the exception of H_2O, NH_3, CO, and NO, as illustrated in Table 20.14.

- *The prefixes mono-, di-, tri-, tetra-, penta-, and hexa- are used to denote the number of simple ligands.* The prefixes *bis-, tris-, tetrakis-,* etc., are also used, especially for more complicated ligands or ones that already contain *di-, tri-,* etc.

- *The oxidation state of the central metal ion is designated by a Roman numeral in parentheses.*

- *When more than one type of ligand is present, they are named alphabetically.** Prefixes do not affect the order.

- *If the complex ion has a negative charge, the suffix -ate is added to the name of the metal.* Sometimes the Latin name is used to identify the metal (see Table 20.15).

The application of these rules is shown in Sample Exercise 20.1.

*In an older system the negatively charged ligands were named first, then neutral ligands, with positively charged ligands named last. We will follow the newer convention in this text.

Table 20.14

Names of Some Common Unidentate Ligands

Neutral Molecules	
Aqua	H_2O
Ammine	NH_3
Methylamine	CH_3NH_2
Carbonyl	CO
Nitrosyl	NO
Anions	
Fluoro	F^-
Chloro	Cl^-
Bromo	Br^-
Iodo	I^-
Hydroxo	OH^-
Cyano	CN^-

Table 20.15

Latin Names Used for Some Metal Ions in Anionic Complex Ions

Metal	Name in an Anionic Complex
Iron	Ferrate
Copper	Cuprate
Lead	Plumbate
Silver	Argentate
Gold	Aurate
Tin	Stannate

Sample Exercise 20.1

Give the systematic name for each of the following coordination compounds.

a. $[Co(NH_3)_5Cl]Cl_2$ **b.** $K_3Fe(CN)_6$ **c.** $[Fe(en)_2(NO_2)_2]_2SO_4$

Solution

a. To determine the oxidation state of the metal ion, we examine the charges of all ligands and counter ions. The ammonia molecules are neutral and the chloride ions each have a $1-$ charge, so the cobalt ion must have a $3+$ charge to produce a neutral compound. Thus cobalt has the oxidation state $+3$, and we use cobalt(III) in the name.

   The ligands include one Cl^- ion and five NH_3 molecules. The chloride ion is designated as *chloro,* and each ammonia molecule is designated *ammine.* The prefix *penta-* indicates that there are five NH_3 ligands present. The name of the complex cation is therefore pentaamminechlorocobalt(III). Note that the ligands are named alphabetically, disregarding the prefix. Since the counter ions are chloride ions, the compound is named as a chloride salt:

$$\underbrace{\text{Pentaamminechlorocobalt(III)}}_{\text{Cation}}\ \underbrace{\text{chloride}}_{\text{Anion}}$$

b. First, we determine the oxidation state of the iron by considering the other charged species. The compound contains three K^+ ions and six CN^- ions. Therefore the iron must carry a charge of $3+$, giving a total of six positive charges to balance the six negative charges. The complex ion present is thus $Fe(CN)_6^{3-}$. The cyanide ligands are each designated *cyano,* and the prefix *hexa-* indicates that six are present. Since the complex ion is an anion, we use the Latin name *ferrate.* The oxidation state is indicated by (III) at the end of the name. The

(top) An aqueous solution of $[Co(NH_3)_5Cl]Cl_2$. *(bottom)* Solid $K_3Fe(CN)_6$.

anion name is therefore hexacyanoferrate(III). The cations are K^+ ions, which are simply named potassium. Putting this together gives the name

$$\underbrace{\text{Potassium}}_{\text{Cation}} \underbrace{\text{hexacyanoferrate(III)}}_{\text{Anion}}$$

(The common name of this compound is potassium ferricyanide.)

c. We first determine the oxidation state of the iron by looking at the other charged species: four NO_2^- ions and one SO_4^{2-} ion. The ethylenediamine is neutral. Thus the two iron ions must carry a total positive charge of six to balance the six negative charges. This means that each iron has a $+3$ oxidation state and is designated as iron(III).

Since the name ethylenediamine already contains *di*, we use *bis-* instead of *di-* to indicate the two en ligands. The name for NO_2^- as a ligand is *nitro*, and the prefix *di-* indicates the presence of two NO_2^- ligands. Since the anion is sulfate, the compound's name is

$$\underbrace{\text{Bis(ethylenediamine)dinitroiron(III)}}_{\text{Cation}} \underbrace{\text{sulfate}}_{\text{Anion}}$$

Because the complex ion is a cation, the Latin name for iron is not used.

Sample Exercise 20.2

Given the following systematic names, give the formula of each coordination compound.

a. Triamminebromoplatinum(II) chloride
b. Potassium hexafluorocobaltate(III)

Solution

a. *Triammine* signifies three ammonia ligands, and *bromo* indicates one bromide ion as a ligand. The oxidation state of platinum is $+2$, as indicated by the Roman numeral II. Thus the complex ion is $[Pt(NH_3)_3Br]^+$. One chloride ion is needed to balance the $1+$ charge of this cation. The formula of the compound is $[Pt(NH_3)_3Br]Cl$. Note that brackets enclose the complex ion.

b. The complex ion contains six fluoride ligands attached to a Co^{3+} ion to give CoF_6^{3-}. Note that the *-ate* ending indicates that the complex ion is an anion. The cations are K^+ ions, and three are required to balance the $3-$ charge on the complex ion. Thus the formula is $K_3[CoF_6]$.

20.4 Isomerism

Purpose

• To introduce and illustrate types of structural isomerism and stereoisomerism.

• To relate molecular structure to optical activity.

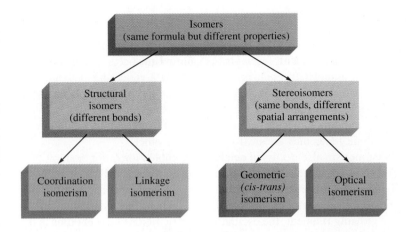

Figure 20.9

Some classes of isomers.

When two or more species have the same formula but different properties, they are said to be **isomers.** Although isomers contain exactly the same types and numbers of atoms, the arrangements of the atoms differ, and this leads to different properties. We will consider two main types of isomerism: **structural isomerism,** where the isomers contain the same atoms but one or more bonds differ, and **stereoisomerism,** where all the bonds in the isomers are the same but the spatial arrangements of the atoms are different. Each of these classes also has subclasses (see Fig. 20.9), which we will now consider.

Structural Isomerism

The first type of structural isomerism we will consider is **coordination isomerism,** in which the composition of the complex ion varies. For example, $[Cr(NH_3)_5SO_4]Br$ and $[Cr(NH_3)_5Br]SO_4$ are coordination isomers. In the first case, SO_4^{2-} is coordinated to Cr^{3+}, and Br^- is the counter ion; in the second case, the roles of these ions are reversed.

Another example of coordination isomerism is the $[Co(en)_3][Cr(ox)_3]$ and $[Cr(en)_3][Co(ox)_3]$ pair, where ox represents the oxalate ion, a bidentate ligand shown in Table 20.13.

In a second type of structural isomerism, **linkage isomerism,** the composition of the complex ion is the same, but the point of attachment of at least one of the ligands differs. Two ligands that can attach to metal ions in different ways are thiocyanate (SCN^-), which can bond through lone electron pairs on the nitrogen or the sulfur atom, and the nitrite ion (NO_2^-), which can bond through lone electron pairs on the nitrogen or the oxygen atom. For example, the following two compounds are linkage isomers:

$[Co(NH_3)_4(NO_2)Cl]Cl$

Tetraamminechloronitrocobalt(III) chloride

(yellow)

$[Co(NH_3)_4(ONO)Cl]Cl$

Tetraamminechloronitritocobalt(III) chloride

(red)

In the first case, the NO_2^- ligand is called *nitro* and is attached to Co^{3+} through the nitrogen atom; in the second case, the NO_2^- ligand is called *nitrito* and is attached to Co^{3+} through an oxygen atom (see Fig. 20.10).

(a)

(b)

Figure 20.10

As a ligand, NO_2^- can bond to a metal ion (a) through a lone pair on the nitrogen atom or (b) through a lone pair on one of the oxygen atoms.

(a)

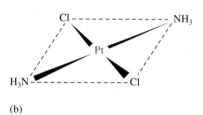

(b)

Figure 20.11

(a) The *cis* isomer of Pt(NH$_3$)$_2$Cl$_2$ (yellow). (b) The *trans* isomer of Pt(NH$_3$)$_2$Cl$_2$ (pale yellow).

Stereoisomerism

Stereoisomers have the same bonds but different spatial arrangements of the atoms. One type, **geometrical isomerism,** or *cis–trans* **isomerism,** occurs when atoms or groups of atoms can assume different positions around a rigid ring or bond. An important example is the compound Pt(NH$_3$)$_2$Cl$_2$, which has a square planar structure. The two possible arrangements of the ligands are shown in Fig. 20.11. In the *trans* **isomer,** the ammonia molecules are across *(trans)* from each other. In the *cis* **isomer,** the ammonia molecules are next *(cis)* to each other.

Geometrical isomerism also occurs in octahedral complex ions. For example, the compound [Co(NH$_3$)$_4$Cl$_2$]Cl has *cis* and *trans* isomers (Fig. 20.12).

A second type of stereoisomerism is called **optical isomerism** because the isomers have opposite effects on plane-polarized light. When light is emitted from a source such as a glowing filament, the oscillating electric fields of the photons in the beam are oriented randomly, as shown in Fig. 20.13. If this light is passed through a polarizer, only the photons with electric fields oscillating in a single plane remain, constituting *plane-polarized light.*

In 1815 a French physicist, Jean Biot (1774–1862), showed that certain crystals could rotate the plane of polarization of light. Later it was found that solutions of certain compounds could do the same thing (see Fig. 20.14). Louis Pasteur (1822–1895) was the first to understand this behavior. In 1848 he noted that solid sodium ammonium tartrate (NaNH$_4$C$_4$H$_4$O$_4$) existed as a mixture of two types of crystals, which he painstakingly separated with tweezers. Separate solutions of these two

Figure 20.12

(a) The *trans* isomer of [Co(NH$_3$)$_4$Cl$_2$]$^+$. The chloride ligands are directly across from each other. (b) The *cis* isomer of [Co(NH$_3$)$_4$Cl$_2$]$^+$. The chloride ligands in this case share an edge of the octahedron. Because of their different structures, the *trans* isomer of [Co(NH$_3$)$_4$Cl$_2$]Cl is green and the *cis* isomer is violet.

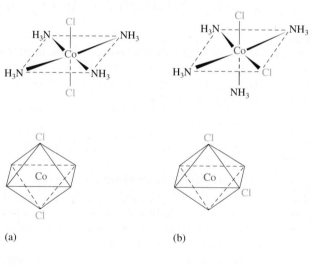

(a)   (b)

Figure 20.13

Unpolarized light consists of waves vibrating in many different planes *(indicated by the arrows).* The polarizing filter blocks all waves except those vibrating in a given plane.

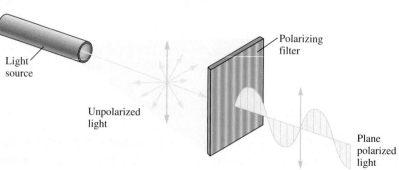

Figure 20.14

The rotation of the plane of polarized light by an optically active substance.
The angle of rotation is called theta (θ).

◀ **CHEMICAL IMPACT** ▶

The Importance of Being *cis*

Some of the most important advancements of science are the results of accidental discoveries, for example, penicillin, Teflon, and the sugar substitutes cyclamate and aspartame. Another important chance discovery occurred in 1964, when a group of scientists using platinum electrodes to apply an electric field to a colony of *E. coli* bacteria noticed that the bacteria failed to divide but continued to grow, forming long fibrous cells. Further study revealed that cell division was inhibited by small concentrations of *cis*-$Pt(NH_3)_2Cl_2$ and *cis*-$Pt(NH_3)_2Cl_4$ formed electrolytically in the solution.

Cancerous cells multiply very rapidly because cell division is uncontrolled. Thus these and similar platinum complexes were evaluated as *antitumor agents,* which inhibit the division of cancer cells. The results showed that *cis*-$Pt(NH_3)_2Cl_2$ was active against a wide variety of tumors, including testicular and ovarian tumors, which are very resistant to treatment by more traditional methods. However, although the *cis* complex showed significant antitumor activity, the corresponding *trans* complex had no effect on tumors. This shows the importance of isomerism in biologic systems.

When drugs are synthesized, great care must be taken to obtain the correct isomer.

Although *cis*-$Pt(NH_3)_2Cl_2$ has proved to be a valuable drug, unfortunately it has some troublesome side effects, the most serious being kidney damage. As a result, the search continues for even more effective antitumor agents. Promising candidates are shown in Fig. 20.15. Note that they are all *cis* complexes.

Figure 20.15

Some *cis* complexes of platinum and palladium that show significant antitumor activity. It is thought that the *cis* complexes work by losing two adjacent ligands and forming coordinate covalent bonds to adjacent bases on a DNA molecule.

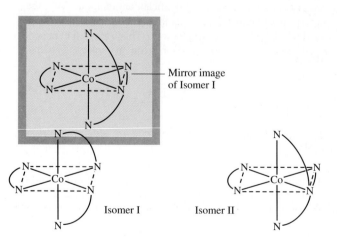

Figure 20.16

A human hand exhibits a nonsuperimposable mirror image. Note that the mirror image of the right hand (while identical to the left hand) cannot be turned in any way to make it identical to (superimposable on) the actual right hand.

types of crystals rotated plane-polarized light in exactly opposite directions. This led to a connection between optical activity and molecular structure.

We now realize that optical activity is exhibited by molecules that have *nonsuperimposable mirror images*. Your hands are nonsuperimposable mirror images (Fig. 20.16). The two hands are related like an object and its mirror image; one hand cannot be turned to make it identical to the other. Many molecules show this same feature, for example, the complex ion $[Co(en)_3]^{3+}$ shown in Fig. 20.17.

Figure 20.17

Isomers I and II of $Co(en)_3{}^{3+}$ are mirror images (the image of I is identical to II) that cannot be superimposed. That is, there is no way that I can be turned in space so that it is the same as II.

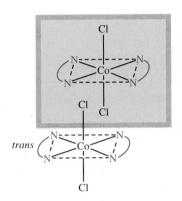

The *trans* isomer and its mirror image are identical. They are not isomers of each other.

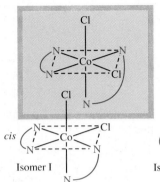

Isomer II cannot be superimposed exactly on isomer I. They are not identical structures.

Isomer II has the same structure as the mirror image of isomer I.

(a)   (b)

Figure 20.18

(a) The *trans* isomer of $Co(en)_2Cl_2^+$ and its mirror image are identical (superimposable). (b) The *cis* isomer of $Co(en)_2Cl_2^+$ and its mirror image are not superimposable and are thus a pair of optical isomers.

Objects that have nonsuperimposable mirror images are said to be **chiral** (from the Greek word *cheir,* meaning "hand").

The isomers of $[Co(en)_3]^{3+}$ (Fig. 20.17) are nonsuperimposable mirror images called **enantiomers,** which rotate plane-polarized light in opposite directions and are thus optical isomers. The isomer that rotates the plane of light to the right (when viewed down the beam of oncoming light) is said to be **dextrorotatory,** designated by d. The isomer that rotates the plane of light to the left is **levorotatory** *(l)*. An equal mixture of the d and l forms in solution, called a **racemic mixture,** does not rotate the plane of the polarized light at all because the two opposite effects cancel.

Geometrical isomers are not necessarily optical isomers. For instance, the *trans* isomer of $[Co(en)_2Cl_2]^+$ shown in Fig. 20.18 is identical to its mirror image. Since this isomer is superimposable on its mirror image, it does not exhibit optical isomerism and is not chiral. On the other hand, *cis*-$[Co(en)_2Cl_2]^+$ is *not* superimposable on its mirror image; a pair of enantiomers exists for this complex ion (the *cis* isomer is chiral).

Most important, biomolecules are chiral, and their reactions are highly structure dependent. For example, a drug can have a particular effect because its molecules can bind to chiral molecules in the body. In order to bind correctly, however, the correct optical isomer of the drug must be administered. Just as the right hand of one person requires the right hand of another to perform a handshake, a given isomer in the body requires a specific isomer of the drug to bind together. Because of this, the syntheses of drugs, which are usually very complicated molecules, must be carried out in a way that produces the correct "handedness," a requirement that greatly adds to the synthetic difficulties.

Sample Exercise 20.3

Does the complex ion $[Co(NH_3)Br(en)_2]$ exhibit geometrical isomerism? Does it exhibit optical isomerism?

Solution

The complex ion exhibits geometrical isomerism because the ethylenediamine ligands can be across from or next to each other:

The *cis* isomer of the complex ion also exhibits optical isomerism because its mirror images

cannot be turned in any way to make them superimposable. Thus these mirror-image isomers of the *cis* complex are shown to be enantiomers that will rotate plane-polarized light in opposite directions.

20.5 Bonding in Complex Ions: The Localized Electron Model

Purpose

- To use the localized electron model to explain the interactions between a metal ion and ligands.

In Chapters 8 and 9 we considered the localized electron model, a very useful model for describing the bonding in molecules. Recall that a central feature of this model is the formation of hybrid atomic orbitals that are used to share electron pairs to form σ bonds between atoms. This same model can be used to account for the bonding in complex ions, but there are two important points to keep in mind:

1. The VSEPR model for predicting structure generally *does not work for complex ions*. However, we can safely assume that a complex ion with a coordination number of 6 will have an octahedral arrangement of ligands, and complexes with two ligands will be linear. On the other hand, complex ions with a coordination number of 4 can be either tetrahedral or square planar, and there is no completely reliable way to predict which will occur in a particular case.

2. The interaction between a metal ion and a ligand can be viewed as a Lewis acid–base reaction with the ligand donating a lone pair of electrons to an *empty* orbital of the metal ion to form a coordinate covalent bond:

Empty metal ion hybrid atomic orbital

Lone pair on the ligand in a hybrid atomic orbital

Coordinate covalent bond

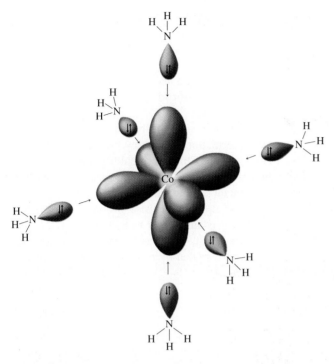

Figure 20.19

A set of six d^2sp^3 hybrid orbitals on Co^{3+} can accept an electron pair from each of six NH_3 ligands to form the $Co(NH_3)_6^{3+}$ ion.

Tetrahedral ligand arrangement; sp^3 hybridization

Square planar ligand arrangement; dsp^2 hybridization

Linear ligand arrangement; sp hybridization

Figure 20.20

The hybrid orbitals required for tetrahedral, square planar, and linear complex ions. The metal ion hybrid orbitals are empty, and the metal ion bonds to the ligands by accepting lone pairs.

The hybrid orbitals used by the metal ion depend on the number and arrangement of the ligands. For example, accommodating the lone pairs from the six ammonia molecules in the octahedral $Co(NH_3)_6^{3+}$ ion requires a set of six empty hybrid atomic orbitals in an octahedral arrangement. As we discussed in Section 9.1, an octahedral set of orbitals is formed by the hybridization of two d, one s, and three p orbitals to give a set of six d^2sp^3 orbitals (see Fig. 20.19).

The hybrid orbitals required on a metal ion in a four-coordinate complex depends on whether the structure is tetrahedral or square planar. For a tetrahedral arrangement of ligands, an sp^3 hybrid set is required (see Fig. 20.20). For example, in the tetrahedral $CoCl_4^{2-}$ ion, the Co^{2+} can be described as sp^3 hybridized. A square planar arrangement of ligands requires a dsp^2 hybrid orbital set on the metal ion (see Fig. 20.20). For example, in the square planar $Ni(CN)_4^{2-}$ ion, the Ni^{2+} is described as dsp^2 hybridized.

A linear complex requires two hybrid orbitals 180 degrees from each other. This arrangement is given by an sp hybrid set (see Fig. 20.20). Thus, in the linear $Ag(NH_3)_2^+$ ion, the Ag^+ can be described as sp hybridized.

Although the localized electron model can account in a general way for metal–ligand bonds, it is rarely used today because it cannot readily account for important properties of complex ions, such as magnetism and color. Thus we will not pursue the model any further.

20.6 *The Crystal Field Model*

Purpose

- To describe the crystal field model and use it to explain the magnetism and colors of coordination complexes.

The main reason the localized electron model cannot fully account for the properties of complex ions is that it gives no information about how the energies of the d orbitals are affected by complex ion formation. This is critical because, as we will see, the color and magnetism of complex ions result from changes in the energies of the metal ion d orbitals caused by the metal–ligand interactions.

The **crystal field model** focuses on the energies of the d orbitals. In fact, this model is not so much a bonding model as it is an attempt to account for the colors and magnetic properties of complex ions. In its simplest form, the crystal field model assumes that the ligands can be approximated by *negative point charges* and that metal–ligand bonding is *entirely ionic*.

Octahedral Complexes

We will illustrate the fundamental principles of the crystal field model by applying it to an octahedral complex. Figure 20.21 shows the orientation of the $3d$ orbitals relative to an octahedral arrangement of point-charge ligands. The important thing to note is that two of the orbitals, d_{z^2} and $d_{x^2-y^2}$, point their lobes *directly at* the point-charge ligands and three of the orbitals, d_{xz}, d_{yz}, and d_{xy}, point their lobes *between* the point charges.

To understand the effect of this difference, we need to consider which type of orbital is lower in energy. Because the negative point-charge ligands repel nega-

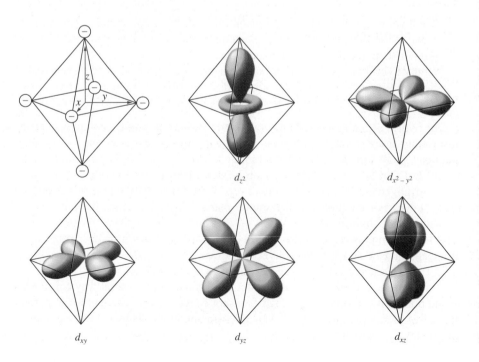

Figure 20.21

An octahedral arrangement of point-charge ligands and the orientation of the 3d orbitals.

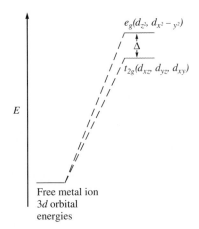

Figure 20.22

The energies of the 3d orbitals for a metal ion in an octahedral complex. The 3d orbitals are degenerate (all have the same energy) in the free metal ion. In the octahedral complex the orbitals are split into two sets as shown. The difference in energy between the two sets is designated as Δ (delta).

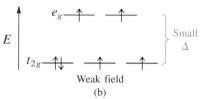

Figure 20.23

Possible electron arrangements in the split 3d orbitals in an octahedral complex of Co^{3+} (electron configuration $3d^6$). (a) In a strong field (large Δ value), the electrons fill the t_{2g} set first, giving a diamagnetic complex. (b) In a weak field (small Δ value), the electrons occupy all five orbitals before any pairing occurs.

tively charged electrons, the electrons will first fill the d orbitals farthest from the ligands to minimize repulsions. In other words the d_{xz}, d_{yz}, and d_{xy} orbitals (known as the t_{2g} set) are at a *lower energy* in the octahedral complex than are the d_{z^2} and $d_{x^2-y^2}$ orbitals (the e_g set). This is shown in Fig. 20.22. The negative point-charge ligands increase the energies of all the d orbitals. However, the orbitals that point at the ligands are raised in energy more than those which point between the ligands.

It is this **splitting of the 3d orbital energies** (symbolized by Δ) that explains the color and magnetism of complex ions of the first-row transition metal ions. For example, in an octahedral complex of Co^{3+} (a metal ion with six 3d electrons), there are two possible ways to place the electrons in the split 3d orbitals (Fig. 20.23). If the splitting produced by the ligands is very large, a situation called the **strong-field case,** the electrons will pair in the lower-energy t_{2g} orbitals. This gives a *diamagnetic* complex in which all the electrons are paired. On the other hand, if the splitting is small (the **weak-field case**), the electrons will occupy all five orbitals before pairing occurs. In this case the complex has four unpaired electrons and is *paramagnetic*.

The crystal field model allows us to account for the differences in the magnetic properties of $Co(NH_3)_6^{3+}$ and CoF_6^{3-}. The $Co(NH_3)_6^{3+}$ ion is known to be diamagnetic and thus corresponds to the strong-field case, also called the **low-spin case,** since it yields the *minimum* number of unpaired electrons. In contrast, the CoF_6^{3-} ion, which is known to have four unpaired electrons, corresponds to the weak-field case, also known as the **high-spin case,** since it gives the *maximum* number of unpaired electrons.

Sample Exercise 20.4

The $Fe(CN)_6^{3-}$ ion is known to have one unpaired electron. Does the CN^- ligand produce a strong or weak field?

Solution

Since the ligand is CN^- and the overall complex ion charge is $3-$, the metal ion must be Fe^{3+}, which has a $3d^5$ electron configuration. The two possible arrangements of the five electrons in the d orbitals split by the octahedrally arranged ligands are

The strong-field case gives one unpaired electron, which agrees with the experimental observation. The CN^- ion is a strong-field ligand toward the Fe^{3+} ion.

From studies of many octahedral complexes, we can arrange ligands in order of their ability to produce d-orbital splitting. A partial listing of ligands in this so-called **spectrochemical series** is

$$CN^- > NO_2^- > en > NH_3 > H_2O > OH^- > F^- > Cl^- > Br^- > I^-$$

Strong-field
ligands
(large Δ)

Weak-field
ligands
(small Δ)

The ligands are arranged in order of decreasing Δ values toward a given metal ion.

It also has been observed that *the magnitude of Δ for a given ligand increases as the charge on the metal ion increases*. For example, NH_3 is a weak-field ligand toward Co^{2+} but acts as a strong-field ligand toward Co^{3+}. This makes sense; as the metal ion charge increases, the ligands will be drawn closer to the metal ion because of the increased charge density. As the ligands move closer, they cause greater splitting of the d orbitals and produce a larger Δ value.

Sample Exercise 20.5

Predict the number of unpaired electrons in the complex ion $[Cr(CN)_6]^{4-}$.

Solution

The net charge of $4-$ means that the metal ion present must be Cr^{2+} ($-6 + 2 = -4$), which has a $3d^4$ electron configuration. Since CN^- is a strong-field ligand (see the spectrochemical series), the correct crystal field diagram for $[Cr(CN)_6]^{4-}$ is

The complex ion will have two unpaired electrons. Note that the CN^- ligand produces such a large splitting that all four electrons will occupy the t_{2g} set even though two of the electrons must be paired in the same orbital.

400   500   600   700
Wavelength (nm)

Figure 20.24
The visible spectrum.

We have seen how the crystal field model can account for the magnetic properties of octahedral complexes. The same model also can explain the colors of these complex ions. For example, $Ti(H_2O)_6^{3+}$, an octahedral complex of Ti^{3+}, which has a $3d^1$ electron configuration, is violet because it absorbs light in the middle of the visible region of the spectrum (see Fig. 20.24). When a substance absorbs certain wavelengths of light in the visible region, the color of the substance is determined by the wavelengths of visible light that remain. We say that the substance exhibits the color *complementary* to those absorbed. The $Ti(H_2O)_6^{3+}$ ion is violet because it absorbs light in the yellow–green region, thus letting red light and blue light pass, which gives the observed violet color. This is shown schematically in Fig. 20.25. Table 20.16 shows the general relationship between the wavelengths of visible light absorbed and the approximate color observed.

The reason that the $Ti(H_2O)_6^{3+}$ ion absorbs a specific wavelength of visible light can be traced to the transfer of the lone d electron between the split d orbitals, as shown in Fig. 20.26. A given photon of light can be absorbed by a molecule only if the wavelength of the light provides exactly the energy needed by the molecule. Or, in other words, the wavelength absorbed is determined by the relationship

$$\Delta E = \frac{hc}{\lambda}$$

where ΔE represents the energy spacing in the molecule (we have used simply Δ in this chapter) and λ represents the wavelength of light needed. Because the d-orbital splitting in most octahedral complexes corresponds to the energies of photons in the visible region, octahedral complex ions are usually colored.

(a)

(b)

$Ti(H_2O)_6^{3+}$

Figure 20.25
(a) When white light shines on a filter that absorbs in the yellow–green region, the emerging light is violet. (b) Because the complex ion $Ti(H_2O)_6^{3+}$ absorbs yellow–green light, a solution of it is violet.

Table 20.16	
Approximate Relationship of Wavelength of Visible Light Absorbed to Color Observed	
Absorbed Wavelength in nm (Color)	Observed Color
400 (violet)	Greenish yellow
450 (blue)	Yellow
490 (blue–green)	Red
570 (yellow–green)	Violet
580 (yellow)	Dark blue
600 (orange)	Blue
650 (red)	Green

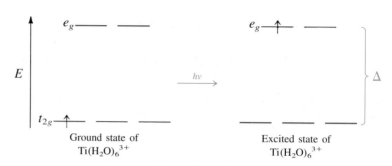

Figure 20.26

The complex ion $Ti(H_2O)_6^{3+}$ can absorb visible light in the yellow–green region to transfer the lone d electron from the t_{2g} to the e_g set.

Ground state of $Ti(H_2O)_6^{3+}$

Excited state of $Ti(H_2O)_6^{3+}$

Solutions of $[Cr(NH_3)_6]Cl_3$ (yellow) and $[Cr(NH_3)_5Cl]Cl_2$ (purple).

Since the ligands coordinated to a given metal ion determine the size of the d-orbital splitting, the color changes as the ligands are changed. This occurs because a change in Δ means a change in the wavelength of light needed to transfer electrons between the t_{2g} and e_g orbitals. Several octahedral complexes of Cr^{3+} and their colors are listed in Table 20.17.

Other Coordination Geometries

Using the same principles developed for octahedral complexes, we will now consider complexes with other geometries. For example, Fig. 20.27 shows a tetrahedral arrangement of point charges in relation to the $3d$ orbitals of a metal ion. There are two important facts to note:

1. None of the $3d$ orbitals "point at the ligands" in the tetrahedral arrangement, as the $d_{x^2-y^2}$ and d_{z^2} orbitals do in the octahedral case. Thus the tetrahedrally arranged ligands do not differentiate the d orbitals as much in the tetrahedral as in the octahedral case. That is, the difference in energy between the split d orbitals will be significantly less in tetrahedral complexes. Although we will not derive it here, the tetrahedral splitting is $\frac{4}{9}$ that of the octahedral splitting for a given ligand and metal ion:

$$\Delta_{tet} = \tfrac{4}{9}\Delta_{oct}$$

Table 20.17	
Several Octahedral Complexes of Cr³⁺ and Their Colors	
Isomer	Color
$[Cr(H_2O)_6]Cl_3$	Violet
$[Cr(H_2O)_5Cl]Cl_2$	Blue–green
$[Cr(H_2O)_4Cl_2]Cl$	Green
$[Cr(NH_3)_6]Cl_3$	Yellow
$[Cr(NH_3)_5Cl]Cl_2$	Purple
$[Cr(NH_3)_4Cl_2]Cl$	Violet

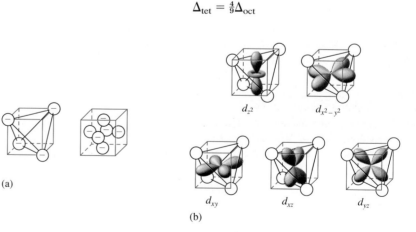

(a)

d_{z^2} $d_{x^2-y^2}$

d_{xy} d_{xz} d_{yz}

(b)

Figure 20.27

(a) Tetrahedral and octahedral arrangements of ligands shown inscribed in cubes. Note that in the two types of arrangements, the point charges occupy opposite parts of the cube: the octahedral point charges are at the centers of the cube faces; the tetrahedral point charges occupy opposite corners of the cube. (b) The orientations of the $3d$ orbitals relative to the tetrahedral set of point charges.

◀ **CHEMICAL IMPACT** ▶

Transition Metal Ions Lend Color to Gems

The beautiful pure color of gems, so valued by cultures everywhere, arises from trace transition metal ion impurities in minerals that would otherwise be colorless. For example, the stunning red of a ruby, the most valuable of all gemstones, is caused by Cr^{3+} ions, which replace about 1% of the Al^{3+} ions in the mineral corundum, which is a form of aluminum oxide (Al_2O_3) that is nearly as hard as diamond. In the corundum structure the Cr^{3+} ions are surrounded by six oxide ions at the vertices of an octahedron. This leads to the characteristic octahedral splitting of chromium's 3d orbitals, such that the Cr^{3+} ions absorb strongly in the blue–violet and yellow–green regions of the visible spectrum but transmit red light to give the characteristic ruby color. (On the other hand, if some of the Al^{3+} ions in corundum are replaced by a mixture of Fe^{2+}, Fe^{3+}, and Ti^{4+} ions, the gem is a sapphire with its brilliant blue color; or if some of the Al^{3+} ions are replaced by Fe^{3+} ions, the stone is a yellow topaz.)

Emeralds are derived from the mineral beryl, which is a beryllium aluminum silicate (empirical formula: $3BeO \cdot Al_2O_3 \cdot 6SiO_2$). When some of the Al^{3+} ions in beryl are replaced by Cr^{3+} ions, the characteristic green color of emerald results. In this environment the splitting of the Cr^{3+} 3d orbitals causes it to strongly absorb yellow and blue–violet light and to transmit green light.

A gem closely related to ruby and emerald is alexandrite, named after Alexander II of Russia. This gem is based on the mineral chrysoberyl, a beryllium aluminate with the empirical formula $BeO \cdot Al_2O_3$ in which approximately 1% of the Al^{3+} ions are replaced by Cr^{3+} ions. In the chrysoberyl environment Cr^{3+} absorbs strongly in the yellow region of the spectrum. Alexandrite has the interesting property of changing colors depending on the light source. When the first alexandrite stone was discovered deep in a mine in the Russian Ural Mountains in 1831, it appeared to be a deep red color in the firelight of the miners' lamps. However, when the stone was brought to the surface, its color was blue. This seemingly magical color change occurs because the firelight of a miner's helmet is rich in the yellow and red wavelengths of the visible spectrum but does not contain much blue. Absorption of the yellow by the stone produces a reddish color. However, daylight has much more intensity in the blue region than firelight. Thus the extra blue in the light transmitted by the stone gives it a bluish color in daylight.

Once the structure of a natural gem is known, it is usually not very difficult to make the gem artificially. For example, rubies and sapphires are made on a large scale by fusing $Al(OH)_3$ with the appropriate transition metal salts at approximately 1200°C to make the "doped" corundum. With these techniques gems of astonishing size can be manufactured: rubies as large as 10 lb and sapphires up to 100 lb have been synthesized. Smaller synthetic stones produced for jewelry are virtually identical to the corresponding natural stones, and it takes great skill for a gemologist to tell the difference.

---

2. Although not exactly pointing at the ligands, the d_{xy}, d_{xz}, and d_{yz} orbitals are closer to the point charges than are the d_{z^2} and $d_{x^2-y^2}$ orbitals. This means that the tetrahedral d-orbital splitting will be opposite to that for the octahedral arrangement. The two arrangements are contrasted in Fig. 20.28. Because the d-orbital splitting is relatively small for the tetrahedral case, the weak-field case (high-spin case) *always* applies. There are no known ligands powerful enough to produce the strong-field case in a tetrahedral complex.

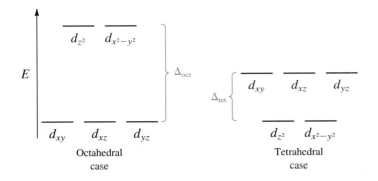

Figure 20.28

The crystal field diagrams for octahedral and tetrahedral complexes. The relative energies of the sets of d orbitals are reversed. For a given type of ligand, the splitting is much larger for the octahedral complex ($\Delta_{oct} > \Delta_{tet}$) because in this arrangement the d_{z^2} and $d_{x^2-y^2}$ point their lobes directly at the point charges and are thus relatively high in energy.

(a)

(b)

Figure 20.29

(a) The crystal field diagram for a square planar complex oriented in the xy plane with ligands along the x and y axes. The position of the d_{z^2} orbital is higher than those of the d_{xz} and d_{yz} orbitals because of the "doughnut" of electron density in the xy plane. The actual position of d_{z^2} is somewhat uncertain and varies in different square planar complexes. (b) The crystal field diagram for a linear complex where the ligands lie along the z axis.

Sample Exercise 20.6

Give the crystal field diagram for the tetrahedral complex ion $CoCl_4^{2-}$.

Solution

The complex ion contains Co^{2+}, which has a $3d^7$ electron configuration. The splitting of the d orbitals will be small, since this is a tetrahedral complex, giving the high-spin case with three unpaired electrons.

The crystal field model also applies to square planar and linear complexes. The crystal field diagrams for these cases are shown in Fig. 20.29. The ranking of orbitals in these diagrams can be explained by considering the relative orientations of the point charges and the orbitals. The diagram in Fig. 20.28 for the octahedral arrangement can be used to obtain these orientations. We can obtain the square planar complex by removing the two point charges along the z axis. This will greatly lower the energy of d_{z^2}, leaving only $d_{x^2-y^2}$, which points at the four remaining ligands as the highest-energy orbital. We can obtain the linear complex from the octahedral arrangement by leaving the two ligands along the z axis and removing the four in the xy plane. This means that only the d_{z^2} points at the ligands and is highest in energy.

20.7 The Molecular Orbital Model

Purpose

• To apply the molecular orbital model to octahedral complexes.

Although quite successful in accounting for the magnetic and spectral (light-absorption) properties of complex ions, the crystal field model has limited use other than explaining those properties dependent on the d-orbital splitting. For example, the model gives a very crude and misleading view of the nature of the metal–ligand bonding.

The molecular orbital model gives a much more realistic view of complex ions, especially of the bonding. As we saw in Section 9.2, this model postulates that a new set of orbitals characteristic of the molecule is formed from the atomic orbitals of the component atoms. To illustrate how this model can be applied to complex ions, we will describe the molecular orbitals in an octahedral species of the general formula ML_6^{n+}. To keep things as simple as possible, we will focus only on those ligand orbitals which have lone electron pairs that interact with the metal ion valence orbitals ($3d$, $4s$, and $4p$). There are two important considerations in predicting how atomic orbitals will interact to form molecular orbitals:

1. *Extent of orbital overlap.* Atomic orbitals must have a net overlap in space to form molecular orbitals. Figure 20.30 shows an octahedral arrangement of ligands with lone-pair orbitals. Recall from our previous discussion that two of the metal ion's $3d$ orbitals (d_{z^2} and $d_{x^2-y^2}$) point at the ligands and thus will form molecular orbitals with the ligand lone-pair orbitals. On the other hand, the d_{xy}, d_{xz}, and d_{yz} orbitals point *between* the ligands and will not be involved in the sigma bonding with the ligands. The spherical $4s$ orbital of the metal ion overlaps with all the ligand lone-pair orbitals, and each of the $4p$ orbitals overlaps with pairs of ligand lone-pair orbitals on the three coordinate axes. Thus both the $4s$ and $4p$ orbitals will be involved in the molecular orbitals in the complex ion.

2. *Relative orbital energies.* Atomic orbitals that are close in energy will interact more than those widely separated in energy.

When we apply these principles to the general complex ML_6^{n+}, we obtain the energy-level diagram shown in Fig. 20.31. Note that the σ_s, σ_p, and σ_d molecular orbitals are bonding MOs; they are *lower* in energy than the ligand orbitals and metal ion orbitals that mix to form them. Electrons in these molecular orbitals will

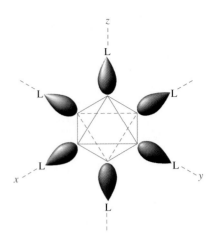

Figure 20.30

An octahedral arrangement of ligands showing their lone-pair orbitals.

The molecular orbital model was introduced in Section 9.2.

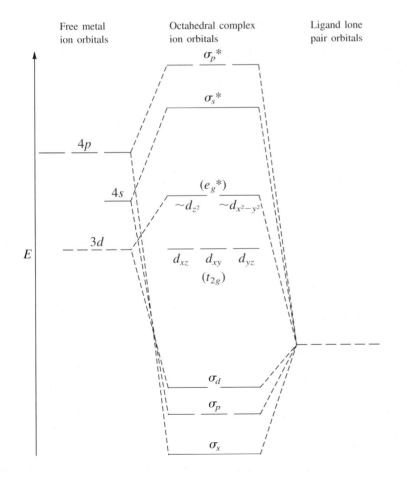

Figure 20.31

The molecular orbital energy-level diagram for an octahedral complex ion ML_6^{n+}. The e_g^* molecular orbitals are essentially pure d_{z^2} and $d_{x^2-y^2}$ orbitals of the metal ion. Little mixing with the ligand orbitals occurs because of the large energy difference between the $3d$ and ligand orbitals.

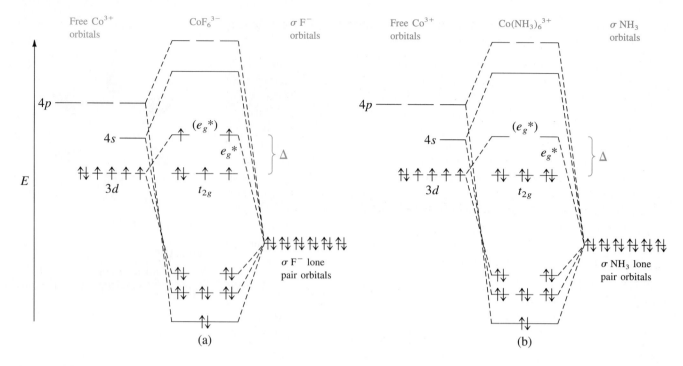

Figure 20.32

(a) The molecular orbital energy-level diagram for CoF_6^{3-}. This yields the high-spin case. (b) The molecular orbital energy-level diagram for $Co(NH_3)_6^{3+}$. This yields the low-spin case.

have lower energies than they do in either the metal ion or the ligands; they are therefore the major contributors to the stability of the complex ion.

Because the d_{xz}, d_{yz}, and d_{xy} orbitals (the t_{2g} set) of the metal ion do not overlap with the ligand orbitals, they remain unchanged. Thus they have the same energy in the complex ion as they had in the free metal ion and make no contribution to the stability of the complex. They are called **nonbonding orbitals.**

The e_g^* molecular orbitals are **antibonding orbitals,** since they are higher in energy than the atomic orbitals that mix to form them. Electrons in these orbitals have higher energies than they do in the free metal ion and destabilize the complex ion relative to the separated metal ion and ligands. However, *the most important characteristic of the e_g^* orbitals is that they are primarily composed of d_{z^2} and $d_{x^2-y^2}$ atomic orbitals,* with relatively little contribution from ligand orbitals. This lack of mixing is due to the large energy difference between the ligand orbitals and the metal ion $3d$ orbitals. Thus we can see that the molecular orbital model predicts the same type of d-orbital splitting as the crystal field model, with the added advantage that it gives a much more realistic picture of the metal–ligand interaction and the origin of the splitting. Thus we can use the molecular orbital model to explain why different ligands produce different magnitudes of splitting. In particular, a ligand with a very electronegative donor atom will have lone-pair orbitals of very low energy (the electrons are very firmly bound to the ligand); these orbitals will not mix very thoroughly with the metal ion orbitals. This will result in a small difference between the t_{2g} (nonbonding) and e_g^* (antibonding) orbitals. For example, in CoF_6^{3-} [see Fig. 20.32(a)] the low-energy orbitals of the very electronegative fluoride ion ligands mix only to a small extent with the cobalt ion orbitals. A small amount of d-orbital splitting results, giving the high-spin case.

On the other hand, in $Co(NH_3)_6^{3+}$ the ammonia lone-pair orbitals are closer in energy to the metal ion orbitals, a situation that produces a larger degree of mixing between them. This in turn gives a relatively large amount of d-orbital splitting, and the low-spin case results [see Fig. 20.32(b)].

We have seen that the molecular orbital model correctly predicts the d-orbital splitting in octahedral complexes, accounting for the magnetic and spectral properties of these species. Moreover, it has a major advantage in that it accounts in a realistic way for metal–ligand bonding. However, it suffers from the disadvantage of being much more complicated to apply than the crystal field model. The molecular orbital model can be applied to all types of complex ions, although we will not pursue the model further in this text.

20.8 *The Biologic Importance of Coordination Complexes*

Purpose

* To describe the function and structure of some biologically important coordination complexes.

The ability of metal ions to coordinate with and release ligands and to easily undergo oxidation and reduction makes them ideal for use in biologic systems. For example, metal ion complexes are used in humans for the transport and storage of oxygen, as electron-transfer agents, as catalysts, and as drugs. Most of the first-row transition metals are essential for human health, as is summarized in Table 20.18. We will concentrate on iron's role in biologic systems, since several of its coordination complexes have been studied extensively.

Iron plays a central role in almost all living cells. In mammals, the principal source of energy comes from the oxidation of carbohydrates, proteins, and fats.

Table 20.18	
The First-Row Transition Metals and Their Biologic Significance	
First-Row Transition Metal	Biologic Function(s)
Scandium	None known.
Titanium	None known.
Vanadium	None known in humans.
Chromium	Assists insulin in the control of blood sugar; may also be involved in the control of cholesterol.
Manganese	Necessary for a number of enzymatic reactions.
Iron	Component of hemoglobin and myoglobin; involved in the electron-transport chain.
Cobalt	Component of vitamin B_{12}, which is essential for the metabolism of carbohydrates, fats, and proteins.
Nickel	Component of the enzymes urease and hydrogenase.
Copper	Component of several enzymes; assists in iron storage; involved in the production of color pigments of hair, skin, and eyes.
Zinc	Component of insulin and many enzymes.

Figure 20.33

The heme complex, in which an Fe^{2+} ion is coordinated to four nitrogen atoms of a planar porphyrin ligand.

A protein is a large molecule assembled from amino acids, which have the general structure

$$H_2N-\underset{\underset{H}{|}}{\overset{\overset{R}{|}}{C}}-COOH$$

in which R represents various groups.

Although oxygen is the oxidizing agent for these processes, it does not react directly with these molecules. Instead, the electrons from the breakdown of these nutrients are passed along a complex chain of molecules, called the **respiratory chain,** eventually reaching the O_2 molecule. The principal electron-transfer molecules in the respiratory chain are iron-containing species called **cytochromes,** consisting of two main parts: an iron complex called **heme** and a protein. The structure of the heme complex is shown in Fig. 20.33. Note that it contains an iron ion (it can be either Fe^{2+} or Fe^{3+}) coordinated to a rather complicated planar ligand called a **porphyrin.** As a class, porphyrins all contain the same central ring structure but have different substituent groups at the edges of the rings. The various porphyrin molecules act as tetradentate ligands for many metal ions, including iron, cobalt, and magnesium. In fact, *chlorophyll,* a substance essential to the process of photosynthesis, is a magnesium–porphyrin complex of the type shown in Fig. 20.34.

In addition to participating in the transfer of electrons from nutrients to oxygen, iron also plays a principal role in the transport and storage of oxygen in mammalian blood and tissues. Oxygen is stored in a molecule called **myoglobin,** which consists of a heme complex and a protein in a structure very similar to that of the cytochromes. In myoglobin, the Fe^{2+} ion is coordinated to four nitrogen atoms of the porphyrin ring and to a nitrogen atom of the protein chain, as shown in Fig. 20.35. Since Fe^{2+} is normally six-coordinate, this leaves one position open for attachment of an O_2 molecule.

One especially interesting feature of myoglobin is that it involves an O_2 molecule attaching directly to Fe^{2+}. However, if gaseous O_2 is bubbled into an aqueous

Figure 20.34

Chlorophyll is a porphyrin complex of Mg^{2+}. There are two similar forms of chlorophyll, one of which is shown here.

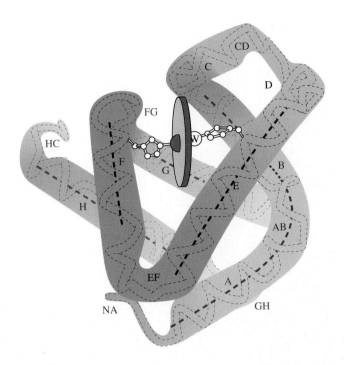

Figure 20.35

A representation of the myoglobin molecule. The Fe^{2+} ion is coordinated to four nitrogen atoms in the porphyrin of the heme (represented by the disk in the figure) and one nitrogen from the protein chain. This leaves a sixth coordination position (indicated by the W) available for an oxygen molecule.

solution containing heme, the Fe^{2+} is immediately oxidized to Fe^{3+}. This oxidation of the Fe^{2+} in heme does not happen in myoglobin. This fact is of crucial importance because Fe^{3+} does not form a coordinate covalent bond with O_2, and myoglobin would not function if the bound Fe^{2+} could be oxidized. Since the Fe^{2+} in the "bare" heme complex can be oxidized, it must be the protein that somehow prevents the oxidation. How? Based on much research, the answer seems to be that the oxidation of Fe^{2+} to Fe^{3+} involves an oxygen bridge between two iron ions (the circles indicate the ligands):

The bulky protein around the heme group in myoglobin prevents two molecules from getting close enough to form the oxygen bridge, and so oxidation of the Fe^{2+} is prevented.

The transport of O_2 in the blood is carried out by **hemoglobin,** a molecule consisting of four myoglobin-like units, as shown in Fig. 20.36. Each hemoglobin can therefore bind four O_2 molecules to form a bright red diamagnetic complex. The diamagnetism occurs because oxygen is a strong-field ligand toward Fe^{2+}, which has a $3d^6$ electron configuration. When the oxygen molecule is released, water molecules occupy the sixth coordination position around each Fe^{2+}, giving a bluish paramagnetic complex (H_2O is a weak-field ligand toward Fe^{2+}) that gives venous blood its characteristic bluish tint.

Hemoglobin dramatically demonstrates how sensitive the function of a biomolecule is to its structure. In certain people, in the synthesis of the proteins needed for hemoglobin, an improper amino acid is inserted into the protein in two places. This

Figure 20.36

A representation of the hemoglobin structure. There are two slightly different types of protein chains (α and β). Each hemoglobin has two α chains and two β chains, each with a heme complex near the center. Thus each hemoglobin molecule can complex with four O_2 molecules.

may not seem very serious, since there are several hundred amino acids present. However, because the incorrect amino acid has a nonpolar substituent instead of the polar one found on the proper amino acid, the hemoglobin drastically changes its shape. The red blood cells are then sickle-shaped rather than disk-shaped, as shown in Fig. 20.37. The misshapen cells can aggregate, causing clogging of tiny capillaries. This condition, known as **sickle cell anemia,** is the subject of intense research.

Our knowledge of the workings of hemoglobin allows us to understand the effects of high altitudes on humans. The reaction between hemoglobin and oxygen can be represented by the following equilibrium:

$$\text{Hb}(aq) + 4O_2(g) \rightleftharpoons \text{Hb}(O_2)_4(aq)$$
$$\text{Hemoglobin} \qquad\qquad \text{Oxyhemoglobin}$$

At high altitudes, where the oxygen content of the air is lower, the position of this equilibrium will shift to the left, according to Le Châtelier's principle. Because less oxyhemoglobin is formed, fatigue, dizziness, and even a serious illness called **high-altitude sickness** can result. One way to combat this problem is to use supplemental oxygen, as most high-altitude mountain climbers do. However, this is impractical for people who live at high elevations. In fact, the human body adapts to the lower oxygen concentrations by making more hemoglobin, causing the equilibrium to shift back to the right. Someone moving from Chicago to Boulder, Colorado (5300 feet) would notice the effects of the new altitude for a couple of weeks, but as the hemoglobin level increased, the effects would disappear. This change is called **high-altitude acclimatization,** which explains why athletes who want to compete at high elevations should practice there for several weeks prior to the event.

Sherpa porters in Nepal are acclimatized to high elevations.

Figure 20.37
Normal red blood cells (round) and sickle-shaped red blood cells.

Our understanding of the biologic role of iron also allows us to explain the toxicities of substances such as carbon monoxide and the cyanide ion. Both CO and CN^- are very good ligands toward iron and so can interfere with the normal workings of the iron complexes in the body. For example, carbon monoxide has about 200 times the affinity for the Fe^{2+} in hemoglobin as oxygen does. The resulting stable complex, **carboxyhemoglobin,** prevents the normal uptake of O_2, thus depriving the body of needed oxygen. Asphyxiation can result if enough carbon monoxide is present in the air. The mechanism for the toxicity of the cyanide ion is somewhat different. Cyanide coordinates strongly to cytochrome oxidase, an iron-containing cytochrome enzyme that catalyzes the oxidation–reduction reactions of certain cytochromes. The coordinated cyanide thus prevents the electron-transfer process and rapid death results. Because of its behavior, cyanide is called a **respiratory inhibitor.**

20.9 Metallurgy and Iron and Steel Production

Purpose

- To describe processes for concentrating minerals in ores.
- To discuss the major processes in hydrometallurgy.
- To describe the blast furnace, open hearth, and basic oxygen processes for steelmaking.
- To discuss the thermodynamics of steelmaking.

In the preceding section we saw the importance of iron in biologic systems. Of course, iron is also very important in many other ways in our world. In this section we will discuss the isolation of metals from their natural sources and the formulation of metals into useful materials, with special emphasis on the role of iron.

Metals are very important for structural applications, electrical wires, cooking utensils, tools, decorative items, and many other purposes. However, because the main chemical characteristic of a metal is its ability to give up electrons, almost all metals in nature are found in ores, combined with nonmetals such as oxygen, sulfur, and the halogens. To recover and use these metals, we must separate them from their ores and reduce the metal ions. Then, because most metals are unsuitable for use in the pure state, we must form alloys that have the desired properties. The process of separating a metal from its ore and preparing it for use is known as **metallurgy.** The steps in this process are typically

1. Mining

2. Pretreatment of the ore

3. Reduction to the free metal

4. Purification of the metal (refining)

5. Alloying

An ore can be viewed as a mixture containing **minerals** (relatively pure metal compounds) and **gangue** (sand, clay, and rock). Some typical minerals are listed in Table 20.19. Although silicate minerals are the most common in the earth's crust, they are typically very hard and difficult to process, making metal extraction relatively expensive. Therefore, other ores are used when available.

After mining, an ore must be treated to remove the gangue and to concentrate the mineral. The ore is first pulverized and then processed in a variety of devices, including cyclone separators (see Fig. 20.38), inclined vibrating tables, and flotation tanks.

In the **flotation process,** the crushed ore is fed into a tank containing a water–oil–detergent mixture. Because of the difference in the surface characteristics of the mineral particles and the silicate rock particles, the oil wets the mineral particles. A stream of air blown through the mixture causes tiny bubbles to form on the oil-covered pieces, which then float to the surface, where they can be skimmed off.

After the mineral has been concentrated, it is often chemically altered in preparation for the reduction step. For example, nonoxide minerals are often converted to oxides before reduction. Carbonates and hydroxides can be converted by simple heating:

$$CaCO_3(s) \xrightarrow{\text{Heat}} CaO(s) + CO_2(g)$$

$$Mg(OH)_2(s) \xrightarrow{\text{Heat}} MgO(s) + H_2O(g)$$

Sulfide minerals can be converted to oxides by heating in air at temperatures below their melting points, a process called **roasting:**

$$2ZnS(s) + 3O_2(g) \xrightarrow{\text{Heat}} 2ZnO(s) + 2SO_2(g)$$

As we have seen earlier, sulfur dioxide causes severe problems if released into the atmosphere, and modern roasting operations collect this gas and use it in the manufacture of sulfuric acid.

Figure 20.38

A schematic diagram of a cyclone separator. The ore is pulverized and blown into the separator. The more-dense mineral particles are thrown toward the walls by centrifugal force and fall down the funnel. The lighter particles (gangue) tend to stay closer to the center and are drawn out through the top by the stream of air.

Table 20.19	
Common Minerals Found in Ores	
Anion	Examples
None (free metal)	Au, Ag, Pt, Pd, Rh, Ir, Ru
Oxide	Fe_2O_3 (hematite)
	Fe_3O_4 (magnetite)
	Al_2O_3 (bauxite)
	SnO_2 (cassiterite)
Sulfide	PbS (galena)
	ZnS (sphalerite)
	FeS_2 (pyrites)
	HgS (cinnabar)
	Cu_2S (chalcocite)
Chloride	NaCl (rock salt)
	KCl (sylvite)
	$KCl \cdot MgCl_2$ (carnalite)
Carbonate	$FeCO_3$ (siderite)
	$CaCO_3$ (limestone)
	$MgCO_3$ (magnesite)
	$MgCO_3 \cdot CaCO_3$ (dolomite)
Sulfate	$CaSO_4 \cdot 2H_2O$ (gypsum
	$BaSO_4$ (barite)
Silicate	$Be_3Al_2Si_6O_{18}$ (beryl)
	$Al_2(Si_2O_8)(OH)_4$ (kaolinite)
	$LiAl(SiO_3)_2$ (spondumene)

The method chosen to reduce the metal ion to the free metal, a process called **smelting,** depends on the affinity of the metal ion for electrons. Some metals are good enough oxidizing agents that the free metal is produced in the roasting process. For example, the roasting reaction for cinnabar is

$$HgS(s) + O_2(g) \xrightarrow{\text{Heat}} Hg(l) + SO_2(g)$$

where the Hg^{2+} is reduced by electrons donated by the S^{2-} ion, which is then further oxidized by O_2 to form SO_2.

The roasting of a more active metal produces the metal oxide, which must be reduced to obtain the free metal. The most common reducing agents are coke (impure carbon), carbon monoxide, and hydrogen. The following are some common examples of the reduction process:

$$Fe_2O_3(s) + 3CO(g) \xrightarrow{\text{Heat}} 2Fe(l) + 3CO_2(g)$$

$$WO_3(s) + 3H_2(g) \xrightarrow{\text{Heat}} W(l) + 3H_2O(g)$$

$$ZnO(s) + C(s) \xrightarrow{\text{Heat}} Zn(l) + CO(g)$$

The most active metals, such as aluminum and the alkali metals, must be reduced electrolytically, usually from molten salts (see Section 17.8).

The metal obtained in the reduction step is invariably impure and must be refined. The methods of refining include electrolytic refining (see Section 17.8),

Figure 20.39

A schematic representation of zone refining.

oxidation of impurities (as for iron, see below), and distillation of low-boiling metals such as mercury and zinc. One process used when highly pure metals are needed is **zone refining.** In this process a bar of the impure metal travels through a heater (see Fig. 20.39), which causes melting and recrystallizing of the metal as the bar cools. Purification of the metal occurs because as the crystal re-forms, the metal ions are likely to fit much better in the crystal lattice than are the atoms of impurities. Thus the impurities tend to be excluded and carried to the end of the bar. Several repetitions of this process give a very pure metal bar.

Hydrometallurgy

The metallurgical processes we have considered so far are usually called **pyrometallurgy** (*pyro* means "at high temperatures"). These traditional methods require large quantities of energy and have two other serious problems: atmospheric pollution (mainly by sulfur dioxide) and relatively high costs that make treatment of low-grade ores economically unfeasible.

In the last hundred years, a different process, **hydrometallurgy** (*hydro* means "water"), has been employed to extract metals from ores by use of aqueous chemical solutions, a process called **leaching.** The first two uses of hydrometallurgy were for the extraction of gold from low-grade ores and for the production of aluminum oxide, or alumina, from bauxite, an aluminum-bearing ore.

Gold is sometimes found in ores in the elemental state, but it usually occurs in relatively small concentrations. A process called **cyanidation** treats the crushed ore with an aqueous cyanide solution in the presence of air to dissolve the gold by forming the complex ion $Au(CN)_2^-$:

$$4Au(s) + 8CN^-(aq) + O_2(g) + 2H_2O(l) \rightarrow 4Au(CN)_2^-(aq) + 4OH^-(aq)$$

Pure gold is then recovered by reaction of the solution of $Au(CN)_2^-$ with zinc powder to reduce Au^+ to Au:

$$2Au(CN)_2^-(aq) + Zn(s) \rightarrow 2Au(s) + Zn(CN)_4^{2-}(aq)$$

The extraction of alumina from bauxite (the Bayer process) leaches the ore with sodium hydroxide at high temperatures and pressures to dissolve the amphoteric aluminum oxide:

$$Al_2O_3(s) + 2OH^-(aq) \rightarrow 2AlO_2^-(aq) + H_2O(l)$$

This process leaves behind solid impurities such as SiO_2, Fe_2O_3, and TiO_2, which are not appreciably soluble in basic solution. After the solid impurities are removed, the pH of the solution is lowered, causing the pure aluminum oxide to re-form. It is then electrolyzed to produce aluminum metal (see Section 17.8).

As illustrated by these processes, hydrometallurgy involves two distinct steps: *selective leaching* of a given metal ion from the ore, and recovery of the metal ion from the solution by *selective precipitation* as an ionic compound.

The leaching agent can simply be water if the metal-containing compound is a water-soluble chloride or sulfate. However, most commonly, the metal is present in a water-insoluble substance that must somehow be dissolved. The leaching agents used in such cases are usually aqueous solutions containing acids, bases, oxidizing agents, salts, or some combination of these. Often the dissolving process involves the formation of complex ions. For example, when an ore containing water-insoluble lead sulfate is treated with an aqueous sodium chloride solution, the soluble complex ion $PbCl_4^{2-}$ is formed:

$$PbSO_4(s) + 4Na^+(aq) + 4Cl^-(aq) \rightarrow 4Na^+(aq) + PbCl_4^{2-}(aq) + SO_4^{2-}(aq)$$

Formation of a complex ion also occurs in the cyanidation process for the recovery of gold. However, since the gold is present in the ore as particles of metal, it must first be oxidized by oxygen to produce Au^+, which then reacts with CN^- to form the soluble $Au(CN)_2^-$ species. Thus, in this case, the leaching process involves a combination of oxidation and complexation.

Sometimes just oxidation is used. For example, insoluble zinc sulfide can be converted to soluble zinc sulfate by pulverizing the ore and suspending it in water to form a slurry through which oxygen is bubbled:

Precipitation reactions are discussed in Section 15.7.

$$ZnS(s) + 2O_2(aq) \rightarrow Zn^{2+}(aq) + SO_4^{2-}(aq)$$

One advantage of hydrometallurgy over the traditional processes is that sometimes the leaching agent can be pumped directly into the ore deposits in the earth. For example, aqueous sodium carbonate (Na_2CO_3) can be injected into uranium-bearing ores to form water-soluble complex carbonate ions.

Recovering the metal ions from the leaching solution involves forming an insoluble solid containing the metal ion to be recovered. This step may involve addition of an anion to form an insoluble salt, reduction to the solid metal, or a combination of reduction and precipitation of a salt. Examples of these processes are shown in Table 20.20. Because of its suitability for treating low-grade ores economically and

Table 20.20

Examples of Methods for Recovery of Metal Ions from Leaching Solutions

Method		Examples
Precipitation of a salt		$Cu^{2+}(aq) + S^{2-}(aq) \rightarrow CuS(s)$
		$Cu^+(aq) + HCN(aq) \rightarrow CuCN(s) + H^+(aq)$
Reduction	Chemical	$Au^+(aq) + Fe^{2+}(aq) \rightarrow Au(s) + Fe^{3+}(aq)$
		$Cu^{2+}(aq) + Fe(s) \rightarrow Cu(s) + Fe^{2+}(aq)$
		$Ni^{2+}(aq) + H_2(g) \rightarrow Ni(s) + 2H^+(aq)$
	Electrolytic	$Cu^{2+}(aq) + 2e^- \rightarrow Cu(s)$
		$Al^{3+}(aq) + 3e^- \rightarrow Al(s)$
Reduction plus precipitation		$2Cu^{2+}(aq) + 2Cl^-(aq) + H_2SO_3(aq) + H_2O(l) \rightarrow$ $2CuCl(s) + 3H^+(aq) + HSO_4^-(aq)$

without significant pollution, hydrometallurgy is becoming more popular for recovering many important metals such as copper, nickel, zinc, and uranium.

The Metallurgy of Iron

Iron is present in the earth's crust in many types of minerals. *Iron pyrite* (FeS_2) is widely distributed but is not suitable for production of metallic iron and steel because it is almost impossible to remove the last traces of sulfur. The presence of sulfur makes the resulting steel too brittle to be useful. *Siderite* ($FeCO_3$) is a valuable iron mineral that can be converted to iron oxide by heating. The iron oxide minerals are *hematite* (Fe_2O_3), the more abundant, and *magnetite* (Fe_3O_4, really $FeO \cdot Fe_2O_3$). *Taconite* ores contain iron oxides mixed with silicates and are more difficult to process than the others. However, taconite ores are being increasingly used as the more desirable ores are consumed.

To concentrate the iron in iron ores, advantage is taken of the natural magnetism of Fe_3O_4 (hence its name, *magnetite*). The Fe_3O_4 particles can be separated from the gangue by magnets. The ores that are not magnetic are often converted to Fe_3O_4; hematite is partially reduced to magnetite, while siderite is first converted to FeO thermally, then oxidized to Fe_2O_3, and then reduced to Fe_3O_4:

$$FeCO_3(s) \xrightarrow{\text{Heat}} FeO(s) + CO_2(g)$$

$$4FeO(s) + O_2(g) \longrightarrow 2Fe_2O_3(s)$$

$$3Fe_2O_3(s) + C(s) \longrightarrow 2Fe_3O_4(s) + CO(g)$$

Sometimes the nonmagnetic ores are concentrated by flotation processes.

The most commonly used reduction process for iron takes place in the **blast furnace** (Fig. 20.40). The raw materials required are concentrated iron ore, coke, and limestone (which serves as a *flux* to trap impurities). The furnace, which is approximately 25 feet in diameter, is charged from the top with a mixture of iron ore, coke, and limestone. A very strong blast (~350 mi/h) of hot air is injected at the bottom, where the oxygen reacts with the carbon in the coke to form carbon monoxide, the reducing agent for the iron. The temperature of the charge increases as it travels down the furnace, with reduction of the iron to iron metal occurring in steps.

$$3Fe_2O_3 + CO \rightarrow 2Fe_3O_4 + CO_2$$

$$Fe_3O_4 + CO \rightarrow 3FeO + CO_2$$

$$FeO + CO \rightarrow Fe + CO_2$$

Iron can reduce carbon dioxide,

$$Fe + CO_2 \rightarrow FeO + CO$$

so complete reduction of the iron occurs only if the carbon dioxide is destroyed by adding excess coke:

$$CO_2 + C \rightarrow 2CO$$

The limestone ($CaCO_3$) in the charge loses carbon dioxide, or *calcines*, in the hot furnace and combines with silica and other impurities to form **slag,** which is mostly molten calcium silicate, $CaSiO_3$,

$$CaO + SiO_2 \rightarrow CaSiO_3$$

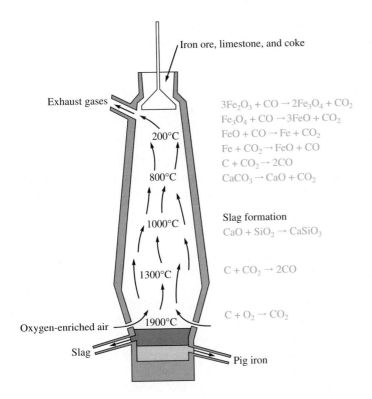

Iron ore, limestone, and coke

Exhaust gases

200°C

$$3Fe_2O_3 + CO \rightarrow 2Fe_3O_4 + CO_2$$
$$Fe_3O_4 + CO \rightarrow 3FeO + CO_2$$
$$FeO + CO \rightarrow Fe + CO_2$$
$$Fe + CO_2 \rightarrow FeO + CO$$
$$C + CO_2 \rightarrow 2CO$$
$$CaCO_3 \rightarrow CaO + CO_2$$

800°C

1000°C

Slag formation
$$CaO + SiO_2 \rightarrow CaSiO_3$$

1300°C

$$C + CO_2 \rightarrow 2CO$$

1900°C

$$C + O_2 \rightarrow CO_2$$

Oxygen-enriched air

Slag

Pig iron

Figure 20.40

The blast furnace used in the production of iron.

and alumina (Al_2O_3). The slag floats on the molten iron and is skimmed off. The gas that escapes from the top of the furnace contains carbon monoxide, which is combined with air to form carbon dioxide. The energy released in this exothermic reaction is collected in a heat exchanger and used in heating the furnace.

The iron collected from the blast furnace, called **pig iron,** is quite impure. It contains ~90% iron, ~5% carbon, ~2% manganese, ~1% silicon, ~0.3% phosphorus, and ~0.04% sulfur (from impurities in the coke). The production of 1 ton of pig iron requires approximately 1.7 tons of iron ore, 0.5 ton of coke, 0.25 ton of limestone, and 2 tons of air.

Iron oxide also can be reduced in a **direct reduction furnace,** which operates at much lower temperatures (1300–2000°F) than a blast furnace and produces a solid ''sponge iron'' rather than molten iron. Because of the milder reaction conditions, the direct reduction furnace requires a higher grade of iron ore (with fewer impurities) than that used in a blast furnace. The iron from the direct reduction furnace is called *DRI (directly reduced iron)* and contains ~95% iron, with the balance mainly silica and alumina.

Production of Steel

Steel is an alloy and can be classified as **carbon steel,** which contains up to about 1.5% carbon, or **alloy steel,** which contains carbon plus other metals such as Cr, Co, Mn, and Mo. The wide range of mechanical properties associated with steel is determined by its chemical composition and by the heat treatment of the final product.

The production of iron from its ore is fundamentally a reduction process, but the conversion of iron to steel is basically an oxidation process in which unwanted impurities are eliminated. Oxidation is carried out in various ways, but the two most common are the open hearth process and the basic oxygen process.

In the oxidation reactions of steelmaking, the manganese, phosphorus, and silicon in the impure iron react with oxygen to form oxides, which in turn react with appropriate fluxes to form slag. Sulfur enters the slag primarily as sulfides, and excess carbon forms carbon monoxide or carbon dioxide. The flux chosen depends on the major impurities present. If manganese is the chief impurity, an acidic flux of silica is used:

$$MnO(s) + SiO_2(s) \xrightarrow{\text{Heat}} MnSiO_3(l)$$

If the main impurity is silicon or phosphorus, a basic flux, usually lime (CaO) or magnesia (MgO), is needed to give reactions such as

$$SiO_2(s) + MgO(s) \xrightarrow{\text{Heat}} MgSiO_3(l)$$

$$P_4O_{10}(s) + 6CaO(s) \xrightarrow{\text{Heat}} 2Ca_3(PO_4)_2(l)$$

Whether an acidic or a basic slag will be needed is a factor that must be considered when a furnace is constructed so that its refractory linings will be compatible with the slag. Silica bricks would deteriorate quickly in the presence of basic slag, and magnesia or lime bricks would dissolve in acid slag.

The **open hearth process** (Fig. 20.41) uses a dishlike container that holds 100 to 200 tons of molten iron. An external heat source is required to keep the iron molten, and a concave roof over the container reflects heat back toward the iron surface. A blast of air or oxygen is passed over the surface of the iron to react with impurities. Silicon and manganese are oxidized first and enter the slag, followed by oxidation of carbon to carbon monoxide, which causes agitation and foaming of the molten bath. The exothermic oxidation of carbon raises the temperature of the bath, causing the limestone flux to calcine:

$$CaCO_3 \xrightarrow{\text{Heat}} CaO + CO_2$$

The resulting lime floats to the top of the molten mixture (an event called the **lime boil**), where it combines with phosphates, sulfates, and silicates. Next comes the

Figure 20.41

A schematic diagram of the open hearth process for steelmaking. The checker chambers contain bricks that absorb heat from gases passing over the molten charge. The flow of air and gases is reversed periodically.

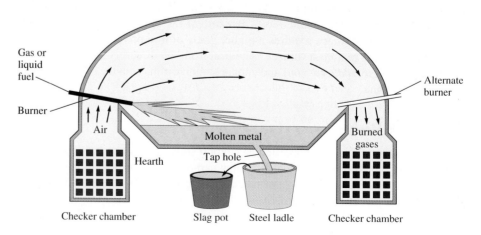

refining process, which involves continued oxidation of carbon and other impurities. Because the melting point increases as the carbon content decreases, the bath temperatures must be increased during this phase of the operation. If the carbon content falls below that desired in the final product, coke or pig iron may be added.

The final composition of the steel is "fine-tuned" after the charge is poured. For example, aluminum is sometimes added at this stage to remove trace amounts of oxygen via the reaction

$$4Al + 3O_2 \rightarrow 2Al_2O_3$$

Alloying metals such as vanadium, chromium, titanium, manganese, and nickel are also added to give the steel the properties needed for a specific application.

The processing of a batch of steel by the open hearth process is quite slow, taking up to 8 hours. The **basic oxygen process** is much faster. Molten pig iron and scrap iron are placed in a barrel-shaped container (Fig. 20.42) that can hold as much as 300 tons of material. A high-pressure blast of oxygen is directed at the surface of the molten iron, oxidizing impurities in a manner very similar to that used in the open hearth process. Fluxes are added after the oxygen blow begins. One advantage of this process is that the exothermic oxidation reactions proceed so rapidly that they produce enough heat to raise the temperature nearly to the boiling point of iron without an external heat source. Also, at these high temperatures only about an hour is needed to complete the oxidation processes.

The **electric arc method,** which was once used only for small batches of specialty steels, is being utilized more and more in the steel industry. In this process an electric arc between carbon electrodes is used to melt the charge. This means that no fuel-borne impurities are added to the steel, since no fuel is needed. Also, higher temperatures are possible than in the open hearth or basic oxygen processes, and this leads to more effective removal of sulfur and phosphorus impurities. Oxygen is added in this process so that the oxide impurities in the steel can be controlled effectively.

Figure 20.42

The basic oxygen process for steelmaking.

Heat Treatment of Steel

One way of producing the desired physical properties in steel is by controlling the chemical composition (see Table 20.21). Another method for tailoring the properties of steel involves heat treatment. Pure iron exists in two different crystalline forms, depending on the temperature. At any temperature below 912°C, iron has a body-centered cubic structure and is called **α-iron.** Between 912°C and 1394°C, iron has a face-centered cubic structure called **austentite,** or **γ-iron.** At 1394°C, iron changes to **δ-iron,** a body-centered cubic structure identical to α-iron.

When iron is alloyed with carbon, which fits into holes among the iron atoms to form the interstitial alloy **carbon steel,** the situation becomes even more complex. For example, the temperature at which α-iron changes to austentite is lowered by about 200°C. Also, at high temperatures iron and carbon react by an endothermic reversible reaction to form an iron carbide called **cementite:**

$$\underset{\text{(Heat)}}{3Fe + C + energy} \rightleftharpoons \underset{\text{Cementite}}{Fe_3C}$$

By Le Châtelier's principle, we can predict that cementite will become more stable relative to iron and carbon as the temperature is increased. This is the observed result.

Refer to Section 10.3 for a review of packing and crystal lattices.

Table 20.21

Percent Composition and Uses of Various Types of Steel

Type of Steel	% Carbon	% Manganese	% Phosphorus	% Sulfur	% Silicon	% Nickel	% Chromium	% Other	Uses
Plain carbon	≤1.35	≤1.65	≤0.04	≤0.05	≤0.60	—	—	—	Sheet steel, tools
High-strength (low-alloy)	≤0.25	≤1.65	≤0.04	≤0.05	0.15–0.9	0.4–1	0.3–1.3	Cu (0.2–0.6) Sb (0.01–0.08) V (0.01–0.08)	Transportation equipment, structural beams
Alloy	≤1.00	≤3.50	≤0.04	≤0.05	0.15–2.0	0.25–10.0	0.25–4.0	Mo (0.08–4.0) V (0–0.2) W (0–18) Co (0–5)	Automobile and aircraft engine parts
Stainless	0.03–1.2	1.0–10	0.04–0.06	≤0.03	1–3	1–22	4.0–27	—	Engine parts, steam turbine parts, kitchen utensils
Silicon	—	—	—	—	0.5–5.0	—	—	—	Electric motors and transformers

Thus steel is really a mixture of iron metal in one of its crystal forms, carbon, and cementite. The proportions of these components are very important in determining the physical properties of steel.

When steel is heated to temperatures in the region of 1000°C, much of the carbon is converted to cementite. If the steel is then allowed to cool slowly, the equilibrium shown above shifts to the left, and small crystals of carbon precipitate, giving a steel that is relatively ductile. If the cooling is very rapid, the equilibrium does not have time to adjust. The cementite is trapped, and the steel has a high cementite content, making it quite brittle. The proportions of carbon crystals and cementite can be "fine-tuned" to give the desired properties by heating to intermediate temperatures followed by rapid cooling, a process called **tempering.** The rate of heating and cooling determines not only the amounts of cementite present but also the size of its crystals and the form of crystalline iron present.

Summary

For the first-row transition metals (scandium through zinc), the last electrons occupy the $3d$ orbitals. Because electrons in these inner orbitals cannot participate as easily in bonding as can electrons in valence s and p orbitals, the chemistry of the transition elements is not greatly affected by the gradual change in the number of electrons. As a class, these elements have metallic physical and chemical properties. In forming ionic compounds with nonmetals, the transition metals exhibit several typical characteristics: more than one oxidation state is often found, the cations often are complex ions, and most compounds are colored and many are paramagnetic.

First-row transition metal ions can form a variety of ions by losing one or more of their electrons. The maximum possible oxidation state for a given element corresponds to the loss of all the $4s$ and $3d$ electrons, but toward the right end of the period the maximum possible oxidation state is not seen. Rather, 2+ ions become the most common because the $3d$ electrons become increasingly difficult to remove.

Transition metals typically form coordination compounds, which consist of a complex ion (a transition metal ion with attached ligands) and counter ions (anions or cations to produce a solid with no net charge). A ligand (a Lewis base) is a neutral molecule or ion having a lone pair of electrons that can be shared with an empty orbital on a metal ion (a Lewis acid) to form a coordinate covalent bond. The coordination number is the number of bonds formed by the metal ion to its ligands and can range from 2 to 8 depending on the size, charge, and electron configuration of the metal ion. A coordination number of 6 means an octahedral arrangement of ligands about the central metal ion; 2 means a linear arrangement, and 4 means either a planar or a tetrahedral arrangement.

Ligands can form one bond (unidentate), two bonds (bidentate), or as many as six bonds to the metal ion. Ligands that can bond to a metal ion through more than one atom are called chelates. For example, ethylenediamine (en) is bidentate, and EDTA is hexadentate (forms six bonds).

When two or more species have the same formula but different properties, they are called isomers. Structural isomers contain the same atoms but one or more different bonds. Coordination isomerism is a type of structural isomerism in which the composition of the coordination sphere around the metal varies. In linkage isomerism, the composition of the coordination spheres is the same, but the point of attachment of at least one of the ligands differs.

In stereoisomerism, the isomers have the same bonds but different spatial arrangements. For example, in geometric isomerism, atoms or groups can assume different relative positions in the coordination sphere around the metal. When two identical ligands lie across from each other, the isomer is *trans;* two ligands located next to each other produce the *cis* isomer.

A second type of stereoisomerism is optical isomerism, which is exhibited by molecules that have nonsuperimposable mirror images, that is, by chiral molecules. The pair of isomers, called enantiomers, rotate plane-polarized light in equal but opposite directions.

Bonding in complex ions can be described in terms of the localized electron model. However, even though this model can account for the bonding in complex ions by use of hybrid orbitals, it does not account for important properties such as magnetism and color. The crystal field model is much more successful at accounting for these properties by focusing on the energies of the d orbitals of the metal ion. To predict the effects ligands will have on the energies of the d orbitals, the ligands are approximated as negative point charges and the metal–ligand bonding is assumed to be completely ionic. The effect of the point charges in an octahedral complex ion is to split the $3d$ orbitals into two groups with different energies. If the splitting is large (the strong-field case), the electrons pair in the lower-energy orbitals before any jump the energy gap. If the splitting is small (the weak-field case), the electrons occupy all five d orbitals singly before pairing occurs. Ligands can be arranged according to their ability to produce splitting, the spectrochemical series.

The crystal field model also accounts for the colors of complex ions. When a substance absorbs a certain wavelength of light in the visible region, its color is determined by the wavelengths of visible light that remain unabsorbed. Complex ions can absorb light as they transfer electrons between the split d orbitals. The relationship between the wavelength of light absorbed (λ) and the magnitude of the splitting (Δ) is given by

$$\Delta = \frac{hc}{\lambda}$$

The molecular orbital model gives the best description of the actual bonding in complex ions. In terms of this model, the d-orbital splitting occurs because the t_{2g} orbitals are nonbonding, while the e_g orbitals are antibonding molecular orbitals and are raised in energy.

Coordination complexes are vitally important in the chemistry of biologic systems, with iron having special importance in electron-transfer processes and the transport and storage of oxygen.

The process of separating a metal from its ore and preparing it for use is known as metallurgy. An ore is a mixture of minerals (relatively pure metal compounds) and gangue (sand, clay, and rock). Minerals can be concentrated by various methods before being processed. Minerals are often converted to the metal oxides (roasted) before the metal ion is reduced in a process called smelting.

Hydrometallurgy extracts metals from ores using aqueous chemical solutions in a process called leaching. An example of this is cyanidation, in which gold is leached with an aqueous cyanide solution.

Iron is often concentrated from iron ore by magnetic methods. The most commonly used reduction process for iron takes place in the blast furnace. The raw materials required are concentrated iron ore, coke, and limestone (which serves as a flux to trap impurities). The iron oxide (Fe_2O_3) is reduced by carbon monoxide to iron metal. The impure product, pig iron, is about 90% iron. Another process using the direct reduction furnace, which yields sponge iron, is coming into increased use.

Steel is a carbon-containing alloy of iron that is manufactured by oxidizing the impurities in pig iron or sponge iron in either the open hearth process or the basic oxygen process. Other metals are often added to form alloy steels.

Key Terms

Section 20.1
complex ion
first-row transition metals
lanthanide contraction

lanthanide series

Section 20.3
coordination compound
counter ion

oxidation state
coordination number
ligand
coordinate covalent bond

monodentate (unidentate) ligand
chelating ligand (chelate)
bidentate ligand

Section 20.4
isomers
structural isomerism
stereoisomerism
coordination isomerism
linkage isomerism
geometrical *(cis–trans)* isomerism
trans isomer
cis isomer
optical isomerism
chiral
enantiomers

Section 20.6
crystal field model
d-orbital splitting
strong-field (low-spin) case
weak-field (high-spin) case
spectrochemical series

Section 20.8
cytochromes
heme
porphyrin
myoglobin
hemoglobin

carboxyhemoglobin

Section 20.9
metallurgy
minerals
gangue
flotation process
roasting
smelting
zone refining
pyrometallurgy
hydrometallurgy

leaching
cyanidation
blast furnace
slag
pig iron
direct reduction furnace
carbon steel
alloy steel
open hearth process
basic oxygen process
electric arc method
tempering

A blue question or exercise number indicates that the answer to that question or exercise appears at the back of this book and a solution appears in the Solutions Guide.

Questions

1. Define each of the following.
   a. Ligand
   b. Chelate
   c. Bidentate
   d. Complex ion

2. What must a ligand have in order to bond to a metal?

3. What do we mean when we say that a bond is a coordinate covalent bond?

4. How would transition metal ions be classified using the Lewis definition of acids and bases?

5. Define each of the following and give examples.
   a. Isomers
   b. Structural isomers
   c. Stereoisomers
   d. Coordination isomers
   e. Linkage isomers
   f. Geometrical isomers
   g. Optical isomers

6. Define each of the following.
   a. Weak-field ligand
   b. Strong-field ligand
   c. Low-spin complex
   d. High-spin complex

7. Compounds of copper(II) are generally colored, but compounds of copper(I) are not. Explain.

8. Would you expect $Cd(NH_3)_4Cl_2$ to be colored? Explain.

9. Compounds of Sc^{3+} are not colored, but those of Ti^{3+} and V^{3+} are. Explain.

10. Why are CN^- and CO toxic to humans?

11. Oxalic acid is often used to remove rust stains. What properties of oxalic acid allow it to do this?

12. Why do transition metal ions often have several oxidation states, while representative metals generally have only one?

13. What is the lanthanide contraction? How does the lanthanide contraction affect the properties of the 4*d* and 5*d* transition metals?

14. Define and give an example of each of the following.
   a. Roasting
   b. Smelting
   c. Flotation
   d. Leaching
   e. Gangue

15. What are the advantages and disadvantages of hydrometallurgy?

16. Describe the process by which a metal is purified by zone refining.

Exercises

In this section similar exercises are paired.

Transition Metals

17. Write electron configurations for the following metals.
   a. Ni
   b. Cd
   c. Zr
   d. Nd

18. Write electron configurations for the following metals.
   a. Mo
   b. Ru
   c. Ir
   d. Mn

19. Write electron configurations for the following ions.
    a. Ni^{2+} c. Zr^{3+} and Zr^{4+}
    b. Cd^{2+} d. Nd^{3+}

20. Write electron configurations for the following ions.
    a. Mo^{4+} c. Ir^+, Ir^{3+}
    b. Ru^{2+}, Ru^{3+} d. Mn^{2+}

21. Write electron configurations for each of the following.
    a. Co, Co^{2+}, Co^{3+}
    b. Pt, Pt^{2+}, Pt^{4+}
    c. Fe, Fe^{2+}, Fe^{3+}

22. Write electron configurations for each of the following.
    a. Au, Au^+, Au^{3+}
    b. Cu, Cu^+, Cu^{2+}
    c. V, V^{2+}, V^{3+}

23. What is the maximum mass of titanium that can be produced from 1.00×10^3 kg of ilmenite ($FeTiO_3$)?

24. Use the following ionization energy values to decide whether ilmenite ($FeTiO_3$) is composed of Fe^{2+} and Ti^{4+} ions or Fe^{3+} and Ti^{3+} ions.

Ionization Energies (kJ/mol)		
	Fe	Ti
First	759	658
Second	1561	1310
Third	2957	2652
Fourth	—	4175

Use the following reduction potentials to answer the same question.

$$TiO^{2+} + 2H^+ + e^- \rightarrow Ti^{3+} + H_2O \qquad \mathscr{E}° = +0.099 \text{ V}$$
$$Fe^{3+} + e^- \rightarrow Fe^{2+} \qquad \mathscr{E}° = +0.77 \text{ V}$$

Which answer is consistent with the information presented in this chapter? Comment on any discrepancies.

25. Molybdenum is obtained both as a by-product of copper mining and from direct mining (primary deposits are in the Rocky Mountains in Colorado). In both cases it is obtained as MoS_2, which is then converted to MoO_3. The MoO_3 can be used directly in the production of stainless steel for high-speed tools, which accounts for about 85% of the molybdenum used. Molybdenum can be purified by dissolving MoO_3 in aqueous ammonia and crystallizing ammonium molybdate. Depending on conditions, either $(NH_4)_2Mo_2O_7$ or $(NH_4)_6Mo_7O_{24} \cdot 4H_2O$ is obtained.
    a. Name MoS_2 and MoO_3.
    b. What is the oxidation state of Mo in each compound in part a?
    c. Complete and balance the following equations.

    $$MoS_2(s) + O_2(g) \rightarrow MoO_3(s)$$
    $$NH_3(aq) + MoO_3(s) \rightarrow (NH_4)_2Mo_2O_7(s)$$
    $$NH_3(aq) + MoO_3(s) \rightarrow (NH_4)_6Mo_7O_{24} \cdot 4H_2O(s)$$

26. Manganese is found in nature in silicate, oxide, and carbonate minerals. Commercially, the most important ores are pyrolusite (MnO_2) and rhodochrosite ($MnCO_3$). Give the systematic names for each compound.

Coordination Compounds

27. Name the following complex ions.
- a. $Ru(NH_3)_5Cl^{2+}$
- b. $Fe(CN)_6^{4-}$
- c. $Mn(NH_2CH_2CH_2NH_2)_3^{2+}$
- d. $Co(NH_3)_5NO_2^{2+}$

28. Name the following complex ions.
- a. $FeCl_4^-$
- b. $Ni(NH_3)_6^{2+}$
- c. $Co(SCN)_4^{2-}$
- d. $Ti(H_2O)_6^{3+}$

29. Name the following coordination compounds.
- a. $[Co(NH_3)_6]Cl_2$
- b. $[Co(H_2O)_6]I_3$
- c. $K_2[PtCl_4]$
- d. $K_4[PtCl_6]$

30. Name the following coordination compounds.
- a. $Na_4[Ni(C_2O_4)_3]$
- b. $K_2[CoCl_4]$
- c. $[Cu(NH_3)_4]SO_4$
- d. $[Co(en)_2(SCN)Cl]Cl$

31. Give formulas for the following.
- a. Hexakispyridinecobalt(III) chloride
- b. Pentaammineiodochromium(III) iodide
- c. Trisethylenediamminenickel(II) bromide
- d. Potassium tetracyanonickelate(II)
- e. Tetraamminedichloroplatinum(IV) tetrachloroplatinate(II)

32. Give formulas for the following complex ions.
- a. Tetrachloroferrate(III) ion
- b. Pentaammineaquaruthenium(III) ion
- c. Iodopentakispyridineplatinum(IV) ion
- d. Amminetrichloroplatinate(II) ion

33. Draw geometrical isomers of each of the following complex ions.
- a. $[Co(C_2O_4)_2(H_2O)_2]^-$
- b. $[Pt(NH_3)_4I_2]^{2+}$
- c. $[Ir(NH_3)_3Cl_3]$
- d. $[Cr(en)(NH_3)_2I_2]^+$

34. Draw structures of each of the following.
- a. *cis*-Dichloroethylenediamineplatinum(II)
- b. *trans*-Dichlorobisethylenediaminecobalt(II)
- c. *cis*-Tetraamminechloronitrocobalt(III) ion
- d. *trans*-Tetraamminechloronitritocobalt(III) ion
- e. *trans*-Diaquabisethylenediaminecopper(II) ion

35. Amino acids can act as ligands toward transition metal ions. The simplest amino acid is glycine ($NH_2CH_2CO_2H$). Draw a structure of the glycinate anion ($NH_2CH_2CO_2^-$) acting as a bidentate ligand. Draw the structural isomers of the square planar complex $Cu(NH_2CH_2CO_2)_2$.

36. The carbonate ion (CO_3^{2-}) can act either as a monodentate or bidentate ligand. Draw a picture of CO_3^{2-} coordinating to a metal ion as a bidentate and as a monodentate ligand. The carbonate ion also can act as a bridge between two metal ions. Draw a picture of a CO_3^{2-} ion bridging between two metal ions.

37. Which of the following ligands are capable of linkage isomerism? Explain your answer.

$$SCN^-, \ N_3^-, \ NO_2^-, \ NH_2CH_2CH_2NH_2, \ OCN^-, \ I^-$$

38. BAL is a chelating agent used in treating heavy-metal poisoning. It acts as a bidentate ligand. What types of linkage isomers are possible when BAL coordinates to a metal ion?

$$CH_2-SH$$
$$|$$
$$CH-SH$$
$$|$$
$$CH_2-OH$$
BAL

39. Draw all the geometrical isomers of $[Cr(en)(NH_3)_2BrCl]^+$. Which of these isomers also has an optical isomer? Draw the various isomers.

40. Draw all geometrical and linkage isomers of square planar $[Pt(NH_3)_2(SCN)_2]$.

Bonding, Color, and Magnetism in Coordination Compounds

41. Draw the *d*-orbital splitting diagrams for the octahedral complex ions of each of the following.
- a. Fe^{2+} (high and low spin)
- b. Fe^{3+} (high spin)
- c. Ni^{2+}
- d. Zn^{2+}
- e. Co^{2+} (high and low spin)

42. How many unpaired electrons are in the following complex ions?
- a. $Ru(NH_3)_6^{2+}$ (low-spin case)
- b. $Fe(CN)_6^{3-}$ (low-spin case)
- c. $Ni(H_2O)_6^{2+}$
- d. $V(en)_3^{3+}$
- e. $CoCl_4^{2-}$

43. The complex ion $NiCl_4^{2-}$ has two unpaired electrons, while $Ni(CN)_4^{2-}$ is diamagnetic. Propose structures for these two complex ions.

44. Tetrahedral complexes of Co^{2+} are quite common. Use a *d*-orbital splitting diagram to rationalize the stability of Co^{2+} tetrahedral complex ions.

45. The compound $Ni(H_2O)_6Cl_2$ is green, while $Ni(NH_3)_6Cl_2$ is purple. Predict the predominant color of light absorbed by each compound. Which compound absorbs light with the shorter wavelength? Predict in which compound Δ is greater and whether H_2O or NH_3 is a stronger field ligand. Do your conclusions agree with the spectrochemical series?

46. The complex ion $Fe(CN)_6^{3-}$ is paramagnetic with one unpaired electron. The complex ion $Fe(SCN)_6^{3-}$ has five unpaired electrons. Where does SCN^- lie in the spectrochemical series relative to CN^-?

Metallurgy

47. Use the data in Appendix 4 for the following.
  a. Calculate $\Delta H°$ and $\Delta S°$ for the reaction

$$3Fe_2O_3 + CO \rightarrow 2Fe_3O_4 + CO_2$$

  that occurs in a blast furnace.
  b. Assume that $\Delta H°$ and $\Delta S°$ are independent of temperature. Calculate $\Delta G°$ at 800°C for this reaction.

48. What roles do kinetics and thermodynamics play in the effect that the following reaction has on the properties of steel?

$$3Fe + C \rightleftharpoons Fe_3C$$

Additional Exercises

49. Titanium dioxide, the most widely used white pigment, occurs naturally but is often colored by the presence of impurities. The chloride process is often used in purifying rutile, a mineral form of titanium dioxide.
  a. Show that the unit cell for rutile, shown below, conforms to the formula TiO_2. (*Hint:* Recall the discussion in Section 10.4.)

● Titanium   ○ Oxygen

  b. The reactions for the chloride process are

$$2TiO_2(s) + 3C(s) + 4Cl_2(g)$$
$$\xrightarrow{950°C} 2TiCl_4(g) + CO_2(g) + 2CO(g)$$

$$TiCl_4(g) + O_2(g) \xrightarrow{1000-1400°C} TiO_2(s) + 2Cl_2(g)$$

  Assign oxidation states to the elements in both reactions. Which elements are being reduced, and which are being oxidized? Identify the oxidizing agent and the reducing agent in each reaction.

50. The melting and boiling points of the titanium tetrahalides are given in the following table.

	mp (°C)	bp (°C)
TiF_4	284	—
$TiCl_4$	−24	136.5
$TiBr_4$	38	233.5
TiI_4	155	377

Rationalize these data in terms of the bonding and intermolecular forces for these compounds.

51. Ores of cobalt have been used to impart a blue color to glass since 2600 B.C. Impure cobalt metal was first isolated in 1735 by G. Brandt, a Swedish chemist. The name is probably derived from *Kobold,* the German word for "goblin" or "evil spirit." The miners of northern Europe thought the spitefulness of such spirits was responsible for ores, which on smelting not only failed to yield the cobalt metal but produced highly toxic fumes (As_4O_6). The principal ores of cobalt are smaltite ($CoAs_2$), cobaltite ($CoAsS$), and linnaeite (Co_3S_4).
  a. Write a reaction for the roasting of smaltite by oxygen, producing cobalt(II) oxide and As_4O_6. Name As_4O_6. Propose a structure for As_4O_6 based on what was discussed about phosphorus chemistry in Chapter 19.
  b. Cobalt is usually obtained as a by-product of the production of copper, nickel, or lead. The ore containing the mixture of metals is first treated with oxygen to form the metal oxides. These oxides are then treated with sulfuric acid, which dissolves the oxides of iron, nickel, and cobalt, but not that of copper, which is left behind. After iron is precipitated as its hydroxide, the basic solution is treated with

hypochlorite ion, which oxidizes the Co^{2+} ion to Co^{3+} and leads to precipitation of cobalt(III) hydroxide:

$$Co^{2+}(aq) + OCl^-(aq) + OH^-(aq)$$
$$\rightarrow Co(OH)_3(s) + Cl^-(aq)$$

Balance this equation.

c. Calculate the concentration of Co^{3+} present in a saturated aqueous solution of $Co(OH)_3$ ($K_{sp} = 2.5 \times 10^{-43}$).

d. Calculate the concentration of Co^{3+} present in a saturated solution of $Co(OH)_3$ buffered at pH = 10.00.

52. Zinc metal tarnishes quickly in moist air. Write a reaction for this process. Using data from Chapter 17 and Appendix 4, calculate $\mathscr{E}°$, $\Delta G°$, and K (at 298 K) for this reaction.

53. Use standard reduction potentials to calculate $\mathscr{E}°$, $\Delta G°$, and K (at 298 K) for the reaction that is used in production of gold:

$$2Au(CN)_2^-(aq) + Zn(s) \rightarrow 2Au(s) + Zn(CN)_4^{2-}(aq)$$

The relevant half-reactions are

$$Au(CN)_2^- + e^- \rightarrow Au + 2CN^- \qquad \mathscr{E}° = -0.60 \text{ V}$$
$$Zn(CN)_4^{2-} + 2e^- \rightarrow Zn + 4CN^- \qquad \mathscr{E}° = -1.26 \text{ V}$$

54. Nickel can be purified by producing the volatile compound nickel tetracarbonyl, $Ni(CO)_4$. Nickel is the only metal that reacts directly with CO at room temperature. What is the oxidation state of nickel in $Ni(CO)_4$?

55. How many bonds could each of the following chelates form with a metal ion?

a. Acetylacetone

b. Diethylenetriamine

$$NH_2-CH_2-CH_2-NH-CH_2-CH_2-NH_2$$

c. Cyclam

d. Porphine

56. A coordination compound of cobalt(III) contains four ammonia molecules, one sulfate ion, and one chloride ion. Addition of aqueous $BaCl_2$ solution to an aqueous solution of the compound gives no precipitate. Addition of aqueous $AgNO_3$ to an aqueous solution of the compound produces a white precipitate. Propose a structure for this coordination compound.

57. Acetylacetone (see Exercise 55, part a), abbreviated acacH, is a bidentate ligand. It loses a proton and coordinates as $acac^-$, as shown below:

a. Draw all the resonance structures for $acac^-$ coordinating to a metal ion.

b. Which of the following complexes are optically active: *cis*-$Cr(acac)_2(H_2O)_2$, *trans*-$Cr(acac)_2(H_2O)_2$, and $Cr(acac)_3$?

c. Acetylacetone reacts with an ethanol solution of $Eu(NO_3)_3$ to give a compound that is 40.1% C and 4.68% H by mass. Combustion of 0.286 g of the compound gives 0.112 g Eu_2O_3. What is the molecular formula of the compound formed from the reaction of acetylacetone and europium(III) nitrate? [Assume that the compound contains one europium(III) ion.]

58. Draw the structure of the complex ion that nickel(II) forms with EDTA (see Table 20.13). Is this complex ion optically active?

59. The complex ion $Ru(phen)_3^{2+}$ has been used as a probe for the structure of DNA.

a. What type of isomerism is found in $Ru(phen)_3^{2+}$?

b. $Ru(phen)_3^{2+}$ is diamagnetic (as are all complex ions of Ru^{2+}). Draw the crystal field diagram for the d orbitals in this complex ion.

(phen = 1,10-phenanthroline =

60. Would it be better to use octahedral Ni^{2+} complexes or octahedral Cr^{2+} complexes to determine whether a given ligand is a strong-field or weak-field ligand by measuring the number of unpaired electrons? How else could the relative ligand field strengths be determined?

61. When an aqueous solution of KCN is added to a solution containing Ni^{2+} ion, a precipitate forms, which redissolves on addition of more KCN solution. No precipitate forms when H_2S is bubbled into this solution. Write equations describing these reactions. *Hint:* CN^- is both a Brønsted–Lowry base ($K_b \approx 10^{-5}$) and a Lewis base.

62. Enterobactin (shown below), a molecule excreted by certain bacteria, is a chelating agent specific for Fe^{3+}. It is used in the transfer of Fe^{3+} from water-insoluble minerals into the bacterial cells. Coordination to the iron ion is through the oxygen atoms on the catechol rings:

Catechol

a. Through how many atoms does enterobactin coordinate to Fe^{3+}?

b. The protons on the catechol —OH groups are lost in complex formation. Draw an approximate picture of the complex ion $Fe(enterobactin)^{3-}$.

Enterobactin

63. Until the discoveries of Werner, it was thought that carbon had to be present in a compound for it to be optically active. Werner prepared the following compound containing OH^- ions as bridging groups and separated the optical isomers.

a. Draw structures of the two optically active isomers of this compound.

b. What are the oxidation states of the cobalt ions?

c. How many unpaired electrons are present if the complex is the low-spin case?

$$\left[Co \left(\begin{array}{c} H \\ O \\ O \\ H \end{array} Co(NH_3)_4 \right)_3 \right] Cl_6$$

64. Using the following equilibrium expressions:

$$[Cu^{2+}][OH^-]^2 = 1.6 \times 10^{-19}$$

$$\frac{[Cu(NH_3)_4^{2+}]}{[Cu^{2+}][NH_3]^4} = 1.0 \times 10^{13}$$

$$\frac{[Cd(NH_3)_4^{2+}]}{[Cd^{2+}][NH_3]^4} = 1.3 \times 10^7$$

$$\frac{[Cd(CN)_4^{2-}]}{[Cd^{2+}][CN^-]^4} = 5.8 \times 10^{18}$$

calculate an equilibrium constant for each of the following.

a. $Cu(OH)_2(s) + 4NH_3 \rightleftharpoons Cu(NH_3)_4^{2+} + 2OH^-$

b. $Cd(NH_3)_4^{2+} + 4CN^- \rightleftharpoons Cd(CN)_4^{2-} + 4NH_3$

(*Hint:* Find reactions that add to give the desired reaction.)

Challenge Problems

65. Ammonia and potassium iodide solutions are added to an aqueous solution of $Cr(NO_3)_3$. A solid is isolated (compound A), and the following data are collected:

i. When 0.105 g of compound A was strongly heated in excess O_2, 0.0203 g of CrO_3 was formed.

ii. In a second experiment it took 32.93 mL of 0.100 M HCl to titrate completely the NH_3 present in 0.341 g of compound A.

iii. Compound A was found to contain 73.53% iodine by mass.

iv. The freezing point of water was lowered by 0.62°C when 0.601 g of compound A was dissolved in 10.00 g of H_2O ($K_f = 1.86$).

What is the formula of the compound? What is the structure of the complex ion present? (*Hints:* Cr^{3+} is expected to be six-coordinate, with NH_3 and possibly I^- as ligands. The I^- ions will be the counter ions if needed.)

66. Henry Taube, 1983 Nobel Prize winner in chemistry, has studied the mechanisms of the oxidation–reduction reactions of transition metal complexes. In one experiment he and his students studied the following reaction:

$$Cr(H_2O)_6^{2+}(aq) + Co(NH_3)_5Cl^{2+}(aq)$$
$$\rightarrow Cr(III) \text{ complexes} + Co(II) \text{ complexes}$$

Chromium(III) and cobalt(III) complexes are substitutionally inert (no exchange of ligands) under conditions of the experiment. Chromium(II) and cobalt(II) complexes can exchange ligands very rapidly. One of the products of the reaction is $Cr(H_2O)_5Cl^{2+}$. Is this consistent with the reaction proceeding through formation of $(H_2O)_5Cr—Cl—Co(NH_3)_5$ as an intermediate? Explain.

67. Chelating ligands often form more stable complex ions than the corresponding monodentate ligands with the same donor atoms. For example,

$$Ni^{2+}(aq) + 6NH_3(aq) \rightleftharpoons Ni(NH_3)_6^{2+}(aq)$$
$$K_f = 3.2 \times 10^8$$
$$Ni^{2+}(aq) + 3en(aq) \rightleftharpoons Ni(en)_3^{2+}(aq) \qquad K_f = 1.6 \times 10^{18}$$
$$Ni^{2+}(aq) + penten(aq) \rightleftharpoons Ni(penten)^{2+}(aq)$$
$$K_f = 2.0 \times 10^{19}$$

where penten is

$$NH_2CH_2CH_2 \diagdown \atop NH_2CH_2CH_2 \diagup N - CH_2 - CH_2 - N \diagup \atop \diagdown \ {CH_2CH_2NH_2 \atop CH_2CH_2NH_2}$$

This increased stability is called the *chelate effect*. Based on bond energies, would you expect the enthalpy changes for the above reactions to be very different? What is the order (from least favorable to most favorable) of the entropy changes of the above reactions? How do the values of the formation constants correlate with $\Delta S°$? How can this be used to explain the chelate effect?

68. Qualitatively draw the crystal field splitting of the *d* orbitals in a trigonal planar complex ion. (Let the *z* axis be perpendicular to the plane of the complex.)

69. Qualitatively draw the crystal field splitting for a trigonal bipyramidal complex ion. (Let the *z* axis be perpendicular to the trigonal plane.)

CHAPTER 21

The Nucleus: A Chemist's View

Since the chemistry of an atom is determined by the number and arrangement of its electrons, the properties of the nucleus are not of primary importance to chemists. In the simplest view, the nucleus provides the positive charge to bind the electrons in atoms and molecules. However, a quick reading of any daily newspaper will show you that the nucleus and its properties have an important impact on our society. This chapter considers those aspects of the nucleus about which everyone should have some knowledge.

Several aspects of the nucleus are immediately impressive: its very small size, its very large density, and the magnitude of the energy that holds it together. The radius of a typical nucleus appears to be about 10^{-13} cm. This can be compared to the radius of a typical atom, which is on the order of 10^{-8} cm. A visualization will help you appreciate the small size of the nucleus: if the nucleus of the hydrogen atom were the size of a Ping-Pong ball, the electron in the 1s orbital would be, on average, 0.5 kilometer (0.3 mile) away. The density of the nucleus is equally impressive— approximately 1.6×10^{14} g/cm^3. A sphere of nuclear material the size of a Ping-Pong ball would have a mass of 2.5 *billion tons!* In addition, the energies involved in nuclear processes are typically millions of times larger than those associated with normal chemical reactions. This fact makes nuclear processes very attractive for feeding the voracious energy appetite of our civilization.

Atomos, the Greek root of the word *atom,* means indivisible. It was originally believed that the atom was the ultimate indivisible particle of which all matter was composed. However, as we discussed in Chapter 2, Lord Rutherford showed in 1911 that the atom is not homogeneous, but rather has a dense, positively charged center surrounded by electrons. Subsequently,

< A scientist stands inside the plasma chamber of a tokamak fusion reactor. The chamber is lined with carbon-fiber tiles to protect against the high temperatures generated in the reaction.

scientists have learned that the nucleus of the atom can be subdivided into particles called **neutrons** and **protons.** In fact, in the last two decades it has become apparent that even the protons and neutrons are composed of smaller particles called **quarks.**

For most purposes, the nucleus can be regarded as a collection of **nucleons** (neutrons and protons), and the internal structures of these particles can be ignored. As we discussed in Chapter 2, the number of protons in a particular nucleus is called the **atomic number** (Z), and the sum of the neutrons and protons is the **mass number** (A). Atoms that have identical atomic numbers but different mass number values are called **isotopes.** However, we usually do not use the singular form *isotope* to refer to a particular member of a group of isotopes. Rather we use the term *nuclide.* A **nuclide** is a unique atom, represented by the symbol

$$_Z^A X$$

> The atomic number Z is the number of protons in a nucleus; the mass number A is the sum of protons and neutrons in a nucleus.

where X represents the symbol for a particular element. For example, the following nuclides constitute the isotopes of carbon: carbon-12 ($_6^{12}C$), carbon-13 ($_6^{13}C$), and carbon-14 ($_6^{14}C$).

> The term *isotopes* refers to a group of nuclides with the same atomic number. Each individual atom is properly called a *nuclide,* not an isotope.

21.1 Nuclear Stability and Radioactive Decay

Purpose

- To relate the stability of a nucleus to the number of protons and neutrons.
- To classify the types of radioactive decay.

Nuclear stability is the central topic of this chapter and forms the basis for all the important applications related to nuclear processes. Nuclear stability can be considered from both a kinetic and a thermodynamic point of view. **Thermodynamic stability,** as we will use the term here, refers to the potential energy of a particular nucleus as compared with the sum of the potential energies of its component protons and neutrons. We will use the term **kinetic stability** to describe the probability that a nucleus will undergo decomposition to form a different nucleus—a process called **radioactive decay.** We will consider radioactivity in this section.

Many nuclei are radioactive; that is, they decompose, forming another nucleus and producing one or more particles. An example is carbon-14, which decays as follows:

$$_6^{14}C \rightarrow\ _7^{14}N +\ _{-1}^0 e$$

where $_{-1}^0 e$ represents an electron, which is called a **beta particle,** or **β particle,** in nuclear terminology. This equation is typical of those representing radioactive decay in that both A and Z must be conserved. That is, the Z values must give the same sum on both sides of the equation ($6 = 7 - 1$), as must the A values ($14 = 14 + 0$).

Of the approximately 2000 known nuclides, only 279 are stable with respect to radioactive decay. Tin has the largest number of stable isotopes—10.

It is instructive to examine how the numbers of neutrons and protons in a nucleus are related to its stability with respect to radioactive decay. Fig. 21.1 shows a plot of

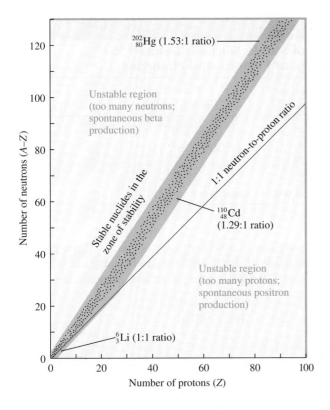

Figure 21.1

The zone of stability. The dots indicate the nuclides that *do not* undergo radioactive decay. Note that as the number of protons in a nuclide increases, the neutron/proton ratio required for stability also increases.

the positions of the stable nuclei as a function of the number of protons (Z) and the number of neutrons ($A - Z$). The stable nuclides are said to reside in the **zone of stability.**

The following are some important observations concerning radioactive decay:

All nuclides with 84 or more protons are unstable with respect to radioactive decay.

Light nuclides are stable when Z equals $A - Z$, that is, when the neutron/proton ratio is 1. However, for heavier elements the neutron/proton ratio required for stability is greater than 1 and increases with Z.

Certain combinations of protons and neutrons seem to confer special stability. For example, nuclides with even numbers of protons and neutrons are more often stable than those with odd numbers, as shown by the data in Table 21.1.

There are also certain specific numbers of protons or neutrons that produce especially stable nuclides. These so-called **magic numbers** are 2, 8, 20, 28, 50, 82, and 126. This behavior parallels that for atoms in which certain numbers of electrons (2, 10, 18, 36, 54, and 86) produce special chemical stability (the noble gases).

Types of Radioactive Decay

Radioactive nuclei can undergo decomposition in various ways. These decay processes fall into two categories: those which involve a change in the mass number of the decaying nucleus and those which do not. We will consider the former type of process first.

Table 21.1

Number of Stable Nuclides Related to Numbers of Protons and Neutrons

Number of Protons	Number of Neutrons	Number of Stable Nuclides	Examples
Even	Even	168	$^{12}_{6}C$, $^{16}_{8}O$
Even	Odd	57	$^{13}_{6}C$, $^{47}_{22}Ti$
Odd	Even	50	$^{19}_{9}F$, $^{23}_{11}Na$
Odd	Odd	4	$^{2}_{1}H$, $^{6}_{3}Li$

Note: Even numbers of protons and neutrons seem to favor stability.

α-particle production involves a change in A for the decaying nucleus; β-particle production has no effect on A.

An **alpha particle,** or **α particle,** is a helium nucleus ($^{4}_{2}He$). **Alpha-particle production** is a very common mode of decay for heavy radioactive nuclides. For example, $^{238}_{92}U$, the predominant (99.3%) isotope of natural uranium, decays by α-particle production:

$$^{238}_{92}U \rightarrow {}^{4}_{2}He + {}^{234}_{90}Th$$

Another α-particle producer is $^{230}_{90}Th$:

$$^{230}_{90}Th \rightarrow {}^{4}_{2}He + {}^{226}_{88}Ra$$

Another decay process in which the mass number of the decaying nucleus changes is **spontaneous fission,** the splitting of a heavy nuclide into two lighter nuclides with similar mass numbers. Although this process occurs at an extremely slow rate for most nuclides, it is important in some cases, such as for $^{254}_{98}Cf$, where spontaneous fission is the predominant mode of decay.

The most common decay process in which the mass number of the decaying nucleus remains constant is **β-particle production.** For example, the thorium-234 nuclide produces a β particle and is converted to protactinium-234:

$$^{234}_{90}Th \rightarrow {}^{234}_{91}Pa + {}^{0}_{-1}e$$

Iodine-131 is also a β-particle producer:

$$^{131}_{53}I \rightarrow {}^{0}_{-1}e + {}^{131}_{54}Xe$$

The β particle is assigned the mass number 0, since its mass is tiny compared with that of a proton or neutron. Because the value of Z is -1 for the β particle, the atomic number for the new nuclide is greater by 1 than for the original nuclide. Thus *the net effect of β-particle production is to change a neutron to a proton.* We therefore expect nuclides that lie above the zone of stability (those nuclides whose neutron/proton ratios are too high) to be β-particle producers.

It should be pointed out that although the β particle is an electron, the emitting nucleus does not contain electrons. As we shall see later in this chapter, a given quantity of energy (which is best regarded as a form of matter) can become a particle (another form of matter) under certain circumstances. The unstable nuclide creates an electron as it releases energy in the decay process. The electron thus results from the decay process rather than being present before the decay occurs. Think of this as somewhat like talking: words are not stored inside us but are formed as we speak. Later in this chapter we will discuss in more detail this very interesting phenomenon where matter in the form of particles and matter in the form of energy can interchange.

A **gamma ray,** or **γ ray,** refers to a high-energy photon. Frequently, γ-ray production accompanies nuclear decays and particle reactions, such as in the α-particle decay of $^{238}_{92}U$:

$$^{238}_{92}U \rightarrow {}^{4}_{2}He + {}^{234}_{90}Th + 2\,{}^{0}_{0}\gamma$$

where two γ rays of different energies are produced in addition to the α particle. The emission of γ rays is one way a nucleus with excess energy (in an excited nuclear state) can relax to its ground state.

Positron production occurs for nuclides that are below the zone of stability (those nuclides whose neutron/proton ratios are too small). The positron is a particle with the same mass as the electron but opposite charge. An example of a nuclide that decays by positron production is sodium-22:

$$^{22}_{11}Na \rightarrow {}^{0}_{1}e + {}^{22}_{10}Ne$$

Note that *the net effect is to change a proton to a neutron,* causing the product nuclide to have a higher neutron/proton ratio than the original nuclide.

Besides being oppositely charged, the positron shows an even more fundamental difference from the electron: it is the *antiparticle* of the electron. When a positron collides with an electron, the particulate matter is changed to electromagnetic radiation in the form of high-energy photons:

$$^{0}_{-1}e + {}^{0}_{1}e \rightarrow 2\,{}^{0}_{0}\gamma$$

This process, which is characteristic of matter–antimatter collisions, is called **annihilation** and is another example of the interchange of the forms of matter.

Electron capture is a process in which one of the inner-orbital electrons is captured by the nucleus, as illustrated by the process

$$^{201}_{80}Hg + \underset{\text{Inner-orbital electron}}{{}^{0}_{-1}e} \rightarrow {}^{201}_{79}Au + {}^{0}_{0}\gamma$$

This reaction would have been of great interest to the alchemists, but unfortunately, it does not occur at a rate that would make it a practical means for changing mercury to gold. Gamma rays are always produced along with electron capture to release excess energy. The various types of radioactive decay are summarized in Table 21.2.

Table 21.2

Various Types of Radioactive Processes Showing the Changes That Take Place in the Nuclides

Process	Change in A	Change in Z	Change in Neutron/proton Ratio	Example
β-particle (electron) production	0	+1	Decrease	$^{227}_{89}Ac \rightarrow {}^{227}_{90}Th + {}^{0}_{-1}e$
Positron production	0	−1	Increase	$^{13}_{7}N \rightarrow {}^{13}_{6}C + {}^{0}_{1}e$
Electron capture	0	−1	Increase	$^{73}_{33}As + {}^{0}_{-1}e \rightarrow {}^{73}_{32}Ge$
α-particle production	−4	−2	Increase	$^{210}_{84}Po \rightarrow {}^{206}_{82}Pb + {}^{4}_{2}He$
γ-ray production	0	0	—	Excited nucleus $\rightarrow$ ground state nucleus + ${}^{0}_{0}\gamma$
Spontaneous fission	—	—	—	$^{254}_{98}Cf \rightarrow$ lighter nuclides + neutrons

Sample Exercise 21.1

Write balanced equations for each of the following processes.

a. $^{11}_{6}C$ produces a positron.
b. $^{214}_{83}Bi$ produces a β particle.
c. $^{237}_{93}Np$ produces an α particle.

Solution

a. We must find the product nuclide represented by $^{A}_{Z}X$ in the following equation:

$$^{11}_{6}C \rightarrow {}^{0}_{1}e + {}^{A}_{Z}X$$
$$\uparrow$$
$$\text{Positron}$$

We can find the identity of $^{A}_{Z}X$ by recognizing that the total of the Z and A values must be the same on both sides of the equation. Thus for X, Z must be $6 - 1 = 5$ and A must be $11 - 0 = 11$. Therefore, $^{A}_{Z}X$ is $^{11}_{5}B$. (The fact that Z is 5 tells us that the nuclide is boron.) Thus the balanced equation is

$$^{11}_{6}C \rightarrow {}^{0}_{1}e + {}^{11}_{5}B$$

b. Knowing that a β particle is represented by $_{-1}^{0}e$ and that Z and A are conserved, we can write

$$^{214}_{83}Bi \rightarrow {}^{0}_{-1}e + {}^{214}_{84}X$$

so $^{A}_{Z}X$ must be $^{214}_{84}Po$.

c. Since an α particle is represented by $^{4}_{2}He$, the balanced equation must be

$$^{237}_{93}Np \rightarrow {}^{4}_{2}He + {}^{233}_{91}Pa$$

Sample Exercise 21.2

In each of the following nuclear reactions, supply the missing particle.

a. $^{195}_{79}Au + ? \rightarrow {}^{195}_{78}Pt$
b. $^{38}_{19}K \rightarrow {}^{38}_{18}Ar + ?$

Solution

a. Since A does not change and Z decreases by 1, the missing particle must be an electron:

$$^{195}_{79}Au + {}^{0}_{-1}e \rightarrow {}^{195}_{78}Pt$$

This is an example of electron capture.

b. To conserve Z and A, the missing particle must be a positron:

$$^{38}_{19}K \rightarrow {}^{38}_{18}Ar + {}^{0}_{1}e$$

Thus potassium-38 decays by positron production.

Figure 21.2
The decay series from $^{238}_{92}U$ to $^{206}_{82}Pb$. Each nuclide in the series except $^{206}_{82}Pb$ is unstable, and the successive transformations (shown by the arrows) continue until $^{206}_{82}Pb$ is finally formed. Note that horizontal arrows indicate processes where A is unchanged, while diagonal arrows signify that both A and Z change.

Often a radioactive nucleus cannot reach a stable state through a single decay process. In such a case, a **decay series** occurs until a stable nuclide is formed. A well-known example is the decay series that starts with $^{238}_{92}U$ and ends with $^{206}_{82}Pb$, as shown in Fig. 21.2. Similar series exist for $^{235}_{92}U$:

$$^{235}_{92}U \xrightarrow[\text{decays}]{\text{Series of}} {}^{207}_{82}Pb$$

and for $^{232}_{90}Th$:

$$^{232}_{90}Th \xrightarrow[\text{decays}]{\text{Series of}} {}^{208}_{82}Pb$$

21.2 *The Kinetics of Radioactive Decay*

Purpose

- To define and show how to calculate the half-life of a radioactive nuclide.

In a sample containing radioactive nuclides of a given type, each nuclide has a certain probability of undergoing decay. Suppose that a sample of 1000 atoms of a certain nuclide produces 10 decay events per hour. This means that over the span of an hour, 1 out of every 100 nuclides will decay. Given that this probability of decay is characteristic for this type of nuclide, we could predict that a 2000-atom sample would give 20 decay events per hour. Thus, for radioactive nuclides, the **rate of**

Rates of reaction are discussed in Chapter 12.

decay, which is the negative of the change in the number of nuclides per unit time

$$\left(-\frac{\Delta N}{\Delta t}\right)$$

is directly proportional to the number of nuclides N in a given sample:

$$\text{Rate} = -\frac{\Delta N}{\Delta t} \propto N$$

The negative sign is included because the number of nuclides is decreasing. We now insert a proportionality constant k to give

$$\text{Rate} = -\frac{\Delta N}{\Delta t} = kN$$

This is the rate law for a first-order process, as we saw in Chapter 12. As shown in Section 12.4, the integrated first-order rate law is

$$\ln\left(\frac{N}{N_0}\right) = -kt$$

where N_0 represents the original number of nuclides (at $t = 0$) and N represents the number *remaining* at time t.

Half-Life

The **half-life** ($t_{1/2}$) of a radioactive sample is defined as the time required for the number of nuclides to reach half the original value ($N_0/2$). We can use this definition in connection with the integrated first-order rate law (as we did in Section 12.4) to produce the following expression for $t_{1/2}$:

$$t_{1/2} = \frac{\ln(2)}{k} = \frac{0.693}{k}$$

Thus, if the half-life of a radioactive nuclide is known, the rate constant can be easily calculated, and vice versa.

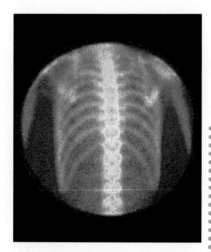

The image of a bone scan of a normal chest (posterior view). Radioactive technetium-99m is injected into the patient and is then concentrated in bones, allowing a physician to look for abnormalities such as might be caused by cancer.

Sample Exercise 21.3

Technetium-99m is used to form pictures of internal organs in the body and is often used to assess heart damage. The m for this nuclide indicates an excited nuclear state that decays to the ground state by gamma emission. The rate constant for decay of $^{99m}_{43}\text{Tc}$ is known to be 1.16×10^{-1}/h. What is the half-life of this nuclide?

Solution

The half-life can be calculated from the expression

$$t_{1/2} = \frac{0.693}{k} = \frac{0.693}{1.16 \times 10^{-1}/\text{h}}$$

$$= 6.0 \text{ h}$$

Thus it will take 6.0 h for a given sample of technetium-99m to decrease to half the original number of nuclides.

As we saw in Section 12.4, the half-life for a first-order process is constant. This is shown for the β-particle decay of strontium-90 in Fig. 21.3; it takes 28.8 years for each halving of the amount of $^{90}_{38}Sr$. Contamination of the environment with $^{90}_{38}Sr$ poses serious health hazards because of the similar chemistry of strontium and calcium (both are in Group 2A). Strontium-90 in grass and hay is incorporated into cow's milk along with calcium and is then passed on to humans, where it lodges in the bones. Because of its relatively long half-life, it persists for years in humans, causing radiation damage that may lead to cancer.

The harmful effects of radiation will be discussed in Section 21.7.

Sample Exercise 21.4

The half-life of molybdenum-99 is 67.0 h. How much of a 1.000-mg sample of $^{99}_{42}Mo$ is left after 335 h?

Solution

The easiest way to solve this problem is to recognize that 335 h represents five half-lives for $^{99}_{42}Mo$:

$$335 = 5 \times 67.0$$

We can sketch the change that occurs, as is shown in Fig. 21.4. Thus, after 335 h, 0.031 mg $^{99}_{42}Mo$ remains.

The half-lives of radioactive nuclides vary over a tremendous range. For example, $^{144}_{60}Nd$ has a half-life of 5×10^{15} years, while $^{214}_{84}Po$ has a half-life of 2×10^{-4}

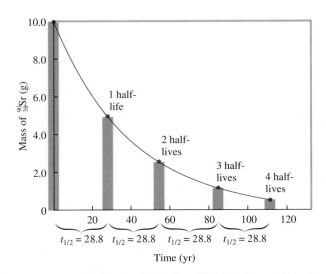

Figure 21.3

The decay of a 10.0-g sample of strontium-90 over time. Note that the half-life is a constant 28.8 years.

Figure 21.4

The change in the amount of $^{99}_{42}Mo$ with time ($t_{1/2} = 67$ h).

second. To give you some perspective on this, the half-lives of the nuclides in the $^{238}_{92}U$ decay series are given in Table 21.3.

Table 21.3		
The Half-Lives of Nuclides in the $^{238}_{92}U$ Decay Series		
Nuclide	Particle Produced	Half-life
Uranium-238 ($^{238}_{92}U$)	α	4.51×10^9 years
Thorium-234 ($^{234}_{90}Th$)	β	24.1 days
Protactinium-234 ($^{234}_{91}Pa$)	β	6.75 hours
Uranium-234 ($^{234}_{92}U$)	α	2.48×10^5 years
Thorium-230 ($^{230}_{90}Th$)	α	8.0×10^4 years
Radium-226 ($^{226}_{88}Ra$)	α	1.62×10^3 years
Radon-222 ($^{222}_{86}Rn$)	α	3.82 days
Polonium-218 ($^{218}_{84}Po$)	α	3.1 minutes
Lead-214 ($^{214}_{82}Pb$)	β	26.8 minutes
Bismuth-214 ($^{214}_{83}Bi$)	β	19.7 minutes
Polonium-214 ($^{214}_{84}Po$)	α	1.6×10^{-4} second
Lead-210 ($^{210}_{82}Pb$)	β	20.4 years
Bismuth-210 ($^{210}_{83}Bi$)	β	5.0 days
Polonium-210 ($^{210}_{84}Po$)	α	138.4 days
Lead-206 ($^{206}_{82}Pb$)	—	Stable

◀ **CHEMICAL IMPACT** ▶

Stellar Nucleosynthesis

How did all the matter around us originate? The scientific answer to this question is a theory called **stellar nucleosynthesis,** literally, the formation of nuclei in stars.

Many scientists believe that our universe originated as a cloud of neutrons that became unstable and produced an immense explosion, giving this model its name—*the big bang theory.* The model postulates that, following the initial explosion, neutrons decomposed into protons and electrons,

$$_0^1n \rightarrow \ _1^1H + \ _{-1}^0e$$

which eventually recombined to form clouds of hydrogen. Over the eons, gravitational forces caused many of these hydrogen clouds to contract and heat up sufficiently to reach temperatures where proton fusion was possible, which released large quantities of energy. When the tendency to expand due to the heat from fusion and the tendency to contract due to the forces of gravity are balanced, a stable young star such as our sun can be formed.

Eventually, when the supply of hydrogen is exhausted, the core of the star will again contract with further heating until temperatures are reached where fusion of helium nuclei can occur, leading to the formation of $_6^{12}C$ and $_8^{16}O$ nuclei. In turn, when the supply of helium nuclei runs out, further contraction and heating will occur, until fusion of heavier nuclei takes place. This process occurs repeatedly,

A mysterious elliptical ring around supernova 1987A (center).

forming heavier and heavier nuclei until iron nuclei are formed. Because the iron nucleus is the most stable of all, energy is required to fuse iron nuclei. This endothermic fusion process cannot furnish energy to sustain the star, and therefore it cools to a small, dense *white dwarf.*

The evolution just described is characteristic of small and medium-sized stars. Much larger stars, however, become unstable at some time during their evolution and undergo a *supernova explosion.* In this explosion, some medium-mass nuclei are fused to form heavy elements. Also, some light nuclei capture neutrons. These neutron-rich nuclei then produce β particles, increasing their atomic number with each event. This eventually leads to heavy nuclei. In fact, almost all nuclei heavier than iron are thought to originate from

supernova explosions. The debris of a supernova explosion thus contains a large variety of elements and might eventually form a solar system such as our own.

Although other theories for the origin of matter have been suggested, there is much evidence to support the big bang theory, and it continues to be widely accepted.

For more information see V. E. Viola, "Formation of the chemical elements and the evolution of our universe," *J. Chem. Ed.* **67** (1990): 723.

21.3 Nuclear Transformations

Purpose

- To show how one element may be changed into another using particle bombardment.

In 1919 Lord Rutherford observed the first **nuclear transformation,** *the change of one element into another.* He found that by bombarding $_7^{14}N$ with α particles, the

Figure 21.5

A schematic diagram of a cyclotron. The ion is introduced in the center and is pulled back and forth between the hollow D-shaped electrodes by constant reversals of the electric field. Magnets above and below these electrodes produce a spiral path that expands as the particle velocity increases. When the particle has sufficient speed, it exits the accelerator and is directed at the target nucleus.

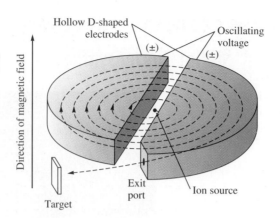

nuclide $^{17}_{8}O$ could be produced:

$$^{14}_{7}N + ^{4}_{2}He \rightarrow ^{17}_{8}O + ^{1}_{1}H$$

Fourteen years later, Irene Curie and her husband Frederick Joliot observed a similar transformation from aluminum to phosphorus,

$$^{27}_{13}Al + ^{4}_{2}He \rightarrow ^{30}_{15}P + ^{1}_{0}n$$

where $^{1}_{0}n$ represents a neutron.

Over the years, many other nuclear transformations have been achieved, mostly using **particle accelerators,** which, as the name reveals, are devices used to give particles very high velocities. Because of the electrostatic repulsion between the target nucleus and a positive ion, accelerators are needed when positive ions are used as bombarding particles. The particle, accelerated to a very high velocity, can overcome the repulsion and penetrate the target nucleus, thus effecting the transformation. A schematic diagram of one type of particle accelerator, the **cyclotron,** is shown in Fig. 21.5. The ion is introduced at the center of the cyclotron and is accelerated in an expanding spiral path by use of alternating electric fields in the presence of a magnetic field. The **linear accelerator** illustrated in Fig. 21.6 employs changing electric fields to achieve high velocities on a linear pathway.

In addition to positive ions, neutrons are often employed as bombarding particles to effect nuclear transformations. Because neutrons are uncharged and thus not repelled electrostatically by a target nucleus, they are readily absorbed by many nuclei, leading to new nuclides. The most common source of neutrons for this purpose is a fission reactor (see Section 21.6).

By using neutron and positive-ion bombardment, scientists have been able to extend the periodic table. Prior to 1940, the heaviest known element was uranium ($Z = 92$), but in 1940 neptunium ($Z = 93$) was produced by neutron bombardment

Figure 21.6

Schematic diagram of a linear accelerator, which uses a changing electric field to accelerate a positive ion along a linear path. As the ion leaves the source, the odd-numbered tubes are negatively charged, and the even-numbered tubes are positively charged. The positive ion is thus attracted into tube 1. As the ion leaves tube 1, the tube polarities are reversed. Now tube 1 is positive, repelling the positive ion, and tube 2 is negative, attracting the positive ion. This process continues, eventually producing high particle velocity.

Table 21.4

Syntheses of Some of the Transuranium Elements

Element	Neutron Bombardment	Half-life
Neptunium (Z = 93)	$^{238}_{92}U + ^{1}_{0}n \rightarrow ^{239}_{92}U \rightarrow ^{239}_{93}Np + ^{0}_{-1}e$	2.35 days ($^{239}_{93}Np$)
Plutonium (Z = 94)	$^{239}_{93}Np \rightarrow ^{239}_{94}Pu + ^{0}_{-1}e$	24,400 years ($^{239}_{94}Pu$)
Americium (Z = 95)	$^{239}_{94}Pu + 2\,^{1}_{0}n \rightarrow ^{241}_{94}Pu \rightarrow ^{241}_{95}Am + ^{0}_{-1}e$	458 years ($^{241}_{95}Am$)

Element	Positive-ion Bombardment	Half-life
Curium (Z = 96)	$^{239}_{94}Pu + ^{4}_{2}He \rightarrow ^{242}_{96}Cm + ^{1}_{0}n$	163 days ($^{242}_{96}Cm$)
Californium (Z = 98)	$^{242}_{96}Cm + ^{4}_{2}He \rightarrow ^{245}_{98}Cf + ^{1}_{0}n$ or $^{238}_{92}U + ^{12}_{6}C \rightarrow ^{246}_{98}Cf + 4\,^{1}_{0}n$	44 minutes ($^{245}_{98}Cf$)
Element 104	$^{249}_{98}Cf + ^{12}_{6}C \rightarrow ^{257}_{104}X + 4\,^{1}_{0}n$	
Element 105	$^{249}_{98}Cf + ^{15}_{7}N \rightarrow ^{260}_{105}X + 4\,^{1}_{0}n$	
Element 106	$^{249}_{98}Cf + ^{18}_{8}O \rightarrow ^{263}_{106}X + 4\,^{1}_{0}n$	

of $^{238}_{92}U$. The process initially gives $^{239}_{92}U$, which decays to $^{239}_{93}Np$ by β-particle production:

$$^{238}_{92}U + ^{1}_{0}n \rightarrow ^{239}_{92}U \xrightarrow[t_{1/2} = 23\ min]{} ^{239}_{93}Np + ^{0}_{-1}e$$

In the years since 1940, the elements with atomic numbers 93 through 106, called the **transuranium elements,**[*] have been synthesized. Many of these elements have very short half-lives, as shown in Table 21.4. As a result, only a few atoms of some have ever been formed. This of course makes the chemical characterization of these elements extremely difficult.

21.4 Detection and Uses of Radioactivity

Purpose

- To discuss radioactivity detection devices.
- To show how objects can be dated using radioactive decay.

Although various instruments measure radioactivity levels, the most familiar of them is the **Geiger–Müller counter,** or **Geiger counter** (see Fig. 21.7). This instrument takes advantage of the fact that the high-energy particles from radioactive decay processes produce ions when they travel through matter. The probe of the Geiger counter is filled with argon gas, which can be ionized by a rapidly moving

Geiger counters are often called survey meters in industry.

[*]For more information, see G. B. Kauffman, ''Beyond uranium,'' *Chem. Eng. News* (Nov. 19, 1990): 18.

Figure 21.7

A schematic representation of a Geiger–Müller counter. The high-energy radioactive particle enters the window and ionizes argon atoms along its path. The resulting ions and electrons produce a momentary current pulse, which is amplified and counted.

Carbon-14 radioactivity is often used to date human skeletons found at archeological sites.

Radioactive nuclides are often called radionuclides. *Carbon dating is based on the radionuclide $^{14}_{6}C$.*

particle as illustrated below. This reaction is demonstrated by the equation:

$$\text{Ar}(g) \xrightarrow[\text{particle}]{\text{High-energy}} \text{Ar}^{+}(g) + e^{-}$$

Normally, a sample of argon gas will not conduct a current when an electrical potential is applied. However, the formation of ions and electrons produced by the passage of the high-energy particle allows a momentary current to flow. Electronic devices detect this current flow, and the number of these events can be counted. Thus the decay rate of the radioactive sample can be determined.

Another instrument often used to detect levels of radioactivity is a **scintillation counter,** which takes advantage of the fact that certain substances, such as zinc sulfide, give off light when they are struck by high-energy radiation. A photocell senses the flashes of light that occur as the radiation strikes and thus measures the number of decay events per unit of time.

Dating by Radioactivity

Archeologists, geologists, and others involved in reconstructing the ancient history of the earth rely heavily on radioactivity to provide accurate dates for artifacts and rocks. A method that has been very important for dating ancient articles made from wood or cloth is **radiocarbon dating,** or **carbon-14 dating,** a technique originated in the 1940s by Willard Libby, an American chemist who received a Nobel Prize for his efforts in this field.

Radiocarbon dating is based on the radioactivity of the nuclide $^{14}_{6}C$, which decays via β-particle production:

$$^{14}_{6}\text{C} \rightarrow \, ^{\;0}_{-1}\text{e} + \, ^{14}_{7}\text{N}$$

Carbon-14 is continuously produced in the atmosphere when high-energy neutrons from space collide with nitrogen-14:

$$^{14}_{7}\text{N} + \, ^{1}_{0}\text{n} \rightarrow \, ^{14}_{6}\text{C} + \, ^{1}_{1}\text{H}$$

Thus carbon-14 is continuously produced by this process, and it continuously decomposes through β-particle production. Over the years, the rates for these two processes have become equal, and like a participant in a chemical reaction at equilibrium, the amount of $^{14}_{6}C$ that is present in the atmosphere remains approximately constant.

Carbon-14 can be used to date wood and cloth artifacts because the $^{14}_{6}C$, along with the other carbon isotopes in the atmosphere, reacts with oxygen to form carbon dioxide. A living plant consumes carbon dioxide in the photosynthesis process and incorporates the carbon, including $^{14}_6C$, into its molecules. As long as the plant lives, the $^{14}_6C/^{12}_6C$ ratio in its molecules remains the same as in the atmosphere because of the continuous uptake of carbon. However, as soon as a tree is cut to make a wooden bowl or a flax plant is harvested to make linen, the $^{14}_6C/^{12}_6C$ ratio begins to decrease because of the radioactive decay of $^{14}_6C$ (the $^{12}_6C$ nuclide is stable). Since the half-life of $^{14}_6C$ is 5730 years, a wooden bowl found in an archeological dig showing a $^{14}_6C/^{12}_6C$ ratio that is half that found in currently living trees is approximately 5730 years old. This reasoning assumes that the current $^{14}_6C/^{12}_6C$ ratio is the same as that found in ancient times.

Dendrochronologists, scientists who date trees from annual growth rings, have used data collected from long-lived species of trees, such as bristlecone pines and sequoias, to show that the $^{14}_6C$ content of the atmosphere has changed significantly over the ages. These data have been used to derive correction factors that allow very accurate dates to be determined from the observed $^{14}_6C/^{12}_6C$ ratio in an artifact, especially for artifacts 10,000 years old or less. Recent measurements of uranium/thorium ratios in ancient coral indicate that dates in the 20,000- to 30,000-year range may have errors as large as 3000 years. As a result, efforts are now being made to recalibrate the $^{14}_6C$ dates over this period.

The $^{14}_6C/^{12}_6C$ ratio is the basis for carbon-14 dating.

Sample Exercise 21.5

The remnants of an ancient fire in a cave in Africa showed a $^{14}_6C$ decay rate of 3.1 counts per minute per gram of carbon. Assuming that the decay rate of $^{14}_6C$ in freshly cut wood (corrected for changes in the $^{14}_6C$ content of the atmosphere) is 13.6 counts per minute per gram of carbon, calculate the age of the remnants. The half-life of $^{14}_6C$ is 5730 years.

Solution

The key to solving this problem is to realize that the decay rates given are directly proportional to the number of $^{14}_6C$ nuclides present. Radioactive decay follows first-order kinetics:

$$\text{Rate} = kN$$

Thus
$$\frac{3.1 \text{ counts/min} \cdot g}{13.6 \text{ counts/min} \cdot g} = \frac{\text{rate at time } t}{\text{rate at time } 0} = \frac{kN}{kN_0}$$

Number of nuclides present at time t

Number of nuclides present at time 0

$$= \frac{N}{N_0} = 0.23$$

We can now use the integrated first-order rate law:

$$\ln\left(\frac{N}{N_0}\right) = -kt$$

A dendrochronologist cutting a section from a dead tree in South Africa.

where

$$k = \frac{0.693}{t_{1/2}} = \frac{0.693}{5730 \text{ years}}$$

to solve for t, the time elapsed since the campfire.

$$\ln\left(\frac{N}{N_0}\right) = \ln(0.23) = -\left(\frac{0.693}{5730 \text{ years}}\right)t$$

Solving this equation gives $t = 12{,}000$ years; the campfire in the cave occurred about 12,000 years ago.

One drawback of radiocarbon dating is that a fairly large piece of the object (from a half to several grams) must be burned to form carbon dioxide, which is then analyzed for radioactivity. Another method for counting $^{14}_6C$ nuclides avoids destruction of a significant portion of a valuable artifact. This technique, requiring only about 10^{-3} g, uses a mass spectrometer (see Chapter 3), in which the carbon atoms are ionized and accelerated through a magnetic field that deflects their path. Because of their different masses, the various ions are deflected by different amounts and can be counted separately. This allows a very accurate determination of the $^{14}_6C/^{12}_6C$ ratio in the sample.

In their attempts to establish the geologic history of the earth, geologists have made extensive use of radioactivity. For example, since $^{238}_{92}U$ decays to the stable $^{206}_{82}Pb$ nuclide, the ratio of $^{206}_{82}Pb$ to $^{238}_{92}U$ in a rock can, under favorable circumstances, be used to estimate the age of the rock.

> Because the half-life of $^{238}_{92}U$ is very long compared with those of the other members of the decay series (see Table 21.3) to reach $^{206}_{82}Pb$, the number of nuclides present in intermediate stages of decay is negligible. That is, once a $^{238}_{92}U$ nuclide starts to decay, it reaches $^{206}_{82}Pb$ relatively fast.

Sample Exercise 21.6

A rock containing $^{238}_{92}U$ and $^{206}_{82}Pb$ was examined to determine its approximate age. Analysis showed the ratio of $^{206}_{82}Pb$ atoms to $^{238}_{92}U$ atoms to be 0.115. Assuming that no lead was originally present, that all the $^{206}_{82}Pb$ formed over the years has remained in the rock, and that the number of nuclides in intermediate stages of decay between $^{238}_{92}U$ and $^{206}_{82}Pb$ is negligible, calculate the age of the rock. The half-life of $^{238}_{92}U$ is 4.5×10^9 years.

Solution

This problem can be solved using the integrated first-order rate law:

$$\ln\left(\frac{N}{N_0}\right) = -kt = -\left(\frac{0.693}{4.5 \times 10^9 \text{ years}}\right)t$$

where N/N_0 represents the ratio of $^{238}_{92}U$ atoms now found in the rock to the number present when the rock was formed. We are assuming that each $^{206}_{82}Pb$ nuclide present must have come from decay of a $^{238}_{92}U$:

$$^{238}_{92}U \rightarrow \, ^{206}_{82}Pb$$

Thus

Number of $^{238}_{92}U$ atoms originally present	=	number of $^{206}_{82}Pb$ atoms now present	+	number of $^{238}_{92}U$ atoms now present

$$\frac{\text{Atoms of } ^{206}_{82}\text{Pb now present}}{\text{Atoms of } ^{238}_{92}\text{U now present}} = 0.115 = \frac{0.115}{1.000} = \frac{115}{1000}$$

Think carefully about what this means. For every 1115 $^{238}_{92}\text{U}$ atoms originally present in the rock, 115 have been changed to $^{206}_{82}\text{Pb}$ and 1000 remain as $^{238}_{92}\text{U}$. Thus

$$\frac{N}{N_0} = \frac{\overset{\text{Now present}}{^{238}_{92}\text{U}}}{\underset{^{238}_{92}\text{U originally present}}{^{206}_{82}\text{Pb} + {^{238}_{92}\text{U}}}} = \frac{1000}{1115} = 0.8969$$

$$\ln\left(\frac{N}{N_0}\right) = \ln(0.8969) = -\left(\frac{0.693}{4.5 \times 10^9 \text{ years}}\right)t$$

$$t = 7.1 \times 10^8 \text{ years}$$

This is the approximate age of the rock. It was formed sometime in the Cambrian period.

Medical Applications of Radioactivity

Although the rapid advances of the medical sciences in recent decades are due to many causes, one of the most important has been the discovery and use of **radiotracers,** radioactive nuclides that can be introduced into organisms in food or drugs and whose pathways can be *traced* by monitoring their radioactivity. For example, the incorporation of nuclides such as $^{14}_{6}\text{C}$ and $^{32}_{15}\text{P}$ into nutrients has produced important information about metabolic pathways.

Iodine-131 has proved very useful in the diagnosis and treatment of illnesses of the thyroid gland. Patients drink a solution containing small amounts of Na^{131}I, and the uptake of the iodine by the thyroid gland is monitored with a scanner (see Fig. 21.8).

Thallium-201 can be used to assess the damage to the heart muscle in a person who has suffered a heart attack, because thallium is concentrated in healthy muscle

Figure 21.8

After consumption of Na^{131}I, the patient's thyroid is scanned for radioactivity levels to determine the efficiency of iodine absorption. (*left*) A normal thyroid. (*right*) An enlarged thyroid.

Table 21.5		
Some Radioactive Nuclides, with Half-Lives and Medical Applications as Radiotracers		
Nuclide	Half-life	Area of the Body Studied
^{131}I	8.1 days	Thyroid
^{59}Fe	45.1 days	Red blood cells
^{99}Mo	67 hours	Metabolism
^{32}P	14.3 days	Eyes, liver, tumors
^{51}Cr	27.8 days	Red blood cells
^{87}Sr	2.8 hours	Bones
^{99m}Tc	6.0 hours	Heart, bones, liver, and lungs
^{133}Xe	5.3 days	Lungs
^{24}Na	14.8 hours	Circulatory system

tissue. Technetium-99m is also taken up by normal heart tissue and is used for damage assessment in a similar way.

Radiotracers provide sensitive and noninvasive methods for learning about biologic systems, for detection of disease, for monitoring the action and effectiveness of drugs, and for early detection of pregnancy, and their usefulness should continue to grow. Some useful radiotracers are listed in Table 21.5.

21.5 Thermodynamic Stability of the Nucleus

Purpose

- To discuss the thermodynamic stability of the nucleus.
- To show how to calculate nuclear binding energies.

We can determine the thermodynamic stability of a nucleus by calculating the change in potential energy that would occur if that nucleus were formed from its constituent protons and neutrons. For example, let's consider the hypothetical process of forming a $^{16}_{8}O$ nucleus from eight neutrons and eight protons:

$$8 \, ^{1}_{0}n + 8 \, ^{1}_{1}H \rightarrow \, ^{16}_{8}O$$

The energy change associated with this process can be calculated by comparing the sum of the masses of eight protons and eight neutrons with that of the oxygen nucleus:

$$\text{Mass of } (8 \, ^{1}_{0}n + 8 \, ^{1}_{1}H) = 8(1.67493 \times 10^{-24} \text{ g}) + 8(1.67262 \times 10^{-24} \text{ g})$$

$$\underset{\text{Mass of } ^{1}_{0}n}{\nearrow} \qquad \underset{\text{Mass of } ^{1}_{1}H}{\nearrow}$$

$$= 2.67804 \times 10^{-23} \text{ g}$$

$$\text{Mass of } ^{16}_{8}O \text{ nucleus} = 2.65535 \times 10^{-23} \text{ g}$$

The difference in mass for one nucleus is

$$\text{Mass of } ^{16}_{8}O - \text{mass of } (8 \, ^{1}_{0}n + 8 \, ^{1}_{1}H) = -2.269 \times 10^{-25} \text{ g}$$

The difference in mass for formation of 1 mole of $^{16}_{8}O$ nuclei is therefore

$$(-2.269 \times 10^{-25} \text{ g/nucleus})(6.022 \times 10^{23} \text{ nuclei/mol}) = -0.1366 \text{ g/mol}$$

Thus 0.1366 g of mass would be lost if 1 mole of oxygen-16 were formed from protons and neutrons. What is the reason for this difference in mass, and how can this information be used to calculate the energy change that accompanies this process?

The answers to these questions can be found in the work of Albert Einstein. As we discussed in Section 7.2, Einstein's theory of relativity showed that energy should be considered a form of matter. His famous equation

$$E = mc^2$$

where c is the speed of light, gives the relationship between a quantity of energy and its mass. When a system gains or loses energy, it also gains or loses a quantity of mass, given by E/c^2. Thus the mass of a nucleus is less than that of its component nucleons because the process is so exothermic.

Einstein's equation in the form

$$\text{Energy change} = \Delta E = \Delta mc^2$$

where Δm is the change in mass, or the **mass defect,** can be used to calculate ΔE for the hypothetical formation of a nucleus from its component nucleons.

Energy is a form of matter.

The energy changes associated with normal chemical reactions are small enough that the corresponding mass changes are not detectable.

Sample Exercise 21.7

Calculate the change in energy if 1 mol $^{16}_{8}O$ nuclei were formed from neutrons and protons.

Solution

We have already calculated that 0.1366 g of mass would be lost in the hypothetical process of assembling 1 mol $^{16}_{8}O$ nuclei from the component nucleons. We can calculate the change in energy for this process from

$$\Delta E = \Delta mc^2$$

where

$$c = 3.00 \times 10^8 \text{ m/s} \quad \text{and} \quad \Delta m = 0.1366 \text{ g/mol} = 1.366 \times 10^{-4} \text{ kg/mol}$$

Thus

$$\Delta E = (-1.366 \times 10^{-4} \text{ kg/mol})(3.00 \times 10^8 \text{ m/s})^2 = -1.23 \times 10^{13} \text{ J/mol}$$

The negative sign for the ΔE value indicates that the process is exothermic. Energy, and thus mass, is lost from the system.

The energy changes observed for nuclear processes are extremely large compared with those observed for chemical and physical changes. Thus nuclear processes constitute a potentially valuable energy resource.

Figure 21.9

The binding energy per nucleon as a function of mass number. The most stable nuclei are at the top of the curve. The most stable nucleus is $_{26}^{56}$Fe.

The thermodynamic stability of a particular nucleus is normally represented as energy released per nucleon. To illustrate how this quantity is obtained, we will continue to consider $_8^{16}$O. First, we calculate ΔE per nucleus by dividing the molar value from Sample Exercise 21.7 by Avogadro's number:

$$\Delta E \text{ per } _8^{16}\text{O nucleus} = \frac{-1.23 \times 10^{13} \text{ J/mol}}{6.022 \times 10^{23} \text{ nuclei/mol}} = -2.04 \times 10^{-11} \text{ J/nucleus}$$

In terms of a more convenient energy unit, a million electronvolts (MeV), where

$$1 \text{ MeV} = 1.60 \times 10^{-13} \text{ J}$$

$$\Delta E \text{ per } _8^{16}\text{O nucleus} = (-2.04 \times 10^{-11} \text{ J/nucleus})\left(\frac{1 \text{ MeV}}{1.60 \times 10^{-13} \text{ J}}\right)$$

$$= -1.28 \times 10^2 \text{ MeV/nucleus}$$

Next, we can calculate the value of ΔE per nucleon by dividing by A, the sum of neutrons and protons:

$$\Delta E \text{ per nucleon for } _8^{16}\text{O} = \frac{-1.28 \times 10^2 \text{ MeV/nucleus}}{16 \text{ nucleons/nucleus}}$$

$$= -7.98 \text{ MeV/nucleon}$$

This means that 7.98 MeV of energy per nucleon would be *released* if $_8^{16}$O were formed from neutrons and protons. The energy required to *decompose* this nucleus into its components has the same numeric value but with a positive sign (since energy is required). This is called the **binding energy** per nucleon for $_8^{16}$O.

The values of the binding energy per nucleon for the various nuclides are shown in Fig. 21.9. Note that the most stable nuclei (those requiring the largest energy per nucleon to decompose the nucleus) occur at the top of the curve. The most stable nucleus known is $_{26}^{56}$Fe, which has a binding energy per nucleon of 8.79 MeV.

Sample Exercise 21.8

Calculate the binding energy per nucleon for the $_2^4$He nucleus (atomic masses: $_2^4$He = 4.0026 amu; $_1^1$H = 1.0078 amu).

Solution

First, we must calculate the mass defect (Δm) for $^4_2$He. Since atomic masses (which include the electrons) are given, we must decide how to account for the electron mass:

$$4.0026 = \text{mass of } ^4_2\text{He atom} = \text{mass of } ^4_2\text{He nucleus} + 2m_e$$

Electron mass

$$1.0078 = \text{mass of } ^1_1\text{H atom} = \text{mass of } ^1_1\text{H nucleus} + m_e$$

Thus, since a $^4_2$He nucleus is "synthesized" from two protons and two neutrons, we see that

$$\Delta m = \underbrace{(4.0026 - 2m_e)}_{\substack{\text{Mass of} \\ ^4_2\text{He nucleus}}} - [\underbrace{2(1.0078 - m_e)}_{\substack{\text{Mass of} \\ ^1_1\text{H nucleus} \\ \text{(proton)}}} + \underbrace{2(1.0087)}_{\substack{\text{Mass of} \\ \text{neutron}}}]$$

$$= 4.0026 - 2m_e - 2(1.0078) + 2m_e - 2(1.0087)$$
$$= 4.0026 - 2(1.0078) - 2(1.0087)$$
$$= -0.0304 \text{ amu}$$

Note that in this case the electron mass cancels out in taking the difference. This will always happen in this type of calculation if the atomic masses are used both for the nuclide of interest and for $^1_1$H. Thus 0.0304 amu of mass is *lost* per $^4_2$He nucleus formed.

The corresponding energy change can be calculated from

$$\Delta E = \Delta mc^2$$

where

$$\Delta m = -0.0304 \frac{\text{amu}}{\text{nucleus}} = \left(-0.0304 \frac{\text{amu}}{\text{nucleus}}\right)\left(1.66 \times 10^{-27} \frac{\text{kg}}{\text{amu}}\right)$$

$$= -5.04 \times 10^{-29} \frac{\text{kg}}{\text{nucleus}}$$

and

$$c = 3.00 \times 10^8 \text{ m/s}$$

Thus

$$\Delta E = \left(-5.04 \times 10^{-29} \frac{\text{kg}}{\text{nucleus}}\right)\left(3.00 \times 10^8 \frac{\text{m}}{\text{s}}\right)^2$$

$$= -4.54 \times 10^{-12} \text{ J/nucleus}$$

This means that 4.54×10^{-12} J of energy is *released* per nucleus formed and that 4.54×10^{-12} J would be required to decompose the nucleus into the constituent neutrons and protons. Thus the binding energy (BE) per nucleon is

$$\text{BE per nucleon} = \frac{4.54 \times 10^{-12} \text{ J/nucleus}}{4 \text{ nucleons/nucleus}}$$

$$= 1.14 \times 10^{-12} \text{ J/nucleon}$$

$$= \left(1.14 \times 10^{-12} \frac{\text{J}}{\text{nucleon}}\right)\left(\frac{1 \text{ MeV}}{1.60 \times 10^{-13} \text{ J}}\right)$$

$$= 7.13 \text{ MeV/nucleon}$$

21.6 *Nuclear Fission and Nuclear Fusion*

Purpose

- To explore the energetics of nuclear fission and nuclear fusion.
- To describe how a nuclear reactor works.

The graph shown in Fig. 21.9 has very important implications for the use of nuclear processes as sources of energy. Recall that energy is released, that is, ΔE is negative, when a process goes from a less stable to a more stable state. The higher a nuclide is on the curve, the more stable it is. This means that two types of nuclear processes will be exothermic (see Fig. 21.10):

1. Combining two light nuclei to form a heavier, more stable nucleus. This process is called **fusion.**

2. Splitting a heavy nucleus into two nuclei with smaller mass numbers. This process is called **fission.**

Because of the large binding energies involved in holding the nucleus together, both these processes involve energy changes more than a million times larger than those associated with chemical reactions.

Nuclear Fission

Nuclear fission was discovered in the late 1930s when $^{235}_{92}\text{U}$ nuclides bombarded with neutrons were observed to split into two lighter elements:

$$^{1}_{0}\text{n} + {}^{235}_{92}\text{U} \rightarrow {}^{141}_{56}\text{Ba} + {}^{92}_{36}\text{Kr} + 3\ {}^{1}_{0}\text{n}$$

This process, shown schematically in Fig. 21.11, releases 3.5×10^{-11} J of energy per event, which translates to 2.1×10^{13} J per mole of $^{235}_{92}\text{U}$. Compare this figure with that for the combustion of methane, which releases only 8.0×10^{5} J of energy per mole. The fission of $^{235}_{92}\text{U}$ produces about 26 million times more energy than the combustion of methane.

Figure 21.10

Both fission and fusion produce more stable nuclides and are thus exothermic.

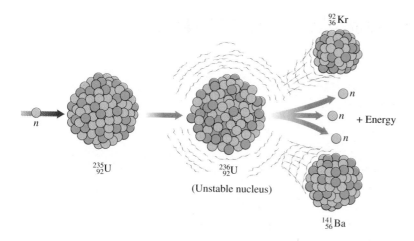

Figure 21.11

On capturing a neutron, the $^{235}_{92}U$ nucleus undergoes fission to produce two lighter nuclides, free neutrons (typically three), and a large amount of energy.

The process shown above is only one of the many fission reactions that $^{235}_{92}U$ can undergo. Another is

$$^{1}_{0}n + ^{235}_{92}U \rightarrow ^{137}_{52}Te + ^{97}_{40}Zr + 2\ ^{1}_{0}n$$

In fact, over 200 different isotopes of 35 different elements have been observed among the fission products of $^{235}_{92}U$.

In addition to the product nuclides, neutrons are also produced in the fission reactions of $^{235}_{92}U$. This makes it possible to have a self-sustaining fission process— a **chain reaction** (see Fig. 21.12). In order for the fission process to be self-sustaining, at least one neutron from each fission event must go on to split another nucleus. If, on average, *less than one* neutron causes another fission event, the process dies out and the reaction is said to be **subcritical.** If *exactly one* neutron from each fission event causes another fission event, the process sustains itself at the same level and is said to be **critical.** If *more than one* neutron from each fission event causes another fission event, the process rapidly escalates and the heat buildup causes a violent explosion. This situation is described as **supercritical.**

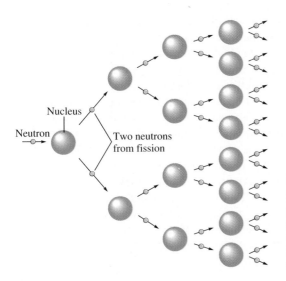

Figure 21.12

Representation of a fission process in which each event produces two neutrons, which can go on to split other nuclei, leading to a self-sustaining chain reaction.

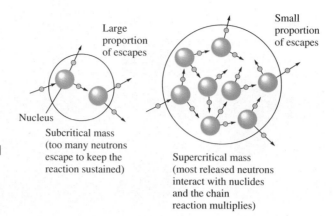

Large proportion of escapes

Small proportion of escapes

Nucleus

Subcritical mass (too many neutrons escape to keep the reaction sustained)

Supercritical mass (most released neutrons interact with nuclides and the chain reaction multiplies)

Figure 21.13

If the mass of fissionable material is too small, most of the neutrons escape before causing another fission event, and the process dies out.

To achieve the critical state, a certain mass of fissionable material, called the **critical mass,** is needed. If the sample is too small, too many neutrons escape before they have a chance to cause a fission event, and the process stops. This is illustrated in Fig. 21.13.

During World War II, an intense research effort called the Manhattan Project was carried out by the United States to build a bomb based on the principles of nuclear fission. This program produced the fission bombs that were used with devastating effects on the cities of Hiroshima and Nagasaki in 1945. Basically, a fission bomb operates by suddenly combining two subcritical masses of fissionable material to form a supercritical mass, thereby producing an explosion of incredible intensity.

Nuclear Reactors

Because of the tremendous energies involved, it seemed desirable to develop the fission process as an energy source to produce electricity. To accomplish this, reactors were designed in which controlled fission can occur. The resulting energy is used to heat water to produce steam to run turbine generators, in much the same way that a coal-burning power plant generates energy. A schematic diagram of a nuclear power plant is shown in Fig. 21.14.

In the **reactor core,** shown in Fig. 21.15, uranium that has been enriched to approximately 3% $^{235}_{92}U$ (natural uranium contains only 0.7% $^{235}_{92}U$) is housed in cylinders. A **moderator** surrounds the cylinders to slow down the neutrons so that the uranium fuel can capture them more efficiently. **Control rods,** composed of substances that absorb neutrons, are used to regulate the power level of the reactor. The reactor is designed so that should a malfunction occur, the control rods are automatically inserted into the core to stop the reaction. A liquid (usually water) is circulated through the core to extract the heat generated by the energy of fission; the energy can then be passed on via a heat exchanger to water in the turbine system.

Although the concentration of $^{235}_{92}U$ in the fuel elements is not great enough to allow a supercritical mass to develop in the core, a failure of the cooling system can lead to temperatures high enough to melt the core. As a result, the building housing the core must be designed to contain the core even if melt-down occurs. A great deal of controversy now exists about the efficiency of the safety systems in nuclear power plants. Accidents such as the one at the Three Mile Island facility in Pennsyl-

Uranium oxide (refined uranium).

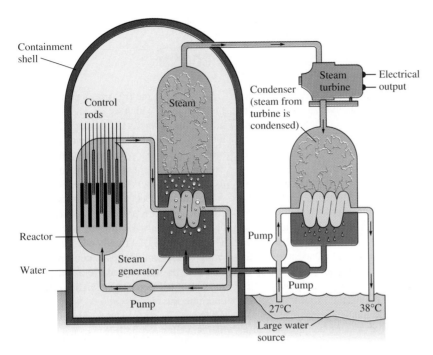

Figure 21.14

A schematic diagram of a nuclear power plant.

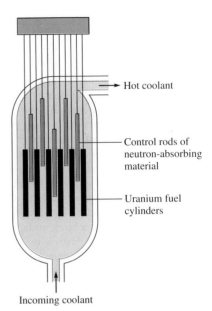

Figure 21.15

A schematic of the reactor core. The position of the control rods determines the level of energy production by regulating the amount of fission taking place.

vania in 1979 and in Chernobyl,[*] USSR, in 1986 have led many people to question the wisdom of continuing to build fission-based power plants.

Breeder Reactors

One potential problem facing the nuclear power industry is the supply of $^{235}_{92}U$. Some scientists have suggested that we have nearly depleted those uranium deposits rich enough in $^{235}_{92}U$ to make production of fissionable fuel economically feasible. Because of this possibility, **breeder reactors** have been developed, in which fissionable fuel is actually produced while the reactor runs. In the breeder reactors now being studied, the major component of natural uranium, nonfissionable $^{238}_{92}U$, is changed to fissionable $^{239}_{94}Pu$. The reaction involves absorption of a neutron, followed by production of two β particles:

$$^{1}_{0}n + {}^{238}_{92}U \rightarrow {}^{239}_{92}U$$
$$^{239}_{92}U \rightarrow {}^{239}_{93}Np + {}^{0}_{-1}e$$
$$^{239}_{93}Np \rightarrow {}^{239}_{94}Pu + {}^{0}_{-1}e$$

As the reactor runs and $^{235}_{92}U$ is split, some of the excess neutrons are absorbed by $^{238}_{92}U$ to produce $^{239}_{94}Pu$. The $^{239}_{94}Pu$ is then separated out and used to fuel another reactor. Such a reactor thus ''breeds'' nuclear fuel as it operates.

Skylab ultraviolet picture of the sun.

[*]See C. A. Atwood, ''Chernobyl—What happened?'' *J. Chem. Ed.* **65** (1988): 1037.

◀ **C H E M I C A L   I M P A C T** ▶

Nuclear Power: Could It Stage a Comeback?

As everyone knows, nuclear power has been a very controversial issue in the United States over the past 30 years. Safety issues and cost, along with the attendant political sensitivities, have stalled the growth of nuclear power. However, this situation might change. The intense concern about the warming effects of the carbon dioxide produced by fossil fuels, the uncertain rate of progress in harnessing solar energy, and innovative reactor designs may lead to a resurgence of interest in fission-powered nuclear plants.

Indeed, the French have demonstrated that nuclear power can be economically and politically feasible. France, which uses breeder reactors to provide most of its electricity, has an excellent safety record and is pioneering new methods for the storage of radioactive wastes.

In the United States, experiments at Argonne National Laboratory in Illinois indicate that a new generation of breeder reactors can be developed that will be inherently safer than the pressurized boiling-water reactors now in use. This research also shows that these reactors can be cost competitive with coal-fired power plants. The reactor under investigation at Argonne, called an *integral fast reactor (IFR)*, is quite different from the current reactors used in power plants. The key differences are that (1) the IFR uses liquid sodium instead of water as the coolant, (2) the IFR uses its fuel much more efficiently and, in fact, breeds new fissionable fuel as it runs, and (3) the IFR produces only a fraction of the radioactive wastes produced by current reactors. Because the boiling point of sodium is near 900°C, the liquid sodium does not need to be under pressure to prevent boiling, as is required for the water in current power reactors. This greatly lessens the chance of a very rapid loss of coolant should a leak develop. Liquid sodium has other advantages over water, such as not being corrosive to steel. Also, the use of sodium as a coolant allows for much faster neutrons than are possible in present water-cooled reactors. These fast neutrons produce extra power and greatly reduce the radioactive waste from the reactor, because they cause the fission (and thus the destruction) of many radioactive products of the fission process.

In addition, the IFR uses a new type of fuel element, which is an alloy of uranium, plutonium, and zirconium. Because these new metal fuel elements conduct heat so much more efficiently than the ceramic fuel elements now commonly in use, lower core temperatures are possible. Also, these metal fuel elements allow electrochemical reprocessing, which leads to very efficient recycling of usable fuel. This means that virtually all the initial uranium fuel is eventually consumed. In contrast, present-day reactors only consume a small percentage of the original uranium; the rest is removed with the radioactive fission products. Because the fuel recycling for the IFR does not require a large facility, it can be done at the reactor site, thus eliminating the transportation of large amounts of radioactive materials.

If development goes as smoothly as projected, the integral fast reactor may be providing safe, economical power shortly after the year 2000 while adding no carbon dioxide or other pollutants to the atmosphere.

Although breeder reactors are now used in France, the United States is proceeding slowly with their development because of their controversial nature. One problem involves the hazards in handling plutonium, which flames on contact with air and is very toxic.

Fusion

Large quantities of energy are also produced by the fusion of two light nuclei. In fact, stars produce their energy through nuclear fusion. Our sun, which presently consists of 73% hydrogen, 26% helium, and 1% other elements, gives off vast quantities of energy from the fusion of protons to form helium:

$$\ce{^1_1H + ^1_1H -> ^2_1H + ^0_1e}$$
$$\ce{^1_1H + ^2_1H -> ^3_2He}$$
$$\ce{^3_2He + ^3_2He -> ^4_2He + 2 ^1_1H}$$
$$\ce{^3_2He + ^1_1H -> ^4_2He + ^0_1e}$$

◀ **CHEMICAL IMPACT** ▶

Cold Fusion

In March of 1989 two chemists, B. Stanley Pons and Martin Fleischmann, reported to an astonished world that they had succeeded in producing nuclear fusion in an aqueous solution. Instead of the millions of degrees assumed to be required to initiate fusion, these scientists reported what they thought was fusion in connection with the electrolysis of D_2O containing LiOD at 25°C using palladium electrodes. *Cold fusion,* as the phenomenon was dubbed, was immediately trumpeted by the media to be the solution to the earth's energy problems.

But now, several years after the first announcement of the phenomenon, it is still not clear whether cold fusion actually occurs. Some of the best scientists in the world have been working with feverish intensity on the problem with, at best, uncertain results. Indeed, this episode is an excellent illustration of how difficult and complex scientific research can be. Given the talent of the scientists and the myriad of modern instruments available for the work, one might assume that this issue would have been resolved quickly.

The possibility of cold fusion arose when Pons and Fleischmann observed very large bursts of heat accompanying the electrolysis of D_2O/LiOD mixtures using palladium electrodes at high current densities. In addition to the extraordinary amounts of energy, the two scientists reported that tritium and neutrons also were produced. None of these things could be explained by any known chemical reactions. The energy production was, at times, 100 to 1000 times that expected from a chemical reaction, and the presence of tritium and/or neutrons would seem to suggest some sort of nuclear process.

However, there are several problems. The excess heat production is intermittent and unpredictable. Some cells run for weeks with no excess energy production, then suddenly will churn out large quantities of energy for hundreds of hours, and

Type of apparatus used by scientists who claimed to observe "cold fusion."

then—just as suddenly—give out. Also, because neutrons are very difficult to detect, great uncertainty remains about how many neutrons, if any, are really produced. Although the detection of tritium is much more straightforward, it is possible that the tritium observed is due to contamination. Also, only about one-fourth of the cells seem to produce tritium, which is very hard to explain. On the positive side, in early 1991 several research groups investigating the electrolysis of D_2O/LiOD using a Pd electrode reported the detection of helium, a product expected in the fusion of deuterium atoms.

So what is going on? Is cold fusion responsible for these effects, or do they arise from a combination of contamination, difficulties in making measurements, and mysterious chemical and/or physical processes? Although hope remains that a process that will prove useful for energy production is occurring, the verdict remains very much in doubt.

◄ **CHEMICAL IMPACT** ►

Nuclear Waste Disposal

Our society has not had an impressive record for safe disposal of industrial wastes. We have polluted our water and air, and some land areas have become virtually uninhabitable because of the improper burial of chemical wastes. As a result, many people are wary about the radioactive wastes from nuclear reactors. The potential threats of cancer and genetic mutations make these materials especially frightening.

Because of its controversial nature, no nuclear waste generated over the last 40 years has been permanently disposed of. However, in 1982 the U.S. Congress passed the Nuclear Waste Policy Act, which established a timetable for choosing and preparing sites for deep underground disposal of radioactive materials. The program is being funded by a tax of 0.1% per kilowatt hour on electricity generated by nuclear power.

The tentative disposal plan calls for the incorporation of the spent nuclear fuel into blocks of borosilicate glass that will be packed in corrosion-resistant metal containers and then buried in a deep, stable rock formation (see figure).

There are indications that this method will isolate the waste until the radioactivity decays to safe levels. One reassuring indication comes from the natural fission "reactor" at Oklo in Gabon, Africa. Initiated about 2 billion years ago when uranium in ore deposits there formed a critical mass, the "reactor" produced fission and fusion products for several thousand

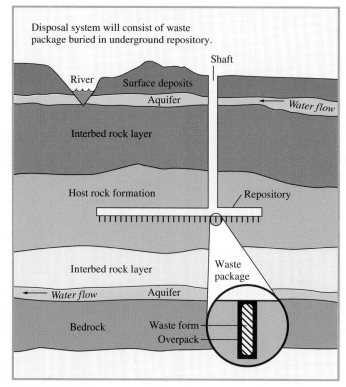

A schematic diagram of the tentative plan for deep underground isolation of nuclear waste. (From *Chem. Eng. News* (July 18, 1983): 20–38. Reprinted with permission. Copyright 1983 American Chemical Society.)

years. Although some of these products have migrated away from the site in the intervening 2 billion years, most have stayed in place. Another indication of the possible success of underground isolation is the disposal program carried out at Oak Ridge National Laboratory over the last 20 years. In this program, the waste has been ground up, mixed with cement, fly ash, and clay, and injected at high pressures into a shale bed 1000 feet underground. This method of injection causes

Intense research is underway to develop a feasible fusion process because of the ready availability of many light nuclides (deuterium, $_1^2H$, in seawater, for example) that can serve as fuel in fusion reactors. The major stumbling block is that high temperatures are required to initiate fusion. The forces that bind nucleons together to form a nucleus are effective only at *very small* distances ($\sim 10^{-13}$ cm). Thus, for two protons to bind together and thereby release energy, they must get very close together. But protons, because they are identically charged, repel each other electrostatically. This means that in order to get two protons (or two deuterons) close

◀ **CHEMICAL IMPACT** ▶

fractures in the rock into which the liquid waste seeps and then solidifies. Monitoring of the wastes has shown little movement of radioactivity. Although this procedure has worked well, the materials involved are not nearly as radioactive as those from power plants, for which this method is not thought suitable. However, this experiment has demonstrated that such wastes can be immobilized.

Choosing the waste repository sites is an especially sensitive issue. Many states have resisted the plan, but Congress has the power to override a state's disapproval. In fact, Congress amended the Nuclear Waste Policy Act in 1987 to make Yucca Mountain in Nevada the primary

potential site. Studies are now being carried out to evaluate the feasibility of this site as a safe repository for nuclear waste.

In a related situation, the Department of Energy (DOE) is preparing the Waste Isolation Pilot Plant (WIPP) near Carlsbad, New Mexico, for the long-term storage of defense-related nuclear waste. This storage facility is sited 2150 feet below the surface in salt beds that have remained stable and free of groundwater for about 225 million years, according to studies by DOE. In the next stages of the testing of WIPP, the Department of Energy will store several thousand drums of waste, which will be monitored for effects such as gas formation.

An alternative to permanent isolation of spent nuclear fuel is monitored, retrievable storage. This method has an advantage since, if reprocessing to remove potentially useful materials such as plutonium becomes feasible, the wastes are still accessible. The argument for this plan is that the technologies and alternatives available to society a few hundred years from now may be so different from those of the present that these wastes could become valuable resources. At the present time, isolation of the wastes seems the most likely event; even so, these underground deposits may become plutonium mines in the future.

---

enough to bind together (the nuclear binding force is *not* electrostatic), they must be "shot" at each other at speeds high enough to overcome the electrostatic repulsion.

The electrostatic repulsion forces between two $_1^2\text{H}$ nuclei are so great that a temperature of 4×10^7 K is required to give them velocities large enough to cause them to collide with sufficient energy that the nuclear forces can bind the particles together and thus release the binding energy. This situation is represented in Fig. 21.16.

Currently, scientists are studying two types of systems to produce the extremely high temperatures required: high-powered lasers and heating by electric currents. At present, many technical problems remain to be solved, and it is not clear which method will prove more useful or when fusion might become a practical energy source. However, there is still hope that fusion will be a major energy source sometime after the year 2000.

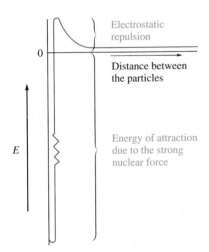

Figure 21.16

A plot of energy versus the separation distance for two $_1^2\text{H}$ nuclei. The nuclei must have sufficient velocities to get over the electrostatic repulsion "hill" and get close enough for the nuclear binding forces to become effective, thus "fusing" the particles into a new nucleus and releasing large quantities of energy. The binding force is at least 100 times the electrostatic repulsion.

21.7 Effects of Radiation

Purpose

* To show how radiation damages human tissue.

The ozone layer is discussed in Section 19.5.

Everyone knows that being hit by a train is very serious. The problem is the energy transfer involved. In fact, any source of energy is potentially harmful to organisms. Energy transferred to cells can break chemical bonds and cause malfunctioning of the cell systems. This fact is behind the concern about the ozone layer in the earth's upper atmosphere, which screens out high-energy ultraviolet radiation from the sun. Radioactive elements, which are sources of high-energy particles, are also potentially hazardous, although the effects are usually quite subtle. The reason for the subtlety of radiation damage is that even though high-energy particles are involved, the quantity of energy actually deposited in tissues *per event* is quite small. However, the resulting damage is no less real, although the effects may not be apparent for years.

Radiation damage to organisms can be classified as somatic or genetic damage. **Somatic damage** is damage to the organism itself, resulting in sickness or death. The effects may appear almost immediately if a massive dose of radiation is received; for smaller doses, damage may appear years later, usually in the form of cancer. **Genetic damage** is damage to the genetic machinery, which produces malfunctions in the offspring of the organism.

The biologic effects of a particular source of radiation depend on several factors:

1. *The energy of the radiation.* The higher the energy content of the radiation, the more damage it can cause. Radiation doses are measured in **rads** (which is short for *r*adiation *a*bsorbed *d*ose), where 1 rad corresponds to 10^{-2} J of energy deposited per kilogram of tissue.

2. *The penetrating ability of the radiation.* The particles and rays produced in radioactive processes vary in their abilities to penetrate human tissue: γ rays are highly penetrating, β particles can penetrate approximately 1 cm, and α particles are stopped by the skin.

3. *The ionizing ability of the radiation.* Extraction of electrons from biomolecules to form ions is particularly detrimental to their functions. The ionizing ability of radiation varies dramatically. For example, γ rays penetrate very deeply but cause only occasional ionization. On the other hand, α particles, although not very penetrating, are very effective at causing ionization and produce a dense trail of damage. Thus ingestion of an α-particle producer, such as plutonium, is particularly damaging.

4. *The chemical properties of the radiation source.* When a radioactive nuclide is ingested into the body, its effectiveness in causing damage depends on its residence time. For example, $^{85}_{36}$Kr and $^{90}_{38}$Sr are both β-particle producers. However, since krypton is chemically inert, it passes through the body quickly and does not have much time to do damage. Strontium, being chemically similar to calcium, can collect in bones, where it may cause leukemia and bone cancer.

Because of the differences in the behavior of the particles and rays produced by radioactive decay, both the energy dose of the radiation and its effectiveness in

Table 21.6

Effects of Short-Term Exposures to Radiation	
Dose (rem)	Clinical Effect
0–25	Nondetectable
25–50	Temporary decrease in white blood cell counts
100–200	Strong decrease in white blood cell counts
500	Death of half the exposed population within 30 days after exposure

causing biologic damage must be taken into account. The **rem** (which is short for *r*oentgen *e*quivalent for *m*an) is defined as follows:

$$\text{Number of rems} = (\text{number of rads}) \times \text{RBE}$$

where RBE represents the relative effectiveness of the radiation in causing biologic damage.

Table 21.6 shows the physical effects of short-term exposure to various doses of radiation, and Table 21.7 gives the sources and amounts of radiation exposure for a typical person in the United States. Note that natural sources contribute about twice as much as human activities to the total exposure. However, although the nuclear industry contributes only a small percentage of the total exposure, the major controversy associated with nuclear power plants is the *potential* for radiation hazards. These arise mainly from two sources: accidents allowing the release of radioactive materials and improper disposal of the radioactive products in spent fuel elements. The radioactive products of the fission of $^{235}_{92}\text{U}$, although only a small percentage of the total products, have half-lives of several hundred years and remain dangerous for a long time. Various schemes have been advanced for the disposal of these

Disposal of nuclear wastes is discussed in the Chemical Impact at the end of Section 21.6.

Table 21.7

Typical Radiation Exposures for a Person Living in the United States (1 millirem = 10^{-3} rem)	
	Exposure (millirems/year)
Cosmic radiation	50
From the earth	47
From building materials	3
In human tissues	21
Inhalation of air	5
Total from natural sources	126
X-ray diagnosis	50
Radiotherapy	10
Internal diagnosis/therapy	1
Nuclear power industry	0.2
TV tubes, industrial wastes, etc.	2
Radioactive fallout	4
Total from human activities	67
Total	193

◀ **C H E M I C A L   I M P A C T** ▶

Nuclear Physics: An Introduction

uclear physics is concerned with the fundamental nature of matter. The central focuses of this area of study are the relationship between a quantity of energy and its mass, given by $E = mc^2$, and the fact that matter can be converted from one form (energy) to another (particulate) in particle accelerators. Collisions between high-speed particles have produced a dazzling array of new particles—hundreds of them. These events can best be interpreted as conversions of kinetic energy into particles. For example, a collision of sufficient energy between a proton and a neutron can produce four particles: two protons, one antiproton, and a neutron:

$$_1^1\text{H} + _0^1\text{n} \rightarrow 2\,_1^1\text{H} + _{-1}^1\text{H} + _0^1\text{n}$$

where $_{-1}^1\text{H}$ is the symbol for an *antiproton*, which has the same mass as a proton but the opposite charge. This process is a little like throwing one baseball at a very high speed into another and having the energy of the collision converted into two additional baseballs.

The results of such accelerator experiments have led scientists to postulate the existence of three types of forces important in the nucleus: the *strong force*, the *weak force*, and the *electromagnetic force*. Along with the *gravitational force*, these forces are thought to account for all types of interactions found in matter. These forces are believed to be generated by the exchange of particles between the interacting pieces of matter. For example, gravitational forces are thought to be carried by particles called *gravitons*. The electromagnetic force (the classical electrostatic force between charged particles) is assumed to be exerted through the exchange of *photons*. The strong force, not charge-related and only effective at very short distances ($\sim 10^{-13}$ cm), is postulated to involve the exchange of particles called *gluons*. The weak force is 100 times weaker than the strong force and seems to be exerted through the exchange of two types of large particles, the W (has a mass 70 times the proton mass) and the Z (has a mass 90 times the proton mass).

The particles discovered have been classified into several categories. Three of the most important classes are as follows:

1. *Hadrons* are particles that respond to the strong force and have internal structure.

2. *Leptons* are particles that do not respond to the strong force and have no internal structure.

3. *Quarks* are particles with no internal structure that are thought to be the fundamental constituents of hadrons. Neutrons and protons are hadrons that are thought to be composed of three quarks each.

The world of particle physics appears mysterious and complicated. For exam-

(*left*) An aerial view of Fermilab, a high-energy particle accelerator in Batavia, Illinois. (*right*) The accelerator tunnel at Fermilab.

◀ C H E M I C A L   I M P A C T ▶

ple, particle physicists have discovered new properties of matter they call "color," "charm," and "strangeness" and have postulated conservation laws involving these properties. This area of science is extremely important because it should help us to understand the interactions of matter in a more elegant and unified way. For example, the classification of force into four categories is probably

necessary only because we do not understand the true nature of forces. All forces may be special cases of a single, all-pervading force field that governs all of nature. In fact, Einstein spent the last 30 years of his life looking for a way to unify the gravitational and electromagnetic forces—without success. Physicists may now be on the verge of accomplishing what Einstein failed to do.

Although the practical aspects of the work in nuclear physics are not yet totally apparent, a more fundamental understanding of the way nature operates could lead to presently undreamed-of devices for energy production and communication, which could revolutionize our lives.

wastes. The one that seems to hold the most promise is the incorporation of the wastes into ceramic blocks and the burial of these blocks in geologically stable formations. At present, however, no disposal method has been accepted, and nuclear wastes continue to accumulate in temporary storage facilities.

Even if a satisfactory method for permanent disposal of nuclear wastes is found, there will continue to be concern about the effects of exposure to low levels of radiation. Exposure is inevitable from natural sources such as cosmic rays and radioactive minerals, and many people are also exposed to low levels of radiation from reactors, radioactive tracers, or diagnostic X rays. Currently, we have little reliable information on the long-term effects of low-level exposure to radiation.

Two models of radiation damage, illustrated in Fig. 21.17, have been proposed: the **linear model** and the **threshold model.** The linear model postulates that damage from radiation is proportional to the dose, even at low levels of exposure. Thus any exposure is dangerous. The threshold model, on the other hand, assumes that no significant damage occurs below a certain exposure, called the **threshold exposure.** Note that if the linear model is correct, radiation exposure should be limited to a bare minimum (ideally at the natural levels). If the threshold model is correct, a certain level of radiation exposure beyond natural levels can be tolerated. Most scientists seem to feel that since there is little evidence available to evaluate these models, it is safest to assume that the linear hypothesis is correct and to minimize radiation exposure.

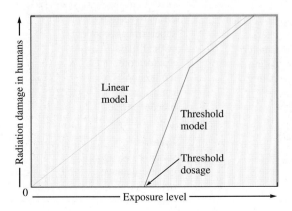

Figure 21.17

The two models for radiation damage. In the linear model, even a small dosage causes a proportional risk. In the threshold model, risk begins only after a certain dosage.

FOR REVIEW

Summary

The stability of the nucleus, which is composed of neutrons and protons, can be considered from kinetic and thermodynamic points of view. Nuclei that are kinetically unstable decompose into more stable nuclei by radioactive decay, which can involve production of an α particle ($_2^4$He), which changes both A and Z, production of a β particle ($_{-1}^0$e), which increases Z, or production of a positron ($_1^0$e), which decreases Z. High-energy photons called γ rays also can be produced.

A radioactive nuclide may undergo a number of decay events, called a decay series, until a stable nuclide is formed. Radioactive decay follows first-order kinetics. The half-life of a radioactive sample is the time required for the amount of the nuclide to reach half the original amount. The transuranium elements, those coming after uranium in the periodic table, can be synthesized by particle bombardment of uranium or heavier elements.

Radiocarbon dating uses the ratio $_6^{14}$C/$_6^{12}$C to date any object containing carbon from living sources.

The thermodynamic stability of the nucleus involves a comparison of the energy of the nucleus to that of its component nucleons. When a system gains or loses energy, it also gains or loses a quantity of mass, given by the relationship $E = mc^2$. The change in mass, called the mass defect, can be obtained by comparing the nuclear mass to the sum of the masses of the component nucleons and can be used to calculate the energy of formation of a nucleus from its nucleons. The binding energy is the energy required to decompose the nucleus into protons and neutrons.

Nuclear fusion is the process of combining two light nuclei to form a heavier, more stable nucleus. Fission is the splitting of a heavy nucleus into two lighter nuclei. Nuclear reactors now in use employ controlled fission.

Radiation damage can cause either direct damage to living organisms or genetic damage to the organism's offspring. The biologic effects of radiation depend on the energy, the penetrating ability, and the ionizing ability of the radiation, and on the chemical properties of the radiation source.

Key Terms

neutron
proton
nucleon
atomic number
mass number
isotopes
nuclide

Section 21.1
thermodynamic stability
kinetic stability
radioactive decay
beta (β) particle
zone of stability
alpha (α) particle
α-particle production

spontaneous fission
β-particle production
gamma (γ) ray
positron production
electron capture
decay series

Section 21.2
rate of decay
half-life

Section 21.3
nuclear transformation
particle accelerator
cyclotron
linear accelerator
transuranium elements

Section 21.4
Geiger–Müller counter
  (Geiger counter)
scintillation counter
radiocarbon dating
  (carbon-14 dating)
radiotracers

Section 21.5
mass defect
binding energy

Section 21.6
fusion
fission
chain reaction

subcritical reaction
critical reaction
supercritical reaction
critical mass
reactor core
moderator
control rods
breeder reactor

Section 21.7
somatic damage
genetic damage
rad
rem

A blue question or exercise number indicates that the answer to that question or exercise appears at the back of this book and a solution appears in the Solutions Guide.

Questions

1. Define *fission* and *fusion*. What types of nuclei are likely to undergo each process?

2. When nuclei undergo nuclear transformations, γ rays of characteristic frequencies are observed. How does this fact, along with other information in the chapter on nuclear stability, suggest that a quantum mechanical model may apply to the nucleus?

3. What assumptions must be made and what problems arise in using carbon-14 dating?

4. How could a radioactive nuclide be used to demonstrate that chemical equilibrium is a dynamic process?

5. There is a trend in the United States toward using coal-fired power plants to generate electricity rather than building new nuclear fission power plants. Is the use of coal-fired power plants without risk? Make a list of the risks to society from the use of each type of power plant.

6. Fusion processes are more likely to occur for lighter elements, while fission processes are more likely to occur for heavier elements. Explain.

7. Why are elevated temperatures necessary to initiate fusion reactions but not fission reactions?

8. Much of the research on controlled fusion focuses on the problem of how to contain the reacting material. Why is containment such a problem? Magnetic fields appear to be the most promising mode of containment. Explain how magnetic fields can be used for containment.

9. How might the discovery of high-temperature superconducting materials affect the feasibility of using fusion as a practical power source?

10. What are the purposes of the moderator and of the control rods in a fission reactor?

Exercises

In this section similar exercises are paired.

Radioactive Decay and Nuclear Transformations

11. Write an equation describing the radioactive decay of each of the following nuclides. (The particle produced is shown in parentheses.)
    a. $^{3}_{1}H$ (β)
    b. $^{8}_{3}Li$ (β followed by α)
    c. $^{7}_{4}Be$ (electron capture)
    d. $^{8}_{5}B$ (positron)
    e. $^{32}_{15}P$ (β)

12. Write an equation describing the radioactive decay of each of the following nuclides.
    a. ^{60}Co (β)
    b. ^{97}Tc (electron capture)
    c. ^{99}Tc (β)
    d. ^{239}Pu (α)

13. Complete the following equations, which describe nuclear reactions that occur in the sun.
    a. $^{1}_{1}H + ^{14}_{7}N \rightarrow$ _____ $+ ^{4}_{2}He$
    b. Two helium-3 nuclei undergo fusion, forming helium-4 and two protons.
    c. $^{1}_{1}H + ^{1}_{1}H \rightarrow ^{2}_{1}H +$ _____
    d. $^{1}_{1}H + ^{12}_{6}C \rightarrow$ _____

14. Many elements have been synthesized by bombarding relatively heavy atoms with high-energy particles in particle accelerators. Complete the following nuclear reactions, which have been used to synthesize elements.
    a. _____ $+ ^{4}_{2}He \rightarrow ^{243}_{97}Bk + ^{1}_{0}n$
    b. $^{238}_{92}U + ^{12}_{6}C \rightarrow$ _____ $+ 6\ ^{1}_{0}n$
    c. $^{249}_{98}Cf +$ _____ $\rightarrow ^{263}_{106}Unh + 4\ ^{1}_{0}n$
    d. $^{249}_{98}Cf + ^{10}_{5}B \rightarrow ^{257}_{103}Lr +$ _____

15. The stable isotopes of boron are boron-10 and boron-11. Four radioactive isotopes with mass numbers 8, 9, 12, and 13 are also known. Predict possible modes of radioactive decay for these four nuclides.

16. There are four stable isotopes of iron with mass numbers 54, 56, 57, and 58. There are also two radioactive isotopes: iron-53 and iron-59. Predict modes of decay for these two isotopes, and write a nuclear reaction for each.

17. Uranium-235 undergoes a decay series in which the following particles are produced in succession: α, β, α, β, α, α, α, α, β, α, β.
   a. What is the final product of the decay of uranium-235?
   b. What are the 10 intermediate nuclides?

18. One type of commercial smoke detector contains a minute amount of radioactive americium-241 (^{241}Am), which decays by α-particle production. The α particles ionize molecules in the air, allowing it to conduct an electric current. When smoke particles enter, the conductivity of the air is changed and the alarm buzzes.
   a. Write the equation for the decay of $^{241}_{95}$Am by α-particle production.
   b. The complete decay of ^{241}Am involves successively α, α, β, α, α, β, α, α, α, β, α, and β production. What is the final stable nucleus produced in this decay series?
   c. Identify the eleven intermediate nuclides.

Kinetics of Radioactive Decay

19. How many disintegrations occur in the first second from 1.00 mol of radioactive nuclides with each of the following half-lives: 12,000 years? 12 h? 12 min? 12 s?

20. The curie (Ci) is a commonly used unit for measuring nuclear radioactivity: 1 curie of radiation is equal to 3.7×10^{10} disintegrations per second (the number of disintegrations from 1 g of radium in 1 s).
   a. What is the activity in mCi (millicuries) of 175 mg Na$_3{}^{32}$PO$_4$? ($t_{1/2}$ for ^{32}P = 14.3 days)
   b. What is the activity in mCi of 1.0 mol plutonium-239 ($t_{1/2}$ = 24,000 years)?

21. Phosphorus-32 is a commonly used radioactive nuclide in biochemical research, particularly in studies of nucleic acids. The half-life of phosphorus-32 is 14.3 days. What mass of phosphorus-32 is left of an original sample of 175 mg Na$_3{}^{32}$PO$_4$ after 35.0 days?

22. A chemist wishing to do an experiment requiring ^{47}Ca (half-life = 4.5 days) needs 5.0 μg of the nuclide. What mass of ^{47}CaCO$_3$ must be ordered if it takes 48 h for delivery from the supplier?

23. Cobalt-60 is commonly used as a source of β particles. How long does it take for 10.0% of a sample of cobalt-60 to decay (the half-life is 5.26 years)?

24. The half-life of sulfur-38 is 2.87 h.
   a. What mass of Na$_2{}^{38}$SO$_4$ has an activity of 10.0 mCi?
   b. How long does it take for 99.99% of a sample of sulfur-38 to decay?

25. What fraction of the original carbon-14 remains in a piece of wood that was cut from a tree 2200 years ago?

26. A living plant contains approximately the same fraction of carbon-14 as in atmospheric carbon dioxide. The observed rate of decay of carbon-14 from a living plant is 15.3 disintegrations per minute per gram of carbon. How many disintegrations per minute per gram of carbon will be measured from a 15,000-year-old sample? Will radiocarbon dating work well for small samples of 10 mg or less?

27. What is the ratio ^{206}Pb/^{238}U by mass in a rock that is 4.5×10^9 years old? (For ^{238}U, $t_{1/2} = 4.5 \times 10^9$ years.)

28. The mass ratios of ^{40}Ar to ^{40}K also can be used to date geologic materials. Potassium-40 decays by two processes:

    $^{40}_{19}$K $\rightarrow$ $^{40}_{18}$Ar (electron capture, 10.7%)

    $$t_{1/2} = 1.27 \times 10^9 \text{ years}$$

    $^{40}_{19}$K $\rightarrow$ $^{40}_{20}$Ca + $^{0}_{-1}$e (89.3%)

   a. Why are ^{40}Ar/^{40}K ratios used to date materials rather than ^{40}Ca/^{40}K ratios?
   b. What assumptions must be made using this technique?
   c. A sedimentary rock has a ^{40}Ar/^{40}K ratio of 0.95. Calculate the age of the rock.
   d. How will the measured age of a rock compare to the actual age if some ^{40}Ar escaped from the sample?

Energy Changes in Nuclear Reactions

29. The sun radiates 3.9×10^{23} J of energy into space every second. What is the rate at which mass is lost from the sun?

30. The earth receives 1.8×10^{14} kJ/s of solar energy. What mass of solar material is converted to energy over a 24-h period to provide the daily amount of solar energy to the earth? What mass of coal would have to be burned to provide the same amount of energy? (Coal releases 32 kJ of energy per gram when burned.)

31. Calculate the binding energy per nucleon for ^{24}Mg and ^{27}Mg. The atomic masses are ^{24}Mg 23.9850 and ^{27}Mg 26.9843. (Since these are atomic masses, they include the mass of magnesium's 12 electrons. See Sample Exercise 21.8.)

32. Calculate the binding energy per nucleon for $^{2}_{1}$H and $^{3}_{1}$H. The atomic masses are $^{2}_{1}$H 2.01410 and $^{3}_{1}$H 3.01605.

33. Consider the following reaction:

$$^{1}_{1}\text{H} + ^{1}_{0}\text{n} \rightarrow 2\ ^{1}_{1}\text{H} + ^{1}_{0}\text{n} + ^{1}_{-1}\text{H}$$

Calculate the energy change for this reaction. Is energy released or absorbed? What is a possible source for this energy?

34. A positron and an electron can annihilate each other upon colliding, producing energy as photons:

$$^{0}_{-1}\text{e} + ^{0}_{+1}\text{e} \rightarrow 2\ ^{0}_{0}\gamma$$

Assuming that both γ rays have the same energy, calculate the wavelength of the electromagnetic radiation produced.

35. Calculate the amount of energy released per gram of hydrogen for the following reaction:

$$^{1}_{1}\text{H} + ^{1}_{1}\text{H} \rightarrow ^{2}_{1}\text{H} + ^{0}_{+1}\text{e}$$

The atomic masses are $^{1}_{1}$H 1.00782 and $^{2}_{1}$H 2.01410. (*Hint:* Think carefully about how to account for the electron mass.)

36. The easiest fusion reaction to initiate is

$$^{2}_{1}\text{H} + ^{3}_{1}\text{H} \rightarrow ^{4}_{2}\text{He} + ^{1}_{0}\text{n}$$

Calculate the energy released per $^{4}_{2}$He nucleus produced and per mole of $^{4}_{2}$He produced. The atomic masses are $^{2}_{1}$H 2.01410, $^{3}_{1}$H 3.01605, and $^{4}_{2}$He 4.00260. The masses of the electron and neutron are 5.4858×10^{-4} and 1.00866 amu, respectively.

Detection, Uses, and Health Effects of Radiation

37. The typical response of a Geiger–Müller tube is shown below. Explain the shape of this curve.

38. When using a Geiger–Müller counter to measure radioactivity, it is necessary to maintain the same geometrical orientation between the sample and the Geiger–Müller tube in order to compare different measurements. Why?

39. A 0.10-cm^3 sample of a solution containing a radioactive nuclide (5.0×10^3 disintegrations per minute per milliliter) is injected into a rat. Several minutes later 1.0 cm^3 of blood is removed. The blood shows 48 disintegrations per minute of radioactivity. Calculate the volume of blood in the rats. What assumptions must be made in performing this calculation?

40. Photosynthesis in plants can be represented by the following overall reaction:

$$6CO_2(g) + 6H_2O(l) \xrightarrow{\text{Light}} C_6H_{12}O_6(s) + 6O_2(g)$$

Algae grown in water containing some ^{18}O (in $H_2{}^{18}O$) evolve oxygen with the same isotopic composition as the oxygen in the water. When algae growing in water containing only ^{16}O were furnished carbon dioxide containing ^{18}O, no ^{18}O was found to be evolved. What conclusions about photosynthesis can be drawn from these experiments?

41. Which do you think would be the greater health hazard: the release of a radioactive nuclide of Sr or a radioactive nuclide of Xe into the environment? Assume the amount of radioactivity is the same in each case. Explain your answer on the basis of the chemical properties of Sr and Xe. Why are the chemical properties of a radioactive substance important in assessing its potential health hazards?

42. Consider the following information:
    i. The layer of dead skin on our bodies is sufficient to protect us from most α-particle radiation.
    ii. Plutonium is an α-particle producer.
    iii. The chemistry of Pu^{4+} is similar to that of Fe^{3+}.
    iv. Pu^{4+} + 4e$^-$ → Pu $\mathscr{E}° = -1.28$ V
    Why is plutonium one of the most toxic substances known?

Additional Exercises

43. The atomic mass of lithium-6 is 6.015126 amu. What is the mass of a lithium-6 nucleus? Calculate the total binding energy per mole of lithium-6.

44. The first atomic explosion was detonated in the desert north of Alamogordo, New Mexico, on July 16, 1945. What fraction of the strontium-90 ($t_{1/2} = 28.8$ years) originally produced by that explosion still remains?

45. Using the kinetic molecular theory for gases (Section 5.6), calculate the average kinetic energy of a $^2_1$H nucleus at a temperature of 4×10^7 K. (See Exercise 35 for the appropriate mass value.)

46. A small atomic bomb releases energy equivalent to the detonation of 20,000 tons of TNT; a ton of TNT releases 4×10^9 J of energy when exploded. Using 2×10^{13} J/mol as the energy released by fission of ^{235}U, estimate a value for the critical mass of ^{235}U. What assumptions must be made in this calculation?

47. In addition to the process described in the text, a second process called the *carbon–nitrogen cycle* occurs in the sun:

$$^1_1H + {}^{12}_6C \rightarrow {}^{13}_7N + {}^0_0\gamma$$
$$^{13}_7N \rightarrow {}^{13}_6C + {}^0_{+1}e$$
$$^1_1H + {}^{13}_6C \rightarrow {}^{14}_7N + {}^0_0\gamma$$
$$^1_1H + {}^{14}_7N \rightarrow {}^{15}_8O + {}^0_0\gamma$$
$$^{15}_8O \rightarrow {}^{15}_7N + {}^0_{+1}e$$
$$^1_1H + {}^{15}_7N \rightarrow {}^{12}_6C + {}^4_2He + {}^0_0\gamma$$

Overall reaction: $4\,{}^1_1H \rightarrow {}^4_2He + 2\,{}^0_{+1}e$

a. What is the catalyst in this process?

b. What nucleons are intermediates?

c. How much energy is released per mole of hydrogen atoms for the overall reaction? (See Exercises 35 and 36 for the appropriate mass values.)

Challenge Problems

48. Many metals become brittle when subjected to intense radiation from radioactive materials. Explain this observation. How might this fact affect the design of nuclear reactors?

49. Because zirconium is one of the few metals that retains its structural integrity upon exposure to radiation, the fuel rods in most nuclear reactors contain zirconium. Answer the following questions about the redox properties of zirconium based on the half-reaction

$$ZrO_2 \cdot H_2O + H_2O + 4e^- \rightarrow Zr + 4OH^-   \mathscr{E}° = -2.36 \text{ V}$$

a. Is zirconium metal capable of reacting water to form hydrogen gas?

b. Write a balanced equation for the reduction of water by zirconium.

c. Calculate $\mathscr{E}°$, $\Delta G°$, and K for the reduction of water by zirconium metal.

d. The reduction of water by zirconium occurred during the accidents at both Three Mile Island in 1979 and Chernobyl in 1986. At Three Mile Island the hydrogen gas was successfully vented, and no chemical explosion occurred. At Chernobyl the hydrogen exploded, destroying the reactor. If 1.00×10^3 kg Zr reacted, what mass of H$_2$ would be produced? What volume of H$_2$ at 1 atm and 1000°C would be produced?

e. Considering all the consequences, do you think it was a correct decision to vent the hydrogen along with other radioactive gases into the atmosphere at Three Mile Island? Explain.

50. Recent attempts to provide a unified field theory for matter have proposed that the fundamental particle is the superstring. A superstring is $\sim 10^{-35}$ m long (10^{-20} times the diameter of a proton). Use the Heisenberg uncertainty principle (see Chapter 7), that is

$$\Delta x \cdot \Delta(mv) \geq \frac{h}{4\pi}$$

to calculate the uncertainty in the mass of a superstring. (Assume that $\Delta x = 1 \times 10^{-35}$ m and that the velocity is 10% the speed of light.) Compare this uncertainty in mass with the electron and proton masses.

Organic Chemistry

T wo Group 4A elements, carbon and silicon, form the basis of most natural substances. Silicon, with its great affinity for oxygen, forms chains and rings containing Si—O—Si bridges to produce the silica and silicates that form the basis for most rocks, sands, and soils. What silicon is to the geologic world, carbon is to the biologic world. Carbon has the unusual ability of bonding strongly to itself to form long chains or rings of carbon atoms. In addition, carbon forms strong bonds to other nonmetals such as hydrogen, nitrogen, oxygen, sulfur, and the halogens. Because of these bonding properties, there are a myriad of carbon compounds; several million are now known, and the number continues to grow rapidly. Among these many compounds are the **biomolecules,** those responsible for maintaining and reproducing life.

The study of carbon-containing compounds and their properties is called **organic chemistry.** Although a few compounds of carbon, such as its oxides

---

< A compound called d-limonene, which has the structure

$$CH_3$$

$$CH_3-C=CH_2$$

and is obtained from orange rinds, is being developed by Raytheon Company for use in cleaning circuit boards. Chlorofluorocarbons (CFCs) are currently used for circuit-board cleaning, but CFCs have been identified as being harmful to the earth's ozone layer. D-limonene is a natural product that has no impact on the ozone and has no known harmful health or environmental effects.

1035

and carbonates, are considered to be inorganic substances, the vast majority are organic compounds that typically contain chains or rings of carbon atoms.

Originally, the distinction between inorganic and organic substances was based on whether or not they were produced by living systems. For example, until the early nineteenth century, it was believed that organic compounds had some sort of "life force" and could only be synthesized by living organisms. This view was dispelled in 1828 when German chemist Friedrich Wöhler (1800–1882) prepared urea from the inorganic salt ammonium cyanate by simple heating:

$$NH_4OCN \xrightarrow{\text{Heat}} H_2N-\overset{\displaystyle \underset{\displaystyle O}{\|}}{C}-NH_2$$

Ammonium cyanate   Urea

Urea is a component of urine, so it is clearly an organic material, yet here was clear evidence that it could be produced in the laboratory as well as by living things.

Organic chemistry plays a vital role in our quest to understand living systems. Beyond this, the synthetic fibers, plastics, artificial sweeteners, and drugs that are such an accepted part of modern life are products of industrial organic chemistry. In addition, the energy on which we rely so heavily to power our civilization is based mostly on the organic materials found in coal and petroleum.

Because it is such a vast subject, we can provide only a brief introduction to organic chemistry in this book. We will begin with the simplest class of organic compounds, the hydrocarbons, and then show how most other organic compounds can be considered to be derivatives of hydrocarbons.

22.1 Alkanes: Saturated Hydrocarbons

Purpose

• To describe the nomenclature system of organic chemistry.
• To discuss isomerism in organic molecules.
• To give the rules for naming alkanes.

As the name indicates, **hydrocarbons** are compounds composed of carbon and hydrogen. Those compounds whose carbon–carbon bonds are all single bonds are said to be *saturated*, because each carbon is bound to four atoms, the maximum number. Hydrocarbons containing carbon–carbon multiple bonds are described as being *unsaturated*, since the carbon atoms involved in a multiple bond can react with additional atoms, as shown by the *addition* of hydrogen to ethylene:

$$
\underset{\text{Unsaturated}}{\overset{\displaystyle H}{\underset{\displaystyle H}{>}}C=C\overset{\displaystyle H}{\underset{\displaystyle H}{<}}} + H_2 \longrightarrow \underset{\text{Saturated}}{H-\overset{\displaystyle \overset{H}{|}}{\underset{\displaystyle \underset{H}{|}}{C}}-\overset{\displaystyle \overset{H}{|}}{\underset{\displaystyle \underset{H}{|}}{C}}-H}
$$

Note that each carbon in ethylene is bonded to three atoms (one carbon and two hydrogens) but can bond to one additional atom if one bond of the carbon–carbon double bond is broken.

The simplest member of the saturated hydrocarbons (also called the **alkanes**) is *methane* (CH_4). As discussed in Section 9.1, methane has a tetrahedral structure and can be described in terms of a carbon atom using an sp^3 hybrid set of orbitals to bond to the four hydrogen atoms (see Fig. 22.1). The next alkane, the one containing two carbon atoms, is *ethane* (C_2H_6), as shown in Fig. 22.2. Each carbon in ethane is surrounded by four atoms and thus adopts a tetrahedral arrangement and sp^3 hybridization, as expected from the localized electron model.

The next two members of the series are *propane* (C_3H_8) and *butane* (C_4H_{10}), shown in Fig. 22.3. Again, each carbon is bonded to four atoms and is described as sp^3 hybridized.

Alkanes in which the carbon atoms form long "strings" or chains are called **normal**, **straight-chain**, or **unbranched hydrocarbons.** As can be seen from Fig. 22.3, the chains in normal alkanes are not really straight but zig-zag, since the tetrahedral C—C—C angle is 109.5° degrees. The normal alkanes can be represented by the structure

where *n* is an integer. Note that each member is obtained from the previous one by inserting a *methylene* (CH_2) group. We can condense the structural formulas by omitting some of the C—H bonds. For example, the general formula for normal alkanes shown above can be condensed to

$$CH_3\!-\!(CH_2)_n\!-\!CH_3$$

The first 10 normal alkanes and some of their properties are listed in Table 22.1. Note that all alkanes can be represented by the general formula C_nH_{2n+2}. For example, nonane, which has nine carbon atoms, is represented by $C_9H_{(2\times9)+2}$, or C_9H_{20}. Also note from Table 22.1 that the melting points and boiling points increase as the molar masses (molecular weights) increase, as we would expect.

Isomerism in Alkanes

Butane and all succeeding members of the alkanes exhibit **structural isomerism.** Recall from Section 20.4 that structural isomerism occurs when two molecules have the same atoms but different bonds. For example, butane can exist as a straight-

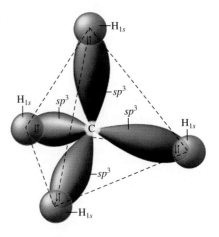

Figure 22.1
The C—H bonds in methane.

(a)

(b)

Figure 22.2
(a) The Lewis structure of ethane (C_2H_6). (b) The molecular structure of ethane represented by ball-and-stick and space-filling models.

(a)

(b)

Figure 22.3
The structures of (a) propane ($CH_3CH_2CH_3$) and (b) butane ($CH_3CH_2CH_2CH_3$). Each angle shown in red is 109.5 degrees.

Table 22.1					
Selected Properties of the First 10 Normal Alkanes					
Name	Formula	Molar Masses	Melting Point (°C)	Boiling Point (°C)	Number of Structural Isomers
Methane	CH_4	16	−183	−162	1
Ethane	C_2H_6	30	−183	−89	1
Propane	C_3H_8	44	−187	−42	1
Butane	C_4H_{10}	58	−138	0	2
Pentane	C_5H_{12}	72	−130	36	3
Hexane	C_6H_{14}	86	−95	68	5
Heptane	C_7H_{16}	100	−91	98	9
Octane	C_8H_{18}	114	−57	126	18
Nonane	C_9H_{20}	128	−54	151	35
Decane	$C_{10}H_{22}$	142	−30	174	75

(a)

(b)

Figure 22.4

(a) Normal butane (abbreviated *n*-butane). (b) The branched isomer of butane (called *isobutane*).

chain molecule (normal butane, or *n*-butane) or with a branched-chain structure (called *isobutane*), as shown in Fig. 22.4. Because of their different structures, these molecules show different properties. For example, the boiling point of *n*-butane is −0.5°C and that of isobutane is −12°C.

Sample Exercise 22.1

Draw the isomers of pentane.

Solution

Pentane (C_5H_{12}) has the following isomeric structures:

1.

$$CH_3—CH_2—CH_2—CH_2—CH_3$$
n-Pentane

2.

$$CH_3—\overset{\overset{\textstyle CH_3}{|}}{CH}—CH_2—CH_3$$
Isopentane

3.

$$CH_3—\overset{\overset{\textstyle CH_3}{|}}{\underset{\underset{\textstyle CH_3}{|}}{C}}—CH_3$$
Neopentane

Note that the structures

$$CH_3—CH_2—\overset{\overset{\textstyle CH_3}{|}}{CH}—CH_3 \qquad CH_3—\overset{\overset{\textstyle CH}{|}}{\underset{\underset{\textstyle CH_3}{|}}{CH}}—CH_2—CH_3 \qquad CH_3—CH_2—\overset{\overset{\textstyle CH}{|}}{\underset{\underset{\textstyle CH_3}{|}}{CH}}—CH_3$$

which might appear to be additional isomers, are actually identical to structure 2.

Nomenclature

Because there are literally millions of organic compounds, it would be impossible to remember common names for all of them. We must have a systematic method for naming them. The following rules are used in naming alkanes.

Rules for Naming Alkanes

1. The names of the alkanes beyond butane are obtained by adding the suffix *-ane* to the Greek root for the number of carbon atoms (*pent-* for five, *hex-* for six, etc.). For a branched hydrocarbon, the longest continuous chain of carbon

Table 22.2

The Most Common Alkyl Substituents and Their Names

Structure*	Name†
—CH_3	Methyl
—CH_2CH_3	Ethyl
—$CH_2CH_2CH_3$	Propyl
CH_3CHCH_3	Isopropyl
—$CH_2CH_2CH_2CH_3$	Butyl
$CH_3CHCH_2CH_3$	*Sec*-butyl
—CH_2—$\overset{H}{\underset{CH_3}{C}}$—$CH_3$	Isobutyl
—$\overset{CH_3}{\underset{CH_3}{C}}$—$CH_3$	*Tert*-butyl

*The bond with one end open shows the point of attachment of the substituent to the carbon chain.

†For the butyl groups, *sec*- indicates attachment to the chain through a secondary carbon, a carbon atom attached to *two* other carbon atoms. The designation *tert*- signifies attachment through a tertiary carbon, a carbon attached to *three* other carbon atoms.

atoms gives the root name for the hydrocarbon. For example, in the alkane

$$CH_3—CH_2—CH—CH_2—CH_3$$

the longest chain contains six carbon atoms, and this compound is named as a hexane.

2. When alkane groups appear as substituents, they are named by dropping the *-ane* and adding *-yl*. For example, —CH_3 is obtained by removing a hydrogen from methane and is called *methyl*, —C_2H_5 is called *ethyl*, —C_3H_7 is called *propyl*, and so on. The compound above is therefore an ethylhexane. (See Table 22.2.)

3. The positions of substituent groups are specified by numbering the longest chain of carbon atoms sequentially, starting at the end closest to the branching. For example, the compound

$$CH_3—CH_2—CH—CH_2—CH_2—CH_3$$

| 1 | 2 | 3 | 4 | 5 | 6 | Correct numbering |
| 6 | 5 | 4 | 3 | 2 | 1 | Incorrect numbering |

is called *3-methylhexane*. Note that the top set of numbers is correct because the left end of the molecule is closest to the branching, and this gives the smallest number for the position of the substituent. Also, note that a hyphen is placed between the number and the substituent name.

4. The location and name of each substituent are followed by the root alkane name. The substituents are listed in alphabetical order (irrespective of any prefix), and the prefixes *di-*, *tri-*, etc. are used to indicate multiple, identical substituents.

Sample Exercise 22.2

Draw the structural isomers for the alkane C_6H_{14}, and give the systematic name for each one.

Solution

We will proceed systematically, starting with the longest chain and then rearranging the carbons to form the shorter, branched chains.

1. $CH_3CH_2CH_2CH_2CH_2CH_3$ Hexane
   Note that a structure such as

   Six carbon atoms

may look different but is still hexane because the longest carbon chain has six atoms.

2. We now take one carbon out of the chain and make it a methyl substituent.

$$\underset{1}{C}H_3\underset{2}{C}H\underset{3}{C}H_2\underset{4}{C}H_2\underset{5}{C}H_3 \qquad \text{2-Methylpentane}$$
$$\qquad\ |$$
$$\qquad CH_3$$

Since the longest chain has five carbons, this is a substituted pentane: 2-methylpentane. The 2 indicates the position of the methyl group on the chain. Note that if we numbered the chain from the right end, the methyl group would be on carbon 4. Because we want the smallest possible number, the numbering shown is correct.

3. The methyl substituent also can be on carbon 3 to give

$$\underset{1}{C}H_3\underset{2}{C}H_2\underset{3}{C}H\underset{4}{C}H_2\underset{5}{C}H_3 \qquad \text{3-Methylpentane}$$
$$\qquad\qquad\ |$$
$$\qquad\qquad CH_3$$

Note that we have now exhausted all possibilities for placing a single methyl group on pentane.

4. Next we can take two carbons out of the original six-member chain:

$$\underset{1}{C}H_3\underset{2}{C}H-\underset{3}{C}H\underset{4}{C}H_3 \qquad \text{2,3-Dimethylbutane}$$
$$\qquad\ |\qquad\ |$$
$$\qquad CH_3\ \ CH_3$$

Since the longest chain now has four carbons, the root name is butane. Because there are two methyl groups, we use the prefix *di-*. The numbers denote that the two methyl groups are positioned on the second and third carbons in the butane chain. Note that when two or more numbers are used, they are separated by a comma.

5. Two methyl groups also can be attached to the same carbon atom as shown here:

$$\qquad\qquad CH_3$$
$$\qquad\qquad\ |$$
$$\underset{1}{C}H_3-\underset{2}{C}-\underset{3}{C}H_2\underset{4}{C}H_3 \qquad \text{2,2-Dimethylbutane}$$
$$\qquad\qquad\ |$$
$$\qquad\qquad CH_3$$

We also might try ethyl-substituted butanes, such as

$$CH_3-CHCH_2CH_3$$
$$\qquad\quad |$$
$$\qquad\ CH_2 \qquad \text{Pentane}$$
$$\qquad\quad |$$
$$\qquad\ CH_3$$

However, note that this is in fact a pentane (3-methylpentane), since the longest chain has five carbon atoms. Thus this is not a new isomer. Trying to reduce the chain to three atoms provides no further isomers either. For example, the structure

$$CH_3-\underset{\underset{\underset{CH_3}{|}}{\overset{|}{CH_2}}}{\overset{\overset{CH_3}{|}}{C}}-CH_3$$

is really 2,2-dimethylbutane.

Thus there are only five distinct structural isomers of C_6H_{14}: hexane, 2-methyl-pentane, 3-methylpentane, 2,3-dimethylbutane, and 2,2-dimethylbutane.

Sample Exercise 22.3

Write the structure for each of the following compounds.

a. 4-ethyl-3,5-dimethylnonane   **b.** 4-*tert*-butylheptane

Solution

a. The root name *nonane* signifies a nine-carbon chain. Thus we have

$$\overset{1\quad2\quad3\quad\quad4\quad\quad5\quad6\quad7\quad8\quad9}{CH_3CH_2CH-CH-CHCH_2CH_2CH_2CH_3}$$
$$\underset{\overset{|}{\underset{\overset{|}{CH_3}}{}}}{CH_3}\;\underset{\overset{|}{CH_2}}{}\;\underset{}{CH_3}$$

b. Heptane signifies a seven-carbon chain, and the *tert*-butyl group is

$$H_3C-\underset{\overset{|}{CH_3}}{\overset{\overset{|}{}}{C}}-CH_3$$

Thus we have

$$\overset{1\quad2\quad\quad3\quad\;4\quad5\quad\;6\quad\;7}{CH_3CH_2CH_2CHCH_2CH_2CH_3}$$
$$\underset{\overset{|}{\underset{CH_3}{}}}{H_3C-\overset{|}{C}-CH_3}$$

Reactions of Alkanes

Because they are saturated compounds and because the C—C and C—H bonds are relatively strong, the alkanes are fairly unreactive. For example, at 25°C they do not react with acids, bases, or strong oxidizing agents. This chemical inertness makes them valuable as lubricating materials and as the backbone for structural materials such as plastics.

At a sufficiently high temperature, alkanes do react vigorously and exothermically with oxygen, and these **combustion reactions** are the basis for their widespread use as fuels. For example, the reaction of butane with oxygen is

$$2C_4H_{10}(g) + 13O_2(g) \rightarrow 8CO_2(g) + 10H_2O(g)$$

The alkanes also can undergo **substitution reactions,** primarily where halogen atoms replace hydrogen atoms. For example, methane can be successively chlorinated as follows:

$$CH_4 + Cl_2 \xrightarrow{h\nu} \quad CH_3Cl \quad + HCl$$
Chloromethane

$$CH_3Cl + Cl_2 \xrightarrow{h\nu} \quad CH_2Cl_2 \quad + HCl$$
Dichloromethane

$$CH_2Cl_2 + Cl_2 \xrightarrow{h\nu} \quad CHCl_3 \quad + HCl$$
Trichloromethane
(chloroform)

$$CHCl_3 + Cl_2 \xrightarrow{h\nu} \quad CCl_4 \quad + HCl$$
Tetrachloromethane
(carbon tetrachloride)

Note that the products of the last two reactions have two names; the systematic one is given first, followed by the common name in parentheses. (This format will be used throughout this chapter for compounds that have common names.) Also, the *hν* above each arrow signifies that ultraviolet light is used to furnish the energy to break the Cl—Cl bond to produce chlorine atoms:

$$Cl_2 \rightarrow Cl\cdot + Cl\cdot$$

A chlorine atom has an unpaired electron, indicated by the dot, which makes it very reactive and able to attack the C—H bond.

As we mentioned before, substituted methanes that contain both chlorine and fluorine as substituents, with the general formula CF_xCl_{4-x}, are called *Freons.* These substances are very unreactive and are extensively used as coolant fluids in refrigerators and air conditioners. Unfortunately, their chemical inertness allows them to remain in the atmosphere so long that they eventually reach altitudes where they may be a threat to the protective ozone layer (see Section 12.8).

Alkanes also can undergo **dehydrogenation reactions,** in which hydrogen atoms are removed and the product is an unsaturated hydrocarbon. For example, in the presence of chromium(III) oxide at high temperatures, ethane can be dehydrogenated, yielding ethylene:

$$CH_3CH_3 \xrightarrow[500°C]{Cr_2O_3} CH_2{=}CH_2 + H_2$$
Ethylene

Cyclic Alkanes

Besides forming chains, carbon atoms also can form rings. The simplest of the **cyclic alkanes** (general formula C_nH_{2n}) is cyclopropane (C_3H_6), as shown in Fig. 22.5(a). Since the carbon atoms in cyclopropane form an equilateral triangle with

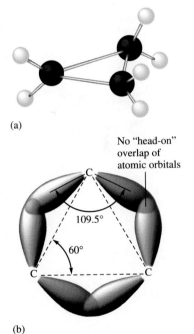

(a)

No "head-on" overlap of atomic orbitals

109.5°

60°

(b)

Figure 22.5

(a) The molecular structure of cyclopropane (C_3H_6). (b) The overlap of the sp^3 orbitals that form the C—C bonds in cyclopropane.

60-degree bond angles, their *sp*³ hybrid orbitals do not overlap head-on as they do in normal alkanes [Fig. 22.5(b)]. This results in unusually weak, or *strained*, C—C bonds, and the cyclopropane molecule is much more reactive than straight-chain propane. The carbon atoms in cyclobutane (C₄H₈) form a square with 90-degree bond angles, and cyclobutane is also quite reactive.

The next two members of the series, cyclopentane (C₅H₁₀) and cyclohexane (C₆H₁₂), are quite stable because their rings have bond angles very close to the tetrahedral angles, which allows the *sp*³ hybrid orbitals on adjacent carbon atoms to overlap head-on and form normal C—C bonds, which are quite strong. To attain the tetrahedral angles, the cyclohexane ring must ''pucker,'' that is, become nonplanar. Cyclohexane can exist in two forms, the *chair* and the *boat* forms, as shown in Fig. 22.6. The two hydrogen atoms above the ring in the boat form are quite close to each other, and the resulting repulsion between them causes the chair form to be preferred. At 25°C more than 99% of cyclohexane is in the chair form.

For simplicity, the cyclic alkanes are often represented by the following structures:

Thus the structure

represents methylcyclopropane.

The nomenclature for cycloalkanes follows the same rules as for the other alkanes except that the root name is preceded by the prefix *cyclo-*. The ring is numbered so as to give the smallest substituent numbers possible.

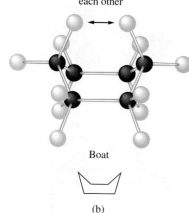

Chair

(a)

These two H atoms repel each other

Boat

(b)

Figure 22.6

The (a) chair and (b) boat forms of cyclohexane.

Sample Exercise 22.4

Name each of the following cyclic alkanes.

a.   CH₃—CH—CH₃

b.   CH₂CH₃

CH₃

CH₂CH₂CH₃

Solution

a. The six-carbon cyclohexane ring is numbered as follows:

CH₃—CH—CH₃

6 1
5 2
4 3

CH₃

There is an isopropyl group at carbon 1 and a methyl group at carbon 3. The name is *1-isopropyl-3-methylcyclohexane,* since the alkyl groups are named in alphabetical order.

b. This is a cyclobutane ring, which is numbered as follows:

$$CH_2CH_3$$

$$CH_2CH_2CH_3$$

The name is *1-ethyl-2-propylcyclobutane.*

22.2 Alkenes and Alkynes

Purpose

- To introduce unsaturated hydrocarbons.
- To discuss isomerism in alkenes.
- To describe common reactions involving multiple carbon–carbon bonds.

Multiple carbon–carbon bonds result when hydrogen atoms are removed from alkanes. Hydrocarbons that contain a carbon–carbon double bond are called **alkenes** and have the general formula C_nH_{2n}. This simplest alkene (C_2H_4), commonly known as *ethylene,* has the Lewis structure

$$H \quad \quad H$$
$$\diagdown \quad \diagup$$
$$C{=}C$$
$$\diagup \quad \diagdown$$
$$H \quad \quad H$$

As we discussed in Section 9.1, each carbon in ethylene can be described as sp^2 hybridized. The C—C σ bond is formed by sharing an electron pair between sp^2 orbitals, and the π bond is formed by sharing a pair of electrons between p orbitals (Fig. 22.7).

The systematic nomenclature for alkenes is quite similar to that for alkanes:

1. The root hydrocarbon name ends in *-ene* rather than *-ane.* Thus the systematic name for C_2H_4 is *ethene* and that for C_3H_6 is *propene.*

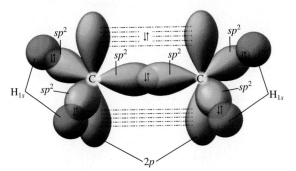

Figure 22.7
The bonding in ethylene.

Figure 22.8
The bonding in ethane.

(a)

(b)

Figure 22.9

The two stereoisomers of 2-butene: (a) *cis*-2-butene and (b) *trans*-2-butene.

2. In alkenes with more than three carbon atoms, the location of the double bond is indicated by the lowest numbered carbon atom involved in the bond. Thus $CH_2=CHCH_2CH_3$ is called *1-butene* and $CH_3CH=CHCH_3$ is called *2-butene*.

Note from Fig. 22.7 that the *p* orbitals on the two carbon atoms in ethylene must be lined up (parallel) to allow formation of the π bond. This prevents rotation of the two CH_2 groups relative to each other at ordinary temperatures and is in contrast to alkanes, where free rotation is possible (see Fig. 22.8). The restricted rotation about doubly bonded carbon atoms means that alkenes exhibit ***cis–trans* isomerism.** For example, there are two stereoisomers of 2-butene (Fig. 22.9). Identical substituents on the same side of the double bond are designated *cis* and on opposite sides are labeled *trans*.

Alkynes are unsaturated hydrocarbons containing a triple carbon–carbon bond. The simplest alkyne is C_2H_2, commonly called *acetylene,* which has the systematic name *ethyne*. As discussed in Section 9.1, the triple bond in acetylene can best be described as one σ bond between two *sp* hybrid orbitals on the two carbon atoms and two π bonds involving two *2p* orbitals on each carbon atom (Fig. 22.10).

The nomenclature for alkynes involves the use of *-yne* as a suffix to replace the *-ane* of the parent alkane. Thus the molecule $CH_3CH_2C\equiv CCH_3$ has the name 2-pentyne.

Like alkanes, unsaturated hydrocarbons can exist as ringed structures, for example:

For cyclic alkenes, number through the double bond toward the substituent.

or

Cyclohexene

or

4-Methyl-cyclopentene

Sample Exercise 22.5

Name each of the following molecules.

a.

b.

$$CH_3CH_2C\equiv CCHCH_2CH_3$$
$$CH_2$$
$$CH_3$$

Solution

a. The longest chain contains six carbon atoms and the chain is numbered as follows:

$$\underset{\underset{CH_3}{|}}{\underset{6\quad 5\quad 4}{CH_3CH_2CH}}\underset{\overset{3}{C}=\overset{2}{C}}{\overset{\overset{1}{H}\quad CH_3}{}}\overset{}{H}$$

Thus the hydrocarbon is a 2-hexene. Since the hydrogen atoms are on opposite sides of the double bond, the molecule is the *trans* isomer. The name is 4-methyl-*trans*-2-hexene.

b. The longest chain consisting of seven carbon atoms is numbered as shown (giving the triple bond the lowest possible number):

$$\underset{\underset{\underset{CH_3}{|}}{CH_2}}{\overset{1\quad 2\quad 3\quad 45\;6\quad 7}{CH_3CH_2C\equiv CCHCH_2CH_3}}$$

The hydrocarbon is a 3-heptyne. The full name is 5-ethyl-3-heptyne, where the position of the triple bond is indicated by the lower-numbered carbon atom involved in this bond.

Reactions of Alkenes and Alkynes

Because alkenes and alkynes are unsaturated, their most important reactions are **addition reactions,** in which π bonds, which are weaker than the C—C σ bonds, are broken, and new σ bonds are formed to the atoms being added. For example, **hydrogenation reactions** involve the addition of hydrogen atoms:

$$CH_2{=}CHCH_3 + H_2 \xrightarrow{\text{Catalyst}} CH_3CH_2CH_3$$
$$\text{Propene} \qquad\qquad\qquad \text{Propane}$$

In order for this reaction to proceed rapidly at normal temperatures, a catalyst of platinum, palladium, or nickel is employed. The catalyst serves to help break the

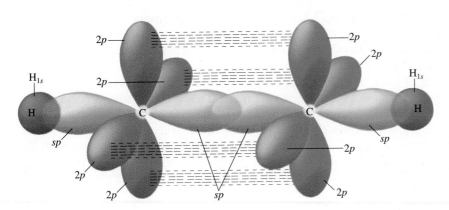

Figure 22.10
The bonding in acetylene.

The reaction of solid calcium carbide with water produces acetylene (C_2H_2), a flammable gas.

(a)

(b)

(c)

Figure 22.11

(a) The structure of benzene, a planar ring system in which all bond angles are 120 degrees. (b) Two of the resonance structures of benzene. (c) The usual representation of benzene. The circle represents the electrons in the delocalized π system. All C—C bonds in benzene are equivalent.

relatively strong H—H bond, as was discussed in Section 12.8. Hydrogenation of alkenes is an important industrial process, particularly in the manufacture of solid shortenings, where unsaturated fats (fats containing double bonds), which are generally liquids, are converted to solid saturated fats.

Halogenation of unsaturated hydrocarbons involves addition of halogen atoms, for example:

$$CH_2{=}CHCH_2CH_2CH_3 + Br_2 \longrightarrow CH_2BrCHBrCH_2CH_2CH_3$$
$$\text{1-Pentene} \qquad\qquad\qquad \text{1,2-Dibromopentane}$$

Another important reaction of certain unsaturated hydrocarbons is **polymerization,** a process in which many small molecules are joined together to form a large molecule. This will be discussed in Section 22.6.

22.3 Aromatic Hydrocarbons

Purpose

• To discuss the structures and reactivities of aromatic hydrocarbons.

A special class of cyclic unsaturated hydrocarbons is known as **aromatic hydrocarbons.** The simplest of these is benzene (C_6H_6), with a planar ring structure as shown in Fig. 22.11(a). In the localized electron model of the bonding in benzene, resonance structures of the type shown in Fig. 22.11(b) are used to account for the known equivalence of all the carbon–carbon bonds. However, as we discussed in Section 9.5, the best description of the benzene molecule assumes that sp^2 hybrid orbitals on each carbon are used to form the C—C and C—H σ bonds, with the remaining $2p$ orbital on each carbon used to form π molecular orbitals. The delocalization of these π electrons is usually shown by a circle inside the ring [Fig. 22.11(c)].

The delocalization of the π electrons makes the benzene ring behave quite differently from a typical unsaturated hydrocarbon. As we have seen previously, unsaturated hydrocarbons typically undergo rapid addition reactions. Benzene does not. Rather, it undergoes substitution reactions where *hydrogen atoms are replaced by other atoms*, for example:

Chlorobenzene

Nitrobenzene

Toluene

In each case the substance shown over the arrow is needed to catalyze these substitution reactions.

Substitution reactions are characteristic of saturated hydrocarbons, and addition reactions are characteristic of unsaturated ones. The fact that benzene reacts more like a saturated hydrocarbon indicates the great stability of the delocalized π electron system.

The nomenclature of benzene derivatives is similar to the nomenclature for saturated ring systems. If there is more than one substituent, numbers are used to indicate substituent positions. For example, the compound

is named 1,2-dichlorobenzene. Another nomenclature system uses the prefix *ortho-* (*o-*) for two adjacent substituents, *meta-* (*m-*) for two substituents with one carbon between them, and *para-* (*p-*) for two substituents opposite each other. When benzene is used as a substituent, it is called the **phenyl group.** Examples of some aromatic compounds are shown in Fig. 22.12.

Benzene is the simplest aromatic molecule. More complex aromatic systems can be viewed as consisting of a number of ''fused'' benzene rings. Some examples are given in Table 22.3.

Mothballs contain napthalene.

1,2-Dibromobenzene
(*o*-dibromobenzene)

1,3-Dibromobenzene
(*m*-dibromobenzene)

1,4-Dibromobenzene
(*p*-dibromobenzene)

Methylbenzene
(toluene)

3-Bromonitrobenzene
(*m*-bromonitrobenzene)

3-Chlorotoluene
(*m*-chlorotoluene)

Phenyl group

4-Chloro-2-phenylhexane

Figure 22.12

Some selected substituted benzenes and their names. Common names are given in parentheses.

Dyed nylon rope used to climb mountains in Nepal.

Table 22.3		
More Complex Aromatic Systems		
Structural Formula	Name	Use or Effect
	Naphthalene	Starting material for dyes
	Anthracene	Dyes
	Phenanthrene	Dyes, explosives, and synthesis of drugs
	3,4-Benzpyrene	Active carcinogen found in smoke and smog

22.4 *The Petrochemical Industry*

Purpose

• To discuss the major aspects of the production of petrochemicals.

As we saw in Section 6.5, petroleum represents an extremely valuable natural resource. The viscous, dark brown liquid pumped from the world's oil fields is a complex mixture of alkanes, alkenes, cycloalkanes, aromatic compounds, and various inorganic components. It contains literally thousands of compounds. Many of the most important chemicals produced in the United States are made from the cracking of petroleum.

More than 90% of the petroleum produced is used for fuels for heating and transportation. However, petroleum is also an extremely valuable source of **petrochemicals,** which serve as raw materials for the chemical industry. Petrochemicals are produced in two major ways: as by-products of refinery operations and from steam cracking of petroleum fractions.

Chemicals from Refineries

Even though petrochemicals represent only a small part (~5%) of the total output of petroleum refineries, which are designed mainly to produce fuels, refineries are an important source of these chemicals. Petroleum is first washed to remove acids and salts and then is transferred to a distillation tower where various fractions are separated by fractional distillation. The approximate compositions of the fractions are shown in Table 22.4.

Distillation is a physical separation of petroleum components, but most refinery operations also involve chemical reactions to maximize the output of the most useful products. **Cracking** is a process whereby large molecules are broken down to smaller ones by breaking carbon–carbon bonds. This can be done at high temperatures in a process called **pyrolysis,** or **thermal cracking,** or it can be done at lower temperatures using a catalyst in a process called **catalytic cracking.** Most cracking in refineries is now carried out catalytically because of lower energy costs and better control. The catalyst most commonly employed is a silica–alumina mixture (SiO_2–Al_2O_3), and temperatures are typically about 500°C. The very finely divided catalyst is usually "fluidized" by the moving stream of gaseous reactants, and a hydrogen atmosphere is often used to promote formation of alkanes (**hydrocracking**) and

A refinery in Carson, California.

Table 22.4			
The Fractions Obtained from the Distillation of Petroleum			
Percentage of Total Volume	Boiling Point (°C)	Approximate Number of Carbon Atoms	Common Names of Products
1–2%	<30	C_1–C_4	Light hydrocarbons (methane, ethane, propane, butane)
15–30%	30–200	C_4–C_{12}	Naphtha or straight-run gasoline
5–20%	200–300	C_{12}–C_{15}	Kerosene
10–40%	300–400	C_{15}–C_{25}	Gas oil
Undistilled	>400	>C_{25}	Residual oil, paraffin, asphalt

to remove nitrogen and sulfur impurities in the form of ammonia and hydrogen sulfide, respectively.

Typical reactions in the cracking operation are

$$n\text{-}C_{30}H_{62} \rightarrow CH_3(CH_2)_5CH{=}CH_2 + CH_3(CH_2)_{10}CH_3 + CH_3(CH_2)_7CH{=}CH_2$$

In the continuous-flow process for the production of gasoline, molecules with about eight carbon atoms are removed as product, and heavier molecules are recycled to be broken down further.

Another refinery process is **catalytic reforming,** in which alkanes and cycloalkanes are converted to aromatic compounds to improve the octane rating of gasoline. For example, toluene can be obtained from *n*-heptane:

The catalyst for this process usually contains platinum and one or more other metals such as rhenium, which specifically promotes conversion of cyclic alkanes to benzenes. Catalytic reforming has replaced coal tar as the major source of BTX (benzene, toluene, and xylenes) for the chemical industry.

Catalytic reforming is also a major source of hydrogen gas. In fact, the rapid increase in the use of ammonia as a fertilizer resulted from the need to use the hydrogen formed as a by-product of the refining process. Petroleum companies constructed many plants in the 1950s to manufacture ammonia by the Haber process,

$$N_2(g) + 3H_2(g) \xrightarrow[\text{High temperature and pressure}]{\text{Catalyst}} 2NH_3(g)$$

and convinced farmers to use the ammonia directly on their fields before planting. In fact, the use of ammonia escalated so rapidly that the hydrogen produced in refining operations could not keep up with the demand. Today, much of the hydrogen used to make ammonia comes from steam reforming of methane:

$$CH_4(g) + 2H_2O(g) \xrightarrow[\text{High temperature}]{\text{Catalyst}} CO_2(g) + 4H_2(g)$$

Other refining processes, which are mainly used to increase gasoline octane ratings, are alkylation, polymerization, and isomerization. In the first two processes, small gaseous molecules are changed to the larger ones needed for gasoline. **Alkylation** involves reactions such as that of 2-methylpropane (isobutane) with a smaller alkene (a propene, butene, or pentene), for example,

The process of combining two, three, or four alkenes to form a larger molecule is called **polymerization** in the oil industry, but **oligomerization** is a more appropriate name, since the products are dimers, trimers, and tetramers rather than long-chain polymers. An example of oligomerization is

$$3CH_3{-}CH{=}CH_2 \xrightarrow{\text{Catalyst}} CH_3{-}\underset{\underset{\displaystyle CH_3}{|}}{CH}{-}CH_2{-}\underset{\underset{\displaystyle CH_3}{|}}{CH}{-}CH{=}CH{-}CH_3$$

In **isomerization,** straight-chain alkanes are converted to branched-chain alkanes. For example,

$$CH_3CH_2CH_2CH_3 \xrightarrow{\text{Catalyst}} CH_3\underset{\underset{\displaystyle CH_3}{|}}{CH}CH_3$$

Isomerization is typically not a separate refinery process but takes place in connection with cracking and reforming operations.

Refineries are always run continuously, with petroleum fed in and products removed on a 24-hour basis. Although all refineries are similar, no two are the same. Operations vary depending on the composition of the crude oil being processed and the seasonality of the products; gasoline is usually a major product in the spring and summer, when driving increases, and the production of heating oil is emphasized in the fall and winter. On the other hand, a refinery with a relatively large petrochemical market tends to maximize its production of ethylene, propylene, BTX, and other commonly used chemicals.

Chemicals and Petrochemical Plants

Although refineries are an important source of chemicals, the great majority of chemicals from petroleum are produced in **petrochemical plants.** These plants are designed specifically to process petroleum fractions for the production of chemicals. The petrochemical industry consumes almost 10% of all the petroleum used in the United States.

The portion of the petroleum used to make petrochemicals is called the **feedstock,** which can vary from *gas oil* (contains the heavy hydrocarbons) to the *light hydrocarbons* (ethane, propane, and the butanes). The particular feedstock used at a given time depends mostly on the price. Because such a large percentage of petroleum goes into the production of fuels, the current fuel prices determine the price of various fractions. In the late summer the price of propane typically increases because home heating is about to increase. Then, in winter, butane prices often rise because butane is added to gasoline to improve its volatility in cold weather. Such price fluctuations affect the cost of feedstocks. Because the prices of the chemicals produced are determined mainly by the price of the feedstock (50–90% of the total cost), petrochemical plants must be able to switch quickly to the cheapest feedstock. Thus *the key to petrochemical plant design is flexibility.* Present economic conditions favor the light hydrocarbon feedstocks (65–75% of the total used).

Another consideration in the design of petrochemical plants is that the natural gas now being obtained from the earth is "drier" (contains less ethane, propane, and heavier hydrocarbons that are more easily liquefied than methane). This may lead to a heavier dependence on gas oil feedstocks in the future unless wells with "wet" gas are discovered.

Oligomer is a term used to describe a molecule assembled by reaction of only a few monomers, in contrast to the term *polymer* for very long-chain molecules.

Natural gas burning.

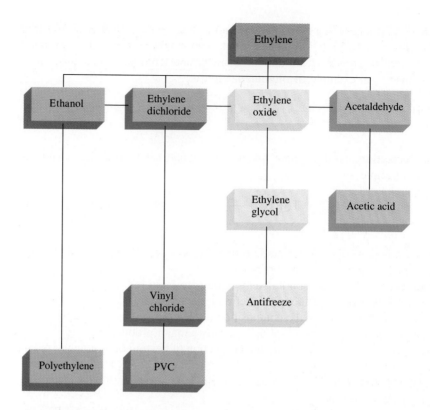

Figure 22.13
Some uses of ethylene.

Capacity refers to the production capability when all plants run at maximum output.

The fundamental operation in a petrochemical plant is **steam cracking,** a process in which hydrocarbon molecules are broken into small fragments by steam at very high temperatures ($\sim 1000°C$). The major product of steam cracking is ethylene; the current U.S. *capacity* is ~ 38 billion pounds per year. (*Actual production* of ethylene is about 35 billion pounds per year.) Some of the uses of ethylene are shown in Fig. 22.13. Ethylene is an important starting material; of the estimated 250 billion pounds of organic chemicals produced annually in the United States, approximately 100 billion pounds (40%) are derived from ethylene.

The petrochemical industry is an important and highly competitive business in which flexibility and innovative solutions to chemical and engineering problems are essential if a given operation is to remain profitable.

22.5 *Hydrocarbon Derivatives*

Purpose

- To introduce the basic functional groups and give a few characteristics of each one.

The vast majority of organic molecules contain elements in addition to carbon and hydrogen. However, most of these substances can be viewed as **hydrocarbon derivatives,** molecules that are fundamentally hydrocarbons but that have additional atoms or groups of atoms called **functional groups.** The common functional

Table 22.5			
The Common Functional Groups			
Class	Functional Group	General Formula*	Example
Halohydrocarbons	—X (F,Cl,Br,I)	R—X	CH_3I Iodomethane (methyl iodide)
Alcohols	—OH	R—OH	CH_3OH Methanol (methyl alcohol)
Ethers	—O—	R—O—R′	CH_3OCH_3 Dimethyl ether
Aldehydes	$-\overset{\overset{\textstyle O}{\|\|}}{C}-H$	$R-\overset{\overset{\textstyle O}{\|\|}}{C}-H$	CH_2O Methanal (formaldehyde)
Ketones	$-\overset{\overset{\textstyle O}{\|\|}}{C}-$	$R-\overset{\overset{\textstyle O}{\|\|}}{C}-R′$	CH_3COCH_3 Propanone (dimethyl ketone or acetone)
Carboxylic acids	$-\overset{\overset{\textstyle O}{\|\|}}{C}-OH$	$R-\overset{\overset{\textstyle O}{\|\|}}{C}-OH$	CH_3COOH Ethanoic acid (acetic acid)
Esters	$-\overset{\overset{\textstyle O}{\|\|}}{C}-O-$	$R-\overset{\overset{\textstyle O}{\|\|}}{C}-O-R′$	$CH_3COOCH_2CH_3$ Ethyl acetate
Amines	$-NH_2$	$R-NH_2$	CH_3NH_2 Aminomethane (methylamine)

*R and R′ represent hydrocarbon fragments.

groups are listed in Table 22.5. Because each functional group exhibits characteristic chemistry, we will consider them separately.

Alcohols

Alcohols are characterized by the presence of the hydroxyl group (—OH). Some common alcohols are shown in Table 22.6. The systematic name for an alcohol is obtained by replacing the final -e of the parent hydrocarbon by -ol. The position of the —OH group is specified by a number (where necessary) chosen so that it is the smallest of the substituent numbers. Alcohols are classified according to the number of hydrocarbon fragments bonded to the carbon where the —OH group is attached,

$R—CH_2OH$

$\overset{R}{\underset{R'}{\diagdown}}CHOH$

$R'-\overset{\overset{\textstyle R}{\|}}{\underset{\underset{\textstyle R''}{\|}}{C}}OH$

Primary alcohol (one R group)

Secondary alcohol (two R groups)

Tertiary alcohol (three R groups)

Table 22.6

Some Common Alcohols		
Formula	Systematic Name	Common Name
CH_3OH	Methanol	Methyl alcohol
CH_3CH_2OH	Ethanol	Ethyl alcohol
$CH_3CH_2CH_2OH$	1-Propanol	n-Propyl alcohol
$CH_3\overset{\displaystyle |}{\underset{\displaystyle OH}{C}}HCH_3$	2-Propanol	Isopropyl alcohol

where R, R′, and R″ (which may be the same or different) represent hydrocarbon fragments.

Sample Exercise 22.6

For each of the following alcohols, give the systematic name and specify whether the alcohol is primary, secondary, or tertiary.

a. $CH_3\underset{\displaystyle OH}{CH}CH_2CH_3$

b. $ClCH_2CH_2CH_2OH$

c. $CH_3\underset{\displaystyle OH}{\overset{\displaystyle CH_3}{C}}CH_2CH_2CH_2CH_2Br$

Solution

a. The chain is numbered as follows:

$$\overset{1}{C}H_3\overset{2}{\underset{\displaystyle OH}{C}}H\overset{3}{C}H_2\overset{4}{C}H_3$$

The compound is called 2-butanol, since the —OH group is located at the number 2 position of a four-carbon chain. Note that the carbon to which the —OH is attached also has —CH₃ and —CH₂CH₃ groups attached:

$$\overset{\displaystyle H}{\underset{\displaystyle OH}{CH_3-C-CH_2CH_3}}$$

R   R′

Thus this is a *secondary* alcohol.

b. The chain is numbered as follows:

$$\overset{3}{Cl}-CH_2-\overset{2}{C}H_2-\overset{1}{C}H_2-OH$$

The name is 3-chloro-1-propanol. This is a *primary* alcohol:

$$Cl-CH_2CH_2-\overset{\displaystyle \overset{H}{|}}{\underset{\displaystyle \underset{H}{|}}{C}}-OH$$

One R group attached to the carbon with the —OH group

c. The chain is numbered as follows:

$$CH_3-\overset{2}{\underset{\displaystyle \underset{OH}{|}}{C}}-\overset{3}{C}H_2-\overset{4}{C}H_2-\overset{5}{C}H_2-\overset{6}{C}H_2Br$$

with CH_3 attached at carbon 2.

The name is 6-bromo-2-methyl-2-hexanol. This is a *tertiary* alcohol because the carbon where the —OH is attached also has three other R groups attached.

Alcohols usually have much higher boiling points than might be expected from their molar masses. For example, both methanol and ethane have a molar mass of 30 g/mol, but the boiling point for methanol is 65°C, while that for ethane is −89°C. This difference can be understood if we compare the intermolecular attractions in these liquids. Ethane molecules are nonpolar and exhibit only weak London dispersion interactions. However, the polar —OH group of methanol produces extensive hydrogen bonding similar to that found in water (see Section 10.1), which results in the relatively high boiling point.

Although there are many important alcohols, the simplest ones, methanol and ethanol, have the greatest commercial value. Methanol, also known as **wood alcohol** because it was formerly obtained by heating wood in the absence of air, is prepared industrially (~4 million tons annually in the United States) by the hydrogenation of carbon monoxide:

$$CO + 2H_2 \xrightarrow[\text{ZnO/Cr}_2\text{O}_3]{400°C} CH_3OH$$

Methanol is used as a starting material for the synthesis of acetic acid and many types of adhesives, fibers, and plastics. It can also be used as a motor fuel. Methanol is highly toxic to humans and can lead to blindness and death if ingested.

Ethanol is the alcohol found in beverages such as beer, wine, and whiskey; it is produced by the fermentation of glucose in corn, barley, grapes, etc.

$$\underset{\text{Glucose}}{C_6H_{12}O_6} \xrightarrow{\text{Yeast}} \underset{\text{Ethanol}}{2CH_3CH_2OH} + 2CO_2$$

The reaction is catalyzed by the enzymes found in yeast and can proceed only until the alcohol content reaches approximately 13% (that found in most wines), at which point the yeast can no longer survive. Beverages with higher alcohol content are made by distilling the fermentation mixture.

Ethanol, like methanol, can be burned in the internal combustion engines of automobiles and is now commonly added to gasoline to form gasohol (see Section

Wine fermentation tanks at Half Moon Bay, California.

6.6). It is also used in industry as a solvent and for the preparation of acetic acid. The commercial production of ethanol (a half million tons per year in the United States) is carried out by reaction of water with ethylene:

$$CH_2{=}CH_2 + H_2O \xrightarrow[\text{Catalyst}]{\text{Acid}} CH_3CH_2OH$$

Many *polyhydroxyl* (more than one —OH group) alcohols are known, the most important being *1,2-ethanediol* (ethylene glycol),

$$\begin{array}{c} H_2C{-}OH \\ | \\ H_2C{-}OH \end{array}$$

a toxic substance that is the major constituent of most automobile antifreeze soluions.

The simplest aromatic alcohol is

which is commonly called **phenol.** Most of the 1 million tons of phenol produced annually in the United States is used to produce polymers for adhesives and plastics.

Aldehydes and Ketones

Aldehydes and ketones contain the **carbonyl group**

$$\diagup\!\!\diagdown\!C{=}O$$

In **ketones** this group is bonded to two carbon atoms, as in acetone,

$$\begin{array}{c} CH_3{-}C{-}CH_3 \\ \| \\ O \end{array}$$

In **aldehydes** the carbonyl group is bonded to at least one hydrogen atom, as in formaldehyde,

$$\begin{array}{c} H{-}C{-}H \\ \| \\ O \end{array}$$

or acetaldehyde,

$$\begin{array}{c} CH_3{-}C{-}H \\ \| \\ O \end{array}$$

The aldehyde vanillin gives the pleasant odor to vanilla beans.

The systematic name for an aldehyde is obtained from the parent alkane by removing the final *-e* and adding *-al*. For ketones the final *-e* is replaced by *-one*, and a number indicates the position of the carbonyl group where necessary. Examples of common aldehydes and ketones are shown in Fig. 22.14. Note that since the aldehyde functional group always occurs at the end of the carbon chain, the alde-

O
‖
H—C—H
Methanal
(formaldehyde)

O
‖
CH₃—C—H
Ethanal
(acetaldehyde)

O
‖
CH₃—C—CH₃
2-Propanone
(acetone)

O
‖
CH₃—C—CH₂CH₂CH₃
2-Pentanone

O
‖
CH₃CHCH₂C—H
|
Cl
3-Chlorobutanal

H   O
 \ //
  C
benzene ring
Benzaldehyde

CH₃CCH₂CH₃
‖
O
2-Butanone
(methyl ethyl ketone,
or MEK)

O   CH₃
 \ /
  C
benzene ring
Methyl phenyl
ketone

Figure 22.14

Some common ketones and aldehydes.

hyde carbon is always assigned as number one for referencing substituent positions in the name.

Ketones often have useful solvent properties (acetone is found in nail polish remover, for example) and are frequently used in industry for this purpose. Aldehydes typically have strong odors. Vanillin is responsible for the pleasant odor in vanilla beans; cinnamaldehyde produces the characteristic odor of cinnamon. On the other hand, the unpleasant odor in rancid butter arises from the presence of butyraldehyde.

Aldehydes and ketones are most often produced commercially by the oxidation of alcohols. For example, oxidation of a *primary* alcohol gives the corresponding aldehyde:

$$CH_3CH_2OH \xrightarrow{\text{Oxidation}} CH_3C\!\!\begin{array}{c} \nearrow O \\ \searrow H \end{array}$$

Oxidation of a *secondary* alcohol results in a ketone:

$$CH_3CHCH_3 \xrightarrow{\text{Oxidation}} CH_3CCH_3$$

with OH below the first carbon and O (double bond) below the second.

H   O
 \ //
  C
benzene ring with
OCH₃ and OH substituents
Vanillin

benzene ring—CH=CH—C
                        \\ O
                        /
                        H
Cinnamaldehyde

CH₃CH₂CH₂C
              \\ O
              /
              H
Butyraldehyde

Carboxylic Acids and Esters

Carboxylic acids are characterized by the presence of the **carboxyl group**

O
‖
—C
 \
  O—H

and have the general formula RCOOH. Typically, these molecules are weak acids in aqueous solution (see Section 14.5). Organic acids are named from the parent alkane by dropping the final -*e* and adding -*oic*. Thus CH_3COOH, commonly called acetic acid, has the systematic name ethanoic acid, since the parent alkane is ethane. Other examples of carboxylic acids are shown in Fig. 22.15.

Many carboxylic acids are synthesized by oxidizing primary alcohols with a strong oxidizing agent. For example, ethanol can be oxidized to acetic acid using

CH₃CH₂CH₂COOH

Butanoic acid

COOH

Benzoic acid

CH₃CHCH₂CH₂COOH
|
Br

4-Bromopentanoic acid

Cl
|
Cl—C—COOH
|
Cl

Trichloroethanoic acid
(trichloroacetic acid)

Figure 22.15

Some carboxylic acids.

potassium permanganate:

$$CH_3CH_2OH \xrightarrow{\text{KMnO}_4(aq)} CH_3COOH$$

A carboxylic acid reacts with an alcohol to form an **ester** and a water molecule. For example, the reaction of acetic acid and ethanol produces ethyl acetate and water:

$$CH_3\overset{O}{\overset{\|}{C}}\text{—}\boxed{OH \qquad H}\text{—}OCH_2CH_3 \longrightarrow CH_3\overset{O}{\overset{\|}{C}}\text{—}OCH_2CH_3 + H_2O$$

React to
form water

Esters often have a sweet, fruity odor that is in contrast to the often pungent odors of the parent carboxylic acids. For example, the odor of bananas is from *n*-amyl acetate,

$$CH_3\overset{O}{\overset{\|}{C}}\underset{OCH_2CH_2CH_2CH_2CH_3}{}$$

and that of oranges is from *n*-octyl acetate,

$$CH_3\overset{}{C}\text{—}OC_8H_{17}$$
$$\overset{}{\underset{O}{\|}}$$

A very important ester can be formed from the reaction of salicylic acid and acetic acid:

$$\text{(reaction scheme)} \qquad + H_2O$$

Salicylic acid   Acetic acid   Acetylsalicylic acid

The product is acetylsalicylic acid, commonly known as *aspirin,* which is used in huge quantities as an analgesic (pain-killer).

Amines

Amines are probably best viewed as derivatives of ammonia in which one or more N—H bonds are replaced by N—C bonds. The resulting amines are classified as *primary* if one N—C bond is present, *secondary* if they contain two N—C bonds, and *tertiary* if all three N—H bonds in NH₃ have been replaced by N—C bonds (Fig. 22.16). Examples of some common amines are given in Table 22.7.

Common names are often used for simple amines; the systematic nomenclature for more complex molecules uses the name *amino-* for the —NH₂ functional group. For example, the molecule

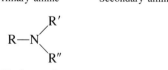

H
|
R—N
|
H

R'
|
R—N
|
H

Primary amine   Secondary amine

R'
|
R—N
\
R″

Tertiary amine

Figure 22.16

The general formulas for primary, secondary, and tertiary amines. R, R', and R″ represent carbon-containing substituents.

Table 22.7		
Some Common Amines		
Formula	Common Name	Type
CH_3NH_2	Methylamine	Primary
$CH_3CH_2NH_2$	Ethylamine	Primary
$(CH_3)_2NH$	Dimethylamine	Secondary
$(CH_3)_3N$	Trimethylamine	Tertiary
NH_2 (aniline structure)	Aniline	Primary
(diphenylamine structure)	Diphenylamine	Secondary

$$CH_3CHCH_2CH_3$$
$$|$$
$$NH_2$$

is named 2-aminobutane.

Many amines have unpleasant "fishlike" odors. For example, the odors associated with decaying animal and human tissues are due to amines such as putrescine ($H_2NCH_2CH_2CH_2CH_2NH_2$) and cadaverine ($H_2NCH_2CH_2CH_2CH_2CH_2NH_2$).

Aromatic amines are primarily used to make dyes. Since many of them are carcinogenic, they must be handled with great care.

22.6 Polymers

Purpose

• To show how polymers are formed from monomers via two types of polymerization reactions.

Polymers are large, usually chainlike molecules that are built from small molecules called **monomers.** Polymers form the basis for synthetic fibers, rubbers, and plastics and have played a leading role in the revolution brought about in daily life by chemistry during the past 50 years.

The simplest and one of the best known polymers is *polyethylene*, which is constructed from ethylene monomers:

$$nCH_2{=}CH_2 \xrightarrow{\text{Catalyst}} \left(\begin{matrix} H & H \\ | & | \\ C-C \\ | & | \\ H & H \end{matrix} \right)_n$$

where *n* represents a large number (usually several thousand). Polyethylene is a tough, flexible plastic used for pipes, bottles, electrical insulation, packaging films, garbage bags, and many other products. Its properties can be varied by using substituted ethylene monomers. For example, when tetrafluoroethylene is the monomer, the polymer Teflon is obtained:

Tetrafluoroethylene   Teflon

Because of the resistance of the strong C—F bonds to chemical attack, Teflon is an inert, tough, and nonflammable material widely used for electrical insulation, non-stick coatings for cooking utensils, and bearings for low-temperature applications.

Other polyethylene-type polymers are made from monomers containing chloro, methyl, cyano, and phenyl substituents, as summarized in Table 22.8. In each case the double carbon–carbon bond in the substituted ethylene monomer becomes a single bond in the polymer. The different substituents lead to a wide variety of properties.

The polyethylene polymers illustrate one of the major types of polymerization reactions, called **addition polymerization,** in which the monomers simply "add together" to form the polymer, with no other products. The polymerization process is initiated with a **free radical** (a species with an unpaired electron) such as the hydroxyl radical (HO·). The free radical attacks and breaks the π bond of an ethylene molecule to form a new free radical,

which can then attack another ethylene molecule:

Repetition of this process thousands of times creates a long-chain polymer. Termination of the growth of the chain occurs when *two radicals* react to form a bond, a process that consumes two radicals without producing any others.

Another common type of polymerization is **condensation polymerization,** in which a small molecule, such as water, is formed for each extension of the polymer chain. The most familiar polymer produced by condensation is *nylon.* Nylon is a

Table 22.8

Some Common Synthetic Polymers, Their Monomers, and Applications

| Monomer | Polymer | |
Name and Formula	Name and Formula	Uses
Ethylene $H_2C=CH_2$	Polyethylene $-(CH_2-CH_2)_n$	Pipes, bottles, electrical insulation, toys
Propylene $\begin{array}{c} H \\ \| \\ H_2C=C \\ \| \\ CH_3 \end{array}$	Polypropylene $-(CH-CH_2-CH-CH_2)_n$ $\quad\;\; CH_3 \qquad\quad CH_3$	Films for packaging, carpets, lab wares, toys
Vinyl chloride $\begin{array}{c} H \\ \| \\ H_2C=C \\ \| \\ Cl \end{array}$	Polyvinyl chloride (PVC) $-(CH_2-CH)_n$ $\qquad\quad\; Cl$	Pipes, siding, floor tile, clothing, toys
Acrylonitrile $\begin{array}{c} H \\ \| \\ H_2C=C \\ \| \\ CN \end{array}$	Polyacrylonitrile (PAN) $-(CH_2-CH)_n$ $\qquad\quad\; CN$	Carpets, fabrics
Tetrafluoroethylene $F_2C=CF_2$	Teflon $-(CF_2-CF_2)_n$	Cooking utensils, electrical insulation, bearings
Styrene $\begin{array}{c} H \\ \| \\ H_2C=C \\ \bigcirc \end{array}$	Polystyrene $-(CH_2CH)_n$ $\bigcirc$	Containers, thermal insulation, toys
Butadiene $\begin{array}{c} H \quad\; H \\ \| \quad\;\; \| \\ H_2C=C-C=CH_2 \end{array}$	Polybutadiene $-(CH_2CH=CHCH_2)_n$	Tire tread, coating resin
Butadiene and styrene (See above.)	Styrene-butadiene rubber $-(CH-CH_2-CH_2-CH=CH-CH_2)_n$ $\bigcirc$	Synthetic rubber

copolymer, since two different types of monomers combine to form the chain; a **homopolymer** results from a single type of monomer. One common form of nylon is produced when hexamethylenediamine and adipic acid react by splitting out a water molecule to form a C—N bond:

$$\underset{\text{Hexamethylenediamine}}{\text{H}_2\text{N}-(\text{CH}_2)_6\text{N}\text{H}} \quad \underset{\text{Adipic acid}}{\text{HO}-\overset{\text{O}}{\overset{\|}{\text{C}}}-(\text{CH}_2)_4\overset{\text{O}}{\overset{\|}{\text{C}}}-\text{O}-\text{H}} \longrightarrow$$

$$\text{H}_2\text{N}-(\text{CH}_2)_6\text{N}-\overset{\text{H}}{\underset{}{}}\overset{\text{O}}{\overset{\|}{\text{C}}}-(\text{CH}_2)_4\overset{\text{O}}{\overset{\|}{\text{C}}}-\text{O}-\text{H} \quad + \text{H}_2\text{O}$$

The molecule formed, called a **dimer** (two monomers joined), can undergo further condensation reactions because it has an amino group at one end and a carboxyl group at the other. Thus both ends are free to react with another monomer. Repetition of this process leads to a long chain of the type

$$\left(\text{N}-(\text{CH}_2)_6\text{N}-\overset{\text{O}}{\overset{\|}{\text{C}}}-(\text{CH}_2)_4\overset{\text{O}}{\overset{\|}{\text{C}}}\right)_n$$

which is the basic structure of nylon. The reaction to form nylon occurs quite readily and is often used as a lecture demonstration (see Fig. 22.17). The properties of nylon can be varied by changing the number of carbon atoms in the chain of the acid or amine monomer.

More than 1 million tons of nylon are produced annually in the United States for use in clothing, carpets, rope, and so on. Many other types of condensation polymers are also produced. For example, Dacron is a copolymer formed from the condensation reaction of ethylene glycol (a dialcohol) and *p*-terephthalic acid (a dicarboxylic acid):

$$\underset{\substack{\text{Ethylene} \\ \text{glycol}}}{\text{HOCH}_2\text{CH}_2\text{O}\,\fbox{H}} \quad \fbox{HO}-\overset{\text{O}}{\overset{\|}{\text{C}}}-\underset{\substack{p\text{-Terephthalic} \\ \text{acid}}}{\text{C}}-\text{O}-\text{H}$$

$$\downarrow \text{H}_2\text{O}$$

The repeating unit of Dacron is

$$\left(\text{OCH}_2\text{CH}_2-\text{O}-\overset{\text{O}}{\overset{\|}{\text{C}}}-\underset{}{\bigcirc}-\overset{\text{O}}{\overset{\|}{\text{C}}}\right)_n$$

Note that this polymerization involves a carboxylic acid and an alcohol to form an ester group:

$$\text{R}-\text{O}-\overset{\text{O}}{\overset{\|}{\text{C}}}-\text{R}_1$$

Thus Dacron is called a **polyester.** By itself or blended with cotton, Dacron is widely used in fibers for the manufacture of clothing.

More details concerning the manufacturing processes for producing polymers are given in Section 22.7.

A nylon Velcro fastener.

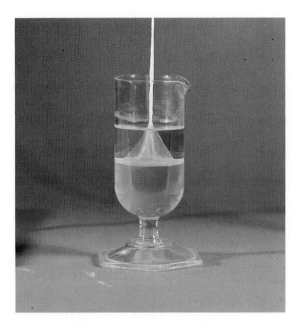

Figure 22.17

The reaction to form nylon can be carried out at the interface of two immiscible liquid layers in a beaker. The bottom layer contains adipoyl chloride

$$Cl-\underset{\underset{O}{\|}}{C}-(CH_2)_4-\underset{\underset{O}{\|}}{C}-Cl$$

in CCl_4, and the top layer contains hexamethylenediamine

$$H_2N-(CH_2)_6-NH_2$$

dissolved in water. A molecule of HCl is formed as each C—N bond forms.

22.7 The Polymer Industry

Purpose

- To discuss the industrial production of polymers.

It has been estimated that approximately 50% of the industrial chemists in the United States work in some area of polymer chemistry, a fact that illustrates just how important polymers are to our economy and standard of living. In Section 22.6 we described the major types of polymers and their uses. In this section we focus on the development of the polymer industry and on the processes used to manufacture several important polymers. These polymers are essential to the production of goods ranging from toys to roofing materials.

The Development and Properties of Polymers

The development of the polymer industry is a striking example of the importance of serendipity in the progress of science. Many discoveries in polymer chemistry arose from accidental observations.

The age of plastics might be traced to a day in 1846 when Christian Schoenbein, a chemistry professor at the University of Basel in Switzerland, spilled a flask containing nitric and sulfuric acids. In his hurry to clean up the spill, he grabbed his wife's cotton apron, which he then rinsed out and hung up in front of a hot stove to dry. Instead of drying, the apron flared and burned. Very interested in this event, Schoenbein repeated the reaction under more controlled conditions and found that the new material, which he correctly concluded to be nitrated cellulose, had some surprising properties. As he had experienced, the nitrated cellulose was extremely flammable and, under certain circumstances, highly explosive. In addition, he found that it could be molded at moderate temperatures to give objects that were, upon cooling, tough but elastic. Predictably, the explosive nature of the substance was initially of more interest than its other properties, and cellulose nitrate rapidly became the basis for smokeless gun powder. Although Schoenbein's discovery cannot be described as a truly synthetic polymer because he simply found a way to modify the natural polymer cellulose (see Section 23.2), it formed the basis for a large number of industries that grew up to produce photographic films, artificial fibers, and molded objects of all types.

The first synthetic polymers were obtained as by-products of various organic reactions and were generally regarded as unwanted contaminants. Thus the first preparations of many of the polymers now regarded as essential to our modern lifestyle were thrown away in disgust. One chemist who refused to be defeated by the ''tarry'' products obtained when he combined phenol and formaldehyde was the Belgian–American chemist Leo H. Baekeland (1863–1944). Baekeland's work resulted in the first completely synthetic plastic, called Bakelite, a substance that when molded to a certain shape under high pressure and temperature cannot be softened again or dissolved. Bakelite is a **thermoset polymer.** In contrast, cellulose nitrate is a **thermoplastic polymer;** that is, it can be remelted after it has been molded.

The discovery of Bakelite in 1907 spawned a large plastics industry, producing telephones, billiard balls, and insulators for electrical devices. During the early days of polymer chemistry, there was a great deal of controversy about the nature of these materials. Although the German chemist Hermann Staudinger speculated in 1920 that polymers were very large molecules held together by strong chemical bonds, most chemists of the time assumed that these materials were much like colloids, where small molecules are aggregated into large units by forces weaker than chemical bonds.

One chemist who contributed greatly to the understanding of polymers as giant molecules was Wallace H. Carothers of the DuPont Chemical Company. Among his accomplishments was the preparation of nylon (see Section 22.6). The nylon story illustrates further the importance of serendipity in scientific research. When nylon is made, by the reaction of a dicarboxylic acid and a diamine,

Casting polyurethane plastic.

Hexamethylenediamine   Adipic acid

the resulting product is a sticky material with little structural integrity. Because of this, it was initially put aside as having no apparently useful characteristics. However, Julian Hill, a chemist in the Carothers research group, one day put a small ball of this nylon on the end of a stirring rod and drew it away from the remaining sticky mass, forming a string. He noticed the silky appearance and strength of this thread and realized that nylon could be drawn into useful fibers.

The reason for this behavior of nylon is now understood. When nylon is first formed, the individual polymer chains are oriented randomly, like cooked spaghetti, and the substance is highly amorphous. However, when the substance is drawn into a thread, the chains tend to line up (the nylon becomes more crystalline), which leads to increased hydrogen bonding between N—H and C=O groups on adjacent chains (see Fig. 22.18). This increase in crystallinity and the accompanying increase in hydrogen-bonding interactions give rise to strong fibers and a highly useful material. Commercially, nylon is produced by forcing the raw material through a *spinneret,* a plate containing small holes, which forces the polymer chains to line up.

Another property that adds strength to polymers is **crosslinking,** the formation of covalent bonds between adjacent chains. The structure of Bakelite is highly crosslinked, which accounts for the strength and toughness of this polymer. Another example of crosslinking occurs in the manufacture of rubber. Raw natural rubber consists of chains of the type

$$\text{~~~~CH}_2\text{—CH}_2\text{—CH=C—CH}_2\text{—CH}_2\text{—CH=C—CH}_2\text{~~~~}$$
$$\qquad\qquad\qquad\quad |\qquad\qquad\qquad\qquad\qquad |$$
$$\qquad\qquad\qquad\ \text{CH}_3\qquad\qquad\qquad\qquad\ \text{CH}_3$$

and is a soft, sticky material unsuitable for tires. However, in 1839 Charles Goodyear (1800–1860), an American chemist, accidentally found that if sulfur is added to rubber and the mixture is heated (a process called **vulcanization**) the resulting rubber is still elastic (reversibly stretchable) but much stronger. This change in character occurs through the formation of covalent bonds to sulfur atoms that link the chains.

Polyethylene and substituted polyethylenes (see Section 22.6) are mainstays of the polymer industry. The discovery of Teflon, a very important substituted polyethylene, is another illustration of the role of chance in chemical research. In 1938 a DePont chemist named Roy Plunkett was studying the chemistry of gaseous perfluoroethylene:

$$\begin{array}{ccc} \text{F} & & \text{F} \\ & \diagdown\quad\diagup & \\ & \text{C=C} & \\ & \diagup\quad\diagdown & \\ \text{F} & & \text{F} \end{array}$$

He synthesized about 100 pounds of the chemical and stored it in steel cylinders. When one of the cylinders produced no perfluoroethylene gas after the valve was opened, the cylinder was cut open to reveal a white powder. This powder turned out to be a polymer of perfluoroethylene, which was eventually developed into Teflon.

Polymers Based on Ethylene

A large section of the polymer industry involves the production of macromolecules made from ethylene or substituted ethylenes. As we saw in Section 22.6, ethylene molecules polymerize by addition, after the double bond has been broken by some initiator:

$$\begin{array}{ccccc}
\text{H} & \text{H} & \text{H} & \text{H} & \\
| & | & | & | & \\
\text{X—C—C}\cdot & & \text{C=C} & \longrightarrow & \\
| & | & | & | & \\
\text{H} & \text{H} & \text{H} & \text{H} &
\end{array}
\quad
\begin{array}{cccc}
\text{H} & \text{H} & \text{H} & \text{H} \\
| & | & | & | \\
\text{X—C—C—C—C}\cdot \\
| & | & | & | \\
\text{H} & \text{H} & \text{H} & \text{H}
\end{array}$$

This process continues by adding new ethylene molecules eventually giving polyethylene, a thermoplastic material.

Charles Goodyear tried for many years to change natural rubber into a useful product. In 1839 he accidentally dropped some rubber containing sulfur on a hot stove. Noting that the rubber did not melt as expected, Goodyear pursued this lead and developed vulcanization.

(a)

(b)

Figure 22.18

(a) Raw (amorphous) nylon with random chain orientations.
(b) Nylon fibers after drawing.

Teflon-coated frying pan. Teflon is a polymer of C_2F_4.

◀ **CHEMICAL IMPACT** ▶

Wallace Hume Carothers

Wallace H. Carothers, a brilliant organic chemist who was principally responsible for the development of nylon and the first synthetic rubber (Neoprene), was born in 1896 in Burlington, Iowa. As a youth, Carothers was fascinated by tools and mechanical devices and spent many hours experimenting. In 1915 he entered Tarkio College in Missouri and so excelled in chemistry that even before his graduation he was made a chemistry instructor.

Carothers eventually moved to the University of Illinois at Urbana–Champaign, where he was appointed to the faculty when he completed his Ph.D. in organic chemistry in 1924. He moved to Harvard University in 1926 and then to DuPont Chemical Company in 1928. At DuPont, Carothers headed the organic chemistry division and during his 10 years there played a prominent role in laying the foundations of polymer chemistry.

By the age of 33, Carothers had become a world-famous chemist whose advice was sought by almost everyone working in polymers. He was the first industrial chemist to be elected to the prestigious National Academy of Sciences.

Carothers was an avid reader of poetry and a lover of classical music. Unfortunately, he also suffered from severe bouts of depression that finally led to his suicide in 1937 in a Philadelphia hotel room, where he drank a cyanide solution. He was 41 years old. Despite the brevity of his career, Carothers was truly one of the finest American chemists of all time. His great intellect, his love of chemistry, and his insistence on perfection all constituted his special genius.

There are two forms of polyethylene: low-density polyethylene (LDPE) and high-density polyethylene (HDPE). The chains in LDPE contain many branches and thus do not pack as tightly as those in HDPE, which consist of mostly straight-chain molecules.

psi is the abbreviation for pounds per square inch; 15 psi ≈ 1 atm.

Traditionally, LDPE was manufactured at high pressure (~20,000 psi) and high temperature (500°C). These severe reaction conditions require specially designed equipment, and for safety reasons, the reaction is usually run behind a reinforced concrete barrier. More recently, lower reaction pressures and temperatures have become possible through the use of catalysts. One catalytic system using triethylaluminum $[Al(C_2H_5)_3]$ and titanium(IV) chloride was developed by Karl Ziegler in Germany and Giulio Natta in Italy. Although this is a very efficient catalyst, it catches fire on contact with air and must be handled very carefully. A safer catalytic system was developed at Phillips Petroleum Company. It uses a chromium(III) oxide (Cr_2O_3) and aluminosilicate catalyst and has become the dominant process in the United States. The product of the catalyzed reaction is highly linear (unbranched) and is often called **linear low-density polyethylene.** It is very similar to HDPE.

The major use of LDPE is for manufacturing the tough transparent film that is used in the packaging for so many consumer goods. Two-thirds of the approximately 10 billion pounds of low-density polyethylene produced annually in the United States is used for this purpose. The major use of HDPE is for blow-molded products such as bottles for consumer products (see Fig. 22.19).

The term molecular weight is used in this section rather than molar mass because the former remains the common terminology in the polymer industry.

The useful properties of polyethylene are due primarily to its high molecular weight (molar mass). Although the strengths of the interactions between specific points on the nonpolar chains are quite small, the chains are so long that these small attractions accumulate to a very significant value so that the chains stick together very tenaciously. There is also a great deal of physical tangling of the lengthy chains. The combination of these interactions gives the polymer strength and toughness. However, a material like polyethylene can be remelted and formed into a new shape (thermoplastic behavior) because in the melted state the molecules can readily flow past one another.

(a)   (b)   (c)   (d)

Compressed air

Open die   HDPE tube

Blow-molded bottle

Figure 22.19
A major use of HDPE is for blow-molded objects such as bottles for soft drinks, shampoos, bleaches, and so on. (a) A tube composed of HDPE is inserted into the mold (die). (b) The die closes, sealing the bottom of the tube. (c) Compressed air is forced into the warm HDPE tube, and it expands to take the shape of the die. (d) The molded bottle is removed from the die.

Two polyethylene bottles. The one on the left is made with high-density polyethylene, while the one on the right is made with low-density polyethylene.

Since a high molecular weight gives a polymer useful properties, one might think that the goal would be to produce polymers with chains as long as possible. However, this is not the case—polymers become much harder to process as the molecular weights increase. Most industrial operations require that the polymer flow through pipes as it is processed. However, as the chain lengths increase, viscosity also increases. In practice, the upper limit of a polymer's molecular weight is set by the flow requirements of the manufacturing process. Thus the final product often reflects a compromise between the optimal properties for applications and those that allow ease of processing.

Although many polymer properties are greatly influenced by molecular weight, other important properties are not. For example, chain length does not affect a polymer's resistance to chemical attack. Physical properties such as color, refractive index, hardness, density, and electrical conductivity are also not greatly influenced by molecular weight.

We have seen that one way to change the strength of a polymeric material is to vary the chain length. Another method for modifying polymer behavior is to vary the substituents. For example, if we use a monomer of the type

the properties of the resulting polymer depend on the identity of X. The simplest example is polypropylene, whose monomer is

and that has the form

The CH$_3$ groups can be arranged on the same side of the chain (called an **isotactic**

Plastic films made from ethylene and its derivatives are used to package most consumer products. This photo shows molten plastic being formed into a bag.

chain) as shown above, can alternate (called a **syndiotactic chain**) as follows:

or can be randomly distributed (called an **atactic chain**).

The chain arrangement has a significant effect on the polymer's properties. Most polypropylene is made by using the Ziegler–Natta catalyst, $Al(C_2H_5)_3 \cdot TiCl_4$, which produces highly isotactic chains that pack together quite closely. As a result, polypropylene is more crystalline, and therefore stronger and harder, than polyethylene. The major uses of polypropylene are for molded parts (40%), fibers (35%), and packaging films (10%). Polypropylene fibers are especially useful for athletic wear because they do not absorb water from perspiration as cotton does. Rather the moisture is wicked away from the skin to the surface of the polypropylene garment, where it can evaporate. The annual U.S. production of polypropylene is about 7 billion pounds.

Another related polymer, **polystyrene,** is constructed from the monomer styrene:

Pure polystyrene is too brittle for many uses, so most polystyrene-based polymers are really *copolymers* of styrene and butadiene,

thus incorporating bits of butadiene rubber into the polystyrene matrix. The resulting polymer is very tough and is often used in furniture as a substitute for wood.

Another polystyrene-based product is acrylonitrile–butadiene–styrene (ABS), a tough, hard, and chemically resistant plastic used for pipes and items such as radio housings, telephone cases, and golf club heads for which shock resistance is an essential property. Originally, ABS was produced by copolymerization of the three monomers:

Acrylonitrile   Styrene   Butadiene

However, it is now prepared by a special process called **grafting,** in which butadiene is polymerized first, and then the cyanide and phenyl substituents are added chemically.

PVC: Additives Make the Difference

Another high-volume polymer, **polyvinyl chloride (PVC),** is constructed from the monomer vinyl chloride:

The production of this polymer is quite representative of the processes used in the polymer industry and will be discussed in detail.

In pure form, PVC is a hard, brittle substance that decomposes easily at the temperatures necessary to process it, making it almost useless. That it has become a high-volume plastic (~10 billion pounds per year produced in the United States by the late 1980s) is a tribute to chemical innovation. By use of the proper additives, PVC can be made rigid or highly flexible, and it can be tailored for use in inexpensive plastic novelty items or for precision engineering applications. PVC is used extensively in modern buildings for floor, wall, and window coverings; waste water pipes; exterior trim; insulation for electrical wiring; and a myriad of other applications. PVC is also widely used for clothing, upholstery, automobile bumpers, packaging materials, and credit cards.

The development of PVC illustrates the interplay of logic and serendipity and also the optimization of properties for processing and for applications. PVC production has been beset with difficulties from the beginning, but a solution has been found for each problem by a combination of chemical deduction and trial and error. For example, many additives have been found that provide temperature stability so that PVC can be processed as a melt and so that PVC products can be used at high temperatures. However, there is still controversy among chemists about exactly how PVC decomposes thermally, and thus the reason that these stabilizers work is not well understood. Also, there are approximately a hundred different plasticizers available for PVC, but the theory of its plasticization is too primitive to predict accurately what compounds might work even better.

PVC was discovered by a German chemical company in 1912, but its brittleness and thermal instability proved so problematical that in 1926 the company stopped paying the fees that maintained its patents. That same year Waldo Semon, a chemist at B. F. Goodrich, found that PVC could be made flexible by the addition of phosphate and phthalate esters. Semon also found that white lead, $Pb_3(OH)_2(CO_3)_2$, provided thermal stability. These advances led to the beginning of significant U.S. industrial production of PVC (~4 million pounds per year by 1936). In an attempt to further improve PVC, T. L. Gresham (also a chemist at B. F. Goodrich) tried approximately a thousand compounds, searching for a better plasticizer, and found that bis-(2-ethylhexyl) phthalate

> A *plasticizer* is a compound added to a polymer to soften it. The type and amount of plasticizer determine the pliability of the final product. One theory suggests that plasticizers cause softening by insertion between polymer chains, where they are held in place only by London dispersion forces. This lessens polymer–polymer interactions and softens the material.

Table 22.9		
Types of Additives Commonly Used in the Production of PVC		
Type of Additive	Effect	Examples
Plasticizer	Softens the material	Bis-(2-ethylhexyl) phthalate
Heat stabilizer	Increases resistance to thermal decomposition	Lead salts, tin compounds, antimony compounds
Ultraviolet absorber	Prevents damage by sunlight	Titanium(IV) oxide (TiO_2), substituted benzophenones
Flame retardant	Lowers flammability	Antimony(III) oxide (Sb_2O_3)
Biocide	Prevents bacterial or fungal attack	Arsenic and tin compounds

Recently, there has been concern about the carcinogenicity of di-2-ethylhexyl phthalate, and other phthalate esters are being studied as possible replacements.

gave the best results. This compound remains the most common plasticizer for PVC. Table 22.9 lists the types of additives commonly used in the production of PVC.

Although the exact mechanism of the thermal decomposition of PVC remains unknown, most chemists agree that the chlorine atoms play an important role. Compounds such as lead phosphite, lead sulfate, or lead phthalate are added to PVC to provide anions less reactive than chloride and to provide lead ions to combine with the released chloride ions. As a beneficial side effect, the lead chloride formed gives the PVC added electrical resistance, making lead stabilizers particularly useful in producing PVC for electric wire insulation.

One major use of PVC is for pipes in plumbing systems. Here, even though the cheap lead stabilizers would be preferred from an economic standpoint, the possibility that the toxic lead will be leached from the pipes into the drinking water necessitates the use of more expensive tin and antimony compounds as thermal stabilizers. Because 45% of the annual production of PVC goes into piping, the PVC formulation used for pipes represents a huge market for companies that manufacture additives, and the competition is very intense. The most recently developed low-cost PVC thermal stabilizer is a mixture of antimony and calcium salts. This mixture has replaced stabilizers containing tin compounds that have become increasingly costly in recent years. (The price for tin rose from less than $2 per pound in the early 1970s to about $4 in the 1980s.)

Outdoor applications of PVC often require that it contain ultraviolet light absorbers to protect against damage from sunlight. For pigmented applications such as vinyl siding, window frames, and building panels, titanium(IV) oxide is usually used. For applications where the PVC must be transparent, various aromatic organic compounds are added.

The additives used in PVC in the largest amounts are the plasticizers, but one detrimental effect of these additives is an increase in flammability. Rigid PVC, which contains little plasticizer, is quite flame-resistant because of the high average chloride content. However, as more plasticizer is added for flexibility, the flammability increases to the point where fire retardants must be added, the most common being antimony(III) oxide (Sb_2O_3). As the PVC is heated, this oxide forms antimony(III) chloride ($SbCl_3$), which migrates into the flame, where it inhibits free radicals (see the discussion of flame retardancy later in this section). However, because antimony(III) oxide is a white salt, it cannot be used for transparent or darkly colored PVC. In these cases sodium antimonate (Na_3SbO_4), a transparent salt, is used.

Once the additives have been chosen for a particular PVC application, the materials must be blended. This is often done in a dry-blending process producing a powder that is then used for fabrication of the final product. The powdered mixture also can be melted and formed into pellets, which are easily shipped to manufacturers, where they are remelted and formed into the desired products.

The production of PVC provides a good case study of an industrial process. It illustrates many of the factors that must be taken into account when any product is manufactured: effectiveness of the product, cost, ease of production, safety, and environmental impact.

Elastomers: Stretchable Polymers

Elastomers are materials that recover their shape after a deforming force. The fundamental elastomer is natural rubber, obtained as a latex from a tree native to tropical America but now grown primarily in the tropical Orient. When the Japanese conquered the major rubber-growing areas at the start of World War II, a crash program was undertaken in the United States to develop a suitable substitute. The results of this program were phenomenal; the U.S. production of synthetic rubber increased from none in 1940 to ~800,000 tons in 1944.

Natural rubber is primarily *cis*-polyisoprene,

which, after crosslinking by vulcanization, is especially useful for tires because of its unusual resistance to heat.

Synthetic rubber, which currently accounts for approximately 50% of the total market, is primarily made from copolymerization of styrene (one part) and butadiene (three parts):

The term *rubber* was apparently coined by Joseph Priestley, best known for the discovery of oxygen, because of its ability to rub out pencil marks.

Table 22.10		
Common Elastomers		
Type	Monomer(s)	Uses
Polychloroprene (Neoprene)	$CH_2{=}\overset{\displaystyle Cl}{\underset{\displaystyle |}{C}}{-}CH{=}CH_2$	Wire covering, automotive drive belts
Polyisoprene	$CH_2{=}\overset{\displaystyle CH_3}{\underset{\displaystyle |}{C}}{-}CH{=}CH_2$	Tires
Nitrile	$CH_2{=}\overset{}{\underset{\displaystyle CN}{\underset{\displaystyle |}{CH}}} + CH_2{=}CH{-}CH{=}CH_2$	Automotive hoses and gaskets
Polybutadiene	$CH_2{=}CH{-}CH{=}CH_2$	Tires

This polymer, called **SBR rubber,** was developed during World War II and is used principally (75%) for the manufacture of tires. Other types of synthetic elastomers are shown in Table 22.10.

Elastomers are characterized by a highly random (noncrystalline) arrangement of the chains in the relaxed state. When the material is stretched, the chains become more ordered. The tendency to snap back to the original state can be described in terms of entropy. Because the energy of interaction between the nonpolar chains is relatively small, the change in free energy is dominated by the positive ΔS term when the elastomer goes from the stretched, relatively ordered state to the relaxed random state. The positive ΔS term results in a negative value for ΔG, making the relaxing process spontaneous.

$\Delta G = \Delta H - T\Delta S$

Flammability of Polymers

One important property of polymers, especially those used for fabrics and construction materials, is flammability. The United States has a serious problem with domestic fires, which cause thousands of deaths and billions of dollars in property damage each year. One way to combat this problem is to make synthetic materials flame retardant. To see how this might be done, we must first understand what happens when something burns. A relatively simple combustion process, that between methane and oxygen, is illustrated in the following Chemical Impact feature. Note that the process takes place via a free-radical chain reaction.

Polymer combustion, although a more complicated process, still involves free radicals. The burning of a polymer (Fig. 22.20) is a cyclic process in which thermal energy is used to break bonds to form polymer fragments. These fragments then react exothermically with oxygen by a free-radical chain mechanism and thus furnish energy to sustain combustion. The polymer can be made flame retardant by providing some means of interrupting this cycle. This is done by solid-phase inhibition or by vapor-phase inhibition. In **solid-phase inhibition** the polymer surface is changed to help prevent fragmentation. If the polymer is extensively crosslinked at the surface, a carbonaceous char forms that insulates the underlying polymer, de-

Figure 22.20

The combustion of a polymer. In the pyrolysis zone, the polymer is broken into small fragments as bonds are disrupted by the thermal energy. These fragments then migrate into the higher-temperature flame zone, where they react with oxygen by free-radical chain reactions. The heat from these exothermic reactions is fed down to the polymer surface to provide energy for more pyrolysis.

◀ **C H E M I C A L   I M P A C T** ▶

The Mechanism of Methane Combustion

The reaction between methane and oxygen,

$$CH_4 + 2O_2 \rightarrow CO_2 + 2H_2O$$

occurs by formation of free radicals (fragments with an unpaired electron) that undergo a series of reactions, producing new radicals in a chain reaction. The radicals are initially formed when energy from an ignition source is fed into the system. The reactions in the chain can be classified into four types: *initiation,* in which radicals are formed; *propagation,* in which one or more radicals react to form a new radical; *branching,* in which one radical reacts to form two radicals; and *termination,* in which two radicals react to form a nonradical.

Examples of the various types of steps are as follows, where $R \cdot$ represents a carbon-containing radical and M is a nonreacting substance that absorbs energy to give M* as the R—H bond forms:

Initiation

$$CH_4 \rightarrow CH_3 \cdot + H \cdot$$
$$O_2 \rightarrow 2O \cdot$$

Propagation

$$CH_4 + H \cdot \rightarrow CH_3 \cdot + H_2$$
$$CH_4 + HO \cdot \rightarrow CH_3 \cdot + H_2O$$
$$CH_3 \cdot + O \cdot \rightarrow CH_2O + H \cdot$$
$$CH_2O + HO \cdot \rightarrow CHO \cdot + H_2O$$
$$CH_2O + H \cdot \rightarrow CHO \cdot + H_2$$
$$CHO \cdot \rightarrow CO + H \cdot$$
$$CO + HO \cdot \rightarrow CO_2 + H \cdot$$

Branching

$$H \cdot + O_2 \rightarrow HO \cdot + O \cdot$$

Termination

$$H \cdot + R \cdot + M \rightarrow RH + M*$$

priving the combustion process of its fuel. As a result, the flame cools, and the fire goes out. **Vapor-phase inhibition** involves changing the chemistry of the combustion process. Substances called **free-radical inhibitors** are built into the polymer. They migrate into the flame to produce additional radical-termination steps or to replace highly reactive radicals with less active radicals. Their effect is to greatly decrease the combustion rate either by radical scavenging:

$$H \cdot + HBr \longrightarrow H_2 + Br \cdot$$
$$HO \cdot + HBr \longrightarrow H_2O + Br \cdot$$

or by radical recombination:

$$HO \cdot + Na \cdot \longrightarrow NaOH$$
$$\underline{NaOH + H \cdot \longrightarrow H_2O + Na \cdot}$$
$$HO \cdot + H \cdot \xrightarrow{\text{Catalyst}} H_2O$$

Many polymers have natural flame retardancy. For example, a polymer containing halogen atoms or aromatic groups burns less readily because large quantities of energy are required to break the bonds in these substances and because these substances tend to char naturally.

Polymers that are naturally flammable have flame retardants either built into the polymer itself or added as separate molecules. The most common additives are phosphorus compounds, which retard flames by solid-phase inhibition as a result of the formation of acids that promote char formation.

Halogens are the substances most often used to modify the polymer itself to decrease flammability. The carbon–halogen bonds break in the flame, releasing the halogen atoms which can then form hydrogen halides that behave as free-radical inhibitors. For example, styrene becomes less flammable if halogens are substituted for hydrogen atoms on the phenyl ring.

◀ **C H E M I C A L   I M P A C T** ▶

Plastic that Talks and Listens

Imagine a plastic so "smart" that it can be used to sense a baby's breath, measure the force of a karate punch, sense the presence of a person 100 ft away, or make a balloon that sings. There is a plastic film capable of doing all these things. It's called **polyvinylidene difluoride (PVDF)**, which has the structure

When this polymer is processed in a particular way, it becomes piezoelectric and pyroelectric. A *piezoelectric* substance produces an electric current when it is physically deformed or alternately when it undergoes a deformation caused by the application of a current. A *pyroelectric* material is one that develops an electrical potential in response to a change in its temperature.

Because PVDF is piezoelectric, it can be used to construct a paper-thin microphone; it responds to sound by producing a current proportional to the deformation caused by the sound waves. A ribbon of PVDF plastic one quarter of an inch wide could be strung along a hallway and used to listen to all the conversations going on as people walk through. On the other hand, electric pulses can be applied to the PVDF film to produce a speaker. A strip of PVDF film glued to the inside of a balloon can play any song stored on a microchip attached to the film—hence a balloon that can sing happy birthday at a party. The PVDF film also can be used to construct a sleep apnea monitor, which, when placed beside the mouth of a sleeping infant, will set off an alarm if the breathing stops, thus helping to prevent sudden infant death syndrome (SIDS). The same type of film is used by the U.S. Olympic karate team to measure the force of kicks and punches as the team trains. Also, gluing two strips of film together gives a material that curls in response to a current, creating an artificial muscle. In addition, because the PVDF film is pyroelectric, it responds to the infrared (heat) radiation emitted by a human as far away as 100 ft, making it useful for burglar alarm systems.

Making the PVDF polymer piezoelectric and pyroelectric requires some very special processing, which makes it costly ($10 per square foot), but this seems a small price to pay for its near-magical properties.

F O R   R E V I E W

Summary

The study of carbon-containing compounds and their properties is called organic chemistry. Most organic compounds contain chains or rings of carbon atoms. The organic molecules responsible for maintaining and reproducing life are called biomolecules.

Hydrocarbons are organic compounds composed of carbon and hydrogen. Those which contain only C—C single bonds are saturated and are called alkanes. All alkanes can be represented by the general formula C_nH_{2n+2}.

Methane (CH_4) is the simplest alkane, and the next three in the series are ethane (C_2H_6), propane (C_3H_8), and butane (C_4H_{10}). In a saturated hydrocarbon, each carbon atom is bonded to four other atoms and is described as being sp^3 hybridized. Alkanes containing long chains of carbon atoms are called normal, or straight-chain, hydrocarbons.

Structural isomerism in alkanes involves formation of branched structures. Specific rules for systematically naming alkanes indicate the point of attachment of any substituent group, the length of the root chain, and so on.

Alkanes can undergo combustion reactions to form carbon dioxide and water or substitution reactions in which hydrogen atoms are replaced by other atoms. Alkanes also can undergo dehydrogenation to form unsaturated hydrocarbons. Cyclic alkanes are saturated hydrocarbons with ring structures.

Hydrocarbons with carbon–carbon double bonds are called alkenes and are said to be unsaturated. The simplest alkene is ethylene (C_2H_4), which is described in terms of sp^2 hybridized carbon atoms. Because the p orbitals on the carbon atoms in ethylene form a π bond, free rotation of the two CH_2 groups relative to each other does not occur (as it does in alkanes). This restriction means that alkenes exhibit *cis–trans* isomerism.

Alkynes are unsaturated hydrocarbons with a triple carbon–carbon bond. The simplest in the series is acetylene (C_2H_2), which is described as containing sp hybridized carbon atoms.

Unsaturated hydrocarbons undergo addition reactions such as hydrogenation (addition of hydrogen) and halogenation (addition of halogen atoms). Ethylene and substituted ethylene molecules can undergo polymerization, a process by which many molecules (monomers) are joined together to form a large chainlike molecule.

Aromatic hydrocarbons, such as benzene, are stable ring compounds with delocalized π electron systems. They undergo substitution reactions rather than the addition reactions characteristic of typical alkenes.

Organic molecules that contain elements in addition to carbon and hydrogen can be viewed as hydrocarbon derivatives: hydrocarbons with functional groups. Each functional group exhibits characteristic chemical properties.

Alcohols contain the —OH group and tend to have strong hydrogen bonding in the liquid state. Aldehydes and ketones contain the carbonyl group:

$$\overset{\diagdown}{\underset{\diagup}{}}C{=}O$$

In aldehydes this group is bonded to at least one hydrogen atom. Carboxylic acids are characterized by the carboxyl group:

$$-C\overset{\displaystyle O}{\underset{\displaystyle OH}{\diagdown\diagup}}$$

They can react with alcohols to form esters. Amines can be thought of as derivatives of ammonia in which one or more N—H bonds have been replaced by an N—C bond.

Polymers can be formed by addition polymerization in which monomers add together via a free radical mechanism. Polymers also can be formed by condensation polymerization, which involves the splitting out of a small molecule (often water) between two monomers to form a dimer, which then undergoes further condensation.

Key Terms

biomolecule
organic chemistry

Section 22.1

hydrocarbons
alkanes

normal (straight-chain or unbranched) hydrocarbons
structural isomerism
combustion reaction
substitution reaction
dehydrogenation reaction
cyclic alkanes

Section 22.2

alkenes
cis–trans isomerism
alkynes
addition reaction

hydrogenation reaction
halogenation
polymerization

Section 22.3

aromatic hydrocarbons
phenyl group

Section 22.4

petrochemicals
cracking
polymerization
feedstock
steam cracking

Section 22.5

hydrocarbon derivatives
functional group

alcohols
phenol
carbonyl group
ketones
aldehydes
carboxylic acids
carboxyl group
esters
amines

Section 22.6

polymers
addition polymerization
free radical
condensation polymerization
copolymer
homopolymer

dimer
polyester

Section 22.7

thermoset polymer
thermoplastic polymer
crosslinking
vulcanization
polyethylene
isotactic chain
syndiotactic chain
atactic chain
polystyrene
polyvinylchloride (PVC)
elastomers
inhibition

A blue question or exercise number indicates that the answer to that question or exercise appears at the back of this book and a solution appears in the Solutions Guide.

Questions

1. The normal (unbranched) hydrocarbons are often referred to as the *straight-chain hydrocarbons*. What does this name refer to? Does this mean that the carbon atoms in a straight-chain hydrocarbon really have a linear arrangement? Explain.

2. Distinguish between structural and geometric isomerism.

3. Distinguish between isomerism and resonance.

4. Distinguish between substitution and addition reactions. Give an example of each type.

5. Define and give an example of each of the following.
   a. Addition polymer
   b. Condensation polymer
   c. Copolymer

6. Define and give an example of each of the following.
   a. Free-radical polymerization
   b. Addition polymerization
   c. Condensation polymerization

7. Distinguish between a thermoset polymer and a thermoplastic polymer.

8. How do the physical properties of polymers depend on chain length and extent of chain branching?

9. Explain how plasticizers and crosslinking agents are used to change the physical properties of polymers.

10. Isotactic polypropylene is harder than atactic polypropylene. Explain.

11. Explain why each of the following changes in a polymer will lead to decreased flammability.
   a. Replacing hydrogen atoms with halogen atoms
   b. Replacing carbon atoms singly bonded to each other in the polymer chain with aromatic rings
   c. Highly crosslinking a polymer

12. How does crosslinking affect the elasticity of an elastomer?

13. Nylon is named according to the number of C atoms between the N atoms in the chain. Nylon-46 has 4 C atoms then 6 C atoms, and this pattern repeats. Nylon-6 always has 6 atoms in a row. Speculate as to why nylon-46 is stronger than nylon-6. (*Hint:* Consider the strengths of interchain forces.)

14. In which polymer, polyethylene or polyvinyl chloride, would you expect to find the stronger intermolecular forces (assuming the average chain lengths are equal)?

Exercises

In this section similar exercises are paired.

Hydrocarbons

15. Draw and name the five structural isomers of hexane (C_6H_{14}). Which isomer would you expect to have the highest boiling point? Why?

16. Name each of the following:

a.

$$CH_3 \quad CH_3$$
$$CH—C—CH_2CH_2CH_3$$
$$CH_3 \quad CH_3$$

b.

$$CH_3$$
$$CH_2CH_2CH$$
$$CH_3$$
$$CH_3—C—CH_2—CH_2—CH—CH_2—CH_3$$
$$CH_3 \qquad CH_2CH_3$$

c.

$$CH_3—CH_2—CH_2—CH—CH_3$$
$$CH_2CH_3$$

17. Draw the structural formula for each of the following.
 a. 2-Methylpentane
 b. 2,2,4-Trimethylpentane, also called isooctane. This substance is the reference (100 level) for octane ratings.
 c. 2-*tert*-Butylpentane
 d. The name given in part c is incorrect. Give the correct name for this hydrocarbon.

18. Draw the structure for 2-ethyl-3-methyl-5-isopropylhexane. This name is incorrect. Give the correct systematic name.

19. Name each of the following alkenes.

a. $CH_2{=}CH—CH_2—CH_3$

b.

$$CH_3$$
$$C{=}CH—CH_3$$
$$CH_3$$

c.

$$CH_3 \qquad\qquad CH_3$$
$$CH_3CH_2CH—CH{=}CH—CH$$
$$CH_3$$

20. Name each of the following alkenes.

a.

$$CH_2{=}C—CH_3$$
$$CH_2CH_3$$

b.

$$CH_2CH_2CH_2CH_3$$
$$CH_2{=}C—CH_2CH_2CH_3$$

c.

$$CH_3$$
$$CH—CH{=}CH_2$$
$$CH_3$$

21. Give the structure for each of the following.
 a. 3-Hexene
 b. 2,4-Heptadiene
 c. 2-Methyl-3-octene

22. Give the structure for each of the following.
 a. 4-Methyl-1-pentene
 b. 2,3,3-Trimethyl-1-hexene
 c. 3-Ethyl-4-decene

23. Give the structure of each of the following aromatic hydrocarbons.
 a. *o*-Xylene
 b. *p*-Di-*tert*-butylbenzene
 c. *m*-Diethylbenzene

24. Cumene is the starting material for the industrial production of acetone and phenol. The structure of cumene is

Give the systematic name for cumene.

25. Name each of the following.

a.   Cl—CH$_2$—CH$_2$—CH—CH$_3$
                                 |
                                Cl

b.   CH$_3$CH$_2$CH$_2$CCl$_3$

c.   CH$_3$ CH$_3$
         CCl—CH—CH
    CH$_3$ Cl   CH$_2$CH$_3$

d.   CH$_2$FCH$_2$F

e.   Cl   f.   Cl   g.   Cl

26. Name each of the following.

a. ▷—CH$_3$

b.   CH$_3$
        C—CH$_3$
        CH$_3$

c.   CH$_3$
   CH$_3$

d. ClCH=CH$_2$

e.   CH$_3$
      CH$_3$

f.   Cl
      Cl

Isomerism

27. Draw all the structural and geometric isomers of C$_3$H$_4$Cl$_2$.

28. Draw all the structural and geometric isomers of bromochloropropene.

29. Draw all the isomers of dimethylnaphthalene.

30. Draw all the isomers of difluoroethene and indicate which ones are polar.

31. Draw the following.
a. *cis*-2-Hexene
b. *trans*-2-Butene
c. *cis*-2,3-Dichloro-2-pentene

32. Name the following.

a.   CH$_3$ CH$_3$
        C=C
     H   H

b.   CH$_3$ CH$_2$CH$_2$CH$_2$CH$_3$
        C=C
     H   CH$_3$

c.   CH$_3$ H
        C=C
     F   F

Functional Groups

33. Identify each of the following compounds as a carboxylic acid, ester, ketone, aldehyde, or amine.
a. Anthraquinone, an important starting material in the manufacture of dyes:

34. Identify the functional groups present in the following pharmaceuticals.
a. Aspirin

     CO$_2$H

     OCCH$_3$
     ‖
     O

b. Morphine

HO

O

N—CH$_3$

HO

b.

c. Naloxone (a narcotic antagonist)

c.

d.

---

35. Mimosine is a natural product found in large quantities in the seeds and foliage of some legume plants and has been shown to cause inhibition of hair growth and hair loss in mice.

Mimosine, $C_8H_{10}N_2O_4$

a. What functional groups are present in mimosine?
b. Give the hybridization of the eight carbon atoms in mimosine.
c. How many σ and π bonds are found in mimosine?

36. Minoxidil ($C_9H_{15}N_5O$) is a compound, produced by the Upjohn Company, that has been approved as a treatment of some types of male pattern baldness.

a. Would minoxidil be more soluble in acidic or basic aqueous solution? Explain.
b. Give the hybridization of the five nitrogen atoms in minoxidil.
c. Give the hybridization of each of the nine carbon atoms in minoxidil.
d. Give approximate values of the bond angles marked a, b, c, d, e, and f.
e. Including all the hydrogen atoms, how many σ bonds exist in minoxidil?
f. How many π bonds exist in minoxidil?

---

37. The structure of ephedrine (adrenaline) is

What functional groups are present?

38. Menthol has the systematic name 2-isopropyl-5-methylcyclohexanol. Draw the structure of menthol.

Reactions of Organic Compounds

39. Complete the following reactions.

    a. $CH_2CH_2 + Br_2 \rightarrow$

    b. $+ Br_2 \xrightarrow{Fe}$

    c. $CH_3CO_2H + CH_3OH \rightarrow$

40. Reagents such as HCl, HBr, and HOH can add across carbon–carbon double bonds. The addition occurs so that the hydrogen atom in the reagent attaches to the carbon atom in the double bond that already has the greater number of hydrogen atoms bonded to it. With this rule in mind, draw the structure of the major product in each of the following reactions.

    a. $CH_3CH{=}CH_2 + HCl \rightarrow$

    b. $CH_3CH{=}CH_2 + H_2O \rightarrow$

    c. $+ HBr \longrightarrow$

    d. $+ H_2O \rightarrow$

    e. $+ H_2O \longrightarrow$

    f. $CH_3{-}C{\equiv}CH + 2HCl \rightarrow$

41. Give the structure of the product resulting from the oxidation of each of the following alcohols.

    a. CH_3CH_2OH

    b. $CH_3CH{-}CH_3$
            $\overset{|}{OH}$

    c. —OH

    d.

    e.

42. Oxidation of an aldehyde yields a carboxylic acid.

    $$R{-}\overset{\overset{O}{\|}}{C}H \xrightarrow{[ox]} R{-}\overset{\overset{O}{\|}}{C}{-}OH$$

    Thus it is very difficult to get only the pure aldehyde from the oxidation of a primary alcohol.

    a. Draw the structures for the products of the following oxidations.

       i. $CH_3\overset{\overset{O}{\|}}{C}H \xrightarrow{[ox]}$

       ii. $\xrightarrow{[ox]}$

       iii. $\xrightarrow{[ox]}$

    b. Which of the reactions in Exercise 41 would result in a mixture of an aldehyde and an acid as products? Draw the structures of the acids formed.

43. How would you synthesize each of the following?
    a. 1,2-Dibromopropane from propene
    b. 1,2-Dibromopropane from propyne
    c. Butyl acetate

44. How would you synthesize each of the following?
    a. Ethylbutyrate
    b. Acetone from an alcohol
    c. *t*-Butylalcohol (2-methyl-2-propanol)

Polymers

45. What monomer(s) must be used to produce the following polymers?

a. $\left(\!\begin{array}{c}\text{CH}-\text{CH}_2-\text{CH}-\text{CH}_2-\text{CH}-\text{CH}_2\\ |\quad\quad\quad\;|\quad\quad\quad\;|\\ \text{F}\quad\quad\quad\text{F}\quad\quad\quad\text{F}\end{array}\!\right)_n$

b. $\left(\!\text{O}-\text{CH}_2-\text{CH}_2-\overset{\displaystyle O}{\overset{\|}{\text{C}}}-\text{O}-\text{CH}_2-\text{CH}_2-\overset{\displaystyle O}{\overset{\|}{\text{C}}}\!\right)_n$

c. $\left(\!\text{O}-\text{CH}_2-\text{CH}_2-\text{O}-\overset{\displaystyle O}{\overset{\|}{\text{C}}}-\text{CH}_2-\text{CH}_2-\overset{\displaystyle O}{\overset{\|}{\text{C}}}\!\right)_n$

d. $\left(\!\begin{array}{ccc}\text{CH}_3 & \text{CH}_3 & \text{CH}_3\\ |\quad\quad & |\quad\quad & |\quad\quad\\ \text{C}-\text{CH}_2- & \text{C}-\text{CH}_2- & \text{C}-\text{CH}_2\end{array}\!\right)_n$

e. $\left(\!\begin{array}{cccc}-\text{CH}-& \text{CH}- & \text{CH}- & \text{CH}-\\ |\quad & |\quad & |\quad & |\quad\\ & \text{CH}_3 & & \text{CH}_3\end{array}\!\right)_n$

Classify these polymers as condensation or addition polymers. Which are copolymers?

46. Kel-F is a polymer with the structure

$$\left(\!\begin{array}{cccccc}\text{F}&\text{F}&\text{F}&\text{F}&\text{F}&\text{F}\\ |&|&|&|&|&|\\ \text{C}-&\text{C}-&\text{C}-&\text{C}-&\text{C}-&\text{C}\\ |&|&|&|&|&|\\ \text{Cl}&\text{F}&\text{Cl}&\text{F}&\text{Cl}&\text{F}\end{array}\!\right)_n$$

a. What is the monomer for Kel-F?

b. Would you expect Kel-F to be more or less reactive than Teflon?

47. Kevlar, used in bulletproof vests, is made by the condensation copolymerization of the monomers

Draw the structure of a portion of the Kevlar chain.

48. The polyester formed from lactic acid,

$$\text{CH}_3-\underset{\overset{|}{\text{OH}}}{\text{CH}}-\text{CO}_2\text{H}$$

is used for tissue implants and surgical sutures that will dissolve in the body. Draw the structure of a portion of this polymer.

49. Polyimides are polymers that are tough and stable at temperatures of up to 400°C. They are used as a protective coating on the quartz fibers used in fiber optics. What monomers were used to make the following polyimide:

50. The Amoco Chemical Company has successfully raced a car with a plastic engine. Many of the engine parts, including piston skirts, connecting rods, and valve-train components, were made of a polymer called *Torlon:*

What monomers are used to make this polymer?

51. Polystyrene can be made more rigid by copolymerizing styrene with divinylbenzene:

$$CH{=}CH_2$$

(benzene ring with)

$$CH{=}CH_2$$

How does the divinylbenzene make the copolymer more rigid?

52. Polyesters containing double bonds are often crosslinked by reacting the polymer with styrene.
    a. Draw the structure of the copolymer of

$$HO{-}CH_2CH_2{-}OH \quad \text{and} \quad HO_2C{-}CH{=}CH{-}CO_2H$$

    b. Draw the structure of the crosslinked polymer (after the polyester has been reacted with styrene).

Additional Exercises

53. Isoprene, the repeating unit in natural rubber, has the structure

$$\overset{\displaystyle CH_3}{\underset{\displaystyle |}{CH_2{=}C{-}CH{=}CH_2}}$$

    Give the systematic name for isoprene.

54. Draw structures for each of the following.
    a. Difluoromethane
    b. 1-Bromo-1,2-dichloropropane
    c. *m*-Difluorobenzene

55. *Cis–trans* isomerism is also possible in molecules with rings. Draw the *cis* and *trans* isomers of 1,2-dimethylcyclohexane.

56. There is only one compound that is named 1,2-dichloroethane, but there are two distinct compounds that can be named 1,2-dichloroethene. Why?

57. Tautomers are molecules that differ in the position of a hydrogen atom. Use bond energies (Table 8.4) to predict which tautomer in each of the following tautomeric pairs is more stable.

    a. $CH_3{-}\overset{\displaystyle OH}{\underset{}{C}}{=}CH_2 \quad$ or $\quad CH_3{-}\overset{\displaystyle O}{\underset{}{C}}{-}CH_3$

    b. (structure) or (structure)

    c. $H_3C{-}\overset{\displaystyle H\;\;H}{\underset{\displaystyle O\;\;O}{C{-}C}}{-}CH_3 \quad$ or $\quad H_3C{-}C{=}C\overset{\displaystyle CH_3}{\underset{\displaystyle OH}{}}$

58. Draw the isomer specified.
    a. An aldehyde that is an isomer of acetone
    b. An ether that is an isomer of 2-propanol
    c. A geometric isomer of *cis*-2-butene
    d. A primary amine that is an isomer of trimethylamine
    e. A secondary amine that is an isomer of trimethylamine
    f. A primary alcohol that is an isomer of 2-propanol

59. Drugs such as morphine (see Exercise 34) are often treated with strong acids. The most commonly used form of morphine is morphine hydrochloride. Draw the structure of morphine hydrochloride. Why are drugs treated in this way?

60. Consider the reaction of propane with chlorine.
    a. How many monochloro products are formed? Draw their structures.
    b. How many dichloro products can be formed? Draw their structures.

61. Ethylene oxide

$$\underset{\displaystyle O}{CH_2{-}CH_2}$$

    is an important industrial chemical. While most ethers are unreactive, ethylene oxide is quite reactive. It resembles C_2H_4 in its reactions in that many addition reactions occur across the C—O bond.
    a. Why is ethylene oxide so reactive? (*Hint:* Consider the bond angles in ethylene oxide as compared with those predicted by the VSEPR model.)
    b. Ethylene oxide undergoes addition polymerization forming a polymer used in many applications requiring a non-ionic surfactant. Draw the structure of this polymer.
    c. Ethylene oxide is also an important intermediate in the chemical industry. Its major use is in the production of ethylene glycol for antifreeze.

$$\underset{\displaystyle O}{CH_2{-}CH_2} \xrightarrow[\substack{H_2SO_4 \\ 50{-}70°C}]{H_2O} HOCH_2CH_2OH$$

This reaction is similar to the addition reactions of alkenes, for example:

$$CH_2{=}CH_2 \xrightarrow[H_2SO_4]{H_2O} CH_3CH_2OH$$

Use bond energies (Table 8.4) to estimate ΔH for the above two reactions.

d. The molecular weight (molar mass) of polymers is often given as part of their trade name by the manufacturers. For example, Carbowax 20M is a polymer of ethylene oxide with an average molar mass of 20,000 g/mol. On average, how many monomer units are in such a polymer? Does this mean that every molecule in a sample of this polymer has the same length? Explain.

62. Polycarbonates are a class of thermoplastic polymers that are used in the plastic lenses of eyeglasses and in the shells of bicycle helmets. A polycarbonate is made from the reaction of bisphenol A (BPA) with phosgene ($COCl_2$):

BPA

$$\xrightarrow[\text{Catalyst}]{2n \text{ NaOH}} \text{polycarbonate} + 2n \text{ NaCl} + 2n \text{ H}_2\text{O}$$

Phenol (C_6H_5OH) is used to terminate the polymer (stop its growth).

a. Draw the structure of the polycarbonate chain formed from the above reaction.

b. Is this reaction a condensation or addition polymerization?

63. A urethane linkage occurs when an alcohol adds across the carbon–nitrogen double bond in an isocyanate:

Alcohol   Isocyanate   A urethane

Polyurethanes (formed from the copolymerization of a diol with a diisocyanate) are used in foamed insulation and a variety of other construction materials. What is the structure of the polyurethane formed by the reaction

64. a. Draw the structures of the polymers formed from the monomers listed in Table 22.10.

b. These polymers also show geometric isomerism. For example, there are two polymers of isoprene: *cis*-polyisoprene (natural rubber) and *trans*-polyisoprene (gutta per-

cha). Gutta percha, which is not an elastomer, has been used as the center of golf balls. Draw the structures of these polymers.

65. Which of the following polymers would be stronger or more rigid? Explain your choices.

a. The copolymer of ethylene glycol and terephthalic acid or the copolymer of 1,2-diaminoethane and terephthalic acid

b. The polymer of $HO{-}(CH_2)_6{-}CO_2H$ or that of

c. Polyacetylene or polyethylene

66. When acrylic polymers are burned, toxic fumes are produced. For example, in many airplane fires, more passenger deaths have been caused by breathing toxic fumes than by the fire itself. Using polyacrylonitrile as an example, what would you expect to be one of the most toxic, gaseous combustion products created in the reaction?

67. Stretch a rubber band while holding it gently to your lips. Then slowly let it relax while still in contact with your lips.

a. What happens to the temperature of the rubber band on stretching?

b. Is the stretching an exothermic or endothermic process?

c. Explain the above result in terms of interparticle forces.

d. What is the sign of ΔS and ΔG for stretching the rubber band?

e. Give the molecular explanation for the sign of ΔS for stretching.

68. All the following observations about the aging of an automobile are related. Explain the relationship among these three observations.

i. On hot days a waxy coating may appear on the inside of the glass of a car.

ii. The "new car" smell gradually goes away.

iii. Vinyl seat covers become brittle and crack.

69. Look up the structures of the following drugs in *The Merck Index*. What functional groups are present? Give a use for each drug.

a. Dopa

b. Amphetamine

c. Ephedrine

d. Acetaminophen

e. Phenacetin

70. Many drugs are sold using trade names or common names. The structures of such substances can be found using the Cross Index of Names at the back of *The Merck Index*. Use *The Merck Index* to find the structure of each of the following and its primary use.

a. Ecotrin   d. Keflex

b. Tylenol   e. Nalfon

c. Lasix   f. Voltaren

Challenge Problems

71. Mycomycin, a naturally occurring antibiotic produced by the fungus *Nocardia acidophilus,* has the molecular formula $C_{13}H_{10}O_2$ and the systematic name 3,5,7,8-tridecatetraene-10,12-diynoic acid. Draw the structure of mycomycin.

72. Ethyl caprate is an ester used in the manufacture of wine bouquets. It is sometimes called "cognac essence." Combustion analysis of a sample of ethyl caprate shows it to be 71.89% carbon, 12.13% hydrogen, and 15.98% oxygen by mass. Hydrolysis (reaction with water) of the ester yields ethanol and an acid. The molar mass of the acid is 172 g/mol. What is the molecular formula of ethyl caprate?

73. The Lewis structure of Dewar's benzene is

Is this another resonance structure for benzene, or would you expect Dewar's benzene to be a different substance?

74. Estimate ΔH for the following reactions, using bond energies (Table 8.4).

$$3CH_2{=}CH_2(g) + 3H_2(g) \rightarrow 3CH_3{-}CH_3(g)$$

The enthalpies of formation of $C_6H_6(g)$ and $C_6H_{12}(g)$ are 82.9 and -90.3 kJ/mol, respectively. Calculate $\Delta H°$ for the two reactions using standard enthalpies of formation from Appendix 4. How do you account for any differences between results obtained by the two methods?

75. Anthraquinone is an important intermediate in the production of dyes. Traditionally, it was prepared by the reaction of phthalic anhydride with benzene:

(i)

In 1974, the company Badische Anilin Soda Fabrik developed an alternative route:

(ii)

Styrene   83% yield   Anthraquinone (52% yield)

Process (iii) was announced in 1977 and process (iv) was introduced in 1978 by Bayer-Ciba-Geigy:

(iii)

80% yield

(iv)

Naphthalene

90% yield

a. What is the overall yield of the process outlined in (ii)?
b. What is the theoretical yield of anthraquinone (molar mass, 208 g/mol) from 1000. kg of styrene? What will be the actual yield?
c. Given the prices in the table at right, calculate the cost of raw materials per pound of anthraquinone produced by both processes (i) and (ii).
d. Would either process (i) or (ii) have an advantage over the other from the standpoint of waste disposal?
e. Given the prices in the table at right, calculate the raw material cost per pound of anthraquinone produced by processes (iii) and (iv).
f. Are there any economic advantages to process (iii) or (iv)?

Compound	Molar Mass	Cost/ Pound	Pounds Used
Phthalic anhydride	148	$0.35	148
Anhydrous $AlCl_3$	133	$0.67	293
Styrene	104	$0.27	208
Benzene	78	$0.61	78

	Molar Mass	Cost/Pound
Benzene	78	$0.61
Benzophenone	182	$2.40
Naphthalene	128	$0.24
1,3-Butadiene	54	$0.12

76. Hexamethylenediamine (1,6-diaminohexane) is one of the raw materials used in the production of nylon. Several processes are available for the production of hexamethylenediamine. Two of them are as follows:

(i)

Furfural

(ii) $CH_2=CH-CH=CH_2 + 2HCN \xrightarrow[\substack{Various \\ catalysts}]{Several steps} NC-(CH_2)_4-CN \xrightarrow[\substack{5000 psi \\ 25-250°C}]{\substack{H_2 \\ Co\ catalyst}} H_2N-(CH_2)_6-NH_2$

The following are the relevant prices:

	Cost/Pound
Furfural	$0.79
Butadiene	$0.12

a. At the quoted prices, assuming all things such as other costs and yields are comparable, which process has the economic advantage?

b. Furfural is derived from corncobs. Butadiene is derived from petroleum. Assuming the raw petroleum represents most of the cost of butadiene, which percentage increase in crude oil prices will make the two processes equivalent from the cost standpoint?

77. Read the label on an over-the-counter medication (Tylenol, cough syrup, etc.) or cosmetic. Look up the structures of the organic compounds listed in a reference such as *The Merck Index*. From the information given, speculate on the function of each of the compounds you looked up.

CHAPTER 23

Biochemistry

Biochemistry, which is the study of the chemistry of living systems, is a vast and exciting field in which important discoveries about how life is maintained and how diseases occur are being made every day. In particular, there has been a rapid growth in the understanding of how living cells manufacture the molecules necessary for life.

We can barely scratch the surface of this important field in this chapter. Instead of taking a necessarily superficial view of the entire field, we will concentrate here on the major types of biomolecules that support living systems. First, however, we will survey the elements found in living systems and briefly describe the constitution of a cell.

At present, 30 elements are known to be essential or are strongly suspected to be essential to human life. These **essential elements** are shown in Fig. 23.1. The most abundant elements are hydrogen, carbon, nitrogen, and oxygen, but sodium, magnesium, potassium, calcium, phosphorus, sulfur, and chlorine are also present in relatively large amounts. Although present only in trace amounts, many of the first-row transition metals are essential for the action of many enzymes. For example, zinc, one of the **trace elements,** is found in more than 200 biologically important molecules. The functions of the essential elements are summarized in Table 23.1. As more studies are performed, additional elements will probably be found to be essential.

Life is organized around the functions of the **cell,** the smallest unit of living things that has the properties normally associated with life, such as reproduction, metabolism, mutation, and sensitivity to external stimuli. There are two fundamental types of cells: *procaryotes*, those without nuclei, and *eucaryotes*, those which have nuclei. Bacteria are examples of procaryotic organisms, and plant and animal cells are examples of eucaryotic cells.

As the fundamental building blocks of all living systems, cells aggregate to form tissues, which in turn are assembled into the organs that make up complex living systems. Thus, to understand how life is maintained and reproduced, we must learn how cells operate on the molecular level. This is the main thrust of biochemistry.

< Magnified strands of a spider web.

1A																	8A
1 H	2A											3A	4A	5A	6A	7A	2 He
3 Li	4 Be											5 B	6 C	7 N	8 O	9 F	10 Ne
11 Na	12 Mg											13 Al	14 Si	15 P	16 S	17 Cl	18 Ar
19 K	20 Ca	21 Sc	22 Ti	23 V	24 Cr	25 Mn	26 Fe	27 Co	28 Ni	29 Cu	30 Zn	31 Ga	32 Ge	33 As	34 Se	35 Br	36 Kr
37 Rb	38 Sr	39 Y	40 Zr	41 Nb	42 Mo	43 Tc	44 Ru	45 Rh	46 Pd	47 Ag	48 Cd	49 In	50 Sn	51 Sb	52 Te	53 I	54 Xe
55 Cs	56 Ba	57 La	72 Hf	73 Ta	74 W	75 Re	76 Os	77 Ir	78 Pt	79 Au	80 Hg	81 Tl	82 Pb	83 Bi	84 Po	85 At	86 Rn
87 Fr	88 Ra	89 Ac	104 Unq	105 Unp	106 Unh	107 Uns	108 Uno	109 Une									

58 Ce	59 Pr	60 Nd	61 Pm	62 Sm	63 Eu	64 Gd	65 Tb	66 Dy	67 Ho	68 Er	69 Tm	70 Yb	71 Lu
90 Th	91 Pa	92 U	93 Np	94 Pu	95 Am	96 Cm	97 Bk	98 Cf	99 Es	100 Fm	101 Md	102 No	103 Lr

Figure 23.1

The chemical elements essential for life. Those most abundant in living systems are shown as purple. Nineteen elements, called the trace elements, are shown as green.

The composition and organization of a typical animal cell is shown in Fig. 23.2. The *nucleus,* which contains the *chromosomes,* is separated from the cell fluid (the *cytoplasm*) by a membrane. The chromosomes store both the hereditary information necessary for cell reproduction and the codes for the manufacture of essential biomolecules. The cytoplasm contains a variety of subcellular structures that carry out various cell functions. For example, the *mitochondria* process nutrients and produce energy to be used as the cell requires it. The *lysosomes* contain enzymes for "digesting" nutrients such as proteins. The *ribosomes* are the sites for protein synthesis. The cell membrane encloses the cytoplasm, protects the cell components, and allows for the passage of nutrients, ions, and wastes.

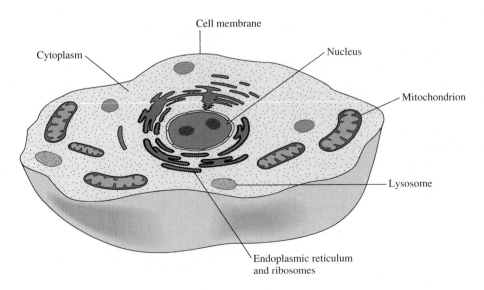

Cell membrane

Cytoplasm

Nucleus

Mitochondrion

Lysosome

Endoplasmic reticulum and ribosomes

Figure 23.2

A typical animal cell (eucaryotic).

Table 23.1

The Essential Elements and Some of Their Functions

Element	Percent by Mass in the Human Body	Function
Oxygen	65	Component of water and many organic compounds
Carbon	18	Component of all organic compounds
Hydrogen	10	Component of water and many inorganic and organic compounds
Nitrogen	3	Component of both inorganic and organic compounds
Calcium	1.5	Major component of bone; essential to some enzymes and to muscle action
Phosphorus	1.2	Essential in cellular synthesis and energy transfer
Potassium	0.2	Cation in intracellular fluid
Chlorine	0.2	Anion inside and outside the cells
Sulfur	0.2	Component of proteins and some other organic compounds
Sodium	0.1	Cation in extracellular fluid
Magnesium	0.05	Essential to some enzymes
Iron	<0.05	In hemoglobin, myoglobin, and other proteins (Section 20.8)
Zinc	<0.05	Essential to many enzymes
Cobalt	<0.05	Found in vitamin B_{12}
Copper	<0.05	Essential to several enzymes
Iodine	<0.05	Essential to thyroid hormones
Selenium	<0.01	Essential to some enzymes
Fluorine	<0.01	Uncertain, found in teeth and bones
Nickel	<0.01	Essential to some enzymes
Molybdenum	<0.01	Essential to some enzymes
Silicon	<0.01	Found in connective tissue
Chromium	<0.01	Essential in carbohydrate metabolism
Vanadium, tin, manganese, lithium, boron, arsenic, lead, cadmium	<0.01	Exact function not known

23.1 *Proteins*

Purpose

• To describe the levels of structure and the functions of proteins.

We have seen that many useful synthetic materials are polymers. Thus it should not be surprising that a great many natural materials are also polymers: starch, hair, silicate chains in soil and rocks, silk and cotton fibers, and the cellulose in woody plants, to name only a few.

Peacock feathers are constructed of fibrous proteins.

In this section we consider a class of natural polymers, the **proteins,** which make up about 15% of our bodies and have molecular weights (molar masses) that range from approximately 6000 to over 1,000,000 grams per mole. Proteins perform many functions in the human body. **Fibrous proteins** provide structural integrity and strength for many types of tissue and are the main components of muscle, hair, and cartilage. Other proteins, usually called **globular proteins** because of their roughly spherical shape, are the "worker" molecules of the body. These proteins transport and store oxygen and nutrients, act as catalysts for the thousands of reactions that make life possible, fight invasion by foreign objects, participate in the body's many regulatory systems, and transport electrons in the complex process of metabolizing nutrients.

The building blocks of all proteins are the **α-amino acids,** where R may represent H, CH_3, or more complex substituents. These molecules are called α-amino acids because the amino group ($-NH_2$) is always attached to the α-carbon, the one next to the carboxyl group ($-CO_2H$). The 20 amino acids most commonly found in proteins are shown in Fig. 23.3.

Note from Fig. 23.3 that the amino acids are grouped into polar and nonpolar classes, determined by the R groups, or **side chains.** Nonpolar side chains contain mostly carbon and hydrogen atoms, whereas polar side chains contain nitrogen and oxygen atoms. This difference is important because polar side chains are *hydrophilic* (water-loving), whereas nonpolar side chains are *hydrophobic* (water-fearing), and this greatly affects the three-dimensional structure of the resulting protein.

The protein polymer is built by condensation reactions of individual amino acids, for example,

The product shown above is called a **dipeptide.** This name is used because the structure

is called a **peptide linkage** by biochemists. (The same grouping is called an *amide* by organic chemists.) Additional condensation reactions lengthen the chain to produce a **polypeptide,** eventually yielding a protein.

You can imagine that with 20 amino acids, which can be assembled in any order, there is essentially infinite variety possible in the construction of proteins. This flexibility allows an organism to tailor proteins for the many types of functions that must be carried out.

The order or sequence of amino acids in the protein chain is called the **primary structure,** conveniently indicated by using three-letter codes for the amino acids

α-Carbon

At the pH of biologic fluids, the amino acids shown in Fig. 23.3 exist in a different form, with the proton of the $-COOH$ group transferred to the $-NH_2$ group. For example, glycine would be in the form $H_3{}^+NCH_2COO^-$.

The peptide linkage is also found in nylon (see Section 22.6).

Figure 23.3

The 20 α-amino acids found in most proteins are shown at right. The R group is shown in color.

Nonpolar R groups

Glycine
(Gly)

Alanine
(Ala)

Proline
(Pro)

Phenylalanine
(Phe)

Isoleucine
(Ile)

Tryptophan
(Trp)

Methionine
(Met)

Leucine
(Leu)

Valine
(Val)

Polar R groups

Serine
(Ser)

Glutamine
(Gln)

Tyrosine
(Tyr)

Histidine
(His)

Asparagine
(Asn)

Threonine
(Thr)

Aspartic acid
(Asp)

Cysteine
(Cys)

Glutamic acid
(Glu)

Lysine
(Lys)

Arginine
(Arg)

(see Fig. 23.3), where it is understood that the terminal carboxyl group is on the right and the terminal amino group is on the left. For example, one possible sequence for a tripeptide containing the amino acids lysine, alanine, and leucine is

$$
\begin{array}{c}
\text{NH}_2 \qquad\qquad\qquad \text{HC(CH}_3)_2 \\
| \qquad\qquad\qquad\qquad | \\
(\text{CH}_2)_4 \quad \text{H} \quad \text{CH}_3 \quad\quad \text{H} \quad \text{CH}_2 \\
| \qquad | \qquad | \qquad\quad | \qquad | \\
\text{H}_2\text{N}-\text{C}-\text{C}-\text{N}-\text{C}-\text{C}-\text{N}-\text{C}-\text{COOH} \\
| \quad \| \quad | \quad | \quad \| \quad | \quad | \\
\text{H} \quad \text{O} \qquad \text{H} \quad \text{O} \qquad \text{H}
\end{array}
$$

$$\underbrace{\qquad\qquad}_{\text{Lysine}} \quad \underbrace{\qquad\qquad}_{\text{Alanine}} \quad \underbrace{\qquad\qquad}_{\text{Leucine}}$$

which is represented in the shorthand notation as

lys–ala–leu

Sample Exercise 23.1

Write the sequences of all possible tripeptides composed of the amino acids tyrosine, histidine, and cysteine.

Solution

There are six possible sequences:

tyr–his–cys	his–tyr–cys	cys–tyr–his
tyr–cys–his	his–cys–tyr	cys–his–tyr

Note from Sample Exercise 23.1 that there are six sequences possible for a polypeptide with three given amino acids. There are three possibilities for the first amino acid (any one of the three given amino acids); there are two possibilities for the second amino acid (one has already been accounted for); and there is only one possibility left for the third amino acid. Thus the number of sequences is $3 \times 2 \times 1 = 6$. The product $3 \times 2 \times 1$ is often written 3! (and is called 3 *factorial*). Similar reasoning shows that for a polypeptide with four amino acids, there are 4!, or $4 \times 3 \times 2 \times 1 = 24$, possible sequences.*

Sample Exercise 23.2

What number of possible sequences exists for a polypeptide composed of 20 different amino acids?

Solution

The answer is 20!, or

$$20 \times 19 \times 18 \times 17 \times 16 \times \cdots \times 5 \times 4 \times 3 \times 2 \times 1 = 2.43 \times 10^{18}$$

*Most calculators have a key for factorials.

A striking example of the importance of the primary structure of polypeptides can be seen in the differences between *oxytocin* and *vasopressin*. Both these molecules are nine-unit polypeptides, and they differ by only two amino acids (Fig. 23.4); yet they perform completely different functions in the human body. Oxytocin is a hormone that triggers contraction of the uterus and milk secretion. Vasopressin raises blood pressure levels and regulates kidney function.

A second level of structure in proteins, beyond the sequence of amino acids, is the arrangement of the chain of the long molecule. The **secondary structure** is determined to a large extent by hydrogen bonding between lone pairs on an oxygen in the carbonyl group of an amino acid with a hydrogen atom attached to a nitrogen of another amino acid:

$$\text{C}=\overset{..}{\text{O}} : \text{---}\underset{\delta^-}{\text{H}}\text{---}\underset{\delta^+}{\text{N}}$$

Such interactions can occur *within* the chain coils to form a spiral structure called an **α-helix**, as shown in Fig. 23.5 and Fig. 23.6. This type of secondary structure gives the protein elasticity (springiness) and is found in the fibrous proteins in wool, hair, and tendons. Hydrogen bonding also can occur *between different* protein chains, joining them together in an arrangement called a **pleated sheet,** as shown in Fig. 23.7. Silk contains this arrangement of proteins, making its fibers flexible but

cys–tyr–ile–gln–asn–cys–pro–leu–gly
(a)
cys–tyr–phe–gln–asn–cys–pro–arg–gly
(b)

Figure 23.4

The amino acid sequences in (a) oxytocin and (b) vasopressin. The differing amino acids are boxed.

● Carbon

○ Nitrogen

Figure 23.5

Hydrogen bonding within a protein chain causes it to form a stable helical structure called the α-helix. Only the main atoms in the helical backbone are shown here. The hydrogen bonds are not shown.

● Carbon

◐ Nitrogen

· Hydrogen

○ Oxygen

⋮ Hydrogen bonding

Hydrogen bond

Figure 23.6

Ball-and-stick model of a portion of a protein chain in the α-helical arrangement showing the hydrogen bonding interactions.

Figure 23.7

When hydrogen bonding occurs between protein chains rather than within them, a stable structure (the pleated sheet) results. This structure contains many protein chains and is found in natural fibers, such as silk, as well as in muscles.

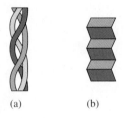

(a)   (b)

Figure 23.8

(a) Collagen, a substance found in tendons, consists of three protein chains (each with a helical structure) twisted together to form a super helix. The result is a long, relatively narrow protein. (b) The pleated-sheet arrangement in which many protein chains are bound together to form the elongated protein found in silk fibers.

very strong and resistant to stretching. The pleated sheet is also found in muscle fibers. The hydrogen bonds in the α-helical protein are said to be *intrachain* (within a given protein chain), and those in the pleated sheet are said to be *interchain* (between protein chains).

As you might imagine, a molecule as large as a protein has a great deal of flexibility and can assume a variety of overall shapes. The specific shape that a protein assumes depends on its function. For long, thin structures, such as hair, wool and silk fibers, and tendons, an elongated shape is required. This may involve an α-helical secondary structure, as found in the protein α-keratin in hair and wool. Collagen, a very important structural protein that is the main component of tendons, ligaments, cartilage, blood vessels, and various other ducts, has the complex helical structure represented in Fig. 23.8(a). Other structural proteins involve a pleated-sheet secondary structure, as found in silk [Fig. 23.8(b)]. Many of the proteins in the body that have nonstructural functions are globular, such as myoglobin (Fig. 23.9). Note that the secondary structure of myoglobin is basically α-helical. However, in the areas where the chain bends to give the protein its compact globular structure, the α-helix breaks down to give a secondary configuration known as the **random-coil arrangement.**

The overall shape of the protein, long and narrow or globular, is called its **tertiary structure** and is maintained by several different types of interactions: hydrogen bonding, dipole–dipole interactions, ionic bonds, covalent bonds, and London dispersion forces between nonpolar groups. These bonds, which represent all the bonding types discussed in this text, are summarized in Fig. 23.10.

The amino acid *cysteine*

$$HS-CH_2-\underset{\underset{\underset{H}{|}}{\overset{\overset{H}{|}}{C}}}{\overset{}{}}-\underset{}{\overset{\overset{O}{\|}}{C}}-OH$$

plays a special role in stabilizing the tertiary structure of many proteins because the

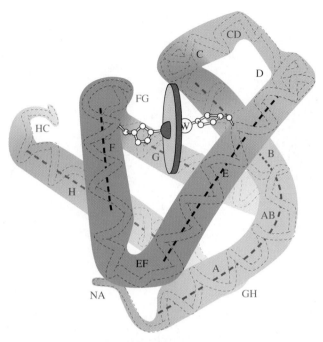

Figure 23.9
The protein myoglobin.

—SH groups on two cysteines can react in the presence of an oxidizing agent to form a S—S bond called a **disulfide linkage:**

$$\overset{\zeta}{C}-CH_2-S-H + H-S-CH_2-\overset{\zeta}{C} \longrightarrow \overset{\zeta}{C}-CH_2-\boxed{S-S}-CH_2-\overset{\zeta}{C}$$

A practical application of the chemistry of disulfide bonds is permanent waving of hair, as summarized in Fig. 23.11. The S—S linkages in the protein of hair are broken by treatment with a reducing agent. The hair is then set in curlers to change the tertiary protein structure to the desired shape. Then treatment with an oxidizing agent causes new S—S bonds to form, which make the hair protein retain the new structure.

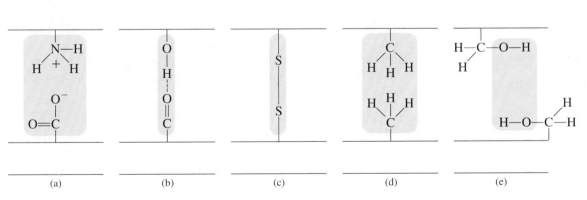

(a) (b) (c) (d) (e)

Figure 23.10

Summary of the various types of interactions that stabilize the tertiary structure of a protein: (a) ionic, (b) hydrogen bonding, (c) covalent, (d) London dispersion, and (e) dipole–dipole.

Natural crysteine
linkages in hair

Reduction

Chains shift

Hair set in curlers
alters tertiary structures

Oxidation

New crysteine linkages
in waved hair

Figure 23.11

The permanent waving of hair.

Figure 23.12

A schematic representation of the thermal denaturation of a protein.

Energy

The three-dimensional structure of a protein is crucial to its function. The process of breaking down this structure is called **denaturation** (Fig. 23.12). For example, the denaturation of egg proteins occurs when an egg is cooked. Any source of energy can cause denaturation of proteins and is thus potentially dangerous to living organisms. For example, ultraviolet or X-ray radiation or nuclear radioactivity can disrupt protein structure, which may lead to cancer or genetic damage. Protein damage is also caused by chemicals such as benzene, trichloroethane, and 1,2-dibromoethane (called EDB). The metals lead and mercury, which have a very high affinity for sulfur, cause protein denaturation by disrupting disulfide bonds between protein chains.

The tremendous flexibility in the various levels of protein structure allows the tailoring of proteins for a wide range of specific functions, some of which are given in Table 23.2.

Enzymes

Enzymes are proteins tailored to catalyze specific biologic reactions. Without the several hundred enzymes now known, life would be impossible. Enzymes are impressive for their tremendous efficiency (typically 1 to 10 million times as efficient as inorganic catalysts) and their incredible selectivity—they ignore the thousands of molecules in body fluids for which they were not designed.

Although the mechanisms of catalytic activity are complex and not fully understood in most cases, a theory called the **lock-and-key model** (see Fig. 23.13) seems

Table 23.2	
Some Functions of Proteins	

1. *Structure*. Proteins provide the high tensile strength of tendons, bones, and skin. Cartilage, hair, wool, fingernails, and claws are mainly protein. Viruses have an outer layer of protein around a nucleic acid core. Proteins called **histones** are bound tightly to DNA in the cells of higher organisms, helping to fold and wrap the DNA in an orderly fashion in chromosomes.

2. *Movement*. Proteins are the major components of muscles and are directly responsible for the ability of muscles to contract. The swimming of sperm is the result of contraction of protein filaments in their tails. The same is true of movements of chromosomes during cell division.

3. *Catalysis*. Nearly all chemical reactions in living organisms are catalyzed by enzymes, which are almost always proteins.

4. *Transport*. Oxygen is carried from the lungs to tissues by the protein hemoglobin in red blood cells. The protein transferrin transports iron in blood plasma from the intestines where the iron is absorbed to the spleen where it is stored and to the liver and bone marrow where it is used for synthesis. Proteins in the membranes of cells allow the passage of various molecules and ions.

5. *Storage*. The protein ferritin stores iron in the liver, spleen, and bone marrow.

6. *Energy transformation and storage*. Myosin, a protein in muscle, transforms chemical energy into useful work. Rhodopsin, a protein in the retina of the eye, traps light energy and, working with other membrane components, converts it into the electrical energy of a nerve impulse. Receptor protein molecules that combine with specific small molecules are responsible for the transmission of nerve impulses.

7. *Protection*. **Antibodies** are special proteins that are synthesized in response to foreign substances and cells, such as bacterial cells. They then bind to those substances or cells, which are called **antigens,** and provide us with immunity to various diseases. We acquire antibodies either from having had the disease or from receiving inactivated viruses in vaccines. Hay fever and food allergies are also caused by the interaction of antibodies with antigens. Interferon, a small protein made and released by cells when they are exposed to a virus, protects other cells against viral infection. Blood-clotting proteins protect against bleeding (hemorrhage). Some antibiotics are polypeptides, which are smaller than proteins.

8. *Control*. **Hormones** are chemical substances produced in the body that have specific effects on the activity of certain organs. Some hormones are proteins. For example, human growth hormone is a protein. Some hormones such as insulin and glucagon, which are made in the pancreas and control carbohydrate metabolism, are polypeptides. Expression of genetic information is also under the control of proteins.

9. *Buffering*. Because proteins contain both acidic and basic groups on their side chains, they can neutralize both acids and bases. Therefore, proteins provide some buffering for blood and tissues.

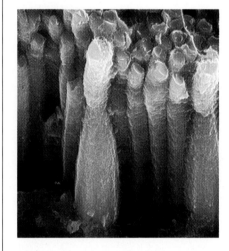

Rods and cones in the human eye (×2500).

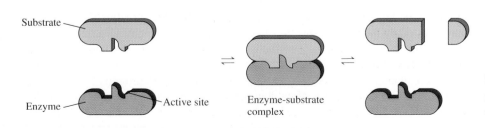

Substrate

Enzyme — Active site

Enzyme-substrate complex

Figure 23.13

Schematic diagram of the lock-and-key model.

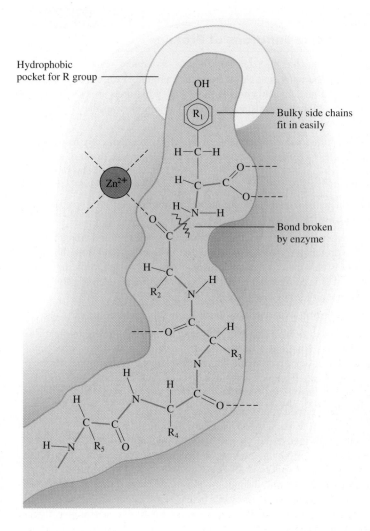

Hydrophobic pocket for R group

Bulky side chains fit in easily

Bond broken by enzyme

Figure 23.14

Schematic of the binding of a protein by carboxypeptidase.

to fit many enzymes. This model postulates that the shapes of the reacting molecule, the **substrate,** and the enzyme are such that they fit together much like a key fits a specific lock. Recent results indicate that the lock-and-key model might be oversimplified. There is now considerable evidence that enzymes often modify their structures significantly to accommodate an incoming substrate. In any case, the substrate and enzyme attach to each other through hydrogen bonding, ionic bonding, metal ion–ligand bonding, or some combination of these, in such a way that the part of the substrate where the reaction is to occur occupies the active site of the enzyme. This process is summarized schematically in Fig. 23.14 for the enzyme carboxypeptidase binding a protein. After the reaction occurs, the products are liberated, and the enzyme is ready for a new substrate. Because the enzyme cycles (''turns over'') so rapidly, only a tiny amount of enzyme is required. This has made the isolation and study of enzymes quite difficult.

The enzyme carboxypeptidase assists in the digestion of proteins by catalyzing the breaking of the peptide linkage that attaches the end amino acid to the protein:

The active site contains Zn^{2+}, which coordinates to the carbonyl group of the end amino acid. There is also a hydrophobic pocket nearby to accommodate a large hydrophobic R group on the terminal amino acid. There are other interactions between groups on the enzymes and substrate, which help hold the substrate in place.

When a substance other than the substrate is bound to the enzyme's active site, the enzyme is said to be *inhibited*. If the inhibition is permanent, the enzyme is said to be *inactivated*. Some of the most powerful toxins act by inhibiting or inactivating key enzymes. "Nerve gases," chemicals used as weapons, act in this way. Nerves transfer messages using small molecules called **neurotransmitters.** An example of a neurotransmitter is acetylcholine.

Once the nerve impulse has been transmitted, for example, to a muscle, the acetylcholine molecules must be destroyed because their continued presence would cause overstimulation and lead to convulsions, paralysis, and possibly death. The acetylcholine molecules are removed by reaction with water.

$$[CH_3COOCH_2CH_2N(CH_3)_3]^+ + H_2O \rightarrow CH_3COOH + [HOCH_2CH_2N(CH_3)_3]^+$$

Acetic acid   Choline

This reaction is catalyzed by the enzyme acetylcholinesterase. The nerve gas diisopropyl phosphorofluoridate (shortened to DIPF) attaches itself permanently to the active site of this enzyme, thus blocking the enzyme's ability to catalyze the removal of acetylcholine. The result is usually death.

There are many other ways that enzymes can be deactivated, in addition to blockage of the active site by foreign molecules. For example, in **metalloenzymes,** which contain a metal ion at the active site, substitution of a different metal ion for the original one usually causes the enzyme to malfunction. And, of course, anything that denatures the enzyme protein destroys its activity.

Because enzymes are so crucial for healthy life, and because we hope to learn how to mimic their efficiency in our industrial catalysts, the study of enzymes occupies a prominent role in chemical research.

23.2 *Carbohydrates*

Purpose

- To describe the structures and isomerism of simple carbohydrates.
- To describe the structures and functions of polymers of glucose.

Another class of biologically important molecules is the **carbohydrates,** which serve as a food source for most organisms and as a structural material for plants. Because many carbohydrates have the empirical formula CH_2O, it was originally believed that these substances were hydrates of carbon, and that accounts for the name.

General Name of Sugar	Number of Carbon Atoms
Triose	3
Tetrose	4
Pentose	5
Hexose	6
Heptose	7
Octose	8
Nonose	9

Most important carbohydrates, such as starch and cellulose, are polymers composed of monomers called **monosaccharides,** or **simple sugars.** The monosaccharides are polyhydroxy ketones and aldehydes. The most important contain five carbon atoms (**pentoses**) or six carbon atoms (**hexoses**). One important hexose is *fructose,* a sugar found in honey and fruit, whose structure is

$$
\begin{array}{c}
CH_2OH \\
| \\
C=O \\
| \\
HO-\overset{*}{C}-H \\
| \\
H-\overset{*}{C}-OH \\
| \\
H-\overset{*}{C}-OH \\
| \\
CH_2OH
\end{array}
$$

Fructose

where the asterisks indicate chiral carbon atoms. In Section 20.4 we saw that molecules with nonsuperimposable mirror images exhibit optical isomerism. A carbon atom with four *different* groups bonded to it in a tetrahedral arrangement *always* has a nonsuperimposable mirror image (see Fig. 23.15), which gives rise to a pair of optical isomers. For example, the simplest sugar, glyceraldehyde,

$$
\begin{array}{c}
H \quad\quad O \\
\diagdown\;C\;\diagup \\
| \\
H-\overset{*}{C}-OH \\
| \\
CH_2OH
\end{array}
$$

which has one chiral carbon, has two optical isomers, as shown in Fig. 23.16.

In fructose each of the three chiral carbon atoms satisfies the requirement of being surrounded by four different groups, which leads to a total of 2^3, or 8, isomers that differ in their ability to rotate polarized light. The particular isomer of fructose represented above is called D-fructose. Generally, monosaccharides have one isomer that is more common in nature than the others. The most important pentoses and hexoses are shown in Table 23.3 on p. 1104.

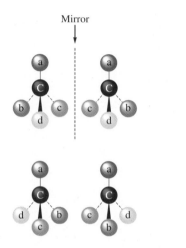

Figure 23.15

When a tetrahedral carbon atom has four different substituents, there is no way that its mirror image can be superimposed on the original molecule. The lower two forms show possible orientations of the molecule. Compare these to the mirror image and note that they cannot be superimposed.

Figure 23.16

The mirror-image optical isomers of glyceraldehyde. Note that these mirror images cannot be superimposed.

Sample Exercise 23.3

Determine the number of chiral carbon atoms in the following pentose:

$$
\begin{array}{c}
H \quad\quad O \\
\diagdown\;C\;\diagup \\
| \\
H-C-OH \\
| \\
H-C-OH \\
| \\
H-C-OH \\
| \\
CH_2OH
\end{array}
$$

Solution

We must look for carbon atoms that have four different substituents. The top carbon has only three substituents and thus cannot be chiral. The three carbon atoms shown in red each have four different groups attached to them as indicated below.

The fifth carbon atom has only three types of substituents (it has two hydrogen atoms) and is not chiral.

Thus the three chiral carbon atoms in this pentose are the ones shown in red.

Note that D-ribose and D-arabinose, shown in Table 23.3, are two of the eight isomers of this pentose.

Although we have so far represented the monosaccharides as straight-chain molecules, they usually cyclize, or form a ring structure, in aqueous solution. Figure 23.17 shows this reaction for fructose. Note that a new bond is formed between the oxygen of the terminal hydroxyl group and the carbon of the ketone group. One cyclic form of fructose is a five-membered ring containing a C—O—C bond. The same type of reaction can occur between a hydroxyl group and an aldehyde group, as shown for D-glucose in Fig. 23.18. In this case a six-membered ring is formed.

More complex carbohydrates are formed by combining monosaccharides. For example, **sucrose,** common table sugar, is a **disaccharide** formed from glucose and fructose by elimination of water to form a C—O—C bond between the rings, which is called a **glycoside linkage** (Fig. 23.19). When sucrose is consumed in food, the above reaction is reversed. An enzyme in saliva catalyzes the breakdown of this disaccharide.

Large polymers containing many monosaccharide units (called **polysaccharides**) can occur when each ring forms two glycoside linkages, as shown in Fig. 23.19. Three of the most important of these polymers are starch, cellulose, and glycogen. All these substances are polymers of glucose, differing from each other in the nature

Figure 23.17

The cyclization of D-fructose.

Table 23.3

Some Important Monosaccharides

Pentoses

D-Ribose	D-Arabinose	D-Ribulose

Hexoses

D-Glucose	D-Mannose	D-Galactose	D-Fructose

Figure 23.18

The cyclization of glucose. Two different rings are possible; they differ in the orientation of the hydroxy group and hydrogen on a particular carbon, as indicated. The two forms are designated α and β and are shown here in two representations.

α-D-glucose

Fructose

$$-H_2O \updownarrow +H_2O$$

Glycoside
linkage

Sucrose

Figure 23.19

Sucrose is a disaccharide formed from α-D-glucose and fructose.

of the glycoside linkage, the amount of branching, and molecular weight (molar mass).

Starch is a polymer of α-D-glucose and consists of two parts: *amylose,* a straight-chain polymer of α-glucose [see Fig. 23.20(a)], and *amylopectin,* a highly branched polymer of α-glucose with a molecular weight that is 10 to 20 times that of amylose. Branching occurs when a third glycoside linkage attaches a branch to the main polymer chain.

Starch, the carbohydrate reservoir in plants, is the form in which glucose is stored by the plant for later use as cellular fuel. Glucose is stored in this high-molecular-weight form because this results in less stress on the plant's internal structure by osmotic pressure. Remember from Section 11.6 that it is the concentration of solute molecules (or ions) that determines the osmotic pressure. Thus combining the individual glucose molecules into one large chain keeps the concentration of solute molecules relatively low and minimizes the osmotic pressure.

Cellulose, the major structural component of woody plants and natural fibers such as cotton, is a polymer of β-D-glucose and has the structure shown in Fig. 23.20(b). Note that the β-glycoside linkages in cellulose give the glucose rings a different relative orientation than is found in starch. Although this difference may seem minor, it has very important consequences. The human digestive system contains α-glycosidases, enzymes that can catalyze breakage of the α-glycoside bonds in starch. These enzymes are not effective on the β-glycoside bonds of cellulose, presumably because the different structure causes a poor fit between the enzyme's active site and the carbohydrate. The enzymes necessary to cleave β-glycoside linkages, the β-glycosidases, are found in bacteria that exist in the digestive tracts of termites, cows, deer, and many other animals. Thus, unlike humans, these animals can derive nutrition from cellulose.

Glycogen, the carbohydrate reservoir in animals, has a structure like that of amylopectin but with more branching. It is this branching that is thought to facilitate the rapid breakdown of glycogen into glucose when energy is required.

A classic test for starch utilizes iodine dissolved in a potassium iodide solution. The iodine reacts with starch to give a dark blue color.

Figure 23.20

(a) The polymer amylose is a major component of starch and is made up of α-D-glucose monomers. (b) The polymer cellulose, which consists of β-D-glucose monomers.

(a)

(b)

Deoxyribose

(a)

Ribose

(b)

Figure 23.21

The structure of the pentoses (a) deoxyribose and (b) ribose. Deoxyribose is the sugar molecule present in DNA; ribose is found in RNA.

23.3 Nucleic Acids

Purpose

• To describe the structures and functions of nucleic acids.

Life is possible only because each cell, when it divides, can transmit to the next generation the vital information about how it works. It has been known for a long time that this process involves the chromosomes in the nucleus of the cell. Only since 1953, however, have scientists understood the molecular basis of this intriguing cellular "talent."

The substance that stores and transmits the genetic information is a polymer called **deoxyribonucleic acid (DNA),** a huge molecule with a molecular weight as high as several billion. Together with other similar nucleic acids called the **ribonucleic acids (RNA),** DNA is also responsible for the synthesis of the various proteins needed by the cell to carry out its life functions. The RNA molecules, which are found in the cytoplasm outside the nucleus, are much smaller than DNA polymers, with molecular weights of only 20,000 to 40,000.

The monomers that comprise the nucleic acids, called **nucleotides,** are composed of three distinct parts:

1. A *five-carbon sugar,* deoxyribose in DNA and ribose in RNA (Fig. 23.21).

Uracil (U)
RNA

Cytosine (C)
DNA
RNA

Thymine (T)
DNA

Adenine (A)
DNA
RNA

Guanine (G)
DNA
RNA

Figure 23.22

The organic bases found in DNA and RNA.

Ribose

−H₂O

Adenosine

Phosphoric acid

Adenosine

−H₂O

Adenosine 5-phosphoric acid

Figure 23.23

(a) Adenosine is formed by reaction of adenine and ribose.
(b) The reaction of phosphoric acid with adenosine to form the ester adenosine 5-phosphoric acid (a nucleotide).

2. A *nitrogen-containing organic base* of the type shown in Fig. 23.22.

3. A *phosphoric acid molecule* (H_3PO_4).

The base and the sugar combine as shown in Fig. 23.23(a) to form a unit that in turn reacts with phosphoric acid to create the nucleotide, which is an ester [see Fig. 23.23(b)]. The nucleotides are connected by undergoing condensation reactions that eliminate water to give a polymer of the type represented in Fig. 23.24; such a polymer can contain a *billion* units.

The key to DNA's functioning is its *double helical structure with complementary bases on the two strands*. The bases form hydrogen bonds to each other, as shown in Fig. 23.25. Note that the structures of cytosine and guanine make them perfect partners for hydrogen bonding, and they are *always* found as pairs on the two strands of DNA. Thymine and adenine form similar hydrogen-bonding pairs.

There is much evidence to suggest that the two strands of DNA unwind during cell division and that new complementary strands are constructed on the unraveled strands (Fig. 23.26). Because the bases on the strands always pair in the same way—cytosine with guanine and thymine with adenine—each unraveled strand serves as a template for attaching the complementary bases (along with the rest of the nucleotide). This process results in two double-helix DNA structures that are identical to the original one. Each new double strand contains one strand from the original DNA double helix and one newly synthesized strand. This replication of DNA allows for the transmission of genetic information when cells divide.

The other major function of DNA is **protein synthesis.** A given segment of the DNA, called a **gene,** contains the codes for a specific protein. These codes transmit the primary structure of the protein (the sequence of amino acids) to the construction "machinery" of the cell. There is a specific code for each amino acid in the protein, which ensures that the correct amino acid will be inserted as the protein chain grows. Each specific amino acid code consists of a set of three bases and is called a **codon.**

DNA stores the genetic information, and RNA molecules are responsible for transmitting this information to the ribosomes, where protein synthesis actually

Figure 23.24

A portion of a typical nucleic acid chain. Note that the backbone consists of sugar–phosphate esters.

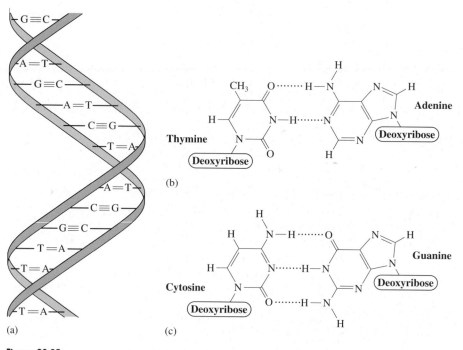

(a) (b) (c)

Figure 23.25

(a) The DNA double helix contains two sugar–phosphate backbones with the bases from the two strands hydrogen bonded to each other. The complementarity of the (b) thymine–adenine and (c) cytosine–guanine pairs.

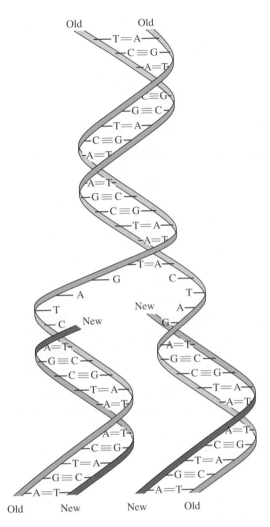

Figure 23.26

During cell division, the original DNA double helix unwinds, and new complementary strands are constructed on each original strand.

occurs. This complex process involves, first, the construction of a special RNA molecule called **messenger RNA (mRNA).** The mRNA is built in the cell nucleus on the appropriate section of DNA (the gene); the double helix is "unzipped," and the complementarity of the bases is utilized in a process similar to that for DNA replication. The mRNA then migrates into the cytoplasm of the cell, where, with the assistance of the ribosomes, the protein is synthesized.

Small RNA fragments, called **transfer RNA (tRNA),** are tailored to find specific amino acids and attach them to the growing protein chain as dictated by the codons in the mRNA. Transfer RNA has a lower molecular weight than messenger RNA. It consists of a chain of 75 to 80 nucleotides, including the bases adenine, cytosine, guanine, and uracil, among others. The chain folds back onto itself in various places as the complementary bases along the chain form hydrogen bonds. The tRNA decodes the genetic message from the mRNA using a complementary triplet of bases called an **anticodon** that governs which amino acid will be brought to the protein under construction.

Computer graphic image of the base pairs of DNA.

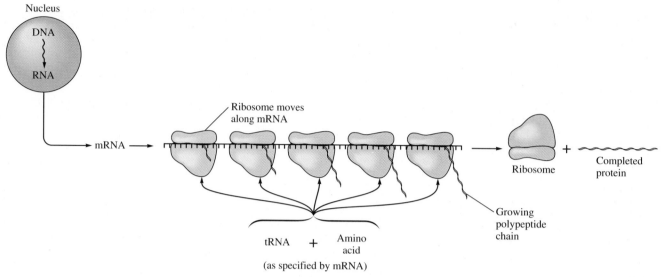

Figure 23.27

The mRNA molecule, constructed from a specific gene on the DNA, is used as the pattern to construct a given protein (with the assistance of ribosomes). The tRNA molecules attach to specific amino acids and put them in place as called for by the codons on the mRNA.

The protein is built as follows: a tRNA molecule brings an amino acid to the mRNA; the anticodon of the tRNA must complement the codon of the mRNA (see Fig. 23.27). Once this amino acid is in place, another tRNA moves to the second codon site of the mRNA with its specific amino acid. The two amino acids link via a peptide bond, and the tRNA on the first codon breaks away. The process is repeated down the chain, always matching the correct tRNA anticodon to the mRNA codon.

23.4 Lipids

Purpose

- To describe the classes of lipids.

The **lipids** are a group of substances classified according to a solubility characteristic. They are defined as water-insoluble substances that can be extracted from cells by nonpolar organic solvents such as ether and benzene. The lipids found in the human body can be divided into four classes according to molecular structure: fats, phospholipids, waxes, and steroids.

The most common **fats** are esters composed of the polyhydroxy alcohol glycerol and long-chain carboxylic acids called **fatty acids** (see Table 23.4). *Tristearin,* the most common animal fat, is typical of these substances.

Table 23.4		
Some Common Fatty Acids and Their Sources		
Name	Formula	Source
Saturated		
Arachidic acid	$CH_3(CH_2)_{18}$—COOH	Peanut oil
Butyric acid	$CH_3(CH_2)_2$—COOH	Butter
Caproic acid	$CH_3(CH_2)_4$—COOH	Butter
Lauric acid	$CH_3(CH_2)_{10}$—COOH	Coconut oil
Stearic acid	$CH_3(CH_2)_{16}$—COOH	Animal and vegetable fats
Unsaturated		
Oleic acid	$CH_3(CH_2)_7CH{=}CH(CH_2)_7$—COOH	Corn oil
Linoleic acid	$CH_3(CH_2)_4CH{=}CH$—CH_2—$CH{=}CH(CH_2)_7$—COOH	Linseed oil
Linolenic acid	$CH_3CH_2CH{=}CH$—$CH_2CH{=}CH$—CH_2—$CH{=}CH$—$(CH_2)_7COOH$	Linseed oil

Fats that are esters of glycerol are called **triglycerides** and have the general structure

where the three R groups may be the same or different and may be saturated or unsaturated. Vegetable fats tend to be unsaturated and usually occur as oily liquids; animal fats are saturated and occur as solids.

Triglycerides can be decomposed by treatment with aqueous sodium hydroxide. The products are glycerol and the fatty acid salts; the latter are known as soaps. This process is called **saponification.**

Unsaturated compounds contain one or more C=C bonds.

Much of what we call dirt is nonpolar. Grease, for example, consists of long-chain hydrocarbons. However, water, the solvent most commonly available to us, is very polar and will not dissolve "greasy dirt." We need to add something to the water that is somehow compatible with both the polar water and the nonpolar

Like dissolves like.

grease. Fatty acid anions are perfect for this role because they have a long nonpolar tail and a polar head. For example, the stearate anion can be represented as

$$CH_3 \overset{CH_2}{\diagup} \overset{CH_2}{\diagdown} \overset{CH_2}{\diagup} \overset{CH_2}{\diagdown} \overset{CH_2}{\diagup} \overset{CH_2}{\diagdown} \overset{CH_2}{\diagup} \overset{CH_2}{\diagdown} \overset{CH_2}{\diagup} \overset{CH_2}{\diagdown} \overset{CH_2}{\diagup} \overset{CH_2}{\diagdown} \overset{CH_2}{\diagup} \overset{CH_2}{\diagdown} \overset{CH_2}{\diagup} \overset{\displaystyle \underset{O^-}{\overset{O}{\parallel}}{C}}{}$$

Such ions can be dispersed in water because they form **micelles** (Fig. 23.28). These aggregates of fatty acid anions have the water-incompatible tails in the interior, while the anionic parts (the polar heads) point outward to interact with the polar water molecules. A soap "solution" is not a true solution; it does not contain *individual* fatty-acid anions dispersed in the water but rather groups of ions (micelles). Thus a soap–water mixture is really a suspension of micelles in water. Because the relatively large micelles scatter light, soapy water looks cloudy.

Soap dissolves grease by taking the grease molecules into the nonpolar interior of the micelle (Fig. 23.29) where they can be carried away by the water. Soap can be viewed as an emulsifying agent, since it acts to suspend the normally incompatible grease in the water. Because of this ability to assist water in "wetting" and suspending nonpolar materials, soap is also called a *wetting agent,* or **surfactant.**

A major disadvantage is that soap anions form precipitates with the cations in hard water, principally Ca^{2+} and Mg^{2+}. This "soap scum" dulls clothes and drastically reduces soap's cleaning efficiency. Water can be softened with slaked lime (see Section 14.6) or by ion exchange (see Section 18.4). In addition, a huge industry has developed to produce artificial soaps, called **detergents.** Any molecule that has nonpolar and polar areas similar to those in the fatty acid anions should act to emulsify grease in water. The most widely used class of detergents is the alkylbenzene sulfonates, for example,

Figure 23.28

The structure of a micelle composed of fatty acid anions. The cations of the salt also surround the negatively charged micelle.

Nonpolar Polar
tail head

$$CH_3 \overset{CH_2}{\diagup} \overset{CH_2}{\diagdown} \overset{CH_2}{\diagup} \overset{CH_2}{\diagdown} \overset{CH_2}{\diagup} \overset{CH_2}{\diagdown} \overset{CH_2}{\diagup} \overset{CH_2}{\diagdown} \overset{CH_2}{\diagup} \overset{CH_2}{\diagdown} \overset{CH_2}{}$$ 〔benzene ring〕$\overset{O}{\underset{O}{\overset{\parallel}{\underset{\parallel}{S}}}}-O^-$ Na^+

Sulfonate group

which can be synthesized from petroleum-based raw materials. Detergent anions have the advantage of not forming insoluble solids with Ca^{2+} and Mg^{2+} ions.

Phospholipids are similar in structure to fats in that they are esters of glycerol. However, unlike fats, they contain only two fatty acids. The third ester linkage involves a phosphate group, which gives phospholipids two distinct parts: the long nonpolar "tail" and the polar substituted phosphate "head" (Fig. 23.30). Because of this dual nature, phospholipids tend to form **bilayers** in aqueous solution with the tails in the interior and the polar heads interfacing with the polar water molecules, as shown in Fig. 23.31(a). Note that this behavior is very similar to that of fatty-acid anions. The bilayers of larger phospholipids can close to form **vesicles** [Fig. 23.31(b)].

Phospholipids form a significant portion of cell membranes. Figure 23.32 shows a cell membrane in the form of a phospholipid bilayer with proteins distributed in it. The cell membrane must first protect the workings of the cell from the extracellular fluids that bathe it. Its second function is to allow nutrients and other necessary chemicals to enter the cell while allowing waste products to leave the cell. The detailed operation of the membrane is very complex and not well understood; however, according to the most widely accepted model, called the **fluid mosaic model,**

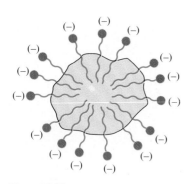

Figure 23.29

Soap micelles absorb grease molecules into their interiors so that the molecules are suspended (emulsified) in the water and can be washed away.

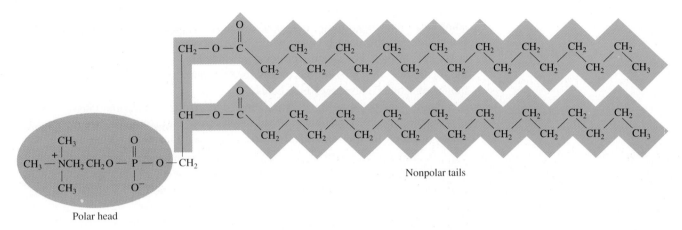

Figure 23.30

Lecithin, a phospholipid, with its long nonpolar tails and polar substituted phosphate head.

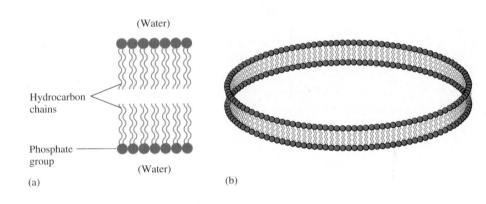

(a)

(b)

Figure 23.31

(a) A bilayer of phospholipids in aqueous solution. The nonpolar tails remain in the interior of the bilayer with the polar heads interacting with water molecules. (b) The bilayers can close to form a spherical vesicle shown here in cross section.

Figure 23.32

A representation of a cell membrane consisting of proteins embedded in a bilayer of phospholipids that are oriented with their polar heads outward.

some small uncharged molecules such as water, oxygen, and carbon dioxide diffuse freely through the lipid bilayer, while other substances pass through "gates and passages" provided by specific proteins imbedded in the membrane. The proteins in the membrane also provide the means for communication between cells, via hormones and other messenger molecules.

Like fats and phospholipids, **waxes** are esters. Unlike the former classes, waxes involve monohydroxy alcohols instead of glycerol. For example, *beeswax,* a substance secreted by the wax glands of bees, is mainly myricyl palmitate,

$$CH_3(CH_2)_{14}-\overset{\overset{\displaystyle O}{\|}}{C}-O-(CH_2)_{29}-CH_3$$

formed from palmitic acid,

$$CH_3(CH_2)_{14}-C\overset{\displaystyle O}{\underset{\displaystyle OH}{<}}$$

and the alcohol

$$CH_3(CH_2)_{29}-OH$$

Waxes are low-melting solids that furnish waterproof coatings on leaves and fruit and on the skins and feathers of animals. Waxes are also important commercially. For example, whale oil is largely composed of the wax cetyl palmitate. It has been used in so many products, including cosmetics and candles, that the blue whale has been hunted almost to extinction.

Steroids are a class of lipids that have a characteristic fused carbon-ring structure of the type

Olives have a shiny wax coating.

Steroids include four groups: cholesterol, adrenocorticoid hormones, sex hormones, and bile acids.

Cholesterol [Fig. 23.33(a)] is found in virtually all organisms and is the starting material for the formation of the bile acids, steroid hormones, and vitamin D [see Fig. 23.33(b)]. Although cholesterol is essential for human life, it has been implicated in the formation of plaque on the walls of arteries (a process called **arteriosclerosis,** or **hardening of the arteries**), which leads to eventual clogging. The phenomenon seems especially important in the arteries that supply blood to the heart. Blockage of these arteries leads to heart damage that often results in death from a heart attack.

The **adrenocorticoid hormones,** synthesized in the adrenal gland, are involved in the regulation of water and the electrolyte balance and in the metabolism of proteins and carbohydrates. For example, *cortisol* [Fig. 23.33(c)] slows the construction of proteins so that the amino acids normally used for this purpose can be used by the liver to synthesize extra glucose.

Figure 23.33

Several common steroids and steroid derivatives.
(a) cholesterol, (b) vitamin D$_3$,
(c) cortisol, (d) testosterone,
(e) progesterone, (f) estradiol,
(g) ethynodiol diacetate, and
(h) cholic acid.

Of the **sex hormones,** the most important male hormone is *testosterone* [Fig. 23.33(d)], a hormone that controls the growth of the reproductive organs and hair and the development of the muscle structure and deep voice characteristic of males. There are two types of female sex hormones of particular significance: *progesterone*

The Chemistry of Vision

Vision, the most remarkable of our senses, is a complex chemical phenomenon. The human eye is roughly spherical with an opening in the front to admit light. The light falls on a rear surface lined with cone-shaped and rod-shaped cells. Each eye contains 7 million cones for detecting color and 120 million rods to detect white light and to provide sharpness of visual images. The molecules responsible for vision are attached to the tops of the rods and cones. We will consider here the function of one of them, rhodopsin.

Rhodopsin has two parts: a protein portion called *opsin* and a small aldehyde portion called *retinal*. The structure of retinal is shown in its all *trans* form in Fig. 23.34(a), where all substituents around the double bonds are *trans*. It is interesting to note that vitamin A, a substance known to aid vision, especially night vision, has the same structure as retinal except that the terminal aldehyde functional group is replaced by a —CH₂OH group to give an alcohol. Retinal can occur in other isomeric forms, one of which is called the 11-*cis* form because of the *cis* arrangement at carbon 11 [see Fig. 23.34(b)]. It is in this *cis* form that retinal is bound to opsin. When rhodopsin absorbs light, the retinal is isomerized to the all-*trans* form, which separates from the opsin.

When the two portions separate, the natural reddish purple color of rhodopsin is lost. In addition, the cell to which rhodopsin is attached becomes excited. This receptor cell then excites other cells and sends a message to the brain. Normally, five closely spaced receptor cells must be excited to produce the sensation of vision. This means that only five photons of light are necessary to stimulate the eye, representing a total energy of only 10^{-18} J.

After the activation of rhodopsin and the separation of the *trans* form of retinal, the retinal returns to the 11-*cis* form and reconnects to the opsin. This process is relatively slow, which is one reason our eyes need time to adapt to low-light conditions. Also, intensely bright light causes saturation of the light receptors, which causes temporary blindness because there is no attached retinal to absorb additional photons of light.

Color discrimination is possible because cone cells occur in three groups: those receptive to blue light, those receptive to green light, and those receptive to yellow–red light. Each type can absorb light in a range around its primary color. Thus light in the blue–green region excites both the blue and green receptors.

Figure 23.34

The retinal portion of rhodopsin. (a) The *trans* form. (b) The 11-*cis* form. Carbon 11 is shown in red.

[Fig. 23.33(e)], and a group of estrogens, one of which is *estradiol* [Fig. 23.33(f)]. These hormones cause the periodic changes in the ovaries and the uterus responsible for the menstrual cycle. During pregnancy, a high level of progesterone is maintained, which prevents ovulation. This effect has led to the use of progesterone-type compounds as birth-control drugs. One of the most common of these is ethynodiol diacetate [Fig. 23.33(g)].

The **bile acids** are produced from cholesterol found in the liver and are stored in the gall bladder. The primary human bile acid is *cholic acid* [Fig. 23.33(h)], a substance that aids in the digestion of fats by emulsifying them in the intestine. Bile acids also can dissolve cholesterol ingested in food. They are therefore important in limiting cholesterol in the body, since too much cholesterol can be detrimental to human health.

Summary

Thirty elements are currently known to be essential or are suspected to be essential for life. The most abundant in the human body are hydrogen, carbon, nitrogen, and oxygen, but sodium, magnesium, potassium, sulfur, and chlorine are also present in large amounts. Other elements found only in trace amounts, such as zinc, are essential for the action of many enzymes.

Proteins are a class of natural polymers with molecular weights ranging from 6000 to 1,000,000. Fibrous proteins are employed in the human body for structural purposes in muscle, hair, and cartilage. Globular proteins are molecules that transport and store oxygen and nutrients, act as catalysts, help regulate the body's systems, fight foreign objects, and so on.

The building blocks of proteins are the α-amino acids, which can be divided into polar and nonpolar classes, depending on whether the side chain (the R group) attached to the α-carbon is hydrophilic or hydrophobic.

A protein polymer is built by successive condensation reactions that produce peptide linkages:

Peptide linkage

The order or sequence of amino acids in the protein chain is called the primary structure. Differences in primary structure are what tailor proteins for specific functions.

The secondary structure refers to the arrangement of the protein chain, which is determined to a large extent by hydrogen bonding between atoms on different amino acids. When such interactions occur within the chain, a spiral structure called an α-helix results. When the hydrogen bonds are between different chains, a pleated sheet results. The overall shape of the protein is called its tertiary structure. The breakdown of tertiary protein structure, called denaturation, can be caused by energy sources or a variety of chemicals.

Enzymes are proteins that act as catalysts in biologic reactions. The specificity and efficiency of an enzyme result from its structure, which is tailored to a specific type of reacting molecule (substrate).

Carbohydrates serve as food sources for most organisms and as structural materials for plants. Simple carbohydrates, called monosaccharides, are most commonly five-carbon and six-carbon polyhydroxy ketones and aldehydes that contain chiral carbon atoms. Monosaccharides combine to form more complex carbohydrates. For example, sucrose is a disaccharide, and starch and cellulose are polymers of D-glucose.

When a cell divides, the genetic information is transmitted via deoxyribonucleic acid (DNA), which has a double helical structure whose two strands are held together by hydrogen bonding between pairs of organic bases—one from each strand. The bases occur only in specific pairs. During cell division, the double helix unravels, and a new polymer forms along each strand of the original DNA to form two double helical DNA molecules. The DNA contains segments called genes, which store the structural information for specific proteins. Various types of ribonucleic acid (RNA) molecules assist in protein synthesis.

Lipids are water-insoluble substances found in cells and can be divided into four classes: fats, phospholipids, waxes, and steroids. Fats are esters composed of glycerol (a polyhydroxy alcohol) and fatty acids (carboxylic acids that contain long-chain hydrocarbons). Soaps are sodium salts of fatty acids. Soaps act as surfactants by forming micelles, with the nonpolar tails of the molecules in the interior and the polar heads toward the exterior where they can interact with the polar water molecules.

Steroids have the characteristic fused-ring structure

and include cholesterol, the adrenocorticoid hormones, the sex hormones, and the bile acids.

Key Terms

biochemistry
essential elements
trace elements
cell

Section 23.1

proteins
α-amino acids
side chain
dipeptide
peptide linkage
polypeptide
primary structure
secondary structure
α-helix
pleated sheet
random-coil arrangement
tertiary structure
disulfide linkage
denaturation
enzymes
lock-and-key model
metalloenzyme

Section 23.2

carbohydrates
monosaccharides (simple sugars)
sucrose
disaccharide
glycoside linkage
starch
cellulose
glycogen

Section 23.3

deoxyribonucleic acid (DNA)
ribonucleic acid (RNA)
nucleotides
protein synthesis
gene
codon
messenger RNA (mRNA)
transfer RNA (tRNA)
anticodon

Section 23.4

lipids

fats
fatty acids
micelle
surfactant
phospholipids
bilayer
waxes
steroids

A blue question or exercise number indicates that the answer to that question or exercise appears at the back of this book and a solution appears in the Solutions Guide.

Questions

1. Distinguish between the primary, secondary, and tertiary structures of a protein. Give examples of the types of forces that maintain each type of structure.

2. Is the primary, secondary, or tertiary structure of an enzyme changed by denaturation?

3. Describe how denaturation and inhibition affect the catalytic activity of an enzyme.

4. Aqueous solutions of amino acids are buffered solutions. Explain.

5. What interactions are responsible for the solubility of starch in water?

6. Distinguish among the following terms: *structural isomerism, geometric isomerism,* and *optical isomerism.*

7. The compounds adenine, guanine, cytosine, and thymine are called the nucleic acid bases. What structural features in these compounds make them bases?

8. Describe the structural differences between DNA and RNA.

9. The deletion of a single base from a DNA molecule can constitute a fatal mutation. Substitution of one base for another is often not as serious a mutation. Explain.

10. Why can lipids be extracted into organic solvents while carbohydrates cannot?

11. What is a polyunsaturated fat?

12. When one spills a solution of sodium hydroxide on one's hands, the skin feels slippery. Why?

Exercises

In this section similar exercises are paired.

Proteins and Amino Acids

13. Glycine can exist in water in two forms as shown below; K_a for the carboxylic acid group is 4.3×10^{-3}; K_b for the amino group is 6.0×10^{-3}.

$$H_2N-CH_2\overset{\overset{\displaystyle O}{\|}}{C}OH \quad \text{or} \quad {}^+H_3N-CH_2-\overset{\overset{\displaystyle O}{\|}}{C}-O^-$$

a. Would you expect the position of the following equilibrium to lie significantly to the right or the left?

$$H_2NCH_2CO_2H \rightleftharpoons {}^+H_3NCH_2CO_2^-$$

b. Two ions of glycine are possible. Which of these would be predominant in a solution with $[H^+] = 1.0\ M$? In a solution with $[OH^-] = 1.0\ M$?

14. When pure crystalline amino acids are heated, decomposition generally occurs before the solid melts. Account for this observation. (*Hint:* See Exercise 13.)

15. Aspartame, the artificial sweetener marketed under the name Nutra-Sweet, is a methyl ester of a dipeptide:

$$H_2N-\overset{\overset{\displaystyle}{\underset{\underset{\displaystyle CH_2CO_2H}{|}}{CH}}}{}-\overset{\overset{\displaystyle O}{\|}}{C}-NH-\overset{\overset{\displaystyle CO_2CH_3}{|}}{CH}-CH_2-\bigcirc$$

a. What two amino acids are used to prepare aspartame?

b. There is concern that methanol may be produced by the decomposition of aspartame. From what portion of the molecule can methanol be produced? Write an equation for this reaction.

16. Two new amino acids, amino malonic acid and β-carboxy aspartic acid, have recently been isolated from the bacteria *E. coli*. Amino malonic acid also has been found in mammals and seems to be associated with the formation of arteriosclerotic plaque. The structures of these amino acids are

$$HO_2C-\overset{\overset{\displaystyle}{\underset{\underset{\displaystyle NH_2}{|}}{CH}}}{}-CO_2H \qquad \begin{array}{c} H_2N-CH-CO_2H \\ | \\ HO_2C-CH-CO_2H \end{array}$$

Amino malonic acid β-Carboxy aspartic acid

Would you classify these as hydrophobic or hydrophilic amino acids? Explain.

17. Give an example of amino acids that could give rise to the interactions pictured in Fig. 23.10 that maintain the tertiary structures of proteins.

18. What type of interactions can occur between the side chains of phenylalanine and isoleucine? Aspartic acid and lysine?

19. Draw the structures of the two dipeptides that can be formed from serine and alanine.

20. How many tripeptides can be formed from the amino acids ala, ala, and gly?

21. How many tetrapeptides can be formed that contain two phenylalanines (phe) and two glycines (gly)?

22. How many tripeptides can be formed containing one phenylalanine (phe), one glycine (gly), and one alanine (ala)?

23. Sickle-cell anemia is a disease resulting from abnormal hemoglobin molecules in which a valine is substituted for a single glutamic acid in normal hemoglobin. How might this substitution affect the structure of hemoglobin?

24. The rate of enzyme-catalyzed reactions often depends on temperature in the manner shown in the graph. Account for the shape of this curve.

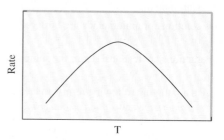

Carbohydrates

25. Draw cyclic structures for D-ribose and D-mannose.

26. Indicate the chiral carbon atoms found in the carbohydrates D-ribose and D-mannose.

Optical Isomerism and Chiral Carbon Atoms

27. Which of the amino acids in Table 23.3 contain more than one chiral carbon atom? Draw the structures of these amino acids and indicate all chiral carbon atoms.

28. Why is glycine not optically active?

29. How many chiral carbon atoms are there in cholesterol? [See Fig. 23.33(a).]

30. Draw the structure of menthol (2-isopropyl-5-methylcyclohexanol), and indicate the chiral carbon atoms.

31. Which of the isomers of bromochloropropene are optically active? (See Exercise 28 in Chapter 22.)

32. The scent of pine trees mainly results from the presence of α-pinene. Oil of turpentine contains roughly 58 to 65% α-pinene. The structure of α-pinene is

Is α-pinene optically active? If it is, identify the chiral carbon atoms.

Nucleic Acids

33. Part of a certain DNA sequence is A-T-G-C-G-G-C-A-T. What is the complementary sequence?

35. Which base will hydrogen bond with uracil within an RNA molecule? Draw the structure of this base pair.

34. The codons (words) in DNA (that specify which amino acid should be at a particular point in a protein) are three bases long. How many such three-letter words can be made from the four bases adenine, cytosine, guanine, and thymine?

36. A tautomeric form (see Exercise 57 in Chapter 22 for a definition of tautomerism) of thymine has the structure

a. Use bond energies (Table 8.4) to predict whether this tautomer or the one given in Fig. 23.22 is more stable.
b. If the tautomer above, rather than the stable form of thymine, were present in a strand of DNA during replication, what would be the result?

37. The base sequences in mRNA that code for certain amino acids are

Glu: GAA, GAG

Val: GUU, GUC, GUA, GUG

Met: AUG

Trp: UGG

Phe: UUU, UUC

Asp: GAU, GAC

These sequences are complementary to the sequences in DNA.
a. Give the corresponding sequences in DNA for the amino acids listed above.
b. Give a DNA sequence that would code for the peptide met–met–phe–asp–trp.
c. How many different DNA sequences can code for the pentapeptide in part b?
d. What is the peptide that is produced from the DNA sequence: C-T-T-A-C-C-A-A-A?
e. What other DNA sequences would yield the same tripeptide as in part d?

38. The change of a single base in the DNA sequence for normal hemoglobin can encode for the abnormal hemoglobin giving rise to sickle-cell anemia. Which base in the codon for glu in DNA is replaced to give the codon(s) for val? (See Exercises 23 and 37.)

Lipids and Steroids

39. Draw the structure of the triglyceride formed from linoleic acid and glycerol.

40. How many moles of H_2 will it take to completely hydrogenate one mole of the triglyceride in Exercise 39? How many products are possible if only four moles of H_2 react with this triglyceride? Draw the structures of these products.

41. The oil of deep water fish is rich in omega-3 fatty acids. The presence of these fatty acids in the diet appears to lower blood cholesterol levels. The term *omega-3* applies to the location of a carbon–carbon double bond. Starting with the terminal methyl group (the omega carbon), the double bond is located after the third carbon atom. Draw the structures of the omega-3 fatty acids that contain a total of 16 carbon atoms and 18 carbon atoms, respectively.

42. Lecithin and sphingomyelin are two phospholipids found in amniotic fluid. During gestation, sphingomyelin levels are relatively constant, but lecithin levels increase. Both substances act as surfactants in the lung, and the ratio of lecithin to sphingomyelin in amniotic fluid is used by physicians to assess whether an infant will be able to breathe unassisted upon birth.
  a. Look up the structures of these two substances in a reference such as *The Merck Index*.
  b. Indicate the hydrophobic and hydrophilic portions of each molecule.

43. Cetyl palmitate is commonly used as a surfactant in many shampoos and related cosmetic products. Look up the structure of cetyl palmitate in an appropriate reference work.

44. Identify the functional group present in the steroids shown in Fig. 23.33.

Additional Exercises

45. Monosodium glutamate (MSG) is commonly used as a flavoring in foods. Draw the structure of MSG.

46. Sucrose polyester (SPE) is a material being developed by the Procter and Gamble Company as a fat substitute in cooking oil. SPE, which is indigestible and thus adds no calories to food cooked in it, is the polyester formed from sucrose (which has eight hydroxyl groups) and a specific fatty acid. The polyesters containing six, seven, or eight fatty acids attached to the hydroxyl groups as esters are not digestible, while those with five or less are digestible.
  a. Draw the structure of the SPE made from sucrose completely esterified with oleic acid.
  b. How many isomers exist when only seven of the hydroxyl groups are esterified (one hydroxyl group remains)?
  c. How many isomers exist when only six of the hydroxyl groups are esterified?
  d. Based on the discussion of enzymes in Chapters 12 and 23, speculate why the SPE molecules with six, seven, or eight ester functional groups are indigestible while the ones containing fewer fatty acids are digestible.

47. Each human DNA molecule contains roughly 5×10^9 base pairs. The spacing between base pairs along a given chain is about 340 pm. If a single human DNA molecule was stretched to its full length, how long would it be?

48. The compound cisplatin (see Chap. 20) appears to kill cancer cells by inhibiting DNA synthesis. Given the following structural information about cisplatin, the information in Exercise 47, and the fact that the chloride ion is easily displaced by other donor molecules in cisplatin, speculate on how cisplatin may interact with DNA.

$$\begin{array}{c} \text{Cl} \quad \uparrow \\ \diagup \text{Pt} \diagup \quad \text{350 pm} \\ \diagup \quad \text{Cl} \quad \downarrow \end{array}$$

49. Look up the structures of the following vitamins in *The Merck Index*. Classify each as water-soluble or fat-soluble.
  a. Vitamin A   c. Vitamin K_5
  b. Vitamin E   d. Vitamin K_6

50. a. Use bond energies (Table 8.4) to estimate ΔH for the reaction of two molecules of glycine to form a peptide linkage.
  b. Would you predict ΔS to favor the formation of peptide linkages between two molecules of glycine?
  c. Would you predict the formation of proteins to be a spontaneous process?

51. The reaction to form a phosphate ester linkage between two nucleotides can be approximated as follows:

$$\text{Sugar}-\text{O}-\overset{\overset{\displaystyle O}{|}}{\underset{\underset{\displaystyle O}{|}}{P}}-\text{OH} + \text{HO}-\text{CH}_2-\text{sugar} \longrightarrow$$

$$-\text{O}-\overset{\overset{\displaystyle O}{|}}{\underset{\underset{\displaystyle O}{|}}{P}}-\text{O}-\text{CH}_2- + \text{H}_2\text{O}$$

Would you predict the formation of a dinucleotide from two nucleotides to be a spontaneous process?

52. Considering your answers to Exercises 50 and 51, how can you justify the existence of proteins and nucleic acids in light of the second law of thermodynamics?

Challenge Problems

53. How many different polypeptides that contain 25 amino acids can be made from a mixture of 5 different amino acids?

54. Use the values of equilibrium constants given in Exercise 13 to calculate equilibrium constants for the following.
  a. $^+\text{H}_3\text{NCH}_2\text{CO}_2\text{H} + \text{H}_2\text{O} \rightleftharpoons \text{H}_2\text{NCH}_2\text{CO}_2\text{H} + \text{H}_3\text{O}^+$

b. $H_2NCH_2CO_2^- + H_2O \rightleftharpoons H_2NCH_2CO_2H + OH^-$

c. $^+H_3NCH_2CO_2H \rightleftharpoons 2H^+ + H_2NCH_2CO_2^-$

55. The isoelectric point of an amino acid is the pH at which the molecule has no net charge. For glycine, this would be the pH at which virtually all glycine molecules are in the form $^+H_3NCH_2CO_2^-$. If we assume that the principal equilibrium is

$2\,^+H_3NCH_2CO_2^-$

$\qquad \rightleftharpoons H_2NCH_2CO_2^- + {}^+H_3NCH_2CO_2H \qquad$ (i)

then at equilibrium

$\qquad [H_2NCH_2CO_2^-] = [^+H_3NCH_2CO_2H] \qquad$ (ii)

Use this result and your answer to part c of Exercise 54 to calculate the pH at which Equation (ii) is true. This will be the isoelectric point of glycine.

56. The structure of tartaric acid is

$$\begin{array}{cc} OH & OH \\ | & | \\ HO_2C-CH & -CH-CO_2H \end{array}$$

a. Is the form of tartaric acid pictured below optically active? Explain.

$$\begin{array}{cc} OH & OH \\ | & | \\ C & -C \\ HOOC\;\; H & \;\; H\;\; COOH \end{array}$$

Note: The dashed lines show groups behind the plane of the page. The wedges show groups in front of the plane.

b. Draw the optically active forms of tartaric acid.

Appendix One *Mathematical Procedures*

A1.1 Exponential Notation

The numbers characteristic of scientific measurements are often very large or very small; thus it is convenient to express them using powers of 10. For example, the number 1,300,000 can be expressed as 1.3×10^6, which means multiply 1.3 by 10 six times, or

$$1.3 \times 10^6 = 1.3 \times \underbrace{10 \times 10 \times 10 \times 10 \times 10 \times 10}_{10^6 \ = \ 1 \ \text{million}}$$

Note that each multiplication by 10 moves the decimal point one place to the right:

$$1.3 \times 10 = 13.$$
$$13 \times 10 = 130.$$
$$130 \times 10 = 1300.$$
$$\vdots$$

Thus the easiest way to interpret the notation 1.3×10^6 is that it means move the decimal point in 1.3 to the right six times:

$$1.3 \times 10^6 = 1\underset{1\ 2\ 3\ 4\ 5\ 6}{\underbrace{3\ 0\ 0\ 0\ 0\ 0}} = 1,300,000$$

Using this notation, the number 1985 can be expressed as 1.985×10^3. Note that the usual convention is to write the number that appears before the power of 10 as a number between 1 and 10. To end up with the number 1.985, which is between 1 and 10, we had to move the decimal point three places to the left. To compensate for that, we must multiply by 10^3, which says that to get the intended number we start with 1.985 and move the decimal point three places to the right; that is:

$$1.985 \times 10^3 = 1\underset{1\ 2\ 3}{\underbrace{9\ 8\ 5}}.$$

Some other examples are given below.

Number	Exponential notation
5.6	5.6×10^0 or 5.6×1
39	3.9×10^1
943	9.43×10^2
1126	1.126×10^3

So far, we have considered numbers greater than 1. How do we represent a number such as 0.0034 in exponential notation? We start with a number between 1 and 10 and *divide* by the appropriate power of 10:

$$0.0034 = \frac{3.4}{10 \times 10 \times 10} = \frac{3.4}{10^3} = 3.4 \times 10^{-3}$$

Division by 10 moves the decimal point one place to the *left*. Thus the number

$$0.\underset{7\;6\;5\;4\;3\;2\;1}{\underbrace{0\,0\,0\,0\,0\,0\,1}}\,4$$

can be written as 1.4×10^{-7}.

To summarize, we can write any number in the form

$$N \times 10^{\pm n}$$

where N is between 1 and 10 and the exponent n is an integer. If the sign preceding n is positive, it means the decimal point in N should be moved n places to the right. If a negative sign precedes n, the decimal point in N should be moved n places to the left.

Multiplication and Division

When two numbers expressed in exponential notation are multiplied, the initial numbers are multiplied and the exponents of 10 are added:

$$(M \times 10^m)(N \times 10^n) = (MN) \times 10^{m+n}$$

For example (to two significant figures, as required),

$$(3.2 \times 10^4)(2.8 \times 10^3) = 9.0 \times 10^7$$

When the numbers are multiplied, if a result greater than 10 is obtained for the initial number, the decimal point is moved one place to the left and the exponent of 10 is increased by 1:

$$(5.8 \times 10^2)(4.3 \times 10^8) = 24.9 \times 10^{10}$$
$$= 2.49 \times 10^{11}$$
$$= 2.5 \ \times 10^{11} \qquad \text{(two significant figures)}$$

Division of two numbers expressed in exponential notation involves normal division of the initial numbers and *subtraction* of the exponent of the divisor from that of the dividend. For example,

$$\frac{4.8 \times 10^8}{\underbrace{2.1 \times 10^3}_{\text{Divisor}}} = \frac{4.8}{2.1} \times 10^{(8-3)} = 2.3 \times 10^5$$

If the initial number resulting from the division is less than 1, the decimal point is moved one place to the right and the exponent of 10 is decreased by 1. For example,

$$\frac{6.4 \times 10^3}{8.3 \times 10^5} = \frac{6.4}{8.3} \times 10^{(3-5)} = 0.77 \times 10^{-2}$$
$$= 7.7 \times 10^{-3}$$

Addition and Subtraction

To add or subtract numbers expressed in exponential notation, *the exponents of the numbers must be the same*. For example, to add 1.31×10^5 and 4.2×10^4, we must rewrite one number so that the exponents of both are the same. The number 1.31×10^5 can be written 13.1×10^4, since moving the decimal point one place to the right can be compensated for by decreasing the exponent by 1. Now we can add the numbers:

$$
\begin{array}{r}
13.1 \times 10^4 \\
+\ 4.2 \times 10^4 \\
\hline
17.3 \times 10^4
\end{array}
$$

In correct exponential notation the result is expressed as 1.73×10^5.

To perform addition or subtraction with numbers expressed in exponential notation, only the initial numbers are added or subtracted. The exponent of the result is the same as those of the numbers being added or subtracted. To subtract 1.8×10^2 from 8.99×10^3, we write

$$
\begin{array}{r}
8.99 \times 10^3 \\
-0.18 \times 10^3 \\
\hline
8.81 \times 10^3
\end{array}
$$

Powers and Roots

When a number expressed in exponential notation is taken to some power, the initial number is taken to the appropriate power and the exponent of 10 is multiplied by that power:

$$(N \times 10^n)^m = N^m \times 10^{m \cdot n}$$

For example,*

$$
\begin{aligned}
(7.5 \times 10^2)^3 &= 7.5^3 \times 10^{3 \cdot 2} \\
&= 422 \times 10^6 \\
&= 4.22 \times 10^8 \\
&= 4.2 \times 10^8 \qquad \text{(two significant figures)}
\end{aligned}
$$

When a root is taken of a number expressed in exponential notation, the root of the initial number is taken and the exponent of 10 is divided by the number representing the root:

$$\sqrt{N \times 10^n} = (N \times 10^n)^{1/2} = \sqrt{N} \times 10^{n/2}$$

For example,

$$
\begin{aligned}
(2.9 \times 10^6)^{1/2} &= \sqrt{2.9} \times 10^{6/2} \\
&= 1.7 \times 10^3
\end{aligned}
$$

Because the exponent of the result must be an integer, we may sometimes have to change the form of the number so that the power divided by the root equals an

---

*Refer to the instruction booklet for your calculator for directions concerning how to take roots and powers of numbers.

integer, for example:

$$\sqrt{1.9 \times 10^3} = (1.9 \times 10^3)^{1/2} = (0.19 \times 10^4)^{1/2}$$
$$= \sqrt{0.19} \times 10^2$$
$$= 0.44 \times 10^2$$
$$= 4.4 \times 10^1$$

In this case, we moved the decimal point one place to the left and increased the exponent from 3 to 4 to make $n/2$ an integer.

The same procedure is followed for roots other than square roots, for example:

$$\sqrt[3]{6.9 \times 10^5} = (6.9 \times 10^5)^{1/3} = (0.69 \times 10^6)^{1/3}$$
$$= \sqrt[3]{0.69} \times 10^2$$
$$= 0.88 \times 10^2$$
$$= 8.8 \times 10^1$$

and

$$\sqrt[3]{4.6 \times 10^{10}} = (4.6 \times 10^{10})^{1/3} = (46 \times 10^9)^{1/3}$$
$$= \sqrt[3]{46} \times 10^3$$
$$= 3.6 \times 10^3$$

A1.2 Logarithms

A logarithm is an exponent. Any number N can be expressed as follows:

$$N = 10^x$$

For example,

$$1000 = 10^3$$
$$100 = 10^2$$
$$10 = 10^1$$
$$1 = 10^0$$

The common, or base 10, logarithm of a number is the power to which 10 must be taken to yield that number. Thus, since $1000 = 10^3$,

$$\log 1000 = 3$$

Similarly,

$$\log 100 = 2$$
$$\log 10 = 1$$
$$\log 1 = 0$$

For a number between 10 and 100, the required exponent of 10 will be between 1 and 2. For example, $65 = 10^{1.8129}$; that is, $\log 65 = 1.8129$. For a number between 100 and 1000, the exponent of 10 will be between 2 and 3. For example, $650 = 10^{2.8129}$ and $\log 650 = 2.8129$.

A number N greater than 0 and less than 1 can be expressed as follows:

$$N = 10^{-x} = \frac{1}{10^x}$$

For example,

$$0.001 = \frac{1}{1000} = \frac{1}{10^3} = 10^{-3}$$

$$0.01 = \frac{1}{100} = \frac{1}{10^2} = 10^{-2}$$

$$0.1 = \frac{1}{10} = \frac{1}{10^1} = 10^{-1}$$

Thus

$$\log 0.001 = -3$$
$$\log 0.01 = -2$$
$$\log 0.1 = -1$$

Although common logs are often tabulated, the most convenient method for obtaining such logs is to use an electronic calculator. On most calculators the number is first entered and then the log key is punched. The log of the number then appears in the display.* Some examples are given below. You should reproduce these results on your calculator in order to be sure that you can find common logs correctly.

Number	Common log
36	1.56
1849	3.2669
0.156	−0.807
1.68×10^{-5}	−4.775

Note that the number of digits after the decimal point in a common log is equal to the number of significant figures in the original number.

Since logs are simply exponents, they are manipulated according to the rules for exponents. For example, if $A = 10^x$ and $B = 10^y$, then their product is

$$A \cdot B = 10^x \cdot 10^y = 10^{x+y}$$

and

$$\log AB = x + y = \log A + \log B$$

For division, we have

$$\frac{A}{B} = \frac{10^x}{10^y} = 10^{x-y}$$

and

$$\log \frac{A}{B} = x - y = \log A - \log B$$

---

*Refer to the instruction booklet for your calculator for the exact sequence to obtain logarithms.

For a number raised to a power, we have

$$A^n = (10^x)^n = 10^{nx}$$

and

$$\log A^n = nx = n \log A$$

It follows that

$$\log \frac{1}{A^n} = \log A^{-n} = -n \log A$$

or, for $n = 1$,

$$\log \frac{1}{A} = -\log A$$

When a common log is given, to find the number it represents, we must carry out the process of exponentiation. For example, if the log is 2.673, then $N = 10^{2.673}$. The process of exponentiation is also called taking the antilog, or the inverse logarithm. This operation is usually carried out on calculators in one of two ways. The majority of calculators require that the log be entered first and then the keys [INV] and [LOG] pressed in succession. For example to find $N = 10^{2.673}$, we enter 2.673 and then press [INV] and [LOG]. The number 471 will be displayed; that is, $N = 471$. Some calculators have a [10^x] key. In that case, the log is entered first and then the [10^x] key is pressed. Again, the number 471 will be displayed.

Natural logarithms, another type of logarithm, are based on the number 2.7183, which is referred to as e. In this case, a number is represented as $N = e^x = 2.7183^x$. For example:

$$N = 7.15 = e^x$$

$$\ln 7.15 = x = 1.967$$

To find the natural log of a number using a calculator, the number is entered and then the [ln] key is pressed. Use the following examples to check your technique for finding natural logs with your calculator:

Number (e^x)	Natural log (x)
784	6.664
1.61×10^3	7.384
1.00×10^{-7}	−16.118
1.00	0

If a natural logarithm is given, to find the number it represents, exponentiation to the base e (2.7183) must be carried out. With many calculators this is done using a key marked [e^x] (the natural log is entered, with the correct sign, and then the [e^x] key is pressed). The other common method for exponentiation to base e is to enter the natural log and then press the [INV] and [ln] keys in succession. The following examples will help you check your technique.

ln N (x)	N (e^x)
3.256	25.9
−5.169	5.69×10^{-3}
13.112	4.95×10^5

Since natural logarithms are simply exponents, they are also manipulated according to the mathematical rules for exponents given above for common logs.

A1.3 Graphing Functions

In interpreting the results of a scientific experiment, it is often useful to make a graph. If possible, the function to be graphed should be in a form that gives a straight line. The equation for a straight line (a *linear equation*) can be represented by the general form

$$y = mx + b$$

where y is the *dependent variable*, x is the *independent variable*, m is the *slope*, and b is the *intercept* with the y axis.

To illustrate the characteristics of a linear equation, the function $y = 3x + 4$ is plotted in Fig. A.1. For this equation $m = 3$ and $b = 4$. Note that the y intercept occurs when $x = 0$. In this case the intercept is 4, as can be seen from the equation ($b = 4$).

The slope of a straight line is defined as the ratio of the rate of change in y to that in x:

$$m = \text{slope} = \frac{\Delta y}{\Delta x}$$

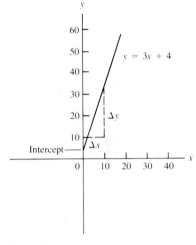

Figure A.1
Graph of the linear equation $y = 3x + 4$.

For the equation $y = 3x + 4$, y changes three times as fast as x (since x has a coefficient of 3). Thus the slope in this case is 3. This can be verified from the graph. For the triangle shown in Fig. A.1,

$$\Delta y = 34 - 10 = 24 \quad \text{and} \quad \Delta x = 10 - 2 = 8$$

Thus

$$\text{Slope} = \frac{\Delta y}{\Delta x} = \frac{24}{8} = 3$$

The above example illustrates a general method for obtaining the slope of a line from the graph of that line. Simply draw a triangle with one side parallel to the y axis and the other parallel to the x axis as shown in Fig. A.1. Then determine the lengths of the sides to give Δy and Δx, respectively, and compute the ratio $\Delta y/\Delta x$.

Sometimes an equation that is not in standard form can be changed to the form $y = mx + b$ by rearrangement or mathematical manipulation. An example is the equation $k = Ae^{-E_a/RT}$ described in Section 12.7, where A, E_a and R are constants, k is the dependent variable, and $1/T$ is the independent variable. This equation can be changed to standard form by taking the natural logarithm of both sides,

$$\ln k = \ln Ae^{-E_a/Rt} = \ln A + \ln e^{-E_a/RT} = \ln A - \frac{E_a}{RT}$$

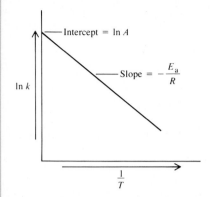

Figure A.2

Graph of ln k versus 1/T.

noting that the log of a product is equal to the sum of the logs of the individual terms and that the natural log of $e^{-E_a/RT}$ is simply the exponent $-E_a/RT$. Thus, in standard form, the equation $k = Ae^{-E_a/RT}$ is written

$$\underbrace{\ln k}_{y} = -\underbrace{\frac{E_a}{R}}_{m} \underbrace{\left(\frac{1}{T}\right)}_{x} + \underbrace{\ln A}_{b}$$

A plot of ln k versus 1/T (see Fig. A.2) gives a straight line with slope $-E_a/R$ and intercept ln A.

Other linear equations that are useful in the study of chemistry are listed in standard form in Table A.1.

Some Useful Linear Equations in Standard Form

Equation ($y = mx + b$)	What is Plotted (y vs. x)	Slope (m)	Intercept (b)	Section in Text
$[A] = -kt + [A]_0$	$[A]$ vs. t	$-k$	$[A]_0$	12.4
$\ln [A] = -kt + \ln [A]_0$	$\ln [A]$ vs. t	$-k$	$\ln [A]_0$	12.4
$\dfrac{1}{[A]} = kt + \dfrac{1}{[A]_0}$	$\dfrac{1}{[A]}$ vs. t	k	$\dfrac{1}{[A]_0}$	12.4
$\ln P_{vap} = -\dfrac{\Delta H_{vap}}{R}\left(\dfrac{1}{T}\right) + C$	$\ln P_{vap}$ vs. $\dfrac{1}{T}$	$\dfrac{-\Delta H_{vap}}{R}$	C	10.8

Table A.1

A1.4 Solving Quadratic Equations

A *quadratic equation*, a polynomial in which the highest power of x is 2, can be written as

$$ax^2 + bx + c = 0$$

One method for finding the two values of x that satisfy a quadratic equation is to use the *quadratic formula:*

$$x = \frac{-b \pm \sqrt{b^2 - 4ac}}{2a}$$

where a, b, and c are the coefficients of x^2 and x and the constant, respectively. For example, in determining $[H^+]$ in a solution of 1.0×10^{-4} M acetic acid the following expression arises:

$$1.8 \times 10^{-5} = \frac{x^2}{1.0 \times 10^{-4} - x}$$

which yields

$$x^2 + (1.8 \times 10^{-5})x - 1.8 \times 10^{-9} = 0$$

where $a = 1$, $b = 1.8 \times 10^{-5}$, and $c = -1.8 \times 10^{-9}$. Using the quadratic formula, we have

$$x = \frac{-b \pm \sqrt{b^2 - 4ac}}{2a}$$

$$= \frac{-1.8 \times 10^{-5} \pm \sqrt{3.24 \times 10^{-10} - (4)(1)(-1.8 \times 10^{-9})}}{2(1)}$$

$$= \frac{-1.8 \times 10^{-5} \pm \sqrt{3.24 \times 10^{-10} + 7.2 \times 10^{-9}}}{2}$$

$$= \frac{-1.8 \times 10^{-5} \pm \sqrt{7.5 \times 10^{-9}}}{2}$$

$$= \frac{-1.8 \times 10^{-5} \pm 8.7 \times 10^{-5}}{2}$$

Thus

$$x = \frac{6.9 \times 10^{-5}}{2} = 3.5 \times 10^{-5}$$

and

$$x = \frac{-10.5 \times 10^{-5}}{2} = -5.2 \times 10^{-5}$$

Note that there are two roots as there always will be for a polynomial in x^2. In this case x represents a concentration of H^+ (see Section 14.3). Thus the positive root is the one that solves the problem, since a concentration cannot be a negative number.

A second method for solving quadratic equations is by *successive approximations,* a systematic method of trial and error. A value of x is guessed and substituted into the equation everywhere x (or x^2) appears, except for one place. For example, for the equation

$$x^2 + (1.8 \times 10^{-5})x - 1.8 \times 10^{-9} = 0$$

we might guess $x = 2 \times 10^{-5}$. Substituting that value into the equation gives

$$x^2 + (1.8 \times 10^{-5})(2 \times 10^{-5}) - 1.8 \times 10^{-9} = 0$$

or $x^2 = 1.8 \times 10^{-9} - 3.6 \times 10^{-10} = 1.4 \times 10^{-9}$

Thus $x = 3.7 \times 10^{-5}$

Note that the guessed value of x (2×10^{-5}) is not the same as the value of x that is calculated (3.7×10^{-5}) after inserting the estimated value. This means that $x = 2 \times 10^{-5}$ is not the correct solution, and we must try another guess. We take the calculated value (3.7×10^{-5}) as our next guess:

$$x^2 + (1.8 \times 10^{-5})(3.7 \times 10^{-5}) - 1.8 \times 10^{-9} = 0$$

$$x^2 = 1.8 \times 10^{-9} - 6.7 \times 10^{-10} = 1.1 \times 10^{-9}$$

Thus $x = 3.3 \times 10^{-5}$

Now we compare the two values of x again:

Guessed: $x = 3.7 \times 10^{-5}$

Calculated: $x = 3.3 \times 10^{-5}$

These values are closer but not close enough. Next we try 3.3×10^{-5} as our guess:

$$x^2 + (1.8 \times 10^{-5})(3.3 \times 10^{-5}) - 1.8 \times 10^{-9} = 0$$
$$x^2 = 1.8 \times 10^{-9} - 5.9 \times 10^{-10} = 1.2 \times 10^{-9}$$

Thus $x = 3.5 \times 10^{-5}$

Again we compare:

$$\text{Guessed: } x = 3.3 \times 10^{-5}$$
$$\text{Calculated: } x = 3.5 \times 10^{-5}$$

Next we guess $x = 3.5 \times 10^{-5}$ to give

$$x^2 + (1.8 \times 10^{-5})(3.5 \times 10^{-5}) - 1.8 \times 10^{-9} = 0$$
$$x^2 = 1.8 \times 10^{-9} - 6.3 \times 10^{-10} = 1.2 \times 10^{-9}$$

Thus $x = 3.5 \times 10^{-5}$

Now the guessed value and the calculated value are the same; we have found the correct solution. Note that this agrees with one of the roots found with the quadratic formula in the first method above.

To further illustrate the method of successive approximations, we will solve Sample Exercise 14.17 using this procedure. In solving for $[H^+]$ for $0.010\ M$ H_2SO_4, we obtain the following expression:

$$1.2 \times 10^{-2} = \frac{x(0.010 + x)}{0.010 - x}$$

which can be rearranged to give

$$x = (1.2 \times 10^{-2})\left(\frac{0.010 - x}{0.010 + x}\right)$$

We will guess a value for x, substitute it into the right side of the equation, and then calculate a value for x. In guessing a value for x, we know it must be less than 0.010, since a larger value will make the calculated value for x negative and the guessed and calculated values will never match. We start by guessing $x = 0.005$.

The results of the successive approximations are shown in the following table:

Trial	Guessed value for x	Calculated value for x
1	0.0050	0.0040
2	0.0040	0.0051
3	0.00450	0.00455
4	0.00452	0.00453

Note that the first guess was close to the actual value and that there was oscillation between 0.004 and 0.005 for the guessed and calculated values. For trial 3, an average of these values was used as the guess, and this led rapidly to the correct value (0.0045 to the correct number of significant figures). Also, note that it is useful to carry extra digits until the correct value is obtained. That value can then be rounded off to the correct number of significant figures.

The method of successive approximations is especially useful for solving polynomials containing x to a power of 3 or higher. The procedure is the same as for quadratic equations: substitute a guessed value for x into the equation for every x term but one, and then solve for x. Continue this process until the guessed and calculated values agree.

A1.5 Uncertainties in Measurements

Like all the physical sciences, chemistry is based on the results of measurements. Every measurement has an inherent uncertainty; so if we are to use the results of measurements to reach conclusions, we must be able to estimate the sizes of these uncertainties.

For example, the specification for a commercial 500-mg acetaminophen (the active painkiller in Tylenol) tablet is that each batch of tablets must contain 450–550 mg of acetaminophen per tablet. Suppose that chemical analysis gave the following results for a batch of acetaminophen tablets: 428 mg, 479 mg, 442 mg, and 435 mg. How can we use these results to decide if the batch of tablets meets the specification? Although the details of how to draw such conclusions from measured data are beyond the scope of this text, we will consider some aspects of how this is done. We will focus here on the types of experimental uncertainty, the expression of experimental results, and a simplified method for estimating experimental uncertainty when several types of measurement contribute to the final result.

Types of Experimental Error

There are two types of experimental uncertainty (error). A variety of names is applied to these types of errors:

$$\text{Precision} \leftrightarrow \text{Random error} \equiv \text{Indeterminate error}$$
$$\text{Accuracy} \leftrightarrow \text{Systematic error} \equiv \text{Determinate error}$$

The difference between the two types of error is well illustrated by the attempts to hit a target shown in Fig. 1.8 in Chapter 1.

Random error is associated with every measurement. To obtain the last significant figure for any measurement, we must always make an estimate. For example, we interpolate between the marks on a meter stick, a buret, or a balance. The precision of replicate measurements (repeated measurements of the same type) reflects the size of the random errors. Precision refers to the reproducibility of replicate measurements.

The accuracy of a measurement refers to how close it is to the true value. An inaccurate result occurs as a result of some flaw (systematic error) in the measurement: the presence of an interfering substance, incorrect calibration of an instrument, operator error, etc. The goal of chemical analysis is to eliminate systematic error, but random errors can only be minimized. In practice, an experiment is almost always done in order to find an unknown value (the true value is not known—someone is trying to obtain that value by doing the experiment). In this case the precision of several replicate determinations is used to assess the accuracy of the result. The results of the replicate experiments are expressed as an average (which we assume is close to the true value) with an error limit that gives some indication of how close the average value may be to the true value. The error limit represents the uncertainty of the experimental result.

Expression of Experimental Results

If we perform several measurements, such as for the analysis for acetaminophen in painkiller tablets, the results should express two things: the average of the measurements and the size of the uncertainty.

There are two common ways of expressing an average: the mean and the median. The mean ($\bar{x}$) is the arithmetic average of the results, or

$$\text{Mean} = \bar{x} = \sum_{i=1}^{n} \frac{x_i}{n} = \frac{x_1 + x_2 \cdots x_n}{n}$$

where Σ means take the sum of the values. The mean is equal to the sum of all the measurements divided by the number of measurements. For the acetaminophen results given previously, the mean is

$$\bar{x} = \frac{428 + 479 + 442 + 435}{4} = 446 \text{ mg}$$

The median is the value that lies in the middle among the results. Half of the measurements are above the median and half are below the median. For results of 465 mg, 485 mg, and 492 mg, the median is 485 mg. When there is an even number of results, the median is the average of the two middle results. For the acetaminophen results, the median is

$$\frac{442 + 435}{2} = 438 \text{ mg}$$

There are several advantages to using the median. If a small number of measurements is made, one value can greatly affect the mean. Consider the results for the analysis of acetaminophen: 428 mg, 479 mg, 442 mg, and 435 mg. The mean is 446 mg, which is larger than three of the four weights. The median is 438 mg, which lies near the three values that are relatively close to one another.

In addition to expressing an average value for a series of results, we must also express the uncertainty. This usually means expressing either the precision of the measurements or the observed range of the measurements. The range of a series of measurements is defined by the smallest value and the largest value. For the analytical results on the acetaminophen tablets, the range is from 428 mg to 479 mg. Using this range, we can express the results by saying that the true value lies between 428 mg and 479 mg. That is, we can express the amount of acetaminophen in a typical tablet as 446 ± 33 mg, where the error limit is chosen to give the observed range (approximately).

The most common way to specify precision is by the standard deviation, s, which for a small number of measurements is given by the formula

$$s = \left[\frac{\sum\limits_{i=1}^{n} (x_i - \bar{x})^2}{n-1} \right]^{1/2}$$

where x_i is an individual result, $\bar{x}$ is the average (either mean or median), and n is the total number of measurements. For the acetaminophen example, we have

$$s = \left[\frac{(428 - 446)^2 + (479 - 446)^2 + (442 - 446)^2 + (435 - 446)^2}{4 - 1} \right]^{1/2} = 23$$

Thus we can say the amount of acetaminophen in the typical tablet in the batch of tablets is 446 mg with a sample standard deviation of 23 mg. Statistically this means that any additional measurement has a 68% probability (68 chances out of 100) of being between 423 mg (446 − 23) and 469 mg (446 + 23). Thus the standard deviation is a measure of the precision of a given type of determination.

The standard deviation gives us a means of describing the precision of a given type of determination using a series of replicate results. However, it is also useful to be able to estimate the precision of a procedure that involves several measurements by combining the precisions of the individual steps. That is, we want to answer the following question: How do the uncertainties propagate when we combine the results of several different types of measurements? There are many ways to deal with the propagation of uncertainty. We will discuss only one simple method here.

A Simplified Method for Estimating Experimental Uncertainty

To illustrate this method, we will consider the determination of the density of an irregularly shaped solid. In this determination we make three measurements. First, we measure the mass of the object on a balance. Next, we must obtain the volume of the solid. The easiest method for doing this is to partially fill a graduated cylinder with a liquid and record the volume. Then we add the solid and record the volume again. The difference in the measured volumes is the volume of the solid. We can then calculate the density of the solid from the equation

$$D = \frac{M}{V_2 - V_1}$$

where M is the mass of the solid, V_1 is the initial volume of liquid in the graduated cylinder, and V_2 is the volume of liquid plus solid. Suppose we get the following results:

$$M = 23.06 \text{ g}$$
$$V_1 = 10.4 \text{ mL}$$
$$V_2 = 13.5 \text{ mL}$$

The calculated density is

$$\frac{23.06 \text{ g}}{13.5 \text{ mL} - 10.4 \text{ mL}} = 7.44 \text{ g/mL}$$

Now suppose that the precision of the balance used is ±0.02 g and that the volume measurements are precise to ±0.05 mL. How do we estimate the uncertainty of the density? We can do this by assuming a worst case. That is, we assume the largest uncertainties in all measurements, and see what combinations of measurements will give the largest and smallest possible results (the greatest range). Since the density is the mass divided by the volume, the largest value of the density will be that obtained using the largest possible mass and the smallest possible volume:

Largest possible mass = 23.06 + .02

$$D_{max} = \frac{23.08}{13.45 - 10.45} = 7.69 \text{ g/mL}$$

Smallest possible V_2 Largest possible V_1

The smallest value of the density is

Smallest possible mass

$$D_{min} = \frac{23.04}{13.55 - 10.35} = 7.20 \text{ g/mL}$$

Largest possible V_2 Smallest possible V_1

Thus, the calculated range is from 7.20 to 7.69 and the average of these values is 7.44. The error limit is the number that gives the high and low range values when added and subtracted from the average. Therefore we can express the density as 7.44 ± 0.25 g/mL, which is the average value plus or minus the quantity that gives the range calculated by assuming the largest uncertainties.

Analysis of the propagation of uncertainties is useful in drawing qualitative conclusions from the analysis of measurements. For example, suppose that we obtained the above results for the density of an unknown alloy and we want to know if it is one of the following alloys:

Alloy A: $D = 7.58$ g/mL

Alloy B: $D = 7.42$ g/mL

Alloy C: $D = 8.56$ g/mL

We can safely conclude that the alloy is not C. But the values of the densities for alloys A and B are both within the inherent uncertainty of our method. To distinguish between A and B, we need to improve the precision of our determination: the obvious choice is to improve the precision of the volume measurement.

The worst case method is very useful in estimating uncertainties when the results of several measurements are combined to calculate a result. We assume the maximum uncertainty in each measurement and calculate the minimum and maximum possible result. These extreme values describe the range and thus the error limit.

Appendix Two The Quantitative Kinetic Molecular Model

We have seen that the kinetic molecular model successfully accounts for the properties of an ideal gas. This appendix will show in some detail how the postulates of the kinetic molecular model lead to an equation corresponding to the experimentally obtained ideal gas equation.

Recall that the particles of an ideal gas are assumed to be volumeless, to have no attraction for each other, and to produce pressure on their container by colliding with the container walls.

Suppose there are n moles of an ideal gas in a cubical container with sides each of length L. Assume each gas particle has a mass m and that it is in rapid, random, straight-line motion colliding with the walls, as shown in Fig. A.3. The collisions will be assumed to be *elastic*—no loss of kinetic energy occurs. We want to compute the force on the walls from the colliding gas particles and then, since pressure is force per unit area, to obtain an expression for the pressure of the gas.

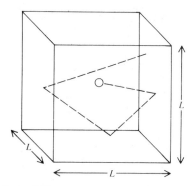

Figure A.3

An ideal gas particle in a cube whose sides are of length L. The particle collides elastically with the walls in a random, straight-line motion.

Figure A.4

(a) The Cartesian coordinate axes.

(b) The velocity u of any gas particle can be broken down into three mutually perpendicular components, u_x, u_y, and u_z. This can be represented as a rectangular solid with sides u_x, u_y, and u_z and body diagonal u.

(c) In the xy plane,
$$u_x^2 + u_y^2 = u_{xy}^2$$
by the Pythagorean theorem. Since u_{xy} and u_z are also perpendicular,
$$u^2 = u_{xy}^2 + u_z^2 = u_x^2 + u_y^2 + u_z^2$$

Before we can derive the expression for the pressure of a gas, we must first discuss some characteristics of velocity. Each particle in the gas has a particular velocity, u, which can be broken into components u_x, u_y, and u_z, as shown in Fig. A.4. First, using u_x and u_y and the Pythagorean theorem, we can obtain u_{xy} as shown in Fig. A.4(c):

$$u_{xy}^2 = u_x^2 + u_y^2$$

Hypotenuse of   Sides of
right triangle   right triangle

Then, constructing another triangle as shown in Fig. A.4(c), we find

$$u^2 = u_{xy}^2 + u_z^2$$

or

$$u^2 = u_x^2 + u_y^2 + u_z^2$$

Now let's consider how an "average" gas particle moves. For example, how often does this particle strike the two walls of the box that are perpendicular to the x axis? It is important to realize that only the x component of the velocity affects the particle's impacts on these two walls, as shown in Fig. A.5(a) on the next page. The larger the x component of the velocity, the faster the particle travels between these two walls, and the more impacts per unit of time it will make on these walls. Remember, the pressure of the gas is due to these collisions with the walls.

The collision frequency (collisions per unit of time) with the two walls that are

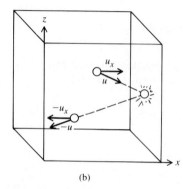

Figure A.5

(a) Only the *x* component of the gas particle's velocity affects the frequency of impacts on the shaded walls, the walls that are perpendicular to the *x* axis. (b) For an elastic collision, there is an exact reversal of the *x* component of the velocity and of the total velocity. The change in momentum (final − initial) is then

$$-mu_x - mu_x = -2mu_x$$

perpendicular to the *x* axis is given by

$$(\text{collision frequency})_x = \frac{\text{velocity in the } x \text{ direction}}{\text{distance between the walls}}$$

$$= \frac{u_x}{L}$$

Next, what is the force of a collision? Force is defined as mass times acceleration (change in velocity per unit of time):

$$F = ma = m\left(\frac{\Delta u}{\Delta t}\right)$$

where *F* represents force, *a* represents acceleration, Δu represents a change in velocity, and Δt represents a given length of time.

Since we assume that the particle has constant mass, we can write

$$F = \frac{m\Delta u}{\Delta t} = \frac{\Delta(mu)}{\Delta t}$$

The quantity *mu* is the momentum of the particle (momentum is the product of mass and velocity), and the expression $F = \Delta(mu)/\Delta t$ implies that force is the change in momentum per unit of time. When a particle hits a wall perpendicular to the *x* axis, as shown in Fig. A.5(b), an elastic collision results in an *exact reversal* of the *x* component of velocity. That is, the *sign*, or direction, of u_x reverses when the particle collides with one of the walls perpendicular to the *x* axis. Thus, the final momentum is the *negative*, or opposite, of the initial momentum. Remember that an elastic collision means that there is no change in the *magnitude* of the velocity. The change in momentum in the *x* direction is then

Change in momentum = $\Delta(mu_x)$ = final momentum − initial momentum

$$= \underset{\substack{\text{Final} \\ \text{momentum} \\ \text{in } x \text{ direction}}}{-mu_x} - \underset{\substack{\text{Initial} \\ \text{momentum} \\ \text{in } x \text{ direction}}}{mu_x}$$

$$= -2mu_x$$

But we are interested in the force the gas particle exerts on the walls of the box. Since we know that every action produces an equal but opposite reaction, the change in momentum with respect to the wall on impact is $-(-2mu_x)$, or $2mu_x$.

Recall that since force is the change in momentum per unit of time,

$$\text{Force}_x = \frac{\Delta(mu_x)}{\Delta t}$$

for the walls perpendicular to the *x* axis.

This expression can be obtained by multiplying the change in momentum per impact by the number of impacts per unit of time:

$$\text{Force}_x = \underset{\substack{\text{Change in} \\ \text{momentum per impact}}}{(2mu_x)} \underset{\substack{\text{Impacts per} \\ \text{unit of time}}}{\left(\frac{u_x}{L}\right)} = \text{Change in momentum per unit of time}$$

That is,

$$\text{Force}_x = \frac{2mu_x^2}{L}$$

So far, we have considered only the two walls of the box perpendicular to the x axis. We can assume that the force on the two walls perpendicular to the y axis is given by

$$\text{Force}_y = \frac{2mu_y^2}{L}$$

and that on the two walls perpendicular to the z axis by

$$\text{Force}_z = \frac{2mu_z^2}{L}$$

Since we have shown that

$$u^2 = u_x^2 + u_y^2 + u_z^2$$

the total force on the box is

$$\text{Force}_{\text{TOTAL}} = \text{Force}_x + \text{Force}_y + \text{Force}_z$$

$$= \frac{2mu_x^2}{L} + \frac{2mu_y^2}{L} + \frac{2mu_z^2}{L}$$

$$= \frac{2m}{L}(u_x^2 + u_y^2 + u_z^2) = \frac{2m}{L}(u^2)$$

Now since we want the average force, we use the average of the square of the velocity $(\overline{u^2})$ to obtain

$$\overline{\text{Force}_{\text{TOTAL}}} = \frac{2m}{L}(\overline{u^2})$$

Next, we need to compute the pressure (force per unit of area)

$$\text{Pressure due to ``average'' particle} = \frac{\overline{\text{Force}_{\text{TOTAL}}}}{\text{Area}_{\text{TOTAL}}}$$

$$= \frac{\dfrac{2m\overline{u^2}}{L}}{6L^2} = \frac{m\overline{u^2}}{3L^3}$$

The 6 sides of the cube   Area of each side

Since the volume V of the cube is equal to L^3, we can write

$$\text{Pressure} = P = \frac{m\overline{u^2}}{3V}$$

So far we have considered the pressure on the walls due to a single, "average" particle. Of course, we want the pressure due to the entire gas sample. The number of particles in a given gas sample can be expressed as follows:

$$\text{Number of gas particles} = nN_A$$

where n is the number of moles and N_A is Avogadro's number.

The total pressure on the box due to n moles of a gas is therefore

$$P = nN_A \frac{m\overline{u^2}}{3V}$$

Next we want to express the pressure in terms of the kinetic energy of the gas molecules. Kinetic energy (the energy due to motion) is given by $\frac{1}{2}mu^2$ where m is the mass and u the velocity. Since we are using the average of the velocity squared ($\overline{u^2}$), and since $m\overline{u^2} = 2(\frac{1}{2}m\overline{u^2})$, we have

$$P = \left(\frac{2}{3}\right) \frac{nN_A(\frac{1}{2}m\overline{u^2})}{V}$$

or

$$\frac{PV}{n} = \left(\frac{2}{3}\right) N_A(\frac{1}{2}m\overline{u^2})$$

Thus, based on the postulates of the kinetic molecular model, we have been able to derive an equation that has the same form as the ideal gas equation,

$$\frac{PV}{n} = RT$$

This agreement between experiment and theory supports the validity of the assumptions made in the kinetic molecular model about the behavior of gas particles, at least for the limiting case of an ideal gas.

Appendix Three **Spectral Analysis**

Although volumetric and gravimetric analyses are still very commonly used, spectroscopy is the technique most often used for modern chemical analysis. *Spectroscopy* is the study of electromagnetic radiation emitted or absorbed by a given chemical species. Since the quantity of radiation absorbed or emitted can be related to the quantity of the absorbing or emitting species present, this technique can be used for quantitative analysis. There are many spectroscopic techniques, since electromagnetic radiation spans a wide range of energies to include X rays, ultraviolet, infrared, and visible light, and microwaves, to name a few of its familiar forms. However, we will consider here only one procedure, which is based on the absorption of visible light.

If a liquid is colored, it is because some component of the liquid absorbs visible light. In a solution the greater the concentration of the light-absorbing substance, the more light is absorbed, and the more intense the color of the solution.

The quantity of light absorbed by a substance can be measured by a *spectrophotometer*, shown schematically in Fig. A.6. This instrument consists of a source that emits all wavelengths of light in the visible region (wavelengths of $\sim$400–700 nm); a monochromator, which selects a given wavelength of light; a sample holder for the solution being measured; and a detector, which compares the intensity of incident light, I_0, to the intensity of light after it has passed through the sample, I. The ratio I/I_0, called the *transmittance*, is a measure of the fraction of light that passes

Figure A.6

A schematic diagram of a simple spectrophotometer. The source emits all wavelengths of visible light, which are dispersed using a prism or grating and then focused, one wavelength at a time, onto the sample. The detector compares the intensity of the incident light (I_0) to the intensity of the light after it has passed through the sample (I).

through the sample. The amount of light absorbed is given by the *absorbance, A,* where

$$A = -\log \frac{I}{I_0}$$

The absorbance can be expressed by the *Beer-Lambert law:*

$$A = \epsilon l c$$

where ϵ is the molar absorptivity or the molar extinction coefficient (in L/mol cm), l is the distance the light travels through the solution (in cm), and c is the concentration of the absorbing species (in mol/L). The Beer-Lambert law is the basis for using spectroscopy in quantitative analysis. If ϵ and l are known, measuring A for a solution allows us to calculate the concentration of the absorbing species in the solution.

Suppose we have a pink solution containing an unknown concentration of $Co^{2+}(aq)$ ions. A sample of this solution is placed in a spectrophotometer, and the absorbance is measured at a wavelength where ϵ for $Co^{2+}(aq)$ is known to be 12 L/mol cm. The absorbance A is found to be 0.60. The width of the sample tube is 1.0 cm. We want to determine the concentration of $Co^{2+}(aq)$ in the solution. This problem can be solved by a straightforward application of the Beer-Lambert law,

$$A = \epsilon l c$$

where

$$A = 0.60$$

$$\epsilon = \frac{12 \text{ L}}{\text{mol cm}}$$

$$l = \text{light path} = 1.0 \text{ cm}$$

Solving for the concentration gives

$$c = \frac{A}{\epsilon l} = \frac{0.60}{\left(12 \dfrac{\text{L}}{\text{mol cm}}\right)(1.0 \text{ cm})} = 5.0 \times 10^{-2} \text{ mol/}L$$

To obtain the unknown concentration of an absorbing species from the measured absorbance, we must know the product ϵl, since

$$c = \frac{A}{\epsilon l}$$

We can obtain the product ϵl by measuring the absorbance of a solution of *known* concentration, since

Measured using a spectrophotometer

$$\epsilon l = \frac{A}{c}$$

Known from making up the solution

However, a more accurate value of the product ϵl can be obtained by plotting A versus c for a series of solutions. Note that the equation $A = \epsilon l c$ gives a straight line with slope ϵl when A is plotted against c.

For example, consider the following typical spectroscopic analysis. A sample of steel from a bicycle frame is to be analyzed to determine its manganese content. The procedure involves weighing out a sample of the steel, dissolving it in strong acid, treating the resulting solution with a very strong oxidizing agent to convert all the manganese to permanganate ion (MnO_4^-), and then using spectroscopy to determine the concentration of the intensely purple MnO_4^- ions in the solution. To do this, however, the value of ϵl for MnO_4^- must be determined at an appropriate wavelength. The absorbance values for four solutions with known MnO_4^- concentrations were measured to give the following data:

Solution	Concentration of MnO_4^- (mol/L)	Absorbance
1	7.00×10^{-5}	0.175
2	1.00×10^{-4}	0.250
3	2.00×10^{-4}	0.500
4	3.50×10^{-4}	0.875

A plot of absorbance versus concentration for the solutions of known concentration is shown in Fig. A.7. The slope of this line (change in A/change in c) is 2.48×10^3 L/mol. This quantity represents the product ϵl.

A sample of the steel weighing 0.1523 g was dissolved and the unknown amount of manganese was converted to MnO_4^- ions. Water was then added to give a solution with a final volume of 100.0 mL. A portion of this solution was placed in a spectrophotometer, and its absorbance was found to be 0.780. Using these data, we want to calculate the percent manganese in the steel. The MnO_4^- ions from the manganese in the dissolved steel sample show an absorbance of 0.780. Using the Beer-Lambert law, we calculate the concentration of MnO_4^- in this solution:

$$c = \frac{A}{\epsilon l} = \frac{0.780}{2.48 \times 10^3 \text{ L/mol}} = 3.15 \times 10^{-4} \text{ mol/L}$$

There is a more direct way for finding c. Using a graph such as that in Fig. A.7

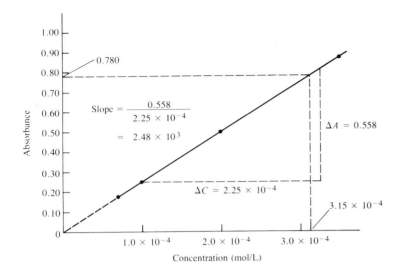

Figure A.7

A plot of absorbance versus concentration of MnO_4^- in a series of solutions of known concentration.

(often called a Beer's law plot), we can read the concentration that corresponds to $A = 0.780$. This interpolation is shown by dashed lines on the graph. By this method, $c = 3.15 \times 10^{-4}$ mol/L, which agrees with the value obtained above.

Recall that the original 0.1523-g steel sample was dissolved, the manganese was converted to permanganate, and the volume was adjusted to 100.0 mL. We now know that the $[MnO_4^-]$ in that solution is 3.15×10^{-4} M. Using this concentration, we can calculate the total number of moles of MnO_4^- in that solution:

$$\text{mol of } MnO_4^- = 100.0 \text{ mL} \times \frac{1 \text{ L}}{1000 \text{ mL}} \times 3.15 \times 10^{-4} \frac{\text{mol}}{\text{L}}$$

$$= 3.15 \times 10^{-5} \text{ mol}$$

Since each mole of manganese in the original steel sample yields a mole of MnO_4^-, that is,

$$1 \text{ mol of Mn} \xrightarrow{\text{Oxidation}} 1 \text{ mol of } MnO_4^-$$

the original steel sample must have contained 3.15×10^{-5} mol of manganese. The mass of manganese present in the sample is

$$3.15 \times 10^{-5} \text{ mol of Mn} \times \frac{54.938 \text{ g of Mn}}{1 \text{ mol of Mn}} = 1.73 \times 10^{-3} \text{ g of Mn}$$

Since the steel sample weighed 0.1523 g, the percent manganese in the steel is

$$\frac{1.73 \times 10^{-3} \text{ g of Mn}}{1.523 \times 10^{-1} \text{ g of sample}} \times 100 = 1.14\%$$

This example illustrates a typical use of spectroscopy in quantitative analysis. The steps commonly involved are as follows:

1. Preparation of a calibration plot (a Beer's law plot) by measuring the absorbance values of a series of solutions with known concentrations.

2. Measurement of the absorbance of the solution of unknown concentration.

3. Use of the calibration plot to determine the unknown concentration.

Appendix Four *Selected Thermodynamic Data*

Note: All values are assumed precise to at least ±1.

Substance and state	ΔH_f° (kJ/mol)	ΔG_f° (kJ/mol)	S° (J/K · mol)
Aluminum			
Al(s)	0	0	28
Al₂O₃(s)	−1676	−1582	51
Al(OH)₃(s)	−1277		
AlCl₃(s)	−704	−629	111
Barium			
Ba(s)	0	0	67
BaCO₃(s)	−1219	−1139	112
BaO(s)	−582	−552	70
Ba(OH)₂(s)	−946		
BaSO₄(s)	−1465	−1353	132
Beryllium			
Be(s)	0	0	10
BeO(s)	−599	−569	14
Be(OH)₂(s)	−904	−815	47
Bromine			
Br₂(l)	0	0	152
Br₂(g)	31	3	245
Br₂(aq)	−3	4	130
Br⁻(aq)	−121	−104	82
HBr(g)	−36	−53	199
Cadmium			
Cd(s)	0	0	52
CdO(s)	−258	−228	55
Cd(OH)₂(s)	−561	−474	96
CdS(s)	−162	−156	65
CdSO₄(s)	−935	−823	123
Calcium			
Ca(s)	0	0	41
CaC₂(s)	−63	−68	70
CaCO₃(s)	−1207	−1129	93
CaO(s)	−635	−604	40
Ca(OH)₂(s)	−987	−899	83
Ca₃(PO₄)₂(s)	−4126	−3890	241
CaSO₄(s)	−1433	−1320	107
CaSiO₃(s)	−1630	−1550	84
Carbon			
C(s) (graphite)	0	0	6
C(s) (diamond)	2	3	2
CO(g)	−110.5	−137	198
CO₂(g)	−393.5	−394	214
CH₄(g)	−75	−51	186
CH₃OH(g)	−201	−163	240
CH₃OH(l)	−239	−166	127
H₂CO(g)	−116	−110	219
HCOOH(g)	−363	−351	249

Substance and state	ΔH_f° (kJ/mol)	ΔG_f° (kJ/mol)	S° (J/K · mol)
Carbon, *continued*			
HCN(g)	135.1	125	202
C₂H₂(g)	227	209	201
C₂H₄(g)	52	68	219
CH₃CHO(g)	−166	−129	250
C₂H₅OH(l)	−278	−175	161
C₂H₆(g)	−84.7	−32.9	229.5
C₃H₆(g)	20.9	62.7	266.9
C₃H₈(g)	−104	−24	270
C₂H₄O(g) (ethylene oxide)	−53	−13	242
CH₂=CHCN(g)	185.0	195.4	274
CH₃COOH(l)	−484	−389	160
C₆H₁₂O₆(s)	−1275	−911	212
CCl₄	−135	−65	216
Chlorine			
Cl₂(g)	0	0	223
Cl₂(aq)	−23	7	121
Cl⁻(aq)	−167	−131	57
HCl(g)	−92	−95	187
Chromium			
Cr(s)	0	0	24
Cr₂O₃(s)	−1128	−1047	81
CrO₃(s)	−579	−502	72
Copper			
Cu(s)	0	0	33
CuCO₃(s)	−595	−518	88
Cu₂O(s)	−170	−148	93
CuO(s)	−156	−128	43
Cu(OH)₂(s)	−450	−372	108
CuS(s)	−49	−49	67
Fluorine			
F₂(g)	0	0	203
F⁻(aq)	−333	−279	−14
HF(g)	−271	−273	174
Hydrogen			
H₂(g)	0	0	131
H(g)	217	203	115
H⁺(aq)	0	0	0
OH⁻(aq)	−230	−157	−11
H₂O(l)	−286	−237	70
H₂O(g)	−242	−229	189
Iodine			
I₂(s)	0	0	116
I₂(g)	62	19	261
I₂(aq)	23	16	137
I⁻(aq)	−55	−52	106

Appendix Four (continued)

Substance and state	ΔH_f° (kJ/mol)	ΔG_f° (kJ/mol)	S° (J/K · mol)
Iron			
Fe(s)	0	0	27
Fe$_3$C(s)	21	15	108
Fe$_{0.95}$O(s) (wustite)	−264	−240	59
FeO	−272	−255	61
Fe$_3$O$_4$(s) (magnetite)	−1117	−1013	146
Fe$_2$O$_3$(s) (hematite)	−826	−740	90
FeS(s)	−95	−97	67
FeS$_2$(s)	−178	−166	53
FeSO$_4$(s)	−929	−825	121
Lead			
Pb(s)	0	0	65
PbO$_2$(s)	−277	−217	69
PbS(s)	−100	−99	91
PbSO$_4$(s)	−920	−813	149
Magnesium			
Mg(s)	0	0	33
MgCO$_3$(s)	−1113	−1029	66
MgO(s)	−602	−569	27
Mg(OH)$_2$(s)	−925	−834	64
Manganese			
Mn(s)	0	0	32
MnO(s)	−385	−363	60
Mn$_3$O$_4$(s)	−1387	−1280	149
Mn$_2$O$_3$(s)	−971	−893	110
MnO$_2$(s)	−521	−466	53
MnO$_4^-$(aq)	−543	−449	190
Mercury			
Hg(l)	0	0	76
Hg$_2$Cl$_2$(s)	−265	−211	196
HgCl$_2$(s)	−230	−184	144
HgO(s)	−90	−59	70
HgS(s)	−58	−49	78
Nickel			
Ni(s)	0	0	30
NiCl$_2$(s)	−316	−272	107
NiO(s)	−241	−213	38
Ni(OH)$_2$(s)	−538	−453	79
NiS(s)	−93	−90	53
Nitrogen			
N$_2$(g)	0	0	192
NH$_3$(g)	−46	−17	193
NH$_3$(aq)	−80	−27	111
NH$_4^+$(aq)	−132	−79	113
NO(g)	90	87	211
NO$_2$(g)	34	52	240

Substance and state	ΔH_f° (kJ/mol)	ΔG_f° (kJ/mol)	S° (J/K · mol)
Nitrogen, *continued*			
N$_2$O(g)	82	104	220
N$_2$O$_4$(g)	10	98	304
N$_2$O$_4$(l)	−20	97	209
N$_2$O$_5$(s)	−42	134	178
N$_2$H$_4$(l)	51	149	121
N$_2$H$_3$CH$_3$(l)	54	180	166
HNO$_3$(aq)	−207	−111	146
HNO$_3$(l)	−174	−81	156
NH$_4$ClO$_4$(s)	−295	−89	186
NH$_4$Cl(s)	−314	−203	96
Oxygen			
O$_2$(g)	0	0	205
O(g)	249	232	161
O$_3$(g)	143	163	239
Phosphorus			
P(s) (white)	0	0	41
P(s) (red)	−18	−12	23
P(s) (black)	−39	−33	23
P$_4$(g)	59	24	280
PF$_5$(g)	−1578	−1509	296
PH$_3$(g)	5	13	210
H$_3$PO$_4$(s)	−1279	−1119	110
H$_3$PO$_4$(l)	−1267	—	—
H$_3$PO$_4$(aq)	−1288	−1143	158
P$_4$O$_{10}$(s)	−2984	−2698	229
Potassium			
K(s)	0	0	64
KCl(s)	−436	−408	83
KClO$_3$(s)	−391	−290	143
KClO$_4$(s)	−433	−304	151
K$_2$O(s)	−361	−322	98
K$_2$O$_2$(s)	−496	−430	113
KO$_2$(s)	−283	−238	117
KOH(s)	−425	−379	79
KOH(aq)	−481	−440	9.20
Silicon			
SiO$_2$(s) (quartz)	−911	−856	42
SiCl$_4$(l)	−687	−620	240
Silver			
Ag(s)	0	0	43
Ag$^+$(aq)	105	77	73
AgBr(s)	−100	−97	107
AgCN(s)	146	164	84
AgCl(s)	−127	−110	96
Ag$_2$CrO$_4$(s)	−712	−622	217
AgI(s)	−62	−66	115
Ag$_2$O(s)	−31	−11	122
Ag$_2$S(s)	−32	−40	146

Appendix Four (continued)

Substance and state	ΔH_f° (kJ/mol)	ΔG_f° (kJ/mol)	S° (J/K · mol)
Sodium			
Na(s)	0	0	51
Na$^+$(aq)	−240	−262	59
NaBr(s)	−360	−347	84
Na$_2$CO$_3$(s)	−1131	−1048	136
NaHCO$_3$(s)	−948	−852	102
NaCl(s)	−411	−384	72
NaH(s)	−56	−33	40
NaI(s)	−288	−282	91
NaNO$_2$(s)	−359		
NaNO$_3$(s)	−467	−366	116
Na$_2$O(s)	−416	−377	73
Na$_2$O$_2$(s)	−515	−451	95
NaOH(s)	−427	−381	64
NaOH(aq)	−470	−419	50
Sulfur			
S(s) (rhombic)	0	0	32
S(s) (monoclinic)	0.3	0.1	33
S^{2-}(aq)	33	86	−15
S$_8$(g)	102	50	431
SF$_6$(g)	−1209	−1105	292
H$_2$S(g)	−21	−34	206
SO$_2$(g)	−297	−300	248
SO$_3$(g)	−396	−371	257
SO$_4^{2-}$(aq)	−909	−745	20
H$_2$SO$_4$(l)	−814	−690	157
H$_2$SO$_4$(aq)	−909	−745	20
Tin			
Sn(s) (white)	0	0	52
Sn(s) (gray)	−2	0.1	44

Substance and state	ΔH_f° (kJ/mol)	ΔG_f° (kJ/mol)	S° (J/K · mol)
Tin, *continued*			
SnO(s)	−285	−257	56
SnO$_2$(s)	−581	−520	52
Sn(OH)$_2$(s)	−561	−492	155
Titanium			
TiCl$_4$(g)	−763	−727	355
TiO$_2$(s)	−945	−890	50
Uranium			
U(s)	0	0	50
UF$_6$(s)	−2137	−2008	228
UF$_6$(g)	−2113	−2029	380
UO$_2$(s)	−1084	−1029	78
U$_3$O$_8$(s)	−3575	−3393	282
UO$_3$(s)	−1230	−1150	99
Xenon			
Xe(g)	0	0	170
XeF$_2$(g)	−108	−48	254
XeF$_4$(s)	−251	−121	146
XeF$_6$(g)	−294		
XeO$_3$(s)	402		
Zinc			
Zn(s)	0	0	42
ZnO(s)	−348	−318	44
Zn(OH)$_2$(s)	−642		
ZnS(s) (wurtzite)	−193		
ZnS(s) (zinc blende)	−206	−201	58
ZnSO$_4$(s)	−983	−874	120

Appendix Five Equilibrium Constants and Reduction Potentials

A5.1 Values of K_a for Some Common Monoprotic Acids

Name	Formula	Value of K_a
Hydrogen sulfate ion	HSO_4^-	1.2×10^{-2}
Chlorous acid	$HClO_2$	1.2×10^{-2}
Monochloracetic acid	$HC_2H_2ClO_2$	1.35×10^{-3}
Hydrofluoric acid	HF	7.2×10^{-4}
Nitrous acid	HNO_2	4.0×10^{-4}
Formic acid	HCO_2H	1.8×10^{-4}
Lactic acid	$HC_3H_5O_3$	1.38×10^{-4}
Benzoic acid	$HC_7H_5O_2$	6.4×10^{-5}
Acetic acid	$HC_2H_3O_2$	1.8×10^{-5}
Hydrated aluminum(III) ion	$[Al(H_2O)_6]^{3+}$	1.4×10^{-5}
Propanoic acid	$HC_3H_5O_2$	1.3×10^{-5}
Hypochlorous acid	$HOCl$	3.5×10^{-8}
Hypobromous acid	$HOBr$	2×10^{-9}
Hydrocyanic acid	HCN	6.2×10^{-10}
Boric acid	H_3BO_3	5.8×10^{-10}
Ammonium ion	NH_4^+	5.6×10^{-10}
Phenol	HOC_6H_5	1.6×10^{-10}
Hypoiodous acid	HOI	2×10^{-11}

A5.2 Stepwise Dissociation Constants for Several Common Polyprotic Acids

Name	Formula	K_{a_1}	K_{a_2}	K_{a_3}
Phosphoric acid	H_3PO_4	7.5×10^{-3}	6.2×10^{-8}	4.8×10^{-13}
Arsenic acid	H_3AsO_4	5×10^{-3}	8×10^{-8}	6×10^{-10}
Carbonic acid	H_2CO_3	4.3×10^{-7}	5.6×10^{-11}	
Sulfuric acid	H_2SO_4	Large	1.2×10^{-2}	
Sulfurous acid	H_2SO_3	1.5×10^{-2}	1.0×10^{-7}	
Hydrosulfuric acid	H_2S	1.0×10^{-7}	1.3×10^{-13}	
Oxalic acid	$H_2C_2O_4$	6.5×10^{-2}	6.1×10^{-5}	
Ascorbic acid (Vitamin C)	$H_2C_6H_6O_6$	7.9×10^{-5}	1.6×10^{-12}	
Citric acid	$H_3C_6H_5O_7$	8.4×10^{-4}	1.8×10^{-5}	4.0×10^{-6}

A5.3 Values of K_b for Some Common Weak Bases

Name	Formula	Conjugate acid	K_b
Ammonia	NH_3	NH_4^+	1.8×10^{-5}
Methylamine	CH_3NH_2	$CH_3NH_3^+$	4.38×10^{-4}
Ethylamine	$C_2H_5NH_2$	$C_2H_5NH_3^+$	5.6×10^{-4}
Diethylamine	$(C_2H_5)_2NH$	$(C_2H_5)_2NH_2^+$	1.3×10^{-3}
Triethylamine	$(C_2H_5)_3N$	$(C_2H_5)_3NH^+$	4.0×10^{-4}
Hydroxylamine	$HONH_2$	$HONH_3^+$	1.1×10^{-8}
Hydrazine	H_2NNH_2	$H_2NNH_3^+$	3.0×10^{-6}
Aniline	$C_6H_5NH_2$	$C_6H_5NH_3^+$	3.8×10^{-10}
Pyridine	C_5H_5N	$C_5H_5NH^+$	1.7×10^{-9}

A5.4 K_{sp} Values at 25°C for Common Ionic Solids

Ionic solid	K_{sp} (at 25°C)	Ionic solid	K_{sp} (at 25°C)	Ionic solid	K_{sp} (at 25°C)
Fluorides		Hg_2CrO_4*	2×10^{-9}	$Co(OH)_2$	2.5×10^{-16}
BaF_2	2.4×10^{-5}	$BaCrO_4$	8.5×10^{-11}	$Ni(OH)_2$	1.6×10^{-16}
MgF_2	6.4×10^{-9}	Ag_2CrO_4	9.0×10^{-12}	$Zn(OH)_2$	4.5×10^{-17}
PbF_2	4×10^{-8}	$PbCrO_4$	2×10^{-16}	$Cu(OH)_2$	1.6×10^{-19}
SrF_2	7.9×10^{-10}			$Hg(OH)_2$	3×10^{-26}
CaF_2	4.0×10^{-11}	**Carbonates**		$Sn(OH)_2$	3×10^{-27}
		$NiCO_3$	1.4×10^{-7}	$Cr(OH)_3$	6.7×10^{-31}
Chlorides		$CaCO_3$	8.7×10^{-9}	$Al(OH)_3$	2×10^{-32}
$PbCl_2$	1.6×10^{-5}	$BaCO_3$	1.6×10^{-9}	$Fe(OH)_3$	4×10^{-38}
$AgCl$	1.6×10^{-10}	$SrCO_3$	7×10^{-10}	$Co(OH)_3$	2.5×10^{-43}
Hg_2Cl_2*	1.1×10^{-18}	$CuCO_3$	2.5×10^{-10}		
		$ZnCO_3$	2×10^{-10}	**Sulfides**	
Bromides		$MnCO_3$	8.8×10^{-11}	MnS	2.3×10^{-13}
$PbBr_2$	4.6×10^{-6}	$FeCO_3$	2.1×10^{-11}	FeS	3.7×10^{-19}
$AgBr$	5.0×10^{-13}	Ag_2CO_3	8.1×10^{-12}	NiS	3×10^{-21}
Hg_2Br_2*	1.3×10^{-22}	$CdCO_3$	5.2×10^{-12}	CoS	5×10^{-22}
		$PbCO_3$	1.5×10^{-15}	ZnS	2.5×10^{-22}
Iodides		$MgCO_3$	1×10^{-15}	SnS	1×10^{-26}
PbI_2	1.4×10^{-8}	Hg_2CO_3*	9.0×10^{-15}	CdS	1.0×10^{-28}
AgI	1.5×10^{-16}			PbS	7×10^{-29}
Hg_2I_2*	4.5×10^{-29}	**Hydroxides**		CuS	8.5×10^{-45}
		$Ba(OH)_2$	5.0×10^{-3}	Ag_2S	1.6×10^{-49}
Sulfates		$Sr(OH)_2$	3.2×10^{-4}	HgS	1.6×10^{-54}
$CaSO_4$	6.1×10^{-5}	$Ca(OH)_2$	1.3×10^{-6}		
Ag_2SO_4	1.2×10^{-5}	$AgOH$	2.0×10^{-8}	**Phosphates**	
$SrSO_4$	3.2×10^{-7}	$Mg(OH)_2$	8.9×10^{-12}	Ag_3PO_4	1.8×10^{-18}
$PbSO_4$	1.3×10^{-8}	$Mn(OH)_2$	2×10^{-13}	$Sr_3(PO_4)_2$	1×10^{-31}
$BaSO_4$	1.5×10^{-9}	$Cd(OH)_2$	5.9×10^{-15}	$Ca_3(PO_4)_2$	1.3×10^{-32}
		$Pb(OH)_2$	1.2×10^{-15}	$Ba_3(PO_4)_2$	6×10^{-39}
Chromates		$Fe(OH)_2$	1.8×10^{-15}	$Pb_3(PO_4)_2$	1×10^{-54}
$SrCrO_4$	3.6×10^{-5}				

*Contains Hg_2^{2+} ions. $K_{sp} = [Hg_2^{2+}][X^-]^2$ for Hg_2X_2 salts.

A5.5 Standard Reduction Potentials at 25°C (298 K) for Many Common Half-reactions

Half-reaction	$\mathscr{E}°$ (V)	Half-reaction	$\mathscr{E}°$ (V)
$F_2 + 2e^- \rightarrow 2F^-$	2.87	$O_2 + 2H_2O + 4e^- \rightarrow 4OH^-$	0.40
$Ag^{2+} + e^- \rightarrow Ag^+$	1.99	$Cu^{2+} + 2e^- \rightarrow Cu$	0.34
$Co^{3+} + e^- \rightarrow Co^{2+}$	1.95	$Hg_2Cl_2 + 2e^- \rightarrow 2Hg + 2Cl^-$	0.34
$H_2O_2 + 2H^+ + 2e^- \rightarrow 2H_2O$	1.78	$AgCl + e^- \rightarrow Ag + Cl^-$	0.22
$Ce^{4+} + e^- \rightarrow Ce^{3+}$	1.70	$SO_4^{2-} + 4H^+ + 2e^- \rightarrow H_2SO_3 + H_2O$	0.20
$PbO_2 + 4H^+ + SO_4^{2-} + 2e^- \rightarrow PbSO_4 + 2H_2O$	1.69	$Cu^{2+} + e^- \rightarrow Cu^+$	0.16
$MnO_4^- + 4H^+ + 3e^- \rightarrow MnO_2 + 2H_2O$	1.68	$2H^+ + 2e^- \rightarrow H_2$	0.00
$2e^- + 2H^+ + IO_4^- \rightarrow IO_3^- + H_2O$	1.60	$Fe^{3+} + 3e^- \rightarrow Fe$	−0.036
$MnO_4^- + 8H^+ + 5e^- \rightarrow Mn^{2+} + 4H_2O$	1.51	$Pb^{2+} + 2e^- \rightarrow Pb$	−0.13
$Au^{3+} + 3e^- \rightarrow Au$	1.50	$Sn^{2+} + 2e^- \rightarrow Sn$	−0.14
$PbO_2 + 4H^+ + 2e^- \rightarrow Pb^{2+} + 2H_2O$	1.46	$Ni^{2+} + 2e^- \rightarrow Ni$	−0.23
$Cl_2 + 2e^- \rightarrow 2Cl^-$	1.36	$PbSO_4 + 2e^- \rightarrow Pb + SO_4^{2-}$	−0.35
$Cr_2O_7^{2-} + 14H^+ + 6e^- \rightarrow 2Cr^{3+} + 7H_2O$	1.33	$Cd^{2+} + 2e^- \rightarrow Cd$	−0.40
$O_2 + 4H^+ + 4e^- \rightarrow 2H_2O$	1.23	$Fe^{2+} + 2e^- \rightarrow Fe$	−0.44
$MnO_2 + 4H^+ + 2e^- \rightarrow Mn^{2+} + 2H_2O$	1.21	$Cr^{3+} + e^- \rightarrow Cr^{2+}$	−0.50
$IO_3^- + 6H^+ + 5e^- \rightarrow \frac{1}{2}I_2 + 3H_2O$	1.20	$Cr^{3+} + 3e^- \rightarrow Cr$	−0.73
$Br_2 + 2e^- \rightarrow 2Br^-$	1.09	$Zn^{2+} + 2e^- \rightarrow Zn$	−0.76
$VO_2^+ + 2H^+ + e^- \rightarrow VO^{2+} + H_2O$	1.00	$2H_2O + 2e^- \rightarrow H_2 + 2OH^-$	−0.83
$AuCl_4^- + 3e^- \rightarrow Au + 4Cl^-$	0.99	$Mn^{2+} + 2e^- \rightarrow Mn$	−1.18
$NO_3^- + 4H^+ + 3e^- \rightarrow NO + 2H_2O$	0.96	$Al^{3+} + 3e^- \rightarrow Al$	−1.66
$ClO_2 + e^- \rightarrow ClO_2^-$	0.954	$H_2 + 2e^- \rightarrow 2H^-$	−2.23
$2Hg^{2+} + 2e^- \rightarrow Hg_2^{2+}$	0.91	$Mg^{2+} + 2e^- \rightarrow Mg$	−2.37
$Ag^+ + e^- \rightarrow Ag$	0.80	$La^{3+} + 3e^- \rightarrow La$	−2.37
$Hg_2^{2+} + 2e^- \rightarrow 2Hg$	0.80	$Na^+ + e^- \rightarrow Na$	−2.71
$Fe^{3+} + e^- \rightarrow Fe^{2+}$	0.77	$Ca^{2+} + 2e^- \rightarrow Ca$	−2.76
$O_2 + 2H^+ + 2e^- \rightarrow H_2O_2$	0.68	$Ba^{2+} + 2e^- \rightarrow Ba$	−2.90
$MnO_4^- + e^- \rightarrow MnO_4^{2-}$	0.56	$K^+ + e^- \rightarrow K$	−2.92
$I_2 + 2e^- \rightarrow 2I^-$	0.54	$Li^+ + e^- \rightarrow Li$	−3.05
$Cu^+ + e^- \rightarrow Cu$	0.52		

GLOSSARY

Accuracy the agreement of a particular value with the true value. (1.3)

Acid a substance that produces hydrogen ions in solution; a proton donor. (4.2)

Acid–base indicator a substance that marks the end point of an acid–base titration by changing color. (15.5)

Acid dissociation constant (K_a) the equilibrium constant for a reaction in which a proton is removed from an acid by H_2O to form the conjugate base and H_3O^+. (14.1)

Acid rain a result of air pollution by sulfur dioxide. (5.9)

Acidic oxide a covalent oxide that dissolves in water to give an acidic solution. (14.10)

Actinide series a group of fourteen elements following actinium in the periodic table, in which the $5f$ orbitals are being filled. (7.11; 18.1)

Activated complex (transition state) the arrangement of atoms found at the top of the potential energy barrier as a reaction proceeds from reactants to products. (12.7)

Activation energy the threshold energy that must be overcome to produce a chemical reaction. (12.7)

Addition polymerization a type of polymerization in which the monomers simply add together to form the polymer, with no other products. (22.6)

Addition reaction a reaction in which atoms add to a carbon-carbon multiple bond. (22.2)

Adsorption the collection of one substance on the surface of another. (12.8)

Air pollution contamination of the atmosphere, mainly by the gaseous products of transportation and production of electricity. (5.9)

Alcohol an organic compound in which the hydroxyl group is a substituent on a hydrocarbon. (22.5)

Aldehyde an organic compound containing the carbonyl group bonded to at least one hydrogen atom. (22.5)

Alkali metal a Group 1A metal. (2.7; 18.2)

Alkaline earth metal a Group 2A metal. (2.7; 18.4)

Alkane a saturated hydrocarbon with the general formula C_nH_{2n+2}. (22.1)

Alkene an unsaturated hydrocarbon containing a carbon-carbon double bond. The general formula is C_nH_{2n}. (22.2)

Alkyne an unsaturated hydrocarbon containing a triple carbon-carbon bond. The general formula is C_nH_{2n-2}. (22.2)

Alloy a substance that contains a mixture of elements and has metallic properties. (10.4)

Alloy steel a form of steel containing carbon plus other metals such as chromium, cobalt, manganese, and molybdenum. (20.9)

Alpha (α) particle a helium nucleus. (21.1)

Alpha particle production a common mode of decay for radioactive nuclides in which the mass number changes. (21.1)

Amine an organic base derived from ammonia in which one or more of the hydrogen atoms are replaced by organic groups. (14.6; 22.5)

α-Amino acid an organic acid in which an amino group and an R group are attached to the carbon atom next to the carboxyl group. (23.1)

Amorphous solid a solid with considerable disorder in its structure. (10.3)

Ampere the unit of electrical current equal to one coulomb of charge per second. (17.7)

Amphoteric substance a substance that can behave either as an acid or as a base. (14.2)

Anion a negative ion. (2.6)

Anode the electrode in a galvanic cell at which oxidation occurs. (17.1)

Antibonding molecular orbital an orbital higher in energy than the atomic orbitals of which it is composed. (9.2)

Aqueous solution a solution in which water is the dissolving medium or solvent. (4.0)

Aromatic hydrocarbon one of a special class of cyclic unsaturated hydrocarbons, the simplest of which is benzene. (22.3)

Arrhenius concept a concept postulating that acids produce hydrogen ions in aqueous solution, while bases produce hydroxide ions. (14.1)

Arrhenius equation the equation representing the rate constant as $k = Ae^{-E_a/RT}$ where A represents the product of the collision frequency and the steric factor, and $e^{-E_a/RT}$ is the fraction of collisions with sufficient energy to produce a reaction. (12.7)

Atactic chain a polymer chain in which the substituent groups such as CH_3 are randomly distributed along the chain. (22.7)

Atmosphere the mixture of gases that surrounds the earth's surface. (5.9)

Atomic number the number of protons in the nucleus of an atom. (2.5)

Atomic radius half the distance between the nuclei in a molecule consisting of identical atoms. (7.13)

Atomic solid a solid that contains atoms at the lattice points. (10.3)

Atomic weight the weighted average mass of the atoms in a naturally occurring element. (2.3)

Aufbau principle the principle stating that as protons are added one by one to the nucleus to build up the elements, electrons are similarly added to hydrogenlike orbitals. (7.11)

Autoionization the transfer of a proton from one molecule to another of the same substance. (14.2)

Avogadro's law equal volumes of gases at the same temperature and pressure contain the same number of particles. (5.2)

Avogadro's number the number of atoms in exactly 12 grams of pure ^{12}C, equal to 6.022×10^{23}. (3.2)

Azimuthal quantum number (ℓ) the quantum number relating to the shape of an atomic orbital, which can assume any integral value from 0 to $n - 1$ for each value of n. (7.6)

Ball-and-stick model a molecular model that distorts the sizes of atoms but shows bond relationships clearly. (2.6)

Band model a molecular model for metals in which the electrons are assumed to travel around the metal crystal in molecular orbitals formed from the valence atomic orbitals of the metal atoms. (10.4)

Barometer a device for measuring atmospheric pressure. (5.1)

Base a substance that produces hydroxide ions in aqueous solution, a proton acceptor. (4.2)

Base dissociation constant (K_b) the equilibrium constant for the reaction of a base with water to produce the conjugate acid and hydroxide ion. (14.6)

Basic oxide an ionic oxide that dissolves in water to produce a basic solution. (14.10)

Basic oxygen process a process for producing steel by oxidizing and removing the impurities in iron using a high-pressure blast of oxygen. (20.9)

Battery a group of galvanic cells connected in series. (17.5)

Beta (β) particle an electron produced in radioactive decay. (21.1)

Beta particle production a decay process for radioactive nuclides in which the mass number remains constant and the atomic number changes. The net effect is to change a neutron to a proton. (21.1)

Bidentate ligand a ligand that can form two bonds to a metal ion. (20.3)

Bilayer a portion of the cell membrane consisting of phospholipids with their nonpolar tails in the interior and their polar heads interfacing with the polar water molecules. (23.4)

Bimolecular step a reaction involving the collision of two molecules. (12.6)

Binary compound a two-element compound. (2.8)

Binding energy (nuclear) the energy required to decompose a nucleus into its component nucleons. (21.5)

Biochemistry the study of the chemistry of living systems. (23)

Biomolecule a molecule responsible for maintaining and/or reproducing life. (23)

Blast furnace a furnace in which iron oxide is reduced to iron metal by using a very strong blast of hot air to produce carbon monoxide from coke, and then using this gas as a reducing agent for the iron. (20.9)

Bond energy the energy required to break a given chemical bond. (8.1)

Bond length the distance between the nuclei of the two atoms connected by a bond; the distance where the total energy of a diatomic molecule is minimal. (8.1)

Bond order the difference between the number of bonding electrons and the number of antibonding electrons, divided by two. It is an index of bond strength. (9.2)

Bonding molecular orbital an orbital lower in energy than the atomic orbitals of which it is composed. (9.2)

Bonding pair an electron pair found in the space between two atoms. (8.9)

Borane a covalent hydride of boron. (18.5)

Boyle's law the volume of a given sample of gas at constant temperature varies inversely with the pressure. (5.2)

Breeder reactor a nuclear reactor in which fissionable fuel is produced while the reactor runs. (21.6)

Brønsted-Lowry model a model proposing that an acid is a proton donor, and a base is a proton acceptor. (14.1)

Buffer capacity the ability of a buffered solution to absorb protons or hydroxide ions without a significant change in pH; determined by the magnitudes of [HA] and [A$^-$] in the solution. (15.3)

Buffered solution a solution that resists a change in its pH when either hydroxide ions or protons are added. (15.2)

Calorimetry the science of measuring heat flow. (6.2)

Capillary action the spontaneous rising of a liquid in a narrow tube. (10.2)

Carbohydrate a polyhydroxyl ketone or polyhydroxyl aldehyde or a polymer composed of these. (23.2)

Carbon steel an alloy of iron containing up to about 1.5% carbon. (20.9)

Carboxyhemoglobin a stable complex of hemoglobin and carbon monoxide that prevents normal oxygen uptake in the blood. (20.8)

Carboxyl group the —COOH group in an organic acid. (14.2)

Carboxylic acid an organic compound containing the carboxyl group; an acid with the general formula RCOOH. (22.5)

Catalyst a substance that speeds up a reaction without being consumed. (12.8)

Cathode the electrode in a galvanic cell at which reduction occurs. (17.1)

Cathode rays the "rays" emanating from the negative electrode (cathode) in a partially evacuated tube; a stream of electrons. (2.4)

Cathodic protection a method in which an active metal, such as magnesium, is connected to steel in order to protect it from corrosion. (17.7)

Cation a positive ion. (2.6)

Cell potential (electromotive force) the driving force in a galvanic cell that pulls electrons from the reducing agent in one compartment to the oxidizing agent in the other. (17.1)

Ceramic a nonmetallic material made from clay and hardened by firing at high temperature; it contains minute silicate crystals suspended in a glassy cement. (10.5)

Chain reaction (nuclear) a self-sustaining fission process caused by the production of neutrons that proceed to split other nuclei. (21.6)

Charles's law the volume of a given sample of gas at constant pressure is directly proportional to the temperature in kelvins. (5.2)

Chelating ligand (chelate) a ligand having more than one atom with a lone pair that can be used to bond to a metal ion. (20.3)

Chemical bond the force or, more accurately, the energy, that holds two atoms together in a compound. (2.6)

Chemical change the change of substances into other substances through a reorganization of the atoms; a chemical reaction. (1.8)

Chemical equation a representation of a chemical reaction showing the relative numbers of reactant and product molecules. (3.6)

Chemical equilibrium a dynamic reaction system in which the concentrations of all reactants and products remain constant as a function of time. (13)

Chemical formula the representation of a molecule in which the symbols for the elements are used to indicate the types of atoms present and subscripts are used to show the relative numbers of atoms. (2.6)

Chemical kinetics the area of chemistry that concerns reaction rates. (12.1)

Chemical stoichiometry the calculation of the quantities of material consumed and produced in chemical reactions. (3)

Chirality the quality of having nonsuperimposable mirror images. (20.4)

Chlor-alkali process the process for producing chlorine and sodium hydroxide by electrolyzing brine in a mercury cell. (17.8)

Chromatography the general name for a series of methods for separating mixtures by employing a system with a mobile phase and a stationary phase. (1.9)

Coagulation the destruction of a colloid by causing particles to aggregate and settle out. (11.8)

Codons organic bases in sets of three that form the genetic code. (23.3)

Colligative properties properties of a solution that depend only on the number, and not on the identity, of the solute particles. (11.5)

Collision model a model based on the idea that molecules must collide to react; used to account for the observed characteristics of reaction rates. (12.7)

Colloid a suspension of particles in a dispersing medium. (11.8)

Combustion reaction the vigorous and exothermic reaction that takes place between certain substances, particularly organic compounds, and oxygen. (22.1)

Common ion effect the shift in an equilibrium position caused by the addition or presence of an ion involved in the equilibrium reaction. (15.1)

Complete ionic reaction an equation that shows all substances that are strong electrolytes as ions. (4.6)

Complex ion a charged species consisting of a metal ion surrounded by ligands. (15.8; 20.1)

Compound a substance with constant composition that can be broken down into elements by chemical processes. (1.8)

Concentration cell a galvanic cell in which both compartments contain the same components, but at different concentrations. (17.4)

Condensation the process by which vapor molecules reform a liquid. (10.8)

Condensation polymerization a type of polymerization in which the formation of a small molecule, such as water, accompanies the extension of the polymer chain. (22.6)

Condensation reaction a reaction in which two molecules are joined, accompanied by the elimination of a water molecule. (19.3)

Condensed states of matter liquids and solids. (10.1)

Conduction bands the molecular orbitals that can be occupied by mobile electrons, which are free to travel throughout a metal crystal to conduct electricity or heat. (10.4)

Conjugate acid the species formed when a proton is added to a base. (14.1)

Conjugate acid-base pair two species related to each other by the donating and accepting of a single proton. (14.1)

Conjugate base what remains of an acid molecule after a proton is lost. (14.1)

Continuous spectrum a spectrum that exhibits all the wavelengths of visible light. (7.3)

Control rods rods in a nuclear reactor composed of substances that absorb neutrons. These rods regulate the power level of the reactor. (21.6)

Coordinate covalent bond a metal-ligand bond resulting from the interaction of a Lewis base (the ligand) and a Lewis acid (the metal ion). (20.3)

Coordination compound a compound composed of a complex ion and counter ions sufficient to give no net charge. (20.3)

Coordination isomerism isomerism in a coordination compound in which the composition of the coordination sphere of the metal ion varies. (20.4)

Coordination number the number of bonds formed between the metal ion and the ligands in a complex ion. (20.3)

Copolymer a polymer formed from the polymerization of more than one type of monomer. (22.6)

Core electron an inner electron in an atom; one not in the outermost (valence) principal quantum level. (7.11)

Corrosion the process by which metals are oxidized in the atmosphere. (17.6)

Coulomb's law $E = 2.31 \times 10^{-19} \left(\dfrac{Q_1Q_2}{r} \right)$, where E is the energy of interaction between a pair of ions, expressed in joules; r is the distance between the ion centers in nm; and Q_1 and Q_2 are the numerical ion charges. (8.1)

Counter ions   anions or cations that balance the charge on the complex ion in a coordination compound. (20.3)

Covalent bonding   a type of bonding in which electrons are shared by atoms. (8.1)

Cracking   a process whereby large molecules of petroleum components are broken down to smaller ones by breaking carbon-carbon bonds. (22.4)

Critical mass   the mass of fissionable material required to produce a self-sustaining chain reaction. (21.6)

Critical point   the point on a phase diagram at which the temperature and pressure have their critical values; the end point of the liquid-vapor line. (10.9)

Critical pressure   the minimum pressure required to produce liquefaction of a substance at the critical temperature. (10.9)

Critical reaction (nuclear)   a reaction in which exactly one neutron from each fission event causes another fission event, thus sustaining the chain reaction. (21.6)

Critical temperature   the temperature above which vapor cannot be liquefied no matter what pressure is applied. (10.9)

Crosslinking   the existence of bonds between adjacent chains in a polymer, thus adding strength to the material. (22.7)

Crystal field model   a model used to explain the magnetism and colors of coordination complexes through the splitting of the d orbital energies. (20.6)

Crystalline solid   a solid with a regular arrangement of its components. (10.3)

Cubic closest packed structure   a solid modeled by the closest packing of spheres with an *abcabc* arrangement of layers; the unit cell is face-centered cubic. (10.4)

Cyanidation   a process in which crushed gold ore is treated with an aqueous cyanide solution in the presence of air to dissolve the gold. Pure gold is recovered by reduction of the ion to the metal. (20.9)

Cyclotron   a type of particle accelerator in which an ion introduced at the center is accelerated in an expanding spiral path by use of alternating electrical fields in the presence of a magnetic field. (21.3)

Cytochromes   a series of iron-containing species composed of heme and a protein. Cytochromes are the principal electron-transfer molecules in the respiratory chain. (20.8)

Dalton's law of partial pressures   for a mixture of gases in a container, the total pressure exerted is the sum of the pressures that each gas would exert if it were alone. (5.5)

Degenerate orbitals   a group of orbitals with the same energy. (7.7)

Dehydrogenation reaction   a reaction in which two hydrogen atoms are removed from adjacent carbons of a saturated hydrocarbon, giving an unsaturated hydrocarbon. (22.1)

Delocalization   the condition where the electrons in a molecule are not localized between a pair of atoms but can move throughout the molecule. (8.9)

Denaturation   the breaking down of the three-dimensional structure of a protein resulting in the loss of its function. (23.1)

Denitrification   the return of nitrogen from decomposed matter to the atmosphere by bacteria that change nitrates to nitrogen gas. (19.2)

Density   a property of matter representing the mass per unit volume. (1.7)

Deoxyribonucleic acid (DNA)   a huge nucleotide polymer having a double helical structure with complementary bases on the two strands. Its major functions are protein synthesis and the storage and transport of genetic information. (23.3)

Desalination   the removal of dissolved salts from an aqueous solution. (11.6)

Dialysis   a phenomenon in which a semipermeable membrane allows transfer of both solvent molecules and small solute molecules and ions. (11.6)

Diamagnetism   a type of magnetism, associated with paired electrons, that causes a substance to be repelled from the inducing magnetic field. (9.3)

Differential rate law   an expression that gives the rate of a reaction as a function of concentrations; often called the rate law. (12.2)

Diffraction   the scattering of light from a regular array of points or lines, producing constructive and destructive interference. (7.2)

Diffusion   the mixing of gases. (5.7)

Dilution   the process of adding solvent to lower the concentration of solute in a solution. (4.3)

Dimer   a molecule formed by the joining of two identical monomers. (22.6)

Dipole-dipole attraction   the attractive force resulting when polar molecules line up so that the positive and negative ends are close to each other. (10.1)

Dipole moment   a property of a molecule whose charge distribution can be represented by a center of positive charge and a center of negative charge. (8.3)

Direct reduction furnace   a furnace in which iron oxide is reduced to iron metal using milder reaction conditions than in a blast furnace. (20.9)

Disaccharide   a sugar formed from two monosaccharides joined by a glycoside linkage. (23.2)

Disproportionation reaction   a reaction in which a given element is both oxidized and reduced. (19.7)

Distillation   a method for separating the components of a liquid mixture that depends on differences in the ease of vaporization of the components. (1.9)

Disulfide linkage   an S—S bond that stabilizes the tertiary structure of many proteins. (23.1)

Double bond   a bond in which two pairs of electrons are shared by two atoms. (8.8)

Downs cell   a cell used for electrolyzing molten sodium chloride. (17.8)

Dry cell battery   a common battery used in calculators, watches, radios, and tape players. (17.5)

Dual nature of light the statement that light exhibits both wave and particulate properties. (7.2)

Effective nuclear charge the apparent nuclear charge exerted on a particular electron, equal to the actual nuclear charge minus the effect of electron repulsions. (7.9)

Effusion the passage of a gas through a tiny orifice into an evacuated chamber. (5.7)

Elastomer a material that recovers its shape after a deforming force is removed. (22.7)

Electrical conductivity the ability to conduct an electric current. (4.2)

Electrochemistry the study of the interchange of chemical and electrical energy. (17)

Electrolysis a process that involves forcing a current through a cell to cause a nonspontaneous chemical reaction to occur. (17.7)

Electrolyte a material that dissolves in water to give a solution that conducts an electric current. (4.2)

Electrolytic cell a cell that uses electrical energy to produce a chemical change that would otherwise not occur spontaneously. (17.7)

Electromagnetic radiation radiant energy that exhibits wave-like behavior and travels through space at the speed of light in a vacuum. (7.1)

Electron a negatively charged particle that moves around the nucleus of an atom. (2.4)

Electron affinity the energy change associated with the addition of an electron to a gaseous atom. (7.13)

Electron capture a process in which one of the inner-orbital electrons in an atom is captured by the nucleus. (21.1)

Electron sea model a model for metals postulating a regular array of cations in a "sea" of electrons. (10.4)

Electron spin quantum number a quantum number representing one of the two possible values for the electron spin; either $+\frac{1}{2}$ or $-\frac{1}{2}$. (7.8)

Electronegativity the tendency of an atom in a molecule to attract shared electrons to itself. (8.2)

Element a substance that cannot be decomposed into simpler substances by chemical or physical means. (1.8)

Elementary step a reaction whose rate law can be written from its molecularity. (12.6)

$E = mc^2$ Einstein's equation proposing that energy has mass; E is energy, m is mass, and c is the speed of light. (7.2)

Empirical formula the simplest whole number ratio of atoms in a compound. (3.5)

Enantiomers isomers that are nonsuperimposable mirror images of each other. (20.4)

End point the point in a titration at which the indicator changes color. (4.9)

Endothermic refers to a reaction where energy (as heat) flows into the system. (6.1)

Energy the capacity to do work or to cause heat flow. (6.1)

Enthalpy a property of a system equal to $E + PV$, where E is the internal energy of the system, P is the pressure of the system, and V is the volume of the system. At constant pressure the change in enthalpy equals the energy flow as heat. (6.2)

Enthalpy of fusion the enthalpy change that occurs to melt a solid at its melting point. (10.8)

Entropy a thermodynamic function that measures randomness or disorder. (16.1)

Enzyme a large molecule, usually a protein, that catalyzes biological reactions. (12.8; 23.1)

Equilibrium (thermodynamic definition) the position where the free energy of a reaction system has its lowest possible value. (16.8)

Equilibrium constant the value obtained when equilibrium concentrations of the chemical species are substituted in the equilibrium expression. (13.2)

Equilibrium expression the expression (from the law of mass action) obtained by multiplying the product concentrations and dividing by the multiplied reactant concentrations, with each concentration raised to a power represented by the coefficient in the balanced equation. (13.2)

Equilibrium position a particular set of equilibrium concentrations. (13.2)

Equivalence point (stoichiometric point) the point in a titration when enough titrant has been added to react exactly with the substance in solution being titrated. (4.9; 15.4)

Essential elements the elements definitely known to be essential to human life. (23)

Ester an organic compound produced by the reaction between a carboxylic acid and an alcohol. (22.5)

Exothermic refers to a reaction where energy (as heat) flows out of the system. (6.1)

Exponential notation expresses a number as $N \times 10^M$, a convenient method for representing a very large or very small number and for easily indicating the number of significant figures. (1.4)

Faraday a constant representing the charge on one mole of electrons; 96,485 coulombs. (17.3)

Fat (glyceride) an ester composed of glycerol and fatty acids. (23.4)

Fatty acid a long-chain carboxylic acid. (23.4)

Feedstock the portion of petroleum used as the raw material in a petrochemical plant; it varies from heavy hydrocarbons to light ones. (24.1)

Fermentation (as in winemaking) the conversion of sugar to ethanol using yeast. (24.5)

Filtration a method for separating the components of a mixture containing a solid and a liquid. (1.9)

First law of thermodynamics the energy of the universe is constant; same as the law of conservation of energy. (6.1)

Fission the process of using a neutron to split a heavy nucleus into two nuclei with smaller mass numbers. (21.6)

Flotation process a method of separating the mineral particles in an ore from the gangue that depends on the greater wettability of the mineral pieces. (20.9)

Formal charge the charge assigned to an atom in a molecule or polyatomic ion derived from a specific set of rules. (8.12)

Formation constant (stability constant) the equilibrium constant for each step of the formation of a complex ion by the addition of an individual ligand to a metal ion or complex ion in aqueous solution. (15.8)

Fossil fuel coal, petroleum, or natural gas; consists of carbon-based molecules derived from decomposition of once-living organisms. (6.5)

Frasch process the recovery of sulfur from underground deposits by melting it with hot water and forcing it to the surface by air pressure. (19.6)

Free energy a thermodynamic function equal to the enthalpy (H) minus the product of the entropy (S) and the Kelvin temperature (T); $G = H - TS$. Under certain conditions the change in free energy for a process is equal to the maximum useful work. (16.4)

Free radical a species with an unpaired electron. (22.6)

Frequency the number of waves (cycles) per second that pass a given point in space. (7.1)

Fuel cell a galvanic cell for which the reactants are continuously supplied. (17.5)

Functional group an atom or group of atoms in hydrocarbon derivatives that contains elements in addition to carbon and hydrogen. (22.5)

Fusion the process of combining two light nuclei to form a heavier, more stable nucleus. (21.6)

Galvanic cell a device in which chemical energy from a spontaneous redox reaction is changed to electrical energy that can be used to do work. (17.1)

Galvanizing a process in which steel is coated with zinc to prevent corrosion. (17.6)

Gamma (γ) ray a high-energy photon. (21.1)

Gangue the impurities (such as clay or sand) in an ore. (20.9)

Geiger-Müller counter (Geiger counter) an instrument that measures the rate of radioactive decay based on the ions and electrons produced as a radioactive particle passes through a gas-filled chamber. (21.4)

Gene a given segment of the DNA molecule that contains the code for a specific protein. (23.3)

Geometrical (cis-trans) isomerism isomerism in which atoms or groups of atoms can assume different positions around a rigid ring or bond. (20.4; 22.2)

Glass an amorphous solid obtained when silica is mixed with other compounds, heated above its melting point, and then cooled rapidly. (10.5)

Glass electrode an electrode for measuring pH from the potential difference that develops when it is dipped into an aqueous solution containing H^+ ions. (17.4)

Glycosidic linkage a C—O—C bond formed between the rings of two cyclic monosaccharides by the elimination of water. (23.2)

Graham's law of effusion the rate of effusion of a gas is inversely proportional to the square root of the mass of its particles. (5.7)

Greenhouse effect a warming effect exerted by the earth's atmosphere (particularly CO_2 and H_2O) due to thermal energy retained by absorption of infrared radiation. (6.5)

Ground state the lowest possible energy state of an atom or molecule. (7.4)

Group (of the periodic table) a vertical column of elements having the same valence electron configuration and showing similar properties. (2.7)

Haber process the manufacture of ammonia from nitrogen and hydrogen, carried out at high pressure and high temperature with the aid of a catalyst. (3.9; 19.2)

Half-life (of a radioactive sample) the time required for the number of nuclides in a radioactive sample to reach half of the original value. (21.2)

Half-life (of a reaction) the time required for a reactant to reach half of its original concentration. (12.4)

Half-reactions the two parts of an oxidation-reduction reaction, one representing oxidation, the other reduction. (4.11; 17.1)

Halogen a Group 7A element. (2.7; 19.7)

Halogenation the addition of halogen atoms to unsaturated hydrocarbons. (22.2)

Hard water water from natural sources that contains relatively large concentrations of calcium and magnesium ions. (18.4)

Heat energy transferred between two objects due to a temperature difference between them. (6.1)

Heat capacity the amount of energy required to raise the temperature of an object by one degree Celsius. (6.2)

Heat of fusion the enthalpy change that occurs to melt a solid at its melting point. (10.8)

Heat of hydration the enthalpy change associated with placing gaseous molecules or ions in water; the sum of the energy needed to expand the solvent and the energy released from the solvent-solute interactions. (11.2)

Heat of solution the enthalpy change associated with dissolving a solute in a solvent; the sum of the energies needed to expand both solvent and solute in a solution and the energy released from the solvent-solute interactions. (11.2)

Heat of vaporization the energy required to vaporize one mole of a liquid at a pressure of one atmosphere. (10.8)

Heating curve a plot of temperature versus time for a substance where energy is added at a constant rate. (10.8)

Heisenberg uncertainty principle a principle stating that there is a fundamental limitation to how precisely both the position and momentum of a particle can be known at a given time. (7.5)

Heme an iron complex. (20.8)

Hemoglobin a biomolecule composed of four myoglobinlike

units (proteins plus heme) that can bind and transport four oxygen molecules in the blood. (20.8)

Henderson-Hasselbalch equation   an equation giving the relationship between the pH of an acid-base system and the concentrations of base and acid: $pH = pK_a + \log\left(\dfrac{[\text{base}]}{[\text{acid}]}\right)$. (15.2)

Henry's law   the amount of a gas dissolved in a solution is directly proportional to the pressure of the gas above the solution. (11.3)

Hess's law   in going from a particular set of reactants to a particular set of products, the enthalpy change is the same whether the reaction takes place in one step or in a series of steps; in summary, enthalpy is a state function. (6.3)

Heterogeneous equilibrium   an equilibrium involving reactants and/or products in more than one phase. (13.4)

Hexagonal closest packed structure   a structure composed of closest packed spheres with an *ababab* arrangement of layers; the unit cell is hexagonal. (10.4)

Homogeneous equilibrium   an equilibrium system where all reactants and products are in the same phase. (13.4)

Homopolymer   a polymer formed from the polymerization of only one type of monomer. (22.6)

Hund's rule   the lowest energy configuration for an atom is the one having the maximum number of unpaired electrons allowed by the Pauli exclusion principle in a particular set of degenerate orbitals, with all unpaired electrons having parallel spins. (7.11)

Hybrid orbitals   a set of atomic orbitals adopted by an atom in a molecule different from those of the atom in the free state. (9.1)

Hybridization   a mixing of the native orbitals on a given atom to form special atomic orbitals for bonding. (9.1)

Hydration   the interaction between solute particles and water molecules. (4.1)

Hydride   a binary compound containing hydrogen. The hydride ion, H^-, exists in ionic hydrides. The three classes of hydrides are covalent, interstitial, and ionic. (18.3)

Hydrocarbon   a compound composed of carbon and hydrogen. (22.1)

Hydrocarbon derivative   an organic molecule that contains one or more elements in addition to carbon and hydrogen. (22.5)

Hydrogen bonding   unusually strong dipole-dipole attractions that occur among molecules in which hydrogen is bonded to a highly electronegative atom. (10.1)

Hydrogenation reaction   a reaction in which hydrogen is added, with a catalyst present, to a carbon-carbon multiple bond. (22.2)

Hydrohalic acid   an aqueous solution of a hydrogen halide. (19.7)

Hydrometallurgy   a process for extracting metals from ores by use of aqueous chemical solutions. Two steps are involved: selective leaching and selective precipitation. (20.9)

Hydronium ion   the H_3O^+ ion; a hydrated proton. (14.1)

Hypothesis   one or more assumptions put forth to explain the observed behavior of nature. (1.1)

Ideal gas law   an equation of state for a gas, where the state of the gas is its condition at a given time; expressed by $PV = nRT$, where P = pressure, V = volume, n = moles of the gas, R = the universal gas constant, and T = absolute temperature. This equation expresses behavior approached by real gases at high T and low P. (5.3)

Ideal solution   a solution whose vapor pressure is directly proportional to the mole fraction of solvent present. (11.4)

Indicator   a chemical that changes color and is used to mark the end point of a titration. (4.9; 15.5)

Inert pair effect   the tendency for the heavier Group 3A elements to exhibit the +1 as well as the expected +3 oxidation states, and Group 4A elements to exhibit the +2 as well as the +4 oxidation states. (18.5)

Inhibition (of combustion)   the process whereby a polymer is made flame-retardant by interrupting the cycle of combustion. (22.7)

Integrated rate law   an expression that shows the concentration of a reactant as a function of time. (12.4)

Interhalogen compound   a compound formed by the reaction of one halogen with another. (19.7)

Intermediate   a species that is neither a reactant nor a product but that is formed and consumed in the reaction sequence. (12.6)

Intermolecular forces   relatively weak interactions that occur between molecules. (10.1)

Internal energy   a property of a system that can be changed by a flow of work, heat or both; $\Delta E = q + w$, where ΔE is the change in the internal energy of the system, q is heat, and w is work. (6.1)

Ion   an atom or a group of atoms that has a net positive or negative charge. (2.6)

Ion exchange (water softening)   the process in which an ion-exchange resin removes unwanted ions (for example, Ca^{2+} and Mg^{2+}) and replaces them with Na^+ ions, which do not interfere with soap and detergent action. (18.4)

Ion pairing   a phenomenon occurring in solution when oppositely charged ions aggregate and behave as a single particle. (11.7)

Ion-product constant (K_w)   the equilibrium constant for the autoionization of water; $K_w = [H^+][OH^-]$. At 25°C, K_w equals 1.0×10^{-14}. (14.2)

Ion-selective electrode   an electrode sensitive to the concentration of a particular ion in solution. (17.4)

Ionic bonding   the electrostatic attraction between oppositely charged ions. (8.1)

Ionic compound (binary)   a compound that results when a metal reacts with a nonmetal to form a cation and an anion. (8.1)

Ionic solid   a solid containing cations and anions that dissolves in water to give a solution containing the separated ions which are mobile and thus free to conduct electrical current. (10.3)

Ionization energy   the quantity of energy required to remove an electron from a gaseous atom or ion. (7.12)

Irreversible process   any real process. When a system undergoes the changes State 1 → State 2 → State 1 by any real pathway, the universe is different than before the cyclic process took place in the system. (16.9)

Isoelectronic ions   ions containing the same number of electrons. (8.4)

Isomers   species with the same formula but different properties. (20.4)

Isotactic chain   a polymer chain in which the substituent groups such as CH_3 are all arranged on the same side of the chain. (22.7)

Isotonic solutions   solutions having identical osmotic pressures. (11.6)

Isotopes   atoms of the same element (the same number of protons) with different numbers of neutrons. They have identical atomic numbers but different mass numbers. (2.5; 21)

Ketone   an organic compound containing the carbonyl group

$$\left(\begin{array}{c} \diagdown \diagup \\ C \\ \parallel \\ O \end{array} \right)$$

bonded to two carbon atoms. (22.5)

Kinetic energy   ($\frac{1}{2} mv^2$) energy due to the motion of an object; dependent on the mass of the object and the square of its velocity. (6.1)

Kinetic molecular theory   a model that assumes that an ideal gas is composed of tiny particles (molecules) in constant motion. (5.6)

Lanthanide contraction   the decrease in the atomic radii of the lanthanide series elements, going from left to right in the periodic table. (20.1)

Lanthanide series   a group of fourteen elements following lanthanum in the periodic table, in which the $4f$ orbitals are being filled. (7.11; 18,1; 20.1)

Lattice   a three-dimensional system of points designating the positions of the centers of the components of a solid (atoms, ions, or molecules). (10.3)

Lattice energy   the energy change occurring when separated gaseous ions are packed together to form an ionic solid. (8.5)

Law of conservation of energy   energy can be converted from one form to another but can be neither created nor destroyed. (6.1)

Law of conservation of mass   mass is neither created nor destroyed. (2.2)

Law of definite proportions   a given compound always contains exactly the same proportion of elements by mass. (2.2)

Law of mass action   a general description of the equilibrium condition; it defines the equilibrium constant expression. (13.2)

Law of multiple proportions   a law stating that when two elements form a series of compounds, the ratios of the masses of the second element that combine with one gram of the first element can always be reduced to small whole numbers. (2.2)

Leaching   the extraction of metals from ores using aqueous chemical solutions. (20.9)

Lead storage battery   a battery (used in cars) in which the anode is lead, the cathode is lead coated with lead dioxide, and the electrolyte is a sulfuric acid solution. (17.5)

Le Châtelier's principle   if a change is imposed on a system at equilibrium, the position of the equilibrium will shift in a direction that tends to reduce the effect of that change. (13.7)

Lewis acid   an electron-pair acceptor. (14.11)

Lewis base   an electron-pair donor. (14.11)

Lewis structure   a diagram of a molecule showing how the valence electrons are arranged among the atoms in the molecule. (8.10)

Ligand   a neutral molecule or ion having a lone pair of electrons that can be used to form a bond to a metal ion; a Lewis base. (20.1)

Lime-soda process   a water-softening method in which lime and soda ash are added to water to remove calcium and magnesium ions by precipitation. (14.6)

Limiting reactant (limiting reagent)   the reactant that is completely consumed when a reaction is run to completion. (3.9)

Line spectrum   a spectrum showing only certain discrete wavelengths. (7.3)

Linear accelerator   a type of particle accelerator in which a changing electrical field is used to accelerate a positive ion along a linear path. (21.3)

Linkage isomerism   isomerism involving a complex ion where the ligands are all the same but the point of attachment of at least one of the ligands differs. (20.4)

Lipids   water-insoluble substances that can be extracted from cells by nonpolar organic solvents. (23.4)

Liquefaction   the transformation of a gas into a liquid. (18.1)

Localized electron (LE) model   a model which assumes that a molecule is composed of atoms that are bound together by sharing pairs of electrons using the atomic orbitals of the bound atoms. (8.9)

Lock-and-key model   a model for the mechanism of enzyme activity postulating that the shapes of the substrate and the enzyme are such that they fit together as a key fits a specific lock. (23.1)

London dispersion forces   the forces, existing among noble gas atoms and nonpolar molecules, that involve an accidental dipole that induces a momentary dipole in a neighbor. (10.1)

Lone pair an electron pair that is localized on a given atom; an electron pair not involved in bonding. (8.9)

Magnetic quantum number m_ℓ, the quantum number relating to the orientation of an orbital in space relative to the other orbitals with the same ℓ quantum number. It can have integral values between ℓ and $-\ell$, including zero. (7.6)

Main-group (representative) elements elements in the groups labeled 1A, 2A, 3A, 4A, 5A, 6A, 7A, and 8A in the periodic table. The group number gives the sum of valence s and p electrons. (7.11; 18.1)

Major species the components present in relatively large amounts in a solution. (14.3)

Manometer a device for measuring the pressure of a gas in a container. (5.1)

Mass the quantity of matter in an object. (1.2)

Mass defect the change in mass occurring when a nucleus is formed from its component nucleons. (21.5)

Mass number the total number of protons and neutrons in the atomic nucleus of an atom. (2.5; 21)

Mass percent the percent by mass of a component of a mixture (11.1) or of a given element in a compound. (3.4)

Mass spectrometer an instrument used to determine the relative masses of atoms by the deflection of their ions in a magnetic field. (3.1)

Matter the material of the universe. (1.8)

Messenger RNA (mRNA) a special RNA molecule built in the cell nucleus that migrates into the cytoplasm and participates in protein synthesis. (23.3)

Metal an element that gives up electrons relatively easily and is lustrous, malleable, and a good conductor of heat and electricity. (2.7)

Metalloenzyme an enzyme containing a metal ion at its active site. (23.1)

Metalloids (semimetals) elements along the division line in the periodic table between metals and nonmetals. These elements exhibit both metallic and nonmetallic properties. (7.14; 18.1)

Metallurgy the process of separating a metal from its ore and preparing it for use. (18.1; 20.9)

Micelles aggregates of fatty acid anions having their hydrophobic tails in the interior and their polar heads pointing outward to interact with the polar water molecules. (23.4)

Millimeters of mercury (mm Hg) a unit of pressure, also called a torr; 760 mm Hg = 760 torr = 101,325 Pa = 1 standard atmosphere. (5.1)

Mineral a relatively pure compound as found in nature. (20.9)

Mixture a material of variable composition that contains two or more substances. (1.8)

Model (theory) a set of assumptions put forth to explain the observed behavior of matter. The models of chemistry usually involve assumptions about the behavior of individual atoms or molecules. (1.1)

Moderator a substance used in a nuclear reactor to slow down the neutrons. (21.6)

Molal boiling-point elevation constant a constant characteristic of a particular solvent that gives the change in boiling point as a function of solution molality; used in molecular weight determinations. (11.5)

Molal freezing-point depression constant a constant characteristic of a particular solvent that gives the change in freezing point as a function of the solution molality; used in molecular weight determinations. (11.5)

Molality the number of moles of solute per kilogram of solvent in a solution. (11.1)

Molar heat capacity the energy required to raise the temperature of one mole of a substance by one degree Celsius. (6.2)

Molar mass the mass in grams of one mole of molecules or formula units of a substance; also called molecular weight. (3.3)

Molar volume the volume of one mole of an ideal gas; equal to 22.42 liters at STP. (5.4)

Molarity moles of solute per volume of solution in liters. (4.3; 11.1)

Mole (mol) the number equal to the number of carbon atoms in exactly 12 grams of pure ^{12}C: Avogadro's number. One mole represents 6.022×10^{23} units. (3.2)

Mole fraction the ratio of the number of moles of a given component in a mixture to the total number of moles in the mixture. (5.5; 11.1)

Mole ratio (stoichiometry) the ratio of moles of one substance to moles of another substance in a balanced chemical equation. (3.8)

Molecular equation an equation representing a reaction in solution showing the reactants and products in undissociated form, whether they are strong or weak electrolytes. (4.6)

Molecular formula the exact formula of a molecule, giving the types of atoms and the number of each type. (3.5)

Molecular orbital (MO) model a model that regards a molecule as a collection of nuclei and electrons, where the electrons are assumed to occupy orbitals much as they do in atoms, but having the orbitals extend over the entire molecule. In this model the electrons are assumed to be delocalized rather than always located between a given pair of atoms. (9.2)

Molecular orientations (kinetics) orientations of molecules during collisions, some of which can lead to reaction while others cannot. (12.7)

Molecular solid a solid composed of neutral molecules at the lattice points. (10.3)

Molecular structure the three-dimensional arrangement of atoms in a molecule. (8.13)

Molecular weight the mass in grams of one mole of molecules or formula units of a substance; the same as molar mass. (3.3)

Molecularity   the number of species that must collide to produce the reaction represented by an elementary step in a reaction mechanism. (12.6)

Molecule   a bonded collection of two or more atoms of the same or different elements. (2.6)

Monodentate (unidentate) ligand   a ligand that can form one bond to a metal ion. (20.3)

Monoprotic acid   an acid with one acidic proton. (14.2)

Monosaccharide (simple sugar)   a polyhydroxy ketone or aldehyde containing from three to nine carbon atoms. (23.2)

Myoglobin   an oxygen-storing biomolecule consisting of a heme complex and a protein. (20.8)

Natural law   a statement that expresses generally observed behavior. (1.1)

Nernst equation   an equation relating the potential of an electrochemical cell to the concentrations of the cell components;

$$\mathscr{E} = \mathscr{E}° - \frac{0.0592}{n}\log(Q) \text{ at } 25°C. (17.4)$$

Net ionic equation   an equation for a reaction in solution, where strong electrolytes are written as ions, showing only those components that are directly involved in the chemical change. (4.6)

Network solid   an atomic solid containing strong directional covalent bonds. (10.5)

Neutralization reaction   an acid-base reaction. (4.9)

Neutron   a particle in the atomic nucleus with mass virtually equal to the proton's but with no charge. (2.5; 21)

Nitride salt   a compound containing the N^{3-} anion. (18.2)

Nitrogen cycle   the conversion of N_2 to nitrogen-containing compounds, followed by the return of nitrogen gas to the atmosphere by natural decay processes. (19.2)

Nitrogen fixation   the process of transforming N_2 to nitrogen-containing compounds useful to plants. (19.2)

Nitrogen-fixing bacteria   bacteria in the root nodules of plants that can convert atmospheric nitrogen to ammonia and other nitrogen-containing compounds useful to plants. (19.2)

Noble gas   a Group 8A element. (2.7; 19.8)

Node   an area of an orbital having zero electron probability. (7.7)

Nonelectrolyte   a substance which, when dissolved in water, gives a nonconducting solution. (4.2)

Nonmetal   an element not exhibiting metallic characteristics. Chemically, a typical nonmetal accepts electrons from a metal. (2.7)

Normal boiling point   the temperature at which the vapor pressure of a liquid is exactly one atmosphere. (10.8)

Normal melting point   the temperature at which the solid and liquid states have the same vapor pressure under conditions where the total pressure on the system is one atmosphere. (10.8)

Normality   the number of equivalents of a substance dissolved in a liter of solution. (11.1)

Nuclear atom   an atom having a dense center of positive charge (the nucleus) with electrons moving around the outside. (2.4)

Nuclear transformation   the change of one element into another. (21.3)

Nucleon   a particle in an atomic nucleus, either a neutron or a proton. (21)

Nucleotide   a monomer of the nucleic acids composed of a five-carbon sugar, a nitrogen-containing base, and phosphoric acid. (23.3)

Nucleus   the small, dense center of positive charge in an atom. (2.4)

Nuclide   the general term applied to each unique atom; represented by $^A_Z X$, where X is the symbol for a particular element. (21)

Octet rule   the observation that atoms of nonmetals tend to form the most stable molecules when they are surrounded by eight electrons (to fill their valence orbitals). (8.10)

Open hearth process   a process for producing steel by oxidizing and removing the impurities in molten iron using external heat and a blast of air or oxygen. (20.9)

Optical isomerism   isomerism in which the isomers have opposite effects on plane-polarized light. (20.4)

Orbital   a specific wave function for an electron in an atom. The square of this function gives the probability distribution for the electron. (7.5)

d-Orbital splitting   a splitting of the d-orbitals of the metal ion in a complex such that the orbitals pointing at the ligands have higher energies than those pointing between the ligands. (20.6)

Order (of reactant)   the positive or negative exponent, determined by experiment, of the reactant concentration in a rate law. (12.2)

Organic acid   an acid with a carbon-atom backbone; often contains the carboxyl group. (14.2)

Organic chemistry   the study of carbon-containing compounds (typically chains of carbon atoms) and their properties. (22)

Osmosis   the flow of solvent into a solution through a semipermeable membrane. (11.6)

Osmotic pressure (π)   the pressure that must be applied to a solution to stop osmosis; $\pi = MRT$. (11.6)

Ostwald process   a commercial process for producing nitric acid by the oxidation of ammonia. (19.2)

Oxidation   an increase in oxidation state (a loss of electrons). (4.9; 17.1)

Oxidation–reduction (redox) reaction   a reaction in which one or more electrons are transferred. (4.9; 17.1)

Oxidation states   a concept that provides a way to keep track of electrons in oxidation–reduction reactions according to certain rules. (4.9)

Oxidizing agent (electron acceptor)   a reactant that accepts electrons from another reactant. (4.9; 17.1)

Oxyacid an acid in which the acidic proton is attached to an oxygen atom. (14.2)

Ozone O_3, the form of elemental oxygen in addition to the much more common O_2. (19.5)

Paramagnetism a type of induced magnetism, associated with unpaired electrons, that causes a substance to be attracted into the inducing magnetic field. (9.3)

Partial pressures the independent pressures exerted by different gases in a mixture. (5.5)

Particle accelerator a device used to accelerate nuclear particles to very high speeds. (21.3)

Pascal the SI unit of pressure; equal to newtons per meter squared. (5.1)

Pauli exclusion principle in a given atom no two electrons can have the same set of four quantum numbers. (7.8)

Penetration effect the effect whereby a valence electron penetrates the core electrons, thus reducing the shielding effect and increasing the effective nuclear charge. (7.12)

Peptide linkage the bond resulting from the condensation reaction between amino acids; represented by

$$\overset{O}{\overset{\|}{-C}}-\overset{H}{\overset{|}{N}}-\qquad (23.1)$$

Percent dissociation the ratio of the amount of a substance that is dissociated at equilibrium to the initial concentration of the substance in a solution, multiplied by 100. (14.5)

Percent yield the actual yield of a product as a percentage of the theoretical yield. (3.9)

Periodic table a chart showing all the elements arranged in columns with similar chemical properties. (2.7)

Petrochemicals chemicals obtained from petroleum either by steam cracking or as by-products of refinery operations. They serve as raw materials for the chemical industry. (22.4)

pH curve (titration curve) a plot showing the pH of a solution being analyzed as a function of the amount of titrant added. (15.4)

pH scale a log scale based on 10 and equal to $-\log[H^+]$; a convenient way to represent solution acidity. (14.3)

Phase diagram a convenient way of representing the phases of a substance in a closed system as a function of temperature and pressure. (10.9)

Phenyl group the benzene molecule minus one hydrogen atom. (22.3)

Phospholipids esters of glycerol containing two fatty acids and a phosphate group. Having nonpolar tails and polar heads, they tend to form bilayers in aqueous solution. (23.4)

Photochemical smog air pollution produced by the action of light on oxygen, nitrogen oxides, and unburned fuel from auto exhaust to form ozone and other pollutants. (5.9)

Photon a quantum of electromagnetic radiation. (7.2)

Physical change a change in the form of a substance, but not in its chemical composition; chemical bonds are not broken in a physical change. (1.9)

Pi (π) bond a covalent bond in which parallel p orbitals share an electron pair occupying the space above and below the line joining the atoms. (9.1)

Planck's constant the constant relating the change in energy for a system to the frequency of the electromagnetic radiation absorbed or emitted; equal to 6.626×10^{-34} J s. (7.2)

Polar covalent bond a covalent bond in which the electrons are not shared equally because one atom attracts them more strongly than the other. (8.1)

Polar molecule a molecule that has a permanent dipole moment. (4.1)

Polyatomic ion an ion containing a number of atoms. (2.6)

Polyelectronic atom an atom with more than one electron. (7.9)

Polymer a large, usually chainlike molecule built from many small molecules (monomers). (22.6)

Polymerization a process in which many small molecules (monomers) are joined together to form a large molecule. (22.2; 22.6; 22.7)

Polypeptide a polymer formed from amino acids joined together by peptide linkages. (23.1)

Polyprotic acid an acid with more than one acidic proton. It dissociates in a stepwise manner, one proton at a time. (14.7)

Porous disk a disk in a tube connecting two different solutions in a galvanic cell that allows ion flow without extensive mixing of the solutions. (17.1)

Porphyrin a planar ligand with a central ring structure and various substituent groups at the edges of the ring. (20.8)

Positional probability a type of probability that depends on the number of arrangements in space that yield a particular state. (16.1)

Positron production a mode of nuclear decay in which a particle is formed having the same mass as an electron but opposite charge. The net effect is to change a proton to a neutron. (21.1)

Potential energy energy due to position or composition. (6.1)

Precipitation reaction a reaction in which an insoluble substance forms and separates from the solution. (4.5)

Precision the degree of agreement among several measurements of the same quantity; the reproducibility of a measurement. (1.3)

Primary structure (of a protein) the order (sequence) of amino acids in the protein chain. (23.1)

Principal quantum number the quantum number relating to the size and energy of an orbital; it can have any positive integer value. (7.6)

Probability distribution the square of the wave function indicating the probability of finding an electron at a particular point in space. (7.5)

Product a substance resulting from a chemical reaction. It is shown to the right of the arrow in a chemical equation. (3.6)

Protein a natural high-molecular-weight polymer formed by condensation reactions between amino acids. (23.1)

Proton   a positively charged particle in an atomic nucleus. (2.5; 21)

Pure substance   a substance with constant composition. (1.8)

Pyrometallurgy   recovery of a metal from its ore by treatment at high temperatures. (20.9)

Quantization   the concept that energy can occur only in discrete units called quanta. (7.2)

Rad   a unit of radiation dosage corresponding to 10^{-2} J of energy deposited per kilogram of tissue (from *radiation absorbed dose*). (21.7)

Radioactive decay (radioactivity)   the spontaneous decomposition of a nucleus to form a different nucleus. (21.1)

Radiocarbon dating (carbon-14 dating)   a method for dating ancient wood or cloth based on the rate of radioactive decay of the nuclide $^{14}_{6}C$. (21.4)

Radiotracer   a radioactive nuclide, introduced into an organism for diagnostic purposes, whose pathway can be traced by monitoring its radioactivity. (21.4)

Random error   an error that has an equal probability of being high or low. (1.3)

Raoult's law   the vapor pressure of a solution is directly proportional to the mole fraction of solvent present. (11.4)

Rate constant   the proportionality constant in the relationship between reaction rate and reactant concentrations. (12.2)

Rate of decay   the change in the number of radioactive nuclides in a sample per unit time. (21.2)

Rate-determining step   the slowest step in a reaction mechanism, the one determining the overall rate. (12.6)

Rate law (differential rate law)   an expression that shows how the rate of reaction depends on the concentration of reactants. (12.2)

Reactant   a starting substance in a chemical reaction. It appears to the left of the arrow in a chemical equation. (3.6)

Reaction mechanism   the series of elementary steps involved in a chemical reaction. (12.6)

Reaction quotient   a quotient obtained by applying the law of mass action to initial concentrations rather than to equilibrium concentrations. (13.5)

Reaction rate   the change in concentration of a reactant or product per unit time. (12.1)

Reactor core   the part of a nuclear reactor where the fission reaction takes place. (21.6)

Reducing agent (electron donor)   a reactant that donates electrons to another substance to reduce the oxidation state of one of its atoms. (4.9; 17.1)

Reduction   a decrease in oxidation state (a gain of electrons). (4.9; 17.1)

Rem   a unit of radiation dosage that accounts for both the energy of the dose and its effectiveness in causing biological damage (from *r*oentgen *e*quivalent for *m*an). (21.7)

Resonance   a condition occurring when more than one valid Lewis structure can be written for a particular molecule. The actual electronic structure is not represented by any one of the Lewis structures but by the average of all of them. (8.12)

Reverse osmosis   the process occurring when the external pressure on a solution causes a net flow of solvent through a semipermeable membrane from the solution to the solvent. (11.6)

Reversible process   a cyclic process carried out by a hypothetical pathway, which leaves the universe exactly the same as it was before the process. No real process is reversible. (16.9)

Ribonucleic acid (RNA)   a nucleotide polymer that transmits the genetic information stored in DNA to the ribosomes for protein synthesis. (23.3)

Roasting   a process of converting sulfide minerals to oxides by heating in air at temperatures below their melting points. (20.9)

Root mean square velocity   the square root of the average of the squares of the individual velocities of gas particles. (5.6)

Salt   an ionic compound. (14.8)

Salt bridge   a U-tube containing an electrolyte that connects the two compartments of a galvanic cell, allowing ion flow without extensive mixing of the different solutions. (17.1)

Scientific method   the process of studying natural phenomena, involving observations, forming laws and theories, and testing of theories by experimentation. (1.1)

Scintillation counter   an instrument that measures radioactive decay by sensing the flashes of light produced in a substance by the radiation. (21.4)

Second law of thermodynamics   in any spontaneous process, there is always an increase in the entropy of the universe. (16.2)

Secondary structure (of a protein)   the three-dimensional structure of the protein chain (for example, α-helix, random coil, or pleated sheet). (23.1)

Selective precipitation   a method of separating metal ions from an aqueous mixture by using a reagent whose anion forms a precipitate with only one or a few of the ions in the mixture. (4.7; 15.7)

Semiconductor   a substance conducting only a slight electrical current at room temperature, but showing increased conductivity at higher temperatures. (10.5)

Semipermeable membrane   a membrane that allows solvent but not solute molecules to pass through. (11.6)

Shielding   the effect by which the other electrons screen, or shield, a given electron from some of the nuclear charge. (7.12)

SI units   International System of units based on the metric system and units derived from the metric system. (1.2)

Side chain (of amino acid)   the hydrocarbon group on an amino acid represented by H, CH_3, or a more complex substituent. (23.1)

Sigma (σ) bond   a covalent bond in which the electron pair is shared in an area centered on a line running between the atoms. (9.1)

Significant figures   the certain digits and the first uncertain digit of a measurement. (1.3)

Silica   the fundamental silicon-oxygen compound, which has the empirical formula SiO_2, and forms the basis of quartz and certain types of sand. (10.5)

Silicates   salts that contain metal cations and polyatomic silicon-oxygen anions that are usually polymeric. (10.5)

Single bond   a bond in which one pair of electrons is shared by two atoms. (8.8)

Smelting   a metallurgical process that involves reducing metal ions to the free metal. (20.9)

Solubility   the amount of a substance that dissolves in a given volume of solvent at a given temperature. (4.2)

Solubility product constant   the constant for the equilibrium expression representing the dissolving of an ionic solid in water. (15.6)

Solute   a substance dissolved in a liquid to form a solution. (4.2; 11.1)

Solution   a homogeneous mixture. (1.8)

Solvent   the dissolving medium in a solution. (4.2)

Somatic damage   radioactive damage to an organism resulting in its sickness or death. (21.7)

Space-filling model   a model of a molecule showing the relative sizes of the atoms and their relative orientations. (2.6)

Specific heat capacity   the energy required to raise the temperature of one gram of a substance by one degree Celsius. (6.2)

Spectator ions   ions present in solution that do not participate directly in a reaction. (4.6)

Spectrochemical series   a listing of ligands in order based on their ability to produce *d*-orbital splitting. (20.6)

Spontaneous fission   the spontaneous splitting of a heavy nuclide into two lighter nuclides. (21.1)

Spontaneous process   a process that occurs without outside intervention. (16.1)

Standard atmosphere   a unit of pressure equal to 760 mm Hg. (5.1)

Standard enthalpy of formation   the enthalpy change that accompanies the formation of one mole of a compound at 25°C from its elements, with all substances in their standard states at that temperature. (6.4)

Standard free energy change   the change in free energy that will occur for one unit of reaction if the reactants in their standard states are converted to products in their standard states. (16.6)

Standard free energy of formation   the change in free energy that accompanies the formation of one mole of a substance from its constituent elements with all reactants and products in their standard states. (16.6)

Standard hydrogen electrode   a platinum conductor in contact with 1 *M* H^+ ions and bathed by hydrogen gas at one atmosphere. (17.2)

Standard reduction potential   the potential of a half-reaction under standard state conditions, as measured against the potential of the standard hydrogen electrode. (17.2)

Standard solution   a solution whose concentration is accurately known. (4.3)

Standard state   a reference state for a specific substance defined according to a set of conventional definitions. (6.4)

Standard temperature and pressure (STP)   the condition 0°C and 1 atmosphere of pressure. (5.4)

Standing wave   a stationary wave as on a string of a musical instrument; in the wave mechanical model, the electron in the hydrogen atom is considered to be a standing wave. (7.5)

State function   a property that is independent of the pathway. (6.1)

States of matter   the three different forms in which matter can exist: solid, liquid, and gas. (1.8)

Steam cracking   a process whereby hydrocarbon molecules are broken into small fragments by steam at very high temperatures. (22.4)

Stereoisomerism   isomerism in which all the bonds in the isomers are the same but the spatial arrangements of the atoms are different. (20.4)

Steric factor   the factor (always less than one) that reflects the fraction of collisions with orientations that can produce a chemical reaction. (12.7)

Steroid   one of a class of lipids with a characteristic fused carbon-ring structure that includes cholesterol, hormones, and bile acids. (23.4)

Stoichiometric quantities   quantities of reactants mixed in exactly the correct amounts so that all are used up at the same time. (3.9)

Strong acid   an acid that completely dissociates to produce an H^+ ion and the conjugate base. (4.2; 14.2)

Strong base   a metal hydroxide salt that completely dissociates into its ions in water. (4.2; 14.6)

Strong electrolyte   a material which, when dissolved in water, gives a solution that conducts an electric current very efficiently. (4.2)

Structural formula   the representation of a molecule in which the relative positions of the atoms are shown and the bonds are indicated by lines. (2.6)

Structural isomerism   isomerism in which the isomers contain the same atoms but one or more bonds differ. (20.4; 22.1)

Subcritical reaction (nuclear)   a reaction in which less than one neutron causes another fission event and the process dies out. (21.6)

Sublimation   the process by which a substance goes directly from the solid to the gaseous state without passing through the liquid state. (10.8)

Subshell   a set of orbitals with a given azimuthal quantum number. (7.6)

Substitution reaction (hydrocarbons)   a reaction in which an atom, usually a halogen, replaces a hydrogen atom in a hydrocarbon. (22.1)

Supercooling the process of cooling a liquid below its freezing point without its changing to a solid. (10.8)

Supercritical reaction (nuclear) a reaction in which more than one neutron from each fission event causes another fission event. The process rapidly escalates to a violent explosion. (21.6)

Superheating the process of heating a liquid above its boiling point without its boiling. (10.8)

Superoxide a compound containing the O_2^- anion. (18.2)

Surface tension the resistance of a liquid to an increase in its surface area. (10.2)

Surfactant a wetting agent, such as soap, that assists water in wetting and suspending nonpolar materials. (23.4)

Surroundings everything in the universe surrounding a thermodynamic system. (6.1)

Syndiotactic chain a polymer chain in which the substituent groups such as CH_3 are arranged on alternate sides of the chain. (22.7)

Syngas synthetic gas, a mixture of carbon monoxide and hydrogen, obtained by coal gasification. (6.6)

System (thermodynamic) that part of the universe on which attention is to be focused. (6.1)

Systematic error an error that always occurs in the same direction. (1.3)

Tempering a process in steel production that fine-tunes the proportions of carbon crystals and cementite by heating to intermediate temperatures followed by rapid cooling. (24.4)

Termolecular step a reaction involving the simultaneous collision of three molecules. (12.6)

Tertiary structure (of a protein) the overall shape of a protein, long and narrow or globular, maintained by different types of intramolecular interactions. (23.1)

Theoretical yield the maximum amount of a given product that can be formed when the limiting reactant is completely consumed. (3.9)

Theory a set of assumptions put forth to explain some aspect of the observed behavior of matter. (1.1)

Thermal pollution the oxygen-depleting effect on lakes and rivers of using water for industrial cooling and returning it to its natural source at a higher temperature. (11.3)

Thermodynamics the study of energy and its interconversions. (6.1)

Thermodynamic stability (nuclear) the potential energy of a particular nucleus as compared to the sum of the potential energies of its component protons and neutrons. (21.1)

Thermoplastic polymer a substance that when molded to a certain shape under appropriate conditions can later be remelted. (22.7)

Thermoset polymer a substance that when molded to a certain shape under pressure and high temperatures cannot be softened again or dissolved. (22.7)

Third law of thermodynamics the entropy of a perfect crystal at 0 K is zero. (16.5)

Titration a technique in which one solution is used to analyze another. (4.8)

Torr another name for millimeter of mercury (mm Hg). (5.1)

Trace elements metals present only in trace amounts in the human body but essential for the action of many enzymes. (23)

Transfer RNA (tRNA) a small RNA fragment that finds specific amino acids and attaches them to the protein chain as dictated by the codons in mRNA. (23.3)

Transition metals several series of elements in which inner orbitals (d or f orbitals) are being filled. (7.11; 18.1)

Transuranium elements the elements beyond uranium that are made artificially by particle bombardment. (21.3)

Triple bond a bond in which three pairs of electrons are shared by two atoms. (8.8)

Triple point the point on a phase diagram at which all three states of a substance are present. (10.9)

Tyndall effect the scattering of light by particles in a suspension. (11.8)

Uncertainty (in measurement) the characteristic that any measurement involves estimates and cannot be exactly reproduced. (1.3)

Unimolecular step a reaction step involving only one molecule. (12.6)

Unit cell the smallest repeating unit of a lattice. (10.3)

Unit factor an equivalence statement between units used for converting from one unit to another. (1.5)

Universal gas constant the combined proportionality constant in the ideal gas law; 0.08206 L atm/K mol or 8.3145 J/K mol. (5.3)

Valence electrons the electrons in the outermost principal quantum level of an atom. (7.11)

Valence shell electron pair repulsion (VSEPR) model a model whose main postulate is that the structure around a given atom in a molecule is determined principally by minimizing electron-pair repulsions. (8.13)

van der Waals's equation a mathematical expression for describing the behavior of real gases. (5.8)

van't Hoff factor the ratio of moles of particles in solution to moles of solute dissolved. (11.7)

Vapor pressure the pressure of the vapor over a liquid at equilibrium. (10.8)

Vaporization the change in state that occurs when a liquid evaporates to form a gas. (10.8)

Viscosity the resistance of a liquid to flow. (10.2)

Volt the unit of electrical potential defined as one joule of work per coulomb of charge transferred. (17.1)

Voltmeter an instrument that measures cell potential by drawing electric current through a known resistance. (17.1)

Volumetric analysis a process involving titration of one solution with another. (4.9)

Vulcanization a process in which sulfur is added to rubber and the mixture is heated, causing crosslinking of the polymer chains and thus adding strength to the rubber. (22.7)

Wave function a function of the coordinates of an electron's position in three-dimensional space that describes the properties of the electron. (7.5)

Wave mechanical model a model for the hydrogen atom in which the electron is assumed to behave as a standing wave. (7.5)

Wavelength the distance between two consecutive peaks or troughs in a wave. (7.1)

Wax an ester similar to a fat or a phospholipid but containing a monohydroxy alcohol instead of glycerol. (23.4)

Weak acid an acid that dissociates only slightly in aqueous solution. (4.2; 14.2)

Weak base a base that reacts with water to produce hydrox-

ide ions to only a slight extent in aqueous solution. (4.2; 14.6)

Weak electrolyte a material which, when dissolved in water, gives a solution that conducts only a small electric current. (4.2)

Weight the force exerted on an object by gravity. (1.2)

Work force acting over a distance. (6.1)

X-ray diffraction a technique for establishing the structures of crystalline solids by directing X rays of a single wavelength at a crystal and obtaining a diffraction pattern from which interatomic spaces can be determined. (10.3)

Zone of nuclear stability the area encompassing the stable nuclides on a plot of their positions as a function of the number of protons and the number of neutrons in the nucleus. (21.1)

Zone refining a metallurgical process for obtaining a highly pure metal that depends on continuously melting the impure material and recrystallizing the pure metal. (20.9)

Chapter 1

1. a. A *law* is a concise statement or equation that summarizes a great variety of observations. A *theory* is a hypothesis that has been tested over a length of time. A law is less likely to be challenged or modified than a theory. **b.** A *theory* is our explanation of why things behave the way they do, while *experiment* is the process of observing that behavior. Theories attempt to explain the results of experiments and are, in turn, tested by further experiment. **c.** A *qualitative* measurement only measures a quality while a *quantitative* measurement attaches a number to the observation. Qualitative observations: The water was hot to the touch. Mercury was found in the drinking water. Quantitative observations: The temperature of the water was 62°C. The concentration of mercury in the drinking water was 1.5 ppm. **d.** Both are explanations of experimental observation. A *theory* is a *hypothesis* that has been tested over time and found to still be valid, with, perhaps, some modifications. **3. a.** No; **b.** Yes; **c.** Yes **5.** Accuracy is a measure of how close a measurement is to the true value, while precision is a measure of the reproducibility of a series of identical measurements. **7.** Experimental results are the facts of science. Theories are attempts to rationalize these facts. If the experiment is done properly and the theory cannot account for the facts, then the theory is wrong. **9.** Chemical changes involve the making and breaking of chemical forces (bonds); physical changes do not. The identity of a substance changes after a chemical change, but not after a physical change. **11. a.** Inexact; **b.** Exact; **c.** Exact; 36 in/yd × 2.54 cm/in × 1 m/100 cm = 0.9144 m/yd (All conversion factors used are exact.) **d.** Inexact; the announced attendance is generally the number of tickets sold, not the number who were actually in the stadium. Some people who paid may not have gone, some may sneak in without paying, etc. **e.** Exact; **f.** Inexact **13. a.** 2, 1.2×10^{-3}; **b.** 3, 4.37×10^5; **c.** 4, 9.000×10^2; **d.** 3, 1.06×10^2; **e.** 6, 1.25904×10^8; **f.** 5, 1.0012×10^0; **g.** 4, 2.006×10^3; **h.** 3, 3.05×10^3; **i.** 4, 1.060×10^{-3} **15. a.** 6×10^8; **b.** 5.8×10^8; **c.** 5.82×10^8; **d.** 5.8200×10^8; **e.** 5.820000×10^8 **17. a.** 467; **b.** 0.24; **c.** 33.04; **d.** 75; **e.** 0.12; **f.** 0.21; **g.** 4.9; **h.** 0.01 **19. a.** 1 km = 10^3 m = 10^6 mm = 10^{15} pm; **b.** 1 g = 10^{-3} kg = 10^3 mg = 10^9 ng; **c.** 1 mL = 10^{-3} L = 10^{-3} dm³ = 1 cm³; **d.** 1 mg = 10^{-6} kg = 10^{-3} g = 10^3 μg = 10^6 ng = 10^9 pg = 10^{12} fg; **e.** 1 s = 10^3 ms = 10^9 ns **21.** 1×10^{-1} nm; 1×10^2 pm **23. a.** 229 cm, 2.29 m; 157 cm, 1.57 m; **b.** 4.0×10^4 km, 4.0×10^7 m; **c.** 1.2×10^{-2} m³, 12 L, 730 in³, 0.42 ft³ **25. a.** 272 leagues, 1.49×10^3 km; **b.** 0.18 km, 1.8×10^4 cm; **c.** 96.0 m, 11 m, 5.25×10^{-1} cable length, 6.2 fathoms **27. a.** 45.06 m/s; **b.** 0.409 s **29. a.** 0.373 kg, 0.822 lb; **b.** 31.1 g, 156 carats; **c.** 19.3 cm³ **31.** 1016 kg, 1.016 tonne **33.** 39.2°C, 312.4 K **35.** 77°F, 298 K **37.** 69.1°F ± 0.2°F **39.** 2.70×10^3 kg/m³, 169 lb/ft³ **41.** 3.2×10^{15} g/cm³ **43.** 0.28 cm³ **45. a.** Both are the same mass; **b.** 1.0 mL mercury; **c.** Both are the same mass; **d.** 1.0 L benzene **47.** Solid: own volume, own shape, does not flow. Liquid: own volume, takes shape of container, flows. Gas: takes volume and shape of container, flows. **49. a.** Pure; **b.** Mixture; **c.** Mixture; **d.** Pure; **e.** Mixture; **f.** Pure; **g.** Mixture; **h.** Mixture; **i.** Pure **51. a.** 8.41; **b.** 16.1; **c.** 52.5; **d.** 5; **e.** 0.009; **f.** 429.59

53. a. 1×10^{18} kg/km³; **b.** 1×10^9 kg/m³; **c.** 1×10^6 g/cm³ **55.** 15 km **57. a.** Maximum = 1.04, Minimum = 1.00, 1.02 ± 0.02; **b.** Maximum = 1.04, Minimum = 1.00, 1.02 ± 0.02; **c.** Maximum = 1.00, Minimum = 0.96, 0.98 ± 0.02. Considering the error limits, a. and b. should be expressed to three significant figures and c. to two significant figures. The division rule differs in b. The rule says b. should be expressed to two significant figures. If we do this for b., we imply that the answer is 1.0 or between 0.95 and 1.05. The actual range is less than this, so we should use the more precise way of expressing uncertainty. **59.** 477 L **61. a.** 4.25 royals, 8.5×10^3 weights; 11 horses; 3.25 royals left; **b.** 52 weights; 187.2 royals **63.** 8.5 g/cm³ ± 0.5 g/cm³ **65.** 10.1 m/s, 36.4 km/hr, 33.3 ft/s, 22.7 mi/hr; 9.01 s **67.** −459.67°F **69.** The object that sinks has the greater density. Since both objects have the same mass, then the sphere that sinks has the smaller volume. The sphere that floats has the larger diameter. **71.** d_{cube} = 5.20 g/cm³ ± 0.05 g/cm³; d_{sphere} = 5.13 g/cm³ ± 0.05 g/cm³. The data are not precise enough to determine if they are the same or different. **73.** In a subtraction, the result gets smaller, but the uncertainties are added. If the two numbers are very close, the uncertainty may be larger than the result. **75.** d_{old} = 8.9 g/cm³, d_{new} = 7.18 g/cm³; d_{new}/d_{old} = mass$_{new}$/mass$_{old}$ = 0.81; The difference in mass is accounted for by the difference in the alloy used. **77. a.** One possibility is that rope B is not attached to anything and rope A and rope C are connected via a pair of pulleys and/or gears; **b.** Try to pull rope B out of the box. Measure the distance moved by C for a given movement of A. Hold either A or C firmly while pulling on the other rope.

Chapter 2

1. No difference. It doesn't matter how a substance is produced; it is still that substance. **3.** Some elements exist as molecules (H_2, Cl_2, O_2, etc.). **5.** Most elements have isotopes. **7.** No. A cathode ray is a stream of β particles. **9.** The atomic number of an element is equal to the number of protons in the nucleus of an atom of that element. The mass number is the sum of the number of protons plus neutrons in the nucleus. The atomic mass is the actual mass of a particular isotope (including electrons). The average mass of an atom is taken from a measurement made from a large number of atoms, and it is this average value we see on the periodic table. **11.** A compound always contains the same number (and type) of atoms. **13. a.** A compound always contains the same number of atoms. **b.** Vol.HCl/Vol.H_2(or Cl_2) = 2 **15.** The F to S mass ratios are simple whole numbers, 1:2:3. **17.** O, 7.94; Na, 22.8; Mg, 11.9; O and Mg are incorrect by a factor of ≈2; correct formulas are H_2O, Na_2O, and MgO. **19.** Using $r = 5 \times 10^{-14}$ cm, $d_{nucleus}$ = 3×10^{15} g/cm³; using $r = 1 \times 10^{-8}$ cm, d_{atom} = 0.4 g/cm³. **21.** 37 **23.** Gold: Au, silver: Ag, mercury: Hg, potassium: K, iron: Fe, antimony: Sb, tungsten: W. **25.** Fluorine: F, chlorine: Cl, bromine: Br, sulfur: S, oxygen: O, phosphorus: P. **27.** Sn: tin, Pt: platinum, Co: cobalt, Ni: nickel, Mg: magnesium, Ba: barium, K: potassium. **29.** The noble gases are He, Ne, Ar, Kr, Xe, and Rn (helium, neon, krypton, xenon, and radon). All isotopes of radon are radioactive. **31. a.** 8; **b.** 8; **c.** 18; **d.** 5 **33. a.** 94 p, 144 n; **b.** 29 p, 36 n; **c.** 24 p, 28 n; **d.** 2 p, 2 n;

A45

e. 27 p, 33 n; **f.** 24 p, 30 n **35.** $^{19}_{9}F$ **37.** $^{151}_{63}Eu^{3+}$ **39.** $^{34}_{16}S^{2-}$
41. $^{75}_{33}As^{3+}$, 30 e; $^{128}_{52}Te^{2-}$, 52 p, 76 n, 2−; $^{32}_{16}S$, 0; $^{204}_{81}Tl^{+}$, 80 e; $^{195}_{78}Pt$,
78 p, 117 n, 78 e, 0 **43.** Metals: Mg, Ti, Au, Bi, Ge, Eu, Am; Non-
metals: Si, B, At, Rn, Br **45.** a, d **47.** Metallic character increases
down a group. **49. a.** lose, Na^{+}; **b.** lose, Sr^{2+}; **c.** lose, Ba^{2+};
d. gain, I^{-}; **e.** lose, Al^{3+}; **f.** gain, S^{2-} **51. a.** chromium(VI)
oxide; **b.** chromium(III) oxide; **c.** aluminum oxide; **d.** selenium
dioxide; **e.** selenium trioxide; **f.** nitrogen triiodide; **g.** phosphorus
trichloride; **h.** sulfur difluoride **53. a.** sodium chloride;
b. magnesium chloride; **c.** rubidium bromide; **d.** cesium fluoride;
e. aluminum iodide; **f.** hydrogen iodide; **g.** nitrogen monoxide or
nitric oxide (common name); **h.** nitrogen trifluoride; **i.** dinitrogen
tetrafluoride; **j.** dinitrogen dichloride; **k.** silicon tetrafluoride;
l. dihydrogen selenide **55. a.** nitric acid; **b.** nitrous acid;
c. phosphoric acid; **d.** phosphorous acid; **e.** sodium hydrogen sulfate or sodium bisulfate (common name); **f.** calcium hydrogen sulfite
or calcium bisulfite (common name); **g.** sodium bromate;
h. iron(III) periodate; **i.** ruthenium(III) nitrate; **j.** vanadium(V)
oxide; **k.** platinum(IV) chloride; **l.** iron(III) phosphate
57. a. CsBr; **b.** $BaSO_4$; **c.** NH_4Cl; **d.** ClO; **e.** $SiCl_4$; **f.** ClF_3;
g. BeO; **h.** MgF_2 **59. a.** SF_2; **b.** SF_6; **c.** NaH_2PO_4; **d.** Li_3N;
e. $Cr_2(CO_3)_3$; **f.** SnF_2; **g.** $(NH_4)(C_2H_3O_2)$; **h.** $(NH_4)(HSO_4)$;
i. $Co(NO_3)_3$; **j.** Hg_2Cl_2; **k.** $KClO_3$; **l.** NaH **61.** No difference
for pure compounds. **63. a.** lead(II) acetate; **b.** copper(II) sulfate;
c. calcium oxide; **d.** magnesium sulfate; **e.** magnesium hydroxide;
f. calcium sulfate; **g.** dinitrogen monoxide or nitrous oxide (common)
65. Yes, 1.0 g hydrogen reacts with 37.0 g ^{37}Cl and 1.0 g hydrogen
reacts with 35.0 g ^{35}Cl. No, the ratio of H/Cl would always be
1 g H/37 g Cl for ^{37}Cl and 1 g H/35 g Cl for ^{35}Cl. **67. a.** BaO, barium oxide; **b.** LiH, lithium hydride; **c.** InF_3, indium(III) fluoride;
d. As_2S_3, diarsenic trisulfide (arsenic(III) sulfide is sometimes used);
e. B_2O_3, diboron trioxide; **f.** OF_2, oxygen difluoride; **g.** AlH_3, aluminum hydride; **h.** InP, indium(III) phosphide **69.** No. The solid
residue must have come from the flask. **71.** Sodium arsenate, arsenic
acid, magnesium antimonate

Chapter 3

1. Boron has isotopes (the major ones are ^{10}B and ^{11}B). The listed
mass of 10.81 is the average mass of all the boron isotopes. **3.** The
molecular formula gives the actual number of atoms of each element in
a molecule (or formula unit) of a compound. The empirical formula
gives the simplest whole number ratio of atoms of each element in a
compound. The molecular formula is a whole number multiple of the
empirical formula. If that multiplier is one, the molecular and empirical
formulas are the same. **5.** 24.31 amu **7.** 48% ^{151}Eu and 52% ^{153}Eu
9. There are three peaks in the mass spectrum, each 2 mass units
apart. This is consistent with two isotopes, differing in mass by two
mass units. **11.** Mn, 54.94 **13. a.** 1.0 mol N, 3.0 mol H;
b. 2.0 mol N, 4.0 mol H; **c.** 2.0 mol N, 8.0 mol H, 2.0 mol Cr,
7.0 mol O **15. a.** 6.0×10^{23} atoms N, 1.8×10^{24} atoms H;
b. 1.2×10^{24} atoms N, 2.4×10^{24} atoms H; **c.** 1.2×10^{24} atoms N,
4.8×10^{24} atoms H, 1.2×10^{24} atoms Cr, 4.2×10^{24} atoms O
17. a. 14 g N, 3.0 g H; **b.** 28 g N, 4.0 g H; **c.** 28 g N, 8.0 g H,
1.0×10^2 g Cr, 1.1×10^2 g O **19. a.** 5.9×10^{-2} mol N, $1.8 \times$
10^{-1} mol H; **b.** 6.2×10^{-2} mol N, 1.2×10^{-1} mol H; **c.** $7.9 \times$
10^{-3} mol N, 3.2×10^{-2} mol H, 7.9×10^{-3} mol Cr, $2.8 \times$
10^{-2} mol O **21. a.** 3.5×10^{22} atoms N, 1.1×10^{23} atoms H;
b. 3.7×10^{22} atoms N, 7.2×10^{22} atoms H; **c.** 4.8×10^{21} atoms N,
1.9×10^{22} atoms H, 4.8×10^{21} atoms Cr, 1.7×10^{22} atoms O

23. Al_2O_3, 101.96 g/mol; Na_3AlF_6, 209.95 g/mol **25.** $2.839 \times$
10^{-3} mol, 1.710×10^{21} molecules **27. a.** 1.661×10^{-22} mol;
b. 5.549 mol; **c.** 8.303×10^{-22} mol; **d.** 8.953 mol; **e.** $2.491 \times$
10^{-22} mol **29. a.** 1.40×10^{-2} g N_2; **b.** 8.41×10^{-2} g N_2;
c. 4.2×10^3 g N_2; **d.** 4.653×10^{-23} g N_2; **e.** 5.60×10^{-14} g N_2;
f. 5.04×10^{-10} g N_2; **g.** 1.4×10^{-7} g N_2 **31. a.** 294.30 g/mol;
b. 3.40×10^{-2} mol; **c.** 459 g; **d.** 1.0×10^{19} molecules; **e.** $4.9 \times$
10^{21} atoms; **f.** 4.9×10^{-13} g; **g.** 4.887×10^{-22} g
33. i. 54.30% F, 45.70% S; ii. 70.37% F, 29.63% S;
iii. 78.08% F, 21.92% S **35.** 13.35% Y, 41.22% Ba, 28.62% Cu,
16.81% O **37.** $Na_3PO_4 < (NPCl_2)_3 < P_4O_{10} < PH_3$ **39.** 1360 g/mol
41. CdS, 77.79% Cd; CdSe, 58.73% Cd; CdTe, 46.83% Cd
43. a. 50.00% C, 5.595% H, 44.41% O; **b.** 55.80% C, 7.025% H,
37.18% O; **c.** 67.90% C, 5.699% H, 26.40% N **45.** i. SF_2;
ii. SF_4; iii. SF_6 **47. a.** $S_4N_4H_4$; **b.** $N_3P_3Cl_6$; **c.** $Co_2C_8O_8$;
d. S_4N_4 **49. a.** 39.99% C, 6.73% H, 53.30% O; **b.** 40.00% C,
6.7140% H, 53.29% O; **c.** 40.00% C, 6.714% H, 53.29% O (all the
same except or rounding differences) **51.** $C_3H_6O_2$ **53.** $Na_2S_2O_3$
55. NO_2, N_2O_4 **57.** $C_7H_5N_3O_6$ **59. a.** $3Fe_2O_3(s) + CO(g) \rightarrow$
$2Fe_3O_4(s) + CO_2(g)$; **b.** $Fe_3O_4(s) + CO(g) \rightarrow 3FeO(s) + CO_2(g)$
61. a. $C_{12}H_{22}O_{11}(s) + 12O_2(g) \rightarrow 12CO_2(g) + 11H_2O(g)$;
b. $2C_6H_6(\ell) + 15O_2(g) \rightarrow 12CO_2(g) + 6H_2O(g)$; **c.** $4Fe(s) +$
$3O_2(g) \rightarrow 2Fe_2O_3(s)$; **d.** $2C_4H_{10}(g) + 13O_2(g) \rightarrow 8CO_2(g) +$
$10H_2O(g)$; **e.** $4FeO(s) + O_2(g) \rightarrow 2Fe_2O_3(s)$ **63. a.** $Cu(s) +$
$2AgNO_3(aq) \rightarrow 2Ag(s) + Cu(NO_3)_2(aq)$; **b.** $Zn(s) + 2HCl(aq) \rightarrow$
$ZnCl_2(aq) + H_2(g)$; **c.** $Au_2S_3(s) + 3H_2(g) \rightarrow 2Au(s) + 3H_2S(g)$;
d. $Ca(s) + 2H_2O(\ell) \rightarrow Ca(OH)_2(aq) + H_2(g)$ **65. a.** $SiO_2(s) +$
$2C(s) \rightarrow Si(s) + 2CO(g)$; **b.** $SiCl_4(\ell) + 2Mg(s) \rightarrow Si(s) + 2MgCl_2(s)$;
c. $Na_2SiF_6(s) + 4Na(s) \rightarrow Si(s) + 6NaF(s)$ **67.** $Pb(NO_3)_2(aq) +$
$H_3AsO_4(aq) \rightarrow PbHAsO_4(s) + 2HNO_3(aq)$ **69.** 6.51 g Cr_2O_3,
1.20 g N_2, 3.09 g H_2O **71.** 4.4 kg **73.** 97 g **75. a.** 76 mg;
b. 52 mg **77. a.** stoichiometric mixture; **b.** I_2; **c.** Mg; **d.** Mg;
e. stoichiometric mixture; **f.** I_2; **g.** stoichiometric mixture; **h.** I_2;
i. Mg **79.** 1.88 g (theoretical), 93.6% **81. a.** 2.3 g; **b.** 1.7 g S_8
83. a. 1050 g; **b.** 2810 g $C_{14}H_8O_2$, 243 g H_2O; **c.** 69.8%
85. a. 242.55 g/mol; **b.** 150.89 g/mol; **c.** 50,000 g/mol;
d. 97.99 g/mol; **e.** 100.09 g/mol **87.** About 700 monomer units
89. a. $2C_8H_{18}(\ell) + 25O_2(g) \rightarrow 16CO_2(g) + 18H_2O(g)$; **b.** $9.6 \times$
10^{13} g **91.** C_3H_4, C_9H_{12} **93.** Sb_2O_3, Sb_4O_6 **95.** $C_4H_3O_2$, $C_8H_6O_4$
97. a. Al; **b.** Al; **c.** Al; **d.** Al; **e.** Al; **f.** Al **99.** 1.12×10^6 g
101. 35.9% **103. a.** 795 g; **b.** 96.2% **105.** Al_2Se_3 **107.** $2.81 \times$
10^6 g HCN, 5.62×10^6 g H_2O **109.** 207 g/mol, Pb
111. 40.% Cu_2O, 60.% CuO

Chapter 4

1. Solubility refers to how much dissolves. Electrolyte refers to
whether or not ions are produced. **3. a.** $NaBr \rightarrow Na^+ + Br^-$;
b. $MgCl_2 \rightarrow Mg^{2+} + 2Cl^-$; **c.** $Al(NO_3)_3 \rightarrow Al^{3+} + 3NO_3^-$;
d. $(NH_4)_2SO_4 \rightarrow 2NH_4^+ + SO_4^{2-}$; **e.** $HI \rightarrow H^+ + I^-$; **f.** $FeSO_4 \rightarrow$
$Fe^{2+} + SO_4^{2-}$; **g.** $KMnO_4 \rightarrow K^+ + MnO_4^-$; **h.** $HClO_4 \rightarrow H^+ +$
ClO_4^-; **i.** $NH_4C_2H_3O_2 \rightarrow NH_4^+ + C_2H_3O_2^-$ **5.** $CaCl_2(s) \rightarrow$
$Ca^{2+}(aq) + 2Cl^-(aq)$ **7. a.** Place 5.8 g NaCl in a 1 L volumetric
flask; add water to dissolve the solid and fill to the mark. **b.** Add
40. mL of 2.5 M stock solution to a 1 L volumetric flask; fill to the
mark with water. **c.** As in a., using 40. g $NaIO_3$. **d.** As in b.,
using 50. mL of the 0.20 M stock solution. **e.** As in a., using 10. g
KHP. **f.** As in b., using 80. mL of the 0.50 m stock solution.
9. a. 0.2677 M; **b.** 1.255×10^{-3} M; **c.** 8.065×10^{-3} M
11. a. $M_{Ca^{2+}} = 0.15$ M, $M_{Cl^-} = 0.30$ M; **b.** $M_{Al^{3+}} = 0.26$ M,

$M_{NO_3^-} = 0.78\ M$;   **c.** $M_{K^+} = 0.50\ M$, $M_{Cr_2O_7^{2-}} = 0.25\ M$;
d. $M_{Al^{3+}} = 4.0 \times 10^{-3}\ M$, $M_{SO_4^{2-}} = 6.0 \times 10^{-3}\ M$ **13.** $M_{NH_4^+} = 0.272\ M$, $M_{SO_4^{2-}} = 0.136\ M$ **15.** 30. mg Mg^{2+}/L = 1.2 × 10^{-3} mol/L; 75 mg Ca^{2+}/L = 1.9 × 10^{-3} mol/L; 1250 mg Mg^{2+}/L = 0.0514 mol/L; 200. mg Ca^{2+}/L = 4.99 × 10^{-3} mol/L **17.** 2.595 × 10^{-3} M **19. a.** $BaCl_2(aq) + Na_2SO_4(aq) \rightarrow BaSO_4(s) + 2NaCl(aq)$; $Ba^{2+}(aq) + 2Cl^-(aq) + 2Na^+(aq) + SO_4^{2-}(aq) \rightarrow BaSO_4(s) + 2Na^+(aq) + 2Cl^-(aq)$; $Ba^{2+}(aq) + SO_4^{2-}(aq) \rightarrow BaSO_4(s)$; **b.** $Pb(NO_3)_2(aq) + 2HCl(aq) \rightarrow PbCl_2(s) + 2HNO_3(aq)$; $Pb^{2+}(aq) + 2NO_3^-(aq) + 2H^+(aq) + 2Cl^-(aq) \rightarrow PbCl_2(s) + 2H^+(aq) + 2NO_3^-(aq)$; $Pb^{2+}(aq) + 2Cl^-(aq) \rightarrow PbCl_2(s)$;   **c.** $3AgNO_3(aq) + Na_3PO_4(aq) \rightarrow Ag_3PO_4(s) + 3NaNO_3(aq)$; $3Ag^+(aq) + 3NO_3^-(aq) + 3Na^+(aq) + PO_4^{3-}(aq) \rightarrow Ag_3PO_4(s) + 3Na^+(aq) + 3NO_3^-(aq)$; $3Ag^+(aq) + PO_4^{3-}(aq) \rightarrow Ag_3PO_4(s)$;   **d.** $3NaOH(aq) + Fe(NO_3)_3(aq) \rightarrow Fe(OH)_3(s) + 3NaNO_3(aq)$; $3Na^+(aq) + 3OH^-(aq) + Fe^{3+}(aq) + 3NO_3^-(aq) \rightarrow Fe(OH)_3(s) + 3Na^+(aq) + 3NO_3^-(aq)$; $Fe^{3+}(aq) + 3OH^-(aq) \rightarrow Fe(OH)_3(s)$ **21. a.** $Ag^+(aq) + I^-(aq) \rightarrow AgI(s)$;   **b.** $Cu^{2+}(aq) + S^{2-}(aq) \rightarrow CuS(s)$;   **c.** $Co^{2+}(aq) + 2OH^-(aq) \rightarrow Co(OH)_2(s)$;   **d.** No reaction **23. a.** $Ba^{2+}(aq) + SO_4^{2-}(aq) \rightarrow BaSO_4(s)$;   **b.** $Pb^{2+}(aq) + 2Cl^-(aq) \rightarrow PbCl_2(s)$;   **c.** No reaction;   **d.** No reaction;   **e.** $Cu^{2+}(aq) + 2OH^-(aq) \rightarrow Cu(OH)_2(s)$
25. Three possibilities are: addition of H_2SO_4 solution to give a white ppt. of $PbSO_4$; addition of HCl to give a white ppt. of $PbCl_2$; addition of K_2CrO_4 solution to give a bright yellow ppt. of $PbCrO_4$ **27.** 2.82 g **29.** 750. mL **31. a.** $2HClO_4(aq) + Mg(OH)_2(s) \rightarrow Mg(ClO_4)_2(aq) + 2H_2O(\ell)$; $2H^+(aq) + 2ClO_4^-(aq) + Mg(OH)_2(s) \rightarrow Mg^{2+}(aq) + 2ClO_4^-(aq) + 2H_2O(\ell)$; $2H^+(aq) + Mg(OH)_2(s) \rightarrow Mg^{2+}(aq) + 2H_2O(\ell)$;   **b.** $HCN(aq) + NaOH(aq) \rightarrow NaCN(aq) + H_2O(\ell)$; $HCN(aq) + Na^+(aq) + OH^-(aq) \rightarrow Na^+(aq) + CN^-(aq) + H_2O(\ell)$; $HCN(aq) + OH^-(aq) \rightarrow H_2O(\ell) + CN^-(aq)$;   **c.** $HCl(aq) + NaOH(aq) \rightarrow NaCl(aq) + H_2O(\ell)$; $H^+(aq) + Cl^-(aq) + Na^+(aq) + OH^-(aq) \rightarrow Na^+(aq) + Cl^-(aq) + H_2O(\ell)$; $H^+(aq) + OH^-(aq) \rightarrow H_2O(\ell)$ **33. a.** $KOH(aq) + HNO_3(aq) \rightarrow H_2O(\ell) + KNO_3(aq)$; $K^+(aq) + OH^-(aq) + H^+(aq) + NO_3^-(aq) \rightarrow H_2O(\ell) + K^+(aq) + NO_3^-(aq)$; $OH^-(aq) + H^+(aq) \rightarrow H_2O(\ell)$;   **b.** $Ba(OH)_2(aq) + 2HCl(aq) \rightarrow 2H_2O(\ell) + BaCl_2(aq)$; $Ba^{2+}(aq) + 2OH^-(aq) + 2H^+(aq) + 2Cl^-(aq) \rightarrow Ba^{2+}(aq) + 2Cl^-(aq) + 2H_2O(\ell)$; $OH^-(aq) + H^+(aq) \rightarrow H_2O(\ell)$;   **c.** $3HClO_4(aq) + Fe(OH)_3(s) \rightarrow 3H_2O(\ell) + Fe(ClO_4)_3(aq)$; $3H^+(aq) + 3ClO_4^-(aq) + Fe(OH)_3(s) \rightarrow 3H_2O(\ell) + Fe^{3+}(aq) + 3ClO_4^-(aq)$; $3H^+(aq) + Fe(OH)_3(s) \rightarrow 3H_2O(\ell) + Fe^{3+}(aq)$ **35. a.** 100. ml;   **b.** 16.7 mL;   **c.** 66.7 mL;   **d.** 50.0 mL
37. Basic, $C_{NO_3^-} = 0.25\ M$, $C_{Na^+} = 2.5\ M$, $C_{OH^-} = 2.3\ M$ **39.** 0.102 M **41. a.** K, +1; O, −2; Mn, +7;   **b.** Ni, +4; O, −2;   **c.** Fe, +2;   **d.** H, +1; O, −2; N, −3; P, +5;   **e.** P, +3; O, −2;   **f.** O, −2; Fe, $+\frac{8}{3}$;   **g.** O, −2; F, −1; Xe, +6;   **h.** S, +4; F, −1;   **i.** C, +2; O, −2;   **j.** Na, +1; O, −2; C, +3 **43.** ClO^-, +1; ClO_2^-, +3; ClO_3^-, +5; ClO_4^-, +7

45.

Redox?	Oxidizing Agent	Reducing Agent	Substance Oxidized	Substance Reduced
a. Yes	O_2	CH_4	CH_4 (C)	O_2 (O)
b. Yes	HCl	Zn	Zn	HCl (H)
c. No	—	—	—	—
d. Yes	O_3	NO	NO (N)	O_3 (O)
e. Yes	H_2O_2	H_2O_2	H_2O_2 (O)	H_2O_2 (O)
f. Yes	CuCl	CuCl	CuCl (Cu)	CuCl (Cu)

47. a. $Zn + 2HCl \rightarrow Zn^{2+} + H_2 + 2Cl^-$;   **b.** $2H^+ + 3I^- + ClO^- \rightarrow I_3^- + Cl^- + H_2O$;   **c.** $7H_2O + 4H^+ + 3As_2O_3 + 4NO_3^- \rightarrow 4NO +$

$6H_3AsO_4$;   **d.** $16H^+ + 2MnO_4^- + 10Br^- \rightarrow 5Br_2 + 2Mn^{2+} + 8H_2O$;   **e.** $8H^+ + 3CH_3OH + Cr_2O_7^{2-} \rightarrow 2Cr^{3+} + 3CH_2O + 7H_2O$ **49. a.** $2H_2O + Al + MnO_4^- \rightarrow Al(OH)_4^- + MnO_2$;   **b.** $2OH^- + Cl_2 \rightarrow Cl^- + ClO^- + H_2O$;   **c.** $OH^- + H_2O + NO_2^- + 2Al \rightarrow NH_3 + 2AlO_2^-$ **51.** $4NaCl + 2H_2SO_4 + MnO_2 \rightarrow 2Na_2SO_4 + MnCl_2 + Cl_2 + 2H_2O$ **53.** $1.622 \times 10^{-2}\ M$ **55. a.** $4.46 \times 10^{-2}\ M$;   **b.** 24.8 mL **57.** 0.942 M **59.** $2H^+ + Mn + 2HNO_3 \rightarrow Mn^{2+} + 2NO_2 + 2H_2O$; $3H_2O + 2Mn^{2+} + 5IO_4^- \rightarrow 2MnO_4^- + 5IO_3^- + 6H^+$ **61.** 18.8 g **63.** 0.3947% **65. a.** 0.8393 M;   **b.** 5.010% **67.** $2.589 \times 10^{-2}\ M$ **69. a.** No, no element shows a change in oxidation number.   **b.** 3.7 g Fe_2O_3 **71.** Fe^{2+} will react with MnO_4^- (purple) producing Fe^{3+} and Mn^{2+} (almost colorless). There is no reaction between MnO_4^- and Fe^{3+}. **73.** 45.3% **75.** 4.03% **77. a.** $8HCl + 2Fe \rightarrow 2HFeCl_4 + 3H_2$;   **b.** $6H^+ + 8I^- + IO_3^- \rightarrow 3I_3^- + 3H_2O$;   **c.** $97Ce^{4+} + 54H_2O + Cr(NCS)_6^{4-} \rightarrow 97Ce^{3+} + Cr^{3+} + 6NO_3^- + 6CO_2 + 6SO_4^{2-} + 108H^+$;   **d.** $64OH^- + 2CrI_3 + 27Cl_2 \rightarrow 54Cl^- + 2CrO_4^{2-} + 6IO_4^- + 32H_2O$;   **e.** $258OH^- + Fe(CN)_6^{4-} + 61Ce^{4+} \rightarrow Fe(OH)_3 + 61Ce(OH)_3 + 6CO_3^{2-} + 6NO_3^- + 36H_2O$;   **f.** $2Fe(OH)_2 + H_2O_2 \rightarrow 2Fe(OH)_3$ **79.** $CaCO_3(s) + H_2SO_4(aq) \rightarrow CaSO_4(aq) + H_2O(\ell) + CO_2(g)$ **81.** 3.72 M **83.** $4.7 \times 10^{-2}\ M$ **85. a.** $6H^+ + 8I^- + IO_3^- \rightarrow 3I_3^- + 3H_2O$;   **b.** $2S_2O_3^{2-} + I_3^- \rightarrow 3I^- + S_4O_6^{2-}$;   **c.** 0.0468 M;   **d.** Place 1.07 g KIO_3 in a 500 mL volumetric flask. Add water to dissolve the KIO_3 and continue adding water to the mark. **87. a.** 0.0559 g;   **b.** 0.242 g;   **c.** 53.1% **89.** 0.123 g SO_4^{2-}, 60.0% SO_4^{2-}, 61% K_2SO_4, and 39% Na_2SO_4 **91. a.** 65 ppm;   **b.** 5.0×10^3 ppb **93.** 100. ppm standard: dilute 10.0 mL of the 1000.0 ppm stock to 100. mL; 75.0 ppm standard: dilute 7.50 mL of the 1000.0 ppm stock to 100. mL; 50.0 ppm standard: dilute 5.00 mL of the 1000.0 ppm stock to 100. mL; 25.0 ppm standard: dilute 2.50 mL of the 1000.0 ppm stock to 100. mL; 10.0 ppm standard: dilute 1.00 mL of the 1000.0 ppm stock to 100. mL. **95.** $0.0785\ M \pm 0.0002\ M$ **97.** The first procedure would give the most accurate concentration.

Chapter 5

1. a. The pressure of the gas inside the can increases with T, causing the can to rupture.   **b.** As you draw a vacuum in your mouth, atmospheric pressure pushes the liquid up the straw.   **c.** The external atmospheric pressure is greater than the internal pressure, so the can collapses. **3.** At constant n and T, nRT = constant, so $PV = k$ (Boyle's law). At constant P and n, $V = nRT/P = kT$ (Charles's law). **5.** 29.92 in. **7.** 65 torr, 8.7×10^3 Pa, 8.6×10^{-2} atm **9. a.** 620. torr, 0.816 atm, 8.27×10^4 Pa;   **b.** 935 torr, 1.23 atm, 1.25×10^5 Pa;   **c.** 495 torr, 810. torr **11. a.** 14.0 L;   **b.** 4.72×10^{-2} mol;   **c.** 678 K;   **d.** 133 atm **13.** $8.315 \times 10^3\ L \cdot Pa/K \cdot mol$ **15.** $P_{H_2} = 317$ torr, $P_{N_2} = 110$ torr, $P_{Tot} = 430$ torr **17.** $V_2 = 1.15\ V_1$ **19.** 0.45 mol **21.** $P_{H_2} = 0.319$ atm, $P_{He} = 0.161$ atm **23.** 239 mL **25. a.** 69.6 K;   **b.** 32.3 atm **27.** 33 Pa **29.** 0.286 g **31.** 5.77 g/L ($SiCl_4$); 4.60 g/L ($SiHCl_3$) **33.** N_2H_4 **35.** 8.172×10^{12} L of N_2, 2.453×10^{13} L of H_2 **37.** 307 L **39. a.** $2CH_4(g) + 2NH_3(g) + 3O_2(g) \rightarrow 2HCN(g) + 6H_2O(g)$;   **b.** 13.3 L **41.** 13.3% **43.** 1.2 L **45.** 3.40×10^3 J/mol (273 K); 6.81×10^3 J/mol (546 K) **47.** 652 m/s (273 K); 921 m/s (546 K) **49.** No, there is a distribution of energies. **51. a.** all the same;   **b.** Flask C **53.** NO **55. a.** 12.24 atm;   **b.** 12.13 atm (one extra sig. fig.);   **c.** The ideal gas law is high by 0.91% (using one extra sig. fig. in b.). **57.** 5×10^{-7} atm, 1×10^{13} molecules/cm^3 **59.** 0.04 mL **61.** $2NO_2(g) + H_2O(l) \rightarrow HNO_3(aq) + HNO_2(aq)$; $2SO_2(g) + O_2(g) \rightarrow 2SO_3(g)$; $SO_3(g) + H_2O(\ell) \rightarrow H_2SO_4(aq)$

63. a.

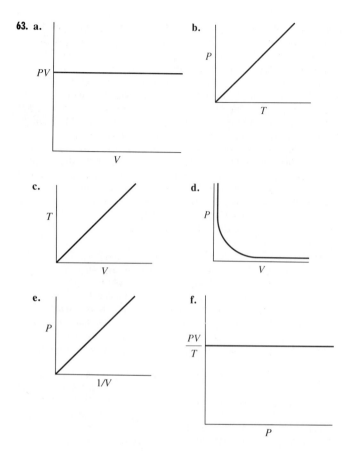

65. a. 46.6 atm; **b.** 1.02×10^3 K; **c.** 171 K **67.** 3.7 L **69.** BrF_3
71. 233 g **73.** The calculated molar mass from the two sets of data
give values close to the expected value of 207.0 g/mol for
$Be(C_5H_7O_2)_2$. **75.** C_2H_3N; C_2H_3N **77.** 1490 **79.** C_3H_8 **81.** $dT = PM/R =$ constant, $d =$ constant$/T$; $-272.6°C$ **83.** 19 min. **85.** At low
P and high T, an^2/V, an^3b/V^2, and nbP are negligible compared to PV.
$PV = nRT$. **87.** 0.921 **89.** XeF_4 **91.** 1.6×10^3 g **93. a.** 0.19 torr;
b. 6.6×10^{21} molecules/m³; **c.** 6.6×10^{15} molecules/cm³
95. benzene: 16 ppbv, 3.9×10^{11} molecules/cm³; toluene: 37 ppbv,
8.9×10^{11} molecules/cm³

Chapter 6

1. A coffee-cup calorimeter is at constant pressure. The heat at constant P equals ΔH. A bomb calorimeter is at constant volume. The
heat at constant V equals ΔE. **3.** A function whose change depends
only on the initial and final states and not on the pathway from the initial to the final state. If H and E were not state functions, the Law of
Conservation of Energy (First Law) would not be true. **5.** Standard
enthalpies of formation provide a reference point, allowing ΔH comparisons. **7.** 150 J **9.** 1.0 kg object with velocity of 2.0 m/s.
11. a. 36 kJ; **b.** 35 kJ; **c.** -85 kJ; **d.** all **13.** 16 kJ
15. 10. L · atm = 1.0×10^3 J **17.** $q = 30.9$ kJ, $w = -12.5$ kJ,
$\Delta E = 18.4$ kJ **19. a.** endothermic; **b.** exothermic; **c.** exothermic;
d. endothermic **21. a.** 2.54×10^3 kJ; **b.** 7.4×10^3 kJ; **c.** 693 kJ
23. a. 54.9 kJ; **b.** 24.3 J/mol · °C **25.** 0.129 J/g · °C, 26.7 J/g · °C
27. 0.45 J/g · °C **29.** 170 J/g, 2.0×10^1 kJ/mol **31.** 2.05 kJ/°C

33. -300 J, -60 kJ/mol **35.** -296.1 kJ **37.** 28.4 kJ **39.** -233 kJ
41. -427 kJ **43.** The enthalpy change for the formation of one mole
of a compound at 25°C from its elements, with all substances in their
standard states. $Na(s) + \frac{1}{2}Cl_2(g) \rightarrow NaCl(s)$; $H_2(g) + \frac{1}{2}O_2(g) \rightarrow$
$H_2O(\ell)$; $6C^{graphite}(s) + 6H_2(g) + 3O_2(g) \rightarrow C_6H_{12}O_6(s)$; $Pb(s) + S(s) +$
$2O_2(g) \rightarrow PbSO_4(s)$ **45. a.** $-940.$ kJ; **b.** -265 kJ; **c.** -176 kJ
47. a. -908 kJ, -112 kJ, $-140.$ kJ; **b.** $12NH_3(g) + 21O_2(g) \rightarrow$
$8HNO_3(aq) + 4NO(g) + 14H_2O(g)$, exothermic **49.** -2677 kJ
51. 132 kJ **53.** -169 kJ/mol **55.** 1.05×10^5 L **57.** -129 kJ
59. a. -55.5 kJ; **b.** -3.55×10^4 kJ **61.** Al. Al has a higher heat
capacity and a lower density than Fe. The same amount of heat could
be dissipated by a smaller mass of Al. **63.** 4.9×10^6 kJ
65. $-390.$ kJ, 30.0°C **67.** -1256 kJ, 11,600°C $\approx$ 12,000°C
69. 2600 g **71. a.** -361 kJ; **b.** -199 kJ; **c.** -227 kJ;
d. -112 kJ **73.** Cooling. Heat is produced by this exothermic reaction. Cooling must be provided to reduce the temperature of the reaction mixture. **75.** -11 kJ **77.** 1×10^4 steps

Chapter 7

1. Planck found it necessary to assume quantized energies to explain
the radiation that heated bodies emit. Einstein's analysis of the photoelectric effect. **3.** Particles with very small mass and large velocities.
5. a. A discrete bundle of light energy; **b.** A number describing a
discrete state of an electron; **c.** The lowest energy state; **d.** An allowed energy state higher than the ground state **7.** Spatial orientation
9. A surface where the probability of finding an electron is zero.
11. We do not know the position of any electron, so we cannot calculate precisely the repulsion energy. **13.** There is a higher probability
of finding the $4s$ electron very close to the nucleus as compared to the
$3d$ electron. **15.** If one more electron is added to a half filled subshell, electron-electron repulsions will increase. **17.** Each element has
a characteristic emission spectrum. **19.** The electron is completely
removed from the atom. **21.** 3.01 m **23.** 3.0×10^{10} s⁻¹; $2.0 \times$
10^{-23} J/photon; 12 J/mol **25.** 276 nm **27.** 8.17×10^{-19} J; 243 nm
29. No **31. a.** 656.7 nm; **b.** 486.4 nm; **c.** 121.6 nm **33.** $n = 1$,
91.20 nm; $n = 2$, 364.8 nm **35.** See Fig. 7.8 **37.** $6 \rightarrow 5$, 7462 nm;
$6 \rightarrow 1$, 93.79 nm **39. a.** 2.6×10^{-5} nm; **b.** 1.6×10^{-2} nm;
c. 9.8×10^{-26} nm **41.** 7.3×10^3 m/s; 7.3×10^5 m/s **43.** $5.79 \times$
10^5 nm; Δx much larger than atom **45.** $n = 1, 2, 3, \ldots$; $\ell =$
$0, 1, 2, \ldots (n-1)$; $m_\ell = -\ell, \ldots, -2, -1, 0, 1, 2, \ldots, +\ell$.
47. b. ℓ must be $<n$; **d.** For $\ell = 0$, $m_\ell = 0$ only
49. a. 1312 kJ/mol; **b.** 5246 kJ/mol; **c.** 1.180×10^4 kJ/mol; The
relative sizes are $1:\frac{1}{2}:\frac{1}{3}$. **51.** 3; 1; 5; 25; 16 **53. a.** 32; **b.** 8;
c. 25; **d.** 10; **e.** 6 **55.** Sc: $1s^22s^22p^63s^23p^64s^23d^1$; Fe:
$1s^22s^22p^63s^23p^64s^23d^6$; S: $1s^22s^22p^63s^23p^4$; P: $1s^22s^22p^63s^23p^3$; Cs:
$1s^22s^22p^63s^23p^64s^23d^{10}4p^65s^24d^{10}5p^66s^1$; Eu:
$1s^22s^22p^63s^23p^64s^23d^{10}4p^65s^24d^{10}5p^66s^24f^65d^1$ (Actual: $[Xe]6s^24f^7$);
Pt: $1s^22s^22p^63s^23p^64s^23d^{10}4p^65s^24d^{10}5p^66s^24f^{14}5d^8$ (Actual:
$[Xe]6s^14f^{14}5d^9$); Xe: $1s^22s^22p^63s^23p^64s^23d^{10}4p^65s^24d^{10}5p^6$; Br:
$1s^22s^22p^63s^23p^64s^23d^{10}4p^5$; Se: $1s^22s^22p^63s^23p^64s^23d^{10}4p^4$ **57.** Cr,
Cu, Nb, Mo, Tc, Ru, Rh, Pd, Ag, Pt, Au **59. a.** F, $1s^22s^22p^5$;
b. K, $[Ar]4s^1$; **c.** Be, $1s^22s^2$; Mg, $[Ne]3s^2$; Ca, $[Ar]4s^2$; **d.** In,
$[Kr]5s^24d^{10}5p^1$; **e.** C, $1s^22s^22p^2$; Si, $[Ne]3s^23p^2$; **f.** 118, $[Rn]$
$7s^25f^{14}6d^{10}7p^6$ **61.** See *Solutions Guide*. **63.** none; an excited state;
energy released **65.** Sc, 1; Ti, 2; Al, 1; Sn, 2; Te, 2; Br, 1
67. a. Be < Mg < Ca; **b.** Xe < I < Te; **c.** Ge < Ga < In
69. a. Ca < Mg < Be; **b.** Te < I < Xe; **c.** In < Ga < Ge
71. a. Be < Mg < Ca; **b.** Te < I < Xe; **c.** Ga < Ge < In **73.** Se

has lower ionization energy because it has two electrons in the same $4p$ orbital. **75. a.** Li; **b.** P; **c.** O^+; **d.** Cl; **e.** Cu **77.** IE $\approx$ 340 kJ/mol; mp $\approx$ 22°C **79. a.** O < S; **b.** I < Br < F < Cl **81. a.** Li, S; **b.** Li, S; **c.** K, Sc **83.** Yes, exothermic **85.** P(g) → $P^+(g)$ + e^- **87. a.** −1445 kJ/mol; **b.** −580 kJ/mol **89.** Li^+ ions, the smallest alkali metal cations, are most strongly attracted to water molecules. **91.** potassium peroxide, K_2O_2; K^{2+} unstable **93.** 6.582 × 10^{14} s^{-1}; 4.361 × 10^{-19} J **95. a.** lithium nitride, Li_3N; **c.** sodium bromide, NaBr; **c.** potassium sulfide, K_2S **97. a.** 4Li(s) + $O_2(g)$ → $2Li_2O(s)$; **b.** 2K(s) + S(s) → $K_2S(s)$ **99.** 119, $[Rn]7s^25f^{14}6d^{10}7p^68s^1$ **101.** 386 nm **103. a.** 18; **b.** 2; **c.** 0; **d.** 1 **105.** No **107.** Each peak corresponds to a subshell with a different n value. Corresponding subshells are closer to the nucleus for heavier elements since the effective nuclear charge increases. **109. b.** and **f.** are possible. **a.** For $\ell = 0$, $m_\ell \neq 1$; **c.** $m_s = \pm\frac{1}{2}$; **d.** For $n = 1$, $\ell \neq 1$; **e.** For $\ell = 2$, $m_\ell \neq -3$ **111. a.** 21; **b.** 21; **c.** 11 **113.** Yes, for $(IE)_{13}$ **115.** The IE of O (and also F and Ne) is lower because of extra electron-electron repulsions in the $2p$ orbital. **117.** Electron-electron repulsions must be considered when adding an electron to an atom. Smaller atoms attract electrons more strongly, yet have larger electron-electron repulsions. The two factors oppose one another, leading to relatively small variations in electron affinities. **119.** $1s^22s^22p^63s^23p^6$; Ar; 1.5205 MJ/mol; 0.94 Å; $1s^22s^22p^63s^2$; Mg; 0.7377 MJ/mol; 1.60 Å; $1s^22s^22p^63s^23p^64s^1$; K; 0.4189 MJ/mol; 1.97 Å **121. a.** 1212 kJ; **b.** −443 kJ; **c.** 146 kJ; **d.** 407 kJ; **f.** 1117 kJ; **g.** 1524 kJ **123.** There are 14 elements between La and Hf, making Hf considerably smaller than La. **125. a.** 3; **b.** first period: 3, second period: 12; **c.** 15; **d.** 21 **127.** None of the noble gases had been discovered when Mendeleev published his periodic table. Thus, no element was out of place in terms of reactivity.

Chapter 8

1. a. Electronegativity: The ability of an atom in a molecule to attract electrons to itself. Electron affinity: The energy change for the reaction M(g) + e^- → $M^-(g)$. The E.A. deals with isolated atoms in the gas phase. **b.** Covalent bond: sharing of an electron pair. Polar covalent bond: unequal sharing of an electron pair. **c.** Ionic bond: electrons are no longer shared. Completely unequal sharing (i.e., transfer) of electrons from one atom to another. **3.** No, more highly charged ions have a greater attraction for an electron. Thus, the electronegativity of an element increases as its oxidation state increases. **5.** 1. polar bonds; 2. a structure such that the polar bonds do not cancel **7. a.** C < N < O; **b.** Se < S < Cl; **c.** Sn < Ge < Si; **d.** Tl < Ge < S **9. a.** Ge—F; **b.** P—Cl; **c.** S—F; **d.** Ti—Cl **11.** Order of E.N. from Fig. 8.3: **a.** C (2.5) < N (3.0) < O (3.5), same; **b.** Se (2.4) < S (2.5) < Cl (3.0), same; **c.** Si = Ge = Sn (1.8), different; **d.** Tl (1.8) = Ge (1.8) < S (2.5), different. Most polar bonds using actual E.N. values: **a.** Si—F and Ge—F equal polarity (Ge—F predicted); **b.** P—Cl (same as predicted); **c.** S—F (same as predicted); **d.** Si—Cl and Ge—Cl equal polarity (TiCl correctly predicted). **13. a.** Cu > Cu^+ > Cu^{2+}; **b.** Pt^{2+} > Pd^{2+} > Ni^{2+}; **c.** Se^{2-} > S^{2-} > O^{2-}; **d.** La^{3+} > Eu^{3+} > Gd^{3+} > Yb^{3+}; **e.** Te^{2-} > I^- > Xe > Cs^+ > Ba^{2+} > La^{3+} **15. a.** Mg^{2+}: $1s^22s^22p^6$; Sn^{2+}: $[Kr]5s^24d^{10}$; K^+: $1s^22s^22p^63s^23p^6$; Al^{3+}: $1s^22s^22p^6$; Tl^+: $[Xe]6s^24f^{14}5d^{10}$; As^{3+}: $[Ar]4s^23d^{10}$; **b.** N^{3-}, O^{2-}, and F^-: $1s^22s^22p^6$; Te^{2-}: $[Kr]5s^24d^{10}5p^6$; **c.** Be^{2+}: [He]; Rb^+: [Kr]; Ba^{2+}: [Xe]; Se^{2-}: [Kr]; I^-: [Xe] **17. a.** Sc^{3+}; **b.** Te^{2-}; **c.** Ce^{4+}, Ti^{4+}; **d.** Ba^{2+} **19.** Se^{2-}, Br^-, Rb^+, Sr^{2+}, Y^{3+}, Zr^{4+} **21. a.** NaCl, Na^+

smaller than K^+; **b.** LiF, F^- smaller than Cl^-; **c.** MgO, O^{2-} greater charge than OH^-; **d.** $Fe(OH)_3$, Fe^{3+} greater charge than Fe^{2+}; **e.** Na_2O, O^{2-} greater charge than Cl^-; **f.** MgO, Mg^{2+} smaller than Ba^{2+} and O^{2-} smaller than S^{2-}. **23.** $\Delta H_f^\circ = -412$ kJ/mol **25. a.** The lattice energy for $Mg^{2+}O^{2-}$ will be much larger than for Mg^+O^-. **b.** Mg^+ and O^- both have unpaired electrons. In Mg^{2+} and O^{2-} there are no unpaired electrons. Hence, Mg^+O^- would be paramagnetic; $Mg^{2+}O^{2-}$ would be diamagnetic. Paramagnetism can be detected by measuring the mass of a sample in the presence and absence of a magnetic field. **27.** Ca^{2+} has greater charge than Na^+, and Se^{2-} is smaller than Te^{2-}. Since charge differences affect lattice energy values more than size differences, we expect the trend from most exothermic to least exothermic to be:

$$CaSe > CaTe > Na_2Se > Na_2Te$$
$$(-2862) \quad (-2721) \quad (-2130) \quad (-2095)$$

29. a. Li_3N (lithium nitride); **b.** Ga_2O_3 (gallium oxide); **c.** RbCl (rubidium chloride); **d.** BaS (barium sulfide) **31.** −42 kJ **33.** −5681 kJ (−4595 kJ, Chapter 6) **35.** −386 kJ (−361 kJ, Chapter 6) **37. a.** Using SF_4 data: $D_{SF} = 342.5$ kJ/mol. Using SF_6 data: $D_{SF} = 327.0$ kJ/mol. **b.** The S—F bond energy in the table is 327 kJ/mol. The value in the table was based on the S—F bond in SF_6. **c.** S(g) and F(g) are not the most stable form of the element at 25°C. The most stable forms are $S_8(s)$ and $F_2(g)$; $\Delta H_f^\circ = 0$ for these two species.

39.

41. a. NO_2^-:

HNO_2:

NO_3^-:

HNO_3:

b. SO_4^{2-}:

$$\left[\begin{array}{c} :\ddot{O}: \\ | \\ :\ddot{O}-S-\ddot{O}: \\ | \\ :\ddot{O}: \end{array} \right]^{2-}$$

HSO_4^-:

$$\left[\begin{array}{c} :\ddot{O}: \\ | \\ :\ddot{O}-S-\ddot{O}-H \\ | \\ :\ddot{O}: \end{array} \right]^{-}$$

H_2SO_4:

$$\begin{array}{c} :\ddot{O}: \\ | \\ :\ddot{O}-S-\ddot{O}-H \\ | \\ :\ddot{O}: \\ | \\ H \end{array}$$

c. CN^-, $[:C\equiv N:]^-$ HCN, $H-C\equiv N:$ **d.** OCN^-,

$\left[:\ddot{O}-C\equiv N: \right]^- \leftrightarrow \left[\ddot{O}=C=\ddot{N}: \right]^- \leftrightarrow \left[:O\equiv C-\ddot{N}: \right]^-$;

SCN^-, $\left[:\ddot{S}-C\equiv N: \right]^- \leftrightarrow \left[\ddot{S}=C=\ddot{N}: \right]^- \leftrightarrow \left[:S\equiv C-\ddot{N}: \right]^-$;

N_3^-, $\left[:\ddot{N}-N\equiv N: \right]^- \leftrightarrow \left[\ddot{N}=N=\ddot{N}: \right]^- \leftrightarrow \left[:N\equiv N-\ddot{N}: \right]^-$;

e. NCCN, $:N\equiv C-C\equiv N:$

43. PAN, $H_3C_2NO_5$:

45.

47. PF_5:

$Be(CH_3)_2$:

$$\begin{array}{ccc} H & & H \\ | & | & | \\ H-C-Be-C-H \\ | & & | \\ H & & H \end{array}$$

BCl_3:

$:\ddot{C}l-B-\ddot{C}l:$ with $:\ddot{C}l:$ below

$XeOF_4$:

XeF_6:

49. Bond length: $CH_3OH > CO_3^{2-} > CO_2 > CO$ bond strength opposite

51. The structure

obeys the octet rule but has a $+1$ formal charge on the most electronegative element (fluorine) and a negative formal charge on a much less electronegative element (boron).

53. a.–f. and **h.** all have similar Lewis structures:

g. ClO_3^- $\left[:\ddot{O}-Cl-\ddot{O}: \atop | \atop :\ddot{O}: \right]^-$

Formal charges: **a.** $+1$; **b.** $+2$; **c.** $+3$; **d.** $+1$; **e.** $+2$; **f.** $+4$; **g.** $+2$; **h.** $+1$

55. [39] **a.** linear, $180°$; **b.** trigonal pyramid, $< 109.5°$; **c.** tetrahedral, $\approx 109.5°$; **d.** tetrahedral, $109.5°$; **e.** tetrahedral, $109.5°$; **f.** bent, $<109.5°$; [41] **a.** NO_2^- bent, $<120°$; HNO_2 bent about O and N, HON angle $<109.5°$, ONO angle $< 120°$; NO_3^- trigonal planar, $120°$; HNO_3 trigonal planar about N, $120°$, bent about N—O—H, angle $< 109.5°$; **b.** tetrahedral about S in all three, angle $= 109.5°$, bent about S—O—H, angle $< 109.5°$; **c.** both are linear, $180°$; **d.** all are linear, $180°$; **e.** linear, $180°$ **57. a.** trigonal planar, $120°$; **b.** bent (V-shaped), $<120°$; **c.** trigonal planar, $120°$ **59. a.** linear, $180°$; **b.** T-shaped, FClF angles are $\approx90°$. Since the lone pair will take up more space, the FClF bond angles will probably be slightly less than $90°$. **c.** $<120°$, $<90°$, see-saw; **d.** $120°$, $90°$, trigonal bipyramid

61.

$H-\ddot{F}:$ (linear)

$$\left[\begin{array}{c} :\ddot{F}:\ddot{F}:\ddot{F}: \\ | \\ Sb \\ | \\ :\ddot{F}:\ddot{F}:\ddot{F}: \end{array} \right]^{-} \text{(octahedral)} \qquad \left[\begin{array}{c} :\ddot{F}: \\ / \backslash \\ H \quad H \end{array} \right]^{+} \text{(bent)}$$

63. a. OCl_2 is $:\ddot{C}l-\ddot{O}-\ddot{C}l:$ bent, polar;

Br_3^- is

$$\begin{array}{c} :\ddot{B}r: \\ | \\ \ddot{B}r: \\ | \\ :\ddot{B}r: \end{array} \quad \text{linear, nonpolar;}$$

BeH_2 is $H-Be-H$ linear, nonpolar;

BH_2^- is

$$\begin{array}{c} \ddot{B} \\ / \backslash \\ H \quad H \end{array} \quad \text{bent, polar.}$$

b. BCl_3 is trigonal planar, nonpolar;

NF_3 is trigonal pyramid, polar;

IF_3 is T-shaped, polar.

c. CF_4 is tetrahedral, nonpolar;

SeF_4 is see-saw, polar;

XeF_4 is square planar, nonpolar;

d. IF_5 is

square pyramid, polar;

AsF_5 is trigonal bipyramid, nonpolar

65. a. −2057 kJ; **b.** −203 kJ **67.** D_{N-N} = 158.4 kJ/mol (calc'd), 160 kJ/mol (table) **69. a.** 1549 kJ; **b.** 1390. kJ; **c.** 1312 kJ; **d.** 1599 kJ **71.** Ionic bonds: strong omnidirectional forces; I. ions cannot move in solid; II. lots of energy needed to disrupt forces between ions; III. as ions slide across each other, strong repulsions cause crystal to snap; IV. polar solvents attracted to ions

73. S_2Cl_2,

SCl_2,

75. a.

b. 109.5° **c.** nonpolar
77. Resonance, the carbon–oxygen bond in CO_3^{2-} is between a single and double bond in strength and length

79. a. **b.** **c.**

trigonal planar trigonal pyramid T-shaped

They have different structures because there are different numbers of electron pairs about the central atom. PF_3 and BrF_3 are polar.

81. I. II.

nonpolar polar

III.

polar

III more polar than II

83. a. ≈120° **b.**

nonpolar

polar

85. Most consistent with structure that obeys the octet rule.
87. 540 kJ ± 50 kJ
89. With resonance all carbon atoms are equal (we indicate this with a circle in the ring), giving three different structures:

Localized double bonds give four unique structures.

91. bent, polar, <109.5°

see-saw, polar, <120°, <90°

octahedral, nonpolar, 90°

nonlinear, polar, <90°, <120°

93. a. CH_2Cl_2 and $CHCl_3$ have dipole moments. **b.** N_2O is polar.
c. all polar

95. a. E.N. is proportional to (I.E. − E.A.). The ionization energies of the noble gases are very high. This causes the E.N. to also be very high. **b.** We also expect F_2 to react with Kr and Rn.

Chapter 9

1. Bond energy is proportional to bond order. Bond length is inversely proportional to bond order. Bond energy and length can be measured.
3. Measure mass on presence of a magnetic field.
5. a. tetrahedral, 109.5°, sp^3, nonpolar

$$\overset{\cdot\cdot}{\underset{\cdot\cdot}{:F:}}\text{—}\overset{\overset{\displaystyle :\overset{\cdot\cdot}{F}:}{|}}{\underset{\underset{\displaystyle :F:}{|}}{C}}\text{—}\overset{\cdot\cdot}{\underset{\cdot\cdot}{:F:}}$$

b. trigonal pyramid, <109.5°, sp^3, polar

$$:\overset{\cdot\cdot}{F}\text{—}N\overset{\displaystyle F}{\underset{\displaystyle \overset{\cdot\cdot}{F}}{}}$$

c. bent, <109.5°, sp^3, polar

$$:\overset{\cdot\cdot}{F}\overset{\displaystyle \overset{\cdot\cdot}{O}\cdot\cdot}{\diagdown}\overset{\cdot\cdot}{F}:$$

d. trigonal planar, 120°, sp^2, nonpolar

$$\overset{\displaystyle :\overset{\cdot\cdot}{F}:}{\underset{\displaystyle \overset{\diagup\diagdown}{F\quad F}}{B}}$$

e. linear, 180°, sp, nonpolar

$$\text{H—Be—H}$$

f. a < 120° see-saw, dsp^3
b < 90° polar
c ≈ 180°

g. a = 90° trigonal bipyramid, nonpolar, dsp^3
b = 120°

h. $:\overset{\cdot\cdot}{F}\text{—}\overset{\cdot\cdot}{Kr}\text{—}\overset{\cdot\cdot}{F}:$ linear, 180°, dsp^3, nonpolar

i.   square planar, 90°, d^2sp^3, nonpolar

j.   octahedral, 90°, d^2sp^3, nonpolar

k.   **l.**
square pyramid, ≈90°,   t-shaped, a <90°,
d^2sp^3, polar   b ≈180°, dsp^3, polar

m.

tetrahedral, 109.5°, sp^3, nonpolar

7. The π-bond forces all six atoms into the same plane.
9. Biacetyl

All CCO angles are 120°. The six atoms are not in the same plane. 11σ and 2π

Acetoin

angle a = 120°, angle b = 109.5°, 13 σ and 1 π bond

11. a. 6; **b.** 4; **c.** The center N in —N=N=N group; **d.** 33 σ;
e. 5 π; **f.** The six-membered ring is planar; **g.** 180°; **h.** <109°;
i. sp^3 **13. a.** 14 sp^3 and 26 sp^2; **b.** 39 σ and 13 π **15. a.** H_2^+,
H_2, H_2^-; **b.** He_2^{2+} and He_2^+ **17. a.** $(\sigma_{1s})^2$; B.O. = 1; diamagnetic;
b. $(\sigma_{2s})^2(\sigma_{2s}*)^2(\pi_{2p})^2$; B.O. = 1; paramagnetic;
c. $(\sigma_{2s})^2(\sigma_{2s}*)^2(\pi_{2p})^4(\sigma_{2p})^2(\pi_{2p}*)^4$; B.O. = 1; diamagnetic;
d. $(\sigma_{2s})^2(\sigma_{2s}*)^2(\pi_{2p})^4$; B.O. = 2; diamagnetic;
e. $(\sigma_{2s})^2(\sigma_{2s}*)^2(\pi_{2p})^4(\sigma_{2p})^1$; B.O. = 2.5; paramagnetic;
f. $(\sigma_{2s})^2(\sigma_{2s}*)^2(\pi_{2p})^4(\sigma_{2p})^2$; B.O. = 3; diamagnetic; **g.** N_2:
$(\sigma_{2s})^2(\sigma_{2s}*)^2(\pi_{2p})^4(\sigma_{2p})^2$; B.O. = 3, diamagnetic; **h.** N_2^+:
$(\sigma_{2s})^2(\sigma_{2s}*)^2(\pi_{2p})^4(\sigma_{2p})^1$; B.O. = 2.5, paramagnetic; **i.** N_2^-:
$(\sigma_{2s})^2(\sigma_{2s}*)^2(\pi_{2p})^4(\sigma_{2p})^2(\pi_{2p}*)^1$; B.O. = 2.5, paramagnetic

19.

π_{2p} σ_{2p}

21. bond length, $CN^- < CN < CN^+$; bond energy, $CN^+ < CN < CN^-$
23. C_2^{2-} has 10 valence electrons. $[:C≡C:]^{2-}$; sp hybrid orbitals
used; $(\sigma_{2s})^2(\sigma_{2s}*)^2(\pi_{2p})^4(\sigma_{2p})^2$; B.O. = 3. Both give the same picture,
a triple bond composed of one σ and two π-bonds. Both predict the
ion to be diamagnetic. C_2^{2-} is isoelectronic with the CO molecule.

25. a. $:\overset{\cdot\cdot}{F}\text{—}\overset{\cdot\cdot}{Cl}\text{—}\overset{\cdot\cdot}{O}:$ bent, sp^3 hybrid;

b. $:\overset{\cdot\cdot}{F}\text{—}\overset{\displaystyle Cl}{\underset{\displaystyle :\overset{\cdot\cdot}{O}:}{}}\text{—}\overset{\cdot\cdot}{O}:$ trigonal pyramid, sp^3;

c. $:\overset{\cdot\cdot}{O}\text{—}\overset{\overset{\displaystyle :\overset{\cdot\cdot}{F}:}{|}}{\underset{\underset{\displaystyle :\overset{\cdot\cdot}{O}:}{|}}{Cl}}\text{—}\overset{\cdot\cdot}{O}:$ tetrahedral, sp^3

d. :F̈: :F̈:
   see-saw, dsp^3;

(Cl with F, O, F substituents)

e. :Ö: :F̈:
   trigonal bipyramid, dsp^3

(Cl—F structure with O, O, F)

27. SbF_5 monomer is trigonal bipyramidal using dsp^3 hybrid orbitals. In the polymer there is a close to octahederal arrangement of fluorines about each antimony.

(Sb-F polymer structure with labels (a), (b), (c))

The three types of fluorines are **(a)** bridging, bonded to two Sb; **(b)** 90° away from one type (a) and 180° away from the other; **(c)** 90° away from both type (a). **29.** 267 kJ/mol **31. a.** sp^3, P—P—P bond angle 60°; **b.** P_4O_6, all P—sp^3, POP angle < 109.5°; OPO angle < 109.5°; **c.** P_4O_{10}, all P are sp^3, POP angle < 109.5°, OPO angle 109.5°

33. a. $COCl_2$

(structure) trigonal planar, polar, 120°, sp^2

b. N_2F_2

can also be

(structures) polar / nonpolar

planar, ≈120°, sp^2

These are distinctly different molecules.

c. N_2O_3

(structure) nonplanar, polar, ≈120°, sp^2

d. COS

(structure O=C=S) linear, polar, 180°, sp

e. ICl_3

(structure with a, a and b labels)

t-shaped, polar, a < 90° b ≈ 180°, dsp^3

35.

(structure showing Cl—P(+1)Cl with O(−1) ↔ Cl—P(0)Cl with O(0))
(a) ↔ (b)

a. Yes; **b.** both sp^3; **c.** P uses a d-orbital to form π bonds; **d.** (b)
37. NO^+, B.O. = 3; NO, B.O. = 2.5; NO^-, B.O. = 2; bond energies: $NO^- <$ NO $< NO^+$; bond lengths, opposite. **39.** N_2: $(\sigma_{2s})^2(\sigma_{2s}*)^2$ $(\pi_{2p})^4(\sigma_{2p})^2$ in ground state, B.O. = 3, diamagnetic; 1st excited state: $(\sigma_{2s})^2(\sigma_{2s}*)^2(\pi_{2p})^4(\sigma_{2p})^1(\pi_{2p}*)^1$, B.O. = 2, paramagnetic (two unpaired electrons)

41.

Ground state   Excited state

It takes energy to pair electrons in the same orbital. Thus, the structure with no unpaired electrons is at a higher energy; it is the excited state.

43.

All five atoms of the ring must be coplanar. All eight atoms (the four carbons and one oxygen in the ring and the three oxygens bonded to the ring) lie in the same plane.

(bracketed resonance structures with 2^- charges)

45. The π bonds between S atoms and between C and S atoms are not as strong. The orbitals do not overlap with each other as well as the atomic orbitals of C and O. **47. a.** The electron removed from N_2 is in the σ_{2p} molecular orbital, which is lower in energy than $2p$ from which the electron in atomic nitrogen is removed. Since the electron removed from N_2 is lower in energy than the electron in N, the ionization energy of N_2 is greater than for N. **b.** F_2 should have a lower ionization energy than F. The electron removed from F_2 is in a $\pi_{2p}*$ antibonding molecular orbital, which is higher in energy than the $2p$ atomic orbitals. **49.** N_2, N, N_2^+, and N^+ will all be present. Light with a wavelength between 85.33 nm and 127 nm will produce atomic nitrogen, but will not cause any ionization.

Chapter 10

1. There is an electrostatic attraction between the permanent dipoles of polar molecules. The greater the polarity, the greater the attraction.

3. As the size of the molecule increases, the strength of the London dispersion forces also increases. As the electron cloud gets larger it is easier for the electrons to be drawn away from the nucleus (more polarizable). **5.** As the strengths of interparticle forces increase; surface tension, viscosity, melting point, and boiling point increase, while the vapor pressure decreases. **7.** Hydrogen bonding is a special type of dipole-dipole force. **9.** Liquids and solids both have characteristic volumes, and are not very compressible. Liquids and gases flow and assume the shape of their containers. **11.** As the interparticle forces increase the critical temperature increases. **13. a.** crystalline solid: long range order; amorphous solid: no long range order; **b.** ionic solid: contain ions held together by ionic bonding; molecular solid: contain discrete covalently bonded molecules held together in the solid by weaker forces (LDF, dipole, or hydrogen bonds); **c.** molecular solid: discrete molecules; covalent network solid: no discrete molecules. A covalent network is like a giant molecule. The interparticle forces are the covalent bonds between the atoms. **d.** metallic solid: contains delocalized electrons; excellent conductor of electricity; covalent network: localized electrons, insulator or semiconductor **15.** No, an example is common glass which is primarily amorphous SiO_2 (a covalent network solid) as compared to ice (a crystalline solid held together by weaker H-bonds). The interparticle forces in the amorphous solid in this case are stronger than those in the crystalline solid. Whether or not a solid is amorphous or crystalline depends on the long range order in the solid and not on the strengths of the interparticle forces. **17. a.** As the temperature is increased, more electrons in the valence band have sufficient kinetic energy to jump to the conduction bands. **b.** A photon is absorbed by an electron which then goes from the valence band to the conduction band. **c.** An impurity either adds electrons at an energy near that of the conduction band (n-type) or adds holes at an energy near that of the valence band (p-type) **19. a.** condensation: vapor $\rightarrow$ liquid; **b.** evaporation: liquid $\rightarrow$ vapor; **c.** sublimation: solid $\rightarrow$ vapor; **d.** A supercooled liquid is a liquid at a temperature below its freezing point. **21. a.** As intermolecular forces increase the rate of evaporation decreases. **b.** increase T: increase rate; **c.** increase surface area: increase rate **23.** The phase change, $H_2O(g) \rightarrow H_2O(l)$ releases heat that can cause additional damage. Also steam can be at a temperature much greater than 100°C. **25. a.** ionic; **b.** dipole, LDF (London dispersion forces); **c.** LDF; **d.** LDF; **e.** metallic; **f.** metallic; **g.** LDF; **h.** hydrogen bonding, LDF **27. a.** OCS; **b.** PF_3; **c.** SF_2; **d.** SO_2 **29. a.** Neopentane is more compact than n-pentane, producing less area of contact between neopentane molecules, leading to weaker interparticle forces and a lower boiling point. **b.** Ethanol exhibits H-bonding; dimethylether does not. **c.** HF exhibits H-bonding; **d.** LiCl, ionic; $TiCl_4$ is a nonpolar molecular substance with relatively weak London dispersion forces. **e.** LiCl, ionic, H—Cl, dipole forces; **f.** Both are ionic. The lattice energy of LiCl is greater than that for CsCl because Li^+ is smaller than Cs^+.
31. As the electronegativity of the atom bonded to H increases, the strength of the hydrogen bond increases.

$$\overset{|}{-}N\text{---}H\text{---}N\overset{/}{\diagdown} < \overset{|}{-}N\text{---}H\text{---}O\overset{/}{\diagdown} < \overset{\diagdown}{/}O\text{---}H\text{---}O\overset{|}{-}$$

33. a. NaCl; **b.** CH_3CN; **c.** H_2; **d.** SiO_2; **e.** $HOCH_2CH_2OH$; **f.** NH_3; **g.** HF; **h.** CO_2 **35.** convex (like Hg in glass) **37.** The structure of H_2O_2 produces greater hydrogen bonding than water. Long chains of hydrogen bonded H_2O_2 molecules then get tangled together.

39. a. CO_2: molecular; **b.** SiO_2: covalent network; **c.** Si: atomic, covalent network; **d.** CH_4: molecular; **e.** Ru: atomic, metallic; **f.** I_2: molecular; **g.** KBr: ionic; **h.** H_2O: molecular; **i.** NaOH: ionic; **j.** U: atomic, metallic; **k.** $CaCO_3$: ionic; **l.** PH_3: molecular **41.** 229 pm **43.** 139 pm; 195 g/mol; Pt **45.** edge, 328 pm; r, 142 pm **47.** 136 pm **49.** $AlNi_3$ **51.** $CaTiO_3$; six oxygens around each Ti **53.** 5.0×10^2 nm **55.** NaCl: $4Na^+$, $4Cl^-$; CsCl: $1Cs^+$, $1Cl^-$; ZnS: $4Zn^{2+}$, $4S^{2-}$; TiO_2: $2Ti^{4+}$, $4O^{2-}$ **57.** p-type **59.** 1.7 atm, 413 K **61.** 1600 kJ **63.** 221 torr **65.** Li, 158 kJ/mol; Mg, 141 kJ/mol. Bonding stronger in Li. **67.** Heating curve plateau is a temperature (and pressure) at which two phases are in equilibrium; gives a point on the phase diagram. **69.** A: solid; B: liquid; C: vapor; D: solid + vapor; E: solid + liquid + vapor (triple point); F: liquid + vapor; G: liquid + vapor (critical point); H: vapor **71.** CH_3CO_2H, H-bonding; CH_2ClCO_2H, H-bonding, Cl (more electronegative atom) replacing H; $CH_3CO_2CH_3$, polar. $CH_3CO_2CH_3$ should have weakest interparticle forces and CH_2ClCO_2H the strongest. **73.** 313 pm **75.** If TiO_2 conducts electricity as a liquid it would be ionic. Because $\Delta EN = 2.0$, we might expect TiO_2 to be ionic. It is actually a covalent network solid. **77.** The bp of HF is higher than expected because of especially strong hydrogen bonding. ΔH_{vap} is lower than expected because some of the H-bonds reform in the gas phase. **79.** 628 pm, 2.00 g/cm^3 **81.** 4.65 kg/hr **83. a.** 2; **b.** At 4000 K, 10^7 Pa: graphite, vapor, liquid; At 4000 K, 10^{10} Pa: graphite, diamond, liquid; **c.** converted to diamond; **d.** diamond **85.** Oil of wintergreen, hydrogen bonding is intramolecular. Methyl-4-hydroxybenzoate, hydrogen bonding is intermolecular, giving it a higher m.p. **87.** The solids with high melting points (NaCl, $MgCl_2$, NaF, MgF_2, AlF_3) are all ionic solids. $SiCl_4$, SiF_4, Cl_2, F_2, PF_5, and SF_6 are non-polar covalent molecules with LDF. PCl_3 and SCl_2 are polar molecules with LDF and dipole forces. In these 8 molecular substances the interparticle forces are weak and the melting points low. $AlCl_3$ is intermediate. The melting point indicates there are stronger forces present than in the nonmetal halides, but not as strong as for an ionic solid. $AlCl_3$ illustrates a gradual transition from ionic to covalent bonding; from an ionic solid to discrete molecules. **89.** body centered, 159 pm **91.** two **93.** 16 Al; 8 Mg; 32 O **95. a.** twenty; **b.** cubic closest packed; **c.** tetrahedron **97.** No, 0°C

Chapter 11

1. 0.365 M **3.** $NiCl_2$, Ni^{2+}: 1.54×10^{-2} M; Cl^-: 3.08×10^{-2} M **5.** 2.5×10^{-2} M **7.** 0.16 L **9.** Molarity **11.** hydrophobic: water hating; hydrophilic: water loving **13.** Negative deviation: solute-solvent attractions are stronger than attractions in pure substances. Positive deviation: solute-solvent attractions are weaker than in pure substances. **15.** No. For ideal solution, $\Delta H_{soln} = 0$ **17.** The osmotic pressure inside bacteria cells is less than outside the cell causing the cells to dehydrate and die. **19.** 0.88 M, 0.91 m, 1.6×10^{-2} **21.** HCl: 12 M, 17 m, 0.23; HNO_3: 16 M, 37 m, 0.39; H_2SO_4: 18 M, 200 m, 0.76; $HC_2H_3O_2$: 17 M, 2000 m, 0.96; NH_3: 15 M, 23 m, 0.29 **23.** 28.5%, 2.69 M, 4.32 m, 0.252 **25.** 23.9%, 1.6 m, 0.028 **27.** 10.%, 2.5 m **29.** Water is a polar molecule capable of hydrogen bonding. Polar molecules, molecules capable of hydrogen bonding, and ions can be hydrated. **a.** CH_3CH_2OH; **b.** $CHCl_3$; **c.** CH_3CO_2H; **d.** Na_2S; **e.** $AlCl_3$; **f.** CO_2 **31.** $KCl(s) \rightarrow K^+(aq) + Cl^-(aq)$; $\Delta H_{soln}^\circ = 31$ kJ/mol **33. a.** Mg^{2+}; **b.** Be^{2+}; **c.** Fe^{3+} **35.** Water (a, c, and e); carbontetrachloride (b, d, and f) **37.** As the length of the hydrocarbon chain increases, the solubility decreases because the hydrophobic chain cannot hydrogen bond to water molecules. **39.** No.

The reaction of CO_2 with OH^- greatly increases the solubility by forming bicarbonate. The solubility depends more on the concentration of OH^- than on the pressure of CO_2. **41.** 23.6 torr **43.** 23.2 torr (25°C), 70.0 torr (45°C) **45. a.** 290 torr; **b.** 0.69 **47.** 0.049 **49.** C **51.** $T_b = 100.042°C$; $T_f = -0.15°C$; $\pi = 2.0$ atm **53. a.** $\Delta T = 2.0 \times 10^{-5}°C$, $\pi = 0.20$ torr; **b.** osmotic pressure **55.** 610 g/mol **57.** 24 atm **59.** d. > b. > c. > a. **61.** −3°C; Measured F.P. should be higher because of ion association **63.** 2.6 (0.091 m); 2.56 (0.279 m); 2.65 (0.475 m) **65.** Formation of hydrogen-bonded dimers increases the solubility in benzene **67.** 10.7 m; 6.77 M; 0.162 **69.** The attraction of water molecules for Al^{3+} and OH^- cannot overcome the larger lattice energy of $Al(OH)_3$. **71. a.** CF_3CF_3 and $CF_3CF_2CF_3$; **b.** $CH_3(CH_2)_5CH_3$ and $CH_3(CH_2)_4CH_3$; **c.** CCl_4 and CF_4 **73.** $\chi_{methanol} = 0.88$ **75.** C_7H_4O, $C_{14}H_8O_2$ **77.** −19.9°C; 105.5°C **79.** 14.5 g **81.** $C_2H_4O_3$; 151 g/mol (exp.); 152.1 g/mol (calc.); $C_4H_8O_6$ **83.** 43% naphthalene **85. a.** 303 ± 9 g/mol; **b.** No; **c.** Make solution more concentrated or use camphor as the solvent

Chapter 12

1. Instantaneous rate: slope of the tangent line to a graph of concentration versus time. Initial rate: instantaneous rate at $t = 0$. Average rate: rate measured over a period of time. **3. a.** The greater the frequency of collisions, the greater the opportunities for molecules to react. **b.** The kinetic energy of the collision can be used to break bonds. **c.** For a reaction to occur, the reactive portion of each molecule must be involved in a collision. Only some collisions have the right orientation. **5.** The probability of the simultaneous collision of three molecules with the correct energy and orientation is exceedingly small. **7.** A catalyst increases the rate of a reaction by providing an alternate pathway (mechanism) with a lower activation energy. **9.** No. The catalyzed reaction has a different mechanism and a different rate law. **11.** $I_2, S_4O_6^{2-}$:0.0040 mol/L · s;I^-:0.0080 mol/L · s **13. a.** mol/L · s; **b.** mol/L · s; **c.** s^{-1}; **d.** L/mol · s; **e.** L^2/mol^2 · s **15.** 7.47 × 10^8 L/mol · s **17. a.** rate = $k[NO]^2[Cl_2]$; **b.** $k = 1.8 \times 10^2$ L^2/mol^2 · min **19. a.** rate = $k[I^-][OCl^-]$; **b.** $k = 3.7$ L/mol · s **21.** rate = $k[ClO_2]^2[OH^-]$; $k = 2.30 \times 10^2$ L^2/mol^2 · s **23.** rate = $k[C_4H_6]^2$; $1/[C_4H_6] = 1/[C_4H_6]_0 + kt$; $k = 1.4 \times 10^{-2}$ L/mol · s **25.** $\ln[H_2O_2] = -kt + \ln[H_2O_2]_0$; $k = 8.3 \times 10^{-4}$ s^{-1}; rate = $k[H_2O_2]$ **27. a.** 2.845×10^{-5} yr^{-1} (^{239}Pu); 1.7×10^{-9} s^{-1} (^{241}Pu); **b.** ^{241}Pu; **c.** 2.1×10^{13} disintegrations/s; 4.7 g (1 yr); 2.9 g (10 yr); 0.024 g (100 yr) **29.** 9.2×10^{-3} s^{-1}; 75 s **31.** 0.12 L/mol · s **33. a.** 1.0×10^{-3} s^{-1}; **b.** 690 s; **c.** 2.9×10^2 s (25%); 1.4×10^3 s (75%); 3 × 10^3 s (95%) **35. a.** rate = $k[CH_3NC]$; **b.** rate = $k[O_3][NO]$ **37.** $H_2O_2 \rightarrow 2OH$ **39.** 4.8×10^3 s^{-1} **41. a.** $E_a = 150$ kJ/mol, $A = 1.0 \times 10^{10}$ **b.** 8.1×10^{-3} L/mol · s **43.** 11.9 kJ/mol **45.** See *Solutions Guide*. **47.** 139 kJ/mol **49. a.** NO; **b.** NO_2; **c.** 2.3 **51.** CH_2DCH_2D **53.** $L^{1/2}/mol^{1/2}$ · s **55.** rate = $k[H_2SeO_3][H^+]^2[I^-]^3$; $k = 5.2 \times 10^5 L^5/mol^5$ · s **57. a.** 0.168 $hr^{-1} = 4.67 \times 10^{-5}$ s^{-1}; **b.** 4.13 hr; **c.** 5.36 atm (0.500 hr), 9.19 atm (12.0 hr); **d.** 0.0347 (3.47%) **59. a.** W; lower E_a; **b.** 1.41×10^{30}; **c.** H_2 decreases the rate of the reaction. For the decomposition to occur, NH_3 molecules must be adsorbed on the surface of the catalyst. If H_2 that is produced from the reaction is also adsorbed on the catalyst, then there are fewer sites for NH_3 molecules to be adsorbed. **61.** rate = $\dfrac{k[I^-][OCl^-]}{[OH^-]}$; $k = 6.0 \times 10^1$ s^{-1} **63. a.** first order; **b.** rate = $k[NO][O_3]$; **c.** $k' = 1.8$ s^{-1}; $k'' = 3.6$ s^{-1}; **d.** $k = 1.8 \times 10^{14}$ cm^3/molecules · s

Chapter 13

1. a. The rates are equal. **b.** No net change. **3.** An equilibrium position is a set of concentrations that satisfy the equilibrium constant expression. More than one equilibrium position can satisfy the same equilibrium constant expression. **5.** When we change the pressure by adding an unreactive gas, we do not change the partial pressure of any of the substances in equilibrium with each other (equilibrium will not shift). Changing the pressure by changing the volume changes the partial pressures of all the substances by the same factor. Unequal numbers of gaseous particles on the two sides causes the equilibrium to shift. **7.** No. The forward and reverse reactions will distribute ^{14}C atoms between CO and CO_2. **9. a.** $K = \dfrac{[NO_2][O_2]}{[NO][O_3]}$; **b.** $K = \dfrac{[O_2][O]}{[O_3]}$; **c.** $K = \dfrac{[ClO][O_2]}{[Cl][O_3]}$; **d.** $K = \dfrac{[O_2]^3}{[O_3]^2}$ **11.** 2.8×10^{-2} atm^2 **13. a.** $K = \dfrac{1}{[O_2]^5}$; **b.** $K = [N_2O][H_2O]^2$; **c.** $K = \dfrac{1}{[CO_2]}$; **d.** $K = \dfrac{[SO_2]^8}{[O_2]^8}$ **15. a.** 16.7; **b.** 3.60×10^{-3}; **c.** 6.00×10^{-2}; **d.** 7.73×10^4 **17.** 0.20 **19.** 2.3 atm **21.** $K_p = 0.72$ atm; $K = 0.017$ mol/L **23. a.** right; **b.** at equilibrium; **c.** at equilibrium; **d.** left **25. a.** decrease; **b.** no change; **c.** no change; **d.** increase **27.** 7.8×10^{-2} atm **29.** $P_{SO_2} = 0.38$ atm; $P_{SO_3} = 0.12$ atm; $P_{O_2} = 0.44$ atm **31. a.** $P_{N_2O_4} = 5.9 \times 10^{-3}$ atm; $P_{NO_2} = 3.8 \times 10^{-2}$ atm; **b.** $P_{N_2O_4} = 0.012$ atm; $P_{NO_2} = 0.056$ atm; **c.** $P_{N_2O_4} = 1.2$ atm; $P_{NO_2} = 0.6$ atm **33. a.** right; **b.** right; **c.** no effect; **d.** left **35. a.** right; **b.** left; **c.** right; **d.** no effect; **e.** no effect; **f.** right **37.** 100% ethanol **39.** A catalyst increases the rates of both reactions. Equilibrium was reached more rapidly with the catalyst. The uncatalyzed reaction takes too long to reach equilibrium. The catalyst reduces the activation energy (increases the rate) for both forward and reverse reactions. **41.** rate$_r = k_r \dfrac{[Br^-][SO_4^{2-}]^3[H^+]}{[SO_3^{2-}]^2}$ **43.** $K_p = P_{O_2}^3/P_{O_3}^2$; **a.** $1/\sqrt{K_p}$; **b.** $1/K_p$ **45. a.** 4×10^3; **b.** 8×10^{-2}; **c.** 8×10^{18} **47.** $[Fe^{3+}] = 4.8 \times 10^{-5}$ mol/L; $[SCN^-] = 1.9$ mol/L; $[FeSCN^{2+}] = 0.10$ mol/L **49.** The SO_2 shifts the equilibrium to the left, producing heat which causes the temperature to increase. **51. a.** $[HOCl] = 9.2 \times 10^{-3}$ mol/L; $[H_2O] = 5.0 \times 10^{-2}$ mol/L; $[Cl_2O] = 1.8 \times 10^{-2}$ mol/L; **b.** $[HOCl] = 0.07$ mol/L; $[H_2O] = 0.22$ mol/L **53. a.** 134 atm^{-1}; **b.** $P_{NO} = 0.052$ atm, $P_{Br_2} = 0.18$ atm, $P_{NOBr} = 0.25$ atm **55. a.** 2×10^3 molecules/cm^3; **b.** There is more NO in the atmosphere than we could expect from the value of K. NO is produced at high temperatures by lightning and in automobile engines. At higher temperatures, K is larger. (See Exercise 13.27.) At 25°C, the rates of the forward and reverse reaction are essentially zero, so that the NO cannot go back to N_2 and O_2 once it gets into the atmosphere. **57.** 0.9 atm

Chapter 14

1. a. A strong acid is 100% dissociated in water. **b.** A strong base is 100% dissociated in water. **c.** A weak acid is much less than 100% dissociated in water. **d.** A weak base has only a small percentage of the molecules that react with water to form OH^-. **3.** $[H^+] = [OH^-] = 1.0 \times 10^{-7}$ M, pH = 7.00 **5. a.** generate H^+ in water; **b.** proton donor; **c.** electron pair acceptor **7.** Nitrogen **9. a.** weaker bond = weaker base; **b.** greater electronegativity = weaker base; **c.** more oxygen atoms = weaker base **11. a.** weak acid; **b.** weak acid; **c.** weak base; **d.** strong base; **e.** weak base; **f.** weak acid **13.** $H_3O^+ > HNO_3 > HOCl > NH_4^+$; H_2O would be the weakest acid **15. a.** HI; **b.** $HClO_2$; **c.** HF

17.

Acid	Base	Conjugate Base of Acid	Conjugate Acid of Base
a. H_2O	H_2O	OH^-	H_3O^+
b. CH_3COCH_3	CH_3O^-	$CH_3COCH_2^-$	CH_3OH
c. H_2S	NH_3	HS^-	NH_4^+
d. H_2SO_4	H_2O	HSO_4^-	H_3O^+
e. H_3O^+	OH^-	H_2O	H_2O
f. H_2O	$H_2PO_4^-$	OH^-	H_3PO_4
g. HCN	H_2O	CN^-	H_3O^+

19. a. $H_3PO_4 + H_2O \rightleftharpoons H_3O^+ + H_2PO_4^-$; $K_{a_1} = \dfrac{[H_3O^+][H_2PO_4^-]}{[H_3PO_4]}$

or $H_3PO_4 \rightleftharpoons H^+ + H_2PO_4^-$; $K_{a_1} = \dfrac{[H^+][H_2PO_4^-]}{[H_3PO_4]}$; Only the first reaction will be written for the rest but both are equivalent.

b. $H_2PO_4^- + H_2O \rightleftharpoons H_3O^+ + HPO_4^{2-}$; $K_{a_2} = \dfrac{[H_3O^+][HPO_4^{2-}]}{[H_2PO_4^-]}$;

c. $HPO_4^{2-} + H_2O \rightleftharpoons H_3O^+ + PO_4^{3-}$; $K_{a_3} = \dfrac{[H_3O^+][PO_4^{3-}]}{[HPO_4^{2-}]}$;

d. $HNO_2 + H_2O \rightleftharpoons H_3O^+ + NO_2^-$; $K_a = \dfrac{[H_3O^+][NO_2^-]}{[HNO_2]}$;

e. $Ti(H_2O)_6^{4+} + H_2O \rightleftharpoons Ti(H_2O)_5(OH)^{3+} + H_3O^+$; $K_a = \dfrac{[H_3O^+][Ti(H_2O)_5(OH)^{3+}]}{[Ti(H_2O)_6^{4+}]}$ **21. a.** $PO_4^{3-} + H_2O \rightleftharpoons HPO_4^{2-} + OH^-$; $K_b = \dfrac{[OH^-][HPO_4^{2-}]}{[PO_4^{3-}]}$; **b.** $HPO_4^{2-} + H_2O \rightleftharpoons H_2PO_4^- + OH^-$; $K_b = \dfrac{[OH^-][H_2PO_4^-]}{[HPO_4^{2-}]}$; **c.** $H_2PO_4^- + H_2O \rightleftharpoons H_3PO_4 + OH^-$; $K_b = \dfrac{[OH^-][H_3PO_4]}{[H_2PO_4^-]}$; **d.** $NH_3 + H_2O \rightleftharpoons NH_4^+ + OH^-$; $K_b = \dfrac{[NH_4^+][OH^-]}{[NH_3]}$; **e.** $CN^- + H_2O \rightleftharpoons OH^- + HCN$; $K_b = \dfrac{[OH^-][HCN]}{[CN^-]}$ **23.** $H^- + H_2O \rightarrow H_2 + OH^-$; $OCH_3^- + H_2O \rightarrow CH_3OH + OH^-$ **25. a.** 2.85; **b.** 9.60; **c.** −0.79; **d.** 12.54; **e.** 3.9; **f.** 14.70; **g.** 3.5; **h.** 11.7 **27. a.** $[H^+] = 3.9 \times 10^{-8} M$, $[OH^-] = 2.6 \times 10^{-7} M$; **b.** $[H^+] = 5 \times 10^{-16} M$, $[OH^-] = 20 M$; **c.** $[H^+] = 10 M$, $[OH^-] = 1 \times 10^{-15} M$; **d.** $[H^+] = 6 \times 10^{-4} M$, $[OH^-] = 2 \times 10^{-11} M$; **e.** $[H^+] = 1 \times 10^{-9} M$, $[OH^-] = 1 \times 10^{-5} M$; **f.** $[H^+] = 4 \times 10^{-5} M$, $[OH^-] = 3 \times 10^{-10} M$ **29. a.** endothermic; **b.** 6.631; **c.** $[H^+] = [OH^-] = 2.34 \times 10^{-7} M$, pH = 6.631; $[H^+] = [OH^-]$ is most general; **d.** 2.35×10^{-14}; **e.** 6.815 **31. a.** H^+, Cl^-, H_2O; 0.602; **b.** H^+, Br^-, H_2O; 0.602; **c.** H^+, ClO_4^-, H_2O; 0.602; **d.** H^+, NO_3^-, H_2O; 0.602 **33. a.** 1.0; **b.** 1.0; **c.** 1.0 **35.** $[H^+] = 1.9 M$, $[OH^-] = 5.3 \times 10^{-15} M$, pH = −0.28 **37.** $9.5 \times 10^{-4} M$, 3.02; $1.3 \times 10^{-3} M$, 2.89; $2.7 \times 10^{-3} M$, 2.57 **39.** $[H^+] = [C_6H_2Cl_3O^-] = 2 \times 10^{-4} M$, $[HC_6H_2Cl_3O] = 0.05 M$, $[OH^-] = 5 \times 10^{-11}$; pH = 3.7 **41.** 4.77 **43.** $[C_6H_5CO_2H] = 4.1 \times 10^{-3} M$, $[C_6H_5CO_2^-] = [H^+] = 5.1 \times 10^{-4} M$, $[OH^-] = 1.9 \times 10^{-11} M$, pH = 3.29 **45.** 0.66 **47.** 1.00 **49.** 21% **51. a.** 0.60%; **b.** 1.9%; **c.** 5.8% **53.** 1.9×10^{-9} **55. a.** 1.7; **b.** 3.68 **57.** $CH_3NH_2 > NH_3 > H_2O \gg NO_3^-$ **59. a.** NH_3; **b.** NH_3; **c.** OH^-; **d.** CH_3NH_2 **61.** 12.049 **63. a.** K^+, OH^-, H_2O; $[OH^-] = 1.50 M$, pH = 13.176; **b.** Cs^+, OH^-, H_2O, $[OH^-] = 0.150 M$, pH = 13.176; **c.** NH_3, H_2O;

$[OH^-] = 1.6 \times 10^{-3} M$; pH = 11.20; **d.** C_5H_5N, H_2O; $[OH^-] = 1.6 \times 10^{-5} M$; pH = 9.20; **e.** CH_3NH_2, H_2O; $[OH^-] = 7.89 \times 10^{-3} M$; pH = 11.897 **65.** $[N_2H_4] = 2.0 M$, $[N_2H_5^+] = 2.4 \times 10^{-3}$; $[H^+] = 4.2 \times 10^{-12} M$; pH = 11.38 **67. a.** $[OH^-] = 1.0 \times 10^{-2} M$, $[H^+] = 1.0 \times 10^{-12} M$, pH = 12.00; **b.** $[OH^-] = 1.6 \times 10^{-2} M$, $[H^+] = 6.5 \times 10^{-13} M$, pH = 12.19; **c.** $[OH^-] = 8.9 \times 10^{-3} M$, $[H^+] = 1.1 \times 10^{-12} M$, pH = 11.96 **69. a.** 1.3%; **b.** 4.2% **71.** 9.59 **73.** 1.0×10^{-9} **75. a.** neutral; **b.** basic; $NO_2^- + H_2O \rightleftharpoons HNO_2 + OH^-$; **c.** acidic; $NH_4^+ + H_2O \rightleftharpoons NH_3 + H_3O^+$; **d.** acidic; NH_4^+ better acid than NO_2^- is a base; **e.** basic; $CO_3^{2-} + H_2O \rightleftharpoons HCO_3^- + OH^-$; **f.** basic; $F^- + H_2O \rightleftharpoons HF + OH^-$ **77.** HCN, NH_4Br, KBr, NH_4CN, KCN, KOH **79. a.** 5.82; **b.** 10.95; **c.** 11.78 **81.** $[HN_3] = [OH^-] = 2.3 \times 10^{-6} M$; $[Na^+] = [N_3^-] = 0.010 M$; $[H^+] = 4.3 \times 10^{-9} M$ **83.** OCl^- **85. a.** $HBrO < HBrO_2 < HBrO_3$; The greater the number of O atoms in an oxy-acid, the stronger the acid. **b.** $HAsO_4^{2-} < H_2AsO_4^- < H_3AsO_4$; For polyprotic acids, the more protons attached, the stronger the acid. **87. a.** $BrO_3^- < BrO_2^- < BrO^-$; The greater the number of O atoms in an oxy-acid, the weaker the conjugate base. **b.** $H_2PO_4^- < HPO_4^{2-} < PO_4^{3-}$; For polyprotic acids, the fewer the protons, the stronger the conjugate base. **89. a.** $B(OH)_3$, acid; H_2O, base; **b.** Ag^+, acid; NH_3, base; **c.** BF_3, acid; NH_3, base **91.** $Al(OH)_3(s) + 3H^+(aq) \rightarrow Al^{3+}(aq) + 3H_2O(l)$; $Al(OH)_3(s) + OH^-(aq) \rightarrow Al(OH)_4^-(aq)$ **93.** Fe^{3+}; Because it is smaller with a greater positive charge, Fe^{3+} will be more strongly attracted to a lone pair of electrons from a Lewis base. **95.** $[H^+] = 0.088 M$; $[OH^-] = 1.1 \times 10^{-13}$; $[Cl^-] = 0.013 M$; $[NO_3^-] = 0.075 M$ **97.** acidic, $HSO_4^- + H_2O \rightleftharpoons H_3O^+ + SO_4^{2-}$; $CO_3^{2-} + HSO_4^- \rightarrow HCO_3^- + SO_4^{2-}$ **99.** 4×10^{-2} mol/L; 0.5 g/100 mL **101.** The N-atom is protonated in each case. **103. a.** $Hb(O_2)_4$ in lungs; HbH_4^{4+} in cells; **b.** Decreasing $[CO_2]$ decreases $[H^+]$, favoring $Hb(O_2)_4$; **c.** lowers acidity from accumulated CO_2 **105.** Weak X—H bonds and the presence of X atoms with favorable electron affinities **107. a.** $SeH^- < SH^- < OH^-$; **b.** $PH_3 < NH_3$; **c.** $HONH_2 < NH_3$ **109. a.** NH_4^+ corresponds to H^+; NH_2^- corresponds to OH^-; **b.** $[NH_4^+] = [NH_2^-]$; **c.** $2Na(s) + 2NH_3(l) \rightarrow 2Na^+ + 2NH_2^- + H_2(g)$; **d.** Since ammonia is more basic than water, the acidity of substances is enhanced (e.g., acetic acid is a strong acid in ammonia). **111. a.** 1.3×10^{-4}; **b.** $[H_2CO_3] = [CO_3^{2-}]$; **c.** pH = $(pK_{a_1} + pK_{a_2})/2$; **d.** 8.31 **113.** 7.4; When an acid is added to water, the pH cannot be basic. Must account for the autoionization of water. **115.** 0.92

Chapter 15

1. An ion that participates in the equilibrium reaction but comes from a source other than that reaction. **3.** The quantity of acid or base that can be absorbed with negligible pH change. All have the same pH. Capacities: $1.0 M > 0.1 M > 0.01 M$ **5.** pH = pK_a + log[base]/[acid]; at halfway point [base] = [acid] so pH = pK_a **7.** No. Since there are three colored forms, there must be two acidic or basic functional groups. **9.** The color is determined by the proportion of the acid and base forms present; this proportion changes as the pH changes. **11.** $H^+ + CH_3CO_2^- \rightarrow CH_3CO_2H$; $OH^- + CH_3CO_2H \rightarrow CH_3CO_2^- + H_2O$ **13. a.** 5.14; **b.** 4.34; **c.** 5.14; **d.** 4.34 **15. a.** 2.94; **b.** 8.94; **c.** 7.00; **d.** 4.89 **17. a.** 1.70; **b.** 5.5; **c.** 1.70; **d.** 4.7 **19. a.** 4.3; **b.** 12.30; **c.** 12.30; **d.** 5.1 **21.** Solution d (which is a buffer). **23.** Solution d **25. a.** 0.56; **b.** 0.35; **c.** 5.6; **d.** 2.2 **27. a.** 40. g; **b.** 12 g; **c.** 51 g **29.** 5.20 **31. a.** 7.97; **b.** 8.73 **33. a.** ≈22 mL; **b.** ≈5 to ≈17 mL; **c.** ≈11 mL; **d.** 0 mL; **e.** at and very near stoichiometric point; **f.** after stoichiometric point

35.

Volume	pH
0.0	2.43
4.0	3.14
8.0	3.53
12.5	3.86
20.0	4.46
24.0	5.24
24.5	5.6
24.9	6.3
25.0	8.28
25.1	10.3
26.	11.3
28.	11.8
30.	12.0

37.

Volume	pH
0.0	11.11
4.0	9.97
8.0	9.58
12.5	9.25
20.0	8.65
24.0	7.87
24.5	7.6
24.9	6.9
25.0	5.28
25.1	3.7
26.	2.7
28.	2.2
30.	2.0

39. a. 3.11; **b.** 9.97 **41.** pH < 0.5 **43. a.** yellow; **b.** orange; **c.** blue; **d.** bluish green **45.** (35) phenolphthalein; (37) bromcresol green; (39a) 2,4-dinitrophenol; (39b) thymolphthalein; *Note:* The titration in 39a is not practical because the pH change at the stoichiometric point is too small. **47. a.** $AgC_2H_3O_2(s) \rightleftharpoons Ag^+(aq) + C_2H_3O_2^-(aq)$; $K_{sp} = [Ag^+][C_2H_3O_2^-]$; **b.** $MnS(s) \rightleftharpoons Mn^{2+}(aq) + S^{2-}(aq)$; $K_{sp} = [Mn^{2+}][S^{2-}]$; **c.** $Al(OH)_3(s) \rightleftharpoons Al^{3+}(aq) + 3OH^-(aq)$; $K_{sp} = [Al^{3+}][OH^-]^3$; **d.** $Ca_3(PO_4)_2(s) \rightleftharpoons 3Ca^{2+}(aq) + 2PO_4^{3-}(aq)$; $K_{sp} = [Ca^{2+}]^3[PO_4^{3-}]^2$ **49. a.** 2.3×10^{-9}; **b.** 3.92×10^{-5}; **c.** 8.20×10^{-19} **51. a.** 2×10^{-11} mol/L, 2×10^{-9} g/L; **b.** 7.32×10^{-4} mol/L, 0.286 g/L; **c.** 7.8×10^{-3} mol/L, 1.1 g/L; **d.** 9.3×10^{-5} mol/L, 9.3×10^{-3} g/L; **e.** 7×10^{-5} mol/L, 1×10^{-2} g/L **53.** $Al(OH)_3$, $CaCO_3$, $Mg(NH_4)PO_4$, Ag_2CO_3, Ag_2CrO_4; $Al(OH)_3 + 3H^+ \rightarrow Al^{3+} + 3H_2O$; $CaCO_3 + H^+ \rightarrow Ca^{2+} + HCO_3^-$; $Mg(NH_4)PO_4 + H^+ \rightarrow Mg^{2+} + NH_4^+ + HPO_4^{2-}$; $Ag_2CO_3 + H^+ \rightarrow 2Ag^+ + HCO_3^-$; $2Ag_2CrO_4 + 2H^+ \rightarrow 4Ag^+ + Cr_2O_7^{2-} + H_2O$; $CaSO_4$ and $SrSO_4$ will be slightly more soluble in acid since SO_4^{2-} is a very weak base ($K_b \approx 10^{-12}$). The effect on solubility won't be as great as the others. $MSO_4 + H^+ \rightarrow M^{2+} + HSO_4^-$ **55. a.** 4×10^{-17} mol/L; **b.** 4×10^{-11} mol/L; **c.** 4×10^{-29} mol/L **57.** $[Pb^{2+}] = [Cl^-] = [Na^+] = 0.010\ M$, $[NO_3^-] = 0.020\ M$

59. a.

$$
\begin{array}{rcll}
Co^{2+} + & NH_3 & \rightleftharpoons CoNH_3^{2+} & K_1 \\
CoNH_3^{2+} + & NH_3 & \rightleftharpoons Co(NH_3)_2^{2+} & K_2 \\
Co(NH_3)_2^{2+} + & NH_3 & \rightleftharpoons Co(NH_3)_3^{2+} & K_3 \\
Co(NH_3)_3^{2+} + & NH_3 & \rightleftharpoons Co(NH_3)_4^{2+} & K_4 \\
Co(NH_3)_4^{2+} + & NH_3 & \rightleftharpoons Co(NH_3)_5^{2+} & K_5 \\
Co(NH_3)_5^{2+} + & NH_3 & \rightleftharpoons Co(NH_3)_6^{2+} & K_6 \\
\hline
Co^{2+} + & 6\,NH_3 & \rightleftharpoons Co(NH_3)_6^{2+} & K_f = K_1K_2K_3K_4K_5K_6
\end{array}
$$

b.

$$
\begin{array}{rcll}
Fe^{3+} + & SCN^- & \rightleftharpoons FeSCN^{2+} & K_1 \\
FeSCN^{2+} + & SCN^- & \rightleftharpoons Fe(SCN)_2^+ & K_2 \\
Fe(SCN)_2^+ + & SCN^- & \rightleftharpoons Fe(SCN)_3 & K_3 \\
Fe(SCN)_3 + & SCN^- & \rightleftharpoons Fe(SCN)_4^- & K_4 \\
Fe(SCN)_4^- + & SCN^- & \rightleftharpoons Fe(SCN)_5^{2-} & K_5 \\
Fe(SCN)_5^{2-} + & SCN^- & \rightleftharpoons Fe(SCN)_6^{3-} & K_6 \\
\hline
Fe^{3+} + & 6\,SCN^- & \rightleftharpoons Fe(SCN)_6^{3-} & K_f = K_1K_2K_3K_4K_5K_6
\end{array}
$$

c.

$$
\begin{array}{rcll}
Ag^+ + & NH_3 & \rightleftharpoons AgNH_3^+ & K_1 \\
AgNH_3^+ + & NH_3 & \rightleftharpoons Ag(NH_3)_2^+ & K_2 \\
\hline
Ag^+ + & 2NH_3 & \rightleftharpoons Ag(NH_3)_2^+ & K_f = K_1K_2
\end{array}
$$

61. $Cu^{2+}(aq) + 2OH^-(aq) \rightarrow Cu(OH)_2(s)$; $Cu(OH)_2(s) + 4NH_3(aq) \rightarrow Cu(NH_3)_4^{2+}(aq) + 2OH^-(aq)$ **63.** $3.3 \times 10^{-32}\ M$ **65.** $pOH = pK_b + \log [acid]/[base]$ **67. a.** 8.08; **b.** pH $= 7.0$, 0.08; pH $= 9.0$, 8; **c.** 8.08, 7.96 **69. a.** KF, HCl; **b.** benzoic acid, NaOH; **c.** sodium acetate, acetic acid; **d.** $(CH_3)_2AsO_2Na$, HCl or ammonium chloride, sodium acetate; **e.** ammonium chloride, NaOH **71. a.** 1.8×10^9; **b.** 5.6×10^4; **c.** 3.2×10^4; **d.** 1.0×10^{14}; a, b, and d can be useful in a titration. Solution c results in a buffer and the equivalence point is difficult to detect (the pH change at the equivalence point is small). **73.** pH $= 8.9$ at the equivalence point; Phenolphthalein **75.** 2.7×10^{-5} mol/L; solubility of hydroxyapitite increases as solution gets more acidic; 6×10^{-8} mol/L; fluorapatite is less soluble, making teeth less susceptible to decay. **77.** $2 \times 10^{-18}\ M$; actual iron concentration is much greater. Must be complexing agents present to increase the solubility. **79.** $2 \times 10^{-37}\ M$ **81.** $0.0620\ M$ **83.** Basic. OH^- removes H^+, driving the second reaction to the right, removing H_4SiO_4, increasing the solubility of silica. **85.** The problem can be solved more quickly and easily by making intelligent approximations. **87.** 1.6×10^{-6} **89.** No. $Q = 1.4 \times 10^{-17} < K_{sp}$

Chapter 16

1. A spontaneous process is one that occurs without any outside intervention. **3. a.** increase; **b.** no change; **c.** decrease **5.** Living organisms need an external energy source to produce the necessary ''ordering.'' **7.** The more widely something is dispersed, the greater the disorder and the greater the work needed to overcome the disorder. It would be more advantageous to prevent contamination of the environment rather than clean it up later. **9.** a, c **11.** The most likely total energy is 2 kJ. **13.** Total energies of 2, 3, or 4 kJ are equally probable. **15.** a, b, c **17. a.** N_2O; **b.** H_2 (100°C, 0.5 atm); **c.** N_2 (STP); **d.** $H_2O(l)$ **19. a.** sucrose; **b.** $H_2O(0°C)$; **c.** $H_2S(g)$ **21. a.** $(-)$; **b.** $(+)$; **c.** $(-)$ **23. a.** -45 J/K; **b.** -137 J/K; **c.** 25 J/K **25.** 238 J/K · mol **27.** b, c, d **29.** 93.8 J/K · mol **31. a.** -803 kJ, -4 J/K, -801 kJ; **b.** 2802 kJ, -262 J/K, 2880. kJ; **c.** -416 kJ, -209 J/K, -354 kJ; **d.** -176 kJ, -284 J/K, -91 kJ **33.** -731 kJ/mol **35. a.** both negative; **b.** β form **37. a.** both positive; **b.** high temperature **39.** -198 kJ, 5.07×10^{34} **41. a.** 79.9 kJ; **b.** 81.1 kJ **43.** -188 kJ **45.** $\Delta H° = -92$ kJ; $\Delta S° = -199$ J/K; $K = 9.1 \times 10^5$; **a.** -67 kJ; **b.** -68 kJ; **c.** -85 kJ; **d.** -41 kJ **47. a.** $\Delta S° = -200$ J/K, $\Delta H° = -128$ kJ, $\Delta G° = -70$ kJ; **b.** $\Delta S° = -220.$ J/K, $\Delta H° = -91$ kJ, $\Delta G° = -25$ kJ; **c.** low temperature **49.** 7; no; yes **51.** 9.65 J/K · mol **53.** ΔS_{univ} **55.** $CH_4(g) + CO_2(g) \rightarrow CH_3CO_2H(l)$, $\Delta H° = -16$ kJ, $\Delta S° = -240.$ J/K, $\Delta G° = +56$ kJ; $CH_3OH(g) + CO(g) \rightarrow CH_3CO_2H(l)$, $\Delta H° = -173$ kJ, $\Delta S° = -278$ J/K, $\Delta G° = -90.$ kJ; The second reaction is preferred. It should be run at temperatures below 622 K. **57.** 8.8 kJ/mol K^+; yes; 0.29 mol ATP **59.** As ΔS_{univ} continually increases, there will be less energy available to do work. When no work can be done, the world ends. **61.** I. 0; II. 1.91×10^{-23} J/K;

III. 2.47×10^{-23} J/K **63.** $\Delta H^\circ = 57.4$ kJ; $\Delta S^\circ = -75.6$ J/K **65. a.** 2.22×10^5; **b.** 94.3 **67.** The hydration of the dissociated ions results in a more ordered "structure" in solution. The smallest ion (F^-) has the largest charge density and should show the most ordering. **69.** $K = 2.0 \times 10^{19}$; $\Delta G^\circ = -110$ kJ/mol; $\Delta S^\circ = 20$ J/K · mol

Chapter 17

1. Oxidation: increase in oxidation number, loss of electrons; Reduction: decrease in oxidation number, gain of electrons **2. a.** H (+1), O (−2), N (+5); **b.** Cl (−1), Cu (+2); **c.** zero; **d.** H (+1), O (−1); **e.** Mg (+2), O (−2), S (+6); **f.** zero; **g.** Pb (+2), O (−2), S (+6); **h.** O (−2), Pb (+4); **i.** Na (+1), O (−2), C (+3); **j.** O (−2), C (+4); **k.** H (+1), N (−3), Ce (+4), S (+6), O (−2); **l.** O (−2), Cr (+3) **3.** a, b, d, and f are oxidation–reduction reactions.

	Oxidizing Agent	Reducing Agent	Substance Oxidized	Substance Reduced
a.	H_2O	CH_4	CH_4	H_2O
b.	$AgNO_3$	Cu	Cu	$AgNO_3$
d.	HCl	Zn	Zn	HCl
f.	HCl	Fe	Fe	HCl

4. a. $4H^+(aq) + NO_3^-(aq) + Cr(s) \rightarrow Cr^{3+}(aq) + NO(g) + 2H_2O(l)$; **b.** $24H^+(aq) + 3MnO_4^-(aq) + 5Al(s) \rightarrow 5Al^{3+}(aq) + 3Mn^{2+}(aq) + 12H_2O(l)$; **c.** $H_2O(l) + CH_3OH(aq) + 6Ce^{4+}(aq) \rightarrow 6Ce^{3+}(aq) + CO_2(g) + 6H^+(aq)$; **d.** $6H^+(aq) + 5SO_3^{2-}(aq) + 2MnO_4^-(aq) \rightarrow 5SO_4^{2-}(aq) + 2Mn^{2+}(aq) + 3H_2O(l)$; **e.** $H_2O(l) + 3PO_3^{3-}(aq) + 2MnO_4^-(aq) \rightarrow 3PO_4^{3-}(aq) + 2MnO_2(s) + 2OH^-(aq)$; **f.** $H_2O(l) + Mg(s) + OCl^-(aq) \rightarrow Mg(OH)_2(s) + Cl^-(aq)$; **g.** $170OH^-(aq) + 4OCe^{4+}(aq) + Ni(CN)_4^{2-}(aq) \rightarrow Ni(OH)_2(s) + 40Ce(OH)_3(s) + 4CO_3^{2-}(aq) + 4NO_3^-(aq) + 24H_2O(l)$; **h.** $5OH^-(aq) + H_2CO(aq) + 4Ag(NH_3)_2^+(aq) \rightarrow 4Ag(s) + 8NH_3(aq) + HCO_3^-(aq) + 3H_2O(l)$ **5.** In a galvanic cell a spontaneous reaction occurs, producing an electric current. In an electrolytic cell electricity is used to force a reaction to occur that is not spontaneous. **7. a.** cathode: where reduction occurs; **b.** anode: where oxidation occurs; **c.** oxidation half-reaction: e^- are products; **d.** reduction half-reaction: e^- are reactants **9.** protective coating; alloying; cathodic protection **11. a.** Cathode: Pt electrode; Cl_2 bubbled into solution, Cl^- in solution; Anode: Pt electrode; Cr^{3+}, H^+ and $Cr_2O_7^{2-}$ in solution; **b.** Cathode: Cu electrode; Cu^{2+} in solution; Anode: Mg electrode; Mg^{2+} in solution **13. a.** Cathode: Pt electrode; Cl_2 bubbled in, Cl^- in solution; Anode: Pt electrode: Br_2 and Br^- in solution; **b.** Cathode: Pt electrode; IO_4^-, IO_3^-, and H_2SO_4 (as a source of H^+) in solution; Anode: Pt electrode; Mn^{2+}, MnO_4^-, and H_2SO_4 in solution **15. 11a.** $Pt|Cr^{3+}$ (1.0 M), H^+ (1.0 M), $Cr_2O_7^{2-}$ (1.0 M) $\|Cl^-$ (1.0 M), Cl_2 (1.0 atm)|Pt; **11b.** $Mg|Mg^{2+}$ (1.0 M) $\|Cu^{2+}$ (1.0 M)|Cu; **13a.** $Pt|Br^-$ (1.0 M), Br_2 (1.0 M) $\|Cl^-$ (1.0 M), Cl_2 (1.0 atm)|Pt; **13b.** $Pt|Mn^{2+}$ (1.0 M), MnO_4^- (1.0 M), H^+ (1.0 M) $\|H^+$ (1.0 M) IO_3^- (1.0 M), IO_4^- (1.0 M)|Pt **17. 11a.** 0.03 V; **11b.** 2.71 V; **13a.** 0.27 V; **13b.** 0.09 V **19. a.** 0.46 V, spontaneous; **b.** −0.53 V, not spontaneous **21. a.** No; **b.** Yes; **c.** Yes; **d.** No **23.** $Mg^{2+} < Fe^{2+} < Fe^{3+} < Cr_2O_7^{2-} < Cl_2 < MnO_4^-$ **25. a.** Br_2; **b.** Ca; **c.** Br^-, H_2, Ca, Cd; **d.** Br_2, H^+ **27. a.** None under standard conditions; Ag^+ ($[Ag^+] > 1$ M); **b.** $Cr_2O_7^{2-}$, O_2, MnO_2, and IO_3^-; **c.** $PbSO_4$, Cd^{2+}, Fe^{2+}, Cr^{3+}, Zn^{2+}, H_2O **29.** Yes, 0.34 $V <$ $\mathscr{E}^\circ < 0.54$ V **31. a.** 0.41 V, −79 kJ, 7.1×10^{13}; **b.** $3H_2O(l) + 6ClO_2(g) \rightarrow 5ClO_3^-(aq) + Cl^-(aq) + 6H^+(aq)$ **33. 11a.** −20 kJ, 1 ×

10^3; **11b.** −523 kJ, 3.55×10^{91}; **13a.** −52 kJ, 1.3×10^9; **13b.** −90 kJ, 2×10^{15} **35.** 77 kJ/mol **37.** −0.829 V (calc'd); −0.83 V (table) **39.** 3.7×10^{-8} **41. a.** 0; **b.** 0.02 V; compartment with $[Ag^+] = 2.0$ M is cathode; **c.** 0.06 V; compartment with $[Ag^+] = 1.0$ M is cathode; **d.** 0.26 V; compartment with $[Ag^+] = 1.0$ M is cathode; **e.** 0 **43.** Yes **45. a.** 0.23 V; **b.** 0.16 V, cell reaction is the opposite of part a. **c.** 1.3×10^{-5}; **d.** Graph $\mathscr{E}$ vs. $\log[Cu^{2+}]$; slope = 0.0296 V **47.** The spontaneous reaction is ($\mathscr{E}^\circ = 0.20$ V): $12 Cl^- + 3Pt + 2NO_3^- + 8H^+ \rightarrow 3PtCl_4^{2-} + 2NO + 4H_2O$; Both NO_3^- and Cl^- must be present. **49. a.** 3.0×10^1 hours; **b.** 33 s; **c.** 1.3 hours **51. a.** Cathode: $K^+ + e^- \rightarrow K$; Anode: $2F^- \rightarrow F_2 + 2e^-$; **b.** Cathode: $2H_2O + 2e^- \rightarrow H_2 + 2OH^-$; Anode: $2H_2O \rightarrow 4H^+ + O_2 + 4e^-$; **c.** Cathode: $H_2O_2 + 2H^+ + 2e^- \rightarrow 2H_2O$; Anode: $H_2O_2 \rightarrow O_2 + 2H^+ + 2e^-$ **53.** Indium **55.** 9.12 L of F_2 (anode); 29.2 g K (cathode) **57.** $4Au(CN)_4^-(aq) + 12OH^-(aq) \rightarrow 4Au(s) + 16CN^-(aq) + 3O_2(g) + 6H_2O(l)$; 96 L **59.** 5.0×10^5 amps **61.** 1.14×10^{-2} M **63. a.** 0.10 V; SCE, anode; **b.** 0.53 V; SCE, anode; **c.** 0.02 V; SCE, cathode; **d.** 1.90 V; SCE, cathode; **e.** 0.47 V; SCE, cathode **65.** 0.36 V, −35 kJ, 1.2×10^6 **67.** $H_2O_2 + 2H^+ + 2e^- \rightarrow 2H_2O$ (ox. agent); $O_2 + 2H^+ + 2e^- \rightarrow H_2O_2$ (red. agent); $\mathscr{E}^\circ = 1.10$ V **69. b.** $Cl_2(g) + 2I^-(aq) \rightarrow I_2(s) + 2Cl^-(aq)$; $\mathscr{E}^\circ = 0.82$ V, $\Delta G^\circ = -160$ kJ, K = 5.0×10^{27}; **d.** $Pb(s) + Cu^{2+}(aq) \rightarrow Cu(s) + Pb^{2+}(aq)$; $\mathscr{E}^\circ = 0.47$ V, $\Delta G^\circ = -91$ kJ, K = 7.6×10^{15}; **e.** $4Fe^{2+}(aq) + 4H^+(aq) + O_2(g) \rightarrow 4Fe^{3+}(aq) + 2H_2O(l)$; $\mathscr{E}^\circ = 0.46$ V, $\Delta G^\circ = -180$ kJ, K = 1.2×10^{31} **71.** Zn provides cathodic protection **73.** 0.0034 V, −660 J, 1.3 **75. a.** 0.242 V; **b.** anode; **c.** $\mathscr{E} = 0.242$ $V - 0.0592 \log [H^+] = 0.242$ $V + 0.0592$ pH; **d.** i. 0.42 V; ii. 0.218 V; iii. 0.77 V; **e.** pH = 0.726, $[H^+] = 0.188$ M; **f.** convenience **77.** Ag **79.** Yes **81.** The energy to recycle Al (4.0×10^2 kJ/kg) is less than 1% of that required by the Hall process (5.4×10^4 kJ/kg). **83.** $w_{max} = 13,200$ kJ; The work done can be no larger than the free energy change. If the process were reversible all of the free energy released would go into work, but this does not occur in any real process. Fuel cells are more efficient in converting chemical energy to electrical energy; they are also less massive. Major disadvantage: they are expensive. **85. a.** $\mathscr{E}^\circ = -1.23$ V, $\Delta G^\circ = 475$ kJ; **b.** $\Delta H^\circ = 572$ kJ, $\Delta S^\circ = 327$ J/K; **c.** 90°C: $\Delta G^\circ = 450$ kJ, $\mathscr{E}^\circ = -1.2$ V; 0°C: $\Delta G^\circ = 483$ kJ, $\mathscr{E}^\circ = -1.25$ V **87.** 1.5×10^{13} **89. a.** 0.40 V; **b.** 1.11 V **91. a.** Uncertainty in pH is ±0.017 pH units. Uncertainty in $[H^+]$ is $±0.06 \times 10^{-4}$ mol/L; **b.** ±1 mV

Chapter 18

1. The gravity of the earth cannot keep H_2 in the atmosphere. **3.** Ionic, covalent, and metallic (or interstitial). The ionic and covalent hydrides are true compounds which differ in the type of bonding. The interstitial hydrides are more like solid solutions of hydrogen and a transition metal and have variable content. **5.** Hydrogen forms many compounds in which its oxidation state is +1. On the other hand hydrogen forms diatomic H_2 molecules and is a nonmetal, while the Group 1A elements are metals. Hydrogen forms the hydride anion H^-; the Group 1A metals do not form anions. **7.** They must be produced in the absence of materials (H_2O, O_2) that are capable of oxidizing them. **9.** The planes of carbon atoms slide easily. Graphite is not volatile so the lubricant will not be lost when used in a high vacuum environment. **11.** The bonds in SnX_4 compounds generally have covalent character, and the SnX_4 molecules interact by dispersion forces. SnX_2 compounds are ionic. **13.** Size decreases from left to right and

increases going down. So going one element right and one element down would result in a similar size for the two elements diagonal to each other. The ionization energies will also be similar for the diagonal elements. Electron affinities are harder to predict, but the similar size and ionization energies would lead to similar properties.
15. a. $\Delta H° = 207$ kJ, $\Delta S° = 216$ J/K; **b.** T > 958 K **17.** Na_2O, NaO_2, Na_2O_2 **19. a.** $Li_3N(s) + 3HCl(aq) \rightarrow 3LiCl(aq) + NH_3(aq)$;
b. $Rb_2O(s) + H_2O(l) \rightarrow 2RbOH(aq)$; **c.** $Cs_2O_2(s) + 2H_2O(l) \rightarrow 2CsOH(aq) + H_2O_2(aq)$; **d.** $NaH(s) + H_2O(l) \rightarrow NaOH(aq) + H_2(g)$
21. $2Li(s) + 2C_2H_2(g) \rightarrow 2LiC_2H(s) + H_2(g)$; oxidation–reduction
23. BaO, BaO_2 **25.** $Mg_3N_2(s) + 6H_2O(l) \rightarrow 2NH_3(g) + 3Mg^{2+}(aq) + 6OH^-(aq)$; $Mg_3P_2(s) + 6H_2O(l) \rightarrow 2PH_3(g) + 3Mg^{2+}(aq) + 6OH^-(aq)$
27. Trigonal planar; Be, sp^2; N, sp^3; Lewis acid **29.** $Be(s) + 2H_2O(l) + 2OH^-(aq) \rightarrow Be(OH)_4{}^{2-}(aq) + H_2(g)$; Be (reducing agent); H_2O (oxidizing agent) **31. a.** thallium(I) hydroxide; **b.** indium(III) sulfide; **c.** gallium(III) oxide or gallium oxide **33.** $B_2H_6 + 3O_2 \rightarrow 2B(OH)_3$ **35.** $In_2O_3(s) + 6H^+(aq) \rightarrow 2In^{3+}(aq) + 3H_2O(l)$; $In(OH)_3(s) + OH^-(aq) \rightarrow$ No reaction; $Ga_2O_3(s) + 6H^+(aq) \rightarrow 2Ga^{3+}(aq) + 3H_2O(l)$; $Ga_2O_3(s) + 2OH^-(aq) + 3H_2O(l) \rightarrow 2Ga(OH)_4{}^-(aq)$ **37.** $2In(s) + 3F_2(g) \rightarrow 2InF_3(s)$; $2In(s) + 3Cl_2(g) \rightarrow 2InCl_3(s)$; $4In(s) + 3O_2(g) \rightarrow 2In_2O_3(s)$; $2In(s) + 6HCl(aq) \rightarrow 3H_2(g) + 2InCl_3(aq)$ or $2In(s) + 6HCl(g) \rightarrow 3H_2(g) + 2InCl_3(s)$
39. a. linear; **b.** sp **41. a.** $K_2SiF_6(s) + 4K(s) \rightarrow Si(s) + 6KF(s)$; **b.** Ionic ($K^+$, $SiF_6{}^{2-}$); $SiF_6{}^{2-}$ is octahedral **43.** $\mathscr{E}° = 0.97$ V. Iron pipes are more easily corroded. **45.** tin(II) fluoride **47.** The π electrons are free to move in graphite, thus giving it a greater conductivity (lower resistance). The electrons have the greatest mobility within the sheets of carbon atoms. Electrons in diamond are not mobile (high resistance). The structure of diamond is uniform in all directions; thus, there is no directional dependence of the resistivity. **49. a.** $2Na + 2NH_3 \rightarrow 2NaNH_2 + H_2$; **b.** 20.09% by mass; $X_{Na} = 0.1570$; 10.94 m
51. ≈20°C, liquid **53.** 1.67×10^5 A, 1.77×10^3 kg of Cl_2
55.

57. Li, +1; Al, +3; H, −1 **59.** If the compound contained Ga(II) it would be paramagnetic. Paramagnetic compounds have an apparent greater mass in a magnetic field. **61.** −83 kJ. H_2CO_3 will spontaneously decompose to CO_2 and H_2O. **63.** Sn and Pb; $Sn(s) + 2H^+(aq) + Sn^{2+}(aq) + H_2(g)$; $Pb(s) + 2H^+(aq) \rightarrow Pb^{2+}(aq) + H_2(g)$
65. The Na^+ ion is encapsulated so that it does not come into contact with the Na^- ion and oxidize it to sodium metal. **67.** grey tin
69. Carbon is much smaller than Si and cannot form a fifth bond in the transition state.

Chapter 19

1. The process is exothermic, so low temperatures are favored for maximum yield of ammonia but the rate is too slow and a catalyst is required. **3.** Pollutants provide nitrogen and phosphorus nutrients, causing the algae to grow, which consumes oxygen, causing fish to die. **5.** Plastic sulfur has long S_n chains which break down into S_8 rings. **7.** Fluorine is the most electronegative element; the F_2 bond is very weak. **9.** Helium, which does not combine with other elements, has a low mass and easily escaped the earth's gravitational pull as the planet was formed. **11.** Nitrogen's small size does not provide room for all

four oxygen atoms, making $NO_4{}^{3-}$ unstable. Phosphorus is larger so $PO_4{}^{3-}$ is more stable. To form $NO_3{}^-$, a pi bond must form. Phosphorus doesn't form strong pi bonds as readily as nitrogen.
13. a. $8H^+(aq) + 2NO_3{}^-(aq) + 3Cu(s) \rightarrow 3Cu^{2+}(aq) + 4H_2O(l) + 2NO(g)$; **b.** $NH_4NO_3(s) \xrightarrow{\text{Heat}} N_2O(g) + 2 H_2O(g)$; **c.** $NO(g) + NO_2(g) + 2 KOH(aq) \rightarrow 2 KNO_2(aq) + H_2O(l)$ **15.** NH_3, sp^3; N_2H_4, sp^3; NH_2OH, sp^3; N_2, sp; N_2O (central N), sp; NO, sp^2; N_2O_3, sp^2; NO_2, sp^2; HNO_3, sp^2. **17.** $\Delta H° = 180.$; kJ, $\Delta S° = 25$ J/K, $\Delta G° = 174$ kJ; At high temperatures, the reaction becomes spontaneous. In the cooler temperatures of the atmosphere, even though the reverse reaction is spontaneous, its rate is very slow. **19. a.** $H_3PO_4 > H_3PO_3$; **b.** $H_3PO_4 > H_2PO_4{}^- > HPO_4{}^{2-}$ **21.** $2Sb_2S_3(s) + 9O_2(g) \rightarrow 2Sb_2O_3(s) + 6SO_2(g)$; $2Sb_2O_3(s) + 3C(s) \rightarrow 4Sb(s) + 3CO_2(g)$; $2Bi_2S_3(s) + 9O_2(g) \rightarrow 2Bi_2O_3(s) + 6SO_2(g)$; $2Bi_2O_3(s) + 3C(s) \rightarrow 4Bi(s) + 3CO_2(g)$ **23.** 821 nm **25. a.** redox; **b.** NO; **c.** $6H^+(aq) + 2HNO_3(aq) + 3S^{2-}(aq) \rightarrow 3S(s) + 2NO(g) + 4H_2O(l)$
27. square pyramid

29. a.

b.

c.

Tetrahedral about each Cl; bent about the central O

d.

Trigonal pyramid

31. $H_2O(l) + BrO_3{}^-(aq) + XeF_2(aq) \rightarrow BrO_4{}^-(aq) + Xe(g) + 2HF(aq)$
33. a. -0.27 V; **b.** No, $\mathscr{E}° < 0$; **c.** $\mathscr{E}$ increases as solution becomes more basic. **35. a.** $IO_4{}^-$; **b.** $IO_3{}^-$; **c.** $IF_2{}^-$; **d.** $IF_4{}^-$; **e.** $IF_6{}^-$; **f.** $IOF_3{}^-$ **37.** XeF_2 can react with oxygen to produce explosive oxides and oxyfluorides. **39.** As the halogen atoms get larger, it becomes more difficult to fit three halogens around the small N. **41.** $\Delta H° = -154$ kJ, $\Delta S° = -173$ J/K, $\Delta G° = -102$ kJ; Reaction is spontaneous at T < 890. K.

43.

All of the resonance structures for fulminate involve greater formal charges than in cyanate, making fulminate more reactive (less stable).

45.

		Bond Order	# Unpaired e^-
M.O.:	NO	2.5	1
	NO^+	3	0
	NO^-	2	2
Lewis:	NO^+, $[:N \equiv O:]^+$		

47. a. $8H_2O(l) + 2Mn^{2+}(aq) + 5NaBIO_3(s) \rightarrow 2MnO_4{}^-(aq) + 16H^+(aq) + 5BiO_3{}^{3-}(aq) + 5Na^+(aq)$; **b.** Bismuthate exists as a co-

valent network: $(BiO_3^-)_x$ **49.** 512 nm, green   **51. a.** $\mathscr{E} > 1.19\ V$;
b. 5×10^9 kJ   **53.** For $NCl_3 \rightarrow NCl_2 + Cl$, only the N—Cl bond is
being broken. For $O=N—Cl \rightarrow NO + Cl$, the NO gets stronger (bond
order increases from 2.0 to 2.5) making ΔH for the reaction smaller
than the energy necessary to break the N—Cl bond.   **55. a.** K_a increases down the group consistent with the bond to hydrogen getting
weaker.   **b.** Po is below Te, so K_a should be larger. The K_a for H_2Po
should be on the order of 10^{-2} or 10^{-1}.

Chapter 20

1. a. ligand: Lewis base;   **b.** chelate: forms more than one bond;
c. bidentate: can form two bonds;   **d.** complex ion: metal ion with attached ligands   **3.** Both shared electrons originally came from a ligand
atom.   **5. a.** isomers: Species with the same formulas but different
properties.   **b.** structural isomers: Isomers that have one or more
bonds that are different.   **c.** stereoisomers: Isomers that contain the
same bonds but differ in how the atoms are arranged in space.
d. coordination isomers: Isomers that differ in what atoms are found in
the coordination sphere.   **e.** linkage isomers: Isomers that differ in
how one or more ligands are attached to the transition metal.
f. geometric isomers: (*cis-trans* isomerism) Isomers that differ in the
positions of atoms with respect to a rigid ring, bond, or each other.
g. optical isomerism: Isomers that differ by being nonsuperimposable
mirror images of each other; that is, they are different in the same way
our left and right hands differ.   **7.** Cu^{2+} is d^9; Cu^+ is d^{10}. Color results from electron transfer between split d orbitals. This cannot occur
for the filled d orbitals in Cu^+.   **9.** Sc^{3+} has no d electrons, while
V^{3+} and Ti^{3+} do.   **11.** A soluble complex ion forms: $Fe_2O_3(s) +$
$6H_2C_2O_4(aq) \rightarrow 2Fe(C_2O_4)_3^{3-}(aq) + 3H_2O(l) + 6H^+(aq)$ **13.** There
is a steady decrease in the atomic radii of the lanthanide elements,
going from left to right. As a result, the properties of the $4d$ and $5d$
elements in each group are very similar because of the similar sizes of
atoms and ions.   **15.** Advantages: low energy cost, less air pollution;
Disadvantages: chemicals used are expensive   **17. a.** Ni: $[Ar]4s^23d^8$;
b. Cd: $[Kr]5s^24d^{10}$;   **c.** Zr: $[Kr]5s^24d^2$;   **d.** Nd: $[Xe]6s^24f^4$
19. a. Ni^{2+}: $[Ar]3d^8$;   **b.** Cd^{2+}: $[Kr]4d^{10}$;   **c.** Zr^{3+}: $[Kr]4d^1$, Zr^{4+}:
$[Kr]$;   **d.** Nd^{3+}: $[Xe]4f^3$ **21. a.** Co: $[Ar]4s^23d^7$; Co^{2+}: $[Ar]3d^7$;
Co^{3+}: $[Ar]3d^6$;   **b.** Pt: $[Xe]6s^14f^{14}5d^9$; Pt^{2+}: $[Xe]4f^{14}5d^8$; Pt^{4+}:
$[Xe]4f^{14}5d^6$;   **c.** Fe: $[Ar]4s^23d^6$; Fe^{2+}: $[Ar]3d^6$; Fe^{3+}: $[Ar]3d^5$
23. 316 kg   **25. a.** Molybdenum(IV) sulfide, Molybdenum(VI) oxide;
b. +4, +6;   **c.** $2MoS_2(s) + 7O_2(g) \rightarrow 2MoO_3(s) + 4SO_2(g)$;
$2NH_3(g) + 2MoO_3(s) + H_2O(l) \rightarrow (NH_4)_2Mo_2O_7(s)$; $6NH_3(g) +$
$7MoO_3(s) + 7H_2O(l) \rightarrow (NH_4)_6Mo_7O_{24} \cdot 4H_2O(s)$
27. a. pentaamminechlororuthenium(III) ion;   **b.** hexacyanoferrate(II)
ion;   **c.** tris(ethylenediamine)manganese(II) ion;   **d.** pentaammine-
nitrocobalt(III) ion   **29. a.** hexaamminecobalt(II) chloride;
b. hexaaquacobalt(III) iodide;   **c.** potassium tetrachloroplatinate(II);
d. potassium hexachloroplatinate(II)   **31. a.** $[Co(C_5H_5N)_6]Cl_3$;
b. $[Cr(NH_3)_5I]I_2$;   **c.** $[Ni(NH_2CH_2CH_2NH_2)_3]Br_2$;   **d.** $K_2[Ni(CN)_4]$;
e. $[Pt(NH_3)_4Cl_2]PtCl_4$

37. SCN^-, NO_2^-, and OCN^- can form linkage isomers; all are able to
bond to the metal ion in two different ways.

43. $NiCl_4^{2-}$ is tetrahedral, $Ni(CN)_4^{2-}$ is square planar.
45. $Ni(H_2O)_6Cl_2$ absorbs red light. $Ni(NH_3)_6Cl_2$ absorbs yellow-green
light. $Ni(NH_3)_6Cl_2$ absorbs the shorter wavelength light: Δ is larger for

$Ni(NH_3)_6Cl_2$; NH_3 is a stronger field ligand than H_2O, consistent with the spectrochemical series. **47. a.** $\Delta H° = -39$ kJ, $\Delta S° = 38$ J/K; **b.** $\Delta G° = -80$ kJ **49. a.** 4O on faces $\times \frac{1}{2}$O/face = 2O atoms; 2O atoms inside body; Total: 4O atoms; 8 corners $\times \frac{1}{8}$Ti/corner + 1Ti/body center = 2Ti; Formula of unit cell, Ti_2O_4; empirical formula, TiO_2
b.

$$\overset{+4-2}{2TiO_2} + \overset{0}{3C} + \overset{0}{4Cl_2} \rightarrow \overset{+4-1}{2TiCl_4} + \overset{+4-2}{CO_2} + \overset{+2-2}{CO}$$

C, oxidized; Cl_2, oxidizing agent
Cl, reduced; C, reducing agent

$$\overset{+4-1}{TiCl_4} + \overset{0}{O_2} \rightarrow \overset{+4-2}{TiO_2} + \overset{0}{2Cl_2}$$

Cl, oxidized; O_2, oxidizing agent
O, reduced; $TiCl_4$, reducing agent

51. a. $2CoAs_2(s) + 4O_2(g) \rightarrow 2CoO(s) + As_4O_6(s)$; tetraarsenic hexaoxide, cage structure similar to P_4O_6; **b.** $2Co^{2+}(aq) + 4OH^-(aq) + H_2O(l) + OCl^-(aq) \rightarrow 2Co(OH)_3(s) + Cl^-(aq)$; **c.** 2.5×10^{-22} M; **d.** 2.5×10^{-31} M **53.** $\mathscr{E}° = 0.66$ V, $\Delta G° = -130$ kJ, $K = 2.0 \times 10^{22}$ **55. a.** 2; **b.** 3; **c.** 4; **d.** 4
57. a.

[chemical structures showing two resonance forms of M(acac) complex with CH₃, O, C, CH groups]

b. *cis*-$Cr(acac)_2(H_2O)_2$ and $Cr(acac)_3$ are optically active.
c. $Eu(acac)_3 \equiv EuC_{15}H_{21}O_6$
59. a. optical isomerism
b. d^6; [orbital diagram with three pairs of arrows]

61. $Ni^{2+}(aq) + 2OH^-(aq) \rightarrow Ni(OH)_2(s)$; $Ni(OH)_2(s) + 4CN^-(aq) \rightarrow Ni(CN)_4^{2-}(aq) + 2OH^-(aq)$

63. a.

[two structures of Co complexes with OH bridges, charge 6+ each]

NH_3 molecules are not shown.
b. All are Co(III); **c.** none

65. $[Cr(NH_3)_5I]I_2$; octahedral **67.** No, since in all three cases six bonds are formed between Ni^{2+} and nitrogen. $\Delta S°$ for formation of the complex ion is most negative for $6NH_3$ molecules reacting with a metal ion (7 independent species become 1). For penten reacting with a metal ion, 2 independent species become 1, so $\Delta S°$ is less negative. Thus, the chelate effect occurs because the more bonds a chelating agent can form to the metal, the more favorable $\Delta S°$ is for the formation of the complex ion, and the larger the formation constant.
69. — d_{z^2}
— — $d_{x^2-y^2}$, d_{xy}
— — d_{xz}, d_{yz}

Chapter 21

1. Fission: splitting a heavy nucleus into two lighter nuclei; Fusion: combining two light nuclei to form a heavier nucleus. Fusion is more likely for elements lighter than Fe; fission is more likely for elements heavier than Fe. **3.** Constant ^{14}C level is a poor assumption and accounting for variation is complicated. **5.** No, coal fired power plants also pose risks. A partial list of risks:

Coal	Nuclear
Air pollution	Radiation exposure to workers
Coal mine accidents	Disposal of wastes
Health risks to miners (black lung disease)	Meltdown
	Terrorists
	Public fear

7. For fusion a collision of sufficient energy must occur between two positively charged particles to initiate the reaction. This requires high temperatures. In fission, an electrically neutral neutron collides with the positively charged nucleus. This has a much lower activation energy. **9.** Magnetic fields are needed to contain the fusion reaction. Superconductors allow the production of very strong magnetic fields, more capable of containing the fusion reaction.
11. a. $^3_1H \rightarrow ^0_{-1}e + ^3_2He$
b. $^8_3Li \rightarrow ^8_4Be + ^0_{-1}e$
$$\frac{^8_4Be \rightarrow 2\ ^4_2He}{^8_3Li \rightarrow 2\ ^4_2He + ^0_{-1}e}$$
c. $^7_4Be + ^0_{-1}e \rightarrow ^7_3Li$; **d.** $^8_5B \rightarrow ^8_4Be + ^0_{+1}e$; **e.** $^{32}_{15}P \rightarrow ^{32}_{16}S + ^0_{-1}e$
13. a. $^1_1H + ^{14}_7N \rightarrow ^{11}_6C + ^4_2He$; **b.** $2\ ^3_2He \rightarrow ^4_2He + 2\ ^1_1H$; **c.** $^1_1H + ^1_1H \rightarrow ^2_1H + ^0_{+1}e$; **d.** $^1_1H + ^{12}_6C \rightarrow ^{13}_7N$ **15.** ^8B and ^9B: positron production or electron capture; ^{12}B and ^{13}B: beta production **17. a.** $^{207}_{82}Pb$;
b. $^{231}_{90}Th$, $^{231}_{91}Pa$, $^{227}_{89}Ac$, $^{227}_{90}Th$, $^{223}_{88}Ra$, $^{219}_{86}Rn$, $^{215}_{84}Po$, $^{211}_{82}Pb$, $^{211}_{83}Bi$, $^{207}_{81}Tl$
19. 1.1×10^{12}; 9.6×10^{18}; 5.8×10^{20}; 3.5×10^{22} **21.** 6.21 mg
23. 0.800 yr **25.** 0.76 **27.** 0.866 **29.** 4.3×10^6 kg/s **31.** ^{24}Mg, 1.324×10^{-12} J/nucleon; ^{27}Mg, 1.324×10^{-12} J/nucleon
33. 3.00657×10^{-10} J absorbed per proton (1.81060×10^{14} J/mol). Kinetic energy. **35.** 2.0×10^{10} J/g **37.** The Geiger-Müller tube has a certain response time. After the gas in the tube ionizes to produce a "count," some time must elapse for the gas to return to an electrically neutral state. The response of the tube levels off because at high activities radioactive particles are entering the tube faster than the tube can respond to them. **39.** 1.0×10^1 mL **41.** Strontium. Xe is chemically unreactive and not readily incorporated into the body. Sr can be easily oxidized to Sr^{2+}. Strontium is in the same family as calcium and could be absorbed and concentrated in the body in a fashion similar to Ca. **43.** 6.013480 amu, 3.086×10^{12} J/mol **45.** 8×10^{-16} J **47. a.** $^{12}_6C$; **b.** ^{13}N, ^{13}C, ^{14}N, ^{15}O, and ^{15}N; **c.** 5.950×10^{11} J/mol H
49. a. Yes; **b.** $3H_2O(l) + Zr(s) \rightarrow 2H_2(g) + ZrO_2 \cdot H_2O(s)$; **c.** 1.53 V, $-590.$kJ, 10^{103}; **d.** 2×10^6 L; **e.** Probably yes. An explosion of the H_2 in the reactor would have created a worse disaster.

Chapter 22

1. A consecutive chain of C-atoms. They are not all in a true straight line since the bond angle at each carbon is 109.5°C. **3.** Resonance: All atoms are in the same position. Only the position of π electrons is different. Isomerism: Atoms are in different locations in space. Isomers are distinctly different substances. Resonance involves multiple Lewis structures to describe the bonding in a single compound.

5. a. Addition polymer: formed by adding monomer units to a double bond. Teflon n $CF_2=CF_2 \rightarrow +(CF_2-CF_2)_n$; **b.** Condensation polymer: two monomers combine, eliminating a small molecule. Nylon and dacron are examples. **c.** Copolymer: formed from more than one monomer. Nylon and dacron are also copolymers. **7.** A thermoplastic polymer can be remelted; a thermoset polymer cannot be softened once it is formed. **9.** Plasticizers make a polymer more flexible. Cross-linking makes a polymer more rigid. **11. a.** Replacement of hydrogen with halogen results in fewer H and OH radicals in the flame, reducing flame temperature. **b.** With aromatic groups present, it is more difficult to "chip off" pieces of the polymer in pyrolysis zone. **c.** It is more difficult to "chip off" fragments of the polymer in the pyrolysis zone. The polymer chars instead of burning. **13.** For a given chain length, there are more hydrogen bonding sites in Nylon-46 as compared to Nylon-6.
15. $CH_3-CH_2-CH_2-CH_2-CH_2-CH_3$ hexane or n-hexane (highest b.p., least branched)

n-Hexane should have the highest boiling point. It is the least branched and, therefore, there will be the strongest dispersion forces between hexane molecules.

17. a.

c.

d. 2,2,3-trimethylhexane

19. a. 1-butene; **b.** 2-methyl-2-butene; **c.** 2,5-dimethyl-3-heptene
21. a. $CH_3CH_2CH=CHCH_2CH_3$; **b.** $CH_3CH=CHCH=CHCH_2CH_3$;
c. $CH_3CHCH=CHCH_2CH_2CH_2CH_3$
   $\quad\;\; CH_3$

23. a.

b.

c.

25. a. 1,3-dichlorobutane; **b.** 1,1,1-trichlorobutane;

c. 2,3-dichloro-2,4-dimethylhexane; **d.** 1,2-difluoroethane;
e. chlorobenzene; **f.** chlorocyclohexane; **g.** 3-chlorocyclohexene

27.

29.

31. a.

b.

c.

33. a. ketone; **b.** aldehyde; **c.** ketone; **d.** amine

35. a.

b. 5 carbons in ring and in —CO$_2$H: sp^2; —CH$_2$— and —CH—NH$_2$: sp^3; **c.** 4 π-bonds and 24 σ-bonds

37. 3 alcohol groups and an amine **39. a.** CH$_2$BrCH$_2$Br; **b.** C$_6$H$_5$Br + HBr

c. CH$_3$\overset{O}{\overset{\|}{C}}OCH$_3$

41. a.

CH$_3$—\overset{O}{\overset{\|}{C}}—H

b.

CH$_3$—\overset{O}{\overset{\|}{C}}—CH$_3$

c.

d. No reaction

e.

H$_3$C—\overset{CH_3}{\underset{CH_3}{\overset{|}{\underset{|}{C}}}}—\overset{O}{\overset{\|}{CH}}

43. a. CH$_3$CH=CH$_2$ + Br$_2$ → CH$_3$CHBrCH$_2$Br;

b. CH$_3$C≡CH + H$_2$ $\xrightarrow{\text{catalyst}}$ CH$_3$CH=CH$_2$ + Br$_2$ → CH$_3$CHBrCH$_2$Br

c. CH$_3$CO$_2$H + CH$_3$CH$_2$CH$_2$CH$_2$OH →

CH$_3$\overset{O}{\overset{\|}{C}}—O—CH$_2$CH$_2$CH$_2$CH$_3$ + H$_2$O

45. a. CHF=CH$_2$ (addition); **b.** HOCH$_2$CH$_2$CO$_2$H (condensation); **c.** copolymer of HOCH$_2$CH$_2$OH and HO$_2$CCH$_2$CH$_2$CO$_2$H (condensation)

d. CH$_3$CH=CH$_2$ (addition)

e. CH=CHCH$_3$ (addition)

47.

49.

51. divinyl benzene acts as a crosslinking agent, making the polymer more rigid **53.** 2-methyl-1, 3-butadiene

55.

trans   *cis*

57. a. ketone; **b.** amide with C=O; **c.** structure with two C=O **59.** The amine group is protonated

---

Morphine hydrochloride is ionic and thus more soluble in water.
61. a. The bond angles in the ring are about 60°. VSEPR predicts bond angles close to 109°. The bonding electrons are close together and electron-electron repulsions are high.
b. —(O—CH$_2$CH$_2$—O—CH$_2$CH$_2$—O—CH$_2$CH$_2$)$_{\overline{n}}$; **c.** ≈0, −37 kJ; **d.** ≈450, No. The molar mass is an average of a large number of chains with varying lengths.

63.

65. a. The polyamide from 1,2-diaminoethane and terephthalic acid is stronger because of the possibility of hydrogen bonding between chains. **b.** The polymer of

because the chains are stiffer. **c.** Polyacetylene is n HC≡CH → —(CH=CH)$_{\overline{n}}$. Polyacetylene is stronger, because the double bonds in the chain make the chains stiffer.
67. a. The temperature increases on stretching. **b.** exothermic; **c.** As the chains of the polymer are stretched they line up with each other resulting in stronger forces between chains. **d.** $\Delta G(+)$, $\Delta S(-)$; **e.** The structure of the stretched polymer is more ordered.
69. Compounds are numbered in *The Merck Index*. The number and page for each compound is given for the 10th edition. **a.** dopa, 3427, p. 497; **b.** amphetamine, 606, p. 84; **c.** ephedrine, 3558, p. 520; **d.** acetaminophen, 39, p. 7; **e.** phenacetin, 7064, p. 1035
71.

C≡C—C≡C—C=C=C—C=C—C=C—C—\overset{O}{\overset{\|}{C}}—OH

73. No, it would be a different molecule with two 4-membered rings.
75. a. 43%; **b.** 1.00×10^3 kg (theoretical), 430 kg (actual); **c.** i. $1.58/lb; ii. $0.63/lb; **d.** The disposal of AlCl$_3$ and H$_2$SO$_4$ in i. would be a major problem. **e.** iii. $0.57/lb using benzene or $2.63/lb using benzophenone. iv. $0.20/lb; **f.** Process iv. is most economical.

Chapter 23

1. Primary: amino acid sequence: covalent bonds; Secondary: features such as α-helix, pleated sheets: H-bonding; Tertiary: three dimensional shape: hydrophobic and hydrophillic interactions, salt linkages, hydrogen bonds, disulfide linkages, dispersion forces **3.** Both denaturation and inhibition reduce the catalytic activity of an enzyme. Denaturation changes the structure of an enzyme. Inhibition involves the attachment of an incorrect molecule at the active site, preventing substrate from interacting with the enzyme. **5.** hydrogen bonding **7.** nitrogen atoms with lone pairs of electrons **9.** A deletion may change the entire code for a protein. A substitution will change only one single amino acid in a protein. **11.** a triglyceride containing more than one carbon-carbon double bond   **13. a.** right;   **b.** $^+H_3NCH_2CO_2H$ in 1.0 M acid; $H_2NCH_2CO_2^-$ in 1.0 M base   **15. a.** aspartic acid, phenylalanine; **b.** $RCO_2CH_3 + H_2O \rightleftharpoons RCO_2H + CH_3OH$ **17. a.** ionic: need —NH_2 on side chain of one amino acid and —CO_2H on other; —NH_2 on side chain: His, Lys, Arg; —CO_2H on side chain: Asp, Glu; **b.** hydrogen bonding: —X—H— – – –O=C—; any amino acid; **c.** covalent: S—S (cys– –cys);   **d.** London dispersion: all nonpolar amino acids;   **e.** dipole–dipole: Tyr and Thr

19.

ser-ala   ala-ser

21. 6   **23.** A polar side chain of the amino acid is replaced by a nonpolar group. This could affect the tertiary structure and the ability to bind oxygen.

25.

D-ribose   D-mannose

27.

isoleucine

threonine

29. 8
31.

33. T-A-C-G-C-C-G-T-A   **35.** adenine

37. a. Glu: CTT, CTC
Val: CAA, CAG, CAT, CAC
Met: TAC
Trp: ACC
Phe: AAA, AAG
Asp: CTA, CTG

b. DNA sequence for Met-Met-Phe-Asp-Trp

TAC-TAC-AAA-CTA-ACC
           or   or
         AAG CTG

c. four

d. C—T—T—A—C—C—A—A—A

‿‿‿ ‿‿‿ ‿‿‿
Glu — Trp — Phe

e. C-T-C-A-C-C-A-A-A; C-T-T-A-C-C-A-A-G; C-T-C-A-C-C-A-A-G

39.

41.

16 carbon omega-3 fatty acid

18-carbon omega-3 fatty acid

43. See *The Merck Index,* 10th Edition, p. 282, 1986.

45. $H_2N—CH—CO_2H$ or $H_2N—CH—CO_2^-Na^+$
          $CH_2CH_2CO_2^-Na^+$ $CH_2CH_2CO_2H$

47. 1.7 m   **49. a.** fat soluble;   **b.** fat soluble;   **c.** water soluble; **d.** water soluble   **51.** not spontaneous   **53.** 2.98×10^{17} **55.** 7.07

Chapter 1 p. xxxii, Courtesy E. S. Garnett et. al., Chedoke-McMaster Hospitals, Hamilton, Ontario, Canada; p. 2, Yoichi Okamoto; p. 3 (left), Archiv fur Kunst und Geschichte, Berlin, Germany; p. 3 (right), H. Mark Weidman; p. 5, The Bettmann Archive; p. 9, METTLER Model AT261 DeltaRange Analytical Balance; p. 14, Tom Pantages; p. 24, Richard Megna/Fundamental Photographs; p. 25, Paul Silverman/Fundamental Photographs; p. 27, Ken O'Donoghue; p. 28 (all), E. R. Degginger; p. 29 (top), Ken Kay/Fundamental Photographs; p. 29 (bottom), Kristen Brochmann/Fundamental Photographs; p. 30, Radian Corporation; p. 31, Procter & Gamble. **Chapter 2** p. 39, IBM Almaden Research Center; p. 42, The Granger Collection; p. 43 (top), Roald Hoffmann; p. 43 (bottom), The Granger Collection; p. 44, The Granger Collection; p. 46, The Granger Collection; p. 48, The Bettmann Archive; p. 49, E. R. Degginger; p. 50 (top left), The Bettmann Archive; p. 50 (center of page), Richard Megna/Fundamental Photographs; p. 52, The Bettmann Archive; p. 56 (top), Tom Pantages/Courtesy Autodesk; p. 56 (center left, bottom left, bottom right), E. R. Degginger; p. 56 (center right, bottom middle), Ken O'Donoghue; p. 57 (top right), Ken O'Donoghue; p. 57 (center right), Tom Pantages/Courtesy Autodesk; p. 57 (bottom), E. R. Degginger; p. 58 (top left), Ken O'Donoghue; p. 58 (center left), William E. Ferguson; p. 60, Kristen Brochmann/Fundamental Photographs; p. 63, Paul Silverman/Fundamental Photographs; p. 64, Ken Eward/Science Source/Photo Researchers; p. 65, Richard Megna/Fundamental Photographs. **Chapter 3** p. 78, Ken O'Donoghue; p. 80, David Pierce/Finnigan Corporation; p. 81, Eric Fordham; p. 82, Tom Pantages; p. 83, Ken O'Donoghue; p. 85 (top), Russ Lappa/Photo Researchers; p. 85 (bottom), Leslie Zumdahl; p. 92, Eli Lilly & Company; p. 93 (all), Ken O'Donoghue; p. 95 (all), Ken O'Donoghue; p. 96, Ken O'Donoghue; p. 97, Ken O'Donoghue; p. 100, Tom Pantages; p. 103 (top and center), Paul Silverman/Fundamental Photographs; p. 103 (bottom), Richard Megna/Fundamental Photographs; p. 105, Runk/Schoenberger/Grant Heilman Photography, Inc.; p. 107, NASA; p. 108, Eric Fordham; p. 112, Focus on Sports; p. 114, Paul Silverman/Fundamental Photographs. **Chapter 4** p. 126, Richard Megna/Fundamental Photographs; p. 128, Tom Pantages/Courtesy Autodesk; p. 132 (both), Ken O'Donoghue; p. 133, The Bettmann Archive; p. 136, Tom Pantages; p. 139 (center left), Ken O'Donoghue; p. 139 (bottom right), Robert Mondavi Winery; p. 143, Richard Megna/Fundamental Photographs; p. 145, Ken O'Donoghue; p. 146, Tom Pantages; p. 147, E. R. Degginger; p. 155 (all), Richard Megna/Fundamental Photographs; p. 159, Richard Megna/Fundamental Photographs; p. 161, E. R. Degginger; p. 162, L. S. Stepanowicz/Panographics; p. 170, E. R. Degginger. **Chapter 5** p. 182, Mark Greenberg/Visions Photo, Inc.; p. 184 (both), E. R. Degginger; p. 193, Ken O'Donoghue; p. 196, Runk/Schoenberger/Grant Heilman Photography; p. 198, Lindsay Lambert; p. 206, Brian Parker/Tom Stack & Associates; p. 208 (all), Ken O'Donoghue; p. 213, Martin Marietta; p. 214, Ken O'Donoghue; p. 218, Jack Finch/Science Photo Library/Photo Researchers; p. 219, Spencer Grant/Stock, Boston; p. 220, © 1989 Field Museum of Natural History, Chicago (Neg. # GN40263); p. 220, © 1989 Field Museum of Natural History, Chicago (Neg. # GN832136); p. 221, John Shaw/Bruce Coleman, Inc. **Chapter 6** p. 232, Alexander Lowry/Science Source/Photo Researchers; p. 235, E. R. Degginger; p. 239, Bernard Asset/Agence Vandystadt/Photo Researchers, Inc.; p. 245, E. R. Degginger; p. 246, Jack Fields/Photo Researchers; p. 248, E. R. Degginger; p. 252, E. R. Degginger; p. 256, E. R. Degginger; p. 259,

Stephenie Ferguson; p. 261, NASA/Goddard Space Center; p. 262, Greg Vaughn/Tom Stack & Associates; p. 265, Mark Heifner/Panographics; p. 267, Ken O'Donoghue. **Chapter 7** p. 278, Micheal Simpson/FPG International; p. 281, Ken O'Donoghue; p. 282, Donald Clegg; p. 283, Dan Guravich/Photo Researchers, Inc.; p. 284, The Bettmann Archive; p. 286 (top), Ken O'Donoghue; p. 286 (bottom), Robert D. Carr/Bruce Coleman, Inc.; p. 288, David Lokey/COMSTOCK; p. 289 (top), NASA; p. 289 (bottom), The Granger Collection; p. 293, Wesley Bocxe/Photo Researchers; p. 306, The Granger Collection; p. 310 (top), Russ Lappa/Science Source/Photo Researchers; p. 310 (middle), Ken O'Donoghue; p. 310 (bottom), Leslie Zumdahl; p. 329, E. R. Degginger. **Chapter 8** p. 340, Walter Klemperer and Todd Marquart/University of Illinois; p. 342 (left), Manfred Kage/Peter Arnold, Inc.; p. 342 (right), Kristen Brochmann/Fundamental Photographs; p. 348 (both), Tom Pantages/Courtesy Autodesk; p. 349 (Table 8.2), Ken O'Donoghue; p. 352, Courtesy of Alcoa; p. 355, E. R. Degginger; p. 360, Ken O'Donoghue; p. 362, Phil Degginger; p. 368, The Bancroft Library/University of California; p. 386 (Table 8.6), Ken O'Donoghue; p. 388, E. R. Degginger; p. 393, Scott Camazine/Photo Researchers. **Chapter 9** p. 402, Runk/Schoenberger/Grant Heilman Photography; p. 412, Ken O'Donoghue; p. 421, David Spears/Science Photo Library/Photo Researchers; p. 425 (both), Donald Clegg; p. 426, Brian Parker/Tom Stack & Associates. **Chapter 10** p. 438, James Bell/Science Source/Photo Researchers; p. 445 (left), Yoav/Phototake; p. 445 (right), Richard Wood/Taurus Photos; p. 446, Brian Parker/Tom Stack & Associates; p. 454, E. R. Degginger; p. 456, Yoav/Phototake; p. 460, Professor Williams, Lehigh University, Department of Materials and Science Engineering; p. 462 (top), Ball-InCon Glass Packaging Corp.; p. 462 (bottom), E. R. Degginger; p. 465 (top), Yoav/Phototake; p. 465 (bottom left and right), E. R. Degginger; p. 475, E. R. Degginger; p. 482, Wide World Photos; p. 486, John Gerlach/Tom Stack & Associates. **Chapter 11** p. 498, Professor E. U. Franck, University of Karlsruhe, Germany; p. 502, Richard Nowitz; p. 503, Len Lessin/Peter Arnold, Inc.; p. 504, R. W. Schreiber/Animals Animals; p. 506, E. R. Degginger; p. 508 (both), USDA; p. 509 (both), Ken Eward/Science Source/Photo Researchers; p. 510, Kristen Brochmann/Fundamental Photographs; p. 511, T. Orban/Sygma; p. 514 (both), Betz/Visuals Unlimited; p. 516, Alfred Pasieka/Taurus Photos; p. 523, E. R. Degginger; p. 524, Leslie Zumdahl; p. 528, E. R. Degginger; p. 529, Southern California Edison; p. 532 (top), Doug Allan/Animals Animals; p. 532 (bottom), Len Lessin/Peter Arnold, Inc. **Chapter 12** p. 542, Professor Sir John Meurig Thomas, Royal Institute of Great Britain; p. 544 (top left), Julie Houck/Stock, Boston; p. 544 (top right), Teri Bloom; p. 544 (bottom left), Leo deWys, Inc.; p. 544 (bottom right) Greg Vaughn/Tom Stack & Associates; p. 572, Kevin Schafer/Tom Stack & Associates; p. 573, Alvin E. Staffan/Photo Researchers; p. 581, Ken Eward/Science Source/Photo Researchers; p. 582 (all), NASA/Goddard Space Flight Center. **Chapter 13** p. 594, Richard Megna/Fundamental Photographs; p. 601, Grant Heilman/Grant Heilman Photography; p. 607, Richard Megna/Fundamental Photographs; p. 622, Ken O'Donoghue; p. 623, Ken O'Donoghue; p. 625, Ken O'Donoghue. **Chapter 14** p. 636, Robert Frerck/Odyssey/Chicago; p. 638, Eric Fordham; p. 647, Ken O'Donoghue; p. 649, E. R. Degginger; p. 658, Bob Daemmrich/Stock, Boston; p. 662, E. R. Degginger; p. 683, Kristen Brochmann/Fundamental Photographs. **Chapter 15** p. 696, Bruce Roberts/Photo Researchers; p. 702, Ken O'Donoghue; p. 703 (both), Ken

Page Numbers of
Some Important Tables

◀ Physical Constants ▶

Constant	Symbol	Value
Atomic mass unit	amu	1.66054×10^{-27} kg
Avogadro's number	N	6.02214×10^{23} mol^{-1}
Bohr radius	a_0	5.292×10^{-11} m
Boltzmann constant	k	1.38066×10^{-23} J/K
Charge of an electron	e	1.60218×10^{-19} C
Faraday constant	F	96,485 C/mol
Gas constant	R	8.31451 J/K · mol
		0.08206 L · atm/K · mol
Mass of an electron	m_e	9.10939×10^{-31} kg
		5.48580×10^{-4} amu
Mass of a neutron	m_n	1.67493×10^{-27} kg
		1.00866 amu
Mass of a proton	m_p	1.67262×10^{-27} kg
		1.00728 amu
Planck's constant	h	6.62608×10^{-34} J · s
Speed of light	c	2.99792458×10^8 m/s